Two-Thirds

Also by David S. Percy
(with Mary Bennett)

Dark Moon: Apollo and the Whistle-Blowers

Also by Mary Bennett

The Only Planet of Choice
(Editor)

Dark Moon: Apollo and the Whistle-Blowers
(with David S. Percy)

Two-Thirds

A History of our Galaxy

David P. Myers

APPENDIX David S. Percy

***Editor* Mary Bennett**

λ

Aulis Publishers
London

Aulis Publishers
25 Belsize Park
London NW3 4DU
England

First Published August 1993
Revised December 1993
Reprinted May 1994
Reprinted May 1995
Revised August 1999

Hardback ISBN 1 898541 000
Paperback ISBN 1 898541 019

Figure 190 photograph Cambridge Newspapers

Ordnance Survey maps reproduced with permission from
The Controller of her Majesty's Stationery Office
Crown Copyrights attached to illustrations including maps pertain only to the maps

A CIP catalogue record for this book is available from the British Library

Printed and bound by SRP Ltd Exeter England

For Alexandra
For Larissa
For Dan Mark
For Kirk
For all the children
of the Universe

Two-Thirds: A History of our Galaxy is written from the heart. The authors and their editor do not belong to any group, either religious or political. This book is presented with magnanimity to all who may read these pages.

Acknowledgements: To those who have gone before.

Special thanks to:

Peter Baillie, Paul Broadhurst, Mark Carlotto, Tony Coulson, Frank Domingo, Colette Dowell, Michael Glickman, Stan Gooch, Hugh Harleston Jr., John Langrish, John Martineau, John Michell, Hamish Miller, Carl Munck, Wolfgang Schindler, Edward Sherwood, Erol Torun, John Anthony West, George Wingfield.

Preface to the 1999 edition

Tradition is the basis for much of this work.
Tradition is the basis for innovation.
Innovation is the reason for this work.
There is an abundance of radically new material in this work.
But also much material that is traditional.

It had been a long day and the man wanted to relax. He took a book from his library and opened it at one of his favourite photographs, so as to immerse himself in the landscape of a place far, far away from the heat of the city. He looked in wonder at the beauty of the largest earthworks in Europe—the great green rampart and ditch encircling the inner grassy platform upon which tall standing stones marked the remains of ancient circles. He saw a tetrahedral-shaped mound on the eastern outer rampart—the rim of the ditch. Suddenly, the picture faded, green gave way to reddish-brown, and a crater was superimposed over the exact dimensions of the earthworks and virtually instantaneously the man 'knew' that this crater was on Mars, in the region of Cydonia. His vision cleared and once again the image before his eyes was an aerial photograph of Avebury Circle in Wiltshire, England. The man was David Percy and the year was 1991.

Having always used his professional skills as a film maker, graphic designer and photographer to assist his life-long research into lost and hidden knowledge, David Percy set about establishing a methodology to test the veracity of his 'vision experience'. Although primarily concerned with examining the possibility of an Earth/Mars connection encoded at

Avebury, his research facilitated production of material for *The Terrestrial Connection*, a lecture by the Mars Mission presented at the headquarters of the United Nations in 1992. It also brought about a meeting with David Myers—this was to be the beginning of an extraordinary team effort that would result in *Two Thirds*. Together they would push the research even further and discover not only the relationship between the Avebury earthworks and the Cydonia crater, but also the match between the entire Avebury complex and the Cydonia region on Mars.

Following these surveys, Percy was beset with further questions: *Why* should these two locations on two different planets correspond? What was the *reason* for these analogues? And why do *other sites and artefacts* on Earth connect with Avebury/Cydonia?

In his search for answers to such questions assistance came from an unexpected source. His colleague Robert Watts (producer of the Indiana Jones trilogy) introduced him to Phyllis Schlemmer, the transceiver of a source known as 'Tom', spokesman for the Council of Nine. David Percy had several sessions with Tom obtaining help with the questions he had already formulated and receiving valuable advice on how to pursue his research. Thanks to this constructive assistance from Tom, Myers and Percy began to liaise extensively, working step by step through the information encoded within the mathematics, the geography and the topography of each artefact or location (including associated crop glyphs) they were studying. Along the way, they discussed their hypotheses with the appropriate professionals such as astronomers, mathematicians and physicists. From this research process evolved the understanding that they were discovering fundamental elements of technologies that mankind does not yet possess. They also realised that the foundations of their research would be beyond the bounds of credibility for most people—as it nearly had been for themselves.

Since the publication of the first edition of *Two-Thirds* in 1993, it is now possible to verify that this book actually contains sense, not nonsense—indeed much that is not known to science today.

Here is a precise example of the truth of this claim.

In late 1993 David Percy asked the evolutionary writer Stan Gooch what he thought the head of the Egyptian Sphinx might represent. Stan had never investigated the matter before. After due consideration, he now stated that in his opinion the head was a combination of the skulls of the two early varieties of man, Neanderthal and Cro-Magnon; and that therefore the Sphinx must be a monument to the hybridisation of the two varieties, which produced ourselves. At this point David Percy showed Stan Gooch the following passage from *Two-Thirds* (pp. 302-3), which he had not before seen:

> "... Modify the face of the statue [the Sphinx] to resemble both the face of the transitional self-aware being resulting from the administration of the first part of the genetic agent [Neanderthal] and the face of the being resulting from the administration of the second part of the genetic agent [Cro-Magnon] . . ."

So in 1993 both Myers/Percy and Gooch independently stated that the head of the Sphinx is a combination of the heads of the first and second stages of a genetic project, resulting in Neanderthal and Cro-Magnon. Their agreement was already remarkable (see Figure 208 on the final page of Appendix for illustration). What is however crucial, and quite apart from the Sphinx, is that *Two-Thirds* and Gooch state unequivocally that we, modern man, are the result of two key stages—a cross between Neanderthal and Cro-Magnon—from which arises our phenomenal hybrid vigour. The scientific establishment for its part has always flatly maintained that Neanderthal man played *no part whatsoever* in our ancestry.

But in April 1999, following new fossil finds in Portugal, the scientific establishment executed a complete U-turn—and announced that Neanderthal and Cro-Magnon did after all interbreed. *Two-Thirds* and Stan Gooch had been absolutely right.

As another example, *Two-Thirds* tells us that there are three different speeds of light throughout the universe. Now in 1999 scientists are suggesting that light might not be a constant after all—the first step towards verification. Revision of scientific consensus as to how light really behaves would have a profound effect on everything to do with our understanding of the size and age of the universe, it would alter our viewpoint on virtually everything.

These two examples very much suggest that other *seemingly* fantastic technological information within the pages of this book should be taken seriously too. Furthermore, *Two-Thirds* proposes the use of a gravity propulsion system that will enable human beings to travel safely and rapidly through deep space—a spacecraft that will open the door to long distance space travel. Traditional ways of doing things are hard to overcome, but without innovation and change to established patterns of behaviour mankind cannot send men safely to Mars and beyond. No matter what NASA's spin doctors may say, sooner or later spacecraft will need total conceptual renewal—such as the development and adoption of spinning disk technology—as described in this book.

The extraordinary text is filled with mathematical proofs demonstrating that the locations and placements on Earth of many of our inherited monuments and structures, such as the Great Pyramid, Teotihuacán, Stonehenge and Avebury, were *intentional*. We are presented with many compelling and logical reasons as to why this construction work was undertaken—and by whom. In counterpart to this we have the story of the occupation of our galaxy—who we really are, where our forbears came from and why we are here on this planet.

This particular history is radically different in many ways including its style: it employs a unique and innovative technique to help us 'get the point' of the various and diverse meanings encoded into the text. The epic storyline and the hard facts *alternate* in varying proportions—sometimes in chapters, sometimes in paragraphs and sometimes in sentences. At some level of our creative/logical perceptual faculty, this mixing of story and factual content can be irritating and this often subconscious activity will in all likelihood bring the reader to a moment of choice: dismiss *Two-Thirds* as nonsense, or put it aside for a while, perhaps forever. That's *exactly* the moment to keep going because your perseverance at this stage will lead to the big pay-off. It is known that each thought we have *literally* alters the shape and structure of our brains, assisting the visualisation of our own individual futures. Our resulting actions create our experience, and so on and so forth.

From start to finish, the backplot and text of *Two Thirds* took just over twelve months to complete—clearly, it is far too complex to have been simply 'dreamt-up' by two individuals either side of the Atlantic in such a short time. Whether you choose to consider this text as sourced from inspiration, by infusion, or 'the Internet without wires' (to quote *Omon Ra* author Victor Pelevin) the truth is that when their research was complete, and David Myers sat at his early Apple computer, he did not expect to be recording the history of our galaxy. The entire text 'came' to him, literally word by word. He was 'given' the exact order in which the paragraphs and chapters were to appear, and quite apart from the unusual alternation of story and fact, this method of writing has given a certain style to the book. It is a style entirely consistent with that of our most ancient planetary myths, verbal or written.

As few of us today are familiar with mythos this style can at first be tedious but the use of this device enforces *reality*. It also enables the reader to exercise the mind's eye (or third eye, if you will). The addition or alteration of one word not only indicates an outcome, it can also switch the reader to another level. The outward patterning created by this device sets up internal, imperceptible wavelengths and rhythms within the text imparting information to the brain, so as editor, wherever I have abbreviated excessively long repetitions in the original manuscript, I have maintained these internal rhythms.

Apart from the text, some months before they were finished David Percy was 'given' the date of publication—August 21st 1993. The authors would later discover that this was the very date that NASA's Mars Observer probe arrived in Martian orbit and promptly stopped communicating. Percy was also 'given' the placement and order of the original 207 illustrations in the Appendix. When illustrated subject matter occurs in the text, it is referred to by an underlined number, for example: 123

In many ways this work is a re-telling of the 'hero's' journey of traditional myth, but there is another innovative storytelling device in *Two-Thirds*. The 'hero' is depicted as a fractal. At any one time 'he' can be singular, a group or an entire civilisation. The heroic qualities of bravery, fidelity, beauty and honour are sometimes expressed within one person, sometimes within the group and then sometimes expressed separately among four people or a group. Each reader's journey through this book will be a fractal of the 'hero's' journey that we as a civilisation have chosen to make by living on this planet, in this solar system, in this galactic experience—NOW.

By opening our minds to the seemingly fantastic information presented in *Two-Thirds: A History of our Galaxy* we can join David Myers and David Percy on THE journey of discovery—about ourselves and our place in the universe.

Mary Bennett
Wiltshire, England
August 1999

Contents

Prologue

Silently, swiftly, the sharp prow of the air ship sliced through the thin atmosphere of the red rock planet; skimming over an arid landscape as it sped towards its secret destination: the magnificent Tor. Already enormous—it loomed ever larger, or so it seemed to the craft's three determined occupants.

Planetary defenses had detected and tracked the air ship but its transponder had returned the correct coded response. The red rock planet was well defended against attack from the outside—but not from treachery and treason.

Horrific events were about to unfold.

Inside the Tor's Aspis Crystal Control Center, Security Director Carl Odkin was preparing to activate various automatic security systems so that he could leave the Tor. He was about to assist in the highly secret security operation covering Hur Square, some eight miles northwest of the Tor and he had to be there on time for the celebration of the 250,000th anniversary of the landing on Daphlay by Altean refugees.

Through his hirelings aboard the air ship, the Altean traitor Paul Bunzler was attempting to sabotage the single most important structure on the red rock planet. A target selected by the Pleiadean renegade Garth Sarkneson—paying Bunzler millions of quid worth of gold for attempting the sabotage, promising him a life of luxury and wealth if successful. Much valuable preparatory time had been lost to Bunzler as Sarkneson had only given his final instructions two days before the designated time of the attack on the Tor. Bunzler had managed to keep to the scheduled destruction of the red rock planet's main defense component together with the primary energy transconversion devices, both located in the

Tor. This act of sabotage was concluded by employing the brothers Henry and Tom Shick as well as their cousin Joe Staliry.

Tom Shick landed their air ship between the Tor's southwestern corner buttress and the Glamyrr Gate buttress, which contained an ascending corridor. This entryway to the highly restricted areas of the Tor was accessible only to authorized maintenance and delivery personnel working under very strict supervision.

Although any of the three on duty Aspis Crystal Security Directors might occasionally leave their station in the Tor during their duty periods, Bunzler had obtained specific highly secret information concerning the departure of Carl Odkin for the Hur Square ceremonies. This information had been key to the timing of the attack—timing that had been specially selected by Sarkneson to inflict maximum terror. To achieve their desired aims, the air ship had to land near Glamyrr Gate precisely 34 minutes before Elder Byron Haley Chee began his opening remarks at the ceremonies.

The hirelings arrived on time, debarked and ran up the stately ramp leading toward Glamyrr Gate and to their first objective: the disablement of the gate's security alarm. Henry Shick held open the satchel around his waist so that his brother could remove an energy slicer. Tom Shick first destroyed the depiction of a dolphin carved on one of the ramp's balustrades, revealing a secret panel. He marked precise points on this steel plate and then used the energy slicer to cut through the alarm component of the Glamyrr Gate security system.

Meanwhile Staliry, standing by the opposite ornamental balustrade, carefully opened his satchel and delicately placed four packets of high explosive on the ramp. Following that, he armed the charges by setting their timers for 30 minutes. Staliry then inserted two of the explosive packets into a double compartmented bandoleer which he then strapped across his shoulder. Finally, he took two single compartmented bandoleers, filled each one with a packet of explosive and handed them to the Shicks after they had finished destroying the supposedly tamper proof alarm system.

Timely entry into the Tor was their next task. Together the cabalists ran up to Glamyrr Gate itself, Tom Shick removed a sonic transmitter from his brother's satchel and pointed it directly at a carving on the five-sided portal. This seemingly innocuous, geometric metaphorical sculpture of a concept of Philosophia was actually linked to the central security computers. Shick's procedure replicated the classified standard method of gaining entry through Glamyrr Gate, and triggered the computers into disarming the security system, opening up the entryway. As the portal opened, the very steep, flat and highly polished surface of the long triangular shaped corridor automatically formed into a translucent crystal stairway.

Staliry ran up the steps, while Tom Shick prepared for their rapid exit by destroying the Portal's locking bolts with an energy slicer. He worked rapidly, aware that if they did not adhere precisely to their exacting schedule they would be entombed in the rubble mound they were about to create.

Two-thirds of the way to the top, Staliry passed a side corridor to his right which would give the Shick brothers access to two of the three enormous energy transcoverter rooms contained in the Tor. The brothers would each place a bandoleer on the tetrahedral crystal casings of these vital energy transconverters, which would then be simultaneously destroyed, along with considerable portions of the Tor itself.

Hopefully achieving their aims with sufficient time to make their escape, the Shicks would then return to the air ship and wait for Staliry, who would be left to his own devices if he failed to join them less than 30 seconds before the devastating explosions took place.

The third energy transconverter—subject of much debate between Bunzler and Sarkneson—would remain unattacked due to its extreme distance from their entrypoint. The Glamyrr Gate entrance was the only unmanned access to the three rooms. These rooms were located in the Tor according to geometric, philosophic and practical considerations. To attempt to destroy all three energy transconverters (and consequently the structural integrity of the Tor) would require more manpower, money and time, and was considered not worth the risk. Bunzler had argued the point successfully, and he believed, correctly. Sarkneson had relented at the last possible moment, threatening Bunzler with dire consequences if the sabotage failed. Livid that Bunzler would even dare question his brilliant plan the instigator of the cabal was outraged that the Tor would remain intact. It would become he thought, an eternal marker; very clearly highlighting the flaws of the weak minded, philosophically corrupt Altean who had defied the finest living example of Pleiadean breeding, intellect and correctness, namely Garth Sarkneson.

When Staliry reached the final step of the ascending corridor he rested for a few seconds and then turned left through an entryway into the Labyrinth Corridor. He wound his way towards the Aspis Crystal Control Center, past a seemingly endless number of dead ends designed to prevent unauthorized access which trailed off in every direction. But Staliry could follow the correct route thanks to his copy of Paul Bunzler's diagram covering nearly all the vital secret defense details for the red rock planet. To insure his rapid escape, and on his own unauthorized initiative, Staliry had brought with him a container of purple dye. As he walked through the Labyrinth Corridor reading Bunzler's diagram, the cabalist sprayed the exquisitely laid and intricately carved crystal tiling, ruining the design, but greatly enhancing his chances of a speedy retreat.

Staliry's target was the Aspis crystal at the apex of the Tor. In conjunction with the planetary magnetic field of the red rock planet, this crystal produced an energy net which effectively neutralized air, and/or space delivered energy attacks by torpedo and cannon, either from beyond or within this anti-weapons shield. Other planetary defenses were used against possible attacks by low flying craft, as were a matrix of powerful magnetic fields (sited far from populated areas) and associated land based energy cannon.

Although the destruction of two-thirds of the Tor's energy transconverters was the main target, and even though there were no other transconverters on the planet of a size capable of activating the Aspis crystal (and thus create an anti-weapons shield), the spiteful Sarkneson nevertheless insisted on destroying the Aspis crystal. It was this insistence on the part of the Pleiadean renegade that caused the rift between Bunzler and himself and was the real reason that the third energy transconverter and the structural integrity of the Tor was spared. Sarkneson's obsessive cabal was his attempt to assuage an ego of gigantic proportions, badly bruised by the sarcastic barbs of his Emperor, Xung Halbert Mavor.

The Aspis Crystal Security Director, Carl Odkin was delayed in leaving his security station due to an unexpected transcommunication from Altean Naval Headquarters on Daphlay. This had been relayed to him from the red rock planet's interplanetary communication system, located in the Bastion, about a dozen miles northeast of the Tor. Not intending to be late for the ceremonies, Carl, the son of Hurmaze Director Joe Lon Odkin, nevertheless checked the Labyrinth Corridor's security system once again before leaving. The system was so secret that the knowledge of its very existence was limited to the three current Aspis Crystal Security Directors, who worked on a weekly rotation basis. Their predecessors had entrusted them with this highly confidential information.

The Labyrinth Corridor's security console showed that all was nominal and Carl Odkin turned to another secret console, with which he would activate the sophisticated and elaborate Aspis Crystal Security System. This action would insure that no intruder could possibly penetrate the Control Center without causing a death-inducing gas to permeate instantly the Upper Tor region. The poison gas system contained a time delay mechanism: once Carl Odkin activated this system he had one minute to be clear of the Upper Tor—or be killed.

Just as he was about to set the poison gas system, the sudden loud alarm of the Labyrinth Corridor security system caused Odkin to spin around and leap back to the first console. One glance told him that an intruder was in the Labyrinth Corridor and heading towards the Aspis Control Center.

In quick sequence Carl Odkin activated the automatic closure of the Control Center entryways, alerted the security team commander at Sustanator Gate, and—drawing his energy pistol—stepped into the Labyrinth Corridor, sealing behind him the interior entryway by using a virtually invisible device that was hidden in the absolutely smooth, seamless crystal wall.

Mindful that without warning he would come face to face with an intruder most certainly bent on destroying the Aspis Crystal, Odkin made his way quickly but carefully along the Labyrinth Corridor. He sought to estimate when and where he might meet a saboteur by recalling in his mind's eye the console's image of the corridor and the speed of the intruder's advance. Carl Odkin knew the time had come as he intuitively sensed another being around the next bend. Standing with legs parted to insure good balance and aim, he firmly gripped his energy pistol and pointed it at the middle of the corridor, angling the barrel so that the charge would disable but not kill, the intruder.

Carl Odkin saw the intruder and immediately fired.

The energy pistol charge struck Staliry a glancing blow in the leg. In great pain and startled out of his dye spraying and diagram reading, he lunged forward and grabbed Odkin by the right wrist. Together they fell onto the tiling.

As they grappled together Staliry knew that death was imminent from the impending explosions. He desperately sought to escape his predicament by suddenly releasing his grip on Odkin's wrist, grabbing the throat of his opponent with both hands and attempting to strangle him. Carl was both physically and mentally on top form and reacted quickly. Releasing one hand from his hold on the intruder, he stretched for his energy pistol, aimed at the intruder's head, and shot him.

Having crawled out from underneath the intruder's body, Carl Odkin immediately saw the bandoleer draped over the shoulder of the dead man. On examination he discovered the high explosive packets and timer. He stopped the timer with eight minutes to go.

Deducing that there would surely be other saboteurs, Carl raced through the Labyrinth Corridor in a desperate attempt to save the Tor from what he thought was a coordinated attack. Guessing that other timers would trigger an explosion, he used the eight minutes as a guide and counted off the seconds as he ran. Reaching the exterior end of the Labyrinth Corridor, he unsealed the entryway, turned left and tore down the steps towards the side corridor which led to the other logical target for saboteurs: the energy transconverter rooms.

With the Aspis Crystal Security Director descending the stairway a mere ten feet above them, the Shick brothers, having successfully completed their tasks, suddenly emerged from the side corridor to Odkin's left and began their own rapid descent, without looking up. Carl Odkin drew his energy pistol and shot the two cabalists in the back. The lifeless bodies of the Shicks tumbled down the stairway ignored by the Security Director. He had by that time reached the side corridor and begun racing toward the transconverter rooms. Carl Odkin turned into the nearest room through the gaping security door. The Shicks had blasted the heavy steel doors open with small but highly explosive charges (placed in locations predetermined by Sarkneson). Ignoring the dangers of entering the powerful magnetic field which surrounded it, Carl Odkin ran toward the energy transconverter.

He knew it would be too late when he reached the ten seconds mark in his countdown.

A flash of memory seared through his mind: a year ago he had been dining in a restaurant in Ell House when he'd heard a voice behind him saying "Same month, next year." Curiously startled by this, he had turned to see Paul Bunzler, Director of Naval Armories on the red rock planet, leaving the restaurant with a stranger. When Bunzler had noticed the Aspis Crystal Security Director looking at him he had deliberately averted his eyes, or so Odkin had thought. Forgotten until now—the last few moments of his life—Bunzler and the stranger, Carl suddenly realized, must belong to a cabal bent on sabotaging the Tor.

Moments after Carl Odkin had deduced this horrific truth the charges on the two energy transconverter casings exploded simultaneously. Only a few seconds later a secondary explosion (caused by the two, still lethal, packets of high explosive left lying on the floor of the Labyrinth Corridor) added to the destruction.

The immense nine-faceted Aspis Crystal of the Tor, having lost its supporting structure, crashed down upon the core of the five-sided pyramid and broke into many pieces. The two energy transconverters disintegrated; following the collapse of the framing beneath them, and several huge crystal panels from the northeast facing of the Upper Tor fell into the firestorm.

In Hur Square nearly one million celebrants looked on in horror as flames rose and heavy black smoke billowed upwards. The body of Aspis Crystal Security Director Carl Odkin, his deeds of heroism unknown, lay crushed under tons of rubble. He shared his permanent tomb with the bodies of the Tor security team. Instantaneously dispatched on receipt of Carl Odkin's alert, they had been unable to gain access to the corridor leading to the energy transconverter rooms.

Sarkneson had foreseen the possibility of an alert. He had ordered Bunzler's men to destroy the security lock mechanisms on the three steel doors separating that corridor from the three ascending stairways, giving access to the energy transconverter corridor, leading from Sustanator Gate. These remotely activated control panels were hidden in the wall of the corridor next to the security doors and were blown up with small charges of high explosive.

Garth Sarkneson, enjoying the company of his long time mistress Suzy Bibbens, received an immediate personal transcommunication into his private quarters of the fortress of his private empire on the planet Colchis. It was sent by the Altean traitor Paul Bunzler, who had been nervously awaiting the outcome of the sabotage from his living quarters in Ell House. Living quarters that overlooked the tragic scenes taking place below. Living quarters that contained a secret transceiver.

Cary Manpure, aged nine, watched the horrific cloud of smoke envelop the southern sky beyond Hur Square in which he stood, surrounded by family and friends.

Tears streamed from his eyes.

Part One ALTEA

Chapter One

The Traditions

Seven billion years ago nearly a million and a half beings, from a planet called Hermur, escaped from their galaxy to look for a new home.

In the area of the galaxy in which Hermur was located, the commander of the galactic naval forces, who was also the local representative of the galactic legal authority, had become a dictator. In fact, legal authority of that now long bygone galaxy had been deteriorating for some time.

The resulting political and social conditions were so bad on Hermur, that the members of a planetary organization—traditionally dedicated to community service—held a secret meeting and decided to seek a new home in another galaxy.

During the years of clandestine planning and preparation that ensued, no hint of this 'cabal,' and the resulting successful escape of those beings, ever reached the Hermurian dictator. This was due to the stringent precautions concerning the dissemination of information, the total dedication of the leaders of the 'cabal' and most importantly, the absolute loyalty of the organization's members.

The members of this established organisation, dedicated to service, had formulated a totally different agenda. Although meetings for such a purpose had been unprecedented on Hermur, intergalactic migrations did indeed have precedent: history told them that massive intergalactic migrations had always carried forward beings from one galaxy to the next, along the chain of galaxies which led to their current galaxy. However, this usually followed the redeeming of their galaxy—the fulfilling of the galactic experience, so that all beings of any given galaxy had the opportunity to live together in harmony. The Hermurian 'cabalists' were extremely disappointed that their departure was not associated with the redeeming of their galaxy—but was precipitated by the need to escape.

The redeeming of the galaxy was the historical imperative under which the galaxy had been developed, but in this case it was not to be. As the 'cabalists' had historical records stating that this had happened several times before, they were not totally downcast when they started preparing their escape. They deduced that fundamental conditions and situations sometimes recur, enabling those aware of their history to take advantage of that knowledge and act accordingly.

The fact that they were able to keep their vast project totally secret from outsiders surprised and uplifted them, and made them feel that they were doing the right thing. Even so, they knew that the reasons for this success were threefold; they were dedicated, they planned well and they worked hard.

All the earlier, highly advanced intergalactic pioneers known to the Hermurian 'cabalists' had, on arrival at their destination, encountered developing beings who were astute but scientifically unsophisticated. Together they formed an enlightened and equal union. The name chosen for their jointly shared galactic seed planet also became the name of the civilization, which eventually spread throughout that union's galaxy.

Having finally escaped Hermur, despite a last minute attempt to stop and destroy them by a lone naval star ship randomly patrolling their area, the Hermurian refugees bravely undertook the daunting prospect of intergalactic travel.

The duration of their migration was totally unknown. Previous intergalactic migrations had lasted from a few years up to a few million years, but an escape from an 'unredeemed' galaxy was always uniformly longer. The Hermurian 'cabalists' had prepared themselves as fully as possible for a very long trek.

Passing the outer fringes of their galaxy in enormous intergalactic space vessels, the escapees maintained their previous speed of near interstellar light speed (over 400,000 times faster than solar system light speed). Accelerating to near intergalactic light speed (nearly three million times faster than solar system light speed) before reaching the precise point—well beyond the galaxy—where interstellar light speed increases by a factor of seven to intergalactic light speed, would have resulted in the escapees' entering an interdimensional zone called complexified three-space. They would immediately disintegrate because the atomic structure of three-dimensional existence would be torn to shreds as a result of exceeding the local speed of light.

In anticipation of this significant historic event of passing through the interstellar/intergalactic light speed crossing point, the Hermurian flotilla formed a loose line abreast, so that they could all pass through the crossing point almost simultaneously.

The six 'cabalist' leaders: Bythe, Mattheron, Murthane, Strumur, Rosurun and Trosumur were more than ready for the moment. They were aware of their purpose and responsibilities, handed down to them through ancient and highly honored family traditions. Their vessel was traveling at the center of the formation, and together they stood on the bridge, surrounded by Mattheron's wife Reinara and his daughters Rulla and Sollura; Trosumur's wife Sereena, his daughter Rissura and son Pasorun—and Rissura's closest friend Serivia.

They stretched out their arms in a gesture of anticipation. For they hoped that they were about to fulfil the purpose of their existence: intergalactic migration.

As the years stretched into decades, the second generation, led by Rissura, Serivia and Pasorun, strongly supported by Rulla and Sollura, maintained the high morale engendered by their pioneering elders.

The high speed dashes were not the most difficult part of the intergalactic migration. It was the patience required between those dashes, as long periods of waiting were necessary in order to synchronize physical time with consciousness time. Changes of speed cause physical time to slow down and speed up; self-aware beings, whose built-in consciousness time is unalterable, cannot tolerate being out of synchronization with physical time for too long.

In order to avoid dying from being out of synchronization, space travelers such as the intergalactic migrators who cover great distances must therefore make frequent and lengthy stops along the way.

Consequently, between voyages, the flotilla made numerous stops in many galaxies, establishing homes on planets they made habitable (staying for up to a million years on some). During these years numerous scout ships were sent out to explore the whole of their temporary galaxy.

Both aboard the intergalactic vessels and on temporary planets countless generations were born, grew to maturity, fulfilled their life's purpose and passed on. Later generations came to accept intergalactic migration as a way of life, maintaining the spirit of those earlier generations.

Their travels led them through many galaxies in various stages of development but the migrators never found indigenous beings that fulfilled the requirements set out by their forebears. These were: purity of heart; an interest in philosophy; a traditional and innovative orientation; good-natured disposition; and above all, loving both of their environment and of one another.

The planet of discovery had to be a planet of harmony. While continually learning of their parent's traditions, the descendants of the early generations of intergalactic travelers were also aware that the planet of discovery would be the seed for a new galactic civilization, which would be required to grow and flourish before the redemption of that galaxy could be accomplished. For this was the all-encompassing mandate of the intergalactic pioneers.

Another tradition of intergalactic migration was originally a secret known only to the family of Trosumur. Just before the increase to near intergalactic light speed, Pasorun had come onto the bridge carrying an old cedar box. No one noticed as he had held the box respectfully while the vessels passed through the point where interstellar light speed increases seven times to intergalactic light speed.

Later Trosumur told everyone the story of the encased book. There existed a tradition he said, which was to be kept secret by his family until the beginning of intergalactic travel. It was then to be revealed. Pasorun had brought the encased book to the bridge according to the formula of the secret tradition. Which then demanded that Trosumur tell them of the history behind the tradition of the encased book:

Trosumur's father had revealed to him that the family's secret history stated that a very ancient adventure book of no apparent literary value, and certainly with no historical fact, actually contained vitally important information on many subjects—included totally unwittingly by its author.

The ancient ancestor who had deduced this startling fact then carefully preserved his precious copy of the adventure book. He himself had originally read it as a youth, at the suggestion of his long deceased father who had bestowed the book to him. The ancient ancestor's father had also received it as a birthday present in his own youth. Before passing on, Trosumur's ancient ancestor had placed this adventure book in an old cedar box and instructed his children to hand the box along with its history, down through the generations.

The secret family tradition, Trosumur concluded, required that the encased book be brought to the bridge during intergalactic migrations and be displayed at the exact moment of the first crossing point, just as Pasorun had done. Once that was over, and the story told to all, the encased book would have served its full purpose, at least in its current form. The legend stated further, that the ultimate purpose of this tradition was to prepare the way for a similar scenario in the ensuing galaxy.

These conditions would engender the actions insuring that some author in the far future would write a seemingly innocuous adventure story. That book would inspire a dreamer in the far future who would subsequently become dedicated to the redeeming of the galaxy.

Thus the secret tradition of the family of Trosumur carried forward the inspiration of his ancient ancestor, a long passed on dreamer, who hoped for better days for the children of the Universe.

Five billion years of sporadic space flight went by, and trillions upon trillions of miles were traversed before the seemingly endless trek ended.

The Hermurian 'cabalists' had finally discovered their new home.

Chapter Two

The Union

On the seed planet they named Altea, the intergalactic migrators and the beings indigenous to this galaxy developed an enlightened joint civilization. Although the locals had never needed to name their planet before (it being the only one they knew and therefore to them their planet was simply home) they participated fully in the decision over the word 'Altea' which was made up of a combination of syllables from both languages and meant 'home to all.'

Among the first of many important procedures agreed by joint committee was the establishment of standard units of time and distance.

The extragalactics knew that for self-aware beings to survive, no matter how favorable all other conditions, a planet must rotate on its axis within a specific time period of 23 hours and 56 minutes. This requirement was essential. Altea rotated naturally at that rate and was therefore a seed planet, whereas Hermur's natural rotation was much slower. Consequently prior to colonization taking place on Hermur, the rotation had to be artificially adjusted and subsequently maintained. Any period of planetary rotation other than 23 hours and 56 minutes only resulted in the slow physical decline and eventual demise of self-aware beings.

The agrarian indigenous beings divided their day into ten periods commencing at what the migrators called six in the morning, while the migrators had always divided their day into 24 hours of 60 minutes composed of 60 seconds, commencing at midnight.

The joint committee dealing with time and distance changed the beginning of the day from rising time until midnight and adopted the 24 hours in a day system, amid considerable grousing by many agriculturally oriented locals, who could see no reason for these changes.

In response to their persistent questioning as to the reasons for planetary rotation adjustment and the methods applied, it was explained to them by their new partners that ancient scientific instructions existed which had enabled them to adjust numerous planets throughout their long trek. However, they would only share this information with them when the locals had learnt enough of the background knowledge necessary for a full understanding of the process.

The locals were affronted by these 'explanations.' Even when the extragalactics insisted that it had taken billions of years to work out the process by which complex scientific knowledge could be understood by indigenous populations, no matter what their level of scientific and technical sophistication, the locals were unimpressed. The migrators also told them that the same held true for an understanding of the required period of revolution.

On measuring the length of Altea's revolution around its sun, the migrators were very pleased to find that at approximately 365 and one-third days, this natural year was an almost exact correlation of the traditional paradigm established aeons ago by their ancestors. The newcomers were very happy about this natural length of year, since their experience had been with a length of year that was totally independent of the period of revolution of a planet around its sun, the true definition of a year. Only those beings from the previous galaxy who had lived on that galaxy's seed planet had ever experienced a year that really was a year.

The locals already puzzled, were utterly bemused by the positively euphoric behaviour of the newcomers over their next scientific revelation, especially as it appeared that the result was expected. Shortly after their arrival the extragalactics had started the difficult and intensive process of attempting to measure the precession of Altea. Precession is a wobbling of the axis of rotation of some planets. This precession, the locals were told, was the least understood of the three processes of planetary movement: rotation, revolution and precession.

The spokesman for the newcomers went on to explain, "As the rate of wobble is very slow, the resulting period of precession is very long (often in the tens of thousands of years). We call it retrograde precession because the wobble is in the opposite direction to the rotation, this creates a tension so powerful that it can cause both the lateral movement of planetary crust plates and earthquakes. It is similar to the tension you feel before sexual release. We'll tell you more about this later."

The indigenous beings understood little of this and stared blankly at the spokesman. They could, however, relate to the feeling of pre-orgasmic tension, and this incited them to listen as the spokesman continued, "It took some time to get an accurate reading of Altea's retrograde precession rate and it turns out to be 25,920 years! This makes Altea a very special, nearly unique planet. Only planets with a retrograde precession period of 25,920 years are capable of creating the environment required for bringing forth, through natural evolutionary processes, self-aware life. Only planets which have a moon in the right orbit and which is the correct size, and only planets which also have a companion planet whose orbit is locked to their own, can have a retrograde precessional period of 25,920 years."

The intergalactic pioneers—having successfully persuaded their indigenous partners to accept the 24 hour day—went on to introduce their vitally important 360 degree system of angular measurement. Possessing only vague notions of measurement and no system of their own, the locals were not very interested in listening to the explanations offered to them, "The 360 degree system combines divisions of both time and planetary location," the spokesman said. "Since the system's most important attribute is its connection with the counting of time: one day is divided into 24 hours of 60 minutes, each consisting of 60 seconds; the 360 degrees are also divided into 60 minutes consisting of 60 seconds each."

The locals were thoroughly confused by this 'revelation,' "How can you say there is a connection between time and angular measurement?" they asked. "We are to have 24 hours in time and 360 degrees in angular measurement."

"We'll get to that later, too," was the reply.

Although they realised that their new partners were becoming frustrated, the extragalactics knew that they were supplying just enough information to make the locals really think and interact, stretching their intellects to near breaking point. In this way the locals were being lovingly guided towards self-realization of much of the great scientific knowledge suddenly made available to them.

The combination of assisting with information (which the locals could never obtain on their own) and their resultant very stretched thinking, was followed by the addition of more information. This process repeated many times was the only way to guarantee an eventual union of equality between the two societies. No other way would work. Any other method would result in either or both groups becoming downcast.

Next, the intergalactic pioneers went on to introduce the indigenous beings to the concept of time and the speed of light.

They managed to grasp the basics fairly well but when the extragalactic spokesman announced that there were actually three types of time and three light speeds, he was greeted by very blank stares. Undaunted he continued, "We call the three types of time: Eternal Time, physical time and consciousness time. Physical time slows down and speeds up in relation to the speed of the observer. Eternal time and consciousness time are constant, no matter what the speed of the observer. Or, if you like: as our ships slow down and speed up so do the devices which measure time. The Universe and our consciousnesses run at a constant speed—always. We'll tell you more about this later."

He paused and then went on, "Now the three light speeds are the result of the effect of gravity on light. (Gravity is the force that holds us onto Altea and keeps us from drifting off into space.) Lots of gravity makes light slow down; very little gravity allows light to speed up. Light, however, likes to travel at only three discreet speeds. As the Universe tends to immediate action rather than dissipated action, light slows down or speeds up suddenly rather than gradually. The Universe likes to do things in blocks rather than just dribbling along. We'll tell you more about these three light speeds later."

The extragalactics did indeed tell the locals much more at a later point, including historical data concerning early understandings. Data that had originated about 100 billion years ago, back along the chain of galaxies from which they came. This data concerned the beginnings of the understanding of time and the speed of light.

After billions of years of observation from numerous vantage points: planetary, solar system, interstellar and intergalactic, the rate at which the Universe evolves—Eternal Time—had been determined as the singular, absolute constant of the Universe. Physical time had been relatively easily evaluated as variable because devices measuring time ran slower in space craft traveling fast. Consciousness time also proved to be constant, as self-aware beings maintain the same life expectancy whether they travel fast in space, or live on a planet (unless they travel too fast for too long, which leads to premature death).

The findings that indicated that there were three speeds of light astonished the discoverers of this phenomenon because early scientists researching the speed of light from a single vantage point—their planet—had incorrectly concluded that light had only one speed. Subsequent experiments carried out within their solar system, though successful, did not give them enough data to define whether the speed of light was really a constant. Nevertheless their theories on the applicable relationships between light and time were both astute and valid. But their inability to measure the speed of light beyond their solar system limited them from gaining a workable understanding of virtually all the forces that govern the physical universe. Furthermore, this inability prevented them from being able to conceive of planets and beings beyond their own. Only when experiments were carried out in the vast reaches of space between stars, and then between galaxies, were the two very much higher speeds of light revealed: interstellar light speed and intergalactic light speed.

Gravity—scientists later discovered—is the force that governs the speed of light.

Planet-based observations, carried out long before the discovery of interstellar and intergalactic light speeds, gave the first hints of this fact: while recording the collapse of massive stars, both visible and non-visible light and the energy emitted by the matter trapped and drawn in by these celestial bodies was detectable.

These collapsing massive stars—celestial bodies of such extreme density that their gravity traps and draws in all matter that comes near them—were not visually observed, only the light emitted by the matter being drawn into them was recorded. They theorized that the gravity of these collapsing massive stars is so strong that nothing, not even light, escapes them. Despite this hint, it had not occurred to those observers, and they had not extrapolated from their observations that light might possibly speed up when beyond the gravitational effects of their solar system.

"Having thoroughly explained all aspects of time," the original spokesman grinned broadly as she continued, "I can add that time becomes a most important factor in planetary measurement and is therefore combined with 360 degree angular measurement to form what we call 'The Nautical Mileage System.' This is quite simple: there are 360 degrees around a planet and 60 minutes in each degree. Multiplying degrees and minutes together results in 21,600 which is the total number of nautical miles around the equator of any given planet." 2

Although intrepid sailors, the indigenous seamen had used very crude methods for reckoning their whereabouts at sea. With the implementation of the nautical mileage system, came the gradual introduction of a planetary-wide grid of automated position locators. As the sailors were keen to learn and as they were anxious to take advantage of the new system, their ships were fitted with automatic position locating devices, giving them instantaneous readouts. Based on that planetary-wide grid reference system these positions were measured from the equator as degrees, minutes and seconds of north or south latitude. Additionally from a prime meridian (located at the centre of Hurtea, the new Altean capital) these positions were measured as degrees, minutes and seconds of east or west longitude (or meridian); with a clearly defined 180 degree demarcation east or west of the prime meridian.

The indigenous beings had never built a capital city, nor named their communities and so they had allowed the extragalactics to choose the name Hurtea (two syllables from the migrator's language meaning 'shining home'). The locals, however, reserved the exclusive right to choose the name of the largest city planned for the eastern hemisphere.

After the locals had accepted the nautical mileage system the new arrivals introduced them to the statute mileage system, known to them since time immemorial, it required updating once per galaxy. This was done by measuring the equatorial circumference of the seed planet. Altea being remarkably similar in size to the preceding galaxy's seed planet, only required an adjustment of about one-tenth of one percent.

"There are precisely 24,901.54558 statute miles around the equator of the seed planet of any given galaxy," explained the pioneer's spokesman. [3]

"How did a scheme like that ever come about?" asked one of the indigenous beings.

"We don't know," answered the spokesman.

After waiting for more questions, but receiving none, she continued her explanations. "The statute mile is divided into 5280 feet, each foot is divided into twelve inches and each inch into 32 parts. We don't really know why 5280 feet make up the mile, but we do know that, though cumbersome, counting by 12s (which is very important) as well as by 10s, is the most logical and convenient system devised during billions of years of experience.

This vital counting by 10s and 12s links directly to an interesting relationship between the nautical mileage system, the retrograde precession of 25,920 years and a very important metaphor: dividing 21,600 (the number of equatorial nautical miles) by 25,920 results in a ratio of 5 to 6. This ratio of 5 to 6 is a metaphor for the vital relationship between the non-living parts of the Universe and living things.

"The non-living parts of the Universe are all six-sided.

"All living things are five-sided."

Having emphasized this strongly she continued, " As a result of this important ratio we have long since concluded that in order to maintain harmony with the vital non-living portions of the Universe we must count by both 10s and 12s. If we were to discontinue this we feel we would become disharmonious with our environment and out of synchronisation with the Universe."

The locals hooted with laughter.

"You know that we have to recalculate the length of the statute mile by slightly less than one-tenth of one percent. This means that everything is the wrong size and we have to recalculate and remeasure everything we possess!" She spread her arms in dismay and gave a wan smile.

The audience laughed uproariously and then gave her a standing ovation. When the applause had died down the spokesman added, "I know that you will be somewhat downcast when I tell you that for convenience sake we often divide miles, feet and inches by tens."

The locals hooted again.

As the lecturer sat down, apparently from nowhere an enormous holographic projection of a sphere circumscribing a tetrahedron suddenly appeared, thoroughly startling the audience of indigenous beings. Another speaker rose and said, "This is a visual aid to help us all understand what I am about to tell you." He cleared his throat and pointedly read from his notes, "The square root of three, divided by two, multiplied by pi, is equivalent to 2.720699046 and is the transdimensional constant. The transdimensional constant is equivalent to the ratio between the surface of a sphere and the surface of the tetrahedron it circumscribes." 4

Producing a light pointer from his lectern, the speaker transferred his notes to his left hand and while continuing to read from them, he used his right hand to aim the thin red beam at the holo-image. "The tetrahedron is the simplest solid shape, contained by four equilateral triangles placed together. It is the basic unit of construction of the physical universe.

A tetrahedron whose four tips just touch the sphere surrounding it is called a circumscribed tetrahedron. A circumscribed tetrahedron is the geometric model for both hyperdimensional and resulting three-dimensional physics processes which devolve from much more complex four-dimensional processes. These four-dimensional processes are also modeled by this same circumscribed tetrahedron representation.

"The physics manifestations of this model drive the physical universe. The four-dimensional manifestations of this model drive the Universe."

The speaker thanked everyone for their kind attention and gave way to the symposeion's director, a stern yet kindly man, whose graying temples contrasted sharply with his black skin.

He looked very intently at the audience and said, "Let's celebrate!"

Having dealt with most matters concerning time and distance to their mutual satisfaction, the joint committee then determined the standards for weights and measures. These took the form of ounces, pounds and tons for weights and liquid ounces, pints and quarts for liquid measuring.

Next came politics.

The galactic newcomers had traditionally elected members to a parliament which then adopted new, and modified existing legal codes. The parliament selected a prime minister by a majority vote system. The prime minister in turn selected a cabinet of ministers and these ministers had to be approved by the parliament. The prime minister was head of the executive branch, parliament was the legislative branch while a legal council supervised the legal system.

Despite their widely separated communities and lack of real time communication technology, the indigenous beings had created remarkably similar political institutions around their planet. Their institutions fulfilled the same traditionally limited role as did the much more sophisticated political institutions of the extragalactics, for the extragalactics. Decision making community councils were made up of locals over the age of 21 selected randomly by drawing lots. A non-voting administrator was appointed by the council to insure the execution of all council decisions. Permitted certain emergency powers, these wise-thinking beings were not necessarily of advanced years, although they were known as Elders.

After the formation of the union, each local community continued with its own system, the extragalactics joining various committees. Eventually, a planetary-wide decision making body called The Over Council Of Altea came into being. The council members were elected from the entire Altean population over 21 years old and served a four year term. An Elder, fulfilling the traditional role, was also appointed.

Though membership of the legal council was open to all Alteans, applicants had first to pass an extremely stiff legal examination set by the Elder before being submitted to the drawing of lots. The successful members each served a single six-year term. The indigenous beings were resistant to the concept of a legal system, having found no need for such a structure, and so the introduction by the extragalactics of the legal codes was a long and carefully staged process.

Various considerations determined the number of members on each council: the Over Council of Altea had 24, the legal council 13 members. While small enough to be efficient these numbers were meaningful to the Alteans: The 24 members of the Over Council metaphorically represented two interlocked tetrahedra, each tetrahedron composed of four equilateral triangles with a total of 12 corners per tetrahedron. 5 Single and interlocked spinning tetrahedra are the basis of Altean transdimensional physics. Together with the Elder, the numbers became 24/25ths, which represented what was known as the Harmonic of the Universe. This harmonic had been discovered billions of years ago by the musician Biederdorf, while researching methods for improving meditation techniques. The repeated playing of a sequence of two tones having an interval of 24/25ths enabled his subjects to achieve higher states of meditation. Biederdorf and his associates subsequently found the harmonic 24/25ths repeated in many things.

The 13 legal council members metaphorically represented the initial growth processes of living things. In plant life, 12 cells form the first growth layer around a single seed, resulting in 13 distinct cells. 6 The beginning of life for all animals and self-aware beings, an embryo, also requires the initial growth of 12 cells around the first cell.

Establishing an equitable financial base for Altean society was the next, complex step, for the locals operated on a barter system and had no idea of monetary concepts. The extragalactics had developed a sophisticated monetary system and were keen to introduce their coinage, including their very fondly named, or 'monikered' monetary unit.

This coin or bill, depending on its denomination, was monikered 'quid' since time immemorial. In fact, the quid had been called thus for so long that the real name of the quid is lost in the mists of time. The word 'quid' never appeared anywhere on the quid, only its numerical value was stamped on the obverse (or imprinted on the notes) and the extragalactic's emblem featured on the reverse: a capstoneless four-sided pyramid with a triangle above it in which there was an eye. The motto of the newcomers formed an arc over this illustration of an eye-triangle proclaiming, 'We forward Its cause!'

The quid was divided into 24 pence and metaphorically represented two interlocked tetrahedra. The word 'quid' had been retained from the phrase 'quid pro quo' meaning 'something given or received for something else' in the language of a distant galaxy. (Many phrases from that galaxy have continued to be used down through the galaxies that followed but the connection between the traditional phrase and the monetary unit has been forgotten.)

In spite of some initial wrangling due to an understandable reluctance to abandon their barter system, once the locals had understood that more advanced types of labor could not operate without some agreed medium of exchange (other than goods), they took to the idea of currency with enthusiasm if not vengeance. They became very shrewd in business practices almost overnight, or so it seemed to the surprised newcomers. The locals negotiated high wages for agricultural workers and other manual laborers—this restored their sagging dignity. It seemed to them that all the technical jobs were filled by the sophisticated newcomers, and this wage negotiation established the tradition that manual labor was esteemed as much as mental labor, preventing the indigenous beings from becoming downcast.

The Altean school system provided both the physical and mental education for all children and was adopted almost intact from the newcomers tried and tested system. Primary schooling lasted for seven years. This included an introductory year of pre-school learning known as the 'Kindergarten.' This word and concept had been taken from the first historically recorded galaxy, indeed, many words from that bygone galaxy's language had survived, and adhered stubbornly to languages which developed along the string of galaxies that followed. (Together with a few words from virtually every language used throughout the string of galaxies that led to this one.) The extragalactics translated 'Kindergarten' into the local Hurengle as 'young children's garden,' the similarity between 'garten' and 'garden' was immediately noticed and remarked upon.

"We don't know why there are so many similarities between words in our language and languages that we know from previous galaxies," their spokesman said. "We are fairly certain that you developed your language without external influences, so we suspect that there may be some intrinsic meaning associated with certain sounds."

The six remaining primary years were known as Enkyklopaideia, meaning 'all-encompassing education' a name derived from the alternative scientific alphabet and partial language brought with them by the extragalactics. This period of basic education was provided by carefully chosen teachers, trained in child development as well as their specialized subjects.

Middle school and high school were both three years in length and separated the adolescents into two groups, as the younger adolescents were especially cantankerous at the onset of puberty. Both schools were continuations of the Enkyklopaideia begun in primary school, albeit to an ever increasing level of sophistication and with some specialization.

Athletic skills were strongly emphasized. Competition was encouraged in both individual and team sports. Many games had been taken up and then dropped throughout the years of travel to various galaxies and planets but golf, swimming and wrestling had become traditional sports, for these three severely tested spirit, mind and body to the limit.

After this schooling the highest achievers were admitted to Akadeimia. Following a rigorous entrance examination and a thorough assessment of each student's personal file concerning their physical, mental and spiritual needs, each student was expected to embark upon an ambitious four-year study in a major discipline together with three ancillary disciplines.

The most respected teachers at Akadeimia were given the honorific title Hurian, meaning 'one who has climbed Mount Hurartu,' by popular acclaim of their students.

In the years that followed, many other points of civilization were established by committees belonging to both groups of beings.

Working on the union project, and having overall supervision of the other committees, was a group of fourteen people (seven from each culture) plus a non-voting chairman. She was an indigenous being of great and varied talent named Melina Renart. The locals had no concept or word for the leader of a committee, since they had never had committees, only Elders and councils. The word chairman was developed as a combining word: 'chair' from the indigenous language's direct translation of the extragalactic word for that object; 'man' meaning 'individual' 'one' or 'person' was another extragalactic word taken from the first historically recorded galaxy. The pronunciation being identical to that of the indigenous word for an adult male, great care was taken in explaining the difference in meanings, for neither the extragalactics nor the locals considered the role of chairman a uniquely male preserve. The plural of the word was therefore made to be 'chairmans' and not 'chairmen.'

Melina Renart was the Altean responsible for the success of the project to combine the highly scientific extragalactic society with the scientifically backward, rustic but very astute, indigenous civilization. A discerning judge of character and devoted student of philosophy, Melina Renart has been remembered down through the ages as an exemplary chairman. It was her tireless efforts to insure a fair hearing of all the very important issues facing the committee, that procured the eventual success of the union. Above all, she stayed aloof from the wrangling over the major issues such as time, measurements, politics and education, thus remaining a cool arbitrator when all others had given up hope of finding a solution. Melina Renart has remained a model for all future chairmans who have been non-voting members of important decision making bodies, and who sometimes have had equally difficult, though not as wide ranging, tasks.

Rather than imposing their own highly sophisticated language, called Hurtegel—meaning 'shining great accomplishment,' the newcomers continued to fulfill their mandate of forming an equal union, by suggesting a synthesis of languages. The locals and the newcomers worked together in committee for many decades to create a new language, which they called Hurengle. Derived from the Hurtegel root syllables of 'hur' meaning 'shining' and 'engle' meaning 'great truth.' The indigenous beings had never needed names for themselves or their language and therefore deferred to the extragalactics on this matter, but they nevertheless insisted that their approbation was essential.

That was the last such deferring by the locals with regard to anything.

The indigenous beings were learning.

Although the choice of name for the combined language was soon decided, there was a long and bitter struggle over every other aspect of Hurengle. Eventually the local language was adopted outright and called Hurengle. The indigenous beings were determined not to be downcast.

The only victory won by the extragalactics throughout these linguistic tussles concerned a collection of syllables so precious and meaningful to them that they refused to relinquish their use. The locals refused to either substitute or combine these syllables into their indigenous language and it was Melina Renart who finally resolved the impasse in a way acceptable to both cultures: use the indigenous word in parallel with the similar word in Hurtegel containing the important syllables and eventually popular usage would determine which word survived.

Almost all the extragalactic words disappeared.

Occasionally, however, some Hurtegel syllables became attached to Hurengle root words (as in 'transportation').

Below are the 16 Hurtegel syllables (with their translations):

Ark: Beginning-Ending
Bury: Mountain
Ergon: Work
Gla: Distant
Gwyn: Clear
Har: Potent
Her: Valiant
Hor: Hyperdimensional Radiating Source
Hur: Shining
Logos: Word
Myrr: Reflection
Pan: All
Tea: Home
Tor: Gate
Trans: Across
Zoos: Life

When the indigenous beings discussed these 16 syllables with the newcomers' translators they did so with both horror and humor.

"We don't like this sound 'hor' that you say means 'Hyperdimensional Radiating Source.' In our language it often has a bad meaning, such as: 'horrible' 'horrific' or 'horror.' We think we understand that 'Hyperdimensional Radiating Source' has something to do with our creation and we don't think that was a horrible thing to have done!"

The extragalactics had to think before replying. Finally, one of their translators said, "Then 'hor' will have to have different meanings in different words."

"What about our word 'horse?'" asked the locals. "A horse is neither horrific nor a hyperdimensional radiating Source, but horses are very important to us and we love them."

"Then horses can be taken as being symbolic of the importance and love of the hyperdimensional radiating Source of the Universe," answered the translator.

From that day on, the horse (an animal the migrators had not seen in five billion years) has been the everyday symbol of Alteans for the Source of the Universe.

"We also have a problem with your syllable 'hur.' You say it means 'shining.' We use that sound in 'hurricane' our word for a dreadful storm."

"That 'hur' sound" replied the translator quickly, "will be spelt with two 'rs'."

The locals stared at him blankly, and then pressed on, "There is another problem with your list of 16 sounds. You never do anything in groups of 16. We think you've tried to sneak in some extra sounds. We have caught you out."

The extragalactics responded, "We have picked out 16 syllables because 16 is two-thirds of 24. Two-thirds is very important." The extragalactics then went on to detail many of the important things about two-thirds.

The extragalactics had also brought with them an alternative scientific script with its own partial language. Somewhat similar to Hurtegel in appearance, the first two letters were called 'alpha' and 'beta' and so they had called this system the alphabet. The word used to denote the original Hurtegel script was the 'a-zed.' Since there had never been a lettered written indigenous language on Altea, the locals had no concept, or need, of a word describing a series of letters. They spoke only one language and inscribed it by drawing pictograms, using one per syllable. This method was unacceptable to the extragalactics, who knew that a letter alphabet was an essential tool for a scientifically advanced culture. After much debate the locals gave in to reason, accepting the loss of their beloved pictograms for the sake of the union.

The extragalactics assigned spellings to Hurengle words that were often more complex than was necessary and frequently differed from their pronunciation. They did this in order to create an equality of effort for both cultures in the mastering of Hurengle. They succeeded beyond their expectations. Alteans have never been able to spell Hurengle.

The locals disliked the term 'a-zed' and insisted on using the word 'alphabet' for Hurengle. The bewildered extragalactics threw up their hands in despair and relented, though this meant that they had then to determine a new name for their scientific alphabet and partial language in order to avoid confusion.

A competition, open to all Alteans, was held to select this all-important name. A committee of judges conversant in both original languages finally selected 'Hellenikos' as the winning word. It had been submitted by an indigenous young lady named Lura White who had used the scientific alphabet and partial language as her source of inspiration, much to everyone's surprise.

The judges were amazed by this word. They had picked 'Hellenikos' merely for its wonderful sound as it rolled off the tongue. Lura White had clearly indicated that the emphasis had to be on the last syllable, 'kos.' When asked how she had made up such a word the 13-year old answered demurely, "I looked through the listing of words in the partial language that accompanied the listing of letters from the scientific alphabet. I found several I thought were interesting. I tried mixing and matching until I nearly went crazy. Finally, I decided to break down the words into their syllables, and that is how I came up with 'Hellenikos.' The complete word 'Hellen' means 'light.' 'Kos' is the first syllable of the word 'Kosmos' meaning 'Universe.'

"Hellenkosmos didn't sound right and was too long, so I chopped off the 'mos' and stuck an 'i' between the first two syllables, producing 'Hellenikos' which means 'Light of the Universe,' or at least, I think it does."

So Hellenikos—meaning 'Light of the Universe'—became the new name for the scientific alphabet and accompanying partial language of the extragalactics.

The young lady made a wonderful presentation of her ideas, speaking forthrightly, expertly and from the heart. Having won the judges' minds, she won their hearts as well.

While the indigenous judges beamed over Lura White's success one of the extragalactic members of the language committee walked up to them and said, "There are many things for which you have no words. We will give you these words along the way."

In the meantime, the personal and family name committee had very little to do, other than to state that everything should remain the same. Not that there was total agreement on this subject, but Melina Renart had stepped in early on and said, "The only solution to this problem is to wait. Everyone keeps her or his name. After living together for a while, the name situation will simply resolve itself by popular usage."

Personal and family names were indeed quite different in the two cultures. The intergalactic pioneers had one-syllable names, sometimes bizarre and of difficult pronunciation for other cultures. Examples of such names were: Chee, Huish and Zuv. Names like these had evolved from the original Hermurian custom of giving offspring one multi-syllabic name without regard to the names of other members of that family.

Although perfectly acceptable on Hermur, this method made it very difficult to keep track of family lineage, and therefore any given being's genetic lineage. During the seemingly endless five billion year intergalactic migration, it became evident that there was an increasing danger of inbreeding through the possibility of too close intermarrying. There was a very real probability of the collapse of their civilization due to genetic disaster.

The intergalactic pioneers became very concerned about the possibility of their genetic collapse as a result of too small a gene pool, and this became an ever increasing problem as time wore on.

The migrators had also had to prevent their physical deterioration and deaths as a result of their periodic but often long space travels. In order to keep themselves alive during these periods in space the travelers instituted a strict maintenance of their standard 24 hour day, induced the appropriate gravitational and magnetic fields in their ships and—most importantly—provided for the appropriate flow of hyperdimensional consciousness energy through those same ships.

The migrators began tracking families by splitting their names into three syllables and using the first syllable as the family name. For instance, Trosumur changed his name to Tros Um Ur, and asked his close friends and associates to call him Ur. His family's names were more difficult to alter but after much debate between them, his wife Sereena became Tros Ser Eena, Rissura became Tros Ris Sura and Pasorun became Tros Pas Orun.

These two children of Sereena and Trosumur had by now grown up, married and had their own children, grandchildren and great grandchildren. (The life expectancy of the intergalactic travelers and their Altean descendants down through the ages usually exceed 200 years.) They insisted that all their descendants conformed to the name splitting. Thus Pas Orun's line had the family name Tros; Ris Sura while not changing her own name, insisted that all her descendants use her husband's family name: Chee.

Tros Ris Sura's husband was a linguist. Born Cheevan, he had been obliged to add another syllable to his name, as had many others. Chee Van Dan's choice of 'Dan,' taken from a language pre-Hurtegel with which he was familiar, was expressly to tease his wife, for the name meant 'stout-hearted,' a pre-requisite for living with such a lady.

By the end of the five billion year intergalactic journey, the pioneers had evolved their naming system even further, so that Tros Ris Sura's multi-great granddaughter was known as Chee Ree Sara. She became the first Elder of Altea.

The indigenous population placed their family names last and frequently picked names that depicted either their most definitive trait, or their particular trade, or the color of their hair. A few examples of these names are: Brown, Miller and White. Their choice of personal name varied widely and was mostly inexplicable in their derivation. Altean names, especially female names, have evolved from the many Hurtegel and indigenous lyrical sounding syllables which have the connotation Light' or 'Radiating light.' This perhaps is an indication as, has been suggested along the way, that there does exist a universal meaning for sounds. Examples of such names are Alana, Lura and Rena.

In the matter of names Melina Renart was proven wrong. Popular usage has never established a permanent policy and the custom of writing the family name first or last has switched back and forth several times.

Visual differences between the two cultures was never an issue, and intermarrying between them began almost from the start. During their uniting ceremony, indigenous ladies traditionally wore a banded hair net and a tiara. Virtually all Altean brides have continued this custom. The tiara is an artistic and complex piece of jewellery representing the union of mind and soul. It consists of a small face superimposed over the forehead of a larger face. The small face and the eyes of the larger face are made of different colored pieces of glass. The chin of the larger face is a diamond. Dyed eagle feathers form a small plume at the top and the band holding the tiara to the head is made of gold.

Indigenous gentlemen traditionally wore a special hat to their uniting ceremony and this custom was also maintained by nearly all Altean bridegrooms. The bridegroom's hat is conical and fits just above the eyebrows. It is decorated with tear-drop shaped colored glass ornaments, ringing it about one-third up from the rim. At the front, and just below these ornaments, are two small agate globes, one either side of a multi-part medallion. Dividing the hat from top to bottom and extending downwards to the bridge of the nose, is this multi-part medallion, made from differently-shaped clam shells inlaid with winged figures. Just below the uppermost and largest winged figure is a ring of diamond-shaped emeralds which extends around the hat. A double-sided face is placed on top of the hat, looking both forward and backward. Uplifted arms, bent at the elbows, extend from the sides of the faces. The hat symbolises the joy of union, looking forward to a happy life and fond remembrances of youth.

The newcomers added a third tradition to the wedding ceremony: their own long-held custom of eating fish at the wedding party. The partaking of fish at Altean weddings throughout the ages has been a ritual which seeks to impart the harmony of the Universe on newly married couples.

The shape of a fish is similar to that of the ellipse formed by two interlocking circles, when the circumference of each circle is tangent to the center of the opposite circle. This ellipse produces the square roots of two, three and five, the numbers which form the basis of geometry and harmonic proportion. 7 Additional lines drawn in relationship to this specific type of interlocking circles produce a hexagon and a pentagon; six-sided and five-sided figures metaphorically representing the non-living parts of the Universe and living things. 8 The Ellipse representing Spirit, reconciles the six-sided and five-sided geometry of the interlocking circles, as the Source of the Universe reconciles the non-living parts of the Universe and living things.

Chapter Three

Altean Culture & Civilization

These intergalactic migrators brought with them to Altea a literary culture rich in tradition and content. Valuable insights were recounted in their numerous and entertaining tales, poems, epic narratives, plus both comic and tragic drama.

The indigenous beings added a rustic aura to the joint culture through the introduction of their oral histories, legends and traditions.

One such legend indigenous to this galaxy is called ODUNSIDE:

ODUNSIDE begins as a ship sailing along a dangerous coast of ancient Altea, seeks to avoid a fierce multi-headed monster known as the hydra. This hideous beast lives in a low marshland area, not far from the site of Altea's future capital city Hurtea.

By repeatedly sailing his ship up the coast by day, in sight of land, and by returning south under cover of night, the tale's hero manages to convince the hydra that an entire fleet of ships seeks its death. Fooled by this clever tactic, the hydra maintains such a constant vigil by day that it becomes exhausted and needs to sleep soundly throughout the night.

Thinking the hydra will be sleeping and therefore an easy prey, the tale's hero Captain Bill Odun sneaks into the marsh one night, rowing a small boat which has been disguised as a female hydra, to look like a 'mate' for the hydra. Odun (or Safeside, as he was called by his Crew, thanks to his concern for their well-being) carefully and quietly opens one of his 'lady hydra's' wooden heads and leaps onto the back of the monster. Having been awoken by the sound of Odun's approach to the small island in the marsh, the hydra is fully alert and looking forward to mating with the 'lady hydra.' Savagely disappointed by the turn of events the hydra is more than ready to do battle.

In an enormously entertaining and frightening narration (especially to young children, for whom it was the tradition to hear ODUNSIDE for the first time sitting by the campfire) the hero and the beast battle to the death on the murky islet. The hydra tries in vain to dislodge Bill Odun from its back by thrashing wildly about, then tries to kill him by breathing fire from its eight heads.

Bill Odun knows that he must sever all eight heads before the monster will die. Clinging for his life to the hydra's scaly back with one hand, the hero repeatedly and deftly swings his broadsword with the other—but to no avail.

The tale's hero begins to realize that nothing can save him, when he suddenly notices a form surging through the trees of the marsh. With one swing of his broadsword this 'form in the marsh' hacks down a dozen trees, and thus hews a pathway before him, until he stands defiantly in front of the monster.

The ensuing battle between the unknown 'form in the marsh' and the hydra is ferocious and only ceases with the death of the hydra.

Bill Odun's first thought is to thank his savior, but the 'form in the marsh' insists on telling his own tale: he and his ship's Crew had been stranded further up the coast by a violent hurricane and he had entered the marsh to look for food for them. The hydra had tried to devour him as he sought the safety of open water and though he had successfully eluded the monster so far, he could not expect to do so forever. While he was summoning up courage to fight the monster he heard the sounds of a battle in progress and had been overjoyed to come across Bill Odun attempting to slay the hydra. This, he pointedly tells the tale's hero, inspired him and gave him the courage to attack the hydra.

After finishing his story for Bill Odun, the 'form in the marsh' sinks onto a broken tree trunk to rest. Having removed 'his' hat, 'he' shakes 'his' head gracefully, loosing 'his' long and flowing hair, which trails beautifully down onto 'his' shoulders.

Meanwhile Bill Odun has dragged his 'lady hydra' boat ashore; he then turns toward the 'form in the marsh,' and SHE gives him a warm smile. Bill Odun asks her why such a beautiful young lady risks herself for him.

"Odunside," she replies, using a combination of his real name and nickname he'd never heard before, "it was not I who did anything, it was love that did everything. My love for you is a power that can work even greater miracles than this small accomplishment you have seen today."

Odunside looks at her for a moment in awe and then sinks to one knee, laying his broadsword at her feet, "I most humbly ask you to be my bride," he says.

"You do not need to be humble, you who should know the answer to your request before you make it," she replies, easily pulling him to his feet with one hand and then placing both hands upon his shoulders so that he can take her in his arms and kiss her.

Thus it was the legend of ODUNSIDE that gave rise to the Altean custom of seafaring vessels traditionally referring to all things of the left as 'odunside' and all things of the right as 'seaside.'

Shortly after they first landed the newcomers, while sitting round a campfire, were told the story of ODUNSIDE by the indigenous beings. Wherupon they immediately fell in love with the tale and began using the terms 'odunside' and 'seaside' when they were aboard their space vessels.

The extragalactics recognized many of their own literary and teaching methods in ODUNSIDE. The omission of important details in ODUNSIDE and other stories was considered by both groups to be an all-important method of adding awe and mystery to their stories, and especially of inducing a sense of wonderment which would stimulate the listener's or reader's imagination. The newcomers were greatly heartened to discover that the indigenous beings also understood the importance of expanding the imagination for both all-encompassing educational purposes as well as for general mind development.

The careful development of individual powers of imagination was an incredibly powerful tool that would be carefully employed by the intergalactic pioneers to guide their new friends lovingly toward the equal union they both sought. The indigenous beings were not to be downcast.

The extragalactics also had their own stories which were historical allegories of the five-billion year trek from their home planet to the seed planet Altea.

They called these stories mythos. —

The Intergalactic travelers wove history and allegory together in an incredible mythos called NOSTOS. The 13 tales of NOSTOS were drawn from the experiences of the migrators during their exploration of many galaxies; when they had lived temporarily on planets that they had made habitable.

The following mythos is included for several reasons.

Firstly it illustrates the rigors of such a trek, continually extended by their failure to find the correct combination of planet and beings, as their traditions demanded. This manifest destiny drove the frustrated intergalactic travelers ever onwards.

Secondly, it is an example of the intergalactic traveler's masterful storytelling abilities.

Thirdly, it demonstrates the power of mythos as a mind expanding and teaching vehicle.

This is the seed tale of the 13 tales of the mythos NOSTOS:

Bill Odun stood by the helm of his mighty ship, observing his Crew as they went about their duties. The sharp bow of the vessel sliced through the dark sea.

Homeward bound, Bill Odun thought. Nostos in the language of my forefathers, he thought further.

As the intrepid, crusty old captain stood beside his helmsman, a man of long experience in whom the ship's officers had every confidence that a course would be steered well and true, Bill Odun reflected on the many adventures that had befallen them all during their cruise of many years. This train of thought was interrupted by his trusted and beloved Number One approaching the bridge to take over the deck watch. So Bill Odun went below to his sea cabin, still thinking about their exploits, and especially the first time they had put into port.

"Perhaps, I will write a book," Odun said to himself.

He drew a pad of paper from a drawer by his knee and placed it on the dark hardwood top of his mighty desk. He then picked up a quill pen and dipped it into a deep ink well. Pausing only a moment to collect his thoughts, chewing on the end of the quill, Bill Odun began to write his NOSTOS . . .

It was a beautiful sun filled and nearly calm day as we put into port. We neared the lone pier, but there was no one there to assist us in mooring, so we lowered one of our small boats over the side so that we could put line handlers onto the pier. Just as these men were climbing the ladder at the end of the pier, a screaming mob surged out of nowhere and began running toward the line handlers.

From my vantage point near the bow of the ship I could see that the mob was extremely menacing, indeed as the creatures came nearer I could see that they carried knives, axes and spears.

We were standing off a hundred yards from the end of the pier. I was terribly concerned for the safety of our line handlers, but was utterly powerless to defend them and though we called out to warn them, by the time they realised what we were shouting about it was too late—the rabble was upon them.

The scene which followed was horrific, and I still anguish as I write about it all these years later. Rather than seek to capture our men, the creatures proceeded to attack and butcher them. There was no defense, and our brave lads died within a few seconds of the onset of the attack, their slaughter a direct result of my blatant omission of care and planning.

Even today, as their captain, I feel I was remiss in not sending an armed escort ashore with them, but it was early on in our journey and I did not have the experience that I have since acquired. Or so I rationalized, as I penned this early episode of our adventures.

The Crew began to clamor for immediate revenge, even as our weapons were being drawn from the armory. This was near my cabin, under lock and key and too far away from the deck to be of use in such an emergency. Later—too much later—I installed a service locker topsides, to prevent subsequent slaughters.

I had to make a quick decision and be utterly ruthless. The aggressors simply had to be taught a lesson, and though I am a man of peace who abhors killing, the Crew needed to understand that I was not a coward who would shirk at protecting them.

I ordered, "Away all boats!" and the other four boats we had aboard ship were quickly loaded to the gunwales with volunteers for the landing party, each having drawn musket and broadsword. I called Number One to my side and told him to assume command of our ship in my absence. Then I was over the side, sliding down the rat lines to the waiting gig.

We quickly reached the beach near the pier head, the men having pulled strongly together on the oars. I did not want to chance another landing on the pier as that was a defenseless position. Once we had firmly established our beachhead and set out pickets, I ordered a few of our men to return to the pier and perform the grizzly task of returning the line handler's bodies to the ship. Later we would bury them at sea, as is proper for all seamen.

At first the men were reluctant to go, but I assured them that this was a necessary task, and that they could return to shore once it was completed. I had another interesting thing to add, which surprised and pleased them greatly. "Bring back the portable two-pounder with you, with plenty of shot and powder," I commanded.

With that instruction in their minds they raced down the pier, and were back with the cannon in less than an hour. I knew that the chances of using it were slim; when we pushed inland I would leave it behind safely chained to the pier with its muzzle spiked. I also knew that psychology was an important discipline, I had learned this during my first days at sea as a 16 year old lad and it has served me well ever since. The Crew should feel that I was avenging their dead comrades with all available means.

I should add here that we had begun firing on the mob from the deck of the ship as soon as we had laid hands on our muskets. I did not want to give them a chance to fulfill any additional purpose they might have, such as booty snatching or any form of desecration of the bodies and I had a strong feeling that their purpose was not simply murderous.

As a result, we had felled four of them and now ordered another team to go and fetch their bodies from the pier head. I wanted to find out more about these creatures.

The bodies were totally naked and outright filthy, as was their hair which was long, stringy and disheveled. While still quite brown, their skins were much lighter than ours. Their only distinguishing feature was the number 6 tattooed on their right buttocks.

I performed an autopsy on one of them. As soon as I cut open the body it became obvious that the internal organs were exactly like ours, so I broke off that part of my autopsy and removed the top of the skull in order to determine the size of the brain.

What I found astonished me. Just inside the skull, right above the left ear, was some sort of device: about the size of the last joint of my little finger, it was metallic, gray and almond-shaped. I did not know what purpose it could have, and as I removed it I could find no connecting wires.

My curiosity was aroused, and I ordered that the other three bodies be brought to me; they all contained the same devices in exactly the same location within their heads.

By this time it was getting toward evening, and having left a substantial watch aboard ship, we set up camp on the beach. We ringed the area with campfires and cooked our supper. Although we had not found time to forage for fresh fruit, grains or vegetables; nor hunt for game in the lush forest which bordered the beach, it was still a rare delight to eat our meal ashore.

After supper, as I began my evening meditation in my tent, it came to me that the pier was the only structure in sight. Perhaps it was a trap, as were the harpies in several of the traditional tales I had read as a youth; lures to lonely seamen since time immemorial.

I also began to wonder what the purpose of the four small almond-shaped devices I now held in my hand might be. My intuitive conclusion was that the devices were some form of control mechanism which made these poor unfortunate creatures act as they had. By admitting this to myself, I was gaining a whole new perspective of our experience, and our plan for revenge was on the verge of becoming—at least for me—a rescue mission. These creatures might very well be just as much victims as were we and I wanted to save those who were still out there somewhere.

In the morning I took the risk of calling the entire Crew ashore, to show all of them my findings and explain my newly gained insights. Normally a captain's word is law, and there is no questioning. But this is not a normal time, I concluded.

I said, "I cannot ask anyone to venture into that forest with me on a rescue mission. I could certainly order you to go on a punitive expedition, but I no longer feel that that is what it will be. Certainly, there is someone or something out there to punish, but I don't know for certain. What I do know is that there are innocents who need to be saved from these."

I held my hand high, and showed the Crew the sinister devices I had removed from the skulls of the dead creatures.

Then I continued, "But I can ask for volunteers to join me so that we can release the other creatures from the bondage they suffer."

I drew my broadsword, drew a line in the sand and said, "Those who will voluntarily join me, cross over."

To a man they did.

Now I had a different problem. I had to send some of them back to the ship, so we drew lots. I held out my hat, and as he passed by, each dropped in the identity ring from his right ring finger.

Next, we blindfolded Number One, much to the delight of my Crew and officers. Number One has to carry out all my orders, even those governing the less attractive side of a seaman's duties. He has to act as if all the orders come directly from him. That is the way of ships at sea—and the fate of being Number One.

Number One drew out 59 names.

Mine was the 60th name. I was exempt from the drawing of lots: sea captains need to have a privilege or two to go along with the long list of weighty responsibilities they have when caring for their Crew, officers and ship.

Except for the slightest hint of grousing from Number One, who was obliged to stay with the ship and therefore 'exempt,' those whose lots had not been drawn returned to the ship without a murmur.

Knowing how and when to use authority is the most important of reasons for choosing a Commander. In this case the use of authority would have been totally divisive. Number One understood this almost as well as myself. I had therefore decided on the traditional method of avoiding unwarranted uses of authority by drawing lots: a simple, direct and conclusive way of making decisions—sometimes.

I divided the remaining seamen into three groups of 20. We then set off into the forest in three columns, our objective being a rocky spur standing well above the forest canopy, a few miles inland. It was my intention that we gain as much information as possible about the intervening territory, and this, I told my Crew, was the reason for dividing into three columns. I also considered it likely that we be ambushed and I wished to minimalize any killing. This, I did not tell my Crew.

I led the right wing column, as I called my group of 20 men. (I borrowed the term 'right wing' from an ancient story: which told of two armies of heavily armed foot soldiers who slaughtered one another to regain—or retain—a beautiful young princess. She had been smuggled from one camp to the other by an effete princeling who was the real cause of the war.)

The center column was led by my third officer, while the left wing column followed the Boatswain, there was no finer Boatswain on any ship anywhere. I would have (and did) entrust him with my life, and I never found nor expected to find my Boatswain lacking in any regard whatsoever.

We had to hack our way through the thick undergrowth of the forest with our broadswords, occasionally sending someone climbing up a tree in order to maintain a bearing to the rocky spur. About 20 minutes after starting out, we heard the sound of musketry off to our left.

The distant and faint report made me think that it must have been the Boatswain's left wing column under attack, so I immediately ordered as rapid an advance as possible, in the direction of the sounds of firing. The way was still frightfully slow, and we had gone perhaps a quarter of a mile when there suddenly sprang up new firing very close on our right, from what I thought must be the center column.

Now that I had determined that both other columns had come under attack, I faced the difficult decision of how to proceed. There was no other choice than to simply take first things first, so I ordered everyone in my column to advance as quickly as possible toward the closer firing. We plunged headlong into the thick underbrush, intent on assisting our shipmates of the center column.

All of a sudden, three of my men and I stumbled into a clearing in the otherwise dense forest. Before we could stop, we were several yards into an open forest glade, and as we stood there the rest of my column appeared one at time, or in small groups from the general direction from which we had come. While my temporary Number One (a young lad who'd quickly shown potential leadership qualities) gathered the rest of the men together, my thoughts were on the best way to locate the center column, or at least what might remain of it.

I quickly realized that everything had grown silent about us—deathly silent. There was no more shooting, and there was certainly no sign of any of the rest of my Crew. The 40 men of the other two columns had disappeared without a trace.

Number One was doing an excellent job setting up a picket line and otherwise organizing my column just outside the clearing, so I turned back to survey our situation. The glade had evidently been fashioned by intelligent beings because it was perfectly circular and one hundred yards in diameter. It was also perfectly empty. Absolutely no vegetation grew within its confines, not even a blade of grass. Not a single rock appeared within my field of vision. The ground was smooth and flat, not tamped down but not loose, either.

Having observed this, I turned back to Number One and asked him to bring the men forward so we could examine the rest of the glade. We fanned out, forming a loose line abreast with myself in the middle and approached the center of the circle.

I was slightly ahead of the others—so I fell in first.

I toppled headlong into a pit, and as I fell I saw every one of my column follow me. Down, down, down we fell, for seconds, for tens of seconds, for at least a minute. I expected we would hit solid ground and be flattened, or impaled on sharp poles, our life blood gushing from our mortal wounds. All this flashed through my mind as we continued to fall helplessly into the bottomless pit.

I expected to be the first to hit bottom, but instead I was the first to land. At the last instant my body righted itself and I landed softly on my feet. I was marveling at what had just occurred when the rest of my men began to land softly about me. I soon spotted Number One and asked him to assemble the column.

Once muster had been taken I began to look around at our new surroundings. We had fallen so far that the sky was only just visible, a small dot in the otherwise totally black overhead. There was a faint luminosity about us, however, and I could see that we were in an enormous cylindrical cavern which stretched from where we now stood up to the surface. The circular wall of the cavern was exceedingly smooth, appearing as if it had been polished by intelligent beings. The floor was hardened dirt.

We had been in the cavern not more than ten minutes when we heard cries from overhead. Seconds later the men of the center column landed softly among us. As we were happily greeting one another we heard more cries, and then the left wing column arrived.

Once again we happily greeted our shipmates, and then a blinding light suddenly appeared from out of the wall. From the light emerged a very short elderly gentleman who hobbled a few feet into the cavern before stopping and leaning on a long staff. Due to the strong light I could barely make out his features, but he was very skinny, had long scraggly arms and legs and a large well formed head. What was most distinctive about him were his large dark eyes, of a strong intelligence, but also revealing a great sadness.

He looked at me and asked politely, "Are you the leader of these men?"

"Yes, venerable gentleman," I replied, trying to be as polite as possible in return.

"Please, follow me," he said as he turned around with the aid of his staff. He then hobbled back through the blinding light and disappeared into it.

I did not have to follow him, but I felt I must.

The way led through a labyrinthine series of galleries which turned every which way with side corridors leading off into blind alleys at every turn. At last, I came upon a small circular chamber, a chair standing in its center. The venerable gentleman—still relying heavily on his staff—had hobbled into the chamber ahead of me, and stood facing me as I entered.

"Please be seated and wait for your host here," he said before making his way from the chamber through an entry in the wall opposite where I was standing.

When she entered the chamber she said, "Bill Odun, I have long awaited your arrival. My venerable voluntary servant and I have been trapped on this island for years by the beast who rules over us from the towering crag above the harbor into which your ship sailed.

"We are not from this planet, but we are prisoners here now because we have been robbed of our flying craft.

"We come here not by magical means, but by flying craft from beyond the confines of your knowledge. Nevertheless, you will be able to understand," she began to explain:

"Instead of using wind to fill our sails—as you do to propel your ship across your seas—we use the gravity that holds you to your planet to propel our craft across the great 'seas' you can see from your ship at night. It is really very simple how we use this force of gravity, but you must first think of gravity as bits of stuff, just as you know a beach is made up of bits of sand.

"We have figured out how to make gravity work for us. Think of it this way, Bill Odun. You know that your ship goes forward through the water because the wind is filling its sails. In our flying craft we make bits of gravity into a stream, and we thrust those bits of gravity out of holes in the sides of the flying craft.

"Can you picture that, Bill Odun?"

"Yes, I think so," I replied, though I could not.

"Good," she continued. "Then now think of what happens to the wind itself when it fills those sails."

"Well, it fills the sails," I suggested, repeating her words.

"I have put it badly," she responded with an enchanting little pout that turned into a smile as she suddenly thought of a new way of trying to explain something which was obviously very simple to her, but which was very difficult for me to understand.

"What would happen," she asked, "if your ship was stoutly moored to a pier, all sails set and a hurricane began to blow?"

"The sails would be torn to shreds!" I replied proudly, finally realizing I was getting somewhere.

"That is correct," she answered. "What would happen though if those sails were so strong they would not tear, and the masts so stout they would not break? What would the wind do then?"

I thought for a moment, befuddled. I had never thought this process through so completely. "The wind would have to bounce back on itself, I think," I finally ventured.

"Exactly!" she shouted with glee. She walked over, gave me a hug as I sat in the chair and kissed me on the lips.

"Now we are making real progress, Bill Odun," she added. "This is difficult, but you are doing fabulously. It took us billions of years to figure just this much out, but you have done it in less than an hour. I know this is tiring, but we must finish it quickly, so I will carry on.

"There is a principle of physics which we know as the following: for every action, there is an equal and opposite reaction. When the wind fills your sails, they billow out and push the ship forward. Action: wind pushing on the sails. Reaction: ship being pushed through the sea..."

"But," I interrupted boldly, "those actions and reactions are in the same direction."

"Very good, Bill Odun," she replied, quite excited by my insight. "It would seem thus, but let me go on and you will see why they are really opposite.

"If the ship is stoutly moored to the pier the wind would bounce back —as you yourself said—if the sails did not shred, and the masts did not fall. The reason the wind has to bounce back is because the ship can't move forward as it wants to.

"The bounce back is the reaction. The reaction when you are under way at sea is not 'necessary' because the forward movement of the ship alleviates the requirement for the specific reaction. Your ship is, however, actually reacting to the original action of the wind filling the sails.

"Do you understand, Bill Odun?"

"Yes," I replied honestly. It really was beginning to make sense now. I clearly understood that if the ship did not move forward due to the wind pushing on the sails, something else had to give, and that was the wind if the sails and masts were strong enough. Otherwise the sails and masts would be the ones to give way.

"The situation with our flying craft is very similar," she went on. "Except we create the 'wind' within those flying craft. 9 The 'wind' is the streams of bits of gravity, and we thrust those streams very rapidly out of the holes of the flying craft.

"The equal and opposite reaction is..."

I could not help but finish her sentence, so I interrupted her again, "The craft going forward...very rapidly..."

She was delighted and I got another kiss, but only a rapid kiss because there was more to learn.

She went on to tell me how the craft worked, and it was merely a process of thrusting the bits of gravity. There are nine different thrusters used in various combinations to make the craft go rapidly in different directions. The thrusters swivel so they can be pointed up and down, so the craft can go up and down as well. I have seen birds fly, I had never expected to do so myself. I never did—but I later saw her fly away and... leave.

The process of creating these little bits of gravity was really quite simple but complex, she explained. They simply flew off a rapidly spinning disk.

I knew about spinning disks. We threw disks for sport, and they became spinning disks as we threw them.

But, she explained, her spinning disks spin much more rapidly than our spinning disks.

When she had finished her explanation, I thought it all through and offered my own summary of what she had explained to me. "You have now told me that you have a rapidly spinning disk in your craft," I said, "from which bits of gravity come flying off and that you then vent these bits of gravity very rapidly through thrusters in order to make your craft fly very rapidly."

She smiled her beautiful smile, and I got another kiss—a long one.

Then she added, "There is something else I need to tell you: the bits of gravity are only somewhat like the grains of sand on the beach. The grains of sand are made up of something. The bits of gravity are made up of nothing, but they still cause an equal and opposite reaction when they are vented through the thrusters, because they act as if they are made of something. We don't know exactly why, but it has to do with the interaction between the different densities of the Universe.

"You know about three of these densities because you have length, width and breadth. None of us can see, touch or even measure the fourth density, but we know it is there because the fourth density interacts with the first three densities.

"We think the reason why bits of gravity do what they do is because of this interaction.

"I know this is getting a little complex, so I won't say any more except that the energy we use to spin our disks works the same way. That energy is also made up of bits of nothing, which thrust against grooves in the spinning disks and make them spin—very rapidly."

As my head was also spinning from all this she turned to me and said, "I need your help...desperately!"

"What may I do for you?" I asked.

She went on to tell me of her plight, and I shall summarize those dire straits in which she and her venerable voluntary servant found themselves; and not forgetting her Crew who, because of the controlling device implanted in their skulls, had been transformed into those creatures who had attacked us.

Initially they had all been sent on an expedition to our planet to observe us and report back. They had been here for some time, having built the pit into which we had fallen as a base for their operation. They knew that their stretch of coastline was uninhabited and therefore did not expect anybody to fall in. However, they had disguised the entrance in order that it be invisible from the air, as there were other interested parties from out there with a totally different attitude toward us.

Their base of operations had nevertheless been discovered by the beast who later became the lord of the crag which towered above the landscape. My host was not quite sure who the beast was or how he got there, but she suspected that he was one of the others. The beast and his cutthroat followers had slipped into my host's base of operations one night, and had stolen her flying craft (the flying craft which thrusts streams of bits of gravity, and which therefore flies very rapidly). These intruders had also slain many of her Crew guarding the craft, strewing their bodies about the earthen floor on which I had been so recently standing. Since then my host and her venerable voluntary servant had been helpless, because within the craft was their means of communication.

My host sent her Number One with the remainder of her Crew to look for the craft. She and her venerable voluntary servant had remained behind, because it was her duty to do so. They had all disappeared, and she and her servant had been left alone for many long months. The two of them had hidden sensors about the forest and the harbor, and she had therefore seen and heard our arrival and the events which had transpired since. She had lured us into the pit by simulating the sound of musketry.

My host had also concluded that her Crew had been turned into those creatures who had attacked our line handlers, four of whom we had killed in retaliation. I felt dreadful about that now, but she would hear nothing of apology.

"You acted out of self-defense, and that is all that need be said," she insisted as tears formed in her eyes.

Before we could continue further, her venerable voluntary servant politely interrupted us to inform me that he had seen to my Crew. He had given them food and drink, told them they would have to remain where they were for the time being and assured them that I was safe.

"You, Bill Odun, must be hungry yourself," suggested my host.

"Yes," I admitted.

She smiled, took my hand and led me to her private quarters.

We enjoyed a wonderful supper in her dining salon, and then retired to her drawing room for further serious discussion.

Now that I understood the overall situation, it was time to discuss what actions we should take, she said. My host had a plan all worked out to rescue her Crew and Number One, to recover her flying craft and to destroy the beast of the crag. As she finished relating her plan to me, my host noticed that I had grown noticeably weary, and suggested I rest. We would have the next day to plan our punitive rescue mission with my Crew, and then that next night we would attack.

My host rose from her seat, walked over to me, reached down with her hand and drew me up to her. This time she really kissed me, and I kissed her with all the passion that had been welling up inside me.

I tried to say those things which I wanted to say, but before I could she backed away from me and put her finger to her lip. "Not now, Bill Odun," she said.

She took my hand and led me through her apartment to her bed chamber.

The following night my lover led me and my Crew to the lift. (The lift was an up and down moving square room that was large enough to hold all of us) and it carried us all the way back to the surface.

We reached the base of the beast's castle walls. They were built into an enormous notch in the crag in such a way that the 'roof' of the castle was actually the crag's upper overhang.

My lover had been carrying a satchel over her right shoulder, and now she removed it. Having placed the satchel on the ground, she reached inside and withdrew its contents: an energy slicer about the size of our musket pistols. She then proceeded to use this slicer to cut through the thick stone wall of the beast's castle.

When she had finished she said, "Follow me."

Once inside the castle it became even darker, but my lover sprinkled luminescent material which looked like sand onto the floor behind her so we could all follow easily without tripping or bumping into things. We made our way across a huge storage room filled with crates toward a wooden stairway that rose against the back wall. She led us up the steps.

We followed the stairway along the back wall until it reached one corner, then turned with it along the side wall, then along the front wall, back along the other side wall and finally half way up the back wall again before arriving at a short landing—before a very large, locked, steel door.

My lover drew her energy slicer and blasted a hole in the door through which we could enter. As she went through, she changed her energy slicer for an energy pistol with which she could shoot the beast and his followers.

We followed her.

After having climbed at least a thousand feet we reached the beast's living quarters. We were passing through a very large dining hall when my lover suddenly dived for the floor. My Crew and I saw this as one, following her onto the flagstones only a few moments later. I held my breath in anticipation.

I could soon see through the dining table chair behind which I was crouching, that shadowy figures were entering the dining hall by way of a far entryway. There were two of them, and when they reached the head of the table they parted ways, one proceeding down either side of the hundred foot long dining table.

I knew we would be discovered, and that really concerned me because I could see from the shadowy projection of their right arms, that they were carrying energy pistols. As they took a few steps in our direction, my lover suddenly stood up and fired a charge from her energy pistol at the shadowy figure nearest to us, who pitched forward as she was firing at the second figure. In that small space between shots, the second figure had found time to react and consequently my lover missed, blasting a hole in the wall beyond the table instead.

The second shadowy figure now began firing in our general direction. The charges flew over our heads and across the table, smashing everything they hit. I was about to express my concern about this firing to my lover when she suddenly lunged under the table.

Sending chairs flying in all directions, she slid across the flagstones on her back, at the same time carefully aiming at the second figure, and killing him.

Once my lover had determined both of the shadowy figures were truly dead she signalled for us to follow, and we proceeded out the entryway through which the figures had come.

Halfway up the next staircase, (no stairway this, it was a magnificent curved staircase in carved oak and led to the beast's bed chamber), we encountered more opposition and my lover shot another of the beast's followers as he was emerging from the entryway beyond the top landing.

Realizing that she might be able to gain quick entry into the beast's bed chamber before its door reclosed, my lover raced up the remaining steps as we followed her. Rushing past the body of the beast's follower, my lover hurled herself at the portal just as it reseated itself in its locking device.

Instead of being able to burst suddenly into the beast's bed chamber, she bounced back, clearly stunned by the portal's failure to give way to her impetuous rush. I dashed up to help, but she would have nothing of personal aid, insisting instead that I pull the energy slicer from her satchel, now laying on the blood-covered landing, the result of my lover not only having shot one of the beast's followers but also having broken her nose which was bleeding profusely.

I handed my lover the energy slicer and she propped herself up enough to aim it at the portal. In a few moments the portal disintegrated before my astonished eyes.

"Get him!" she ordered.

The Boatswain stood next to me, and I ordered him, "See to her wounds, immediately!"

Without hesitation I dashed into the bed chamber of the beast and found him after much searching, cowering under his own bed. I dragged him kicking, scratching and screaming all the way across the bed chamber and presented him to my lover.

Propped up against the balustrade, she glowered at the sniveling creature she had called the beast. He seemed most pathetic to me, though I knew he was evidently capable of deeds of bestiality.

"Don't kill me, don't kill me!..." the beast shrieked repeatedly, cowering before my lover.

My bloodied lover could only stare at the beast in total disgust until the beast became so exhausted that he could only stop and pant like a dog, but calling him a dog is an insult to one of our most beloved animals!

Finally, my lover spoke to the beast, "I will spare you, but only under one condition. You must immediately reveal to me the location of the device you use to control my Crew through the skull implants."

"There," the beast responded abjectly, raising a finger and weakly pointing into his bedchamber.

"Bring him!" ordered my lover as she rose to her feet.

She strode through the entryway and by the scruff of the neck I dragged him after us.

"Where?" my lover demanded as she stood next to the beast's bed.

"In here, let me show you," the beast replied, squiggling loose from my grip and crawling to the wall next to the headboard. The beast clawed his way up the paneled wall and touched some hidden button on it. The panel before him slid quickly to one side revealing a large niche in which stood what was obviously a control mechanism.

Although he seemed to be cooperating I felt that the beast was up to something. Suddenly he reached up, grabbed something from inside the niche and wheeled about quickly, aiming that 'something,' an energy pistol, directly at my lover.

I reacted instantly, and leaped for the beast pushing him off balance. Before anyone could react I was upon him and crushed the beast's skull with the ruby on the pommel of my broadsword.

My lover deactivated the mind control mechanism hidden in the large niche by blasting it with energy pistol shots.

She already knew where her Crew was incarcerated, so we quickly gathered up my Crew and proceeded to that place within the castle. We released her Crew—including her Number One, a man whom I instantly liked for his caring attitude toward my lover's Crew.

They were all dazed by events and their sudden release. They remembered nothing of what had happened to them since their capture. They were amazed to see how they looked, and how they were 'dressed,' but most of all by how they had been branded with the number 6—a number which was a metaphor of great significance to them, but a number which in the context of the branding meant death.

Once she had been assured that her Crew was safe, my lover led me back to the storage room through which we had originally entered the castle.

As we entered the store room the floor began to slide back and I thought I might fall into another pit. The floor stopped moving before I was forced to take another plunge however, a spiral ramp suddenly appearing before us in the hole left by the receded floor.

We descended the long spiral ramp and then made our way through a labyrinthine series of corridors. With my lover still leading the way we eventually entered a cavern in which were two flying craft.

My lover said that the one nearer to us was hers and that the other belonged to the beast. Surprisingly to me, she was more interested in the craft of the beast, and we boarded it. She rummaged around its bridge a while, familiarizing herself with it. Then she immobilized the craft by blasting the navigation computer with her energy pistol.

Then she turned to me and kissed me long and passionately on the lips.

"Bill Odun, you must go back to your ship, and I must leave on mine."

The extragalactics also constructed the mythos NOSTOS to help them begin the task of lovingly guiding the indigenous beings of developing Altea toward understanding the newcomer's scientific knowledge.

Much later those known as Essenes allegorized the story of the beast of the mythos NOSTOS and infused their allegorical story into the culture of the planet whose beings were being prepared to lead the redeeming of the galaxy. Essenes infused this story into that culture in order to juxtapose the beast—the refusal to accept ideas beyond one's own—and the lover of the hero—the thirst for knowledge. Essenes marked the beast of this allegorized story with the number 666 to show that bestiality makes one thrice dead.

The use of mythos was an enormously important tool of the extragalactics to greatly assist them in carefully and lovingly guiding their partners in the formation of an equal union. The plan to use mythos had been decided upon by the very first leaders shortly after they left Hermur. Trosumur had loved mythos, and he had been the driving force behind the adoption of mythos as teacher—billions of years before the discovery of Altea.

The best way to approach the scientifically unadvanced beings of the seed planet that the intergalactic migrators would eventually find had also been worked out billions of years before discovery. Sereena had proposed the original idea, and her plan was never changed. When the migrators came upon the future Altea they did not show themselves at once. They secretly gathered as much information as they could about the indigenous population while awaiting an inevitable severe storm to strike somewhere on the planet. When a hurricane (called a typhoon in Hurtegel) ravaged the eastern coast of one of the large land masses of the future Altea, the extragalactics appeared alongside those helping the victims of the storm. Working together—and almost totally unaware of their differences—the indigenous beings and the intergalactic pioneers accomplished great feats of rescue. When the storm abated and the crisis was past, the two groups sat down together to begin forming the union.

There had been great unanimity at the onset of the migration, but—mostly as the result of time and continued disappointment—a rift had erupted between those who wanted to continue with the imperative of the traditions and those who wearied of the trek.

About two billion years into the trek about half of the intergalactic travelers decided to stay behind on a planet the migrators had made habitable and on which they had lived temporarily for a thousand years while searching for a seed planet in the galaxy of the planet which was their temporary home.

Bloodshed was avoided, but the two factions parted very angrily.

About ten years later tragedy struck those who had chosen to stay.

A distress transcommunication asking for immediate assistance was received aboard the vessels of the flotilla of those continuing on. Those who had chosen to stay were under attack from an unknown disease and were dying even as the message was sent. The command went out for all vessels to immediately alter course and to return to the planet (on which those who had chosen to stay were dying). In a matter of days (the return trip was to take two years) the transcommunications suddenly ceased. Even so, the returners continued with their rescue mission.

They were too late.

A landing party made up entirely of volunteers wearing ultra protective sterile clothing was dispatched to the surface of the planet. They sent back sad news. The disease had been so devastating that not a living thing, neither plant, nor animal, nor self-aware being had remained alive.

Badly shaken by their experience, the landing party insisted, however, on returning to a quarantine vessel. It was a wise precaution, for despite their vigilance they all died very quickly.

The flotilla commander sadly ordered that the quarantine vessel, together with the bodies of its former occupants, be totally destroyed. This was to be done in such a way that the disease would not be able to contaminate any future visitor who might happen to pass by that spot in space.

A method was devised using the energy lances of two vessels, and in an instant the quarantined vessel and its contents disappeared. During high speed space transits all space craft divert the energy from their weapons defense systems to their energy lance, which is projected forward from space craft. Energy lances are used to destroy objects in space that are large enough to damage craft, if in a collision with them. Space craft navigate around known objects in space, but the only way to avoid others is to destroy them. This procedure works because there are no large objects in interstellar and intergalactic space, and space craft travel slowly enough within solar systems to be able to locate and navigate around large unknown objects.

This experience taught the remaining intergalactic travelers an incredibly invaluable lesson: remain steadfast to the imperative, no matter what. Without this lesson the following generations of intergalactic travelers realized that they would never have been able to continue on for another...three...billion...years!

The intergalactic pioneers finally discovered the seed planet which would soon be called Altea, the planet which fulfilled the imperatives of the traditions. Everything on Altea began relatively smoothly.

The indigenous beings were precisely the developing beings the migrators had long sought, and Altea was perfect in every way: a beautiful blue-green planet with the potential of being the seed of a galactic-wide civilization.

After their arrival on Altea many of the extragalactics began to think about how they would colonize from Altea, and what that experience would be like. Most of them came to the conclusion that the galactic experience in this new galaxy would be easier than it had been in the previous galaxy. (This consideration was based both on the knowledge that the Hermurians were obliged to flee from the preceding galaxy and the subsequent rigors of their five-billion year trek.) It was, therefore, with a great deal of optimism that most of the newcomers began their new galactic experience.

Not all of the newcomers were certain that this galactic experience would be easy, so a group of doubters reformed the organization which had originally led them from Hermur, calling themselves Essenes—just as those who had gone five billion years before had. Essenes were ready to be the preparers of the new galaxy. They were ready for whatever eventualities might arise in the many years they knew it would take before galactic redeeming.

The original members of this new group of Essenes were all extragalactics, but soon indigenous beings also joined, including many young adults. Among them were Lura White, when she was 18, and her friend Richy Drake, when he was only 17—but nearly 18.

Ever since she had been picked as the winner of the contest to name the scientific alphabet and partial language brought by the intergalactic travelers, Lura White had been known for her astute insights into the manner of things.

Richy Drake, on the other hand, had been a restless youth, totally the opposite of his friend Lura White, until suddenly one day something struck him. He turned to Lura as they walked home together and said to her quite unexpectedly, "I have a very strange feeling that everything is not going to turn out quite as well as we are being told. I think it is going to be very difficult. We must be prepared for everything."

The next day, Lura White and Richy Drake became the first two indigenous Essenes. And although they had discussed the matter with their parents, the decision was entirely theirs.

The two mythos related above ODUNSIDE and NOSTOS (the latter only in one of its 13 parts) and many other legends and tales of Altean mythos have been handed down over the ages to the entire galaxy. Fragments, including some of their original texts, have been infused into many indigenous stories of the beings inhabiting the planet prepared for them by Essenes. This has been done as part of their role as preparers of the galaxy, and in order to stimulate the imagination and intellect of these beings.

Essenes have also behaved in such a way as to counterbalance the horrific intervention in the affairs of these beings by the Pleiadeans—

descendants of rebellious cabalists who have enslaved almost the entire galaxy.

The going has been difficult—excruciatingly difficult—more excruciatingly difficult than even Richy Drake could have foreseen two billion years ago as a result of his intuitive understanding of the way things might develop.

It has been a titanic struggle to keep all the children of the galaxy from being downcast.

Chapter Four

Philosophia

The now united Alteans joined together to enhance their understanding of the Universe through study, using the traditional name for such study that had been brought to this galaxy by the intergalactic travelers: Philosophia.

According to Philosophia the Universe was created by the Source of the Universe so that the Source could share the Universe with self-aware beings.

According to Philosophia the Source lovingly guides self-aware beings toward an understanding of love. Thus self-aware beings will gain harmony with themselves, their fellow self-aware beings, their environment and the Universe.

According to Philosophia the ultimate goal of the Universe is harmony.

According to Philosophia the Source of the Universe radiates Everything from the zero-dimension point where the tip of the cone-shaped physical universe meets the tip of the hypercone-shaped hyperdimensional universe.

According to Philosophia the physical universe, the hyperdimensional universe and their Source combine to form the Universe.

According to Philosophia the physical universe is finite with clearly defined conical limits. However, at the interface of three-dimensions, complexified three-space and four-dimensions (caused by the very rapid vorticular spinning of matter along the rim of the physical universe) the physical universe loops back on itself, connects to the rim of the hyperdimensional universe and forms a hyperdimensional four-torus: a four-dimensional mathematical doughnut. 10

The age of the Universe has not been determined, and it may be impossible to do so. The stuff of which the Universe is made streams from the Source, proceeds up the cone of the physical universe and eventually reaches the upper limit of that cone, then extremely high speed rotation transdimensions the stuff of the physical universe into the hyperdimensional universe. This then spirals inward to the Source. The Source transconverts the stuff of the hyperdimensional universe into the stuff of the physical universe and extrudes that stuff into the physical universe. The process is repeated over and over and over again.

According to Philosophia the Source of the Universe is nothing in three-dimensions, and Everything in four-dimensions.

Since the Source is a four-dimensional Entity, Its extrusions into three-dimensions are necessarily only approximations of Its true four-dimensional self. This is so because four-dimensions is too complex to be modeled exactly in three-dimensions.

According to Philosophia the Source extrudes Itself into the physical universe by means of a process which unfolds over time. Time is the carrier which streams outward from the Source, and in time is embedded the stuff of which the physical universe is made. The Source of the Universe extrudes Itself into the three-dimensional physical universe by means of time in three ways. One of these extrusions forms the physical universe, the second binds it together and the third carries forward souls.

These extrusions can be modeled by a tetrahedron with data, information and knowledge representing these three extrusions at the three corners of its base. 11 Wisdom, the zero-dimension point at the apex of the tetrahedron is the radiating Source from which these extrusions emanate. The lines connecting the apex to its three lower corners of the tetrahedron represent Eternal Time, physical time and consciousness time.

Eternal Time, which is eternally invariant, carries forward the non-living parts of the physical universe.

Physical time, which varies greatly with environment, carries forward those things which hold the physical universe together.

Consciousness time, is also invariant, carries forward souls and measures the duration of self-aware consciousness and the conditions under which self-aware consciousness can exist.

The non-living parts of the physical universe are organized in a less complex way than both living things and self-aware consciousness. Therefore, the conditions under which the non-living parts of the physical universe can exist are also less complex, usually resulting in a long period of existence.

Living things are more complex and require a more complex set of conditions under which they can live, usually for a short life-span.

Souls are extruded into the physical universe by the Source so that they may gain experience and knowledge. To do this souls attach themselves to three-dimensional beings. Together, souls and the beings to whom they are attached form self-aware consciousness.

Self-aware consciousness requires not only the conditions required by both the non-living parts of the physical universe and living things in order to exist in three-dimensions, but also another, highly complex set of conditions.

Consciousness time is the carrier in which all the conditions required by the non-living parts of the physical universe, living things and self-aware beings are embedded so that all of them can exist in the physical universe.

The radiating of Eternal Time is accomplished in a spiraling fashion. There are spirals of ascending size, from the smallest at the sub-atomic level to the largest: the enormous vortex which is the conical physical universe. As a result of this vorticular unfolding, spin is imparted on everything. Spin is what makes everything work.

The radiating of physical time contains four-dimensional gravity and the three-dimensional manifestations of four-dimensional gravity: the weak force, the strong force, light and three-dimensional gravity.

These three-dimensional manifestations of four-dimensional gravity can also be represented tetrahedrally, with three-dimensional gravity at the apex.

Four-dimensional gravity and three-fourths of its four manifestations in three-dimensions—the weak force, the strong force and three-dimensional gravity—hold the physical universe together.

Although the natures of the weak force, the strong force and three-dimensional gravity are somewhat understood, light remains a mystery. Light is complex, multi-faceted and unfathomable. Light does, however, seem to be a governor on how fast things can travel.

Three-dimensional and four-dimensional gravity govern the speed of light.

Working together, three-dimensional and four-dimensional gravity are sometimes strong enough to even stop light, due to the coalescing of an enormous amount of extremely dense matter—as in the collapse of certain types of stars.

The strength of three-dimensional gravity decreases at greater and greater distances from matter. Similarly, and at the same rate, the strength of four-dimensional gravity decreases at greater and greater distances from matter. However, as the initial strength of three-dimensional gravity is weaker than that of four-dimensional gravity, the ability of three-dimensional gravity to help govern the speed of light decreases at a closer distance from a large mass than that of four-dimensional gravity. Due to the fact that galaxies are close enough together throughout the physical universe, four-dimensional gravity never actually loses its ability to govern the speed of light.

As a result of the increasing inability of three-dimensional gravity to govern the speed of light, there are three greatly different speeds of light depending upon how far distant light is from a large amount of matter. It is unknown why light suddenly changes speed by discreet amounts, instead of gradually as it gets farther and farther from large amounts of matter, but the Universe likes to do things in blocks rather than just dribbling on.

Solar system light speed is approximately 186,000 miles per second and extends well beyond the limits of a solar system. 12

Interstellar light speed is the speed of light between solar systems. Over 400,000 times faster than solar system light speed, interstellar light speed begins well beyond the limits of a solar system and extends well beyond the fringes of galaxies.

Intergalactic light speed is seven times faster than interstellar light speed. Intergalactic light speed is the speed of light in the physical universe well beyond the fringes of galaxies.

Physical time is affected by the speed of travel: slower speed results in faster time; faster speed results in slower time.

The rate of physical time is determined by the total speed component of the observer.

Only a certain band of physical time rates is compatible with the existence of physical matter. An even narrower band of physical time rates allows for the existence of life. A band of physical time rates narrower yet, produces the environment in which self-aware beings can live.

Only a retrograde precession rate of 25,920 years produces the off-center rotation which calibrates and fine tunes the physical time rate to the point where natural evolutionary forces can work to produce a life form. A life form which can evolve highly enough to become that vital three-dimensional being to which the four-dimensional soul can attach itself, in order to have the opportunity to experience and learn, the very important and vital process that insures galactic redeeming and eventual redemption of the Universe.

Any given cross-section, cut perpendicular to the central axis of the cone of the physical universe, results in a circular slice of the physical universe. Any given circular slice contains data, information and knowledge extruded into the physical universe by the Source; though the composition of that data, information and knowledge is always different from one slice to the next. Nevertheless, any given circular slice (even one which is so thin that it is no thicker than the ink with which it can be drawn on a piece of paper) is still three-dimensional—and only deemed two-dimensional as a convenience for geometric calculation. Any given circular slice contains something of everything, including the all-important spinning which makes everything work.

The lengths of the vast number of the regularly varying circumferences of three-dimensional circular slices of the conical physical universe—which can be geometrically modeled to be so thin that they can be called two-dimensional and therefore deemed to have only one circumference—are calculated by multiplying their diameters by pi, the Universal Constant of the Universe.

Much of Philosophia is tremendously old, but it is always subject to alteration, due to new insights deduced by beings studying and practicing Philosophia.

According to Philosophia there exists an all-encompassing dualism which helps to explain the twistings and turnings of life. This dualism consists of the Eternal and the temporal, and it is necessary to balance these opposites in order to be in harmony.

According to Philosophia there exists the transarking of souls. Transarking means that immortal souls attach themselves to mortal beings for the duration of the lives of those mortal beings, and in so doing gain experience and knowledge.

The transarking of souls is the most important function that beings have.

According to Philosophia the soul is a synthesis of vital four-dimensional concepts—including the matrix of current galaxy transarkings; transdimensional requirements for interfacing with three-dimensional beings and a vast collection of accumulated data, information and knowledge.

The soul transcommunicates continuously to provide the being currently transarking the soul with important guidance in ever increasing intensity and timeliness. This occurs as both the soul and the being transition together toward understanding their combined purpose during that particular transarking.

The process of transarking varies greatly as to number of transarkings per galaxy, experience gained per transarking and intervals between transarkings. In every galaxy, each soul undergoes one complete cycle of the transarking process: nominal state, various stages of development and completion.

The results of galactic transarkings remain the same from galaxy to galaxy, but the scenarios vary. The redeeming of any particular galaxy depends on the active participation of all the immortal souls in that particular galaxy, and on the ways in which souls react to varying circumstances.

Souls always have the same purpose in each galaxy they inhabit: it is essential for each soul to fulfill its cycle before galactic redeeming is complete.

Refusal to accept the requirement to voluntarily accomplish the goals of any given transarking only results in more transarkings, and the delay of redeeming that particular galaxy, which in turn delays the redeeming of the Universe.

Therefore, it is the role of each soul during each transarking in each galaxy to seek to discover the purpose of that particular transarking, and then to voluntarily seek to fulfill that purpose.

Certain pairs and small groups of souls have special relationships. These include:

Soul partners—a vital relationship in which soul partners form marriages during specified transarkings;
Soul parents and soul children—when soul partners marry they often have offspring, some of whom are soul children, resulting in their becoming soul parents. These two types of relationships provide for two distinct and beneficial soul interactions;
Soul mates—three to seven souls who always transark together to provide mutual support;
Soul companions—pairs which assist one another during specified transarkings.

According to Philosophia souls have a period of existence in each galaxy when they remember everything; when the memories of different transarkings share their specific memories. This is also a time when souls can interact with other souls and share memories with one another.

Philosophia is important to those who study it, as Philosophia assists and guides them in their personal relationships.

In various tenets, Philosophia shows that it is essential for beings to follow voluntary guidelines of behavior which promote harmonious interactions between beings. Perhaps the most important of these tenets is the continuous striving to see the perspective of others.

Deciding how to act in any given circumstance is determined by both tradition and timely thinking, and allows individuals wide latitude of action within a specified framework. Another purpose of this tenet is to promote open and wide ranging discussion and relationships between beings.

By practicing this rational approach to the important source of insight (searching with others for new ideas) beings are able to expand their abilities in such areas as: realization of self-worth, formulation of personal habits, understanding the relative merit of opposing views, finding purpose in seemingly purposeless situations and establishing loving relationships.

Loving relationships include sexually intimate relationships. Observation has shown that during sexual excitement and at the point of sexual release enormous amounts of hyperdimensional energy are released from the hyperdimensional soul. Therefore, Philosophia concludes that the requirement for self-aware beings to have sexually intimate loving relationships is the result of the hyperdimensional soul's needs. The difference between animals and self-aware beings is that self-aware beings have souls which are hyperdimensional and therefore spiritual. Although some animals enjoy sexual release and form loving relationships, animals do not enjoy sexual intimacy and release to the extent that self-aware beings do. Animals do not have souls, self-aware beings do. Therefore the self-aware beings' far greater sexual enjoyment is spiritual in nature.

Translating concepts into metaphor is an important way of assisting beings to understand and practice Philosophia.

Exemplifying this concept are the Five Symbols of Philosophia:

The keirykeion consists of three lines representing two drakon entwined about a straight rod. 13 The drakon are a metaphor for the continuous wanderings of the two opposites of the Universe: the Eternal and the temporal. The rod represents the process of resolving the opposites. The crossings of the drakon indicate moments of resolution and harmony. When the drakon are wide apart disharmony reins.

The Hellenikos word 'drakon' as used in Philosophia means 'dragon,' 'serpent' or 'snake.' Drakon are used in the keirykeion because of various drakon body shapes.

The second symbol is the Waldark soul print, a two-dimensional representation of the three-dimensional energy disturbance pattern of the soul together with a small portion of the three-dimensional secondary energy disturbance pattern. That small portion is virtually the same for all souls. The Waldark soul print is composed of a circle, from which extend the points of a five pointed star—but the points are irregular: some are elongated, others foreshortened. Inside the circle is a six pointed star. At the center of the six pointed star is a point.

Billions upon billions of years ago, far back in the chain of galaxies preceding the latest galaxy, lived Waldark, the first being known to have demonstrated that the soul must exist. He was able to record both the three-dimensional energy disturbance pattern and the three-dimensional secondary energy disturbance pattern of souls, each soul having its own absolutely unique pattern.

Later students of Philosophia conceived the Waldark soul print in order to present an easily recognized representation of the soul and part of the three-dimensional secondary energy disturbance pattern of the soul. The circle depicts the principal spherical three-dimensional energy disturbance patterns emanating from the soul. The elongated and foreshortened points of a five pointed irregular star which extend from the circle depict part of the three-dimensional secondary energy disturbance pattern. The six pointed star is a representation of two spinning interlocked tetrahedra, (Waldark's model for the way in which the soul transredimensions the energy streaming from the Source of the Universe). The point at the center of the six pointed star represents the zero-dimension point, through which the Source of the Universe extrudes Itself into three-dimensions.

The third symbol is the triphylon, in the form of a flower, it is a three-dimensional metaphor for the unfolding process of the Universe.

The fourth symbol is two interlocked tetrahedra, a three-dimensional 'representation' of Horun, the hyperdimensional energy which streams from the Source. 14 The computed geometric modeling of the three-dimensional disturbance patterns of Horun shows both tetrahedra simultaneously spinning about all of the seven axes of tetrahedral spin symmetry, a total of 14 spins.

The fifth symbol of Philosophia is the apple. Used as a symbol of Philosophia because the uppermost part of the three-dimensional secondary energy disturbance pattern of a soul print looks like a large apple with progressively smaller apples piled on top of one another, all with their stems pointing downward. This pattern continues through the top of the skull and onward indefinitely with the 'apples' getting progressively smaller and weaker.

Philosophia is an ever expanding and dynamic study, constantly modified by those who study it.

Chapter Five

Waldark

Waldark lived about one hundred billion years ago, but the results of his work are of such magnitude that Waldark has become legendary. His very important and vital findings are the basis for significant portions of the body of scientific knowledge, and many of the philosophic concepts handed down from galaxy to galaxy, along the chain of galaxies which have followed since Waldark uncovered many secrets of the Universe.

The galaxy in which Waldark lived is the oldest galaxy recorded in the ongoing history carried forward along the chain of galaxies leading to the current galaxy, but it has always been acknowledged that there were galaxies before the galaxy in which Waldark lived; and that there must have been intergalactic migrations previous to the first recorded migration. (The first recorded migration from Waldark's galaxy to the second historically recorded galaxy in the chain of galaxies leading to this galaxy.)

Indeed there are strong indications that much scientific knowledge must have existed during earlier times and the scientific alphabet and partial language (which came to be called Hellenikos by Alteans) is known to have come down from a galaxy previous to that in which Waldark lived. It is also known that during the time of his galaxy, albeit before he was born, this knowledge was lost due to a cataclysmic natural disaster on Waldark's planet. At the time of this catastrophe no other planets in that galaxy had been colonised.

The devastation was so great that incredible amounts of knowledge were lost. Centuries later, scattered and incomplete records were found by chance in a deserted, hermetically sealed tunnel containing shattered crystal tubes, strange looking cars, and what turned out to be control mechanisms. A damaged lexicon was also found in the sealed tunnel and through much hard labor the lexicon was translated into the language of the day, ultimately resulting in the preservation of what was to became known as Hellenikos. Grave robbers found the tunnel initially, but had been seen by seekers of that time, and those seekers preserved, aired, catalogued and published what had been so miraculously discovered. Waldark is therefore not the first to figure things out, but he is the first to have been historically recorded as having done so.

Waldark worked on nearly everything, but he began with the most important manifestation of the Source: self-aware consciousness.

This work turned out to be the point of departure on a long and increasingly internally consistent voyage of discovery which led him along the following path: from consciousness to energy production; to sexual and physical well being; and on to space travel.

Initially, Waldark had to 'prove' that self-aware beings actually have a soul or consciousness different from other animals. From his background in philosophy Waldark thought that the soul resides in a dimension higher than the body.

Therefore, Waldark knew that he could only 'prove' that the soul exists by demonstrating some manifestation of it in three-dimensions. He knew that he could never prove its physical existence, because the soul simply does not reside in three-dimensional reality.

Waldark reasoned that before he could delve into the mysterious realm of the soul and self-aware consciousness, he had to first learn, through the study of brain functions, everything he could about the very observable workings of the three-dimensional aspects of the mind of self-aware beings. His inescapable conclusion: the physical brain operates on electricity.

Based on this conclusion, Waldark theorized that the soul might also operate on heretofore unknown higher-dimensional energy. If he could somehow demonstrate that the soul operated on such an energy, then by inference the soul must exist. One could not have process without cause.

Although Waldark considered his tentative ideas extremely radical, for he was a man of extreme conservatism in all things, they actually meshed with existing philosophic thinking which had long since postulated that the Source of the Universe radiated some kind of energy from a zero-dimension point at the center of the Universe. And that in some way, some self-aware beings were sometimes able to tap into that energy and become at one with the Source.

Waldark knew of this thinking that energy radiated from the Source of the Universe and concluded that if his own theory of 'self-aware consciousness energy' had any chance of being a reasonable model for how the soul operates, he would have to first demonstrate that this energy from the Source actually exists.

This required many years of arduous labor on Waldark's part before he finally perfected a device which could 'detect' higher-dimensional energy by detecting anomalies in three-dimensional energy fields.

Waldark knew that it would never be possible to actually record higher-dimensional energy using three-dimensional devices, but he strongly suspected that the energy anomalies of the physical universe that were already known and partially observed were the result of interaction with theoretical higher dimensions. This had been previously postulated by leading researchers of his day. What Waldark sought were patterns in these anomalies.

Using the relatively crude initial device he had made, Waldark spent years of detailed observation and painstaking cataloging of energy anomalies. Only then did Waldark begin to see that long hoped for patterns were emerging out of apparent disorder. After more years he found that they fitted into a highly logical framework, but before announcing his tentative conclusions, Waldark insisted—to the detriment of his well being—that there could not be one single inconsistency in these patterns.

At last, and still before revealing any of his work, Waldark began the attempt to conceive and subsequently build a second and much more sophisticated higher-dimensional 'measuring' device. When perfected it was able to accurately measure and record many different apparent three-dimensional manifestations of energy streaming from the Source. The key to Waldark's success was twofold, consisting of a positive frame of mind as to the device's capabilities and the use of previous data, meticulously gathered. This information enabled Waldark to predict both the location and the intensity of energy anomalies in a wide variety of physical environments.

Once he assured himself that he was really dealing with something substantive (and not just with wishful thinking) Waldark turned his attention back to his original intent: 'proving' that the soul exists.

Slowly and meticulously Waldark, using the same device, sought and immediately found patterning in the energy anomalies emanating from self-aware beings. No such anomalies were located around any type of animal examined by Waldark, suggesting that he might be dealing with more than just wishful thinking.

Due to his vast experience in plotting anomalies thought to be caused by energy from the Source, Waldark quickly detected patterns in these newly discovered, though quite different, three-dimensional manifestations of higher-dimensional energy, related to self-aware consciousness.

Waldark was astounded by how much less complex these patterns were: self-aware consciousness was simple when compared with Consciousness.

The results amazed Waldark. His careful and meticulous readings of his device showed the following: when a self-aware being's eyes are open, the anomaly patterns completely surround the head, spiraling outward in rapidly changing vortices of varying shapes and intensities; when the being's eyes are closed the same amount of energy is emitted, but it is always focussed into two opposing vortices, aligned with the vertical axis of the head.

Pondering over his results for some time, Waldark moved ahead with his work only after he was completely satisfied that his test results were absolutely accurate, and that his tentative conclusions—reached as a result of his seemingly endless musings and ponderings—followed a totally consistent internal logic.

Waldark also concluded that he had to now refine his device so that it could more accurately define the subtleties of the anomalies spiraling out from the self-aware consciousness, and try to locate their source.

He then clearly demonstrated with his improved device that the soul emits higher-dimensional energy in two distinctively different patterns. It radiates this energy, not from a zero-dimension point like the Source, but from a spherical area, approximately one-fifth inch diameter. This small area is located halfway through the brain to the back of the skull measured from the bridge of the nose, and slightly to the right side of the brain. This point is tangential to the centerline of the being's bi-symmetry.

Waldark had actually 'seen' the soul! The sceptical old man successfully demonstrated to himself that self-aware consciousness manifests itself in three-dimensions as a 'shadow' of its higher-dimensional reality. Much like a back lit three-dimensional sphere casts a shadow on a two-dimensional plane and appears as a circle.

The vortices suggested—and Waldark demonstrated—that the soul spins at a tremendous rate: precisely at 750,000 revolutions per minute, with the eyes open. To determine this spin rate, Waldark measured the repetitions of the constantly changing patterns of the omni-directional vortices observed emanating from 'eyes-open' self-aware beings.

For a long time it proved impossible for Waldark to measure the spin rate from 'eyes closed' self-aware beings, but he suspected that it had to be slower. Reasoning that the opposed cone vortices were a lower order manifestation of a spinning process that became more complex as the spin rate increased. To resolve his problem, Waldark reverted to yet more years of study—this time reading every book on geometry he could find, intuitively feeling that the solution to modeling his observations lay in that traditional branch of mathematics.

The answer was to be found in the moldering pages of the most ancient of all the weighty tomes through which Waldark had been endlessly wading. In a brief dissertation titled "Circumscribed Solids," the awestruck Waldark had a blinding flash of inspiration and was immediately able to construct a theory that is still the basis for understanding how the soul manifests itself in three-dimensional reality.

The circumscribed solids were described in the tome as the five simplest, regular three-dimensional building blocks of the physical universe: the tetrahedron, the cube, the octahedron, the icosahedron and the dodecahedron. 15 To circumscribe these solid shapes meant to surround each of them with a sphere so that their varying numbers of points just touch the sphere.

Waldark chose the circumscribed tetrahedron as his initial model since it was the lowest order and simplest form; all other shapes could be reduced to the tetrahedron, but the tetrahedron could not be made into any simpler shape that was both regular and three-dimensional.

Since both the 'eyes open' and 'eyes closed' modes gave patterns that were the same above and below the head, Waldark reasoned that he should not use a single circumscribed tetrahedron as his geometric model: one spinning tetrahedron he felt would produce a pattern different above its spinning point than below its spinning base. So he chose two circumscribed tetrahedra, interlocked so that—if the sphere was spun—one point of one tetrahedron would just touch the north pole of the sphere, while another such point of the other tetrahedron would just touch the south pole. 16 Viewed from either pole this arrangement looked like a six-pointed star with a dot in the exact center, where the two pole points touched the two poles of the sphere. Further, lines drawn between the lower six points of the nested tetrahedra formed a hexagon in two-dimensions. It was geometrically pleasing, if nothing else, thought Waldark.

He next began to spin his actual physical model, and—as the revolutions began to build up—energy anomalies identical to those that emanated from the 'eyes closed' self-aware consciousness began to manifest themselves before a greatly pleased Waldark! His model was apparently correct!

Waldark could now show conclusively that two spinning interlocked tetrahedra create three-dimensional energy field anomalies like those created by closed eyed self-aware beings, but he could not yet model the 'eyes open' phenomenon. Waldark mused and pondered further until he finally realized that it was impossible: the means to spin his model at speeds anywhere near 750,000 rpms did not exist at the time.

Then he suddenly understood that he did not have to: when the spinning tetrahedra reached exactly 750,000 rpms they would suddenly (due to forces that are still not understood to this day) begin to act as if they successively 'became' the four other higher order solids listed above. Acting exactly as if the tetrahedra were each one of these four solids, they would form distinctively different anomaly patterns, and thus create a constantly changing, but absolutely regular, pattern of vortices.

Although Waldark could not form all of these patterns at once, he could make them individually by assembling circumscribed models of cubes, octahedra, icosahedra and dodecahedra. By spinning each separately he could record the anomaly patterns of all four. Waldark realized that there would be additional interference patterns created as one solid gave way to the next which would result in transitory residual vortices, but he knew the proper order in which the solids were formed, so predicting these interference patterns was possible.

Eventually he put all of his test data together: the anomaly patterns for each of the four higher spinning circumscribed solids along with their various mutual interference patterns. The exciting results were as predicted: the total package of his experimentally produced anomaly patterns matched those patterns previously recorded by his device as being emitted by 'eyes open' self-aware beings.

Waldark had not proven that the soul exists, but he had never hoped to. Instead, he had demonstrated that there was some process going on which resulted in the disturbance of three-dimensional energy fields, and the most likely source of those disturbances was energy from a higher dimension. Secondly, he had found that those disturbances emanated from a small spherical area in the head, which was most likely the three-dimensional manifestation of a higher-dimensional soul. Waldark had also been able to recreate these interference patterns with simple geometric modeling.

Waldark at last felt compelled to announce his findings. The main reason for this, he reasoned, was so that other seekers, particularly those in his and related fields, could not only test his data and results, but might also be able to correlate his findings with some of their own research.

As Waldark was finishing his lengthy presentation before a very august body of academicians and scholars gathered at an interdisciplinary symposeion, bedlam broke out. Skeptics berated Waldark and shouted him down.

Waldark, a very timid man of great integrity, was stunned by this severe traducing. He had checked and rechecked everything many times, and his data, modeling and conclusions were beyond reproach. What he had forgotten was that he would be dealing with emotion, not reason, when he spoke before such a gathering, extolling revolutionary ideas which were destined to sweep aside all previous notions of how the Universe is.

Extremely upset he left the speaker's stand and began to leave by a back exit, when he was approached by a group of six young men in whose eyes the fire of sudden awareness burned with such intensity that Waldark stopped to listen to them.

Their spokesman, Segelman, told Waldark that they were all Akadeimia students assigned to the same living quarters and they had become great friends. By sheer coincidence, or so it seemed, they had different areas of study, but they shared the unique quality of open mindedness and took an interest in each others disciplines.

Although Segelman was "only a student of art," he said, he was considered by the others to be the most concise and persuasive speaker among them. In a hasty consultation after Waldark's presentation (which they had attended spontaneously having seen it advertised on an Akadeimia notice board) they therefore delegated the role of spokesman to him. Nodding at one of the taller of his friends, and introducing him as Althoch a student of astrophysics, Segelman came quickly to the point.

Althoch had been researching their planet's solar system, including its sun. As a result, he had observed anomalies on virtually all of those spinning celestial bodies at nearly the same latitude: 19 to 20 degrees north or south. These apparent vorticular upwellings of energy were almost always in the hemisphere towards which the magnetic field of that particular celestial body flowed.

Althoch had been trying to find a model to explain this phenomenon, with no success whatever, a fact he had relayed to his five friends. Bergman, the other tall member of the group and a student of mathematics, while researching the history of geometry, had stumbled upon exactly the same old weighty tome of geometry as had Waldark. Bergman had read the same section on "Circumscribed Solids," and had remembered his friend's difficulties. Overtaken by sudden inspiration, Bergman had left the library on the run, dragging the weighty tome with him.

Together, the prospective astrophysicist and the budding mathematician had conceived and constructed their model, it was of two interlocked spinning tetrahedra.

They had then shown their other four close friends how the model worked: the three non-polar points of the spinning interlocked tetrahedra all touched their circumscribing sphere between 19 and 20 degrees latitude, in the hemisphere opposite their polar points, and that was the latitude at which Althoch had observed the energy anomalies. None of them had been able to figure out why this model worked, and more especially why the anomalies occurred in only one hemisphere—almost always in the hemisphere of the inflow of the magnetic field.

When they had heard Waldark's speech, they all had virtually simultaneous inspirations and following the presentation, they huddled together, and exchanged the most astounding series of hypotheses they had ever set themselves. The spokesman had summed them up for Waldark:

Does the physical universe operate in the same way as self-aware consciousness? Do spinning bodies, such as planets, actually have a kind of 'consciousness' by virtue of their spinning and creating this interlocked tetrahedra geometric model? Does the fact that Althoch's observed energy phenomena occurred consistently in the hemisphere of the magnetic field inflow, have anything to do with the planet's (or other celestial body's) possession of a 'consciousness?'

He looked expectantly at Waldark, who said sternly, "Young man, we shall test the data."

Together all seven left the hall, and all the grousers were left behind forever. The proverbial line had been drawn in the sand by Waldark, and only he and the six young students had stepped across it. Such is the way of the Universe: a very few ordinary ladies and gentlemen—inspired by circumstance or by that which is undefinable, take enormous strides down the path of understanding and accomplish the extraordinary.

The 'cabalists'—as they later came to call themselves—duly finished their studies and joined Waldark as soon as they could. Althoch and Bergman were first, followed by Segelman and his close friend Biederdorf, a musician. Last came Ahnenhof, a philosophy student, and Herzman, the historian. They were a diverse and dedicated group of 'cabalists.'

Waldark, Althoch and Bergman immediately went to work to see if they could find anomalies in their planet's natural three-dimensional energy fields which matched the anomalies caused by the higher-dimensional energy emanating from self-aware beings. Their efforts were immediately rewarded, but in order to actually map those anomalies they had to modify Waldark's device again so that it was capable of picking up even the faintest trace of the much subtler disturbances they were now researching.

Once this task was accomplished the three set out in earnest to discover what sort of patterning they would encounter while seeking the 'consciousness energy' emitted by their own spinning planet.

It was Althoch who recognized the pattern immediately: the anomalies followed exactly the lines of the magnetic field of the planet! Excited beyond belief he reported his discovery to Waldark, who retorted, "Not enough data."

It took some time before the three had completed their mapping of major portions of the planet from sea level to 100,000 feet, the highest altitude at which they were capable of taking measurements. When they were finally done, Waldark looked at everything several times, then turned to his partners and grudgingly admitted, "You may be right, Althoch."

Waldark and his partners continued their work, this time trying to figure out why there were three-dimensional energy upwellings at 19-20 degrees latitude on many celestial bodies, and why those anomalies almost always occurred in the hemisphere of the inflow of the magnetic field.

Since they knew the circumscribed tetrahedral model seemed to geometrically describe this location, and since they had discovered that the higher-dimensional energy associated with their spinning planet followed along the lines of the planet's magnetic field, they thought there might be some connection between this higher-dimensional energy and both the hemispheric and latitudinal location of the three-dimensional energy upwellings. 17

Even before they could deal with the question of location, they had to determine the reason for the upwellings, and whether they were due to an energy transfer or actual energy that was in some way 'generated' by the planet itself. Why an upwelling proved to be relatively simple to track down: recent studies by others in the field of vorticular fluid flow clearly demonstrated that a spinning body with a liquid core causes vortices to form in that liquid and that they try to rise to the surface. They do so through weaknesses in the crust, but relatively quickly coalesce into one vortex which organizes itself below the weakest spot in the crust.

In an attempt to determine if the energy was generated by the planet, they decided to look to other planets of their solar system. Althoch suggested this because he felt that the answer might lie in some of the recent data returned by unmanned rocket propelled probes to the outer planets of that system. He again quickly found a pattern which was germane to their study: the planets in question radiated more energy than they received from their sun. The reports included much speculation as to the reason for this, but subsequent reports by the same, or different authors invalidated any previous conclusions.

But Althoch knew: spinning celestial bodies somehow generate energy.

He had an additional proof for Waldark which nearly convinced the old man: contemporary theory held that all stars generated their energy entirely by means of nuclear fusion. That complex process (replicated on their planet) emitted all manner of radiation and particles, among them a zero rest mass particle called a neutrino.

According to planetary test results nuclear fusion produces a certain set number of neutrinos. Very elaborate, well conceived, expertly run and completely documented experiments to measure the quantity of neutrinos streaming from the planet's sun utterly failed to find anywhere near the expected number of neutrinos—two-thirds were 'missing.'

Althoch knew: since spinning celestial bodies somehow generate energy, fusion was responsible for only a part—perhaps one-third—of the energy produced by his planet's sun.

"Perhaps," Waldark responded when he read his younger colleague's report.

Even the excited Althoch knew, though, that there had to be some source of the energy being generated by spinning celestial bodies. The laws of thermodynamics had to be conserved. Energy generation was in reality merely energy conversion. So, at best, the planets were converting energy; they were tapping energy from some source. Energy had to come from somewhere. The source remained a mystery to them for some time; that is, until Bergman—who continued to read more arcane books—began to devour obscure treatises written by mathematicians working at the leading edge of their discipline.

These mathematicians had been dealing for some extended period of time with theoretical higher-dimensions, by means of geometrically constructing higher-dimensional models of three-dimensional geometric shapes. From their modeling these advanced thinkers had predicted the possible 'existence' of higher-dimensional universes, which would necessarily be more complex than the physical universe and therefore contain more energy.

When he read this, Bergman experienced another flash of inspiration: perhaps the very act of spinning allowed celestial bodies to rotate themselves partially into a higher dimension, and then to open a 'gate' from that higher dimension into the physical universe; thereby allowing energy to flow down from one dimension to the next, as when the spillway in a dam is opened.

When Waldark heard this totally outrageous tentative hypothesis, he said, "I think you are right, Bergman."

The reason why the very conservative Waldark could say this was on account of his own, private, tentative conclusions with regard to consciousness. He knew that there was no way self-aware consciousness could actually generate the energy he had been able to detect emanating from the soul; self-aware consciousness needed a source into which it could tap so that it could convert the energy it received into the energy which he had been able to detect. The obvious source of that energy was the Source of the Universe.

Waldark and his two partners had long since recognized that by generating the same sort of energy spinning celestial bodies were operating in very much the same way as did self-aware consciousness. This planetary consciousness energy must therefore also be transredimensioned from energy streaming from the Source, Waldark reasoned.

The anomalies originally detected by Althoch were simply lower order manifestations of the same process, Waldark concluded. 18 The three-dimensional manifestation of the higher-dimensional gating of energy was emitted at one of the points of the tetrahedron; the higher-dimensional energy was emitted at the pole point of the tetrahedron. The planetary consciousness energy radiated out of the hemisphere with the magnetic field, while the much weaker, lower order three-dimensional energy could only escape in the opposite hemisphere, away from the tremendous out welling of planetary 'consciousness energy.'

The only source for the observed vorticular energy anomalies was the Source of the Universe, the entity of higher-dimensionality which radiates everything.

They had come full circle: the Source of the Universe to self-aware consciousness to celestial bodies and back to the Source, a name as well as an Entity, taking on ever increasing meaning to Waldark, Althoch and Bergman.

The three mused and pondered about their discoveries and conclusions for some time before deciding on their next course of action. They agreed that there had to be a 'practical' result from the years of research, and that that must lie in the area of energy 'generation' for planetary-wide usage. Since there were both three-dimensional and higher-dimensional energy manifestations of what seemed to be a fantastic new source of limitless energy: higher-dimensionality. They quickly concluded that a division of labor was necessary. Waldark would consider the practicality of tapping self-aware 'produced' consciousness energy for everyday use; Althoch and Bergman would explore the possibility of developing spinning devices that would emulate a celestial body's ability to gate energy.

The younger partners soon ran into a dead end. They discovered that celestial bodies produce these vorticular upwellings due to enormous amounts of angular momentum: a combination of diameter and spin rate. Devices small enough to be practical would simply have to spin faster than was currently possible to make them spin, in order to generate enough angular momentum to 'generate' enough energy to compensate for the energy it took to spin them.

When he had finished hearing his partners' verbal report detailing their conclusions, Waldark responded, "Is it not convenient, gentlemen, that celestial bodies are already spinning, and therefore do not need our help to create enough angular momentum to gate energy?"

In the meantime, Waldark had been 'charging ahead' at his accustomed pace to determine if there was a way to capture and convert self-aware consciousness energy for practical usage. He started by remeasuring in much more detail the disturbance fields surrounding the head. Waldark was particularly interested in the 'eyes closed' mode which produced the simpler pattern, and also the mode whose spin rate he had been unable to determine.

This time Waldark began taking measurements farther and farther above the top of the head. 19 When he reached a point about nine inches above the skull, the clockwise vorticular disturbance he had been recording shifted dramatically, rose straight upward for just over two inches, and then reversed its spin to counterclockwise. Not only that, but—as the vortex changed rotational direction—the vortex began to tighten its spin, forming an inward tapering cone whose length was about 16 inches. This cone ended not at a point, but was reduced to about one-fifth inch in cross section. Then the process suddenly reversed again and—in about one-fifth of an inch—began its original clockwise spin in an outward tapering cone, identical to the original cone emanating from the soul. This process: outward cone, straight up, inward cone repeated itself every 30 inches or so, for as high as Waldark could practically measure.

Waldark was overwhelmed by the complexity of all this, but totally intrigued by the fact that all the energy once again, seemed to be concentrated at the points of the inward tapering cones, as if semi-representational of the soul area inside the skull. If—and this was a big if—the higher-dimensional energy could ever somehow be captured, this would be the spot at which to do so.

Waldark had absolutely no idea of how to do that, so he read and thought. There was no particular subject on which to concentrate, so he read everything. As luck would have it, he stumbled onto part of the solution one evening, by the simple act of putting on his hat before going out to buy a snack to ease his hunger.

"A hat!" he shouted.

With the assistance of Biederdorf and Segelman, the musician and the artist (who had just 'officially' joined the 'cabalists' after finishing their studies) Waldark was soon designing a hat—later termed the Waldark hat 20 —which would serve to capture, refocus and then transmit higher-dimensional consciousness energy to a receiver and thus begin the process of transdimensioning and reconfiguring consciousness energy for practical usage.

The Waldark hat is infused with a magnetic field which modifies the shape of the first set of cones into an oblate spheroid and shortens the length of this modified pattern to two-thirds the original length of the first set of cones. The top of the oblate spheroid is the refocusing point of the first set of cones and that refocused energy is captured in the knob at the top of the Waldark hat.

There was a long way to go, but the three worked steadily for some time on the effort which had now been reduced to engineering by way of art and music. Theory had led to investigation; investigation to tentative conclusion; tentative conclusion to art and music; art and music to engineering. Engineering would later lead to practical results.

The 'cabalists' met with many surprises along the way, the most important being that the amount of usable three-dimensional energy resulting at the end of their process was much less than the energy they had had to infuse into the system to make the process work. They were facing a situation very similar to the one encountered by Althoch and Bergman when they were trying to build spinning devices emulating the ability of celestial bodies to gate energy.

They were discouraged, but undaunted. Again the 'cabalists' resorted to a division of labor. The four young men looked for ways to improve the process after the capture of the consciousness energy; Waldark sought a way to boost the amount of consciousness energy emanating from the soul.

The old man had long thought that the 'eyes closed' spin rate of the self-aware consciousness was slower than the 'eyes open' mode, but he still did not know by how much. He also knew that both modes generated the same amount of energy, so he knew it would do no good to build a contraption to try to capture all the various vortices of the 'eyes-open' mode. Somehow—and he did not know if this was possible—there might be a way to increase the 'eyes closed' spin rate thereby increasing the amount of energy generated. This would have to be done in a very controlled manner (without allowing the interlocked tetrahedra of the geometric modeling of self-aware consciousness to transform themselves into the higher order shapes, thus disrupting the flow of energy from the two opposing cones).

Waldark knew absolutely nothing about meditation (the act of thinking deeply about one's self, the Universe and the interrelationships between them) so he consulted Ahnenhof, who was nearing completion of his studies at that time, and who knew a lot about meditation due to "extra-curricular studies." Ahnenhof intuitively felt that meditation could increase the spin rate of self-aware consciousness, simply because it puts oneself in harmony with the Universe. Harmony was a word that was not included in the conservative Waldark's everyday speech, so the very precise Waldark looked it up in his massive lexicon, and discovered that in one of its definitions harmony meant to be 'in tune.' Since Waldark knew 'in tune' could mean having the right wavelength, he therefore thought that the right wavelength must have a correlation with the right spin rate. This was a loose extrapolation, Waldark conceded, but the 'cabalist' felt that he was very much in harmony with his own thinking.

Waldark therefore read about meditation, but he knew that the best way to find out whether his theory would work was not through reading, but through testing those who meditated. Ahnenhof found several willing volunteers for this purpose in an institute for meditation that looked rather seedy, and to the orthodox thinker, somewhat disreputable.

The results were adequate, if not fantastic. The meditators clearly generated more energy than any previous subjects, but still not enough to result in more energy produced than input. Nevertheless, Waldark was so encouraged that he took it upon himself to learn meditation, not only from books and the institute, but especially through the guidance of Ahnenhof. According to the somewhat bemused but always respectful Ahnenhof, Waldark became "only adequate" and then "fairly good" at the subtle art. Together Waldark and Ahnenhof tested the former's ability to generate energy under a state of meditation. Much to the amazement of all, Waldark surpassed everyone else ever tested.

"Still not good enough," grumbled the old man.

So he resorted to musing and pondering again, and did so while he was in his meditational state. Finally, an inspiration came to him: since self-aware consciousness and the resulting energy both emanate from the Source in a higher-dimension, it might help the process of meditation to achieve higher levels and greater understanding—and therefore a higher spin rate—by trying to visualize what a higher-dimension might look like.

Waldark grabbed all Bergman's articles and books on higher-dimensional geometry and began to read them, but more importantly he looked at the 'depictions' of the hypercubes, hyperspheres, hypertetrahedra and so on. Waldark was extremely disappointed. These 'shapes' did not resemble anything; he could visualize nothing.

In desperation he showed the books and their drawings to Ahnenhof. The student of philosophy looked at one of the 'crazy' drawings, then at Waldark.

With a touch of impudence the young man said, "You don't see this stuff. You feel it!"

So Waldark returned to his studying, and tried to 'feel' the higher-dimensional geometric figures, still without much result. One evening all the other 'cabalists'—including Herzman, who was also just finishing his studies—gathered to discuss the difficulty Waldark was having. As their symposeion continued into the night they gradually became hungry, so they sent Herzman out for a snack and he returned with doughnuts.

Neither Herzman nor the others made any progress at all until Segelman, the heartiest eater among them began to feel a strange empathy for one of the simpler three-dimensional drawings, it was strikingly similar to what he was eating: the last doughnut.

He, at least, felt better for this as he held it in his right hand, nibbling at it in small bites. The artist was suddenly inspired to close his eyes and enjoy the triple 'feel' of the doughnut: in his hand, in his stomach and in his mind's eye. He was suddenly at great peace with himself and the Universe—in harmony for the first time in his life. Now he knew what 'feel' should connote to them: not only the ability to sense with the emotions—as Ahnenhof meant when he spoke with Waldark—but also the ability to sense in a tactile fashion should be included.

Segelman was instantly able to intuit that to achieve an increase of the spin rate of self-aware consciousness sufficient for usable quantities of three-dimensional energy to be produced, a mental image of higher-dimensionality, together with a physical stimulus was required. This would help the mind achieve the necessary higher states of meditation.

The doughnut was the key, Segelman thought.

The others saw Segelman's expression and realised it was a significant moment. When he was at last ready, the young artist told them everything.

As a result, it was decided that Bergman and Segelman should delve into a comprehensive study of mathematical doughnuts, which had both three-dimensional forms and higher-dimensional 'forms.'

When the report of their study was presented to Waldark, he said, "Let's see what we can do."

Waldark struggled with trying to imagine in his mind's eye a suitable three-dimensional model of the "hyper-doughnut," as he called it. Finally, he was inspired with the mental image of a totally-asymmetrical "thing," (as he immediately named it) of bent and twisted ribbon that Waldark thought would also wrap around a real three-dimensional doughnut.

He spent some time constructing the thing out of metal until it fit his mental image of a hyper-doughnut, until it wrapped around a real doughnut shape and, most importantly, until it felt good in his right hand.

When he was ready, Waldark picked up the thing—later to become the irreplaceable Waldark thing—placed it is his right hand so that it lay along the arc from his right thumb to his right index finger and squeezed it sufficiently so that he could feel the thing's smooth shape along its entire length. Then, while seated comfortably under the energy receiving and transmitting hat, Waldark went into as high a meditational state as he could. At the other end of the process, the three-dimensional energy flowed; for the first time energy output exceeded energy input.

About this time Althoch and Bergman came bursting through the doors of the old man's experiment room, thoroughly overexcited.

Althoch blurted out his exciting news, "Waldark, we have just perfected a way to boost the energy output of our system by 2160 times. It costs a little, and it takes a little energy, but the net result is still very worthwhile!"

The old man looked at them, and said rather blandly, "Very good, gentlemen, we can combine that with the thing which already allowed me to produce more energy than we input. Together, we have a good chance of achieving something at last."

The old man went back to his research.

Waldark had very carefully measured the multi-cone patterns which emanated from the top of the head, but he had no idea whether the combinations of patterns would differ in the as yet unmeasured cone pattern which (he knew) projected down from the head during the 'eyes closed' mode.

All examinations were conducted with adult subjects standing with their heads held straight and eyes closed. His first observation was that the initial downward vortex rotated counterclockwise, opposite the vortex in the first upward cone. 21 Otherwise, in an individual, the first lower cone was identical to the first upward cone, when compared to the first upward cone. His second observation was that the cone system through the body was an analog to the cone system above the head. At chest level the vorticular motion ceased and the energy projected itself straight downward for slightly over two inches. The Vortex then reversed itself, this time with a clockwise rotation and formed a downward tapering cone which closed to a one-fifth inch cross section at the genital area. The second outward tapering cone then formed down the legs; the straight down section located itself around the knees; and lastly another downward tapering cone projected itself pointing toward the feet. With some beings this second cone set did not complete its full length before apparently penetrating the ground, perhaps infusing the planet itself with energy. With others, the second cone set ended right at ground level. With still others, the second cone set ended above the feet, a third cone set therefore started before the energy apparently began to infuse the ground.

Waldark was amazed by the stunning implications. Not only concerning the apparent transmission of energy by self-aware beings into the planet on which they live, but even more by the relationship that consciousness energy might have with sexuality.

The one consistency Waldark had found in his linear body measurements of adult subjects—the cones were always the same angular shape—was that the first downward pointing cone always terminated at exactly the same spot in the body: the genitals. The obvious initial conclusion: both opposing consciousness energy cones emanating from the soul had lengths adjusted to the distance between the soul and the genitals.

To test his hypothesis further, Waldark decided to test new subjects at various stages of growth and development. He was startled to find that in babies and in children the cones were much shorter when compared with their bodies. The first downward pointing cone ended in the area of the abdomen, and it was most often the third downward pointing cone which went beyond the feet. It was during adolescence that the cones grew—along with the body—so that the first downward pointing cone permanently ended with the genitals.

Waldark shook his head at this revelation and said to himself, "So now we know."

Circumstances dictated that Waldark do some further experimenting. Enlisting several voluntary loving pairs, he very discretely proceeded to investigate if there was any reaction of consciousness energy emission to sexual intimacy, and especially to moments of sexual release. The results were again astonishing:

As sexual arousal began, a tightly wound vortex formed with ever increasing intensity as arousal continued. This vortex measured from the soul to the genitals approximately one-fifth of an inch in diameter. At release this vortex attained maximum intensity and differed in females and males. In females the vortex became somewhat longer, somewhat larger in diameter and conical at its end. In males the vortex bent and extended upward through and out of the male reproductive organ. This vortex extended several inches beyond the male reproductive organ and also became conical at its end. At release the energy infused the sex partners with an incredible burst of energy which Waldark was unable to measure because it was beyond the limits of his devices.

Waldark said to himself again, "So now we know."

Intrigued by his findings with regard to sex and the incredible power sexual release unleashed, Waldark wondered if perhaps consciousness energy might be helpful to the general physical well being of self-aware beings. In order to be able to discover if this was true, Waldark knew he had to do two things. Firstly, build a device which mimicked self-aware consciousness by 'generating' higher-dimensional energy in the same multi-cone pattern as did the soul. Secondly he needed volunteers, with various and diverse ailments and injuries.

Waldark conceived the device fairly quickly, and built it through much thought, labor and assistance. As conceived, the device was to be hand held and would consist of a single circumscribed tetrahedron at the end of a handle. The tetrahedron would be spun very rapidly by some manner of device at its base; the energy for that device would be held in a spherical storage compartment at the end of the handle opposite the spinning tetrahedron. The handle itself serving as a conduit for the energy. Achieving the very rapid spin rate necessary was a possibility too, as Waldark was now producing enormous amounts of energy on his own.

The end result of the process beginning with consciousness energy was three-dimensional energy which was not unlike electricity; the standard energy of the day. Following the incredible boosting it received in the device invented by Waldark's partners, this newly discovered type of energy flowed incredibly rapidly in a way similar to the electron flow of electric current, but consisting of massless corpuscles—analogous to previously discovered photons of light. The experiments conducted by Waldark's partners, while the old man carried out his sex research, showed that the rapidly flowing corpuscles could also be effectively used as thrusters—to turn spinning devices which could be grooved to receive the full force of the corpuscles. The younger partners had already built one such spinning device, connected it to a dynamo, and generated more than enough electricity for their usage.

As a result of his partners' efforts, Waldark would be able to build the first device originally designed to be run by consciousness energy corpuscles. However, first he had to devise a way to store the corpuscles in the spherical storage compartment at the end of the handle opposite the spinning circumscribed tetrahedron. Waldark's partners would also have to miniaturize a radially grooved disk and corpuscle thruster to fit below the base of the tetrahedron. After completing their individual components, they were to jointly work on the conduiting, and on a system which would regulate the spin rate of the disk-tetrahedron component.

The younger partners' work took only a few days, but storing corpuscles proved very difficult.

"The corpuscles are very active and want to do something immediately," Waldark said aloud to himself in exasperation one day, "or they give up and die—just like electricity when the circuit is interrupted by a break in the wire and the electricity drains out.

"How am I supposed to understand these corpuscles of consciousness energy when no one even understands electricity?"

Then the answer struck him, "I'll make a continuous loop conduit for the corpuscles, and they'll race all around, thinking they're doing something," he said to himself.

In the meantime, the younger partners had gone ahead with the conduiting through the handle, and were in the process of connecting it to the corpuscle thruster at the base of the disk-tetrahedron component. Waldark approached them with his solution to the storage problem. Together they engineered the conduiting system into a much modified storage compartment. A sphere would not work, but a volute casing with a shape similar to some types of sea shells would. The conduiting spiraled up from the base of the cone to its top and then turned straight down the center to near its starting point, where it completed the loop. A shunt opposite the handle joint allowed varying numbers of corpuscles to be transferred by way of the handle conduit to the thruster which spun the tetrahedron. Much to their satisfaction it worked, and the volute casing storage component could be easily reinfused with more corpuscles when usage had drained off most of the corpuscles.

Now that the device—later called the Waldark healer—was ready, Waldark needed patients. Bergman—having a deficiency in his immune system, eagerly volunteered to try it out. It was difficult, however, to know which part of his body to treat. Despite having been a patient at a reputable immune system clinic for some time, Bergman knew virtually nothing about his condition and the 'cabalists' knew that they would never be given access to his records.

So instead, they obtained several weighty tomes on immune system deficiencies, and by patiently listening, Waldark was able to determine that the source of his partner's malady was the spleen, a highly vascular ductless organ near the stomach and intestines; responsible for destroying worn-out red blood cells; filtering the blood; the production of lymphoid tissue and white blood corpuscles.

Now that he knew the area for possible treatment, Waldark had to figure out what that treatment might entail. He knew that spin rate was important, but everything else was unknown.

Based merely on the intuitive feeling that the device's spin rate needed to be in harmony with the nominal spin rate of self-aware consciousness, Waldark's first idea was to spin the tetrahedron at 750,000 rpms, and to see what type of anomalies they could detect in the three-dimensional energy field of his experiment room. To their utter amazement 750,000 rpms obtained from his single spinning tetrahedron reproduced the multi-cone pattern produced by the 'eyes closed' mode, but only in one direction—toward the spinning point of the tetrahedron. It was also notably weaker in intensity.

Having observed this, Waldark began to slowly increase the speed of his device. As he moved off 750,000 rpms, the uni-directional multi-cone system collapsed into disorder. He continued to increase the spin rate until it reached 762,836.8 rpms, when a most amazing transformation took place: incredible amounts of energy began shooting upward in the exact same multi-cone pattern as at 750,000 rpms, but with much more intensity. Excitedly, he increased the spin by only a fraction of one revolution-per-minute, causing disorder to return. He kept increasing the spin rate, until once again he discovered another, even more powerful manifestation of the uni-directional multi-cone pattern at 762,914.5 rpms. Twice more—at 762,992.4 rpms and at 763,070.1 rpms—he uncovered progressively more powerfully constructed single direction multi-cone patterns.

Beyond 763,070.1 rpms Waldark began to find the onset of the same vorticular disturbance he had encountered earlier. (When measuring the effects on consciousness energy generation during sexual arousal and release.) This tightly wound, uni-directional, increasingly powerful vortex—much stronger than anything he had measured at lower spin rates—increased even more as he spun the device ever faster. At 768,167.9012 rpms—Waldark measured this spin rate much more precisely—the vortex reached its maximum intensity; at slightly higher spin rates disorder returned.

Waldark increased the rotation of the tetrahedron, and for quite some time nothing changed—there was only disorder. Finally, he nudged the rpm indicator to 777,777 and instantaneously the device disintegrated. Waldark, who always took every precaution, was standing behind heavy plate glass windows in a separate control room when the disintegration occurred. That saved his life. Everything in the experiment room had been pierced by billions of high speed particles emitted by the device, which was totally obliterated—nothing whatsoever remained.

As Waldark and his younger partners surveyed the damage, the old man said, "I spun it too fast. We need to build another."

When the replacement device was ready, Waldark began spinning it at 750,000 rpms, and then slowly decreased the spin rate. The results were very similar to his previous findings when he had increased the spin rate: at 748,370.3, 747,825.9, 747,203.6, and 746,659.2 rpms there appeared the exact same uni-directional multi-cone patterns, but in decreasing amounts of intensity. Between these spin rates there was disorder.

Something else first occurred at 699,993 rpms. Waldark, random testing as he went, continued to slow down the spin rate with ever decreasing intensity, to precisely 10,000 rpms: the multi-cone pattern appeared not only above, but also below the spinning tetrahedron.

Somehow, all the spin rates of a single tetrahedron from 10,000 to approximately 699,993 rpms acted as if there were interlocked tetrahedra by 'replicating' themselves in an inverse fashion, thereby producing mirrored opposing energy disturbance patterns. Below 10,000 rpms, two actual interlocked tetrahedra were required to form the opposing multi-cone patterns.

It took Waldark a long time to analyze his data, but he finally came to understand it enough to catalog it as follows:

1. A minimum spin rate of 10,000 rpms is required for a single spinning tetrahedron to create opposing multi-cone three-dimensional energy field disturbances, as a result of interacting with energy from the Source. Both the energy from the Source and the energy manifested by this process reside in a dimension higher than the reality of the physical universe.

2. The self-aware consciousness 'eyes closed' mode spins at 699,993 rpms (the highest spin rate allowable for the phenomenon described being initiated at 10,000 rpms).

3. The self-aware consciousness 'eyes open' mode spins at 750,000 rpms, and creates a complex pattern of vorticular three-dimensional energy fields by apparently acting as if two interlocked tetrahedra transform themselves into the four higher order solid shapes. An actual single tetrahedron spinning at this rate creates a uni-directional multi-cone disturbance pattern in the direction to which it points.

4. Actual spinning single tetrahedra produce incredibly strong single-direction multi-cone disturbance patterns at eight specific harmonic frequencies of spin rate, four below and four above 750,000 rpms. The higher the harmonic spin rate, the more intense the three-dimensional energy field disturbance. All are much more intense than the 750,000 rpm single tetrahedron spin rate disturbance.

5. Actual spinning tetrahedra—between just over 763,070.1 rpms and at 768,167.9012 rpms—produce a completely different, inexplicable and increasingly intense three-dimensional energy field disturbance pattern. This is the same energy disturbance pattern observed during sexual arousal, and at the moment of sexual release of self-aware beings.

6. At 777,777 rpms some inexplicable threshold is reached and destruction ensues. This spin rate is apparently just beyond the maximum spin rate allowable in the physical universe.

Waldark was rather mystified by these tentative conclusions, boggled by all the numbers and unsure of what they meant.

However, the old man did say, "Sex really must be the most powerful thing around. If sex were any more powerful, we'd blow ourselves right out of the Universe."

Waldark still felt that the 750,000 rpm spin rate was the one to use in treating his partner, because it was in harmony with the soul. The 'eyes closed' spin rate seemed nearly as good, but that was not the spin rate of self-aware beings for two-thirds of their lives; that is, when they are awake and active.

Waldark considered briefly using one or more of the four harmonic spin rates higher than 750,000 rpms (which also formed single direction multi-coned disturbance patterns), since the energy emitted at those spin rates was very intense. The old man abandoned that idea because he felt more at ease with 750,000 rpms, and because those other spin rates were achieved through meditation, and were not the day to day spin rate of all souls.

Waldark's partners agreed, so they began the treatment of Bergman immediately, 'irradiating' the area of the young man's spleen directly from above, three times a day for five minutes each time. To their great disappointment none of the symptoms improved and Bergman's health declined further. The only thing left to do was to increase the number and length of the treatments. There was still no improvement.

Finally, Bergman became desperate. As they were finishing one of the sessions Bergman grabbed the device from Segelman and shouted at him, "I'll do it. I'll hold this thing and blast myself with it until I die."

The failing Bergman was bedridden by this time so the others relented and sadly turned away, leaving their beloved friend to the device which had so far failed them miserably.

The young man was so weak that he could not actually hold the device. Therefore, he stuck its handle under an armpit and pointed the spinning tetrahedron at an angle toward his abdominal area.

In a day Bergman was remarkably improved.

In two days he was walking.

In a week he was cured.

When the seven discussed Bergman's remarkable recovery, the only reason they could find as to the cause of his cure was the young man's inability to hold the device. This had resulted in an oblique entry of the energy into his body, and that apparently made the difference.

"Waldark's device does indeed heal," shouted Herzman. "It's the Waldark healer."

In order to test the Waldark healer, they went on to cure secretly many other beings. It bothered them greatly that they could not help even more cases, but the risk was too great. If legal authority found out what they were doing, everything would be lost.

They found that the device worked on many ailments, but not on all. Notable exceptions included the common cold, headaches, nerve damage and sensory losses. All of them suffered from some or all of these, and they thought it ironic that they could not help themselves.

"We'll have to just settle for Bergman," Herzman said ruefully.

In the ensuing weeks and months, Waldark did an exceptional amount of musing and pondering, even for him, and he reviewed all his work several times. The old man also remeasured many three-dimensional energy field disturbances caused both by his spinning tetrahedron device and by the soul.

Still he published nothing, and no one other than his partners knew anything that happened at "Waldark's place," as the wags called his increasingly dilapidated abode.

Inside Waldark's facility, however, incredibly fantastic and revolutionary ideas continued to become reality.

While Waldark's partners were "tinkering" (according to Waldark) the old man finally linked his consciousness energy measurements to his experimental measurements obtained from his spinning single-tetrahedron device. This included the results of differing meditational states gleaned from himself and several other meditators.

His next set of conclusions were as follows:

1. The spin rate of 10,000 rpms is vitally important being the lowest minimum spin rate at which higher-dimensional energy emanates from single spinning tetrahedra in opposing multi-cone patterns. From this Waldark deduced that a higher-dimensional 'transformation' takes place at 10,000 rpms during which spinning tetrahedra reduplicate themselves into imaginary interlocked tetrahedra (a concept he extrapolated from the very useful imaginary number system used in mathematics).

2. This imaginary interlocked tetrahedra model works up to a maximum spin rate of 699,993 rpms; the 'eyes closed' spin rate of the soul of self-aware beings. Waldark calculated that the spin rate of this mode is 90 percent of 777,777, the observed threshold destruction spin rate of three-dimensional objects in the physical universe.

3. The 750,000 rpm spin rate of single spinning tetrahedra models and of self-aware consciousness, seemingly manifest themselves in totally different ways: the former with a single direction multi-cone interference pattern; the latter with a complex but regular series of vorticular interference patterns.

4. The observed eight harmonic frequencies of single spinning tetrahedra, which produce progressively more intense uni-directional multi-cone disturbance patterns are matched by identical patterns (produced by inexplicable leaps of meditational states), which also produce actual leaps of energy emission into the energy transproduction system, built by Waldark and his partner. Once again Waldark calculated these spin rates as percentages of 777,777 and found them to be the following (shown to

two significant figures): 96.00, 96.07, 96.15, 96.22, 98.08, 98.09, 98.10, and 98.11 percent.

5. The singularly intense disturbance vortex which is most intense at 768,167.9012 rpms and during sexual release was the most powerful—by far—manifestation of energy Waldark ever observed in the physical universe. Its maximum spin rate percentage of 777,777 is 98.7654321, a very interesting combination of numerals, which has an exact fractional equivalent of 80/81sts.

6. The 777,777 rpm spin rate Waldark deemed to be the spin rate which literally spins matter out of its three-dimensional existence.

Waldark considered these conclusions to be all rather tidy—except for the 750,000 rpm spin rate, which made no sense to him at all. In one case this spin rate produced a uni-direction multi-cone pattern; in the other a complex, omni-directional, multi-vortex pattern.

Waldark struggled to understand why, with its two distinctive disturbance patterns, this spin rate was different from all the others which emitted identical patterns from both a single spinning tetrahedron model, and from the soul.

One day, when Waldark had almost given up, the answer came to him in a flash: 750,000 rpms is a transdimensional spin rate. In its three-dimensional manifestation 750,000 rpms acted like the single spinning tetrahedron model; when self-aware consciousness spins in its 'eyes open' mode, the 750,000 rpms is a 'shadow' of what 750,000 rpms might be in a higher-dimension.

But Waldark knew that self-aware consciousness exists in both three-dimensions and in a higher dimension. Then both patterns should coexist if his hypothesis was correct. He went back to his data concerning 'eyes open' self-aware consciousness and discovered very minute perturbations directly over the head. Following many more testings of more subjects in the 'eyes open' mode, painstaking further investigations indicated the faintest hint of the multi-cone pattern of the single spinning tetrahedron model. Elsewhere, he found only the original already modeled multi-vortex pattern.

The answer was evident: the tremendous power of the higher-dimensional pattern of the higher-dimensional soul overwhelmed and nearly obliterated the higher-dimensional pattern of the three-dimensional shadow of the soul.

All other spin rates—including the highest spin rate recorded during sexual release—emitted higher-dimensional energy from the higher-dimensional soul, not its three-dimensional shadow, Waldark concluded.

The old man came to this conclusion because he found that due to their intensity, the spin rates of the multi-cone patterns, and the unique tightly wound vortex of the sexual release spin rate, were fundamentally different from the multi-cone pattern of the 750,000 rpm spin rate.

Waldark had previously noted the much higher intensity of the disturbance patterns of all the other spin rates, and was now able to correctly interpret this much higher intensity as being due to the higher-dimensional source of that energy; in that it emanates directly from the higher-dimensional soul, and not from its three-dimensional shadow. The seeming similarities between the multi-cone pattern of the 750,000 rpm spin rate and the multi-cone patterns of the other spin rates had misled him for some time, but Waldark was now sure that they were different.

He immediately leaped to the sexual implications of this revelation: the incredibly strong and loving sex drive of self-aware beings was rooted, not so much in animal instinct, or in even the three-dimensional shadow of the soul, but in the higher-dimensional soul itself.

Waldark said to himself, "So now we know."

The old man tried to explain all this to his younger partners, who all found it too incredible to accept. Though barely able to cope with these conclusions himself, the frustrated Waldark tried a simpler explanation: "Young men, your soul spins slowly while you have your eyes closed so you can be off in another world, thinking deep thoughts, concentrating or just plain dreaming. It spins very fast when you meditate so you can bring down more stuff from somewhere out there. When you engage in sexual activity, you need everything you can get. But when you are wide awake with your eyes open, you need to deal with both the here and now, and with those other things you were dealing with when you had your eyes closed, when you were meditating and when you were making love. Now do you understand?"

That was the end of the discussion, and no one has ever explained it better since.

The young men had indeed been doing some 'tinkering,' and now that Waldark was 'through' with his other studies, his partners invited him to see what they had been doing in the meantime.

Althoch had gone back to astrophysics, with an eye to the fact that celestial bodies were spinning themselves partially into a higher-dimension. If they did so, he reasoned, they must be losing mass, and if so, then they must have less gravity. Where were the lost mass and gravity going?

He and his colleagues then set about trying to replicate this phenomenon by rapidly rotating a sphere in their joint experiment room.

True to Althoch's hypothesis, the sphere lost mass as it was spun, losing more the faster its speed of rotation. Waldark's partners were even able to observe where the mass went: straight up and straight down from the axis of rotation—the poles.

It was at this time that Waldark was made aware of his younger partners' work, and he became immediately interested. Although his partners had clearly shown loss of mass by this rapidly spinning process, they had not been able to find out anything at all about the required loss of gravity, and how that might manifest itself. So, it was back to the books again for more reading by Waldark.

He quickly discovered that no one had the slightest idea whatsoever what gravity was or how it worked, only that mass attracts mass according to how voluminous the masses are. They knew less about gravity than they did about electricity. Waldark threw away all the books on gravity and began to muse and ponder some more.

Since Waldark and his partners had clearly shown that the Source of the Universe emits higher-dimensional energy through the physical universe; that self-aware consciousness somehow absorbs and then retransmits that energy; that celestial bodies do essentially the same thing and also 'gate' energy from a higher-dimension; and considering that everything else they had studied had connections with higher-dimensionality, Waldark thought that this might also be true of gravity.

Waldark thought some more and wondered if a tetrahedral model might work with gravity as well. To test this tentative hypothesis he suggested to his younger partners that perhaps they should look for a disturbance in the three dimensional energy field around their spinning, mass losing sphere; at a latitude of 19-20 degrees north and south.

The results were immediate and positive: an incredibly powerful disruption was found emanating from both hemispheres in a circular cone from 19.47 degrees to 22.48 degrees latitude.

"This must be the result of gravity waves being given off to compensate for the loss of mass," the excited Althoch shouted.

"Not enough data, young man," Waldark responded.

Months later—after exhaustive experimentation—Waldark had to admit that Althoch's initial conclusion was probably correct; however, they still did not know much about gravity itself. Waldark went back to his musing and pondering.

Finally, he came up with another idea, "Since gravity waves are being emitted in two circular cones around a spinning sphere," Waldark said to his partners, "why not try to capture those waves in a device, and see if they do anything. Perhaps they will be similar to light waves and contain something like photons. Perhaps the photon type bits of gravity will want to thrust like the corpuscles of our new, usable energy from consciousness. Perhaps gravity is another source of energy."

When Waldark made this suggestion to his partners the younger men were elated. By this time they had already made some modifications to their previous experiment. Instead of using a spinning sphere, they were now using a spinning disk, a much simpler model with which to work. They had already been able to measure the loss of mass up and down the axis of rotation, and had measured the emission of gravity waves. Since there was no latitude on a disk, the results were somewhat different: the circular cone began two-thirds of the way from the center of the disk to its rim, and was canted at an angle to the disk itself between, 19.47 and 22.48 degrees. 22

With Waldark's help the younger men constructed a double gravity wave capture ring which fitted just above and just below the spinning disk, designed so that the outflowing gravity waves would enter them through slots. A Y-shaped attachment connected the rings to a gravity emission shaft which also held the double rings in place. At the open end of the gravity emission shaft they placed a multi-armed free spinning wheel with cup-like projections at the end of its arms. If all went as planned when they spun the disk at a high rate of speed the emitted gravity waves would be captured by the double rings, forced by the emission shaft down its length and thrust against the cups of the free-spinning wheel, activating it, or so they hoped.

At the outset of the first trial—at the very instant the gravity waves issued forth from the emission shaft—the free-spinning wheel was sent flying by the force of the first gravity wave hitting its first cup.

In the months that followed they refined their model to an incredible degree. They determined soley by trial and error where to place the capture rings, and to their great surprise, they found that the optimum spin rate—by a very significant amount—was 750,000 rpms.

This sent Waldark back to more musing and pondering, before he finally came up with the reason: since 750,000 rpms was the transdimensional spin rate, only 750,000 rpms would bridge both the three-dimensional and higher-dimensional components of the physics acting to make the system operate efficiently.

As Waldark had suspected, they were also able to determine that the gravity waves consisted of massless particles which behaved not unlike the massless corpuscles of their newly discovered energy, the massive electrons of electric current and the massless photons of light. They did this by conducting experiments very similar to previous researchers' work on light photons.

Waldark and his younger partners were not just playing with a new toy to see how powerful a thrust they could create to blow away increasingly strongly made free-spinning wheels. They had something else in mind: a flying craft!

Althoch and Bergman had presented Waldark with a plan soon after the first experiments with gravity thrust. Their idea was to loop the gravity emission shaft back up over the upper gravity capture ring, and form it into another bigger ring. This ring could not be a closed system (that would cause a backup of the gravity particles and a rupture in some part of the system as the gravity particles sought an extremely high speed escape). Instead, the younger men proposed a series of vents around this ring through which the gravity particles could escape. 23

The idea was to control the number of gravity particles being emitted from each vent, (in other words a gravity particle distributor ring) and then project these particles at tremendous velocity in many different directions, using manipulatable, thrusters connected to these vents.

With this accomplished, all that was needed was a craft in which to place their revolutionary new propulsion unit. They completed their prototype which contained a disk six feet in diameter, a size they calculated was the minimum disk diameter required to generate enough gravity particles for both hovering and movement of any craft.

The disk was magnetically levitated. From previous experiences they knew that it would burn up due to friction while spinning at 750,000 rpms if this were not so.

The disk was made of an extremely strong material, the result of a tremendous amount of work and chemical engineering. Without such precautions the disk would fly apart while spinning at 750,000 rpms, as had earlier disks which were not correctly constructed.

The extremely strong material of the disk was also a super conductor, in order to assist the process of magnetic levitation.

The length of the craft was twelve feet and its width eight feet.

The craft was powered by a combination of electricity and consciousness energy corpuscles, the latter used to spin the craft's spinning disk and to create the magnetic fields required for the gravity particle drive to work.

The spinning disk was grooved with half-hexagon shaped radial grooves top and bottom to make it easier for the energy corpuscles to spin the disk.

The spinning disk was sculpted so that its steel banded rim was slightly thicker than its center. This sculpting also helped to keep the disk from distorting and flying apart while spinning.

The three sides of the half-hexagon grooves of the disks were lined with bands of steel which stretched from the center of the disk to its rim, where the radial bands connected to the wide steel band on the rim. The radial steel bands provided a hard surface against which the consciousness energy corpuscles could thrust; gave additional strength to the disk; and allowed the disk to be magnetically levitated.

Once the craft was ready, and crammed full of every type of sensory gear they could obtain (mostly to record its flight path and velocity) and all the associated devices constructed and tested, the 'cabalists' waited impatiently for a very dark night during which they could conduct their first test flight.

Finally, that night came. They set the craft on a docking frame in an open field, and set up "flight control"—as Herzman called it—under a tree. The younger men offered to let Waldark take the controls, but the old man demurred.

Taking a deep breath, Althoch activated the spinning disk and adjusted the thrusters to a slow ascent setting. The craft reacted virtually instantaneously as directed.

Excitedly Althoch changed the thrusters to the hover position, and the craft responded, hovering above the ground, some 20 feet from where they were grouped.

Next, Althoch turned the craft slowly in a circle clockwise, then counter clockwise, until he stopped the craft as it faced directly away from them.

Satisfied with the initial tests, Waldark nodded that Althoch should continue.

Althoch set the altitude controller so that the ship would rise to 100,000 feet, then hover. He relayed the message to the craft and it rose quickly up out of sight.

Then Althoch ordered the ship ahead at half-thrust for a distance of 10 miles, the maximum range they thought they could send their craft without fear of detection.

It reached its destination and hovered.

The final test was preprogrammed: return by fastest speed and shortest distance to hover over its dock at ten feet for ten seconds, then descend at dead slow to docking position.

Althoch ordered this maneuver and very soon the craft was hovering over its dock.

A few moments later Waldark shook his head and said, "So now we know."

Later that same night the 'cabalists' discussed everything that they had accomplished together: they had discovered a means to convert consciousness energy into a very powerful and practical energy source, they had built a device based on higher-dimensional energy, which would help immensely with the physical healing of many maladies and they had built a prototype flying craft propelled by vented gravity particles generated by a rapidly spinning disk.

Ahnenhof concluded the discussion. "We have been able to do all this because we understand that everything devolves from the Source of the Universe," he said. "Everything works in the same way."

"What do we do about telling everyone?" Herzman asked the next day.

"Nothing," Waldark responded. "When I am gone, you do it."

Several years later Waldark passed on, and Herzman and Segelman worked together to produce an enormous volume containing all of Waldark's work—and published it on their own.

"Waldark accomplished much," said Herzman as he presented each of his friends with copies of "Waldark's weighty tome," as he nicknamed the work.

Everyone read it, and forced those who worked in the disciplines covered by Waldark's work to take heed—and test the data!

Chapter 6

From Hope to Despair

Through the aeons that have followed since the time of Waldark and his 'cabalists' successive seekers have built upon and perfected the ideas and devices introduced by Waldark so long ago. Consciousness energy has become the mainstay of civilization and the graviton drive along with the spinning disk, the means by which civilization has been able to migrate from galaxy to galaxy. The Waldark healer has helped provide for a much healthier life for self-aware beings.

The knowledge gained by Waldark and his successors—and the highly sophisticated devices resulting from that knowledge—came with the intergalactic migrators from the last galaxy and were introduced to the indigenous beings of this galaxy. The union which created Altean society benefited greatly from Waldark's work, and for the first billion years of its existence that society improved and grew steadily with none of the turmoil which had taken place in the last galaxy.

Nevertheless, there continued to be those who intuitively felt that all would not go so well indefinitely. These individuals banded together down through the generations as Essenes.

Although there had been much colonization in the solar systems relatively close to Altea, there had been no attempt to spread Altean civilization to the center or far reaches of the galaxy. Following the billionth anniversary of the beginning of the union the thoughts of many Alteans began to expand outward, and Essenes knew that the time to begin their preparation of the galaxy was coming nearer, for they knew that with a great expansion came greater risk of confrontation and conflict between competing interests.

About 950 million years ago Essenes migrated from Altea and became the first beings in the galaxy to venture beyond the confines of Altean territory.

About 260 million years after Essenes migrated from Altea, a band of preparers of another kind departed Altea to undertake an enormous task: to finally survey and begin to settle in the center of the galaxy in preparation for the eventual migration of billions more colonists to follow in their paths.

The great hopes of both filling the galaxy with Altean civilization and redemption of the galaxy had begun.

The surveying, migrating and colonization continued at a steady pace under a system which operated from a star group the first surveyors named the Pleiades, after the daughters of the surveyor of the first mapping expedition, whose name was Folen Pleiade Xian. It was a spot well chosen, due to its location near the transition zone between ongoing exploration and Altean territory.

Altea is located in one of the spiraling arms of the galaxy, about three-quarters of the way from the galactic center to its outermost fringes. This would take nearly a month's journey by space craft traveling at near interstellar light speed. The Pleiades are only about nine hours distant from Altea, so both the distance and travel time to the center of the galaxy where colonization was to proceed were very great from the operations base of the colonization effort. Nevertheless, the Pleiades were ideally located between Altea and the center of the galaxy.

The inclusion of a survey team was a major part of each colonial expedition, and its leader was the coordinator of the expedition's interdisciplinary committee, which decided all important matters pertaining to exploration and colonization. During a preparatory period before departure from the Pleiades operations base, surveyors asked for volunteers to accompany them on the extensive scouting missions required to find an appropriate new place from which to seek a permanent home.

In the very first expedition, one such volunteer was the nephew of the deputy commander of an Altean naval station in the remote area of the center of the galaxy into which his group would be journeying. Some one hundred years previously, the Altean Naval Service had been given the mandate to go ahead and insure all was safe for the pioneers who would follow. Its stations and bases dotted the interior of the galaxy by the time this first and important pioneering expedition took place.

Mavor Tovon Liu, the young volunteer, was very bright, so the head surveyor accepted him as his assistant for a holographic mapping project.

Taking on this work was just what the youth wanted, it afforded him the opportunity to both accompany the survey team and to learn the position of stars, which he needed to know, as he wanted to master the skills of navigating space craft. Mavor Tovon also made sure he did the best possible job he could, so that the surveyor would be certain to show him everything about the galactic holo-map they were producing. As a result the two spent many extra hours together, becoming good friends. When the task of holo-mapping the area had been completed, Folen Pleiade and Mavor Tovon sadly parted ways, and the youth went with his family to their new home.

Soon afterwards, his uncle Mavor Gin Jing came to visit, and after learning of Mavor Tovon's experience, convinced his nephew to go with him and seek an appointment to the Altean Naval Institute for possible future commissioning as a naval officer.

Having completed his training and in receipt of his commissioning patent, young Ensign Mavor Tovon was posted to the star ship commanded by this very same uncle, Captain Mavor Gin Jing, a procedure not without precedent. Captain Mavor was a strict disciplinarian valuing leadership above all else, but he also treated his Crew and officers with respect, appreciating their skills and experience in naval matters.

Ensign Mavor became Captain Mavor's best navigator and to veteran naval personnel Ensign Mavor seemed to have skills beyond his age and experience.

For over four years the two worked together as the star ship's commanding officer and assistant navigator—until Lieutenant Mavor Tovon was suddenly attacked by a totally debilitating disease. Having been transferred to a naval medical facility, Lieutenant Mavor Tovon slowly recovered.

When he was fit for duty again Lieutenant Mavor returned to his uncle's ship. The disease had almost killed him and as Mavor Tovon was not a student of Philosophia he merely stated his own belief when he said, "I had a close contact with the maker of all living things, and I somehow managed to hold off death before it could overwhelm the forces of light and good."

Lieutenant Mavor so impressed the star ship's Crew with his apparent insight regarding death they began to form a similar belief in the way the transition between life and what follows takes place. Even Mavor Tovon's uncle and his officers joined this new way of viewing the most intriguing mystery of the Universe.

In the months that followed word of this 'explanation' for one of the most important philosophic matters surrounding the lives of every self-aware being spread like a powerful light throughout the Altean territory being developed within the Pleiades star group—where Lieutenant Mavor's star ship patrolled.

Eventually this 'explanation' became the primary 'philosophy' of those settlers who were becoming prosperous in the Pleiades star group and among many Altean Naval Service officers assigned there.

Known as "The Purity of the White Light" and evolved from the few words spoken by the innocent and unsophisticated Mavor Tovon Liu, this myopic framework of beliefs held that the illumination of the mind devolves from actually experiencing resurgences of life after death-defying situations. Such as mortal combat; searching for new homes in unexplored areas of the galaxy; being determined to succeed in all aspects of life, no matter what the cost or odds. All are used to achieve this state.

By preparing for death, these "seekers of the white light" (as they dubbed themselves) taunted the inevitable and came to despise all who did not embrace their mockery of anything that did not advance this credo.

They became the dreaded opponents of Philosophia, and it was this group of devotees of this life of seeking constant challenge to their very existence who developed the fierce undercurrent which led to the eventual rebellion against Altea.

Essenes had been correct from the start, and Richy Drake had been prescient.

Only a few years had passed before an act of treason resulted in the secession and the onset of Pleiadean confederacy. This event was instigated by some groups of disgruntled colonists and a few dissident naval officers, convicted that they would benefit by taking total command of all positions of authority within the Pleiades star group. They were led by the deputy commander of Altean Naval Service forces in the Pleiades, Xung Ping Wyan.

Thanks to their leader's connection with the local Altean naval supplier of arsenals, they were able to arm themselves with naval weapons and use a transport vessel for the surprise nighttime attack that left over 1000 dead among the defenders. In this way did the dissenting cabalists take over the main Altean Naval Service base in the Pleiades star group.

Following their initial success, these rebellious followers of mutinous officers of the Altean Naval Service attacked other installations, star ships, local shuttles and transport vessels in the Pleiades star group. They captured and executed any remaining Altean Naval Service personnel and showed no mercy in tracking down and executing all others who stood in their way. Soon the entire star group was under their heel.

By the time the Altean Naval Service could be mobilized to respond to this onslaught against its forces in the Pleiades star group, it was too late to prevent the total loss of the Pleiades to the cabalists. The cabalists then declared themselves the rulers of the so-called Pleiadean confederacy, which their tribunal sought to project as an instrument of the will of the beings who lived in the Pleiadean star group. The number of daring escapes made by the desperate inhabitants bore witness to that lie.

Since the declaration of the confederacy was a clear act of treason, the Over Council of Altea directed Admiral Liu Jing Mavor, the commandant of the Altean Naval Institute, to lead a large fleet of Altean Naval Service star ships to recover the Pleiades star group. In a bold attack on Altea itself the cabalists defeated the Altean fleet before it was fully combat ready, and forced the Over Council to recognize the secession of the Pleiades and the legality of the founding of the confederacy.

Xung Ping Wyan became the Pleiadean confederacy's first elder, and its council was composed of his closest associates. Through a combination of the most pernicious acts of repression of individual rights, and through the systematic dismantling of all previous legal institutions and codes, they started what would eventually become the Pleiadean empire.

Next the traitors began to build an enormous naval force which they used to consolidate and then expand their area of control, and to bully the already severely weakened Altean Naval Service, which by then could do no more than defend the remnants of Altean territory surrounding Altea itself.

By the start of the next century after the founding of the Pleiadean confederacy, most beings in the galaxy were reduced to subordinate status in what was now declared the Pleiadean empire by Xung Gin Mavor, who had proclaimed himself emperor as a result of his victory over the Pleiadean council in a war which had pitted his family against the other families descended from the original cabalists.

Xung instituted a new privileged order called the "Pleiadean Order of Initiates of Vital Knowledge," a patrilineal hereditary group of close followers of the emperor, thus thoroughly limiting the power base to a very few.

Xung Gin Mavor's father was Xung Tovon Mavor. He named his own son Mavor Gin Jing, after the ancestor responsible, or so he claimed, for developing his nephew and namesakes Mavor Tovon's supposed belief in the strength of fighting at all times against the oblivion produced by death.

In a wrenching break with the past, Xung Gin Mavor decreed all Pleiadean subjects must immediately eliminate their middle name, since its usage was a remnant of the tradition of honoring one's mother's clan. Due to the emphasis on more manly attributes that tradition was no longer permitted.

New territories (colonized before the founding of the Pleiadean confederacy by Alteans using the Pleiades as an operational base) were annexed by force with armed attacks into the center of the galaxy. Subjected to Pleiadean systematic targeting of undesirable thought, more and more beings were put into serious jeopardy of losing every possession, their lives and those of their family and associates.

In a very short span of years the Pleiadean empire came to envelop the entire center of the galaxy. Only Altea and Altean territory colonized during those first billion years of Altean society remained outside the empire, a constant threat to Pleiadean naval supremacy, and a constant reminder to the Pleiadean emperor and his followers that Altean civilization still lived.

Among the privileged Pleiadean few there was a horrific struggle for power following the death of Xung Gin Mavor. After years of strife, a new emperor finally gained ascendancy and appended Xung to his own name thereby "insuring the continuity of imperial succession." All following Pleiadean emperors have adopted this 'tradition' of appending Xung to their own name, and among the Pleiadeans and their subjects only the emperor has three names.

The Pleiades star group had been known out of time immemorial by the indigenous beings of this galaxy, as seven distinct pinpoints of light located in the middle of the brightest part of a glowing band which spanned the night sky of Altea in a more or less single fairly broad ribbon. The indigenous beings had no idea what either the pinpoints of light or the glowing band of light were, but their seafarers learned to navigate by pointing the bows of their ships at the seven distinct pinpoints of light and at certain other pinpoints of light which they called stars because their twinkling made them appear like shapes they also called stars. What was to later become the Pleiades star group was one of the most important seasonal navigation guides of the indigenous beings, and they used those seven distinct pinpoints of light to help them travel cross the wide oceans of Altea.

When the intergalactic pioneers and the indigenous beings worked together to form a language of synthesis they discovered that many words in their two original languages which meant the same thing were similar in sound. The indigenous beings called a pinpoint of light in the night sky a star; the extragalactics called an gigantic ball of extremely hot glowing gas an astir. The indigenous beings called the gigantic glowing ball which gave them light and heat the sun; the extragalactics called the gigantic ball of extremely hot glowing gas of any given solar system which contained a planet or planets which were either habitable or could be made habitable a sustanator. The extragalactics liked the much shorter word sun—which they considered a foreshortening of their word sustanator—and did not press to use their word sustanator in the language of synthesis. The indigenous beings refused to give up their word star—just as they refused to give up any of their other words.

When colonization of the center of the galaxy was about to begin, Folen Pleiade Xian was traveling by space craft from Altea toward the Pleiades base of operations and he noticed how the Pleiades star group split the glowing heart of the galaxy which he was about to begin to survey. Just to the odunside of Folen's vessel was half of the galactic core, the Pleiades star group was directly ahead and to seaside was the other half of the center of the galaxy.

At that moment, Pleiade decided for surveying purposes, to split the enormous center of the galaxy into two halves: odunside and seaside. Later those two halves of the galactic core became the Odunside and Seaside territories of Altean colonization. Later still the Odunside and Seaside territories became the far flung Odunside and Seaside provinces of the Pleiadean empire, ruthlessly ruled from the distant Pleiades star group.

The emblem of the Pleiadean empire is a circle divided by a diagonal line with the Pleiades star group superimposed over the circle and the diagonal line.

Chapter Seven

The Preparers

Sara Eland was an inquisitive young lass of nine, in her fourth grade class of a primary school in Hurtea, the capital of Altea, when she first read about Essenes. As far back as she could remember Sara had always thought highly of voluntary service, and she often helped out whenever she could at home, at school and in her community.

Her interest in Essenes was immediate and heartfelt. Though very young to be an Essene, she became an Essene before her tenth birthday as a result of a thorough study of the group by herself and her parents, several meetings between the three of them with Essene representatives and Sara's steadfast, almost stubborn, insistence that her life lay with that ancient, mysterious, highly honorable and dedicated group of voluntary servants.

She excelled not only in her major discipline art, but also in her three minor disciplines biology, mathematics and Philosophia. And by the time Sara concluded her Akadeimia studies, the young lady had already become 'one of the leaders' of Essenes.

(Essenes had long since adopted much obscure nomenclature for their very different, mysterious and difficult to understand 'organization' and 'leadership.' This nomenclature defies description. Therefore, the use of the phrase 'one of the leaders' with regard to Sara Eland's 'position' is at best a poor rendition of the Essene concept. All terms and references used in this work with regard to Essene 'organization' and 'leadership' are merely terms of convenience.)

Sara was particularly motivated by the growing concept in Altean society of a monumental migration designed to fill the galaxy with Altean civilization and culture. She was also enough of a student of history to know that such an expansion could very well lead to those situations which had been feared by early Essenes such as Lura White and Richy Drake: the cataclysmic stoppage of steady progress toward galactic redeeming as a result of forces unleashed by a massive colonization of the galaxy.

The young Essene spent much of her spare time reading history and reflecting on what had happened in past galaxies during such times of rapid change: the road to colonization was often strewn with conflict, greed and untimely death. Sara hoped this would not be the case in her own galaxy, but she considered the absolute manifest destiny of Essenes to be preparers for such a negative eventuality. If all turned out well, so much the better; but if something went badly wrong during the process of colonization, there had to be a group of beings who could reverse things, and put the galaxy back on course. The time to act was now, before the colonization actually began and before anything went wrong, Sara thought.

What to do in view of the broadened thinking of Alteans, and how to proceed—these were the challenges confronting Essenes.

For the next few years, Essenes, including Sara Eland, talked of little else among themselves. They agreed that they had to withdraw even further from society to avoid outside pressures and to insure that their eventual plans would be kept absolutely secret. Whatever their final decision, they knew it would be bold, resolute and might not sit well with popular thought and with legal authority. As a result, they adopted new Essene names so that their actions would be untraceable should their plans be discovered.

(In this work, however, the original names of Essenes are used.)

To some extent this clandestine behavior in a very open and free society seemed odd to them, but after one of their number changed his mind and left the organization, it soon proved to be absolutely necessary. He had been so overwhelmed by the realization of what Essenes were contemplating that he simply could no longer continue with them. When he resurfaced having been away from family and community for some time, he was immediately bombarded with questions. He was obliged to reveal at least some of what was going on within the Essene movement, but he knew none of their names. If he had, ensuing investigations would have been embarrassing and traumatic for uninvolved relatives, ignorant of Essenes activities.

As it was, there was not much any one could do except wonder at what this odd group was doing, being so concerned about galactic redemption due to possible upheavals caused by galactic colonization, when colonization was still only an idea.

Among those shaking their heads at the reports of Essene thinking was a relatively young man, called Peter Odun, of very conservative views.

Odun was a teacher of history, coincidentally at the same Akadeimia that Sara Eland had attended, but she had never been in any of his classes. He invariably always began the first day's discussion with a comical self-effacing account of how he was a distant descendant of the famous Bill Odun, hero of Peter Odun's two favorite mythos ODUNSIDE and NOSTOS.

Although Odun was very conservative in his thinking regarding Akadeimia policy and the politics of the day, he was a favorite among his students for his sense of humor and his biting sarcasm against those who felt self-important.

It was therefore not surprising to them that Odun penned a scathing article which was published in Hurtea's largest daily newspaper which thoroughly lambasted the "presumptuous Essenes for thinking they have some sort of monopoly on correct thinking with regard to how matters should proceed." He also skewered them for their secrecy, concluding: "If one single member of the Essene 'movement' will reveal himself to me, and convince me of the rightness of his mission, then I will quit my job and become an Essene myself."

Sara Eland read the article with growing anger until she came to its ending. Inspired by the impudent challenge of this Peter Odun—about whom she knew very little from her Akadeimia days—Sara decided to lay down the gauntlet.

Armed with her own wit, knowledge and wise-thinking, Sara emerged from her Essene hideout so she could track down and find her newly discovered tormenter.

That was not difficult as Odun lived alone, not far from his place of work, in a relatively modest home directly on the beach. Early one evening she rang his bell and he opened the door after turning on the porch light.

"May I help...you?" He inquired, pausing somewhat as he discerned that an absolutely beautiful young lady was standing before him.

"Yes," she answered resolutely, "I am an Essene. We have a lot to talk about."

He invited her into his home. After Sara had expressed her concerns to Peter Odun about the possibility of conflict arising during the projected colonization of the galaxy, he responded, "I don't think we should be so concerned. Alteans have Philosophia. Since Alteans study Philosophia I don't think the problems which you foresee will arise."

"How many Alteans do you think actually study Philosophia?" asked Sara.

Peter Odun shrugged his shoulders.

"Your type of mind is perfectly suited to the study and enjoyment of Philosophia," Sara continued. "Not all minds are like yours. Philosophia requires thinking. Not all Alteans think. You are very comfortable with Philosophia at all levels of thinking. Others need to have everything explained to them, or they reject everything. Others simply want to be told what to believe.

"The others, those who reject everything, will do anything.

"The others, those who want to be told what to believe, will become the slaves of those who will do anything."

The next day Peter Odun became an Essene.

Seven weeks later Sara Eland and Peter Odun were married, and their undying love for one another is still known as the romance of the galaxy.

Peter Odun had been smitten not only by Sara's beauty, charm and wit; he had been especially struck by her reasoning and her devotion to the imminent and decisive voluntary service proposed by Essenes, for she had almost immediately entrusted him with very confidential information concerning that organisation. As a result of their almost instantaneous meeting of hearts and minds, the Essene movement was propelled rapidly ahead following Odun's enrolment, thanks to his skills as catalyst, organizer and strategist.

Peter Odun set out at once to recruit new members of the organization through his Akadeimia colleagues and friends. The first to be won over was his friend Peter Taylor, a teacher of Philosophia. Next came Hal Ward, another of Odun's closest friends, an Akadeimia teacher of art.

Taylor was especially enthusiastic, and promised to enlist his close friend from childhood Ken Michaels, an actor of some renown; he failed in that attempt because Michaels was emotionally unable to accept the eventual departure of Essenes from Altea, bound for destinations unknown. Taylor's friend was nevertheless sympathetic, and he not only kept the secret of their confidential discussions, he also contributed considerable funds to Essenes.

Odun had also hoped to convince his own childhood friend Ron Wood to join them, but Wood, trying to save his family's failing financial concerns—ruined by too many leaders and not enough followers—was too embroiled to have the time to be able to give his full attention to Odun's persuasive request that his friend join in the historic events which were about to unfold.

Saddened by Wood's being trapped by more important personal affairs—and Odun did not doubt they were truly important—the former history teacher resolved to gain Wood's attention later. When the time eventually came for Essenes to depart, Odun's close friend Ron Wood was still in such a state that all he could do was wish the expedition well.

In the meantime the art teacher Hal Ward had introduced another Akadeimia teacher Roger Towns to Essene thinking, and the very precise, stolid physics teacher had actually decided to join them.

A student of Ward's named Alana Woodman, known fairly widely amongst her peers and others for being slightly erratic and very erotic, overheard Towns and Ward discussing Essene ideas after class one day, when she was working on a sculpture of a nude male in the back of Ward's classroom. When Alana had heard enough she walked right up to the two of them and said steadfastly, "I want to join."

As it turned out Alana Woodman was a key figure in the next phase of the Essene movement because her lover was a well known businessman named Will Jones. She quickly convinced him of the merits of Essene thinking and he poured huge sums of money into the relatively meager Essene coffers. Not only that, Jones recruited another businessman and friend Marty Nelsson, who matched Jones quid for quid in his donations. The two were not merely philanthropists, they were dedicated members of the Essene movement, who suddenly realized that the earlier stages of their lives—when they were amassing huge fortunes—were merely meant to prepare them for now.

The two businessmen met with Sara Eland and her new husband Peter Odun to work out strategy and a timetable for their eventual departure from Altea, a plan now possible, mostly due to the sudden influx of funds. The logistics alone were staggering and it was evident to the four of them that it would take considerable time and effort to carry such a project forward to fruition.

Essenes were thinking of leaving Altea to find a completely unknown planet on which to live permanently, a planet which would, in turn, serve as a base for their future voluntary preparatory work designed to insure the redemption of the galaxy. Since they would be cutting themselves off from Altea, they had to take everyone and everything they would need with them—and prepare to do so in a totally secret manner.

It could not be just a few Essenes either; they had to carefully recruit a vast number. The four knew well of the potential for genetic collapse, faced by the intergalactic pioneers of old, and they knew that Essenes would face the same problem. Additionally, they knew Essenes would not meet up with beings with whom they could intermingle—so they had to have a large enough gene pool to be able to survive indefinitely.

Essene leaders therefore consulted Essene mathematicians and geneticists to calculate precisely the minimum number of Essenes required for their genetic survival on the journey from Altea. This calculation took into account a myriad of factors, including the many variables of the gene pool with which they started. The final result: a minimum of two-thirds of a million.

The challenge was incredible, but the leaders were undaunted, and the funding sufficient. Through the business networks of Jones and Nelsson everything they needed was acquired or constructed. Through careful and secret recruiting methods, especially by Sara Eland and her closest childhood friend Roz Jones—more than enough dedicated Essenes were ready when the time came. Their model for accomplishing their eventual departure from Altea was the clandestine departure from Hermur billions of years before by their ancestors: the intergalactic pioneers, the 'original' Essenes.

Though all the subterfuge might not have been necessary, everyone felt that it was the way to proceed. Indeed it was their only regret, that such behavior take place on Altea, which was as open and free a society as anyone could hope would ever exist. However, they also agreed that once on their way, they would broadcast a single transcommunication back to Altea, revealing the reasons for their actions, and the manner of their doing.

So with all this in mind, the two businessmen met with the recently married couple again to work out the opening procedures for their massive project. What was needed most was a secret base of operations. Beside affording them a location at which Essenes could meet, there had to be a place for the storage of everything they would take with them, and a staging area from which the thousand specially constructed oversize space transporters (in which they would all travel) could depart.

Odun came up with what turned out to be the perfect idea. His widowed mother lived several hundred miles inland from Hurtea, in a ramshackle villa up in the mountains, near the town where he had grown up. Odun thought that his mother would be willing to give up her place of residence and move into town, where she could live more comfortably.

Sara—who had just visited the villa and her husband's mother—immediately understood his idea, and finished up his presentation in the way only she could, and much to his relief, since he liked to think more than talk, "The villa is absolutely perfect," said Sara enthusiastically. "No one lives nearby and it is surrounded by hundreds of acres of forest land in which we can hide everything. The villa itself needs a lot of fixing up, and perhaps an addition or two, but I could design all that, so everything will be just perfect."

Within a year Sara Eland and Peter Odun were the new inhabitants of the villa, and his mother was happily living in town nearer her friends, contented that although she didn't quite know how and what, she was helping something greatly.

Under cover of writing a joint art history book the couple lived an immensely happy double life: actually writing the book, and manning the secret Essene base of operations. Many friends from their previous lives in Hurtea came to visit them, and no one knew they were all Essenes working toward the eventual day of departure. At night secret landings of shuttle craft were made at various well camouflaged sites within the estate, and crews quickly hid their contents in specially prepared bunkers in the forest. No locals suspected anything.

This was despite the massive redecoration project which Sara began as soon as the two had moved into the villa. All local labor and contractors were used to complete Sara's plans, so that work was well known. There were no secrets as far as the villa was concerned, and the pair occasionally entertained locals, many of whom had known Peter Odun from childhood. The announcement that Sara would be having their first child was an excuse for a party, and also served to justify some of the reconstruction. After their son arrived, a daughter followed fairly quickly thereafter, and that provided the excuse for Roz Jones to move in with them as Nanny.

The villa was gorgeous and decorated with exquisite taste by Sara. She loved to coordinate colors and styles, and her choices were impeccable. Mostly she loved her husband, and she indulged him shamelessly. He was particularly fond of swimming, so she had a large pool installed "for the children."

They were an exceedingly romantic couple. During the many hours they spent together Sara taught Peter the finer arts of loving, while Nanny taught the children the fine arts. This is not to say that they were not devoted parents; their care and love for their children is legendary (and these children contributed significantly to the Essene movement in later years). They were a happy and loving family, a family about to embark together on one of the most important, selfless ventures of all time.

The preparations became more intense as Essenes neared the time for their departure. The massive storage bunkers dug into the forested hillsides surrounding the villa were first partially occupied by the transport vessels needed for the lengthy deep space voyage. These vessels had been constructed a few at a time by companies owned by either Will Jones or Marty Nelsson, and subsequently flown to the estate by highly trusted pilots. After all the craft had been assembled, the next stage began: filling those enormous vessels with everything necessary for the great Essene migration.

In the meantime, the recruiting network had grown significantly, and more and more Alteans became Essenes during the years of logistical preparation. The massive effort to acquire over two-thirds of a million members was faced with enormous challenges. Firstly, the absolute need for secrecy which required a closed mouth in the case of either acceptance or refusal. Secondly, there was the mandate for a very diverse gene pool among the migrators. Lastly—and by far most importantly—all Essenes had to be thoroughly and irrevocably dedicated to the project and its goal: preparing the galaxy for redemption; the ultimate completion of the galactic experience so that all beings therein would have the opportunity to live in harmony.

Sara and her team worked with the utmost diligence on this all-important phase of the project, using an overall strategy mostly conceived by her husband. The essence of the plan called for nearly all active recruiting to be carried out at various Akadeimia by means of the direct recruitment of those students and teachers thought to be favorably inclined toward the Essene movement. Those of this grouping who became members would then informally discuss the Essene concept in general terms with their associates and friends. Those considered to be very interested would then be contacted by Essene members who would carry through the recruitment to either success or failure.

The success rate using this method was extremely high. Mostly, it was simply a formalization of the tactics used by Peter Odun and Peter Taylor right after they became Essenes. The interpersonal network of students and teachers spread through Altean society, but always very secretly. Often business partners, friends and even relatives did not know that their partners, friends and relatives were Essenes until they met at a local meeting.

Essenes were very careful, however, not to drain away too many of any Akadeimia's students and teachers, or to disrupt any institution or company by taking away too many of its employees or directors. Often hard decisions had to be made even after membership, so many Essenes had to remain behind to insure that businesses could continue to function and provide employment, essential goods and services.

The outfitting of the expedition was completed some time before the recruiting effort. Therefore, many Essenes who had been involved in logistics were able to switch their attention to the vital task of acquiring new members, which they did tirelessly.

At last, it was time for Essenes to depart. A final planning session was held at the villa, and there were tears in the eyes of everyone present as they began to understand fully the great significance of what they were about to do, and how much they would miss Altea. For Sara Eland, Roz Jones, Peter Odun and the two children, Lars and Leena, it was especially wrenching because they would also be leaving their wonderful home.

It would have been impossible for all migrators to assemble in secret for departure from the villa, so a thousand different gathering points around Altea were carefully chosen. The passengers of a vessel were to make their way independently to their designated departure site for a very rapid nighttime boarding and departure. Crews for the vessels began arriving in small numbers at the bunkers over a period of several days. None could be away from their usual place of work long enough to arouse suspicion, neither could they swoop down upon the area of the villa in large numbers as that would also arouse suspicion. Therefore, they came at night and by various means of transport. All vessels were manned without incident according to plan.

The only thing missing at this point was the final meet and assemble announcement, a coded message which had previously been given to all members of the departing expedition. Only the actual date of departure was kept secret and only three Essenes were in the know: Sara Eland, Peter Taylor and Marty Nelsson.

When the time came, the phrase "Rare thunderheads were reported over many coastal areas today" was included in the planetary weather report broadcast across Altea. It was read without comment by a completely unwitting news commentator, but the inserter of the phrase was very excited. He had received the timely signal to proceed through his highly secret transceiver as he rose that morning. As planned, he had inserted the extra 'weather report' into the bulletin he wrote each day for the news.

This news was broadcast in the morning from his area of the planet and was received across Altea at whatever time of day it might then be. When his daily work was completed, he left his place of employment as usual, but did not return to his residence. Instead, he made his way steadily to his predetermined meet and assemble site.

And so it was all over Altea that critical morning, day and night. Ladies and gentlemen, young ladies and youths, lasses and lads all proceeded as prescribed by local planning to their designated meet and assemble sites. The seemingly endless waiting and listening through many broadcasts—for some at very odd hours of the day or night—for the critical 'weather report' was over.

As dawn crept around Altea, signalling the beginning of a new day, all Essene transport vessels had departed Altean space, spiraling outward from the planet as midnight local time was observed.

Sara Eland turned to her husband as the vessel they and their children traveled in rose above Altea, "I wasn't sure we'd make it," she confessed. "I wasn't sure we could keep it a secret."

Peter Odun opened the musty tome he was carrying and said, "Sara, this is a history of the Hermurian intergalactic migration:

> Although meetings for such a purpose had been unprecedented on Hermur, intergalactic migrations did indeed have precedent: history told them that massive intergalactic migrations had always carried forward beings from one galaxy to the next, along the chain of galaxies which led to their current galaxy. However, this usually followed the redeeming of their galaxy—the fulfilling of the galactic experience, so that all beings of any given galaxy had the opportunity to live in harmony. The Hermurian 'cabalists' were extremely disappointed that their departure was not associated with the redeeming of their galaxy—but was precipitated by the need to escape.
>
> The redeeming of the galaxy was the historical imperative under which the galaxy had been developed, but in this case it was not to be. As the 'cabalists' had historical records stating that this had happened several times before, they were not totally downcast when they started preparing their escape. They deduced that fundamental conditions and situations sometimes recur, enabling those aware of their history to take advantage of that knowledge and act accordingly.
>
> The fact that they were able to keep their vast project totally secret from outsiders surprised and uplifted them, and made them feel that they were doing the right thing. Even so, they knew that the reasons for this success were threefold; they were dedicated, they planned well and they worked hard.

"Sara, we have succeeded because we have read and understood history, because we have been dedicated, because we have planned well and because we have worked hard."

"I will not accept this as a mere escape, though," Sara responded. "Maybe the Hermurian refugees were not downcast, but everyone else was. This galaxy will not be downcast."

Only a few hours after the departure of Essenes in their thousand ships bound for a new life of voluntary service to the galaxy, other Alteans began to realize that some of their co-workers, family members, friends and neighbors were failing to appear for their everyday business, family and social engagements. Worried reports in the thousands were just beginning to be received around the planet by various local legal authorities, when all planetary broadcasting was temporarily disrupted by Essenes, who sent a single, lengthy transcommunication back to Altea from the flotilla. Essenes wanted everyone to know immediately and directly from them what had transpired over the last few hours, what Essenes were doing and what they hoped to accomplish.

The leaders of Essenes spoke in turn assuring Alteans that Essenes were leaving Altea to assume their roles as preparers of the galaxy, not because they had lost hope for Altea or because they did not love their planet or Alteans, but because the time had arrived when the long ago conceived imperative of the Essene movement demanded that they take bold and resolute action. Essenes apologized for the secrecy of their preparation and outward voyage, but explained that they had concluded (even before preparations for departure were begun) that secrecy was in the best interests of all. It not only precluded the possibility of a negative reaction to Essenes, it also, they hoped insured a minimum disruption of Altean society before, during and after the departure. The Essene leadership went on to say that at the end of the main transcommunication there would follow another even more lengthy transcommunication which contained a personal message from each member of the expedition, which Essenes hoped Altean authorities would intercept and then redirect to the families concerned.

In concluding their very thoughtful, candid and loving remarks the Essene leadership asked for understanding and well wishes as Essenes embarked on their journey into the unknown. This would be the last transcommunication they said, but Essenes wanted all Alteans to know that the hearts and minds of all Essenes were with their fellows—forever—on Altea, and wherever Alteans might one day travel to in the galaxy.

There was much grieving throughout Altean society, but even more grieving accompanied the private viewing of the many personal messages by friends and relatives of those who had departed. Alteans everywhere were deeply shocked. Many resented the secrecy with which Essenes had accomplished their goal of leaving Altea. Others were horrified that such a massive—though benevolent—undertaking could have been conceived and executed without anyone even suspecting. Families cried out in agony at the loss of loved ones, as much lost to them as if they had died. Despite their efforts, Essenes had underestimated the breadth and depth of the feelings unleashed by their sudden, resolute and irrevocable departure.

A malaise continued to hang over Altea for months as the full import and impact of events sank into the minds of Alteans. They began to doubt everything, but mostly themselves, and for the first time as a culture, started to come to full grips with the possible ramifications of galactic colonization. Not only from the standpoint of those dire warnings issued by Essenes about possible confrontation and conflict, but from the sheer magnitude of the extensive operation that would be required to plan, outfit and send expeditions far from Altean space.

During their first billion years of development, Alteans had reached beyond Altea to a dozen relatively nearby planets, using the technology brought by the intergalactic pioneers. These they had colonized, but only through great effort and expense. There were simply very few suitable planets in the vicinity. Many stars are really multi-star systems, and therefore produce constantly varying gravitational fields around themselves. Very few planets can exist under such conditions. It is only at the center of the galaxy where stars are relatively close together, that there are more than a few planets. To be able to colonize extensively Alteans had to journey to the center of the galaxy.

Planets also have to be of a certain composition and relatively small. Giant planets consisting mostly of gases are totally unacceptable. The inner rocky planets of star systems are the only likely targets for colonization.

Preparation of these rocky planets includes many things, but most importantly the adjustment of each individual planet's speed of rotation so that it turns on its axis once every 23 hours and 56 minutes—no matter what its diameter. This period of rotation is absolutely vital because it results in just the right magnetic field for a planet, just the right magnetic field to carry with it planetary consciousness energy—long-since called planetary torun. This planetary torun is also produced in exactly the right amount by means of a rotational period of 23 hours, 56 minutes. Alteans also knew from information brought from previous galaxies that no self-aware being can exist for long without living on a planet across which flows the proper amount of planetary torun, as this torun allows four-dimensional souls to survive within a three-dimensional being and environment.

Planetary rotation speeds could only be increased by Altean technology, so planets spinning too rapidly, as well as planets without large amounts of water, were simply uninhabitable.

To accomplish the task of increasing planetary spin rates, gravitron infusion complexes containing two very large spinning disks are constructed on planetary surfaces at two widely separated sites predicated by the geography of the particular planet and by the transdimensional physics known to Alteans. These spinning disks, accompanied by their attendant gravitron capture rings (the particles of gravity waves have long since been known as gravitrons) increase the effective mass of planets near their surfaces through a process of continuous bombardment and infusion of gravitrons. The results, obtained by carefully planned and monitored continuing processes, are planets which turn on their axis once every 23 hours and 56 minutes.

Next comes the project of infusing the (usually very thin) natural atmospheres of planets being prepared for habitation with a mixture of gases. Enormous amounts of nitrogen and other gases (in super-cooled and compressed-to-liquid form) are transported from an already inhabited planet, (where the gases have been extracted or manufactured). These gases are then released into the existing natural atmosphere of planets being prepared, and are kept from drifting away from the planet by the planet's gravity which is now stronger due to the massive infusion of gravitrons. Finally, oxygen joins the combined atmosphere, following its separation from water on the planet being prepared. Planets are given combined atmospheres with a density and resulting thickness which enables the suns of those planets to heat their atmospheres to comfortable temperatures.

The procedures for gravitron infusion, rotation rate increasing, combined atmosphere making and subsequent warming had long since been worked out in previous galaxies, so Alteans knew before embarking on a planetary adjustment project that the planet in question could meet the several parameters necessary to qualify as a planet which could be made habitable. That experience reduced even further the number of planetary candidates for colonization. Qualifying planets therefore 'only' required massive amounts of money and effort, not new scientific inventions.

The processes of rotation and atmosphere adjustments take from five to ten years, during which time workers have to live inside in controlled temperature, atmosphere and induced torun-flow environments, just as those traveling in space vessels do.

Once these adjustments are completed, the real work of planetary development begins. Considering the expense, logistics, manpower and dedication involved, several hundred years of work are required to fully colonize a planet.

Only a relatively few planets around Altea had therefore been thoroughly developed, and Alteans had not had the wherewithal to undertake the daunting task of colonizing the galaxy.

Now the departure of Essenes made Alteans rethink everything.

After months of planetary-wide thought and discussion, the Over Council of Altea finally issued a statement of findings regarding galactic colonization. The findings were based on invaluable lessons learned from the preparation and departure of Essenes. And as a result of the jarring awakening that Alteans had received. Following public discussion of these statements, the Over Council stated it would take action according to the will of Alteans.

Before there could be any thought of colonization, the Over Council stated, there would have to be a thorough exploration of the center of the galaxy, an area completely unknown to Alteans. Although it had always been physically possible to visit the heart of the galaxy, the expense and effort had always been prohibitive. Additionally, unknown dangers, even the possibility of beings hostile to Altean exploration could be lurking beyond Altean space.

In order to undertake this vast proposition and to insure that exploration was carried out safely, the Over Council proposed the formation of a fully armed Altean Naval Service. The navy would explore and establish bases and stations along the route and in the center of the galaxy. It would serve as guide and protector of the colonists who might follow.

The Over Council also stated that a large percentage of the planetary wealth would be required over a lengthy period of time to finance the Altean Naval Service from initial planning through to deployment.

Only after this first phase of exploration and preparation was well under way could any sort of rational decision be made as to the feasibility of undertaking actual colonization—colonization which would take much more dedication, effort and sacrifice than even the exploration would, the Over Council added.

The Over Council would take action only if at least two-thirds of Altea's adult population approved a plan for preliminary or primary exploration.

The Over Council also dedicated its future members to another two-thirds majority vote, if and when—sometime in the far distant future, they knew—actual colonization was contemplated.

These possibilities raised by the Over Council caused an immediate planetary-wide debate, concerning the merits of perhaps finally translating a state of amorphous longing for planetary action into a series of precisely planned, properly financed moves toward exploration and possible eventual colonization of the galactic core.

What eventually resulted through a series of decisions made about a year after the departure of the Essene expedition, was not the clear mandate envisioned by the Over Council, but several partially funded procedures to begin a very down scaled Altean Naval Service, a navy which was designed to make a few tentative explorations to see if more explorations were feasible.

Altea therefore embarked on a very conservative 'go slow, look and see' policy, resulting in a series of convulsive steps which nonetheless crept toward the ultimate goal. The Altean Naval Service began with much fanfare, was reduced to only a pair of star ships for hundreds of years following an initial disappointing exploration, then revived again when interest was regenerated by a private expedition's finding of a planet rich in various ores along the way toward the heart of the galaxy. This same pattern was repeated many times, and each time new discoveries and slight advances were made.

A full 260 million years passed by—or more correctly was allowed to slip by—before the Altean Naval Service had finally been allowed to grow to sufficient size and capability to accomplish those things which the far-sighted Over Council of Altea of 260 million years previously had sought to accomplish during its own time.

The results of the work of the Altean Naval Service had shown that colonization was feasible. A new round of discussions ensued, finally over two-thirds of Altean adults approved a recommendation to begin colonization.

That was some 690 million years ago.

Essenes eventually settled underground in an otherwise uninhabitable planet, but this suited their purposes entirely, since Essenes wanted to work by themselves and in total secrecy.

Following the collapse of the Altean effort to colonize the center of the galaxy, Essenes determined that the time for major preparation was at hand. Secretly they had followed every event of importance which had occurred in the galaxy for over a quarter of a billion years. Essenes were therefore intimately familiar with Altean society and thinking, concluding that for Alteans to eventually carry out their mandate of redeeming the galaxy, Altean society would require considerable assistance in order to reverse its state of continuing deterioration.

Essenes knew that they themselves were only preparers, and not redeemers. Essenes observed Altean society for millions more years before finally concluding that due to Altea's long slide toward losing its societal courage (a society's ability to take decisive action counter to prevailing doctrine or current events) would never be able to take those resolute steps necessary to counter either current or future events so that galactic redeeming could take place. Essenes therefore concluded that what was needed was a partner society for Altean society, a partner society composed of courageous free-willed self-aware beings who could provide the Alteans with guiding assistance.

Essenes knew that no such courageous free-willed self-aware beings currently existed or would exist under current or projected conditions in the galaxy. Therefore, a qualifying planet needed to be found and prepared in such a way that natural evolution would eventually bring about such a being.

This was the specific mandate that Essenes had always sought.

Explorations by Essenes discovered a planet which was nearly the same size as Altea and which contained vast amounts of water, mostly in gigantic oceans that covered most of its surface. Primitive sea life existed in those oceans, but Essenes knew that there was not the slightest possibility that evolutionary processes would continue much farther on this planet without major adjustments to the planetary environment.

Essenes concluded that the way to effect major adjustments to the environment of this planet was through working on the three most important planetary motions in space: rotation, revolution and retrograde precession. Essenes knew that they could bring about these desired changes through the introduction of a moon, whose mass and resulting gravity could be used to alter the planet's periods of rotation and revolution; and most importantly to induce the required retrograde precessional period of 25,920 years.

Essenes were in the process of finding a suitable moon for the planet they would be preparing when one of their extragalactic ships received a distress call from a very distant source: beings on a dying planet were desperately seeking aid. The Essene ship diverted immediately in order to render assistance, but arrived at the planet too late to save its beings.

As a result of internal pressures and a weak crust the planet had suddenly burst open along a long fissure, allowing molten rock to flow freely across much of its surface. The resulting release of poison gases so polluted the atmosphere that those beings not killed by fire were asphyxiated.

Essenes watched in great sorrow for some time as the planet convulsed again and again before the fissure collapsed into itself, quelling the fires.

As part of standard Essene procedure aboard ship sensors were directed at the dying planet, and Essenes thereby determined that its mass and size made it a suitable candidate to become the projected moon of the planet they were about to prepare.

The Essene leadership discussed the appropriateness of using this now dead planet for the project, and decided to proceed, as they concluded that the dead planet could become a reminder to those who came later, of those who had gone before, in the endless repetition of birth, life, death and rebirth.

The formerly dead planet become moon was brought into orbit around the planet of preparation some 572 million years ago. Its crust had been completely transformed and pockmarked by numerous craters of varying size in order to appear as if it really were the natural satellite of the planet of preparation.

The rotation rate of the new moon was synchronized with its period of revolution so that only one hemisphere would ever face the planet of preparation. The side visible from the planet of preparation was unlike the arrangement of craters on its far side, as was the distribution of the lowlands and the highlands, resulting in very distinct topographical differences between the two sides. The mass of the new moon was redistributed resulting in distinct differences in crustal thickness between the near side and the far side. Moreover, the new moon was cosmetically dressed with dust and rocks of vastly differing ages.

Only hints of the former dead planet's previous existence remained, among them the presence of isotopes near its surface which could not possibly be present as a result of radiation from the sun of the planet of preparation. The dead planet's sun was an older star which had produced these isotopes due to countless aeons of nuclear fusion; the much younger sun of the planet of preparation would not be capable of emitting such isotopes until far into the future, when its own processes of nuclear fusion would have had time to construct such isotopes.

By far the most important adjustment made to the planet of preparation, however, was the creation of a retrograde precessional period of 25,920 years. This period of retrograde precession—which produced a very slow off-center rotation on the surface of the planet of preparation—was absolutely necessary to provide the proper environment for natural evolution to bring about self-aware life.

In a relatively short time the evolutionary process began on the planet of preparation, and there ensued a literal explosion of life, first in the great oceans, and later on the emerging land masses.

Essenes observed this process unfolding for hundreds of millions of years from an underground underwater base on the planet of preparation, a base from which they kept the planet of preparation's moon in the orbit that insured the maintenance of the planet of preparation's all-important 25,920 year retrograde precession.

Chapter Eight

The Tri-Naval Authority

While Essenes were preparing, Alteans managed to survive the onslaught of the Pleiadeans by committing vast resources to their defenses, and for over 650 million years the Altean Naval Service vigilantly served as protector of the remaining Altean territory. The Pleiadean navy managed to overwhelm some outposts, but it never attempted another direct assault on Altea.

The restriction of Alteans to a relatively small territory caused the eventual predictable depletion of vital natural resources on Altea and nearby planets, and resulted in the introduction of rationing. The Over Council delegated the Altean Naval Service overseer of mining, transportation, processing and distribution of selected ores.

Thus the Altean Naval Service became involved in non-naval activities for the first time. Initially all went smoothly, but with time—due to pressures resulting from the continuing necessity for vital ores as they became rarer—and due to the natural proclivity of structured organizations to become dictatorial when dealing with outsiders—the Altean Naval Service became overbearing in its zeal to carry out its mandate efficiently.

There were therefore an increasing number of complaints lodged by many Alteans before the Over Council, concerning the methods employed by the Altean Naval Service. The Over Council felt compelled to take action and called members of the Altean Naval Service high command before it, to review policy. The Altean Naval Service commanders resented this intrusion into what they considered their area of total responsibility and refused to appear before the Over Council. This action in turn precipitated a major political crisis without precedent in Altean history. The Altean Naval Service high command remained steadfast and was supported all down its chain of command. The Over Council insisted the naval commanders appear before them not only to explain their procedures regarding rationing, but now also to explain their insubordination.

The standoff continued for several days before the Over Council ordered the members of the Altean Naval Service high command to resign forthwith, giving them 48 hours to present themselves unarmed to legal authority.

The bitter confrontation between the Altean Naval Service and the Over Council caused increasing anxiety throughout Altean society. On the one hand everyone knew their navy was obliged to submit to civilian legal authority, but on the other hand they all feared a massive attack by the Pleiadeans if the Altean Naval Service was severely crippled by the Over Council.

Sensing the mood of the planet swinging in favor of the navy, the Altean Naval Service high command broadcast its position—emphasizing the Pleiadean threat—in a planetary-wide temporary interruption of normal programming. This outraged the Over Council which then retaliated by preempting the resumption of normal programming with its own broadcast.

The legal and ethical positions of the Over Council were unimpeachable, but the overriding fear of Pleiadean domination resulted in the Over Council's relenting and allowing the Altean Naval Service to continue as before. At this point, Odkin Lon, the Elder of Altea, attempted to preserve traditional civilian legal authority by issuing an emergency order to the members of the Altean Naval Service high command to resign forthwith and to present themselves unarmed to him. This traditional emergency authority of the Elder of Altea was seldom invoked and could be overruled by a two-thirds vote of the Over Council of Altea. The badly demoralized council members voted to overrule the emergency order of Odkin Lon.

Although the full ramifications of the defeat of the Over Council and the Elder were not at first widely understood, they became evident to everyone over time, as the Altean Naval Service increasingly intruded into Altean politics and society. In the ensuing years, the Over Council saw its authority severely limited as the naval high command gradually increased its power in order to "insure adequate defenses."

Eventually, Over Council membership came to be virtually handed out by naval commanders who offered Alteans a slate of candidates guaranteed to be fully capable of working alongside their naval counterparts for the betterment and especially the defense of Altea. Statements made about the candidates were perfectly accurate as those candidates were always committed to the notion that the Altean Naval Service must always come first, due to its commitment to the defense of Altea. The candidates' commitment to the betterment of Altea was always subordinate to their commitment to defense. The naval slate was invariably elected by the thoroughly cowed populace of Altea.

Gradually, the entire planet became subordinate to the defense effort and Alteans lost most of their political and many of their social freedoms. Elders came to be chosen by the high command of the Altean Naval Service. Rationed goods and services became a way of life, even in the area of energy transproduction and usage, due to the growing scarcity of gold—the singularly most vital and rare component of energy transproduction.

Long ago the intergalactic pioneers had brought with them the single most important technological advance in history: the ability to transproduce nearly limitless amounts of energy transdimensionally by using the single most important resource in the Universe: consciousness.

The process of consciousness energy production—rediscovered and to a large extent perfected by Waldark and his 'cabalists' aeons before—had become increasingly sophisticated to the point where it took only a few beings to 'generate' enough consciousness energy to run an entire planet.

To begin the process meditators hold in their right hand a Waldark thing to help them achieve the extremely high states of meditation required. Using their own consciousness, meditators transredimension consciousness energy from the Source which permeates the Universe—long since called Horun—and thus produce hyperdimensional consciousness energy—long since called torun.

As Waldark had established, torun produced by meditation emanates in vast quantities from the top of the head. Therefore, meditators wear Waldark hats—conical hats about 20 inches high—which capture, refocus and transmit the torun to the next device in the chain leading toward usable energy. 20

The next critical step in the process requires an energy transdimensioner, this device transdimensions hyperdimensional torun into three-dimensional torinum. This torinum is then conduited to an energy transconverter—another device developed by Waldark's 'cabalists.' Energy transconverters transconvert torinum into tornum, a rapidly flowing stream of consciousness energy corpuscles called conscitrons by Alteans.

Tornum is used to run everything.

Without gold, energy transconverters cannot transproduce tornum.

Without tornum nothing runs.

Therefore, the vital energy transproduction industry came under the control of the naval high command, which predicated production and distribution of energy based on its own sense of rationing. First priority went to the Altean Naval Service star ships; next came the spinning disks regulating the rotation of outlying planets; other naval considerations came third and last were the needs of Altean society in general.

The supply of gold steadily dwindled and Alteans suffered greatly.

The high command decided to take bold action.

In a totally unprecedented master stroke the Altean Naval Service fleet attacked several key, gold-producing planets deep in Pleiadean territory. Groups of Altean star ships, in simultaneous assaults, blasted Pleiadean defenses and destroyed Pleiadean navy craft sent against them.

As the battles raged, heavily escorted Altean Naval Service transport vessels landed at gold facilities on the targeted planets. Supported by energy cannon and energy torpedo, Altean Naval Service marines assaulted Pleiadean ground positions and temporarily seized control of the gold works. Altean Naval Service cargo vessels descended to the ground and on loaded vital gold. Once the gold was safely on its way toward Altea, the main battle group withdrew, forming a virtually impenetrable shield behind the cargo vessels.

The smashed and demoralized Pleiadean defenders pursued not at all.

As a result of their successful attack enough gold had come into the possession of the Altean Naval Service to fulfill Altean needs for years.

On announcing their great victory over the Pleiadean navy and the seizure of much gold, the naval high command also announced the formation of a new command structure designed to fully protect Altean territory from anticipated Pleiadean counterattack.

Thus the Tri-Naval Authority came into existence.

Its establishment dissolved the Altean Naval Service high command and divided the defense of Altean territory into three sectors, each with its own command and defense structure, capable of acting alone or in concert with the other sectors to successfully repel any Pleiadean attack.

The three sectors were: East Altean Defense Command whose headquarters were in Altea's largest city of the eastern hemisphere, West Altean Defense Command headquartered in Hurtea, and Outer Altean Defense Command, which had no permanent headquarters but physically located itself randomly at outlying naval bases and stations for varying periods of time.

Three high ranking members of the former high command became Commanders of the three sectors. Each commander was responsible for his own sector, but all three met frequently to establish policy concerning matters germane to all Altean territory. The Over Council carried out the wishes of the three commanders of the Tri-Naval Authority. By issuing a number of decrees designed primarily to improve the defense of Altean territory, the Tri-Naval Authority came to control virtually all economic and political policy of the Alteans.

As the years passed, the Tri-Naval Authority continued to provide the same expert shield over Altean territory as had the Altean Naval Service previously. By periodically conducting raids against Pleiadean territory, the Altean Naval Service was able to replenish its supply of gold, and thus insure the ability of Alteans to continue to exist as a viable societal group, but individual liberties almost vanished.

As part of their responsibilities the Tri-Naval Authority protected vulnerable Altean outposts, established after the initial Altean attack on Pleiadean territory. These outposts mined gold and other vital priority metal ores, and served to supplement Altean Naval Service supplies, seized in raids.

Altean Naval Service star ships patrolled the space surrounding these outposts in varying search patterns at random intervals, but they were not completely successful in discouraging Pleiadean raids. Most times the Pleiadean craft turned back to their own territory when intercepted by patrolling Altean Naval Service star ships, but some tried to evade their interceptors, or even attack them. Those Pleiadean craft were invariably destroyed.

Occasionally, a Pleiadean raider would slip undetected past the Altean Naval Service patrollers. It was following such an intrusion that a young Altean naval officer so distinguished himself—by locating, tracking and destroying a Pleiadean raider about to launch an attack on a mining center on a small planet near the transition between Altean and Pleiadean territory—that he became a Luminary of Altea, a hero.

The officer, whose name was Zuv Lon Ell, let the enemy raider approach its intended victim, and then prepared to attack himself. Ensign Zuv was constantly monitored by his commanding officer, who was ultimately responsible for the success of the action, but allowed Ensign Zuv to proceed without jeopardizing either the Altean outpost or his star ship. By carefully measuring junior officers, the Altean Naval Service was able to train a continuous flow of highly capable commanders who were vastly superior to their Pleiadean counterparts.

The attack doctrine employed by the Altean Naval Service in such situations called for use of energy cannons against the Pleiadean craft, but on this occasion that tactic would have threatened Alteans as well as the Pleiadean raider, because the Altean outpost lay directly on the line of fire beyond the Pleiadean craft. Mindful of this fact, Ensign Zuv maneuvered his star ship to come within range of the Pleiadean energy torpedoes. Mere seconds separated the combatants and any mistake might have proven fatal to Ensign Zuv's star ship, as he patiently waited for the firing solution for an energy torpedo salvo.

By restricting all active transcommunications and relying solely on his passive holo-plot to track the enemy—a procedure which was much more time consuming and less accurate than conventional active tracking—the young Altean officer managed to prevent detection of his star ship by the Pleiadean raider's passive locating devices.

Ensign Zuv turned on the energy torpedo transmagnetic acquisition and tracking device at the last possible moment so as to insure the correctness of his firing solution. Seeing that the active and passive holo-plots matched, the commanding officer of the Altean star ship nodded to his officer, indicating that authorization to attack was granted. Ensign Zuv launched the energy torpedo salvo.

The Pleiadean raider had only six seconds from the time the energy torpedo transmagnetic acquisition and tracking device was activated to when the energy torpedoes impacted, and no time for any defensive response. The Pleiadean craft was struck and instantly turned into a burning hulk as it fell toward the planet, where it impacted harmlessly.

When his star ship returned to Altea, Ensign Zuv was greeted by a completely unexpected, overwhelming reception from the Tri-Naval Authority commanders. They had decided to use the young officer's extremely competent and professional actions to publicize the ability of the Altean Naval Service to defend Altean territory.

Ensign Zuv, very dedicated and rather shy, did not know how to react to this sudden attention bestowed upon him by the highest ranking Altean commanders. At the ceremony honoring him as a Luminary of Altea—broadcast throughout Altean territory at the wishes of the Tri-Naval Authority—Ensign Zuv Lon Ell stood erect and received with great dignity the medal placed on his chest by one of those commanders.

The young man was much relieved when two weeks later, following a round of ceremonies and public appearances, he was allowed to return to his star ship. Ensign Zuv tried to return to his duties, but he was haunted by the spectacles to which he had been subjected. He had merely done his job by defending Altean territory as he was trained and dedicated to do, he thought, and for doing that the highest naval authority had made him a Luminary of Altea.

Ensign Zuv was unable to cope with his elevated status which he felt was unearned, and he began to realize it had been granted to him only for propaganda purposes. Two weeks after Ensign Zuv returned to duty he was found dead in his aboard ship stateroom, the wound from a self-inflicted energy pistol shot in the side of his head still bleeding.

Chapter Nine

The Rivalry

About 489,000 years ago Admiral Renford Arbrath became commander of the East Altean Defense Command. He therefore joined Admiral Edwards Evard, commander of the West Altean Defense Command, and Admiral Home Robb, commander of the Outer Altean Defense Command, as the third member of the Tri-Naval Authority.

The three were at odds immediately.

Renford replaced a relatively docile commander who had spent over twenty years at his post and who had increasingly given way to the very aggressive Edwards. Renford was a tough battle hardened commander, and had led many daring raids against Pleiadean strongholds seeking ever precious gold.

Renford was accustomed to acting as he pleased.

Edwards had long enjoyed a preeminent position among the three, theoretically equal, commanders who controlled virtually all Altean society.

Edwards was not about to give way to anyone, let alone accommodate the upstart Renford.

Home was the mild mannered and level headed member of the group, but he was indecisive when it came to making major decisions. Rather than clawing his way to the top as almost all other Tri-Naval Authority commanders had done, Home had been inserted into his current position at a time when it had proven impossible to choose between any of the more aggressive candidates.

Home therefore attempted to appease both Edwards and Renford, but succeeded only in infuriating the two of them.

Edwards and Renford each accused Home of taking the side of the other on every occasion. The pressures on Home became immense, so he followed the line of least resistance and submitted his resignation. This may have solved one problem for the two quarreling commanders, but it created a new one, because it became apparent very quickly that no new commander of the Outer Altean Defense Command could be selected, nor did any lesser commander actively seek the position. Those drafted by either Edwards or Renford proved unacceptable to the other.

The Tri-Naval Authority had succeeded in precipitating its own military and political crisis. Other Alteans—especially the thoroughly cowed Over Council—distanced themselves from the rivalry, fearing they might be caught up in the conflict.

Edwards and Renford raged. The administration of Altean territory deteriorated. The morale of the Altean Naval Service sagged, and so did its defense posture.

The Pleiadeans attacked.

Scores of Pleiadean naval craft swooped down upon Altea's main outer defense base and left it a burning shambles.

Many Altean Naval Service star ships were destroyed on the ground.

Something had to be done.

At last, the two rivals Edwards and Renford understood that they needed to make some accommodation, or the next Pleiadean attack would threaten Altea itself.

Overnight, they found a 'solution.'

Instead of the appointment of a third commander for the Tri-Naval Authority, two joint commanders would be chosen, one from Edwards's staff, one from Renford's staff. Edwards would have the authority to reject Renford's selection; Renford would have the power to reject Edwards's appointee.

This would insure—Edwards and Renford declared in an Altean territory-wide broadcast—that Altean defenses could be properly reestablished, and that Altean territory would return to normal. What the 'solution' really did was preserve Edwards and Renford in their positions.

From the East staff came Admiral Masters Sam, and from the West staff Admiral Halburn All. Neither man sought the position or appeared very outspoken, so both were accepted by the rivals.

Halburn and Masters had both been involved in the investigation following the Pleiadean attack, and both knew that immediate action was required to save Altea from another disastrous defeat. They therefore met privately and agreed to try to collaborate closely to prop up the crumbling Altean defenses while continuing to appease their masters. In public Halburn and Masters showed the appropriate amount of disdain and distrust for one another; behind the scenes they got things done.

The inevitable follow up attack by the Pleiadean navy was met inside Pleiadean space by a determined and ferocious Altean Naval Service counterattack which sent the forces of the empire reeling in defeat.

Edwards and Renford had themselves declared Luminaries of Altea.

Despite the quiet and diligent efforts of the joint commanders of the Outer Altean Defense Command, the overall defense effort against the Pleiadeans continued to deteriorate due to the continued bitter and hateful rivalry between the commanders of East and West. Halburn and Masters realized that they had just enough forces at their disposal to repel a medium sized Pleiadean attack, but they feared that if the Pleiadeans broke through the Outer defenses, the combined defenses of East and West would no longer be capable of halting the imperials.

Edwards and Renford were busily redeploying their forces for possible use against each other.

The realization that there was a distinct possibility of civil war completely traumatized Altean society. A few Alteans were at last galvanized into action in an attempt to restore the traditional authority of the Over Council, and to once again subordinate the Altean Naval Service to civilian control.

Risking everything, these bold Alteans from all three defense sectors secretly joined together to form a very dedicated, highly motivated and absolutely resolute organization.

They were to call themselves Lotharians.

Chapter Ten

At the Brink

The enmity between Edwards and Renford deepened and their forces divided the planet into two armed camps.

Altea was at the brink of disaster.

Only the Lotharians worked to try to halt the inexorable slide toward devastating civil war; other Alteans were simply too cowed by the prospect of combat to do more than hope.

Halburn and Masters continued their valiant efforts to hold the Pleiadeans at bay by employing all the energies and resources of the Outer Altean Defense Command. The Pleiadeans had been severely stung by their last attempt, but Altean intelligence sources reported that imperial forces would probably return to Altean territory in the near future; the Pleiadeans understood the deteriorating situation on Altea, and were clearly waiting for just the right moment to strike and destroy their longtime enemy.

All communications between East and West were severed, and families separated by this division could only meet within the bounds of the Outer Altean Defense Command. Despite the ferocious antagonism between Edwards and Renford they were both well aware of the Pleiadean threat, and they 'cooperated' to the extent of giving limited support to the outer defenses. This included a severely restricted schedule of shuttle flights to the outer planets from both East and West. Some passengers were allowed aboard the shuttles along with the standard cargo of naval supplies, but only if they could prove a legitimate need for the journey. Family hardship was sometimes honored.

It was in this very tense atmosphere that the Lotharians strove toward their goal of reestablishing civilian legal authority.

The organization had been founded by two ladies shortly after Renford became commander of East and the already poor situation quickly became intolerable. Fosgood Lura was visiting her longtime friend Cunard Anna when the two began to discuss those weighty issues that were bearing down upon them.

"The naval control of Altea has not only gone on for too long," stated Lura, "it is now totally out of control."

Anna looked at her friend, was suddenly inspired and said, "Then let's do something about it. Let's work to restore the Over Council and therefore the individual rights and freedom of all Alteans."

They talked long into the night, and the more they talked the more they realized someone had to do something, and that someone was really two someones: Cunard Anna and Fosgood Lura.

They also decided on a name: the Lotharians. Lotharian was a double edged combining word, built around the syllable brought to this galaxy by the intergalactic pioneers: 'har,' meaning 'potent.'

Therefore, to them a Lotharian meant someone who loathed 'har,' the potency or power of the corrupt—but also one who was a lot 'har,' very powerful (in the sense of being powerful enough to overcome great odds).

At first the two ladies went about discussing the issues with friends, inviting them into their homes, and enlisting some of them into their fledgling organization. The ladies soon realized, however, that this way of doing things would eventually lead to public disclosure of their organization, and consequently put them at risk of being apprehended by 'legal' authority.

Living next door to Cunard Anna was a youth named Spaty Astir, an avid and astute student of history. Young Astir understood Cunard Anna's ideas and her dilemma about procedure. One of the first and youngest to become a Lotharian, he had an immediate suggestion. "When the intergalactic pioneers left Hermur billions of years ago they were able to do so because they built up an organization, planned carefully and attracted many followers," he said. "When Essenes departed Altea 950 million years ago, they were able to do so because they also built up an organization, planned carefully and attracted many followers.

"What else did they have in common?

"They both worked secretly."

So the Lotharians went immediately underground.

Spaty Astir had a brother; a very interesting relative and—a sweetheart.

Spaty Astir's brother's name was Roger, and he was on one of the outer planets, studying architecture at Akadeimia.

Astir's very interesting relative's name was Ell Dan, who had sometime earlier been awarded the honorific title 'Art Hurian' by the Altean Arts Council for his innate and incredible skills as an artist. Ell Dan's mastery of the arts was indeed unprecedented. He was known throughout Altean territory and the bestowing of the honorific title upon him, the first time a living artist had been honored in this way, was applauded by all, disapproved by none.

Ell Dan was the first cousin of Astir and Roger; their mothers were sisters.

When Spaty Roger finished high school it was only natural that he would want to study under his older cousin Ell Dan, who held a fairly new teaching position at Akadeimia on one of the outer planets. Ell Dan and his wife Lana had quietly moved to that outer planet the year before; only their families knew this move was a silent protest against political and social developments on Altea.

Astir's sweetheart lived just down the street. Her name was Zuv Sofy, and she was a direct descendent—as was Ell Dan—of Ensign Zuv Lon Ell, the Luminary of Altea who had killed himself (when he realized that he had become a pawn of the Tri-Naval Authority).

Sofy loved Astir, Astir loved Sofy. They always had, they always would.

Nearby lived another friend of the Spaty family, Folen Lana, who held a very important position with the company which had the concession to fly shuttles to the outer planets.

Astir invited Folen Lana to his home one evening under the pretext of discussing plans for a marriage trip for Sofy and himself, but mostly with the intent of having a very private meeting concerning the Lotharians. Astir's parents were fully aware of the main intent of the assembly, Cunard Anna, Fosgood Lura and Sofy were all to be there, and although they chose not to participate, they did not discourage their younger son's efforts.

When Folen Lana was seated she was quite surprised to see the extra guests.

Fosgood Lura wasted no time. "Astir invited you here this evening, but in doing so he committed a slight deception," she said. "We don't really want to talk about marriage trips...yet. But we do want to talk about trips...business trips aboard your shuttle."

Folen Lana had, of course, never heard of the Lotharians, but she soon found out about their concerns as the others in the room took turns outlining them for her.

When the Lotharians completed their presentation Folen Lana smiled and said: "I want to join. Let's talk about Sofy and Astir's wedding trip."

Later, much later, Sofy and Astir were snuggled together in a secret hiding place they knew. The young lady and her adoring companion had just made love to one another, and now they lay peacefully in one another's arms contemplating the future when they would be married and such slight deceptions would no longer be required.

They only hoped that there would be a future.

As a result of Folen Lana's willing and expert interceding on his behalf, Astir was able to board the next shuttle bound for the outer planet where his brother was 'gravely ill.'

Once at his destination, the young Lotharian immediately met privately with both his cousin Ell Dan and his 'gravely ill' brother Roger.

They did not talk of someone being gravely ill, but of a society being gravely ill.

Two more seriously concerned Alteans became Lotharians.

During Astir's four day stay, the three of them delved deeply into the problem of organization. By combining information that had been passed down to them about the organization of the escaping Hermurians, together with help from the documentation of Essenes organization, planning and pre-departure procedures from Altea (obtained from ancient writings recording the personal transcommunications from the departed flotilla, transcommunications made public by the parties concerned), the three Lotharians made great strides toward the beginnings of real organisation.

Once again Akadeimia would become the targets of their recruiting. Both Ell Dan and Spaty Roger had many contacts within their Akadeimia on the planet on which they were meeting, so they would begin there, using the same tactics of recruitment Essenes had used many millions of years before.

Ell Dan had contacts throughout the many other Akadeimia of Altean territory, and indeed throughout Altean society. He was well known and respected everywhere, and now he was determined to use his well deserved social position to good ends. He would think about how to proceed, but he was sure he could come up with a plan to personally renew his many contacts.

As he was about to depart for Altea, where he could hold Sofy in his arms again, Astir lamented the cyclical nature of history. "Here we are today delving back into musty old tomes, trying to figure out what to do, making our decisions as a result of having tried to understand situations and organizations of long ago," he said.

"We go along for a while, and then get ourselves back into the same old rut. We never seem to get anywhere. This time—unless we do something extraordinary—there won't even be a next time.

"So much for the traditions; there won't be any intergalactic pioneer lad to carry an old cedar box with an encased adventure book to the bridge.

"There will only be the Pleiadeans."

Astir's brother and cousin looked at Astir, feeling great sorrow for the defiant, discouraged youth, who really only wanted one thing from life—Sofy.

Ell Dan retrieved one of the musty old tomes they had been reading and opened it at a place he had previously marked.

"Astir," he said, "I would like you to listen to something written about Essenes which I thought was very interesting. This passage describes the first meeting of Sara Eland and Peter Odun, who you know were among the leaders of Essenes when they left Altea nearly a billion years ago. The passage reads:

> As it was, there was not much any one could do except wonder at what this odd group was doing, being so concerned about galactic redemption due to possible upheavals caused by galactic colonization, when colonization was still only an idea.
>
> Among those shaking their heads at the reports of Essene thinking was a relatively young man, called Peter Odun, of very conservative views.
>
> Odun was a teacher of history, coincidentally at the same Akadeimia that Sara Eland had attended, but she had never been in any of his classes. He invariably always began the first day's discussion with a comical self-effacing account of how he was a distant descendant of the famous Bill Odun, hero of Peter Odun's two favorite mythos ODUNSIDE and NOSTOS.
>
> Although Odun was very conservative in his thinking regarding Akadeimia policy and the politics of the day, he was a favorite among his students for his sense of humor and his biting sarcasm against those who felt self-important.
>
> It was therefore not surprising to them that Odun penned a scathing article which was published in Hurtea's largest daily newspaper which thoroughly lambasted the "presumptuous Essenes for thinking they have some sort of monopoly on correct thinking with regard to how matters should proceed." He also skewered them for their secrecy, concluding: "If one single member of the Essene 'movement' will reveal himself to me, and convince me of the rightness of his mission, then I will quit my job and become an

Essene myself."

Sara Eland read the article with growing anger until she came to its ending. Inspired by the impudent challenge of this Peter Odun—about whom she knew very little from her Akadeimia days—Sara decided to lay down the gauntlet.

Armed with her own wit, knowledge and wise-thinking, Sara emerged from her Essene hideout so she could track down and find her newly discovered tormenter.

That was not difficult as Odun lived alone, not far from his place of work, in a relatively modest home directly on the beach. Early one evening she rang his bell and he opened the door after turning on the porch light.

"May I help...you?" He inquired, pausing somewhat as he discerned that an absolutely beautiful young lady was standing before him.

"Yes," she answered resolutely, "I am an Essene. We have a lot to talk about."

He invited her into his home. After Sara had expressed her concerns to Peter Odun about the possibility of conflict arising during the projected colonization of the galaxy, he responded, "I don't think we should be so concerned. Alteans have Philosophia. Since Alteans study Philosophia I don't think the problems which you foresee will arise."

"How many Alteans do you think actually study Philosophia?" asked Sara.

Peter Odun shrugged his shoulders.

"Your type of mind is perfectly suited to the study and enjoyment of Philosophia," Sara continued. "Not all minds are like yours. Philosophia requires thinking. Not all Alteans think. You are very comfortable with Philosophia at all levels of thinking. Others need to have everything explained to them, or they reject everything. Others simply want to be told what to believe.

"The others, those who reject everything, will do anything.

"The others, those who want to be told what to believe, will become the slaves of those who will do anything."

The next day Peter Odun became an Essene.

Seven weeks later Sara Eland and Peter Odun were married, and their undying love for one another is still known as the romance of the galaxy.

Ell Dan closed the dusty old tome and said, "Sara Eland was right.

"The others who reject everything have done that anything—again.

"The others who want to be told what to believe have become the slaves of those who will do that anything — again.

"It is time for those who can think to think — and act — extraordinarily.

"That makes these extraordinary times, Astir.

"It is time for us to do the extraordinary.

"The cycle must be broken."

As the shuttle sped through space on its way toward Altea, Astir mused about the future, but those thoughts always took him back to the past. You can't know where you are going, he thought, if you don't know where you've been.

Where he had just been was a planet called Colchis, so named nearly two billion years before by the intergalactic pioneers who had found gold in abundance on Colchis.

The name Colchis had come out of time immemorial, from a mythos in which earlier brave sailors had sought a golden fleece, across the sea, far from home.

Chapter Eleven

The Lotharian

As he tried to decide how he could further the efforts of the Lotharian movement, Ell Dan soon realized that the idea of returning control of Altea and its outer planets to the civilian legal authority of the Over Council would not succeed. The long entrenched power of the Altean Naval Service through the Tri-Naval Authority and lately through the additional excesses of the East and West commanders was out of control, and there was no counter force available to dislodge those two madmen.

There was only one alternative: escape.

The Lotharians would therefore have to take their organization one step further in emulating the Essene movement; they would have to undertake a massive build-up of supplies and space vessels so that at least two-thirds of a million of them—the genetic minimum—could leave Altean territory. The Lotharians would not know where to travel, but in order to survive they would have to leave, Ell Dan concluded. The fate of Essenes was unknown to Alteans, but the artist knew that the Lotharians would have to take the same risk. There was no other choice. How to proceed? he asked himself.

Although Ell Dan's plan was to recruit Alteans from the outer planets and to eventually escape therefrom, he was also intent on including as many residents of Altea as possible. After all, he knew it was on Altea that everything had begun, including the Lotharian movement.

Fortunately Ell Dan also knew the open secret of Colchis and of the other outer planets, and that turned out to be the secret of success for the Lotharians. Ell Dan knew that Halburn and Masters, the joint commanders of the Altean outer defenses, were not only cooperating, but also that they were friendly with one another. If properly persuaded, Halburn and Masters could provide incalculable support for the escape.

Although the understanding between the two commanders was an open secret on the outer planets, the residents of those planets were very careful not to let out to strangers that Halburn and Masters might be conducting themselves counter to the orders of the East and West commanders. Neither Edwards nor Renford suspected that Halburn and Masters were thinking and acting on their own. The joint commanders were therefore extremely cautious in carrying out their duties, and Ell Dan knew that he had to proceed with similar caution when he approached them.

Ell Dan also suspected that as Ell 'Art Hurian,' it would be easier. In fact it turned out to be very easy, but only because Ell Dan thought of something else.

Ell 'Art Hurian's' additional thinking called for a traveling art exhibit and lecture series to be led and conducted by himself and which he hoped would be able to travel throughout Altea. Although his plan appeared on the surface to have little chance of success, Ell Dan thought it might work. He had read a few history books himself and he therefore knew that autocrats such as Edwards and Renford, by appearing to be champions of cultural pursuits, often used the furthering of the arts to their own purposes.

The way to begin, he thought, was to go through the joint commanders of the outer defenses, and that is precisely what Ell Dan did.

The meeting was easily arranged and Ell 'Art Hurian' explained his art tour and lecture series. Ell 'Art Hurian' told the joint commanders that he understood there would be difficulties, especially with regard to travel arrangements, but that he felt strongly that an art exhibit and lecture series could help to ease the mounting tensions. The joint commanders indicated they were in full agreement with Ell 'Art Hurian's' stated plans and promised that they would forward the artist's requests to the commanders of East and West.

As Ell 'Art Hurian' was being ushered from the meeting room and just before reaching its door, the Lotharian turned back toward the joint commanders and said, "Gentlemen, I have something more to discuss with you, if you do not mind. There is something we three have to do together."

Masters nodded to the artist's escort, who left the room, shutting the door behind him. Ell 'Art Hurian' was invited back before the joint commanders, and the Lotharian stood before them as they sat at their respective desks.

"Gentlemen," the Lotharian began, "I want to tell you about an organization which you are about to join . . ."

When the Lotharian had completed his presentation, Halburn looked at Masters and Masters looked at Halburn. Masters looked the Lotharian straight in the eyes and said, "We want to join, we want in."

As the Lotharian had suspected, both Edwards and Renford agreed to the art tour and lectures. Halburn and Masters had sent their separate transcommunications to the staffs of East and West at precisely the same time, indicating that they were doing so "in keeping with standard procedures of insuring that both commanders are kept equally informed of Outer Altean Defense Command activities." The two commanders on Altea were paralyzed with fear that the other would immediately agree to Ell 'Art Hurian's' plan, and then make swift propaganda of that acceptance. As a result both Edwards and Renford sent back separate but nearly identical positive responses within an hour of receiving the messages from the joint commanders of the outer defenses.

The art tour and lectures came about as planned and were very successful both in terms of culture and recruitment. Ell 'Art Hurian' was treated with great respect wherever he went, and his artistic talents and knowledge well received.

The Lotharian renewed old acquaintances and contacts, recruited many new members and because there was absolutely no communication between East and West, began the establishment of two large Lotharian organizations on Altea.

Ell 'Art Hurian' was obliged to transit through Colchis in order to get from the West to the East and he used this 'inconvenience' to keep the outer planets' Lotharian organization abreast of happenings on Altea.

Following major recruiting successes in the western region of East (where he was also able to meet with all of the original Lotharians including Sofy and Astir) the Lotharian was more than pleased with the results to date, as Ell 'Art Hurian' departed for the last stops of the tour, in the eastern region of East.

When Ell 'Art Hurian' landed, the Lotharian was shocked beyond belief as he realized he must insist that the Lotharians escape as soon as possible. The Lotharian had seen the Shield.

The Shield was a powerful magnetic field stretching along both meridians, 180 degrees apart, the Shield separated East and West, and had recently been put in place by East in order to eliminate the possibility of a surprise attack by West. The western boundary of East was entirely oceanic, but the eastern boundary of East included a long continental border with West. A large section of this border ran through highly populated areas dividing cities, towns, villages and sometimes even houses. This recently imposed border had not been willingly accepted by any Alteans outside the command structures of East and West. No borders had ever been envisaged for Altea, and this one had become the object of much hatred. Alteans living on and near the hated demarcation had been ruthlessly uprooted. Heavily armed naval marine forces of East and West faced each other across a barren strip a hundred yards wide.

Above and beyond its presence as a sign of impending doom, what upset the Lotharian most about the Shield was its powerful magnetic field. While essential elements of many devices vital to Alteans, magnetic fields are always heavily shielded due to the negative affects which powerful magnetic fields have on self-aware beings: magnetic fields disrupt the normal flow of planetary torun, a flow which is required by self-aware beings in order to exist.

It was Waldark and his associates who discovered that Horun is trans-redimensioned into planetary torun by rotating celestial bodies, and that that torun is directed along the lines of the magnetic field of rotating celestial bodies by the magnetic fields of those celestial bodies. 18 Although this information was contained in Herzman's exhaustive and thorough presentation of Waldark's work, its importance was at first not understood by those who carried forward Waldark's work toward practical fruition.

As a result, beings were sent into space and onto other planets and were consequently required to live in environments which had no flow of planetary torun. Those who were away from the required flow of planetary torun of their planet for lengthy periods first became ill, often suicidal and, if they did not return to their home planet in time, eventually died.

Beside the obviously devastating practical, emotional and psychological effects these tragedies had upon this space exploration program, a most serious philosophic question arose: (were self-aware beings meant to leave their planet of existence?)

The debate raged.

Space exploration ceased.

Waldark's 'cabalists' had long since gone their separate ways, but all of them were extremely interested and involved in the planetary-wide discussions surrounding the failed space exploration projects. It was Segelman who suggested that they get back together and review the work which had been done earlier by Waldark and themselves.

"I have this feeling that we'll find the answer," the artist told his friends.

The work was long and arduous, but the 'cabalists' arrived at a possible solution to the dilemma facing their planet, and asked those directing the space program to listen to what they had to say. What the 'cabalists' proposed was that self-aware beings require planetary torun in order to exist. Not only that, but self-aware beings require this torun in specific amounts and in a more or less uninterrupted flow.

Utilising a strong magnetic field to divert the natural flow of planetary torun away from their working and living areas, the 'cabalists' had conducted experiments on themselves. They had all become ill and did not recover until the magnetic field was removed. Then, in order to insure that the problem was not the magnetic field itself, they diverted the planetary torun flow by carefully placing large geometrically shaped blocks of very dense stone in a pattern which deflected the planetary torun, in a way similar to the bending force of a magnetic field. They became ill again.

Additionally, the 'cabalists' had conducted experiments to evaluate the relationship between the direction of planetary torun flow and the physical orientation of meditators transredimensioning energy. This was Segelman's suggestion, he felt that there might be some connection. The investigators discovered that positioning so that one's left side is toward the inflow of planetary torun while looking straight ahead makes the meditational process much easier.

Upon reading the results Herzman, who could not meditate at all, said "The inflow of energy blows away the left side of the brain. That helps artists like you.

"I'll have to be sure to always face another way so I can do some real historical thinking."

As a result of their experiments, the 'cabalists' suggested (feeling qualified to do so) that an existing space craft be modified by the inducement of a magnetic field, and that the correct induced flow of torun be released along the lines of that induced magnetic field. The craft could then be sent into space for an extended period to see if its occupants became ill. If they did, the experiment would be a failure but the ship could return in time to save those occupants.

The 'listeners' from the space program were somewhat impressed, but refused to take any action. It was too risky, they said. They could not withstand the violent opposition which would arise from the undertaking of such an experiment. They rose and began to leave the meeting.

Utterly frustrated, Herzman leaped in front of the 'listeners' and slammed shut the door behind him, cutting off their escape route.

"Listen to me!" he raged at them. "If you won't take the risk, we will. We'll be the occupants of the ship, and we'll see what happens. Once more, we'll do the modifications ourselves."

The other 'cabalists' nodded in agreement. They would not allow the 'listeners' to leave the room until they agreed to take appropriate action.

The experiment was a partial success. The 'listeners' would not allow the 'cabalists' to go into space, but the 'listeners' did allow them to oversee the modifying of an existing space craft to their specifications. They were to include a device which induced a magnetic field and a device which insured that the correct induced flow of torun be released along the lines of that induced magnetic field.

When the occupants of the craft returned from an extended period in space they were ill, but not as ill as others had previously been under similar conditions and over the same period of time. The 'cabalists' had insisted that a previous space mission be replicated so that accurate comparisons could be made.

"We haven't figured it all out yet," said Segelman.

Despite the negativety of the 'listeners' to requests that the 'cabalists' be able to continue their research into the space program's illness problem, and the reluctance of the 'listeners' to admit that the 'cabalists' had accomplished anything, the 'cabalists' continued on.

"What we have to figure out," said Herzman, "is what other differences there are between being in a space craft and being on our planet."

They all sat down together and made up a list.

They crossed off everything except for light from the sun.

"There is light aboard space craft, so it is not the light we can scc that is missing in space craft," said Herzman. "The problem must have something to do with the part of sunlight we cannot see."

They read about sunlight and found out that the sunlight which reached the surface of their planet included some ultraviolet light and some infrared light.

The 'cabalists' drew lots to see who would be the volunteer. Herzman 'won.' Herzman and his pet dog sat in a room for a long time that was illuminated by artificial light, containing neither ultraviolet nor infrared light. The light was on for 12 hours a day and off for another 12 . The others let Herzman out after he became ill. The dog was better and glad not to be cooped up any longer!

Then Herzman sat alone in a room for a long time that was illuminated by artificial light, to which the same amount of ultraviolet light was added as occurred naturally in sunlight. The light was on for 12 hours a day and off for another 12. The others let Herzman out after he became ill—and he became ill after about the same period of time as in the previous test.

Then Herzman sat alone again in a room for a long time that was illuminated by artificial light, to which the same amount of infrared light was added as occurred naturally in sunlight. The light was on for 12 hours a day and off for another 12. The others let Herzman out when he failed to become ill—after a much longer period of time than he had previously stayed in the room.

The answer was: infrared light for 12 hours a day.

The 'cabalists' talked to the 'listeners' again and detailed their experiments. Very grudgingly the 'listeners' permitted another space flight in the previously modified space craft, which would be modified further, so that its occupants would be exposed to the same amount of infrared light as occurred naturally in sunlight 12 hours a day.

The experiment was a complete success. None of the occupants of the space craft became ill.

Some time later Herzman and Segelman reflected on what Waldark's work had come to mean to their planet.

Segelman read to Herzman from Waldark's book:

> "I'm no expert in physics," Waldark told them, "but it seems to me that for a long time we have had an excellent physics covering three-dimensional phenomena. That physics has correctly told us that energy is never lost or gained—it just changes form. Yet we do have energy, and that energy has to come from somewhere. If one believes in three-dimensional physics then the only conclusion one can come to about the source of energy is that it must come from somewhere beyond three-dimensions. Energy comes from the Source of the Universe. Period."

Because Waldark's 'cabalists' had proven that either a certain flow of planetary torun or a like induced flow of torun is required for self-aware life to exist—and that those flows can be disrupted by geometrically shaped dense objects and by magnetic fields—the Lotharian knew that the powerful magnetic field of the Shield would significantly disrupt the flow of planetary torun near it, and that those Alteans living within the area of disruption would suffer and eventually die.

Although naval marine forces of East and West had forced those living within 50 yards of the border to move beyond this lifeless strip, those same forces had prevented the refugees from moving much further. In fact, everyone else living in the vicinity of the border had been forced to remain where they were, despite the known dangers of the Shield's powerful magnetic field.

The East and West forces both told their victims that this procedure was necessary in order to demonstrate that "Nothing has changed; everything is the same here on this side of the border." The real reason being, of course, that they could use the victims themselves as shields.

Now everyone expected West to emplace its own Shield to prevent a surprise attack from East, but there were no signs of that as Ell 'Art Hurian' toured—artistically—and the Lotharian recruited—desperately.

Both sides feared a surprise attack by low-flying star ships, an attack which could only be detected by such a strong magnetic field. Star ships are immensely sophisticated, tremendously fast and carriers of deadly weapons.

Since the first spinning disk and gravitron drive had been constructed and a prototype craft flown by Waldark, space craft had been improved over the aeons to fly ever faster, farther and more safely. The engineering effort had been long and arduous, but the results were spectacular. 24 Over time the devices essential for tornum production, together with the spinning disk and the gravitron drive, were continually redesigned for compactness, and eventually came to be stacked together amidships. Several of these aboard ship engineering components require powerful magnetic fields in order to function, so all of the engineering spaces are always encased in a steel box to prevent their induced magnetic field from adversely affecting those aboard the craft.

Ship design had also been perfected to a high degree over time. Altean Naval Service star ships are 108 feet long and have a maximum beam width of 72 feet. 25

A circular two-level bridge is enclosed in a crystal pod on top of the steel box surrounding the engineering spaces, while a similar weapons and defense pod is attached to the underside of the steel box.

During overhaul, the weapons and defense pod is removed so that a spinning disk which has lost two-thirds of its density, due to having spun for a long time, can be removed and replaced by a new spinning disk. The pod is also removed for periodic maintenance and other procedures.

Forward of the midships engineering spaces are Crew's berthing and auxiliary equipment.

Astern of the engineering spaces is a large multi-purpose auxiliary space, about 26 feet fore and aft. A large section of the deck of this auxiliary space opens allowing access from outside both to the auxiliary space and to the ship, and serving as the star ship's in port quarter deck.

The upper level of the bridge is the command and control center of the star ship. 26 Its circular outer section is divided into three equal modules: ship's maneuvering and navigation forward; weapons control odunside, midships and aft; engineering control seaside, midships and aft. Consoles three foot high occupy the outer half of the upper bridge, except for the center one-third of the maneuvering and navigation section. This is unoccupied so that the commanding officer can have an unobstructed view forward.

A raised circular command station two foot high is in the center, a position from which the commanding officer can oversee everything; it is surrounded by consoles two foot high and three feet wide. These are for maneuvering and navigation, engineering control and weapons control.

Surrounding the command station is the approximately 37 inch wide roundabout. Access from the lower bridge is gained through a hatch in the roundabout directly forward of the commanding officer's command station. This hatch is closed except during change of watch; during once each hour personal relief breaks; during access/departure of the commanding officer or Number One and for emergencies.

The lower bridge is divided into three unequal modules. 27 Forward are the mess decks with attendant galley and scullery, odunside midships. Odunside aft is the communications and transcommunications center; seaside, midships and aft are officers' staterooms. Directly below the commanding officer's command station is a circular compartment identical in size, but divided fore and aft at the center line of the star ship. To odunside is the commanding officer's cabin; to seaside an isolated meditation compartment where the on duty meditator sits, facing seaside while transredimensioning energy. Access to the lower bridge is gained by a ladder aft from the auxiliary space and a ladder forward from Crew's berthing. A double doored light-sealed ladder—attached to the aft round bulkhead of the mess decks—leads to the upper bridge, always darkened at sea for best vision.

Under normal underway conditions, either the commanding officer or her/his Number One is at or near the commanding officer's command station.

The officer of the deck is the commanding officer's personal representative, responsible for all ship's operations. The officer of the deck normally stations herself or himself in the roundabout seaside near the helmsman, but makes frequent trips around the roundabout—especially to the navigation area. The helmsman monitors the course and speed of the ship as the ship's course and speed are relayed to the helm by the aboard ship navigational computers; the helmsman can override those computer inputs as ordered.

The engineering duty officer assists the officer of the deck and supervises the controlling of all functions from the engineering control station on the upper bridge, a procedure done remotely, the midships engineering spaces being off limits during underway operations. The engineering duty officer stations herself or himself in the section of the roundabout in engineering control and oversees her or his watch seated at diverse engineering consoles.

A star ship's complement is 40 Crew and eight officers. Except for the ship's cook, commanding officer and Number One, all ship's company stand a three-section watch routine of four hours each watch. Thirteen ship's Crew members—including an all-important energy transredimensioning meditator—along with the officer of the deck and the engineering duty officer, make up each watch section.

During combat operations all ship's company man battle stations. The weapons control officer stations herself or himself in the section of the roundabout in weapons control and oversees those manning the various weapons control consoles located in that section.

The sailors of the Altean Naval Service traditionally refer to a star ship as a "40 plus 8."

In order to assist meditators in their meditation—and to provide ship's company with the appropriate amount of torun commensurate with good health practices—an induced magnetic field carrying with it the correct induced flow of torun flows from forward to aft. This flow of torun is made available through the energy transredimensioning of meditators.

Star ships are highly maneuverable due to the instantaneous, minute regulation of the distribution of gravitrons flowing from the controlled directional gravitron thrusters, and due to the instantaneously, minutely controlled directional thrusting of those gravitron thrusters. Gravitron flow and thruster positioning are controlled by the aboard ship navigation and steering system, which itself is controlled by extremely precise and instantaneously reactive aboard ship navigational computers.

Since radical and repeated maneuvering, especially during combat—and very rapid acceleration/deceleration can be sudden and potentially devastating to both those aboard and the ship—the induced gravitational field aboard ship is virtually instantaneously adjustable to counter forces created by maneuvering and acceleration/deceleration. Space craft are only inhabitable and able to maneuver as they do on account of their computers, which react virtually instantaneously to changing conditions because these computers do their calculations hyperdimensionally.

The gravitron distributor ring distributes gravitrons throughout the space between the ship's inner and outer hulls. 28 By use of magnetic fields most of these gravitrons are used to propel the ship, and by use of magnetic fields some of these gravitrons are used to make the induced and adjustable gravitational field. Aboard ship computers control these magnetic fields.

Altean star ships carry two main armaments.

Energy torpedoes—incredibly powerful individualized packets of energy—are launched in salvos, the number of energy torpedoes in any given salvo is determined by the type of target being attacked. Energy torpedoes are a short-range weapon, and at close range their capability to destroy targets far exceeds the star ship's long-range weapon, the energy cannon.

Twelve energy cannon are located (like the numbers on a clock face) around the weapons pod and they transmit a high powered stream of energy in a tightly wound vortex that includes many smaller and more powerful tightly wound vortices arrayed in a series of concentric rings. The smaller, more powerful vortices of energy arrive at the target a fraction of a second ahead of the main stream of energy and are designed to puncture small holes in the target. The main stream then follows and completely destroys the weakened target.

In order to protect the star ship from detection and/or attack, three energy fields are induced all around the outside of the ship's hull.

A portion of the powerful magnetic field which surrounds the engineering devices is diverted so that an exterior induced magnetic field completely surrounds the ship. This magnetic field is induced for the purpose of providing an all-encompassing carrier for the ship's two vital defense shields.

The ship's anti-weapons shield is projected through a large nine-faceted Aspis crystal attached to the center of the underside of the weapons pod. 29 Tornum is conduited to the Aspis crystal—named Aspis from the Hellenikos word meaning 'shield'—which then separates the tornum into nine streams. These nine streams of tornum are then bent by the exterior induced magnetic field so that they form a net of hyperdimensional energy surrounding the entire ship. When energy torpedoes or streams of energy from energy cannon hit this hyperdimensional energy net, they are deflected. Only very powerful direct hits by continuous streams of energy from energy cannon or very rapidly repeated hits by energy torpedoes can penetrate the anti-weapons shield of a star ship.

Gravitrons are released through special hull vents and bent around the ship by the exterior induced magnetic field. The resulting induced, immensely strong exterior gravitational field bends light as light enters this field, making the ship electromagnetically invisible.

Both planetary and aboard ship long and short range detection and tracking devices work on the principle of transmagnetic anomaly. Special transceivers have their hyperdimensional transmissions infused with transmagnetic anomaly detection and tracking capabilities, rendering detection and tracking virtually instantaneous—even at distances into billions of miles. Transmagnetic anomaly detection and tracking devices work because space craft have steel hulls made of an alloy composed mainly of titanium and iron.

Only when a space craft is flying low, parallel to the ground and at right angles to the lines of the planetary magnetic field, can they escape detection by transmagnetic anomaly detection and tracking devices. This deception is the result of interaction between the magnetic field of a planet and the hyperdimensional component of that magnetic field. Approaches and/or attacks at any other angle, different altitudes or attitudes to the lines of the planetary magnetic field, make space craft vulnerable to transmagnetic anomaly devices.

The Shield was a powerful magnetic field whose lines were always at right angles to the lines of the planetary magnetic field. In the few moments it would take West star ships to pass through the Shield they could be detected, tracked and destroyed by East's magnetic anomaly devices and their attendant land based energy cannon, which were powerful enough to overpower a ship's anti-weapons shield, no matter how forceful it might be.

The Lotharian returned to Colchis and discussed the situation on Altea with Halburn and Masters at the first opportunity. Such a meeting would normally have had to be held secretly, but due to the fact that the joint commanders had arranged the art and lecture tour, it was only natural that Ell 'Art Hurian' should report back to them when the trip had been completed. Halburn and Masters sadly agreed with the Lotharian's assessment that all haste was required.

"What is the situation with supplies and ships?" the Lotharian asked. "How soon can we leave?"

"It will take us a few days to know for sure," replied Halburn, "but I can give you an estimate now. We have emulated the Essene method of hiding the stores along with vessels, including not actually on loading anything until the last moment, which provides great flexibility of action. I think that in three weeks we will have enough vessels so that at least the required two-thirds of a million Alteans can escape."

That was all the Lotharian needed to know. Later that same day he met with his wife Lana, Spaty Roger and other close Lotharian associates to discuss implementation of the escape plan. They soon realized that they had many more than two-thirds of a million Lotharians—and their count included only those who lived on the outer planets.

Long into the night they agonized over how to proceed. On the one hand they all felt that to wait would be to invite total disaster; on the other hand they did not want to leave anyone behind. The fact that they currently had no method for helping any Lotharians on Altea further complicated their thinking. At last, however, they did decide on one thing: they would have to split up, some going immediately, others to follow soon after.

The Lotharian then had another—this time secret—meeting with Halburn and Masters in order to ascertain if such a two-phased escape was possible. The joint commanders assured him it was. They also gave him a departure date of three weeks hence in enough vessels—on loaded and manned by volunteers from their joint command—to carry exactly 717,199 Lotharians. As Essenes had done hundreds of millions of years before, departure would be at midnight local time in a spiraling out fashion from each of the planets. Halburn handed the Lotharian a list of pickup sites detailing how many Lotharians should be at each location.

"I have two special requests of you two gentlemen," the Lotharian said. "First I need one ship after its on loading of passengers, but with a totally empty hanger bay, made available at my Akadeimia the night of departure. That is for the art. Secondly I need one additional ship reconfigured to hold plant and animal life. Most importantly, the ship needs to have a large holding tank nearly filled with circulating salt water, with fresh circulating air pumped into it above the waterline. I intend to take 24 dolphins with us.

"If we can't take the dolphins, none of us leaves," the Lotharian added with finality.

"We'll do it," responded Masters.

"Good," said the Lotharian, rising from his chair. "I will have Woods Garth, director of the Colchis Institute of Zoology, report to you in three days time, to work out the details."

Altean dolphins had evolved from a heredity that included ancestors from beyond the galaxy. The Hermurian escapees had made a special point of taking dolphins with them as they began what turned out to be a five-billion year trek. During all that time the descendants of those dolphins were lovingly cared for by the descendants of those Hermurian escapees. When the intergalactic pioneers finally arrived at Altea, they released their dolphins into the seas of that blue-green planet to join the millions of native Altean dolphins already inhabiting the waters.

Dolphins had long since won the hearts and minds of the beings inhabiting the chain of galaxies back into the mists of time, and dolphins were traditionally carried along with all intergalactic pioneers.

Dolphins are known from time immemorial to be astonishingly intelligent, by far the most intelligent of all animals and also to be incredibly friendly toward self-aware beings, often in a playful way, but also frequently as rescuers of self-aware beings in distress at sea. Traditional stories are filled with tales of dolphins saving everyone from lasses and lads to sailors gone adrift.

Although self-aware beings have always loved to see dolphins roam the seas at will, they have never been able to resist capturing a few dolphins so as to interact more closely with them. This interaction has resulted in the time honored dolphin show. Trained dolphins have traditionally provided self-aware beings with spectacular swimming and diving performances, often witnessed by huge audiences of exceedingly pleased children, adolescents and adults.

Tradition has also held that the last act of a dolphin show be a lad seated on a dolphin as it swims around the course, signifying the very close long-held, loving relationship between dolphins and self-aware beings.

In dealing with inquisitive learning dolphins, their loving trainers have frequently found themselves being influenced by the dolphins. On occasions somehow trainers have intuitively known what the dolphins were going to do next and have been able to think and actually feel along with the dolphins.

It was on Altea some 780 million years before Ell 'Art Hurian's' time that a dolphin trainer named Lor Dur Xian acquired the ability to read some of the thoughts of dolphins, including being able to perceive their innermost feelings. Fascinated by this unexpected discovery, Lor Dur Xian began to develop this relationship further. After many years of working with dolphins the trainer concluded that he and these mamals were able to communicate with one another by mental telepathy, and that dolphins also express their innermost thoughts by such means.

No one following the passing of Lor Dur Xian has ever been able to achieve the same results, Ell 'Art Hurian' recalled as he sought out Woods Garth, the zoological institute director. The ability to communicate telepathically, the artist thought, would allow all of us to convey more fully our innermost thoughts to one another. Such communication might prevent recurrences of the positively horrific prospects facing Alteans, he mused.

We must take the dolphins with us, the Lotharian firmly concluded.

When the Lotharian returned that evening Astir had arrived unexpectedly on the afternoon shuttle from Altea. Folen Lana had gotten him a seat so he could visit "his still gravely ill brother" again.

After supper the Lotharians met again to discuss their escape plans, clearer now, thanks to Halburn and Master's decisive actions. Although the logistics of having Lotharians meet the escape ships were not considered a problem, deciding who could go and who must stay proved to be beyond their powers. The Lotharian was absolutely paralyzed by the prospect of such a difficult reckoning. Although he was very optimistic that a second group would follow—including many Lotharians who were residents of Altea who would be shuttled to the outer planets by means of a plan which would rely on the consummate skills and determination of Folen Lana—the Lotharian could not be sure that anyone after those of the first group could escape.

"I will remain, of course," he told them all.

This revelation caused a loud outcry from the others.

You must go, everyone strongly admonished the Lotharian.

It was Astir who suggested the plan. They adopted it immediately.

"The mist has been before our eyes," Astir told the Lotharians, citing a somewhat arcane metaphor which often appeared in traditional mythos as a way of explaining slow thinking and indecision.

"We draw lots," he concluded, drawing upon that same tradition.

Ell Lana resolved the problem by stating, "Dan and I will draw lots to see which one of us goes with the first group and which one of us stays to help prepare for the departure of the second group. Before we do, however, I insist that there be proper administration of our drawing of lots, and that Dan swears he will abide by the irrevocable outcome. I so swear now."

Ell Dan nodded reluctantly.

Ell Lana drew the lot to remain.

On schedule the first group of Lotharians escaped from Altean territory, bound for a far distant point near the edge of the galaxy and about 12 days distant, at the near interstellar light speed speed to be maintained by the Lotharian flotilla. With them was their treasure of art and the gigantic, if somewhat clumsy appearing, converted star ship rescue vessel HURARTU, named after the mythos enshrouded mountain of Altea.

Aboard HURARTU were many plants and animals.

Aboard HURARTU were the dolphins.

Together, far from the Pleiadeans and the two Altean madmen Edwards and Renford, they would all await the arrival of the second group of Lotharians.

Chapter Twelve

The Death of Altea

First as he flew with the vast fleet of escapees and then as he awaited with nervous anticipation the departure of the second group of refugees, the Lotharian continually worried about what those two madmen Edwards and Renford might do.

He could not possibly have anticipated what two other madmen did do.

Lin Tiu was a nuclear physicist, and a long time employee of a navy controlled energy transproduction complex near Hurtea in West. Specifically he dealt with energy transconverters and more specifically he dealt with the process in which gold is used to transconvert torinum into tornum.

Large dolphin shaped lead lined casings—each containing a canister of pure fine grain gold—are tipped at either end with lead lined spheres, and these are connected by a long hollow tube through the long axis of the gold dolphins. The casings and attendant spheres are then inserted into a large, lead lined cylindrical outer casing which, after having its breech closed, is inserted into the transconverter sphere of energy transconverters. 30

The casings, dolphins and spheres are lined with lead to prevent leakage of radioactivity. The lead content in the crystal of the tetrahedral casings of energy transconverters is the shield which prevents leakage of radioactivity from the transconverter spheres of energy transconverters.

The gold dolphin's sphere, attached toward the breech end of the outer casing, contains a precisely regulated neutron emitter. Following a further refining process (carried out inside the gold dolphin) single atoms of gold are injected in a steady stream into the hollow tube where they are bombarded by neutrons. The first five neutrons to hit a gold atom have the correct velocity to knock five neutrons from the nucleus of that gold atom. Due to their velocity, the sixth neutron adheres to the nucleus of the gold atom, while the seventh neutron propels the gold atom down the tube to the steel sphere projecting into the transconverter sphere of the energy transconverter. 31

It is in this second sphere that a critical nuclear reaction takes place. Though the gold atoms try to decay into two other elements, 99 percent of the time these gold atoms are prevented from doing so by induced forces within this lead lined sphere. Except in the one percent of cases when decay does result, a positron is emitted. It is this positron which interacts with torinum to transproduce tornum.

After giving up this positron, the radioactive residue—99 percent gold and one percent two other elements—is channelled in a lead lined conduit from the lead lined sphere so that it can be separated under the most stringent purity and safety conditions. The radioactive gold is reconstituted into its non-radioactive fine pure grain form and reused.

The other one percent—the two radioactive elements—is what constitutes the gradual loss of gold in the process of transconverting torinum into tornum. These radioactive elements provided Lin with a scheme.

Having heard of the Shield erected by East, Lin feared West would fall victim to a surprise attack. Lin was not as concerned about the ascendancy or even survival of West as he was totally consumed by his own survival and the relatively high standard of living he enjoyed. Events had shaken him badly and Lin deemed an appropriate countermeasure by West would restore order.

Lin had read a number of history books and he had learned something by having done so. Among the lessons he believed were for him was the notion that an incredibly powerful deterrent always deters. Agreeing with this, Liu came up with his scheme. Additionally he believed he might gain a certain amount of notoriety, perhaps even wealth, by being known as the inventor of the ultimate deterrent.

With the assistance of his legal brother, who was a staff aide, Lin presented his plan directly to Edwards' team. It consisted of the following points:

The still radioactive one percent residue of the energy transconverter process, could be transported to the various energy transproduction complexes of West and restowed in close proximity to energy transconverters. At present this residue, accumulated over nearly two billion years, was contained in casings and very safely stowed in precisely engineered and maintained vaults which had never leaked contamination into the air or planet.

All energy transconverters at transproduction complexes in West could be fitted with high explosive charges. Detonation devices attached to the explosives could then be linked together so that on command, they could all be exploded simultaneously.

These explosions would not only release the radioactivity contained in the energy transconverters, it would also tear apart the stored casings of radioactive residue. In the process the still radioactive residue would be further irradiated and the result would be released into the atmosphere as a result of the explosions. Lin estimated that it would take three or four days for this radioactivity to completely enshroud Altea in death.

The setting up of the ultimate deterrent would have to be done in complete secrecy, Lin told the staff. Those performing the tasks involved in this process and those working in the energy transproduction complexes must not even suspect what was being done. East could not know of the Deterrent—as Lin suddenly decided to call his scheme—until it was completely in place and activated in such a way that it could not be deactivated.

The most important feature of the Deterrent—Lin proclaimed, ever more impressed with this new name for the ultimate deterrent as determined by himself—was that once activated, it would be automatically triggered by a certain set of parameters. This was relatively simple to achieve: all West naval assets were linked by transcommunication and computers. If any part of that network was interrupted, a signal would be sent automatically to explode the high explosive charges. All facets of the Deterrent would be connected to this same naval transcommunication network, and any interruption of those inner-workings and interworkings of the Deterrent itself would also activate the triggering signal.

Even the programming of the three randomly alternating West naval computers which could activate the Deterrent would include this same interruption parameter. So anyone trying to deactivate the program would also activate the triggering signal. The plan and the Deterrent were perfect, Lin concluded before leaving the West staff briefing room.

The next day Lin received a summons from Edwards.

Following their brief meeting Lin began work on the Deterrent. There had been only one change made to his previous plan. Edwards had insisted there be a half-hour delay built into the Deterrent, a delay Edwards secretly wanted in order that he could make good his escape if something went wrong.

Admiral Harder Garth was commander of an East star ship squadron. He was extremely frustrated by the unresolved confrontation between the two Altean forces. Harder hated the Pleiadeans and wanted to be after them rather than embroiled in internal conflict. Having known Edwards through service with him in the years before the split, he considered West commander Edwards to be obnoxious and intransigent. Harder did not think much of his own East commander either, since Renford had shown himself to be a power driven opportunist.

The longer Harder considered his frustrations the more he came to believe the only way out of the current impasse was through action. East had an incredible advantage, Harder knew, due to the Shield. West would never dare attack because its star ships would be destroyed within minutes. On the other hand, Harder believed that West must be doing something to even the imbalance. Harder was afraid Renford would not see this coming before it was too late. West would gain parity with East and the impasse would continue while the real enemy—the Pleiadeans—remained unscathed.

However, the most chilling notion that came to Harder's mind was not parity with West, but the possible domination by a superior West. They had not responded by building their own Shield. What were they up to? he asked himself.

The more Harder considered these notions the more upset he became. Harder decided it was up to him to break the impasse. It had to be done, and Renford never would act. A scheme formed in Harder's mind: when the opportunity presented itself, he, Admiral Harder Garth, would personally lead his squadron of star ships in an attack—any attack—on West. He would set in motion a conflict which could not be stopped, but Harder believed East would win this war quickly with few losses. Then the entire Altean Naval Service could go back to killing Pleiadeans.

In the meantime, with the massive resources of the commander of West behind him, Lin was building the Deterrent. Each day and week brought new parts of the scheme together, but both Lin and Edwards chafed at even the slightest delay. Until it was completely in place, activated and announced to all Alteans, the Deterrent was no deterrent whatsoever.

Life on Altea went from intolerable to horrific.

Naval forces of East and West controlled everything, and the vast resources of the planet were being channeled to an enormous extent toward defending Altea from its other half. Civilians caught up in this hopeless morass lost hope, resigning themselves to an existence they had imagined would only ever have to be endured by the enslaved billions of the Pleiadean empire.

Meanwhile, those Lotharians still remaining in Altean territory continued making preparations for the second escape, they hoped it would come soon; they hoped it would free them from the two madmen, Edwards and Renford. In the absence of both her husband and Spaty Roger, who had drawn a lot of departure, Ell Lana coordinated everything from Colchis. The outer defense joint commanders Halburn and Masters continued their efforts to assemble stores and vessels for the second escape, while maintaining their constant alert for the growing probability of a Pleiadean attack. Both had long since resolved to remain at their posts no matter what. Folen Lana had begun the long and arduous task of shuttling Lotharian residents of Altea to the outer planets so that they would be able join the second escape. Sofy and Astir grew even more desperately in love—and desperate.

Harder prepared his squadron for attack and waited impatiently for the opportune time. He kept even his Number One from knowing his true intentions as the squadron engaged in a series of exercises designed to sharpen its combat readiness.

It had been almost a year since the escape of the first group of Lotharians, but their disappearance—even that of the well known Ell Dan 'Art Hurian'—had gone unnoticed by authorities on Altea, and Halburn and Masters said nothing.

Ell Lana not only kept the Lotharian organization going, she also secretly transcommunicated frequently with her far distant husband, informing him of developments. The Lotharian continued to be extremely concerned, even when his wife told him that the second escape was only a week away.

The Deterrent was completed at about the same time, but no one apart from Edwards, Lin and a few others knew of its existence. Lin chafed for the public announcement, but Edwards delayed. He wanted to make his dramatic pronouncement on the anniversary of the first devastating attack by the Altean Naval Service on Pleiadean territory; the attack which had resulted in the seizure of huge quantities of gold at a time when Altean supplies of vital gold were nearly depleated. Like the rebirth experienced at that time, Edwards would proclaim another rebirth for Altea. East, seeing its folly, would capitulate before the Deterrent, and united once more, Alteans would defeat the real enemy—the Pleiadeans.

Sofy and Astir set their wedding date to coincide with the second escape. They would be married one afternoon, and after their wedding party would board the shuttle bound for Colchis, where they would enjoy their week-long wedding trip—their halkyon days—made possible by Folen Lana. What Sofy and Astir would also be doing on Colchis during their halkyon days would be to help in the final evacuation preparations.

Late in the day one day, and deep in the excavations of the buried city on the planet where Waldark later lived, workers came upon an extremely hard metallic 'plate.' They called their supervisor—one of the seekers who had observed the grave robbers—and he immediately dismissed them. When the site was clear, he gathered together his fellow seekers and together they found a large casing made of what came to be known as titanium steel. Together they secretly dug it up and removed the casing from the site to their private residence.

They opened the casing and found within it—insulated by a thick layer of what later became known as synthetic asbestos—a wooden table encased in a surrounding transparent cube of a material which later became known as resin. The table was exquisite, its surface inlaid with different types of wood, depicting a columned structure full of style and grace. They were awed by what they had found.

They also found a written message, stuck down one side of the resin cube between the cube and the insulation. It was only after they had laboriously translated the previously found lexicon that they could read it. The message was to whomever found the table, from the one who had insured its safety during a time of grave danger. The message stated that the table had come down to the time of the writer from 20 billion years previously and had originally belonged to a man named Eumares. The descendants of Eumares had so loved the table that they had taken it with them from galaxy to galaxy encased in its protective resin cube, so that the table would not deteriorate. The writer closed the message by asking that the encased table be cared for by whomever found it and that it be once again passed down from galaxy to galaxy.

The seekers agreed to keep their find a secret for the time being and then they elected one of their number as administrator of the encased table. As it turned out, many generations passed before the existence of the encased table was made known. The encased table was revealed to the planet by a descendant of its original administrator, but only after she decided that the time was right. Much later, when the beings of that galaxy undertook the first now historically recorded intergalactic migration, an even later descendant of the first administrator of the encased table accompanied it toward its next galactic home, and the responsibility of its administration was passed on and on and on to succeeding members of the family.

Many adventures befell the encased table along the way from galaxy to galaxy, especially during those times when intergalactic migration was really escape. In the galaxy before the current galaxy, it was entrusted to a museum on the seed planet of that galaxy by one of its administrators, and it remained there up until the time when the Hermurian 'cabalists' were planning their escape.

Just before escape, during one of the final secret meetings between the leaders of the Hermurian 'cabalists,' Trosumer said, "We must take the encased table of Eumares with us.

"We will get it."

Trosumur was in the newspaper business and he contacted the museum and told them that he would like to write an article about the encased table and asked if he and his family might come to the museum so that he could gather information and image it. He received a positive response.

Sereena and Trosumur with their children Rissura and Pasorun took an intergalactic passenger vessel from Hermur to the seed planet of the galaxy and stayed at a hotel very close to the museum. As Trosumur worked, he secretly transcommunicated with other Hermurian 'cabalists' who were aboard a transport vessel headed for the seed planet, their arrival timed to coincide with Trosumur's for the removal of the encased table. At last, all was worked out and Trosumur and his family went to the museum together to image the encased table.

As they were doing so, under the watchful eyes of museum officials and guards, Hermurian 'cabalists' suddenly smashed through the room's domed crystal ceiling. Trosumur and his family were expecting this and they instantaneously dived, and took cover under benches along the curved walls of the room. In the resulting confusion the Hermurian 'cabalists'—disguised as rebels from another part of the galaxy—dropped into the room and rounded up the museum officials and guards, all of whom were dazed by the sudden unexpected attack, several had been cut by falling pieces of crystal. Trosumur and his family were also taken 'captive.'

Next an insulated titanium steel casing was lowered into the room from the space vessel hovering overhead. The Hermurian 'cabalists' carefully placed the table inside the casing and it was lifted up and into the waiting space vessel. As alarm systems continued to blare, the 'cabalists' were also lifted up into the space vessel along with their 'hostages' Sereena, Rissura, Pasorun and Trosumur. Before they could be apprehended the 'cabalists' sped off in their space vessel and returned to Hermur just before the scheduled escape. Due to the concentration of galactic forces looking in the wrong place, only a single galactic star ship on routine patrol confronted the Hermurian escapees.

The descendants of Trosumur never relinquished control of the encased table of Eumares and it came to be that the father of Spaty Astir became its administrator. He named Astir the new administrator just before his marriage, and with the help of Folen Lana Astir shipped the encased table in a wooden crate labeled "Machine Parts" to Ell Lana on Colchis.

Both Cunard Anna and Fosgood Lura the co-founders of the Lotharian movement, would be at the wedding; Folen Lana had procured seats for them a couple of days later on a shuttle bound for a different outer planet. Neither Sofy's nor Astir's parents could bring themselves to leave Altea, but they were extremely hopeful for the young couple, and grateful that Sofy and Astir had decided to marry before departing forever.

During the wedding party they heard of the attack of East star ships across the Shield. 'Their' side had started the war!

Harder had found his chance. As a result of the general rotation of star ship squadrons Harder had found himself and his star ships stationed near the border. Routine exercises called for simulated attacks through the Shield and across the border, but star ships always veered away at the last instant when their commanding officers received their recall orders automatically from their central command.

Harder first believed that in order to be able to carry out his attack scheme he would have to devise a method for overriding the automatic recall order. However, several simulated attacks by his squadron convinced him that such an override was not possible. Instead, he would disregard the recall orders, continue across the border and attack West forces there. As he did so he would personally order the commanding officers of his squadron to follow his lead and attack rather than veer off. These commanding officers had been carefully wooed by him, and he therefore felt they afforded him great personal loyalty. They would have to make a split-second decision. Harder felt that they would follow him.

For the simulated attack the squadron's formation was a loose line abreast, with the commander's star ship in the center. This formation obliged an enemy to use independent targeting and tracking of each star ship; it also helped maintain a semblance of order for the squadron. Harder took advantage of this formation to forge ahead of the other star ships. When the recall order came Harder personally took the helm and charged toward the border. Next Harder stared down the commanding officer of his star ship and ordered him to attack. Then Harder transcommunicated orders to all the other commanding officers of the squadron to follow his lead and attack through the Shield and across the border. All except two obeyed Harder.

West forces were not caught off guard. A horrific air battle followed and Harder, his commanders, along with their Crews and star ships—were all destroyed.

Several West star ships were also destroyed.

The West transcommunication link was broken.

The Deterrent was activated.

All across West horrific explosions ripped through the energy transproduction complexes. Great plumes of fire and smoke rose into the air of Altea. Deadly radiation was being released into the atmosphere of Altea at a horrific rate.

The planet began to die.

Lin was just rising in the morning when he heard the sound of distant explosions. Only one thought seared through him: those madmen have started something, and now the Deterrent will kill me. Lin knew it was too late. He walked into his bathroom, filled the tub and drowned himself.

Edwards was already at his desk in his Hurtea headquarters when he received the first transcommunication alerting him of the attack by East star ships across the border thousands of miles to the west. As soon as the second report was received—claiming total victory, but detailing West casualties—Edwards knew that Altea was doomed.

The West commander ordered an all out attack. A few moments later Edwards heard the same distant reports of explosions as had Lin. Edwards immediately left his office, took his private elevator to a heavily armored subterranean hanger and boarded his private star ship which was always manned and ready. A few moments later Edwards took off in that star ship and headed for safety—safety in a specially prepared bunker on an outer planet. Edwards entered that bunker and waited.

Edwards was not saved by his distant bunker, nor was Renford in his bunker on Altea.

Within 15 minutes of Edwards's order for an all out attack, West star ships began a well-coordinated assault on East, taking horrific casualties due to the Shield, but nevertheless inflicting heavy damage on East. Renford ordered the counterattack and through the smoke billowing upward from the explosions caused by the Deterrent, East star ships began attacking West.

Alteans everywhere began dying from radiation poisoning.

The news of the attacks smashed through the wedding party of Sofy and Astir, as if it was the wedding party that was under attack. The realization that their plans of escape were dashed, immediately seared through the minds of the young couple. The others—including the Lotharians present—left at once for their homes.

There would be no more shuttle flights to the outer planets.

Only Astir's Voluntary Best Servant and best friend: Douglas Lee lingered. He was overwhelmed by the prospect of what was to come, but nevertheless offered his best wishes to the wedding pair.

"Thank you, Lee," Astir responded. "You have been a most devoted friend. No one could ask for more than what you have meant to me."

Douglas Lee turned and left the hall in which the wedding party had once been joyously progressing.

Astir held Sofy as they stood alone in the middle of the dance floor.

"We'll make it, Sofy," he said. "Don't give up hope."

Neither Sofy nor Astir yet knew about the Deterrent. They might well have survived a war, for both sides quickly exhausted themselves and a new stalemate ensued only hours after hostilities had broken out. Neither side had the capacity to inflict any more damage on the other.

Only the Deterrent moved inexorably forward.

It was the morning of the next day in East when Sofy and Astir learned of the horrific radiation which was continuing to encircle Altea. Astir could no longer tell Sofy to not give up; he knew that they were doomed. Astir knew that they had some time together, and he wanted to make the most of it. Once again Astir took Sofy in his arms.

"Sofy, I love you—forever."

Only two days later, those were also Astir's last words to Sofy as they lay together in their secret hiding place to which they had returned to await the end, and to enjoy memories and one another. Sofy never removed the banded hair net she wore during her uniting with Astir, but she and Astir removed her tiara and his hat and secreted them in their secret hiding place.

Surrounding their secret hiding place was the dead city in which Sofy and Astir had grown up, the city of the eastern hemisphere of Altea which had been named by the indigenous beings nearly two billion years before, the city called Danebury. After deferring to the intergalactic migrators over the naming of Hurtea, the new capital of Altea, they had insisted on naming what was to become the second largest city of Altea. The newcomers had been totally surprised when they were told that the name of the city was to be Danebury—they had expected the indigenous beings to choose a name from their indigenous language.

"The name Danebury," the locals said when announcing their choice, "means 'mountain of the very stout-hearted,' we think."

The intergalactic migrators were overcome. Tears flowed. They had succeeded. Neither group was downcast.

Now Danebury was dead.

Now Altea was dead.

Alteans living on Colchis and on the other outer planets learned of the horror and were devastated.

The Lotharians were at first confused about how they should proceed, but Ell Lana, having transcommunicated with her far distant husband, told them, "We depart as scheduled. We cannot tell anyone who is not a Lotharian what we are doing because if we do chaos will result. The outer defense command is still capable of defending against the Pleiadeans, so those who remain behind will have a very good chance of surviving. One day we can all reunite."

A few hours later the Pleiadeans struck.

Well aware of events transpiring on Altea, imperial commanders believed they would face only the outer defense forces if they attacked, and there would be no reinforcement from Altea as there had been in the past. The time had come to finally obliterate their hated enemies, and the Pleiadean imperial command seized the moment.

Sweeping across the boundaries between Altean and Pleiadean space in unprecedented numbers, wave after wave of Pleiadean craft attacked the defending forces of the Outer Altean Defense Command. On Colchis Halburn and Masters instantly understood what was happening. The joint commanders immediately activated all of their forces, and personally led the powerful fleet sent to meet the imperials.

Halburn deferred overall command to Masters.

Despite the heroic efforts of Halburn, Masters and the entire Altean outer defense fleet, the remnant of the Altean Naval Service was overwhelmed by the onslaught of the Pleiadeans.

Not one Altean star ship survived because not one single Altean star ship failed to continue fighting until it was destroyed.

Colchis and the other outer planets lay defenseless before the imperial forces, who encircled them so that there could be no escapees.

The Lotharians and all the other Altean residents of those planets were trapped.

On the very day that the second group of Lotharians had been scheduled to escape, Pleiadean craft began releasing poisonous gas into the atmospheres of Colchis and the other outer planets of Altea.

All perished.

Edwards died in his bunker. Other Alteans died in their homes.

The Pleiadeans believed they had expunged Alteans from the galaxy.

Several years later a Pleiadean craft returned to the vicinity on random patrol and its commander—one Halbert Sarkneson—decided to personally determine what Colchis might be like after having been deserted for so long. Aboard his personal scout craft Sarkneson descended to the surface of the planet. To his astonishment instruments indicated Colchis was not far from being habitable. Sarkneson's further investigation on foot and wearing protective environmental gear revealed that although the planet's vital gravitron-infusing spinning disks had ceased to operate and the rotation of the planet had therefore slowed somewhat, those spinning disks were in such good condition they could be readily returned to operation. Through the reactivation of those spinning disks Colchis would once again be infused with gravitrons, thereby increasing the planet's effective mass and returning it to the required rotational period of 23 hours, 56 minutes.

As Sarkneson was about to transcommunicate this information back to imperial headquarters he was struck by a sudden notion: I, Halbert Sarkneson, will keep this place to myself and set up my own domain. Although Sarkneson did not know it, he was not the first Pleiadean to come up with such a scheme. Once before, an equally devious, treacherous and self-aggrandizing Pleiadean named Carl Halverson had attempted to carve out an empire elsewhere for himself—with disastrous results.

Sarkneson knew nothing of either Halverson or his disastrous scheme. Sarkneson did not report his findings on Colchis to his emperor. He even kept his discoveries well hidden from those aboard the imperial vessel during the return journey to the Pleiades.

Once home, Sarkneson, who was already a very wealthy Pleiadean of the imperial set, put into operation his most secret scheme to build a private empire for himself on Colchis, and thus become even wealthier and more powerful. He subsequently led a private expedition to Colchis and was accompanied by his sons and several trusted members of his retinue. On Colchis they restarted the spinning disks and in only a few months returned the planet to its proper rotational speed.

The private empire of the family Sarkneson had begun.

Chapter Thirteen

The First Essene Panlogos

From their far distant location near the outer reaches of the galaxy, the Lotharians received increasingly horrifying news of the tragedy on Altea and of the outer planets. They were utterly devastated.

The Lotharian had to be physically restrained and sedated after his wife transmitted her final message to him, "Continue on."

Accordingly, despite all the suffering, the Lotharians eventually did so.

Following weeks of anguishing at the place where they were to have been joined by the second group of escapees, the Lotharian flotilla finally got underway in search of a new home.

Ell Dan 'Art Hurian' the Lotharian was resigned to circumstances, but he was never the same. That special light which had burned in him had been extinguished. There would be no more joy, only resolve.

Much later and just before passing on, Ell Dan 'Art Hurian' the Lotharian called his associates together and asked them to listen to an ancient history of the departure of Essenes from Altea which he read from a musty tome:

> As dawn crept around Altea signalling the beginning of a new day, all Essene transport vessels had departed Altean space, spiraling outward from the planet as midnight local time was observed.
>
> Sara Eland turned to her husband as the vessel they and their children traveled in rose above Altea. "I wasn't sure we'd make it," she said. "I wasn't sure we could keep it a secret."
>
> Peter Odun opened the musty tome he was carrying and said, "Sara, this is a history of the Hermurian intergalactic migration:

Although meetings for such a purpose had been unprecedented on Hermur, intergalactic migrations did indeed have precedent: history told them that massive intergalactic migrations had always carried forward beings from one galaxy to the next, along the chain of galaxies which led to their current galaxy. However, this usually followed the redeeming of their galaxy—the fulfilling of the galactic experience, so that all beings of any given galaxy had the opportunity to live in harmony. The Hermurian 'cabalists' were extremely disappointed that their departure was not associated with the redeeming of their galaxy—but was precipitated by the need to escape.

The redeeming of the galaxy was the historical imperative under which the galaxy had been developed, but in this case it was not to be. As the 'cabalists' had historical records stating that this had happened several times before, they were not totally downcast when they started preparing their escape. They deduced that fundamental conditions and situations sometimes recur, enabling those aware of their history to take advantage of that knowledge and act accordingly.

The fact that they were able to keep their vast project totally secret from outsiders surprised and uplifted them, and made them feel that they were doing the right thing. Even so, they knew that the reasons for this success were threefold; they were dedicated, they planned well and they worked hard.

"Sara, we have succeeded because we have read and understood history, because we have been dedicated, because we have planned well and because we have worked hard."

"I will not accept this as a mere escape, though," Sara responded. "Maybe the Hermurian refugees were not downcast, but everyone else was. This galaxy will not be downcast."

"We cannot allow," Ell Dan 'Art Hurian' the Lotharian concluded, "this galaxy to be downcast."

It took 2000 years of wandering before the Lotharians settled on a suitable planet. In the center of the galaxy there would have been many, but near the outer fringes of the galaxy, far from the dreaded, hateful Pleiadeans, there were few planets. None of those planets discovered in those 2000 years had had the prerequisites necessary to sustain life, even though the Lotharians were just as capable of adjusting planets, because their expertise consisted of the same adjustment capabilities that Alteans always had. The Lotharians could adjust rotation rates of planets to the required 23 hours and 56 minutes, and they could infuse thin natural atmospheres with nitrogen and other gases, but they could not find a rocky planet with sufficient water in any form. Water is absolutely necessary for life to exist, and it was from water that the Lotharians would extract oxygen to create a breathable, combined atmosphere.

The way about the outer reaches of the galaxy was also slow. The Lotharians could travel very fast; but, like all self-aware beings, they could not travel fast for extended periods of time. The faster that a space craft travels through space, the slower physical time becomes. That slowing of physical time puts physical time out of synchronization with consciousness time; the time on which self-aware beings run. Short periods of very high speed travel do not appreciably affect self-aware beings, but prolonged periods of very high speed travel will kill them.

Young Alteans of later ages had always been amazed by the history of the intergalactic travelers and how they could have possibly spent five billion years in migration—given the enormous speeds at which they traveled, nearly three million times faster than solar system light speed.

Most of the time aboard ship the intergalactic travelers had to travel relatively slowly in order to synchronize physical time with consciousness time. Most of the time they lived on a series planets, in a series of galaxies while they searched the galaxy in which they were temporarily living.

Some galaxies they searched more than once. In five billion years life could emerge, grow to maturity and die out in any given galaxy. The migrators had established an intricate, well conceived and well executed search pattern of the parts of the Universe in which they knew self-aware beings could exist. Eventually they had succeeded in finding Altea.

Before they left on their trek, the Hermurian escapees had devised two ways of measuring physical time. They knew that there were three types of time: Eternal Time, physical time and consciousness time. They knew that physical time slowed down and sped up, as space vessels sped up and slowed down, and they knew that Eternal Time and consciousness time were constant. They knew that clocks had been observed speeding up and slowing down as space vessels changed speed. The Hermurians knew that the Universe and their consciousnesses would continue to run at a constant speed. So they constructed compensators in their clocks in order that their clocks would always run at a constant speed, which was the speed at which physical time needs to run for self-aware beings to live.

In order to know when to slow down, so as to synchronize times, the Hermurians constructed chronometers which would slow down and speed up with the velocity of their intergalactic space vessels. When the migrators arrived at Altea their clocks (having always run at the constant speed which is the speed at which physical time needs to run for self-aware beings to live) showed that it had been five billion years since their ancestors had escaped from Hermur.

Like the intergalactic travelers the Lotharians mostly had to go slow while traveling, and through the succeeding generations stretching over 2000 years they had stopped and started so many times (often as a result of finding what eventually turned out to be very disappointing planets) that they were thoroughly exhausted and abjectly discouraged.

The Lotharians were becoming downcast.

Then one day as the Lotharian flotilla crept slowly through space synchronizing physical time with consciousness time, it suddenly happened.

Without warning, what the Lotharians were later told was a holo-image, suddenly appeared next to the commanding officer's raised circular command station on the flotilla command vessel.

The commanding officer was startled from her chair, and the current leaders of the Lotharians with whom she had been talking shrank back in amazement.

The holo-image said, "I am an Essene holo-image and I am directed by Essenes to deliver the First Essene Panlogos to you. Alteans are to travel immediately to a new home for Alteans. Lotharians are no longer Lotharians. Lotharians are once again Alteans. The course to your destination has been infused into the navigational computers of all your space vessels. Alteans are required to obey the First Essene Panlogos NOW!"

The holo-image disappeared.

There was no choice.

The Altean flotilla got underway bound for the new home of Alteans.

Part Two SILBURY

Chapter One

Daphlay

When the surviving Alteans arrived at the planet selected for them by the Essene holo-image they were bitterly disappointed. They were not unsurprised by what they found, for they had not expected to find another blue-green planet like Altea. Their disappointment stemmed from the realization that finally struck them: they would not be going home.

Nevertheless, Alteans did have a new home at last, on a barren planet about half the size of Altea, with only a very thin natural atmosphere. However, it was a planet with a tremendous amount of water in the form of ice frozen in its polar caps. They knew that they would have to do much planetary adjusting in order to provide themselves with a habitable environment, but it was well within their capacity to adjust the planet and they began immediately—after naming their new home Daphlay.

Taken from Hurengle and Hellenikos, Daphlay is a combining word: 'lay' is a foreshortening of the Hurengle phrase 'laying on;' 'Daph' is a foreshortening of the Hellenikos word 'daphne' which, in Hurengle, had long since been equated with the Laurel plant. The combining of these two syllables 'daph' and 'lay' was meant to evoke the traditional phrase 'laying on of the laurel,' a phrase evoking many metaphors, but evoking most of all the victor's crown. Alteans of Daphlay had survived and were ready to take up the daunting challenge of becoming victorious, not over others, but over those weaknesses inherent in self-aware beings which had so far prevented the redeeming of the galaxy.

Once the planetary environmental adjustments had been made to Daphlay, those Alteans not directly involved in either that work or the construction of Daphlay's first cities, left the space vessels and joined their fellow Alteans on the planet. Beings living on planets which require these environmental adjustments usually reside in just a few cities, the landscape is usually arid and it is far more practical to concentrate the population into areas where it is easy to conduit water, usually sourced from the polar ice caps. Daphlay was no exception.

Due to Spaty Roger's ideas, the cities on Daphlay were to be even more concentrated than had previously occurred on such planets. The architect had been among the first, and as it turned out, the only group of Lotharians to escape from Altean territory. In the remaining years of his life, all of which he spent aboard ship, Spaty Roger first conceived and then designed enormous pyramidal structures which he saw as complete cities within themselves.

A million inhabitants can live in a small number of Spaty's structures. Principally made of crystal, because of their size and composition, Spaty's houses, as they came to be called, must be sited so that their disruption of the natural flow of planetary torun is virtually nil.

To achieve this, these houses are placed in combination with each other in such a way that the energy flow takes precedent over geometric regularity. Even so, the overall pattern made by these differently shaped crystal houses is still somewhat geometric and definitely pleasing to the eye.

All such houses are designed as microcosms. Besides being the home for Alteans who live in the many individual living quarters contained in crystal houses, each house is also home to a large number of businesses which provide a variety of goods and services, and to numerous recreational facilities.

The capital of Daphlay was named Altea City in honor of the seed planet of the galaxy.

The construction of Daphlay's cities and the resettling of Altean society was accomplished very quickly. With the resettling came the realization that once again, there existed the imperative need for defense. Consequently the Altean Naval Service was immediately revived, under the strict control of the new civilian authority of Altean society, the Council of Daphlay. The population and resources of the Alteans were relatively small so a large navy was out of the question. However the Lotharians, during their 2000 year search for a new home, had worked out a very intricate defense plan. The Alteans were prepared: Daphlay was to be hidden.

Although deep space is almost empty, there are particles scattered in apparently random and definitely varying degrees of concentration throughout all deep space. These particles, like particles suspended in a planet's atmosphere, diffuse light. Normally the pockets of concentration are insufficient to be effective light diffusers, but the Lotharians devised a method whereby, over vast stretches of space, they could collect these widely scattered particles. This 'space dust' could be subsequently released in the solar system of their eventual new home planet.

When the Alteans of Daphlay completed their space dust shield it had the effect of diffusing the light emitted by Daphlay's sun, when observed from beyond Daphlay's solar system. This prevented the establishing, by means of luminosity, the distance from an observer to that star, its solar system and Daphlay. This means of evaluation is the only practical method for an approaching space craft to accurately calculate such a rapidly decreasing distance. The only known alternative is to slow craft dramatically in order to use standard ranging devices. These devices do not function effectively at near interstellar light speed due to interference caused by space dust particles. Slowing craft to speeds at which this interference is eliminated prohibit craft from arriving at destinations in a timely manner. It would take years, rather than a few hours, to travel from solar system to solar system if navigational computers and luminosity sensors of space craft could not work together and virtually instantly calculate, by means of luminosity, the given distance to a star.

Alteans of Daphlay did not stop at visually hiding the planet—they protected Daphlay from any potential Pleiadean attackers by using star ships, which patrolled the approach points of Daphlay's solar system; and they established an intricate program to conceal from the Pleiadeans the information concerning Daphlay's location in the galaxy.

Space craft are only able to approach a solar system by limited attitudes of approach. 32 These limited attitudes of approach necessitate the use of two braking methods for space craft approaching a solar system: one external and one aboard ship. Space craft in interstellar space are traveling at near interstellar light speed and need to reduce their speed to below the local speed of light in and around a solar system—solar system light speed—which is more than 400,000 times slower, otherwise they will destroy themselves. The exterior braking component is provided for by the outward streaming of gravitrons from that solar system.

Solar systems are composed of a rotating star or stars, around which revolve and rotate many other celestial bodies. Waldark and his 'cabalists' demonstrated that spinning bodies rotate themselves partially into complexified three-space, thereby losing mass and thereby emitting gravitrons in a cone between 19.47 and 22.48 degrees north and south of their equator. A solar system is made up of its individual components, but it also acts in many ways as a unit. Therefore, a solar system, which is relatively flat, acts in many ways like a spinning disk. A solar system emits lost mass from its center—both north and south—and perpendicular to its ecliptic plane—its flatness; and a solar system emits a stream of gravitrons in a cone between 19.47 and 22.48 degrees north and south of its ecliptic plane. The origin of the gravitron stream cone—like spinning disks—is two-thirds of the way from the center of the solar system to the outermost celestial bodies which comprise that system. Therefore for space craft, the limited attitudes of approach to a solar system are the two cones that extend from a point situated two-thirds of the way from its center to its outer edge; and these are found above and below the ecliptic plane and at angles of between 19.47 and 22.48 degrees to it.

The approach points of a given solar system are located along the axis perpendicular to the ecliptic plane passing through the center of that solar system. The distance from the center of a solar system to its two approach points is directly proportional to the total mass of that system and situated at the point at which solar system light speed increases by over 400,000 times to interstellar light speed.

Space craft approaching a solar system transit one of the two approach points of the solar system they are approaching. That is why the new Altean Naval Service of Daphlay immediately established a permanent patrol sector around the two approach points of the solar system in which Daphlay is located. Those patrol sectors have never been unoccupied.

In interstellar flight the braking system aboard ship suffers severe damage, especially during the approach and braking procedures. Space craft brake themselves on approaching a solar system by periodically thrusting high speed gravitrons through their number nine gravitron thruster, located at the point of their bow. This stream of vented, high-speed, massless gravitrons 'smashes' against the stream of massless gravitrons streaming from a solar system, and the reaction to this action helps space craft to slow down.

During interstellar flight the number nine thruster is only used during the breaking procedure. Otherwise this thruster is protected by double clamshell doors. 33 Made of extremely tough steel, these doors at the bow of the craft act as the cutting edge of the ship as it travels at high velocity through empty space (though this emptiness in fact contains space dust). The resulting high speed collisions between the doors of the thruster and space dust particles cause damage to the doors. During the braking procedure they are even more damaged due to the increased number of space dust particles encountered. The thruster itself is damaged during the braking procedure, but being exposed to the particles for considerably less time than the doors themselves, the amount of damage is relatively lessened; the clamshell doors open automatically (when the thruster emits its stream of gravitrons) exposing the number nine thruster to minor damage from space dust particles. Upon completion of this emission the doors close, and again are exposed to collisions with space dust.

The braking procedure completed and now traveling at below solar system light speed, space craft go to one of the two approach points. As a result of that solar system's celestial bodies' partial spinning into complexified three-space, escaping particles stream up and down around the line passing through the center of that system, perpendicular to its ecliptic plane. These streaming particles, including metallic particles, also pass through or near to the two approach points of the solar system. Hence, to be able to enter a solar system, space craft have to pass through a solar system approach point.

The doors of the number nine thruster are so severely damaged during solar system approach that they have to be rethickened. Energy is run through the doors causing the metallic particles to adhere, thus rethickening the double clamshell doors and preventing the space craft from breaking up while traveling in the solar system they have just entered. The number nine gravitron thruster unit is replaced on space craft after several interstellar flights.

In order to safeguard Daphlay from intrusion by the Pleiadeans, Alteans of Daphlay initiated a highly secret, very sophisticated galactic grid reference system.

This system used by the Alteans on Daphlay employs a highly secret matrix having three axes. 34 At irregular intervals computers generate a randomly changing reference point. One axis gives distance above the reference point; a second axis gives distance from the reference point; a third indicates azimuth. The orientation of the grid also changes irregularly.

To find Daphlay, the current reference point, the orientation of the grid and all axial components must be known. The computers that store this information are themselves rotated at irregular intervals, and are kept secret and expertly guarded.

Transceivers continuously transmit this information to traveling Altean space craft, especially space craft bound for Daphlay, by way of specially assigned Altean Naval Service personnel.

In their transmit mode, transceivers operate by streaming data infused tornum on a spherical bearing, varying in size. This produces a chain reaction along a line of space dust particles and attaches bits of data to each succeeding particle.

The process of attaching bits of data to space dust particles imparts a spin rate of 750,000 rpms to each particle. The 750,000 rpm spin rate of the first particle of space dust to be so spun causes all particles within the spherical bearing between the transmitting and receiving transceiver—whatever the distance—to virtually instantly spin at 750,000 rpms and transcommunicate the message between the two transceivers. This is possible because 750,000 rpms is the spin rate which bridges three-dimensional and four-dimensional physics, and because in four-dimensions events are non-sequential. Four-dimensional 'processes,' when observed from three-dimensional reality, appear to occur virtually instantaneously.

In their receiving mode transceivers intake the bits of data previously attached to the particles of space dust.

Incoming transcommunications are first filtered through special computers which contain current and randomly changing communication code keys. These code keys are made up of billions of irrelevant bits of intelligent information which must be removed before messages become decipherable. Communication can only take place when both transmitting and receiving transceivers are connected to the appropriate computers with the current code keys.

The galactic location of Daphlay was known only to very few Alteans when they first landed. Since then this information resides only within the computers. Any attempt to gain unauthorized access to that information would cause the entire grid reference system to self-destruct immediately.

The specially assigned Altean Naval Service personnel use a device located on their belt buckles to relay the information concerning the galactic grid reference system and Daphlay's location from the Altean space craft's transceiver into the ship's navigational computers. Only Altean space craft bound for Daphlay receive the planet's location.

Whenever a specially assigned member of the Altean Naval Service thinks that the galactic grid reference system and/or the location of Daphlay is about to be compromised, she or he is directed to immediately remove the depiction of a dolphin from her or his belt buckle, a procedure which can be accomplished very easily and without attracting attention.

This action permanently removes, in an instant, all the relevant information concerning the grid reference system and Daphlay's location from the computers aboard that particular ship. It also sends out a warning about the space craft involved to all other Altean Naval Service space craft and installations.

All space craft not belonging to the Altean Naval Service are routinely assigned six Altean Naval Service personnel aboard. All six work completely alone with no knowledge of those responsible for the safety of

Daphlay, for three of those six are specially assigned holders of the grid information.

Two-thirds of those three specially assigned Altean Naval Service personnel have depictions of dolphins on their belt buckles, which can break the relaying of Daphlay's location and the galactic grid reference system.

When the Pleiadean renegade Garth Sarkneson penetrated the highly secret Altean Naval Service computers, about 250,000 years after this system for hiding Daphlay was installed, he was able to obtain much valuable data. However, in spite of holding two members of the specially assigned personnel with depictions of dolphins on their belt buckles, Sarkneson was never able to discover the location of Daphlay.

The inability of the fanatically driven Sarkneson to find Daphlay drove the Pleiadean to distraction substantiating the merits of Daphlay's camouflage systems and fully justified the reasoning behind these elaborate, expensive and essential procedures.

Chapter Two

The Second Essene Panlogos

Two thousand years after the First Essene Panlogos, an Essene holo-image suddenly appeared and delivered the Second Essene Panlogos to the Council of Daphlay. It said, "I am an Essene holo-image and I am directed by Essenes to deliver to the Council of Daphlay the Second Essene Panlogos. Alteans are now to settle on another planet. The planet on which Alteans are to settle is the fourth planet out from the star in a solar system to which Alteans are directed. The third planet out from the star of this solar system is not to be approached by Alteans. I await your answer NOW!"

The befuddled council members began shouting back and forth to one another as they tried to determine how to respond. The din created by the council members grew, and it became obvious to the Elder that the Council of Daphlay would be unable to come to the immediate decision demanded by the Essene holo-image.

The voice of Elder Dan Reed Colwell roared above the noise. "Ladies and gentlemen, please be quiet!" Elder Dan shouted three times. After each attempt the din created by the council members diminished. Finally there was complete silence.

Elder Dan spoke swiftly, distinctly and with great resolve, "Ladies and gentlemen, we have been presented with the necessity to make a decision of great importance immediately. I gather from your reactions that you are not now ready to make such a decision. Therefore—in accordance with age old tradition—the Elder now makes that decision.

"The Elder states to the Essene holo-image that Alteans will proceed as directed by Essenes to settle on the planet described. Alteans await your further instructions."

The holo-image responded immediately, "Your naval computers have been infused with the location of the solar system in which the designated planet is located. Essenes anticipate your arrival at that planet in 11 days. For you to be able to arrive there on time you must leave Daphlay NOW!"

The holo-image disappeared.

Bedlam broke out.

To the shouting of "You cannot do this!" "Your decision is counter to legal statute!" and "Elder Dan has greatly exceeded his authority!" Elder Dan, when he was finally given the chance, responded, "The traditional authority granted to Elders allows Elders to make important decisions when the council cannot make such important decisions. I made the decision. However, that same tradition also allows the council to override the decision of the Elder by a two-thirds majority vote before the decision becomes effective. Ladies and gentlemen, you failed to vote amongst yourselves to determine if you could override the decision of the Elder by a two-thirds majority vote before the statements and actions of the Essene holo-image made that decision effective."

Elder Dan left the meeting room of the Council of Daphlay.

Dan Reed Colwell immediately contacted his friend Captain Hartman Dan, commanding officer of the Altean Naval Service star ship INTREPID, and asked him if they could meet as soon as possible at Captain Hartman's living quarters. Captain Hartman agreed.

Dan Reed Colwell informed Captain Hartman of the situation and asked him to fly him aboard INTREPID to the planet whose location had been infused into its naval computers.

"Of course, Reed" responded Captain Hartman, "but don't resign as Elder until we are well along the way to the planet. I can only bend, not break regulations."

Shortly thereafter, Dan Reed Colwell and Hartman Dan boarded the Altean Naval Service star ship INTREPID and took off together—bound for the fourth planet in a solar system previously unknown to Alteans, on a journey which would take about 11 days with the INTREPID traveling at near interstellar light speed.

On the way to that planet—and far from Daphlay—Dan Reed Colwell transmitted his letter of resignation as Elder of Daphlay to all Alteans.

He never returned to Daphlay.

Chapter Three

The Red Rock Planet

As the Altean Naval Service star ship carrying Dan Reed Colwell approached the solar system containing the designated planet, Captain Hartman ordered the sequencing of the braking procedure which would slow the space craft sufficiently so that it could proceed to one of the two approach points of that solar system, approximately 800 million miles from the medium sized bright yellow star of that solar system. Following the rethickening of the double clamshell doors of its number nine thruster at the approach point, the star ship made its way toward the fourth planet of that solar system, on a course which kept it more than 50 million miles from the orbit of the third planet out from the star of that solar system—the planet forbidden to Alteans by Essenes.

Captain Hartman then ordered the braking sequence which would slow the star ship from near solar system light speed to a velocity which would allow the space craft to commence orbiting the fourth planet. The solar system braking sequence does not require the use of the bow-mounted number nine thruster. Instead, numbers seven and eight thrusters (mounted seaside and odunside and a few feet aft of the number nine thruster) are pointed forward and thrust a steady stream of high speed gravitrons forward to slow the ship. In a few minutes the solar system braking sequence was completed, and the star ship was inserted into a polar orbit around the fourth planet.

The fourth planet should be called the Red Rock Planet, Dan Reed Colwell thought as he looked at it for the first time.

Aboard ship devices calculated that the planet was slightly larger than Daphlay but because the red rock planet was rather misshapen it was impossible to measure and only an average diameter could be calculated. West of an area of extensive labyrinthine canyons, three huge shield volcanoes towered over an enormous bulge covering a good portion of the red rock planet's equatorial section. 35 Northwest of the bulge, a fourth shield volcano—the largest at some 300 miles across—stood silently over a vent leading to the planet's core. Dan Red Colwell knew this because aboard ship devices had already calculated that this massive shield volcano was located within the 19-20 degree vorticular upwelling zone, the area in which the three-dimensional energy manifestation of the rotation of celestial bodies into complexified three-space manifests itself. Upon seeing this shield volcano in the northern hemisphere Dan Reed Colwell deduced that the red rock planet's magnetic field would also have its inflow point near the north pole of the planet.

"What is your measurement of the magnetic field?" he asked Captain Hartman Dan.

"Erratic and weak," replied his friend.

This would mean that, at best, there would be an erratic and weak flow of planetary torun across the red rock planet, Dan Reed Colwell also knew.

"We have a lot of work to do," Dan Reed Colwell said to Captain Hartman as the star ship's orbit carried them toward and over the north polar area of the red rock planet.

It was as they approached the most northerly region that Dan Reed Colwell first saw hope for the future of Alteans on the red rock planet. Before them lay an extensive sheet of white.

"What's it made of?" Dan Reed Colwell demanded impatiently.

A young ensign at the environmental console responded excitedly, "Ice! Frozen water! VERY THICK!"

Dan Reed Colwell's heart leaped.

"WATER!" he shouted.

A few hours, and a few orbits later, the star ship reported a summary of its findings to Daphlay.

Bedlam had broken out throughout the new home of Altean society as a result of the visit of the Essene holo-image, and the decision of Elder Dan to accept the Second Essene Panlogos. But mostly because a friend of Elder Dan's, the commanding officer of an Altean Naval star ship, was using that craft to escort the former Elder of Daphlay to the planet designated by Essenes.

Only 4000 years before, Altean society had suffered a series of crises which had culminated in a gigantic convulsion. Colonization of the center of the galaxy had led to revolt and the spawning of the Pleiadean empire. This had led to hundreds of millions of years of armed confrontation and combat between Alteans and the Pleiadeans. In turn, this armed confrontation between Alteans and the Pleiadeans had led to the loss of basic rights of Alteans and to the ascendancy of autocratic naval rule. This had resulted in the death of Altea. Only the Lotharian escapees, whose descendants continued to live on Daphlay, had survived.

When the Council learned of what former Elder Dan had done they met in emergency session and then transmitted a message to Dan Reed Colwell aboard the star ship ordering him to return immediately to Daphlay and to present himself before the Council. If Dan Reed Colwell did not comply with this order the Council would send Altean Naval Service star ships to retrieve him.

The possibility of conflict as a result of the divisive confrontation between former Elder and Council paralyzed Alteans with fear.

Having anticipated what would happen as a result of his actions Dan Reed Colwell was ready: he transmitted another message to all Daphlay.

After admitting that he had provoked the confrontation, Dan Reed Colwell went on to explain why he had done so. For some time he had felt a growing unease with the way things were 'progressing' on Daphlay, Dan Reed Colwell told them. The facade of Altean culture and civilization had been recreated on Daphlay, but the spirit was lacking. Beyond simply living, there seemed to be no purpose to life in Altean society. There were no goals.

The mandate of Alteans had always been to spread Altean civilization and culture throughout the galaxy. The destiny of Alteans had always been to redeem the galaxy. The mandate and the destiny of the Alteans was the legacy of the intergalactic pioneers, seekers who had brought that legacy with them, inherited from previous intergalactic seekers.

Alteans were on the verge of breaking the chain of mandates and destinies which had been passed on as legacies from galaxy to galaxy, along the chain of galaxies leading back into the mists of time, he stated.

"Who are we to break this chain?" asked Dan Red Colwell.

He paused a few moments, and then he continued, "We are Alteans and Essenes are Alteans. Essenes are Alteans who decided long ago to voluntarily serve and to prepare the galaxy for redeeming. Essenes are not redeemers. Alteans are the redeemers.

"Essenes—who know much more than other Alteans—have directed us to renew our mandate of spreading Altean culture and civilization throughout the galaxy so that we will be able to fulfill our destiny as redeemers of the galaxy. Settling on another planet is the first step toward fulfillling both our mandate and our destiny. To refuse to act in accordance with the dictates of our mandate and therefore to not attain our destiny is to commit suicide. If Altean society fails to respond now with renewed vigor, then Altean society is doomed."

Dan Reed Colwell switched off the transceiver he had been using aboard the Altean star ship in polar orbit around the red rock planet and waited.

The next day the Council of Daphlay announced its unanimous support for the project of settling on the planet chosen by Essenes.

Popular support for Dan Reed Colwell's actions as a result of Dan Reed Colwell's message to Alteans had forced the Council to reconsider its position.

Funds were quickly raised, vessels on loaded with the necessities required to carry the project forward and an expedition dispatched to join the lone Altean Naval Service star ship which continued to orbit the red rock planet.

The planetary adjustments needed to make the red rock planet habitable turned out to be relatively simple.

Although the magnetic field of the red rock planet was erratic and weak, the planet's period of rotation was only about 40 minutes too slow. Increasing the rotational rate by this small amount of 40 minutes or so, produced a magnetic field which carried with it the required flow of vital planetary torun so that Alteans could inhabit the planet. How the magnetic fields of planets come about and why a planetary period of rotation of 23 hours 56 minutes produces the appropriate magnetic field for life on planets has always remained beyond the grasp of self-aware beings.

Two gravitron infusion complexes are required to infuse gravitrons into the surface of a planet being prepared for habitation, in order to increase the effective mass of that planet near its surface, and thereby increase its rotation to the required rate. On the red rock planet the massive shield volcano located between 19 and 20 degrees north latitude served the same purpose as would the infusion of gravitrons into the planet's surface by one gravitron infusion complex. Alteans speculated that in times past the increasing size and mass of all the four, then active shield volcanoes, may have gradually increased the rotational rate of the planet to near that which is acceptable for habitation.

With the exception of galactic seed planets—which always naturally rotate in 23 hours and 56 minutes—Alteans knew that the red rock planet was the only planet that had ever been recorded to have a rate of rotation anywhere near to the only acceptable rate for self-aware beings: 23 hours, 56 minutes.

The red rock planet was special.

Therefore, they only needed to find one site where spinning disks would be used to infuse gravitrons into the surface of the planet in order to speed up its rate of rotation by about 40 minutes. From their transdimensional physics, Alteans knew that the gravitron infusion complex should be sited approximately 120 degrees either east or west of the massive shield volcano located between 19 and 20 degrees north latitude and in the northern hemisphere.

The latitudinal locations and longitudinal separations between gravitron infusion complexes are based on the geometry of circumscribed tetrahedra. When one point of a circumscribed tetrahedron is placed at the pole of a spinning sphere, which circumscribes that tetrahedron, the other three points of the tetrahedron touch that sphere at intervals of 120 degrees of longitude. That is the reason for the longitudinal separation of 120 degrees between gravitron infusion sites on planets being prepared for habitation. Those same three points also touch at 19.47 degrees latitude in the hemisphere opposite the pole point of the tetrahedron.

Thus, on planets being made habitable, two gravitron infusion complexes are always constructed at about 19.47 degrees in the same hemisphere and separated by about 120 degrees of longitude.

The red rock planet was special.

The red rock planet required only a gentle 'push'—through the infusion of gravitrons and a resulting increase of apparent mass near its surface—to increase its rate of rotation to the required rate. Because the red rock planet had to complete each rotation only about 40 minutes faster not as much 'push' would be required by its single—and not at about 19.47 degrees—gravitron infusion complex. There were three possibilities for the latitude of this complex: about 30, 41 or 60 degrees north latitude. The farther north the site, the less the 'push.'

All three possible sites reflected trigonometric functions relating to the geometry of circumscribed tetrahedra. The ratio of the surface area of a circumscribing sphere to the surface area of the tetrahedron it circumscribes, is 2.720699046 to 1. The square root of three divided by two times pi, is 2.720699046; the transdimensional constant of the Universe. The square root of three divided by two, is the hyperdimensional component of the transdimensional constant, and pi is the three-dimensional component.

The angle whose cosine is the square root of three divided by two is 30 degrees; the angle whose tangent is the square root of three divided by two is 40.89 degrees; the angle whose sine is the square root of three divided by two is 60 degrees.

Approximately 41 degrees north latitude was chosen for the gravitron infusion complex because 40.89 degrees was the most flexible of the three options. 36

Approximately 120 degrees east of the massive shield volcano was chosen due to its favorable surface geography.

The area chosen was relatively level, dotted with knobbly hills and impact craters, and it was within one of those larger impact craters that the gravitron infusion complex was constructed.

Before the complex could be constructed, a coolant had to be provided to keep the magnetically levitated spinning disks from burning up due to friction caused by their spinning at 750,000 rpms. Aboard ship spinning disks are cooled by the induction of the external atmosphere, or space, in which the ship is located. Ground based spinning disks are cooled by water.

The first step in the process of increasing the effective mass of a planet near its surface is to conduit large amounts of water to the two sites of gravitron infusion. This is often a massive, lengthy and expensive project carried out under conditions not conducive to life.

The red rock planet was special.

The red rock planet required only one water conduit, a conduit from its north polar ice cap to about 41 degrees north latitude (not to about 19.47 degrees latitude). The conduit at over 1000 miles was long, but only one was needed and at only half the length that might have otherwise been required.

When the conduit was completed, cool fresh water was piped into the extensive basin of the crater and allowed to fill that basin to a predetermined level on the supporting uprights of the bases of the two enormous spinning disks. Once the cooling water—fanned into water vapor by the rapidly spinning disks—was available, the process of gravitron infusion could begin.

In less than three years the red rock planet was ready for the next step in the process of making it habitable: the infusion of a breathable combined atmosphere. This too was accomplished comparatively quickly because the Council of Daphlay had previously financed a massive program to produce vast amounts of liquified nitrogen, and to provide for the transportation of nitrogen and other required liquified gases to the red rock planet. When the red rock planet was ready for those liquified gases, those liquified gases had been readied for the red rock planet.

Altean Naval Service transport vessels carried the liquified gasses to the planet, they swept low over its surface, spraying their liquid cargo behind them. When the liquified gases hit the thin natural atmosphere of the planet they abruptly returned to their natural gaseous states. In doing so, these gases created gigantic clouds of mist which eventually dissipated as the atmosphere of the planet became denser and warmed by the energy emitted from the star around which the red rock planet orbited.

Once the calculated amount of nitrogen and other gases had been infused into the newly combined artificial and natural atmosphere of the red rock planet, the next phase of the process to produce breathable air began. Oxygen extracted from the ice sheets of both poles of the planet was allowed to mix freely with the transitional combined atmosphere. The hydrogen released by the extraction process floated up into the atmosphere and beyond, too light to be held by the gravity of the planet. When the projected amount of oxygen had mixed into the atmosphere the extraction process was ceased, and the new combined atmosphere of the red rock planet was almost ready.

The air was breathable but still too cool, especially at night, for Alteans to settle on the planet. The red rock planet's orbit is far from its star, so the heat absorbed by its thin natural atmosphere, almost totally composed of carbon dioxide, only managed occasionally to raise the midday equatorial temperature above the freezing point of water. The infusion of a breathable atmosphere about 1500 feet thick and extremely shallow when compared with a naturally breathable atmosphere like that of Altea, still did not insure much greater warming. On its own, the infused artificial atmosphere's ability to absorb and retain more heat from the red rock planet's star was still insufficient to raise atmospheric temperatures.

The presence of the natural atmosphere, plus the added artificial atmosphere brought about the slow climb of atmospheric temperatures to an afternoon temperature of about 75 degrees at mid-latitudes. Incoming short-wave radiation from the red rock planet's star was able to pass directly through the combined atmospheres, but most of the incoming ultraviolet radiation was absorbed at the upper limits of the combined atmosphere, thereby protecting life below. The short-wave radiation which penetrated to the surface of the red rock planet was absorbed by the surface and then, as long-wave infrared radiation, sent the heat out into the combined atmosphere.

Without the natural atmosphere of the red rock planet this infrared radiation would, for the most part, have continued upward and beyond the artificial atmosphere which would have remained too cool for Alteans. However, the natural atmosphere of the planet consisted almost entirely of carbon dioxide, a gas which absorbs infrared radiation and therefore gives off heat. Some of that heat is directed toward space but the rest is directed back toward the surface of the planet. So the combined atmosphere of the red rock planet gradually warmed to near ideal.

When the atmosphere stopped warming, additional carbon dioxide was transported from Daphlay and carefully and precisely released into the combined atmosphere of the planet so that atmospheric temperatures rose to prescribed levels.

The process of warming the combined atmosphere of the planet was relatively easy and of short duration compared with many other planets which had received artificial atmospheres in addition to their natural atmospheres, as part of their preparation for habitation. The red rock planet's natural atmosphere was almost perfect in its ability to provide the temperature raising component of the combined atmosphere.

The red rock planet was special.

Even though the temperature at mid-latitudes was around 75 degrees, the temperature near the polar ice caps remained below the freezing point of water—even during periods when one or the other ice cap pointed at the star of the red rock planet. For a non-seed planet, the red rock planet had a relatively large inclination of its axis, but its great distance from its star kept the water ice of its polar caps from melting.

When all was ready, Dan Reed Colwell was the first to remove his environmental helmet and to draw into his lungs the first breath of the new warm combined atmosphere. Dan Reed Colwell watched as his associates, who had greatly assisted the process of preparing the red rock planet, also removed their helmets and breathed the air of the planet. As they did so, Dan Reed Colwell had a sudden inspiration.

"The red rock planet needs a real name," he said, "and I have that name.

"Let us call this planet Silbury, meaning 'planet of the mountain of silicate'."

The others nodded agreement.

The red rock planet had a name.

Silbury was special in another way too.

The average circumference of the planet was very nearly 13,275 miles. Dividing 13,275 by 36,000—which is 100 times the standard 360 degrees around any given planet—results in .36875. Multiplying .36875 by 5280 results in 1947, 1000 times 19.47, a representation of the latitude at which the three non-polar corners of spinning tetrahedra touch the sphere which circumscribes them.

As a result, the Alteans instituted a completely new distance unit on Silbury: the Silbury mile. The Silbury mile was 1947 feet long and had been calculated by dividing the number of miles in the near average circumference of the misshapen planet by 36,000 and then by multiplying the result by 5280.

Silbury was indeed special.

Chapter Four

Dan 'Pan Hur'

Dan Reed Colwell, the former Elder of Daphlay, became the first Elder of Silbury. From the time Dan Reed Colwell had asked Captain Hartman, the commanding officer of the star ship INTREPID, to take him forthwith to the planet designated by Essenes, Dan Reed Colwell had led the way for the settling of Alteans on Silbury.

The early days of that process had been fraught with contention and the possibility of conflict, but Dan Reed Colwell had quickly defused the situation by forcefully imploring Alteans to do their duty, to live up to the requirements of their mandate and to work toward achieving their destiny as redeemers of the galaxy. Those days had also given Dan Reed Colwell much insight concerning Essenes and the role that group of Alteans played as preparers of the galaxy. Dan Reed Colwell was convinced that Essenes and their work were essential ingredients in the process of redeeming the galaxy; he was determined to not only cooperate with Essenes, but to insist that others did so too.

Once the Council of Daphlay had been persuaded of its need to cooperate fully with Essenes, the rest of the project was reduced to logistics, engineering and work; the work had been long, somewhat difficult but definitely rewarding.

Silbury was special, Dan Reed Colwell knew. Once the single site for the gravitron infusion complex had been selected by Dan Reed Colwell and his associates, the construction of the complex could proceed in parallel with the conduiting of water from the north polar ice cap. Once those two projects were completed, the basin of the impact crater filled with water to its specified height and the rotational period of the planet fixed at 23 hours and 56 minutes, the project to infuse the correct atmosphere could begin.

Silbury was ready to support and bring forth life.

Just west of the ancient impact crater containing the gravitron infusion complex, Dan Colwell Reed and his associates constructed a long narrow structure to house the first Altean inhabitants of Silbury. Due to its shape it soon became known as 'The Wall' and was constructed on top of material removed from the floor of the crater. 37

The location and design of the Wall were both utilitarian and part of a larger scheme. Dan Reed Colwell and his associates had created a layout which would, in all its various components and by its overall design, represent their heartfelt thanks to the Source of the Universe. The Wall was the first of two structures, and the first of three components, to be completed during phase one of the project. Dan Reed Colwell hoped that the Horz complex, as it was to be called, would be completed in his lifetime.

The second structure was an enormous tetrahedral pyramid, constructed on the northeastern rim of the crater. Housing the Horz complex medical facilities, it came to be known as the Tetrahedron—its location and design were also part of the overall design of the Horz complex. The impact crater itself became known as the Tetrahedron Crater. The spinning disks of the gravitron infusion complex in the Tetrahedron Crater were also used for a vital process: the high speed off-center rotation of reproductive material into complexified three-space at 750,000 rpms. This process reconfigured that reproductive material and made it useful for various healing procedures. The close proximity of the Tetrahedron to the crater's spinning disks greatly facilitated the process of reconfiguring the highly perishable reproductive material and practically eliminated any loss of material through delays in transportation.

The Tetrahedron also served as a pumping station for the water conduit. This conduit ran from the north polar ice cap, to the grave circle north of the Horz complex and to the northeastern rim of the Tetrahedron Crater. At this point on the crater, the water was pumped up and over the rim and allowed to free fall into the combination reservoir and cooling lake for the spinning disks.

The third component of the first phase was a huge spiral mound constructed several miles due south of the Tetrahedron. Its location and design were in accordance with its representational purpose in the layout of the Horz complex.

Dan Reed Colwell and his associates named the huge spiral mound Hurbury, meaning 'shining mountain.' It was intended to be a monument to self-aware life. 38 Hurbury's equiangular spiral — a spiral based on the twelfth root of two—was meant to represent the harmonics of the natural environment necessary for the evolution of self-aware life from life; harmonics which have a logarithmic progression and intervals equal to the twelfth root of two.

A deep broad ditch was constructed outward from Hurbury so that the azimuth of that ditch was 27.2 degrees gyro from the center of Hurbury. The bottom of the ditch was lined with beacons to assist the approach of space craft. The azimuth 27.2 degrees gyro was a metaphorical representation of 10 times the transdimensional constant 2.720699046.

Hurbury was constructed due south of the Tetrahedron so that the angle formed at the apex of Hurbury, between the Tetrahedron and the southern end of the Wall, was 19.47 degrees (the latitude at which the three non-polar points of a circumscribed tetrahedron touch the spinning sphere which circumscribes it).

The long axis of the Wall was 22.48 degrees west of due north.

This 22.48 degree alignment was intended to be combined with the 19.47 degree angle formed at the apex of Hurbury, as these two angles represent the upper and lower angular limits of cones of emitted gravitrons which form on either side of spinning disks.

Before the conduiting of water, before the infusion of gravitrons and gasses and before there could be construction, vast quantities of energy had to be available on Silbury to operate the devices used in the implementation of the projects which prepared the planet for habitation.

That energy was available to the preparers of Silbury from the Source by means of meditators transredimensioning Horun into torun; energy transdimensioners transdimensioning torun into torinum; and energy transconverters transconverting torinum into tornum. It was the conscitrons of tornum that did the work necessary to accomplish the tremendous tasks of first preparing Silbury, and then building the Horz complex.

The melting of the north polar ice cap required a mobile energy transproduction unit, which was flown in by an Altean Naval Service transport vessel. Adjacent to this unit a prefabricated structural unit providing the required environmental conditions for meditators and other workers was erected. After that, three mobile ice melting devices were shipped from Daphlay and they began melting ice into a very large fabricated holding tank. The many workers who performed their tasks outside the environmental structural unit were required to wear protective environmental suits and helmets and they worked outside for no more than four hours at a time.

In the meantime, other Altean Naval Service transport vessels were laying the water conduit along a route predetermined by overhead holo-mapping. The sections for this conduit were made of an extremely durable steel alloy, with an exterior diameter of 21 feet, a thickness of 9.18 inches, and a resulting interior diameter of 19.47 feet. The size of the pipe was both representational and practical. Precise sections of conduit were fabricated to match each topographical turning and change of elevation on Silbury. Using the guidance of remote sensors, each section of pipe was robotically fitted carefully into place. The joints between the sections were then precisely fused by extremely high temperature welding devices and these were also guided by remote sensors. In this way the entire water conduit, from the edge of the ice cap to the Tetrahedron Crater, was laid without exposing Alteans to potentially hazardous tasks in a hostile environment.

While the water conduit work was progressing, the Tetrahedron Crater project was also under way. Three mobile energy transproduction units were landed together with three prefabricated environmental structural units. Altean Naval Service sappers created a level platform just west of the Tetrahedron Crater for those units, by precisely placing high explosive charges in the rugged terrain of the solidified outflow, and all the units were then sited.

Sappers then blew a huge gap in the southwestern arcing of the crater's rim. Scores of mobile excavation and hauling machines were then landed by transport vessels and they began the task of removing material from the crater floor, hauling that material up out of the crater through the gap in its southwestern rim and over a roadway which led to the dumping site on which the Wall was to be constructed. These special mobile excavation machines only need one operator. Their control modules are environmentally safe and include the introduction of the appropriate induced flow of torun.

The excavations in the floor of the Tetrahedron Crater were undertaken for three reasons: to provide foundation material for the Wall; to increase the potential water holding capacity of the crater; to prepare a portion of the floor of the crater for the uprights belonging to the bases required for the two spinning disks. The bases had to be very large and strong, for these spinning disks were to have diameters of over 1000 feet. Each base consisted of a ring of 30 steel alloy uprights connected at their tops by 30 steel alloy lintels.

Once the gravitron infusion complexes were completed, large amounts of energy were needed to magnetically levitate and spin the disks. These two enormous bronzed limestone, steel banded and rimmed spinning disks had been cast on the outer of the two 'natural' satellites in circular orbits around Silbury's equator. This was necessary because their considerable weight on the planetary surface would have caused them to break up as they were cooling.

From the time that Dan Reed Colwell first learned of Satyr and Nymph (as he had named these two orbiting chunks of space material, forever chasing one another across the sky), he had suspected that the 'natural' satellites of Silbury were not natural at all, but had been placed in orbit by Essenes. The simple explanation for the existence of Silbury's two satellites would be that of wandering asteroids which had been captured by the gravity of Silbury at some distant time in the past. Dan Reed Colwell thought that the orbits of Satyr and Nymph were too perfect—including the exact 5:2 ratio of the radii of those orbits—to have been the result of chance captures. If such captures had taken place, the resulting orbits would have been very elliptical and most likely unstable. The orbits of Satyr and Nymph were perfectly circular and they never varied any detectable amount.

Silbury was special.

Satyr and Nymph—its 'natural' satellites—were very special.

Satyr and Nymph were rich in the various minerals required by Altean society, Silbury contained virtually no valuable minerals whatsoever.

At the same time as the lower bases of the Tetrahedron Crater spinning disks were being constructed, and following the removal of the material from the crater, an energy conduit was buried in the floor. Near the energy conduit's exit from the crater, another conduit was also being laid. This would carry water from the future Tetrahedron Crater Reservoir to other places in the Horz complex.

The energy conduit was laid in a ditch which led southwesterly from the Tetrahedron Crater, through the previously created gap in its southwestern rim and then through the solidified outflow from the crater. From there, a branch conduit was laid to conduit energy to the Wall; the main energy conduit continued straight across the planetary surface. The conduit then passed over the Bastion (the large, artificially flattened mesa being developed as the main Altean Naval Service base on Silbury) a short distance across the planetary surface again, and then to a smaller, fairly flat mesa which was to become known as Dolphin Mesa.

The water conduit was laid north of the energy conduit in a ditch which also led southwesterly from the Tetrahedron Crater, through the previously created gap in its southwestern rim and then through the solidified outflow from the crater. From there a branch conduit was laid west of the energy conduit taking water to the Wall; the main water conduit continued straight across the planetary surface over the mesa of the Bastion, a short distance across the planetary surface again and to and under Dolphin Mesa. A large pump house containing three centrifugal water pumps was constructed tangential to the southern side of the water conduit and west of the Bastion. The operation of two-thirds of those pumps was required to provide a continuous flow of water from the Tetrahedron Crater Reservoir to the various existing components and structures of the Horz complex.

The ditches for the conduits were dug by mobile excavating machines. The material removed was piled up nearby and when both the energy and water conduits were laid, the material was carefully replaced in such a way that it was impossible to tell where the conduits ran. (With the exception of the conduits buried in the floor of the Tetrahedron Crater, as this crater was to be subsequently filled with water.)

At the southwestern end of the conduits lay Dolphin Mesa. This was the site of a longhouse and two pyramidal structures, each one housing a large energy transconverter and three energy transdimensioners. 39 The beautifully designed, long, narrow, hexagonal longhouse was constructed of gleaming transparent crystal and named Chapter One by Dan Reed Colwell to signify the new beginning of the colonization of the galaxy by Alteans.

These long, narrow, hexagonal buildings like Chapter One had been constructed from out of time immemorial along the chain of galaxies leading to this galaxy and had originally been called kirks. The intergalactic pioneers had proposed the construction of four churs, as kirks were known by that time, to help mark the prime meridian in the center of Hurtea, the new capital of Altea. The observant indigenous beings saw that the shape of the proposed churs was identical to that of the shape of the longhouses in which they had always held their community meetings.

According to legend, longhouses were constructed as stylized representations of Mount Hurartu on Altea, because that mountain, by being only a little mountain and therefore relatively easy to climb, represented the first step in climbing every mountain, the philosophic metaphor of the indigenous beings for striving to learn as much as possible. The name Mount Hurartu predated the arrival of the extragalactics and the meaning of the word 'hurartu' has become lost in the mists of time.

The indigenous beings had laughed at their 'sophisticated' friends for calling a longhouse by the quaint name chur.

"Your buildings are not churs," they had said, "they are longhouses.

"We very much like the idea of constructing four beautiful new longhouses in the middle of Hurtea."

Chapter One, the longhouse on Dolphin Mesa, was to be the permanent home of the dolphin trainers. It was intended to be the 'temporary' site of energy transredimensioning by meditators and the 'temporary' home of the Horz complex main library. When, at some future date, the western components of the Horz complex were constructed, these two temporary sites were to be transferred to new locations.

Once the 'permanent' energy transproduction complex of Dolphin Mesa became operational, the magnetic levitation system of the Tetrahedron Crater gravitron infusion complex also became operational. Then the two enormous spinning disks which had been cast on Satyr were transported to Silbury and very carefully and expertly inserted between their conscitron thruster armatures, so that they could be held in place by the magnetic levitation system of the gravitron infusion complex. After the completion of the complex the two disks were spun to their nominal rotation speed of 750,000 rpms, whereupon gravitrons began to be infused into the surface of Silbury.

Dolphin Mesa had been hollowed out to make room for another body of water which gave its name to the mesa: 'The Sea of Dolphins' and the three structures of Dolphin Mesa were therefore constructed on small islands in the Sea of Dolphins.

Following the completion of the gravitron infusion process to artificially fix the period of rotation of Silbury at the required 23 hours, 56 minutes and the readying of a warm breathable, combined atmosphere, Silbury was ready for the dolphins.

After Dan Reed Colwell had tested the air of Silbury he then personally supervised the careful and loving placement of 24 dolphins into the cool salt water of the Sea of Dolphins—water salinated as it entered the Sea. Not only do these marine animals require salt water but also the cooling systems of energy transconverters require a circulating mixture of salt water and liquified jade.

The two energy transconverters and six energy transdimensioners in structures on the islands in the Sea of Dolphins were also seen as 'temporary' because the energy transproduction process was projected to be incorporated into a single structure in the western part of the complex. At some point, the island structures in the Sea of Dolphins would be turned into resorts where future residents of the Horz complex could enjoy a seaside setting.

Right now, Dan Reed Colwell and his associates oversaw everything and Dan Reed Colwell astutely and lovingly guided everyone through the arduous and exacting days of preparing Silbury for settlement.

Dan Reed Colwell was beyond the age of normal retirement when the Essene holo-image delivered the Second Essene Panlogos, and well beyond the age of retirement when Silbury became a thriving Altean community. Nevertheless, the members of the fledgling Altean community on Silbury asked Dan Reed Colwell to become the first Elder of Silbury, and he reluctantly agreed.

In later years Dan Reed Colwell took up gardening as his hobby, sharing a garden with his longtime friend Hartman Dan. This garden was adjacent to the farming area northwest of the Tetrahedron Crater. Hartman Dan, long since retired from the Altean Naval Service, had been the officer in charge of logistical support for Silbury. He shared a love of art with his friend Dan Reed Colwell and having spent their lives almost exclusively using their minds, they found that their gardening enabled them to enjoy the satisfaction of physical labor. Indeed, Dan Reed Colwell's work on the merits of combining mental and physical labor has been an inspiration and guide to many Alteans since that time.

Just before passing on, Dan Reed Colwell attended one last meeting of the Council of Silbury.

"I am tired of writing my name Dan Reed Colwell," he said to the council. "It's time to change back to the method of those indigenous to this galaxy. From now on I'm Reed Colwell Dan."

Everyone on Silbury and on Daphlay eventually reverted to the indigenous method of writing the family name last, but when Reed Colwell Dan finally did pass on he was given the honorific title 'Pan Hur,' and he has always been known since as Dan 'Pan Hur.'

Reed Colwell Dan's body was buried in the grave circle north of the Horz complex, in the manner of his ancestors.

Over 100,000 years later, the seventh and final component of the overall design of the Horz complex—the corbelled dome for the grave circle—was conceived, designed and completed by a young architect named Dan Manty. 40 Manty's work was so enthusiastically received by the Altean community of Silbury that he was asked to change his family name to Manpure. The community felt that only a "manpure" (meaning a 'pure one') could have conceived and designed such a magnificent monument. Dan Manpure reluctantly agreed.

The magnificent corbelled dome enclosing the huge grave circle in which the bodies of all those who died on Silbury could be buried—in the manner of their ancestors—was constructed in such a way that its monumental Lion Gateway was closest to the grave of Reed Colwell Dan. This Lion Gateway consisted of two pairs of large upright megaliths and a single massive lintel stone. In the weight-relieving triangle above the lintel a sculptured relief was carved, portraying part of a soul print flanked by two lions. Dan Manty had been completely unaware of Lura Redmand's plans for the Hurmaze when he designed the Lion Gateway, but his metaphorical representation was similar.

"Two lions to one soul," Dan Manpure said to his daughter when she asked him to explain the Lion Gateway to her. "It takes a lot more courage than soul to survive."

Dan 'Pan Hur' had thought about many things during his long life, but the one thing which puzzled him most was the forbidden planet, whose orbit was next inside the orbit of Silbury toward the star, become sun of the solar system. In accordance with the instructions of the Essene holo-image, Alteans had gone no closer to the third planet of the solar system than Silbury.

Nevertheless, Dan 'Pan Hur' had always wondered. Especially when he saw the forbidden planet among the myriad of stars in the night sky above Silbury. (Planets being one of the few things he ever saw from Daphlay, because everything beyond the solar system of Daphlay is obscured by Daphlay's space dust shield.) The obvious blue-green color of the forbidden planet fascinated Dan 'Pan Hur' and reminded him of Altea and what Altea must have looked like from a distance.

Dan 'Pan Hur' thought it curious that the solar system of the forbidden planet was relatively near to Altea (about nine hours' travel time at near interstellar light speed). In the two-billion year existence of Altean society, it was odd that this solar system had never been discovered. Odd, but not surprising since the main thrust of exploration had always been toward the center of the galaxy and not transversally along the spiralling arm in which both Altea and the forbidden planet are located. There must be some connection between our being here, the first Elder of Silbury thought, and the forbidden blue-green planet.

During a solitary stroll late one night in the flower gardens surrounding the Wall, Dan 'Pan Hur' looked up and saw the forbidden planet shining above him.

"The blue-green planet seems special," he said to himself.

The next day Elder Dan opened the meeting of the Council of Silbury as follows, "The forbidden planet seems special to me. I think that one day an Essene holo-image will return and tell us that we of Silbury have something very special to do with the blue-green planet. We, or future Councils of Silbury and Elders, need to be prepared for that eventuality.

"It is not just our inhabiting Silbury which allows us to call the star about which Silbury orbits, the sun. I think that the blue-green planet qualified this star to be called a sun long before we arrived."

After the passing of Dan 'Pan Hur' the Council of Silbury raised a monument to him, west of the Wall. It was in the form of an obelisk. 41

"It's an aptly shaped monument to the man who named Satyr," said Dan 'Pan Hur's' widow, Avena.

Chapter Five

Renewal

For 100,000 years the Altean settlement on Silbury continued to thrive, though its size did not increase significantly, and the western part of the Horz complex as envisioned by Dan 'Pan Hur' and his associates was not constructed. The Altean Naval Service provided a defensive shield for Silbury by maintaining a continuous patrol of four star ships—two of those star ships always at, or near, the approach points of the solar system containing Silbury and the forbidden blue-green planet.

About 100,000 years after an Essene holo-image had delivered the Second Essene Panlogos, an Essene holo-image suddenly appeared on Silbury and delivered the Third Essene Panlogos to the Council of Silbury. It said, "I am an Essene holo-image and I am directed by Essenes to deliver to the Council of Silbury the Third Essene Panlogos. Until somewhat over a million years ago there existed in this solar system, on the planet which is forbidden to Alteans, beings who were naturally evolving toward the eventual development of a self-aware being on that planet. Pleiadeans interfered with this process in such a way, that now these beings will become extinct, due to a genetic catastrophe brought on by inbreeding. Essenes have infused Altean computers in the Tetrahedron with biological and genetic data pertaining to the current beings living on the planet forbidden to Alteans. Alteans are to develop a genetic agent which will avert this genetic catastrophe. I await your answer NOW!"

Even though it had been 100,000 years since the last appearance of an Essene holo-image, the members of the Council of Silbury and the Elder knew well what had happened immediately following that previous appearance. They also knew well of the prescience of Dan 'Pan Hur' who had thought that an Essene holo-image would return some day and who had also thought that there existed a special relationship between Alteans of Silbury and the forbidden blue-green planet. Therefore, both the current Council of Silbury and the current Elder of Silbury were prepared for the eventual return of an Essene holo-image and for whatever that holo-image would direct Alteans of Silbury to do.

The Elder looked around the silent room and at the resolute faces of all members of the Council. Then she looked at the holo-image and replied resolutely, "Alteans of Silbury accept the Third Essene Panlogos."

The holo-image disappeared.

The Council of Silbury immediately reported the gist of the Third Essene Panlogos and their response to the Council of Daphlay. The Council of Silbury, although autonomous in its decision making processes, routinely informed the Council of Daphlay of important decisions it had made. Both Daphlay and Silbury considered themselves to be planetary outposts of Altea. An Altea, which despite the horrific environmental catastrophe it had suffered, would eventually recover and once again be inhabited by Alteans. Daphlay and Silbury therefore cooperated enormously, but did not defer one to the other on issues of local importance. On matters of defense against the Pleiadeans the Councils of both planets met and jointly decided on how to proceed.

In the case of the Third Essene Panlogos, the Council of Daphlay offered full cooperation and its much greater financial resources to Silbury. The Council of Silbury politely declined financial assistance.

The project of developing a genetic agent on Silbury that would prevent the Pleiadean-instigated impending genetic disaster on the blue-green planet commenced immediately amid great enthusiasm.

This enthusiasm carried over into the start-up of the construction of the western part of the Horz complex. The project continued through the Council of Silbury's invitation to Alteans of Silbury and Daphlay to invest in the project. Dan 'Pan Hur' had successfully enlisted investors at the beginning of the Altean settlement on Silbury; now large numbers of investors stepped forward to help with the great expansion of that settlement.

Both the overall design for the completion of the Horz complex and specific plans for each component to be constructed in the projected western part of the complex had been conceived by Dan 'Pan Hur' and his associates and had been kept in the library in Chapter One. A design committee was appointed to review and if necessary update that overall design and those plans.

Dan 'Pan Hur' and his associates had intended that three major new components of the Horz complex be added far to the west of the three eastern components and far to the southwest of the grave circle. The completed Horz complex would therefore have seven components (the grave circle was to be considered the seventh component, and therefore represent spirit). In the southwest, on top of a large knobbly hill which would have to be partially leveled, an enormous five-sided pyramid was to be constructed. Northwest of this pyramid, and west of Hurbury there would be a city. Between this projected city and the Wall on a high, relatively flat mesa a conical tower was to be built as a monument to all those who had gone before. The main library of the Horz complex, which was open continuously, was to be moved from Chapter One to that same mesa, so that five of the six components comprising the eastern and western parts of the Horz complex were inhabited. Thus the overall Horz complex would represent 6, 5 and 7—the numbers which represent the interaction between the components of the Universe: the non-living parts of the Universe, living things and spirit.

The first meeting of the committee was called after they had all studied the designs and plans that had been distributed, and each member was offered the opportunity to voice her or his thoughts on the subject of the western development of the Horz complex. Several members said that they found the design and plans flawless.

Then a member rose and told the committee that she thought that due to the recently revealed purpose of the Altean settlement on Silbury there should be a number of major revisions made to the design and purpose of the projected western components of the Horz complex.

Some of the other members of the committee were rather taken aback by the suggestion that there was a "recently revealed purpose of the Altean settlement on Silbury."

"What are you talking about with this 'recently revealed purpose of the Altean settlement on Silbury'?" one shouted.

"Please be patient, and I'll explain," she responded.

They were even more taken aback by the specific recommendations made by this member of the committee: The massive five-sided pyramid—named the Tor by Dan 'Pan Hur'—would still house three enormous energy transconverters. These would replace the two smaller energy transconverters on the islands in the Sea of Dolphins and become the energy transconverters of the Horz complex. But the 12 previously projected energy transdimensioners and the primary site of energy transredimensioning would be located instead on the high flat mesa between the projected city and the Wall. The conical tower which was to have been constructed on top of that mesa would be constructed in the middle of a huge square set in the center of the projected city. Placed around this monument to those who had gone before would be four longhouses. Built on a scale larger than Chapter One, these four longhouses would represent the four points of tetrahedra, and be named data, information, knowledge, and Wisdom. 42

"The high flat mesa will be completely transformed so that it can hold three gigantic computers, the energy transdimensioners and the primary site of energy transredimensioning for the Horz complex. As a result, the main library of the Horz complex remains in Chapter One," she continued.

"The mesa will become an architectural, artistic and philosophic monument to the recently revealed purpose of the Altean settlement on Silbury. The mesa will become the Hurmaze, a representation of the emergence of self-aware life," she concluded.

"Your proposal is totally impractical and would result in prohibitive additional expenses," shouted Paul Gravenson, another committee member. "To move the entire energy transproduction process of the Horz complex to its southwestern corner is bad enough, but to then split that process into two widely separated components is ridiculous, and what is the purpose of these three incredibly oversized computers?"

Lura Redmand explained her plan further, "The computers are for defense. Admiral Lura Sanders will discuss that later.

"The torinum transdimensioned by the 12 energy transdimensioners in the Hurmaze will be conduited to Chapter One and then further conduited to the Tor for transconversion into tornum..."

"Do you mean to tell us," Gravenson interrupted, "that you do not propose to conduit the torinum directly to the Tor, but only by way of Chapter One? That is even more impractical, expensive and to no purpose. Even if we were to do as you first suggested, the energy conduit should run directly from the flat mesa to the Tor."

Lura Redmand answered, "The reason for conduiting by way of Chapter One is to provide for a backup in case of failure of the primary energy transconversion facilities. The plan I propose calls for maintaining the current capabilities of all the facilities on Dolphin Mesa. As a result, the resorts envisioned for the two islands in the Sea of Dolphins should be combined into one retreat on the shore of the Tetrahedron Crater Reservoir."

"There is no reason for such a backup," insisted Gravenson. "Failures are very rare, and we already have three large new energy transconverters planned for the Tor, when two will suffice."

"There are the Pleiadeans," said Lura Redmand, "and we therefore need backups for our vital energy and defense components so that the Pleiadeans cannot destroy us."

"The two energy transconverters on Dolphin Mesa are not capable of providing enough tornum to run the Tetrahedron Crater spinning disks and the newly enlarged Horz complex," said Gravenson.

"I would not expect them to," Lura Redmand answered. "The backup system can power the entire Horz complex except the Tetrahedron Crater spinning disks. Those spinning disks could remain shut down for an extended period of time without jeopardizing life on Silbury while any necessary repairs were being made to the primary energy transconverters. I have calculations from the director of the Tetrahedron Crater gravitron infusion complex stating that the spinning disks could remain shut down for almost 10 years before there is a significant problem. I cannot conceive of a situation wherein we would all be still alive and wherein we could not repair our primary energy transconverters within 10 years."

"What is this so called Hurmaze to look like?" demanded Gravenson.

Lura Redmand opened her large briefcase and removed a drawing of the Hurmaze.

The others gasped when they saw it. 43

"Firstly, the northern end of the Wall will need its length slightly extended in order to provide an appropriate backdrop for the Hurmaze when it is viewed from the west. The Hurmaze itself," Lura stated, "is to be sculpted out of the top of the mesa and is to be two sided. Facing the Wall is the eastern side, which is to be the left side of a lion's head. Facing the city is the western side, which is to be the head of a primate."

"That makes no sense," said Gravenson. "Your sculpture of a primate AND a lion hardly represents 'the emergence of self-aware life.' It's just an ape and a cat."

"Give Lura Redmand a chance to explain," intervened Rena Cosgood, the committee chairman, as Gravenson began to laugh.

Lura Redmand was becoming somewhat dismayed by Gravenson's berating negativety but Rena Cosgood's timely words encouraged her. She continued, "The sculpture represents the right side of a primate's head because a single type of primate on a seed planet eventually evolves into a being, who evolves into a being, who evolves into a being, whose children are one day born with souls and are therefore self-aware. 44 The children born with souls have minds to which souls can attach as a result of the evolution of the mind of that single type of primate. The union of the evolved minds and souls of the children born self-aware is represented in the right side of the Hurmaze by the sculpting of the right halves of the banded hair net and the tiara, worn by Altean ladies when they unite with their husband.

Lions have traditionally represented courage. 45 Courage has been traditionally held to reside in the heart. The heart is on our left side as our souls are on our right. To not only be self-aware, but also to be able to function, we have to have a heart. This not only sustains our lives by pumping blood through us, it also sustains us by providing us with courage. Self-aware beings therefore require courage, evolved minds and souls. The half lion head is also wearing half of a soul print around its neck. A soul print associated with a representation of courage intensifies the union of heart and soul.

"The half lion wears half of the hat worn by Altean gentlemen when they unite with their wives. This half hat joins the half tiara of the right side of the Hurmaze to underline union. 43

"Essenes have recently told us that we are now to work to save the beings on the forbidden planet from genetic catastrophe. If we accomplish the goal set for us by Essenes, then I think that the beings on the forbidden planet will then eventually evolve into beings who are self-aware.

"I think that the purpose of our being on Silbury is to greatly assist beings on the forbidden planet to become self-aware.

"The purpose of the Hurmaze therefore is not only to represent the emergence of self-aware life, but also to signify reason for our presence on Silbury."

"I have never in my life," said Gravenson, "heard a more ridiculous assortment of naive notions combined with sheer impracticality." He then got up and walked out of the meeting.

Before anyone could say anything Rena Cosgood rose and stared them all down. Then the chairman of the committee called for an immediate adoption of Lura Redmand's plans. There were NO dissenting votes.

As they were leaving the meeting together Rena asked Lura why she had named the Hurmaze the Hurmaze.

"The hur part is obvious, I think. But why maze?" asked Rena.

"Because to get from one end to the other end of anything important, it seems that we always have to go through a maze. The accomplishment of anything worthwhile seems to require seemingly endless twistings and turnings along the way. The most shining accomplishment for which we can ever hope is the saving of those beings on the forbidden planet who are currently genetically doomed. The realization of that goal will undoubtedly be maze-like."

"You are amazing," responded Rena.

Lura smiled at her new friend and asked, "Why did you call for the adoption of my plans today? I thought today's meeting was supposed to be a general discussion about the design and plans."

"Because your plans and thinking are flawless," responded Rena, "and because I was afraid that your plans would not be adopted if that horrific

Paul Gravenson was present. His head is full of the most ridiculous assortment of stupidity and pomposity—but he very fortunately walked out."

The construction of the western part of the Horz complex went forward and was completed in the lifetime of both Lura Redmand and Rena Cosgood.

The Hurmaze was sculpted as envisioned by Lura Redmand, but several small pyramids were erected at various locations on the sculpture to serve as sight line benchmarks for the various and diverse geometric alignments of the Horz complex of which the Hurmaze became an integral component. The one pyramid that Lura Redmand had originally planned was constructed on the bridge of the right half of the nose—directly over the 'soul' of the Hurmaze—and became the site of energy transredimensioning on Silbury. Since the Hurmaze represented the emergence of self-aware life, it was fitting and logical that the energy of the Horz complex should emerge from above the 'soul' of the Hurmaze, Lura Redmand had concluded.

The three gigantic computers were installed in the Hurmaze as Lura Redmand had suggested, one under each cheek, and one under the two chins. The excavations for the caverns housing the computers were also extensive: each computer's exterior was a four-sided pyramid; each side was over 2250 feet long, while the height of each pyramid—including unconstructed capstone—was over 1440 feet. All three pyramid shaped computers had energy transdimensioners located just above each of their four facings.

Energy transdimensioners receive four-dimensional torun consciousness energy and transdimension that torun into three-dimensional torinum. 47 The initial torun is transmitted to the transdimensioner by Waldark hats that are worn by energy transredimensioning meditators.

Icosahedral shaped energy transdimensioners require the most exacting engineering. Within these energy transdimensioners are three precisely positioned phi section rectangles which are the heart of the transdimensioning process. These rectangles transdimension four-dimensional torun through complexified three-space into three-dimensional torinum, (doing so through a process which is partially the result of the rectangle's ability to be cylinderized and folded end to end, thus forming a three-dimensional representation of a four-dimensional torus—Waldark's hyper-dimensional doughnut).

These phi section rectangles are made of a silver alloy, and have a 13 to 1 length to thickness ratio. Scribed into both facings of all three, exactly one-third of the way through each facing, are logarithmic Transdimensional Spirals which manifest themselves in the growth pattern of living things and in transdimensioning processes. Each of these six spirals is made up of 153 rhombus shaped inscribings. Each composed of 16 rhomboid synthetic rubies; there are therefore 2448 rubies on each facing.

Torinum is transmitted to 27 locations within the icosahedral shell of energy transdimensioners and transdimensioned as a result of the geometric shape of the three phi section rectangles and the six Transdimensional Spirals. It is the precision of energy transdimensioners that brings about the near 99 percent transdimensioning of torun into torinum.

Computers are extremely vital, hyperdimensional computational, as well as data, information and knowledge storage devices—a harmonious balance between analog and digital. 48 Computers vary in size from roughly one inch in height to those of an unprecedented size which were constructed inside the mesa on which the Hurmaze was sculpted. Computers have an invariant four-sided pyramidal exterior, because aeons ago, that particular form was found to be the geometric form which allows them to function.

The four-sided pyramidal exterior form of computers is also a geometrically shaped, three-dimensional representation of any thin nearly two-dimensional circular slice of the conical physical universe. If the capstone of computers existed, a line drawn from the apex of the capstone perpendicular to the base of the computer, would form four angles at the apex of the capstone with the four edges of the facings of computers of 38.14602598 degrees each. The tangent of 38.14602598 degrees when multiplied by four is a very close approximation of pi. Pi is the Universal Constant of the Universe which defines the relationship between a circle's diameter and its circumference; a circumference which all-encompasses everything contained within a circle. Circles are only nearly two-dimensional and therefore contain a sampling of the data, information and knowledge contained in the physical universe.

The capstoneless, pyramid shaped exterior casings of computers are made of crystal. In order to function they are always surrounded by a powerful magnetic field. Their interiors (except as described below) are filled with chalk—or manufactured chalk when naturally occurring chalk is not readily available.

When the intergalactic pioneers landed on Altea they were delighted to find such things as chalk in abundance. For aeons they were obliged to manufacture and/or search for substances vital to the sophisticated devices on which they depended. Altea proved to have almost all those substances in at least modest amounts.

Computers—from those about an inch in height to the largest—are the same internally. 49 Computers have a central cylindrical column which extends from their base to their top. In the core of that column runs a central conduit from the base of the central column past the top of the computer, this also serves as a connector to various networks and devices external to computers. About mid-way up from the base, a cylindrical ring surrounds the central column. This ring relays exterior commands to the appropriate components of the computer by way of the central conduit and smaller individual conduits connected to the computer's storage components.

The data, information, knowledge and program storage components are contained in a doughnut shaped circular cylinder located at the base. This occupies the bottom one-third of the computer. This doughnut is divided by slats of mica into 999 circular wedge shaped compartments. 990 of these contain removable circular wedge shaped crystal disks; the other nine compartments are disrupted by conduits—and in the gigantic computers inside the Hurmaze, by service access passages. 50

The 990 circular wedge shaped crystal disks are separated into three storage units of 330 disks each. One set of smaller conduits connects each storage unit with the central conduit and the command relay ring.

The disks of each of the three computational units of 330 crystal disks are loaded with the complete package of data, information and knowledge and programs stored in any given computer. The solution to any given command is computed three times, compared, and computation only continues if at least two-thirds of those solutions match.

Computations are achieved as follows: exterior commands are received, by way of the central conduit, in the command relay ring surrounding the central column. These commands are then relayed to all three storage units by way of the central conduit and smaller conduits. The appropriate disks in all three units then transfer the necessary data, information and knowledge and programs required for computation to their interfaces with the chalk. When these packets of data, information and knowledge, together with their programs, reach the chalk interface they are spun into the fourth-dimension and impelled toward the central column. 49

Computation takes place as those packets are impelled across the chalk. When the computational results physically reach the central column, a process begins which transdimensions the four-dimensional computational results first into complexified three-space, then into three-dimensions as the computational results reach the central conduit. The three separate results from each of the three storage units are then compared and the final computational results are transmitted through the central conduit to exterior devices—if at least two-thirds of those computational results match.

Computers are constructed in this manner so that the combination of geometric shapes, structural and other materials and the surrounding powerful magnetic field can all work together to transdimension data, information and knowledge and programs so that computations can be made in the fourth-dimension. The reason for having computations take place in the fourth-dimension is because the fourth-dimension is non-sequential. From the perspective of three-dimensional reality these computations that are taking place in four-dimensions, no matter how simple or complex, appear to be occurring virtually instantaneously.

The central cylindrical conduit is divided transversally into three pie shaped sections. From the base to just opposite the midpoint of the doughnut, the central conduit's three transverse sections receive the three computational results from the three storage units of the computer. Located just above this point is a geometrically shaped open space between the lowest part of the conduit and its upper parts. Devices located within a niche in the walling of this open space compare the three incoming computations—and only if at least two-thirds of those three results agree— relay those final results three times up the (now continuous) three transverse sections of the central conduit. At a point in the central conduit (opposite the top of the doughnut) another comparison of the final computational results is made—and only if all three final computations agree exactly—the final result is transmitted up one of the three transverse sections of the upper portion of the central conduit, and out of the computer.

Incoming commands use another of the three transverse sections of the central conduit down as far as the command relay ring, which then transmits its own commands down the continuation of that same transverse section of the central conduit to the point (opposite the top of the doughnut) where those commands are shunted to the three groups of smaller conduits leading to the three computational units of the doughnut.

All components of computers are made of crystal, except for the chalk filling; the mica slats; and the third pie shaped section of the central conduit, as far down as the point opposite the top of the doughnut, which is hollow for ventilation purposes.

A large, geometrically shaped, precisely located open space in the central column and command relay ring is also used for ventilation, and connects to the exterior by small air vents.

Before the sculpting of the Hurmaze could begin, caverns which were to house the three computers and 12 energy transdimensioners were dug out of the high flat mesa in such a way that the mesa would not collapse due the removal of much of its interior. Temporary steel shoring was placed throughout the excavation and later replaced by the permanent crystal structural components of the interior of the Hurmaze. Following the completion of the hollowing process, the computers were put together on their precisely leveled base pads. The phi section rectangles of the energy transdimensioners were precisely cast on Satyr and carefully transported to the surface of Silbury where they were very carefully fitted together and inserted into the specially made crystal icosahedral shells of the energy transdimensioners. The 12 completed energy transdimensioners were then arrayed around the three computers in frames suspended from the ceiling inside the Hurmaze.

Only as the final work of connecting the Hurmaze internal components was beginning did the work on the surface of the Hurmaze commence. Lura Redmand was there every day for years as the meticulous work of sculpting the Hurmaze was executed. When the project was completed, Lura invited Rena Cosgood for a tour. As they stood together on the center of the foreheads of the Hurmaze the two ladies could see over the entire sculpture.

"You did it, Lura," said Rena emphatically. "With heart, mind and soul you did it!"

"And with the absence of Paul Gravenson," added Lura Redmand.

During the construction of the Hurmaze a considerable amount of material was removed from the interior of the mesa and taken to the south of the chins where it was spread out in an expansive but relatively low crescent shaped mound. The tips pointed back toward the western and eastern sides of the mesa. Hanging from the neck of the lion side of the Hurmaze and going up to the mound, half a soul print was constructed. In the low area between the chins and the mound, Lura Redmand created a park, so that when entering the park from the direction of the chins, the crescent shaped mound became a backdrop. She named this park the Park of Meditation and it was for the meditators who transredimensioned energy in the Hurmaze. 43

Those residents of Silbury who wanted to become meditators who could transredimension energy underwent rigorous testing in the Park of Meditation. Those who had proven themselves capable then underwent rigorous training in the Park of Meditation to become meditators who transredimension energy. Meditators already transredimensioning energy periodically returned to the Park in order to undergo ongoing training. Such meditators often went to the Park of Meditation to rest and/or think.

Between a grassy knoll and the structure used to test and train aspirant meditators, Lura Redmand supervised the construction of a large oval shaped pond. The testing and training structure was named the Labyrinth and was actually part of the half soul print worn by the lion; it was one-twelfth as long as the 98.11 percent of a mile (the length of the partially crescent shaped, banded hair net from bottom to the crown of the head). The Labyrinth was beautifully colonaded with downward tapering columns which were representations of a portion of soul prints. Representations of bulls horns—representations of another part of soul prints—lined the top of the Labyrinth's facade. Inside were hundreds of rooms connected by labyrinthine passageways. Those who sought to become meditators who could transredimension energy achieved or failed in their ambition, within these rooms.

What Lura Redmand did not tell Rena Cosgood (nor anyone else) was the fact that, when viewed from above and facing southward, the grassy knoll above the pond, the pond and the ridge of the backdrop for the Park of Meditation formed the right cheek, the right eye and the right hairline of Sara Eland. <u>46</u> Because these things formed part of Sara Eland's face and to scale, then the half soul print hanging from the neck of the lion was also a representation of half of Sara Eland's soul print.

No Altean ever knew what Lura Redmand had done, even though she left two hints. She named the pond after Sara Eland and she had the soul half print hanging upside down from the lion.

In the meantime, to the south of the Hurmaze, the construction of the massive Tor was well under way. The knobbly hill on which the pyramid would stand had two-thirds of its height removed. The Lower Tor—which was to be two-thirds of the height of the Tor—was constructed of stone blocks quarried from a vast canyon far away across Silbury. Water had flowed at one time through this now dry canyon. The much steeper-sloped Upper Tor was to be constructed of huge crystal panels laid over an extremely strong frame of crystal beams.

Following the construction of the Lower Tor but before any work was begun on the Upper Tor, the three enormous energy converters of the Tor were installed on their carefully constructed and leveled base pads. <u>51</u> The steel alloy transconverter sphere, two concentric spherical steel cooling casings of the transconverter sphere and the tetrahedral crystal casing (over 500 foot per side) of all three energy converters were separately cast on Satyr before being transported to Silbury. On arrival they were encased between the upper and lower halves of the steel alloy spheres designed to contain the powerful magnetic fields with which energy converters need to be surrounded to make them function. The two immense steel alloy hemispherical magnetic field encasing spheres of each energy transconverter were also cast on Satyr. After one half of each sphere was buried in the stone of the Lower Tor the main components of the energy transconverters were put in place and then the upper halves of the spheres were lowered and the two halves precisely welded together.

So that the construction of the Upper Tor could proceed, the new plan for what to put in the Upper Tor had been adopted. The proposal of Dan 'Pan Hur' and his associates to have 12 energy transdimensioners and the site of energy transredimensioning of meditators placed in the projected Upper Tor was no longer valid, on account of the decision to accept Lura Redmand's plan to move them to the Hurmaze. The Upper Tor would have been virtually empty without these things.

It was Admiral Lura Sanders, a friend of Lura Redmand, who conceived the bold new purpose for the Upper Tor which transformed it into a vital and revolutionary planetary defense component. Admiral Sanders thought of placing a huge Aspis crystal at the apex of the Tor in order to create an anti-weapons defense shield that would completely envelope Silbury.

Aspis crystals and the anti-weapons defense shields they create had been brought by the intergalactic travelers to this galaxy and had been used for defense by space craft for aeons. Aspis crystals had never—at least to anyone's knowledge—been used to create land based defensive energy shields. When Lura Sanders told Lura Redmand what she was thinking, Lura Redmand was taken totally aback, but nevertheless she listened.

"Aboard ship Aspis crystals create anti-weapons shields which completely surround the craft because nine-faceted Aspis crystals divide tornum into nine streams and those nine streams of tornum follow the lines of the exterior induced magnetic field surrounding the craft, thus forming a net of energy. 29 Planets such as Silbury have magnetic fields which surround them. I think that we can create a powerful anti-weapons defense shield around Silbury by passing extremely large amounts of tornum through a huge Aspis crystal. The nine streams of tornum would then be carried around Silbury by Silbury's magnetic field and form an energy net.

"Now that Silbury is growing up, Silbury is becoming a bigger target for the Pleiadeans. We are presumably not allowed by Essenes to put a light diffusion shield around this solar system—that could be seen as interacting with the forbidden planet—but we need to do something more to defend Silbury. An anti-weapons defense shield seems to me to be the best way, along with plans I have to help prevent low level attack by Pleiadean craft: this would be a labyrinthine pattern of magnetic fields—far away from the Horz complex. To makc this system of magnetic fields worthwhile we will also have to install land based transmagnetic anomaly detection and tracking devices, with accompanying energy cannon batteries all around Silbury.

"A tremendous amount of computational power would be required to coordinate the defense network, but I think the expense and effort worthwhile—and more than justified," Lura Sanders concluded.

Lura Redmand incorporated Lura Sanders' ideas into her plans for the western components of the Horz complex and Admiral Sanders presented her plans to the design committee (from which Gravenson continued to absent himself). They deferred to the Council of Silbury which approved all the plans. The three gigantic computers of the Hurmaze came to be.

The additional conduits for energy and water required by the construction of the western part of the Horz complex were completed. 52 An energy conduit was laid in a ditch dug straight southwestward from Dolphin Mesa to the Tor (as a straight extension of the energy conduit at whose eastern end was the Tetrahedron Crater gravitron infusion complex). Both the torinum and the tornum conduiting components of the previous dual energy conduit were also extended from Chapter One to the Tor; so that torinum could be received in the Tor from the Hurmaze by way of Chapter One, and so that tornum could be conduited from the Tor to the entire Horz complex, including the vital Tetrahedron Crater gravitron infusion complex.

A ditch dug from just southwest of Dolphin Mesa to the southwestern corner of the Hurmaze contained another dual energy conduit; this connected Chapter One, the Hurmaze and the Tor. Another ditch was dug from the southwestern corner of the Hurmaze to the city, and an energy conduit was laid to supply tornum to the city, the Crystal Palace and the Crystal Works.

The long straight water conduit which had run as far as underneath the western end of Dolphin Mesa was extended southwestward, until it was north of the Tor and then it turned southward to the northeastern corner of the Tor. At the bend, a booster pump house was constructed and the operation of two-thirds of its booster pumps was required to insure a proper flow of water to the Tor.

Two-thirds of the way along the straight water conduit, from the western edge of Dolphin Mesa to the booster pump house, a branch water conduit was laid straight northwestward to run along the western side of the Hurmaze where it bent sharply southwestward and continued to the city. Near the center of the triangular area formed by Dolphin Mesa, the Hurmaze and the Tor along the western tangent of the branch water conduit, a large booster pump house containing three large booster pumps was constructed. The operation of two-thirds of those booster pumps was required to insure a proper flow of water to the city, the Crystal Palace, the Crystal Works and the Hurmaze.

Convicts dug a ditch for energy conduit and another for water conduit from the city to the Crystal Palace and the Crystal Works. Once those conduits were laid and thoroughly tested, convicts filled in the ditches and returned the terrain to its natural state.

Once all other conduits had been laid and thoroughly tested, those ditches were also filled in and the terrain returned to its natural state.

The city—named Altea City in honor of the seed planet of the galaxy—was constructed as the westernmost component of the Horz complex. Altea City was composed of twelve main structures, varying in size from large to enormous and constructed around the conical tower. (The tower that was originally planned for the top of the high flat mesa which became the Hurmaze), now named the Tower of Ancestors as the monument to those who had gone before.

The Tower of Ancestors tapered to a very sharp point at its top, four times as high as its base diameter of 96 feet. Set in the middle of a huge square—named Hur Square—it was surrounded by four longhouses named data, information, knowledge and Wisdom.

The Tower of Ancestors was positioned so that a sight line from it passed through the mouths of the Hurmaze, across the Wall to the Tetrahedron. 53 This sight line was the most important sight line representation in the Horz complex, and was to be understood as starting in the east. In this sight line the Tetrahedron represented the Source of the Universe; the Wall the boundary between hyperdimensionality and three-dimensions; the mouths of the Hurmaze speech and therefore self-awareness; and the Tower of Ancestors: civilization. The sight line represented the unfurling process of the Universe as it is extruded from four-dimensions into three-dimensions, bringing about the birth of self-aware life and subsequently the birth of civilization.

Other sight lines from the Tower of Ancestors defined the new northern and southern ends of the Wall, by way of the energy transredimensioning pyramid on the bridge of the right nose of the Hurmaze and the southern tangent of the Hurmaze.

The long west to east axis of Altea City, and the sight line from the Tower of Ancestors to the southern tangent of the Hurmaze, were both 22.48 degrees north of due west-east. This 22.48 degree alignment was established to form a relationship to the 19.47 degree angle formed (at the apex of Hurbury between the southern end of the Wall and the Tetrahedron) because 19.47 divided by 22.48 is a near equivalent of the square root of three divided by two: the hyperdimensional component of 2.720699046, the transdimensional constant.

Hur Square was aligned differently. 54 The centers of the four longhouses were sited so that they had bearings of 041.95, 131.95, 221.95

and 311.95 degrees gyro from the Tower of Ancestors. Hur Square's north-south axis was aligned 3.05 degrees east of due north. This alignment was determined by subtracting the total of 19.47 and 22.48 from 45.

Hur Square was not a square but an enormous rectangle covering over 139 acres. Its north-south width was 2248 feet while its east-west length was 2698 feet. The ratio of 2248 to 2698 feet is a near equivalent to the ratio of 5 to 6, the metaphorical representation of the relationship between the non-living parts of the Universe and living things. The width 2248 feet was determined first in ratio with the 1947 foot length of the Silbury mile. The ratio of 1947 to 2248 feet is a near equivalent to the square root of three divided by two.

The alignments, locations and dimensions of the four longhouses were such that the sight line from the Tower of Ancestors to the northern tangent of the Hurmaze was the southeastern tangent of Wisdom, the center of which had an azimuth of 041.95 degrees gyro from the Tower of Ancestors. 54

Similarly the sight line from the Tower of Ancestors to the northern tangent of the Tor was the northeastern tangent of Data, the center of which had an azimuth of 131.95 degrees gyro from the Tower of Ancestors.

These two sight lines from the Tower of Ancestors to the northern tangents of the Hurmaze and the Tor were marked in the large hexagonal tiling of Hur Square by an inch-wide line made of bronze. The triangle formed by the Tower of Ancestors and the two points at which the two bronze sight lines reached the eastern edge of Hur Square, was a two-dimensional representation of the cone of the physical universe.

The observed top of the cone of the physical universe forms an angle of 56.4426902 degrees with the outward slope of this cone, an angle whose sine is 5/6ths, a fraction which metaphorically represents the ratio of 5 to 6, which is the representation of the relationship between the non-living parts of the Universe and living things.

To calculate the shape of the cone of the physical universe that cone must be reduced geometrically to two-dimensions, resulting in an isosceles triangle having two angles of 56.4426902 degrees and a resulting third angle of 67.1146196 degrees. 10 Therefore, it is projected that the physical universe expands outward from its zero-dimension point of origin (as extruded from four-dimensions) in a three-dimensional cone which expands transversally at an angle of 67.1146196 degrees.

By reducing those cones geometrically to two-dimensions, Waldark calculated very precisely the various angles of the conical disturbance patterns caused by the transredimensioning of energy by self-aware consciousness. He found that the first upward cone tapered outward at an angle of 55.92884964 degrees. 55 Waldark also found that the first inwardly tapering cone did so at an angle of 67.1146196 degrees from above its top, meaning that the two angles of the two-dimensional triangle representing that cone (opposite where the energy is refocused) are both 67.1146196 degrees. Waldark had no way to relate these angles to anything, but subsequent observers have noted that not only the angle 67.1146196 degrees appears in both the cones of transredimensioning and in the cone of the physical universe, but also that the ratio of 55.92884964 degrees to 67.1146196 degrees is equivalent to 5/6ths.

The isosceles triangle formed by the Tower of Ancestors and the two points at which the two bronze marked sight lines reached the eastern edge of Hur Square, had an angle of 67.1146196 degrees at the Tower; two angles of 56.4426902 degrees with the eastern edge of the square; an edge which ran perpendicular to the centerline axis the isosceles triangle representing the cone of the physical universe. Just inside the eastern edge of Hur Square and halfway between its northern and southern edges was a 12 foot high model of a Waldark thing.

Hur Square was located in the center of a very large, phi section, rectangular city site area. The twelve large to enormous structures of Altea City were arrayed somewhat geometrically with the long axis of the phi section rectangular city site area, but they were positioned and designed principally so that the interference patterns that those structures caused in the natural flow of planetary torun would virtually cancel each other out.

Following is a description of those twelve structures, starting in the northeastern corner of Altea City and progressing counterclockwise: 56

1. Ell House: The second largest structure in Altea City, a huge three sided house. Most structures on Silbury were constructed with large exterior crystal support beams from which the rest of their support network and facing panels were suspended. Ell House was constructed in this manner, its enclosed portion being three-quarters of its total height.

The three corner support beams of Ell House formed an irregular tripod above the flat roof of the structure, this roof was covered with a garden which were planted with a wide variety of flowers. Attached to the crystal beamed apex of Ell House, was an irrigation sprayer which soaked the garden early each morning. At their request, young children were frequently brought to the garden for its morning spraying so that they could run naked through the 'rain.' The design of the interior construction of Ell House and other structures on Silbury adopted the widespread use of arches and vaults.

2. Council House: Constructed very close to Ell House as the meeting place for the Council of Silbury, the administration center for the limited government of Silbury and as the Elder's office, which was always accessible.

3. Dan House: The largest structure in Altea City, an enormous four sided house.

4. The Air Port: A relatively low rectangular structure aligned with the long axis of the rectangular city site area. The Air Port was Altea City's mooring facility for air ships.

5. Zuv House: A five sided house.

6. The Gymnasion/Stadion: Located in the northwestern corner of the city site this immense structure was for sports. The Gymnasion/Stadion was rectangular with rounded ends. Along its two sides and two rounded ends was a continuous line of tall arched windows, 3600 in number, including entryways. The Gymnasion/Stadion was about one and one-half miles long and two-thirds as wide. In the northern rounded end was the grass turfed Stadion with a seating capacity of 83,333. Special lighting which had been developed aeons before, meant that grass could grow inside the Stadion. In the southern rounded end was the Gymnasion with the same seating capacity.

Although the Gymnasion and the Stadion were both very large, each covering only about one-fifth of the ends of the Gymnasion/Stadion, they were dwarfed by the size of the overall structure. Surrounding both the Gymnasion in the south and the Stadion in the north were indoor parks. The Gymnasion and the Stadion were completely enclosed by the outer facing of the Gymnasion/Stadion because the very low humidity of the combined atmosphere of Silbury might prevent some athletes from performing their best.

The extensive center section of the Gymnasion/Stadion had many facilities including sports retail stores, dressing rooms, smaller athletic facilities and several very large swimming pools. There was also a perierchomai transportation system station in the complex.

7. The Shopping Center: Located east of the Gymnasion/Stadion, this structure contained numerous stores and eating establishments.

8. Hurartu House: A four sided house.

9. The Quid Building: Located in the southwestern part of the city site area this structure was the financial facility of Altea City.

10. Philosophia House: A structure dedicated to the study of Philosophia.

11. The Legal Building: Located just south of Hur Square, this structure was the legal facility of Altea City.

12. Waldark House: Located east of Hur Square and the Waldark thing, a four sided house.

The four longhouses of Hur Square were also constructed with exterior support beams. Their six curved support beams met directly over their centers.

Structures containing offices and businesses were constructed throughout the Horz complex and some were sited as benchmarks along the many sight lines between major components of the Horz complex. The components and structures of the Horz complex were sited to repeatedly convey and reconvey the geometric representations of the Horz complex, these endeavored to respectfully thank the Source of the Universe for being the Source of the Universe.

Although some of the structures containing offices and businesses were over 30 miles from Altea City, they were only a few minutes away from the city by privately owned or community provided air ships which moored at the Air Port.

After the completion of the structures of Altea City, Dan Park was laid out surrounding Hur Square. The park meandered through much of the western two-thirds of Altea City.

Lura Redmand also designed a perierchomai transportation system for travel within Altea City and between Altea City and the Carnival, the Hurmaze and the Space Port and to near the Memorial and Stathmos.

Perierchomai transportation systems had come down to Alteans from before the time of Waldark together with the scientific alphabet and partial language Alteans came to call Hellenikos. The word 'perierchomai' means 'to go round and about' in Hellenikos.

Perierchomai transportation systems are designed to move many beings rapidly, and to do so by sending magnetically levitated cars at high speeds through hermetically sealed tubes made of crystal. Passengers get on and off at various stations along the way, but through cars are shunted around stations at which no one aboard a car wants to exit. The cars themselves are open and small, holding up to six passengers in three rows. These passengers are held safely in place by a bar which automatically closes upon leaving the embarking station. Stations and tubes may be above or below ground, but the areas of embarkation are always sealed from the outside so that the correct atmospheric pressure can be maintained inside the tubes. This requires a double set of revolving doors with a space in between for entering and leaving stations.

The perierchomai transportation system designed by Lura Redmand had its seed station under the Tower of Ancestors in the center of Hur Square. 56.1 Near the Tower of Ancestors, four entrances spaced 90 degrees apart, and spaced 45 degrees from the sightlines between the Tower of Ancestors and the four longhouses of Hur Square, allowed access by way of escalators to and from the Tower of Ancestors Seed Station.

Twelve other stations—two-thirds of them within Altea City—completed the first and only growth ring of the system designed by Lura Redmand. The eight stations within Altea City were as follows: Ell House, Dan House, Zuv House, the Air Port, the Gymnasion/Stadion, Hurartu House, Philosophia House and Waldark House. There were no stations for Council House, the Legal Building, the Quid Building, or the Shopping Center.

The other four stations were for the Carnival (located in two different sized impact craters east of Waldark House and south of Ell House); the Space Port (located in an impact crater near and south of the Hurmaze); Stathmos (located west northwest of the Hurmaze); and the Hurmaze Station, located under the site of energy tranredimensioning in the Hurmaze.

The Space Port, under the floor of the crater, was used by non-Altean Naval Service space craft. A small opening in the crater floor gave access to the Space Port below. The Carnival consisted of many things, but its main attractions were a gigantic ferris wheel in the center of the smaller crater and a very large snail shaped structure in the center of the other crater which also housed many fun rides. Stathmos, meaning 'campground' in Hellenikos, was a children's campground, and everyone had to hike to it from the Stathmos Station.

The perierchomai transportation system of Altea City—known affectionately as the Peri and so designated by station signs—was laid out so that its crystal tubes formed a grid consisting of seven triangles. 56.1 Two-thirds of the angles of three of these triangles were of significance in the layout of the Horz complex. Two triangles had an angle which represented star ships; and one of those triangles had an angle that was important when added to an adjacent angle of the next triangle. One triangle was basic to the makeup of the Universe. One triangle included the verifying angle of the system layout.

Two of the angles formed by the triangle between the Gymnasion/Stadion Station, the Tower of Ancestors Seed Station and the Zuv House Station were 22.48 degrees at the Gymnasion/Stadion Station and 45 degrees at the Tower of Ancestors Seed Station.

Two of the angles formed by the triangle between the Tower of Ancestors Seed Station, the Ell House Station and the Zuv House Station were 22.48 degrees at the Ell House Station and 90 degrees at the Tower of Ancestors Seed Station.

Two of the angles formed by the triangle between the Tower of Ancestors Seed Station, the Carnival Station and the Ell House Station were 85.36 degrees (one of the apparent two-dimensional angles of the Tor) at the Carnival Station and 45 degrees at the Tower of Ancestors Seed Station.

One of the triangles representing star ships was formed by the Ell House Station, the Hurmaze Station and the Space Port Station. The angle formed at the Hurmaze Station in that triangle was 51.84 degrees, thereby representing a star ship's height of 51.84 feet.

The angle at the Space Port Station (in the triangle formed by the Carnival Station, the Ell House station and the Space Port Station) added to the angle at the Space Port Station (in the triangle formed by the Ell House Station, the Hurmaze Station and the Space Port Station) resulted in 138.56 degrees, twice 69.28 degrees—another of the apparent two-dimensional angles of the Tor.

The Philosophia House Station was located near the southern and only entrance to Philosophia House, an entrance far away from everything else in Altea City. The triangle formed by the Gymnasion/Stadion Station, the Tower of Ancestors Seed Station and the Philosophia House Station was a 30/60/90 triangle, the triangle which, in the system layout is the triangle basic to the makeup of the Universe.

The angle at the Philosophia House Station in the triangle formed by the Carnvial Station, the Tower of Ancestors Seed Station and the Philosophia House Station was also 51.84 degrees and therefore also represented star ships.

The 72 degree angle at the Carnival Station in the triangle formed by the Carnival Station, the Ell House Station and the Space Port Station was the verifying angle of the system layout because 72 x 5 = 360, with 5 representing life and 360 representing the angular measuring system of the Universe, the 360 degree system used to lay out all the angles in the Horz complex.

In the meantime, the project to head off the impending genetic catastrophe on the forbidden planet was progressing. The Tetrahedron became the center of a well conceived and steadfast effort to formulate a genetic agent capable of preventing the eventual extinction of the beings then currently inhabiting the forbidden planet. The data, information and knowledge infused into Silbury computers by Essenes proved invaluable, without it, nothing could have been achieved.

The genetic project was begun on Silbury as a result of the Third Essene Panlogos. There was no precedent on how to conduct such a project or on how to organize it, but Alteans had always tried to keep government minimal in their lives, so a private corporation was set up with many investors and donors. A board of trustees was elected by the donors and investors with one vote each, no matter what their donation or investment. The board of trustees set policy for the genetic program. The director and associates of the genetic program carried out these policies. The program came to be modeled after Altean school systems (though school trustees were elected by everyone). The board of trustees of the genetic project chose a director and the director chose associates.

The relationship between the genetic project and the government of Silbury was simple. The government did not involve itself in any way whatsoever with the project. A vote of Alteans living on Silbury mandated that the government supply the genetic project with its requirements and things that were only available through government sources. The genetic project would pay for those supplies. A two-thirds majority vote had been required and the actual vote was over 90 percent in favor.

By the time Altea City was completed those working on the genetic project were on the verge of completing their task. They had used reconfigured male reproductive material to produce a non-living agent, which if introduced into the reproductive system of female beings of the forbidden planet would cause pregnancy. The agent was not just one agent but an overall agent divided into numerous sub-agents, all of which had a slightly different genetic makeup. These numerous sub-agents would then be introduced to numerous different females providing a wide variety of 'fathers' for the resulting children.

Great care was taken in producing this agent and its sub-agent to avoid altering in any way the current beings other than to give them male genetic diversity.

The director of the genetic project and his associates were in a meeting planning a presentation to the Council of Silbury on the conclusion of the project when an Essene holo-image suddenly appeared and said, "I am a holo-image of Essenes and I have new instructions for you. It is not enough for Alteans to simply provide genetic diversity to the beings of the planet forbidden to Alteans. Alteans must produce a genetic agent which will both provide genetic diversity and bring about a self-aware being for the planet forbidden to Alteans."

The holo-image disappeared.

So the genetic project continued with the added goal of greatly speeding up the natural evolutionary processes on the forbidden planet which were leading toward a self-aware being.

The additional requirements proved exceedingly difficult to fulfil. The breakthrough did not come for nearly a hundred years. The breakthrough was the addition of reconfigured female reproductive material to the genetic agent. The non-living agent (which now combined both female and male reconfigured reproductive material) was again divided into sub-agents having diverse genetic makeups and would produce pregnancy when introduced into the female reproductive system of the beings currently living on the forbidden planet. The introduction of this agent/sub-agent would not only resolve the problem of the lack of genetic diversity in those beings but would also result in the birth of a self-aware being in the third generation after the first introduction of the agent/sub-agent. All three intervening generations would also have to be similarly impregnated by the same agent/sub-agent.

The fifth and current director of the genetic project and her associates were in a meeting planning a presentation to the Council of Silbury on the second conclusion of the project when an Essene holo-image suddenly appeared and said, "I am an Essene holo-image and I have new instructions for you. It is not enough for Alteans to provide genetic diversity to the beings of the planet forbidden to Alteans and to introduce an agent/sub-agent which will result in a self-aware being in the fourth generation, providing that agent/sub-agent is introduced to the three succeeding generations. Alteans must produce a genetic agent which will provide genetic diversity to the beings living on the planet forbidden to Alteans, and Alteans must introduce an agent which will result in a self-aware being in one generation."

The holo-image disappeared.

The additional requirements proved beyond the capabilities of Alteans to fulfil. There was no breakthrough, only endless altering of the genetic agent and endless failure to improve the agent significantly beyond those capabilities achieved in the first hundred years of the project. Only the required introduction of the agent/sub-agent to the succeeding generations was eliminated. Those working on the genetic formula could simply not figure out a way to make a self-aware being evolve in one generation.

Nearly 100,000 more agonizing and frustrating years dragged by. Alteans working on the genetic project achieved nothing. Enthusiasm for the project had dwindled. No one wanted to work on it any longer. No one cared any more about the beings headed for extinction on the forbidden planet. Alteans had long since had a way to save those beings, but the added impossible requirement of Essenes prevented Alteans from helping those beings. The genetic project ground to a halt. Alteans lived out their lives on Silbury without thinking about the purpose for their being there. The visions of Dan 'Pan Hur,' Lura Redmand and others were gone.

About 285,000 years ago and 100,000 years after an Essene holo-image had delivered the Third Essene Panlogos—an Essene holo-image suddenly appeared on Silbury and delivered the Fourth Essene Panlogos to the Council of Silbury. It said, "I am an Essene holo-image and I am directed by Essenes to deliver to the Council of Silbury the Fourth Essene Panlogos. Alteans have discontinued work on the genetic project because it has proven impossible to fulfil all the requirements given to Alteans by Essenes. Alteans are now directed to proceed with the genetic project: which is to produce two succeeding self-aware beings, one to follow the other by about 200,000 years. Alteans are to immediately begin to develop a genetic agent which will avert the genetic catastrophe on the planet forbidden to Alteans and which will fulfil the requirements just described."

The holo-image disappeared.

The genetic project was started up again with a new board of trustees, director and associates. Previously, the genetic project had dragged on and on, with the investors realizing nothing from their investments. The project had quickly devolved to being funded by donors and there were many, mostly from Silbury, but some were from Daphlay. Thus the project had remained alive over a very long period of time and when things were active enough money was always available. Now, many more new donors gave to the genetic project and another favorable vote of around 90 percent authorized the government to sell what was required to the project. However, those working on the project could not even conceive of how to proceed, so nothing was accomplished for some years. The project was alive, but barely.

Then a breakthrough occurred that propelled the genetic project forward again.

Tommy Burr was a first year Akadeimia student on Silbury. He was studying biology and to fulfil one of the requirements of his program he decided to investigate what was known about the early development of self-aware beings as they evolved toward being both creative and linear thinkers.

Tommy Burr found the information he needed not in any computer he searched, but in a moldering and weighty tome in one of the upper shelves of the main library of the Horz complex in Chapter One.

He discovered that the natural evolutionary process of the development of self-aware beings always follows the same pattern: a self-aware transitional being develops creative-thinking and then evolves into another species of self-aware being which develops linear-thinking. In order to function and survive the resulting fully developed self-aware being must rely on both the creative-thinking developed by its immediate predecessor in the evolutionary chain and on its own species' development of linear-thinking.

He presented his findings to his teacher, a teacher who was so intrigued by what she read that she immediately forwarded Tommy Burr's report to the current director of the genetic project. The director of the project read Tommy Burr's report that very day and the mist cleared from before his eyes.

"So now we know," he said to himself.

Chapter 6

The Interferers

Well over a million years before the settling on Silbury by Alteans (over 1.6 million years ago) a Pleiadean scout craft on random patrol in the outer reaches of the galaxy happened upon the solar system containing both the planet later to be called Silbury by Alteans, and the planet long since called the planet of preparation by Essenes. After passing through one of the two approach points of that solar system, the Pleiadean craft proceeded directly toward the outer limits of the solar system and then turned back inward, making a cursory 'inspection' of the outer gigantic, gas-filled planets of the solar system and then of a particularly misshapen red colored planet. The next planet inward was found to be more interesting.

The mission of this Pleiadean scout craft was identical to that of numerous other scout craft which had randomly searched the outer reaches of the galaxy for hundreds of millions of years: look and report.

Therefore this particular Pleiadean scout craft looked at the blue-green planet of preparation and reported. It reported that the planet had enormous quantities of both salt and fresh water; a breathable atmosphere; a wide variety of plant life; both its waters and its land had diverse animal life. And there were being-like creatures on the planet which appeared to be very intelligent when compared with all other animals. It also reported the planet's size, its periods of rotation and revolution, the presence and specifications of a natural satellite and the planet's distance from its star.

These data were transmitted to Pleiadean naval headquarters, as the scout craft left the vicinity of the blue-green planet of preparation on its way out of that particular solar system and onwards, randomly searching the outer reaches of the galaxy. The inbound message was routinely passed to Pleiadean intelligence where it was scanned by the duty officer, who routed it to the department which handled data-gathering reports from the outer reaches of the galaxy. Two weeks later that department's duty officer glanced at the report and routed it to the third deputy commander. The third deputy also glanced at it and routed it to the second deputy who glanced at it and routed it to the first deputy who glanced at it and routed it to the department commander. The department commander scanned the report and routed it to the commander of Pleiadean intelligence. The commander of Pleiadean intelligence read the report and conjured up a scheme.

At his next routinely scheduled briefing with the Pleiadean emperor, the commander of Pleiadean intelligence gave the emperor a summary of the report. He mentioned the scout craft on random patrol in the outer reaches of the galaxy, the finding of a planet which had a breathable atmosphere, water and both plant and animal life. The commander wondered if he might personally oversee a return to that planet to investigate further. The emperor nodded his approval and the two turned to the next item on the intelligence commander's briefing list.

About a month later the commander of Pleiadean intelligence Carl Halverson left the Pleiades aboard a Pleiadean naval craft captained by Halverson's legal son, his daughter's husband Lee Arnholt. Also aboard was another legal son of Halverson, Barth Holbert, a member of the Pleiadean institute of biology. Halverson had revealed his scheme to his daughters' husbands and they had both immediately agreed to join him on the expedition.

Unknown to the rest of the officers and crew, Halverson's wife and two daughters were hidden in his personal stateroom.

Halverson had not invited any of his four sons. They were "totally irresponsible" he had screamed at his wife when she had dared to suggest "her boys" be allowed to accompany them.

Within hours the craft arrived at its destination and the search for the "being-like creatures" who appeared to be "very intelligent" began. These were the currently developing beings of the planet of preparation who were evolving toward the eventual emergence of a free-willed self-aware being. After completing a planet-wide scanning, the Pleiadeans returned to the area with the greatest concentration of these creatures: the eastern central section of a large continent which was almost equally divided by the planet's equator. Having pin-pointed several fairly large gatherings of these beings through visual search (their craft was totally invisible behind its gravitational shield) the Pleiadeans swooped down on these unsuspecting groupings one after another, spraying the creatures with a non-lethal but extremely debilitating sickness inducing gas.

Having completed this procedure the Pleiadeans returned to the area of each grouping whereupon they shot all the creatures with energy pistols, except for young females whom the Pleiadeans believed would be capable of giving birth. These females were herded aboard the Pleiadean craft and kept under armed guard in the craft's hanger bay while Holbert inseminated them one after another with sperm from Halverson which had been collected over the preceding month. The thoroughly cowed females were drugged before being taken to the craft's mess decks for the insemination procedure, after which they were carried from the craft and deposited in a group nearby.

When the Pleiadeans were finished they took off and settled in a more equitable climate, establishing Halverson's private empire in an area he had already selected during their preliminary planet-wide scanning. 57 Halverson's private empire was located between two rivers which flowed southeasterly into a shallow gulf, some 2500 miles north of where he had left a large number of females pregnant, or so he hoped.

After establishing his own secret empire Halverson intended to return south a few years later to see how his 'experiment' was proceeding. Halverson believed that it would result in the creation of new, reasonably intelligent creatures on this distant from the Pleiades planet. Halverson thought that the indigenous "being-like creatures" had bodies remarkably similar to Pleiadeans. It was only their heads and faces which were misshapen. Halverson hoped the cross-breeding he had just accomplished would create creatures who were both more intelligent and better looking. In any case he fully intended to make slaves of these sons and daughters.

But Halverson and his family never did return to the scene of their horrific butchery and forced impregnation of the developing beings on the planet of preparation. Halverson, Arnholt, Holbert and their wives lived for a while in splendor in Halverson's private empire between the two rivers. The other officers and crew of the Pleiadean craft worked hard carving out that empire, but they had no wives with them. Eventually they revolted, executed the six would-be imperialists and murdered the three young children of Arnholt and Holbert and their wives.

When the officers and crew attempted to take off in the Pleiadean space craft, that craft exploded.

Pleiadean authorities never knew the fate of Halverson and his space craft, for Halverson had eradicated all data before leaving. So he and his craft were simply listed as missing after a data search failed to find anything whatsoever concerning the solar system and planet previously discovered during the random search. A routine appointment was made to replace Halverson as commander of Pleiadean intelligence; Halverson's wife's "boys" noted that their mother was also missing and fought over how they should divide up their father's estate.

Pleiadeans have never known of the brutalities heaped upon the developing beings of the planet of preparation by Halverson and his 'expedition.'

Essenes have always known all about Halverson, Arnholt and Holbert and their deeds.

Essenes observe everything of importance that takes place within the galaxy. Essenes were not surprised to witness the deceit, treachery and self-aggrandizement of Halverson. The Pleiadean empire was founded on such behavior but it nevertheless managed to survive. Even though Halverson's attempt to establish his own private empire would not have been tolerated by his emperor—had he been discovered—such a blatant manifestation of deceit, treachery and self-aggrandizement was only a minor extrapolation of 'normal' Pleiadean behavior.

Essenes had insured that no Pleiadean of the Halverson 'expedition' remained alive.

Essenes observed the beings who resulted from the brutal interference of the Halverson 'expedition.' Although these beings were much more developed than their predecessors (who became extinct, mostly as a result of the Halverson 'expedition') the beings resulting from Halverson's interference suffered from an irreversible genetic flaw: the offspring of the females who had been brutally inseminated with Halverson's sperm could only mate with other offspring from that same group of mothers, and they all had the same father.

Essenes knew that unless something was done to correct this catastrophic genetic flaw, inbreeding would eventually destroy the emergence of free-willed self-aware life on the planet of preparation.

Essenes continued to watch and observe. Essenes were not allowed to stop the interferers but when the time was right, Essenes took action to execute the accomplices of the perpetrators.

Chapter Seven

The Lads

The director of the genetic project who had read Tommy Burr's report—and immediately coopted him into the program—was correct in thinking that a major breakthrough had just taken place. Alteans of Silbury were unable to fulfill their required task to both correct genetic problems and to speed up evolution on the forbidden blue-green planet. Each time they were on the verge of doing so, an Essene holo-image would suddenly appear with new requirements.

This situation dragged on for nearly 48,000 years.

With the assistance of Tommy Burr thc agent was modified within a period of a few years to meet the new requirements of the Fourth Essene Panlogos.

The director of the genetic project and his associates, including Tommy Burr, were planning a presentation to their board of trustees when an Essene holo-image interrupted that meeting and said, "I am a holo-image of Essenes and I have new instructions for you. It is not enough for Alteans to fulfill the requirements of the Fourth Essene Panlogos. Alteans must produce an agent which not only fulfills the requirements of the Fourth Essene Panlogos, but an agent which also insures that the creative and linear-thinking self-aware beings who are to be the end result of that agent have great diversity of both culture and physical characteristics."

The holo-image disappeared.

In possession of Tommy Burr's important breakthrough information concerning the development of self-aware beings toward becoming both creative and linear thinkers, the director of the genetic project and his associates decided to make a thorough search of computers and libraries on Daphlay and Silbury, to see what could be found with regard to both the physical and cultural diversity of self-aware beings. They located much data and information which they entered into computers in the Tetrahedron.

These Alteans found that although all self-aware beings are basically the same physically, there had always existed a great diversity of physical appearances among them. This diversity was not only that which was apparent to Alteans on a daily basis: different physical statures, facial features, eye colors, hair colors and types; it included differences of anatomy and skin color.

Those working on this part of the genetic project very quickly developed several sub-sub-agents to fulfill the Essene requirement for the great diversity of physical characteristics.

As for the requirement for great cultural diversity, the director and his associates felt it should be dealt with in two stages: first they needed to establish a way of infusing cultural diversity into sub-sub-sub-agents and secondly they had to determine what cultural diversities to infuse. The information contained in the computers in the Tetrahedron pertaining to cultural diversity was extensive. That information would have to be carefully synthesized and then the board of trustees would have to make the choices.

This stage was never reached. Alteans could not figure out a way of infusing any cultural diversity into a sub-sub-sub-agent. Alteans working on the genetic project achieved nothing. Enthusiasm for the project had dwindled. No one wanted to work on it any longer. No one cared any more about those beings headed for extinction on the forbidden planet. Alteans had long since had a way to save those beings, but the latest additional requirement of Essenes prevented Alteans from helping those beings. The genetic project ground to a halt. Alteans lived out their lives on Silbury without thinking about the purpose for their being there. The visions of Dan 'Pan Hur,' Lura Redmand and others were gone.

Nearly 48,000 agonizing and frustrating years had dragged by, following the Fourth Essene Panlogos. Until one day, the Council of Silbury was in session when an Essene holo-image suddenly appeared and said, "I am an Essene holo-image and I am directed by Essenes to deliver to you the Fifth Essene Panlogos. Alteans have discontinued work on the genetic project because it has proven impossible to fulfill all the requirements given to Alteans by Essenes. Essenes have infused computers in the Tetrahedron with those things which will enable Alteans to complete the genetic project. Alteans are to immediately resume working on the genetic project."

The holo-image disappeared.

The genetic project was immediately started up again with a new board of trustees, director and associates. Many more new donors subscribed to the genetic project and another favorable vote of over 90 percent authorized the government to supply the project.

Three days after the Essene holo-image delivered its message to the Council of Silbury, an Altean Naval star ship on patrol near one of the two approach points of the solar system containing both Silbury and the forbidden blue-green planet received a message. Lana Manpure, wife of Lieutenant Mark Manpure, one of the star ship's officers, had just delivered the couple's third son. She had named him Cary.

While the genetic project went forward once again Cary Manpure grew from infancy to childhood.

Cary Manpure lived in Zuv House with his family, and when he was about five and a half years old, he began Kindergarten in the Zuv House primary school.

Altea City had been constructed to house up to a million inhabitants and after the initial influx of new settlers, following the completion of the western part of the Horz complex, the Altean community of Silbury preferred to remain relatively small and voluntarily maintained a birth rate at about that level.

Due to the life span of Alteans lasting over 200 years, two-thirds of the population of Altea City was older than the traditional retirement age of 72. Therefore, at any given time, out of a total population of around one million on Silbury there were about 175,000 children and adolescents, from newly born through age 20. Almost everyone lived in the five crystal houses, which varied greatly in size. Zuv House and Hurartu House were the smallest with designed maximum capacities of 83,333 inhabitants each. The other three houses had capacities which were multiples of 83,333: Waldark House twice 83,333; Ell House three times 83,333; and Dan House five times 83,333. Altogether there were 12 multiples of 83,333 as the designed maximum population of Altea City.

There were also 12 different school systems, each system composed of one primary school, one middle school and one high school. The number of school systems for any given house corresponded to its multiples of 83,333. Each school system was named: Zuv House was Zuv; Hurartu House was Renart; the two Waldark House systems were Transtea and Hartea; the three of Ell House were Zootea, Transpan and Hertea; the five belonging to Dan House were Hermur, Zooher, Hurtea, Pantea and Panher. Two-thirds of these names were derived from the important syllables brought to this galaxy by the intergalactic pioneers. Of the remaining third—two, Hermur and Hurtea, were place names from Altean history; two were named by Alteans of Silbury in honor of ancient Alteans: Melina Renart and Zuv Lon Ell.

All 12 school systems were therefore about the same size, thereby allowing all to compete against each other more or less equally.

Since there were always about 83,333 Alteans living in the attendance area of any given school system, there were always approximately 9000 students in the three schools making up a complete system—about 700 per grade. A primary school consisted of a Kindergarten plus six grades. Each grade had 21 different classes; so a primary school had about 147 classes and 4900 students at any one time. The middle and high schools of all 12 school systems always had three grades and therefore about 2100 students each.

Even though there were 21 classes in each grade of the Zuv Primary School, Cary Manpure and his cousin Vicky Manpure always found themselves in the same class. Which was a pity as the two did not get along with each other. Cary thought Vicky was always trying to outdo him; Vicky thought Cary was always trying to outdo her.

One time Cary Manpure said to his cousin Vicky, "Why do you think you're so smart?"

"I don't think I'm so smart," she retaliated. "Data gathered over billions of years proves males are only 98 percent as smart as females."

Cary Manpure tried to have the last word, "That is an average with a very large sample. I'm just talking about you."

Vicky's older brother Dan, however, was Cary's favorite. Dan Manpure had been born with a physical disability—his leg bones had never formed properly so he had to wear braces to be able to walk. Dan Manpure was an artist beyond compare, and Dan Manpure was a being beyond compare.

Vicky and Dan's parents were Anna and Arnhold Manpure, Arnhold being the brother of Cary's father.

Cary Manpure's home life was ideal and he dearly loved his mother, father and two brothers Ames and Frank.

Cary Manpure's mother was from the clan Burr and she was a direct descendant of Tommy Burr. In accordance with Altean tradition all three of her sons had Burr as a middle name. The clan Burr was among the large group of settlers who had come to Silbury from Daphlay when the Horz complex was being completed almost 150,000 years before. Dan Manty had arrived at the same time. The clan Manpure had descended from Dan Manty, and the name Dan, always very popular with Alteans, was always given to the first born grandson of each alternating generation. Cary Manpure's grandfather was named Dan according to this family tradition.

Lana Manpure named her son Cary after her friend Milly Jackman's son Cary, six months old at the time of Cary Manpure's birth. This was followed six months later by the birth of Rena, Milly and (another Dan) Dan Jackman's daughter. Rena Jackman and Vicky Manpure became best friends. However, Rena only appeared in Cary Manpure's class occasionally. A year after Rena was born, the Jackmans had another son whom they named Tommy. The Jackman family also lived in Zuv House.

When Cary Manpure was in the third grade, he signed up to take an art class for primary school lasses and lads given by his cousin Dan Manpure. Cary Jackman and Vicky Manpure did the same.

As it turned out the two Carys and two other lads (whom they did not know at the time) ended up working on a joint art project. All four of them had to spend a lot of time together outside class, working on this project and that is how they all came to be inseparable friends.

The two other lads were Tommy Untiman and Terry Wellton.

Terry Wellton was very tall and two years older than Cary Manpure. He had an older brother named Hal and his parents were Sara and Mark Wellton. The Welltons lived in Hurartu House.

Tommy Untiman was six months younger than Cary Manpure and lived in Waldark House with his mother, Marta Untiman. She was very embittered and claimed that her husband had been killed in a mining accident about the time of Tommy's birth, and that she had moved from Daphlay to Silbury shortly thereafter to escape from the sad memories.

By trying to prevent Tommy from participating in activities that interested him, Marta Untiman vented her bitterness on her son. She was very upset when she learned that Tommy had signed up for the art class without asking her permission, but he insisted to such an extent that she eventually relented.

The lads worked on the art project alternately at the Jackmans, the Manpures and the Welltons. Marta Untiman would not allow them into her place. Tommy Untiman got along especially well with Milly Jackman, who became a second mother to him during his formative years. Her deep interest in Philosophia awakened in him an incredibly strong desire for study.

The lads became a unit of four friends, which bonded even more tightly together when their group art project, lead by Vicky Manpure won first prize. Especially as it had not been judged by her brother Dan but by a group of Akadeimia art students. However, the unit of four friends did have one problem; there were two Carys and a Terry, which, from afar, could sound like Cary. They drew lots to decide who should make up secret nicknames for whom; and so it was that Terry Wellton named Tommy Untiman 'Pazzy'—an old word from a previous galaxy for a short haircut—and certainly applicable to Tommy. Cary Jackman named Terry Wellton 'Fliff' as Terry was tall, and 'fliff' was an old word from another ancient galaxy meaning 'measuring stick.' Cary Manpure named Cary Jackman 'Buff,' meaning 'a stack of old books.' This phrase, taken from some previous galaxy's forgotten language, was often used by Alteans and indeed Cary Jackman was always studying. Tommy Untiman named Cary Manpure 'Ollun' which he made up from the expression 'all in one,' and meaning that Cary Manpure knew something about everything. Cary Manpure did not think that he knew something about everything, but rather that he knew a lot of somewhat worthless things about obscure subjects. I am just that way, Cary Manpure thought, and I enjoy knowing these worthless things.

No one else knew these names, because the unit of four friends only used them amongst themselves.

Even though Cary Jackman was always studying, he found time to be very good at athletics, especially the age old game of golf. He and Cary Manpure had played golf a few times before the formation of the unit of four friends, so when they no longer had to spend their free time working on the joint art project, the two Carys decided to invite their two new friends to play their first rounds of golf with them. Terry was delighted, but Tommy was afraid his mother would not allow him to play. The lads therefore enlisted Milly Jackman's help, for she had a way about her. In fact she helped Tommy many times. And on this occasion too, Marta Untiman gave in to Milly Jackman's persuasive way.

The seven golf links of Silbury were all in Dan Park which covered an expansive area of the western two-thirds of Altea City. Early one morning, the lads of the unit of four friends played their first game of golf together. With the exception of Cary Jackman, they were terrible. Though they did laugh a lot. Afterwards they walked to the Shopping Center and had a snack at a place that was to become their favorite eatery. Later that day, Cary Manpure invited Tommy to sleep over. Tommy was afraid of that too, but Cary convinced him to come along to his place for a while anyway. When the two lads arrived, Lana Manpure was at home, so Cary asked her to call Tommy's mother to see if Tommy could stay and sleep over. She did and he did. As a result, a very strong sub-unit was formed within the unit of four friends.

None of the four friends were in the same class or the same grade. Only the two Carys were even in the same school system. So they got together after school, usually at their favorite eatery in the late afternoon. When they could, they invariably played golf. Tommy Untiman often slept over at Cary Manpure's place. Marta Untiman at first tried to restrict her son from this routine, but eventually gave in to the ways of Lana Manpure and Milly Jackman. The mothers of the two Carys took responsibility for Tommy's well being as if he was their son. The lads of the unit of four friends were not permitted to go about freely. They were allowed to enjoy themselves within the limits of their established routine—which could only be varied with special permission—as long as they maintained good deportment and good study habits.

Finally, they said, they talked their parents into letting them go alone to the Carnival. The two Carys boarded a Peri car at the Zuv House Station and designated the Hurartu House Station as their destination. They were automatically routed there, passing around the Air Port Station and the Tower of Ancestors Seed Station, and Terry Wellton joined them in their car. Next they designated the Waldark House Station and they sped eastward around the Tower of Ancestors Seed Station to the Waldark House Station where Tommy Untiman jumped into the car. The four of them then went together the short distance to the Carnival Station.

You only rode in a car with those whom you knew and there were therefore six separate waiting line areas at Peri stations. A seventh area, with no line, was for those waiting to join others already aboard Peri cars.

Later in the day when he became bored with the Carnival, Cary Manpure devised a Peri car game whereby they would race one another to the Gymnasion/Stadion Station by way of the Hurmaze Station and any other five stations. Both teams of two had to stop at all six stations and one of the two in each car had to retrieve a system map from each station at which they stopped. They drew lots to see who would have to go by way of the Ell House Station and the Stathmos Station, and who would get to go by way of the Space Port Station. 56.1

Cary Manpure and Tommy Untiman jumped into their car having drawn the longer, Ell House routing.

Cary Jackman and Terry Wellton sped eastward around the Space Port Station, arriving just ahead of their opponents at the Hurmaze Station.

After they had both retrieved station system maps from holders outside the double set of revolving doors of the Hurmaze Station, Cary Manpure overtook Cary Jackman in a race on foot back to their cars, squeezed ahead of him and took off with Tommy Untiman, leaving Cary Jackman looking on from the loading platform.

Cary Manpure and Tommy Untiman won the race. The unit of four friends walked together to their favorite eatery in the Shopping Center, and the losers hosted refreshments. Later, they walked to Hurartu house and while Terry Wellton rode up an elevator to his family's living quarters, the other three re-entered the Peri system. Tommy Untiman stood in one line and took a car to Waldark House while the two Carys stood in two line and rode together back to Zuv House.

It was only a few weeks after their first golf game and just days after their first unsupervised excursion to the carnival together that the Tor was rocked by explosions. The unit of four friends were all together at the celebration in Hur Square, along with their families, and Marta Untiman. The Welltons were becoming friends of the Manpures and the Jackmans, who were already good friends; but this was the first time any of them ever met Marta Untiman.

Tears streamed down Cary Manpure's cheeks when he saw the rising smoke. He was very upset and angry. Nine-year-old Cary Manpure, and everyone else, knew that the Pleiadeans had to be responsible for the catastrophe, and so everyone was also very frightened. The ceremonies immediately broke up. While his family returned home, Altean Naval Service Commander Mark Manpure reported immediately to the Bastion.

Chapter Eight

Sabotage

Like Vicky Manpure, Tom Roon was always in the same class as Cary Manpure, and the two boys did not get along either. This was not for the same reason that Cary and Vicky failed to get along, but simply because Tom Roon was a lad with whom it was hard for anyone to be friends. By contrast Tom Roon's sister Sara, a year younger than he, was a delight to be with and also very beautiful.

Dan Sardman was Sara Roon's age and they grew up to be good friends later to became sweethearts too. Dan had a brother named Clark, who was the same age as Vicky Manpure and Cary Manpure. Clark and Dan's parents were Margina and Kurt Sardman, the family lived in Zuv House. Clark Sardman was also someone with whom it was hard to get along. Clark Sardman was friends with Tom Roon. Cary Manpure and Dan Sardman liked one another a lot.

Tom and Sara Roon lived with their parents Avena and Kirk Roon in Zuv House, very near to Cary Manpure. Although Cary Manpure did not get along with Tom Roon, the four parents were good friends. Kirk Roon was the director of Roon Mining Company, which mined gold.

Roon Mining was apparently successful, but that success was being jeopardized by Kirk Roon's younger brother Hal. He had used his position as the company's director of finance to secretly siphon company funds in support of his particular life style.

Hal Roon was desperate. He had thus far been able to keep his misdeeds from his brother, but he was aware that very soon the company's director would discover something amiss. Hal Roon knew he would have to act to stave off the personal disaster which would result from the impending collapse of Roon Mining. Hal Roon could not bring himself to action and squandered much of his time avoiding any decision making. He flitted away his work day. At night he took to reading everything, anything to pass away the time. His once active life style dwindled to nothing but mindless reading.

Then late one night Hal Roon read something that conjured up a notion in his mind. In learning about the horrific war which resulted in the destruction of Altea, Hal Roon was very interested to discover how the outer planets of Altean territory had come under attack by Pleiadeans. He came to the conclusion there must have been little or no damage to the planets themselves, as the Pleiadeans had simply gassed everyone. If the report was accurate, Hal Roon thought, then the structures on those planets must be still fairly well intact. If so, then their energy transproduction complexes must still contain huge amounts of gold. Hal Roon looked through the listing of those planets and found the one that had been the most thoroughly developed—Colchis.

Colchis was to have been the temporary home of the intergalactic migrators while they searched this galaxy for a seed planet. While initial preparations were underway to make Colchis habitable, scout craft discovered the blue-green planet which was to become the seed planet of the galaxy. While some migrators began the process of forming a union with the indigenous beings of the seed planet, others continued to develop Colchis. Colchis, Hal Roon thought, is where I will go, and Colchis will provide me with gold.

Roon Mining was perfectly equipped for the undertaking envisioned by Hal Roon, and the next morning he boarded one of the company's exploration vessels at the Space Port and told its captain he had two hours to prepare for flight. He added that as this was going to be an exploration for ore, before accepting a possible new contract offered by the Council of Silbury, he, Hal Roon, as director of finance, would be aboard as observer. While the vessel was being readied, Hal Roon took the Peri to Waldark House Station, walked to Roon Mining headquarters and spoke with his brother Kirk. This time he said that he had just received information concerning the discovery of a significant lode of gold by a company exploration vessel, and he personally wished to evaluate how much gold might be there. Hal Roon reminded his older brother of the problems they had endured in the past, due to incorrect assessments of such finds, that he, the director of finance should thoroughly investigate this lode before they committed company resources to it. Kirk Roon agreed with his brother and wished him well.

As ordered by Roon Mining's director of finance, the company exploration vessel took off from the Space Port of Silbury and took about an hour and a half to reach the outer limit of solar system light speed (about 800 million miles above the solar system's ecliptic plane). From there it increased its speed to near interstellar light speed and some eight hours later, following its braking procedure, arrived at one of the approach points of the solar system containing Colchis. About an hour after completing the rethickening process on its number nine thruster doors, the vessel approached and began orbiting the planet.

For over a quarter of a million years, ever since the Pleiadean Halbert Sarkneson had happened upon the stricken planet and restarted its graviton infusing spinning disks, Colchis had been the private empire of the family Sarkneson. For over a quarter of a million years, the eldest son of the family Sarkneson had lived two lives: one life as servitor of the Pleiadean emperor, the other as absolute master of this own empire.

The private empire of the family Sarkneson was very secret. No one outside the private empire other than father, eldest son and a few loyal retainers, had ever heard of it for anyone who even came close to mentioning its existence disappeared. On Colchis the family Sarkneson maintained a fortress. Set into the side of a deep canyon, it had been built by slave laborers drawn from Pleiadean work projects which the family Sarkneson supervised for the Pleiadean emperor. A well equipped defense unit of over a thousand men protected the fortress from the slaves who worked for the Sarkneson empire—nearly five thousand of them. It was also capable of defending the planet from unwelcome intruders. The defense unit consisted of descendants of the private expedition team that Halbert Sarkneson had taken to Colchis, and included Halbert Sarkneson's direct descendants, through his sons' offspring. The mothers of male offspring fathered by these defenders of the Sarkneson empire were rewarded by an 'elevation' from slavery to a relative freedom.

The gold of Colchis had made the family Sarkneson incredibly wealthy. They had used that wealth to build their empire and those who defended it were well paid. The private empire afforded virtually unlimited wealth, luxury and power to each succeeding head of the family Sarkneson and his eldest son. The private empire offered considerable wealth, luxury and power to its defenders. The private empire kept those who worked it in miserable slavery.

Minutes before the Roon Mining exploration vessel reached one of the two approach points of the solar system containing the private empire of the family Sarkneson, the current head of the family had just landed within the confines of his fortress on Colchis. Garth Sarkneson was angry; he angered easily, but had never been as livid as he was right now. His retainers and guards scattered before him. As he entered his private chambers Suzy Bibbens, his mistress, tried to kiss him but he pushed her aside roughly.

That morning, Garth Sarkneson had been at a meeting of Pleiadean notables and the Pleiadean emperor. The Pleiadean emperor had belittled Sarkneson in front of his contemporaries. No emperor—nobody—was allowed to belittle Garth Sarkneson. He seethed quietly and as soon as the meeting finished, immediately left imperial headquarters, boarded his personal space craft and ordered his retainers to take him to Colchis. Throughout the 12 hour trip Sarkneson fumed and vainly sought to conger up a scheme whereby he could take his revenge on Xung Halbert Mavor, the Pleiadean emperor. Unable to think of a plan, Sarkneson grew even angrier.

Only a few minutes after Sarkneson entered the fortress, the defense unit's transmagnetic anomaly detection and tracking devices detected an unidentified object. It was entering the solar system on a course that would bring that object toward Colchis. The watch commander was alerted and he immediately called the defense unit's commander, informing him of the appearance of the object approaching them. Since the establishment of the Sarkneson empire, no craft other than Sarkneson craft had ever entered their solar system. The unit commander hesitated to inform Sarkneson of the unknown object because he wanted to be personally sure the detection was valid. So the unit commander told the watch commander to await his arrival at the surveillance center and that he would then take the appropriate action.

It took the unit commander nearly five minutes to reach the surveillance center and by that time the unknown object was only a few minutes away from Colchis and was slowing as if to go into orbit around the planet. Still the unit commander hesitated. Perhaps this was a Sarkneson craft having communications difficulties. The unit commander finally decided that even if it was, he would have to call an alert. As the Roon Mining exploration vessel went into orbit around Colchis, the Sarkneson empire's defense unit commander sounded the emergency alarm, sending the entire unit to defense stations.

Jolted out of his thoughts by the blaring alarm, Sarkneson reached for the nearest communication device. The unit commander explained the situation to Sarkneson.

"I'm coming up!" Sarkneson shouted.

The unknown object was clearly in orbit by the time Sarkneson could view the plot. He glared at the unit commander as he spoke, "Why was I not informed of this intrusion sooner? Do I have to wait for the emergency alarm to learn of possible threats? If this thing, whatever it is, had been intent on attacking us, the first I would have heard of it would have been the sound of walls crashing about me."

Sarkneson drew his energy pistol and shot the unit commander dead.

"Send three scout craft to intercept that thing. Use gas, but not death-inducing gas. I want them alive," the Pleiadean ordered the watch commander.

With that Sarkneson turned and left the surveillance center, returning to his quarters where he was much more receptive to the advances of Suzy Bibbens. Sarkneson had still not thought of a way to strike back at Xung Halbert Mavor, but he somehow felt that the timely arrival of the intruder might lead to something interesting. That calmed his anger and Suzy Bibbens sated his sexual drive, at least temporarily.

Hal Roon was so intent on finding gold that he had not thought of switching on his transmagnetic anomaly detection and tracking device. The three Sarkneson scout ships approached the Roon Mining vessel and when in position, each drove its single armored spear through the vessel's hulls. As they pierced the interior of the ship, debilitating gas was released from the spear tips and the occupants of the Roon Mining vessel were completely overcome.

At the same time, a quick drying mastic was released along the shafts of the spears and this virtually instantly sealed the shafts to the edges of the holes in the hulls of the Roon Mining vessel.

With their speared victim between them, the three scout ships returned to base. Sarkneson's forces then broke into the Roon Mining vessel, removed its unconscious occupants to a dungeon, where they were shackled to a wall by their arms and legs.

The watch commander reported to Sarkneson that his orders had been carried out and that a space vessel containing 20 occupants had been captured.

"Bring the one who was in charge of that vessel to me immediately," ordered the Pleiadean.

When Roon faced Sarkneson he crumbled under the fierce gaze of the Pleiadean. Sarkneson, disgusted by the weakling before him, demanded who he was.

Roon had no idea whom he was facing, but he knew he could only be a Pleiadean. Therefore, he did not respond.

The lack of response enraged Sarkneson, so he struck Roon's face with the back of his hand. Roon fell to the floor, blood spurting from his nose. Sarkneson picked Roon up and shook him with both hands.

"Tell me who you are!" screamed the Pleiadean.

Roon did not know what to do. He knew that he should not divulge that he was an Altean, but he was terrified of the man berating and beating him. "If you don't hit me again," ventured Roon. "I will tell you."

Sarkneson could hardly abide such a response, but managed to restrain his urge to beat Roon senseless. "Speak," he commanded.

Roon's voice cracked as he blurted out his answer, "My name is Hal Roon. I am director of finance of Roon Mining Company. We are here exploring for gold."

Sarkneson did not flinch as Roon's words seared through him. Roon had not said so, but it was clear to Sarkneson that this man was an Altean, even though ALL Alteans had been dead for a quarter of a million years. Sarkneson now knew that this man would provide him with whatever he needed to gain revenge over the Pleiadean emperor, Xung Halbert Mavor.

Sarkneson turned to Suzy Bibbens who stood nearby. "Attend to our guest," he ordered. "Be sure to take care of his needs."

With that Sarkneson strode out of the room and into his private quarters where even Suzy Bibbens was not permitted.

The next day Sarkneson sent for Roon. Roon was tired, not from the rigors of incarceration, but from the delights of Suzy Bibbens. He was beginning to wonder what this place really was.

"I need access to your computers," demanded Sarkneson as Roon stood before him.

Roon had been so engrossed in his thoughts he was totally taken aback by this request. He had already divulged too much, he knew, but what he had said, not only saved his skin, it had brought him pleasure. Roon decided to use the same tactic as before, only this time he would ask for more.

"If you help me," Roon said boldly, "I will give you the access code."

Sarkneson could barely tolerate such an answer, but the Pleiadean restrained his urge to execute his captive on the spot. Sarkneson had done a lot of thinking during the night and he was doubly sure that this Altean was going to be useful to him. "Speak," he ordered. "If there is anything useful in your computers then perhaps we can come to a mutually agreeable resolution to your visit here."

Roon's mind raced. Perhaps he had stumbled onto something even greater than he had anticipated. Perhaps he could not only salvage his life, but also come away with a fortune.

"Before I give you the access code," Roon ventured, "I want you to know there are many things of interest in those computers. I would therefore expect that your proposed 'mutually agreeable resolution' includes remuneration."

The instant Sarkneson heard those words he knew that he was dealing with a man who would do anything for money. Sarkneson would dole out wealth to this man just as long as this man's information and assistance pleased him.

"I meant just exactly that," the Pleiadean lied.

When Sarkneson had completed his investigation of the information contained in the computers of the Roon Mining exploration vessel his mind surged ahead. He learned of the exact location of Silbury, much about the Altean settlement there and that Silbury was a relatively small settlement, as the majority of Alteans lived on a planet called Daphlay.

He did not learn the location of Daphlay.

"Where is Daphlay?" Sarkneson demanded of Roon.

"I don't know," answered Roon. "The location of Daphlay is a closely held secret of the Altean Naval Service. Only specially assigned Altean Naval Service personnel are allowed to navigate civilian space craft. Only by having six of these members of the navy aboard can any space craft go anywhere."

"Do you mean to tell me," the Pleiadean roared, "that you had six members of the Altean navy aboard your vessel when you came here?"

"Yes," Roon responded.

Sarkneson leaped at Roon and grabbed him by the throat choking him. "Do not lie to me!" Sarkneson screamed. "The Altean navy would not put six of their personnel aboard every civilian ship. Tell me where Daphlay is!"

Roon did not know what to do. He knew nothing more than he had already told his interrogator. He gasped for breath and was barely able to respond, "I don't know where Daphlay is. I am telling the truth about the navy men. They are in uniform. Go and look."

Roon's answer only enraged Sarkneson further. Now that the Pleiadean knew that Alteans were living on a planet called Daphlay he was obsessed with finding that planet. Once found, he—Garth Sarkneson—would personally destroy the last of the Alteans and permanently finish the task which everyone considered accomplished a quarter of a million years before. Then and only then, would he—Garth Sarkneson—tell Xung Halbert Mavor and the Pleiadean notables that Alteans had been living and multiplying for the past quarter million years, but that he—Garth Sarkneson—had personally exterminated them; and then he would be master of two empires!

Sarkneson drew his energy pistol and aimed it at Roon. "You have ten seconds to tell me where Daphlay is, or you die," the Pleiadean screeched.

Roon became crazed. He could not answer. He fell to the floor and began babbling gibberish.

Sarkneson looked down at Roon and was about to fire when he suddenly changed his mind. Perhaps this man is telling the truth, he thought. If I kill him I gain nothing. With him alive I can go to the Altean outpost planet and find out for myself where Daphlay is. Then I will carry out my other plans.

"Get up!" the Pleiadean shouted at Roon.

Seeing he was not dead yet Roon gathered himself enough to stand.

Sarkneson stared into Roon's face. "You may not know where Daphlay is," the Pleiadean snapped at Roon, "but you will take me back with you to your planet. I shall find out myself."

Those words seared into the badly shaken Roon. He lost consciousness and collapsed on the floor.

When Roon awoke he found himself in a richly appointed bedchamber and lying next to him in the sumptuous bed, not Suzy Bibbens, but another of Sarkneson's dalliances.

The next day Sarkneson invited Roon to breakfast in his private quarters.

"I have a plan," announced Sarkneson as they were eating.

Roon looked at his 'host,' afraid to say anything. Sarkneson could see that his 'guest' was terrified, and that pleased the Pleiadean. Sarkneson would dole out favors to this man, but Sarkneson would hold all the power in their 'relationship.' Sarkneson needed Roon's knowledge of things Altean in order to achieve his first goal of finding the location of Daphlay, so he acted accordingly.

"I have a plan," the Pleiadean repeated, "but I need your assistance."

Roon was suddenly put at ease. His hopes rose again. He remembered his erotic nights in this place. He also remembered his host's acceptance of his request for remuneration. Roon saw visions of great wealth and endless nights of sexual delight.

"I will do as you ask," he responded.

Sarkneson told Roon that they were going to go to Silbury aboard the exploration vessel. Sufficient tornum for the quick interstellar trip could be brought with them in volute casings and infused into the aboard ship energy system. Between them Roon and Sarkneson could fly the vessel to Silbury and back. They would be detected and tracked by the Altean Naval Service from the time they approached the solar system containing Silbury, but Roon and vessel could respond properly to encoded transponder interrogations. Upon landing at the Space Port of Silbury, Roon would take Sarkneson to his living quarters and then Roon would go alone to report to his brother, the company's director. Hal Roon would 'confess' to Kirk Roon.

Hal Roon was to 'confess' the following: Roon Mining Company had not discovered a huge new lode of gold, a company from Daphlay had. Hal Roon had found out about the discovery through a transcommunication from a friend highly placed in that company. That friend knew the lode was too big for his company to mine alone, and wanted to help his friend Hal Roon by insuring that Roon Mining shared the lode. The best way for that to happen, Hal Roon and his friend had agreed, was for a vessel belonging to Roon Mining to find—while exploring for gold—the planet on which this lode had been discovered. This might be seen as collusion but the two had worked out a procedure by which it could be shown Roon Mining had been exploring in the area for some time and the arrival of their ship at that planet was the result of their search pattern.

When the Roon Mining vessel had begun orbiting the planet on which the company from Daphlay was conducting ongoing mining operations—Hal Roon would continue to 'confess'—the vessel had been detected and asked to identify itself. The Roon Mining vessel had responded, and the director had then asked the Roon Mining vessel not approach until the director had consulted with his company headquarters on Daphlay. The directors of the company had been considering asking another company to assist them. They would much prefer to work with a company from Silbury rather than with one of their direct competitors, so they had invited Roon Mining to participate in the mining operations.

Hal Roon would tell his brother that he was sorry he had proceeded in such a way, but it was a very confidential matter and a tremendous opportunity. Hal Roon had negotiated a 25 percent holding for Roon Mining in an incredibly rich lode of gold. He had brought back the company's first share of the gold, jointly mined and refined by the two companies: a million quid worth of near pure gold.

The employees of Roon Mining who had accompanied Hal Roon had all remained at the mining site to help with the operations.

Hal Roon had returned in the Roon Mining exploration vessel with the other company's assistant director of ongoing mining operations, who would provide vital assistance to Hal Roon in the on loading of Roon Mining equipment needed for the operation. They would be on Silbury for a only a couple of days before returning to the mining operation.

When Sarkneson finished this scenario Roon looked at him in amazement.

"I think it will work," Roon said, "except that you have forgotten we need Altean navy personnel to navigate for us.

"I can navigate the ship," Sarkneson retorted, bristling at Roon's questioning his plan, but managing to subdue his anger. "I know where this planet Silbury is, I know where we are now, I know how to get from here to there. Just in case there is something extra that has to be done by the navy I will take all six along. If I need information I will ask them. If they fail to answer, I will shoot them until one tells me what I want to know."

Hal Roon cringed.

"The only possible problem I foresee is the navy men might have to report at some point," Sarkneson stated.

"They don't," Roon responded. "During the time that they are assigned to us they don't report to the navy at all. They talk about this. They like duty aboard civilian space craft because they don't have to deal with officers."

"They must have families," Sarkneson stated, realizing things were getting more complex. "They would see or at least contact their families when they got to your planet."

"That's true," Roon answered, suddenly seeing his input becoming valuable to Sarkneson. "I can work around that. I can make up a false schedule to put into our computer so it will seem like those men are away all the time. I've done that once or twice before at the request of men who haven't wanted to see their families."

Sarkneson saw that Roon was feeling good about himself, so he drew his energy pistol and pointed it at Roon's head. "Just see that you do," he growled.

Roon cringed again.

After Sarkneson's men had loaded tornum and gold into the cargo bay of the Roon Mining vessel, guards chained the six heavily shackled members of the Altean Naval Service to the bulkhead of the secret compartment Sarkneson had built into the Roon Mining vessel while it was repaired.

As Roon watched this procedure Sarkneson said to him, "You feed them by placing food in their mouth. You clean the place up. You don't talk to them. You don't let anybody find them."

Roon and Sarkneson took off from Colchis and landed at the Space Port of Silbury. Sarkneson had no difficulty navigating the vessel. The incoming transmission from the Altean Naval Service, not interruptable and navigationally meaningless unless the craft was bound for Daphlay, was relayed to the vessel's navigational computer by the device in the belt buckle of two of the six men shackled in the secret compartment in the vessel. This message was also a transponder message and required a response from the devices in both belt buckles. Without that response an Altean Naval Service star ship would have intercepted the Roon Mining Vessel and taken Garth Sarkneson into custody.

But neither of the two men now shackled aboard the vessel had been able to remove the depiction of a dolphin from their belt buckles. They were desperately worried and chafed at their shackles.

While Sarkneson waited in Roon's living quarters, Hal reported to his brother. Kirk Roon accepted his story at face value and thanked him for a job well done. The director of Roon Mining completely understood the requirement for secrecy, and forgave his brother for his previous act of deception.

Hal Roon returned to his living quarters and reported to Sarkneson all had gone according to plan.

When he arrived home for supper Kirk Roon told his wife Avena that his brother had returned to Silbury with incredibly good news about a new joint mining operation with a company from Daphlay.

When Avena Roon had heard the whole story she looked at her husband and said, "I don't trust Hal. I never have, and I never will."

Sarkneson believed his mere presence on Silbury would enable him to discover the location of Daphlay. The Pleiadean realized that the information was most likely kept in Altean Naval Service computers and therefore restricted to authorized personnel. Sarkneson also knew he faced the additional problem of being totally unfamiliar with Altean society in general and Silbury in particular. The Pleiadean knew he would be successful because he believed he was the most intelligent, the best looking and the greatest seducer any female Altean could ever hope to meet.

After Roon had finished reporting to him, Sarkneson responded. "You will tell me how to get to your best nighttime entertainment."

"You are going out tonight by yourself?" asked Roon in total surprise.

"You do not ask me questions!" exploded Sarkneson. The Pleiadean continued to berate Roon not only because he enjoyed doing so, but also because he needed to keep Roon in such a terrified state that Roon would not even contemplate revealing him to Altean legal authority.

"You should go to the Golden Triangle," said Roon. "To get there you'll have to go to the Air Port on the Peri. At the Air Port you can get an air ship to take you to the Golden Triangle."

"Go feed the men in the ship." Sarkneson ordered Roon. "And clean it up. No smells."

When Sarkneson entered the Golden Triangle that evening he immediately looked for the female singer at the bar, because he knew such singers always knew the type of man Sarkneson wanted to find. Sarkneson found Althena Chee, daughter of the Elder of Silbury.

Althena Chee led Sarkneson to Paul Bunzler, the Director of Naval Armories on Silbury. Bunzler knew he was the most intelligent, the best looking and the greatest seducer any female Altean could ever hope to meet. Bunzler was the one Sarkneson wanted to meet.

Sarkneson met Bunzler the next evening at the Golden Triangle. The Pleiadean and Bunzler left a short time later and went to Bunzler's living quarters near the top of Ell House and located in the middle of its southern facing. Their conversation continued well into the night.

The next morning Bunzler went to his office with the intention of obtaining the location of Daphlay for Sarkneson. He was unsuccessful.

That evening Bunzler reported to Sarkneson the location of Daphlay was not stored in the Altean Naval Service computers on Silbury which Bunzler had been able to access that day.

Sarkneson exploded. The Pleiadean's anger exceeded even his recent fits of rage relating to Pleiadean emperor Xung Halbert Mavor and Sarkneson's previous failures to find Daphlay.

Bunzler was shocked by Sarkneson's outburst. The man with whom he had been dealing; the man who had already given him a small fortune in gold; the man who had offered him fabulous wealth, up until then this man had been charming, soft spoken and rational. The man who stands before me is a madman, thought Bunzler.

"I am sorry," Sarkneson 'apologized,' calming down. The Pleiadean realized he had shaken Bunzler and he knew he could not afford to antagonize Bunzler. He could not berate Bunzler as he did Roon.

"Tomorrow I leave, but I will be back in a month," Sarkneson continued. "See what you can find out in the meantime. Be discreet. I appreciate your position, so don't do anything that will get you caught."

The next morning the Pleiadean hauled the director of finance of Roon Mining out of his bed before dawn. Roon, half-asleep, cringed as Sarkneson shouted at him again, "Get up and get going. We leave in an hour."

When they arrived on Colchis the shackled men were returned to the dungeon and reshackled to a wall. When they left Colchis again the procedure was reversed from the dungeon to the secret compartment of the vessel.

"We will do this each time we travel back and forth," Sarkneson told Roon as Roon watched the shackling process. "There may be information I will need, and get, from them."

A month later Roon and Sarkneson returned to Silbury. The director of finance of Roon Mining presented his brother with another share of gold, enough to assure that Kirk Roon would never investigate the company's finances. Hal Roon's month of erotic pleasure had been supplemented by more gold doled out by Sarkneson. The Pleiadean's tactic of doling out wealth while continually berating him, had effectively turned Roon into Sarkneson's slave. Roon never considered reporting the Pleiadean to Altean legal authority, because he both feared the man yet thoroughly enjoyed the wealth and the sexual gratifications granted by Sarkneson.

When the Pleiadean met with Bunzler in Ell House, Bunzler reported that he had still found nothing on the location of Daphlay. Because of his position, Bunzler told Sarkneson, he had access to all Altean Naval Service secrets kept in computers on Silbury. There was nothing to be found on Silbury about the location of Daphlay.

"What about the men who navigate civilian ships?" Sarkneson asked, his anger rising.

"That is the only information available: they navigate civilian ships," answered Roon.

Sarkneson exploded, "I navigated the ship by myself. They didn't do anything. Find out about what those men do!"

Bunzler nodded.

Sarkneson felt his anger growing, but he controlled himself, knowing that if he alienated Bunzler now, his plan for smashing Xung Halbert Mavor was doomed. He spoke calmly, "Perhaps you could find it necessary to travel to Daphlay soon. Perhaps aboard ship you might find out something."

Much relieved, Bunzler agreed. Sarkneson doled out more gold.

"I will be back in a month," Sarkneson told Bunzler as he prepared to leave.

Roon and Sarkneson left the next morning with another load of 'vital' mining equipment. Bunzler made his trip to Daphlay. Roon and Sarkneson returned a month later with more gold for Roon Mining.

When the Pleiadean met with Bunzler again in Ell House, Bunzler informed him that he had been unable to find out anything about the naval men who were aboard civilian ships. Despite his position, he did not have access to all Altean Naval Service secrets kept in computers aboard ship or on Daphlay. Those computers that he had been able to access did not have the location of Daphlay stored in them.

Sarkneson's anger surged, but he again controlled himself, even as he began to realize his plan for smashing Xung Halbert Mavor was doomed.

"How can it be you cannot give me the location of Daphlay?" the Pleiadean asked. "Space craft travel back and forth to and from it. Alteans live on it. Yet no one seems to know where it is. How can this be?"

"Because Alteans fear Pleiadeans," responded Bunzler, "Alteans have very carefully hidden Daphlay. Even Silbury is incredibly well defended, and Silbury is only an outpost."

Sarkneson thought about what Bunzler had just said. Daphlay was hidden. Silbury was not. Daphlay might escape the Pleiadean. Silbury would not.

A new scheme began to form in Sarkneson's mind. He would deliver a devastating blow to Silbury that would make all Alteans cringe in fear. Sarkneson began to relish that prospect even more than he had relished the prospect of smashing Xung Halbert Mavor.

The mind of Garth Sarkneson was so put together he could flit from one scheme to the next without regrets. Sarkneson gave no more thought to the problem of Altean Naval Service personnel aboard civilian space craft. Sarkneson's approach to problem solving was not through logic. Sarkneson's way was to be impulsive.

"Tell me about the defenses of Silbury," said Sarkneson.

When Bunzler was done, Sarkneson, who had brought with him a large rectangular case, pulled a heavy box from it and handed this to Bunzler.

"Open it," said the Pleiadean.

Bunzler's eyes flashed when he saw the box was full of gold.

"I need your assistance further," said Sarkneson. "As a result of your giving me more assistance, you will have to leave this planet. I will then provide you with a new home, unlimited wealth and limitless opportunities for you to indulge yourself in sexual pleasures."

"What would you like me to do?" responded Bunzler, overwhelmed at the prospect.

"Supply me with information and manpower so that you can perform an act of sabotage for me," said Sarkneson.

Bunzler did not flinch, so Sarkneson added, "I'm hungry."

The two left Bunzler's living quarters and had supper at a restaurant in Ell House. As they were leaving Bunzler asked, "When?"

Sarkneson replied, "Same month, next year."

As Sarkneson finished speaking, Bunzler saw Aspis Crystal Security Director Odkin turn in his seat and look directly at him. A feeling of unease surged through Bunzler, and he avoided Odkin's eyes.

When the two cabalists were outside the restaurant, Sarkneson turned to leave the crystal house. "I will be back in a month," he told Bunzler.

Roon and Sarkneson left the next morning with another load of 'vital' mining equipment. They returned a month later with more gold for Roon Mining and some other cargo Sarkneson carried in an oversized rectangular case.

When the Pleiadean met with Bunzler in his living quarters that night, Sarkneson opened up the case. First he doled out more gold for Bunzler. Then the Pleiadean took out a large block of high explosive and a portable transceiver.

"I will hide these," said Sarkneson.

Sarkneson hid the block of high explosive in Bunzler's bedroom. Sarkneson entered code keys and the very narrow spherical bearing on which Bunzler was to transcommunicate into the transceiver, instructed Bunzler on how to operate the transceiver and hid it in Bunzler's bathroom.

"I leave in the morning," said Sarkneson. "Contact me in exactly one week, early evening, after you return to your living quarters."

Roon and Sarkneson left the next morning with another load of 'vital' mining equipment. When they arrived on Colchis, Sarkneson had Roon shackled separately in the dungeon.

During the following months Bunzler and Sarkneson secretly transcommunicated with each other and based on information supplied by Bunzler, the Pleiadean continued to formulate his plan.

When Hal Roon failed to return and no messages were received from the Crew who had accompanied him on his initial trip, Kirk Roon began to think something was amiss. He contacted the mining company on Daphlay with which Hal Roon had said he was working. The company denied any knowledge of any dealings with either Hal Roon or Roon Mining. Very disturbed by these revelations, Kirk Roon ordered a thorough audit of the company finances. The results showed how close the company had been to collapse and how that had been avoided, thanks to the gold that Hal Roon had brought to Silbury.

Kirk Roon informed legal authority of the situation and invited the families of the missing Crew and of the missing members of the Altean Naval Service to a meeting.

He told them everything he had discovered.

"My brother has obviously been involved in illegal activities. We don't know where he took our vessel, so we don't know where to look. Nevertheless, Roon Mining accepts responsibility for his actions and with my deepest regrets and sympathy Roon Mining will do the best it can to try to make up for the loss of your loved ones."

Later Kirk Roon spoke privately with his wife. "I can't figure this out," he said. "Hal obviously stole from the company, somehow found a huge lode of gold, paid the company back, provided the company with enough gold to keep us going for years and then disappeared. It makes no sense."

"I never trusted your brother," replied Avena Roon.

As the time grew nearer to "same month, next year" the transcommunications between Bunzler and Sarkneson became filled with acrimonious arguments about how the sabotage should be carried out; Bunzler wanted to proceed in a practical manner. Sarkneson insisted they should stick to his original plan. This was based entirely on bitter hatred of Alteans and an obsessive desire to make all Alteans cringe in fear. Sarkneson finally gave in to Bunzler, but not until he had threatened the Altean traitor with certain death should the sabotage fail.

The sabotage did not fail. Explosions rocked the Tor. The shattered Tor burned. Fire fighting air ships dropped tons of fire retardant on the inferno, but it was only extinguished after three days of horrific struggle. It took another week for the Tor to cool enough to permit an on scene investigation to be carried out by Alteans wearing special protective equipment, necessitated by escaping radioactivity.

That investigation quickly determined the cause of the explosion: sabotage.

The frightened Alteans of Silbury, who had fled to their houses following the explosions, were not allowed to venture out for three weeks. The Altean Naval Service of Silbury conducted a planet-wide search for saboteurs. A combined Daphlay-Silbury force of star ships fanned out across interstellar space, ready to intercept the anticipated Pleiadean attack. No saboteurs were found. No Pleiadean craft threatened Silbury.

About a month after the blast, and after the radioactivity had been thoroughly removed from the Tor and its vicinity, Mark Manpure took his youngest son to see the remains of the Tor. Young Cary Manpure was amazed to see that the structure was largely intact. Some of the facing panels of the northeastern portion of the Upper Tor had collapsed and the Aspis crystal had fallen into the center of the Tor, but from outside the Tor still looked like the Tor. The interior had been gutted; only one energy transconverter had been spared, saved by its fireproof steel alloy encasing sphere. But the conduits within the Tor had been badly damaged, so even that energy transconverter lay useless.

Cary asked, "How soon can we repair the Tor, Daddy?"

"It will take a long time," Cary's father replied, "but in the meantime we can reactivate the undamaged energy transconverter and get the spinning disks of the gravitron infusion complex going again. Once that energy transconverter is operational we can take all the time that is necessary to fix up the Tor just like it was before."

Neither Cary Manpure nor his father understood then what they would understand later: The Tor was not going to be rebuilt.

Silbury was going to be abandoned.

Chapter Nine

The Youths

When two of the Tor's energy transconverters were destroyed and the third ceased functioning, transconversion of torinum into tornum was automatically switched to the backup energy transconverters on Dolphin Mesa. Saved by Lura Redmand, these energy transconverters provided enough tornum to power all the Horz complex—except the vital gravitron infusing spinning disks in Tetrahedron Crater. They had spun to a halt when the Tor's energy transconverters ceased functioning, and were never restarted. Silbury began to rotate more slowly and lose its magnetic field. The artificial part of Silbury's combined atmosphere began to float off into outer space.

After the sabotage, the Council of Silbury feared an attack by the Pleiadeans; for they thought that the destruction of the Aspis crystal—which caused the removal of the anti-weapons defense shield from around Silbury—was a prelude to a major assault on the planet. They became incapable of making any decisions which were unrelated to the defense of Silbury, despite the fact that none of their star ship patrols—including those that probed near the Pleiades—ever detected any sign of a Pleiadean craft. This situation continued for months, even after it became perfectly obvious that the sabotage of the Tor was an isolated incident.

Once the Council of Silbury overcame its reluctance to make decisions, it agreed to arrange for an assessment of the cost and time required to reconstruct the heavily damaged Tor. Despite the estimated cost being exceedingly high, the Council of Daphlay offered to help defray a large portion of those costs from its much larger resources. The Council of Silbury accepted.

The Council of Silbury concluded that the estimated time factor for the repair work to the Tor was a major consideration. The Tor had originally taken 15 years to build; repairs would take nearly as long, as a substantial amount of wreckage clearing had to be done before reconstruction could even begin. Without the operation of the gravitron infusing spinning disks the estimate was that the atmosphere of Silbury would not be of sufficient density to sustain life on the planet for more than ten years, but the magnetic field of the planet, together with the required flow of planetary torun, would deteriorate to the point of being unacceptable in just over nine years. The council stated that the Tor could be made operational on Silbury without a breatheable atmosphere and a proper magnetic field, but by the time it was done, everyone would have had to be evacuated. They would have to start from the beginning with the processes of gravitron infusion, artificial atmosphere infusion and combined atmosphere warming—and it would take at least another five years.

The Council of Silbury finally came to the conclusion that their solution would be to undertake temporary repairs, sufficient to render the undamaged energy transconverter in the Tor operational again. This could be done by shunting both energy and water conduiting from the main conduits leading to the Tor from Dolphin Mesa around the Tor and connecting them to the remaining energy transconverter's conduiting systems. This could be completed relatively inexpensively and in only a few weeks. The combined tornum output of the undamaged energy transconverter in the Tor plus the tornum output of the energy transconverters on Dolphin Mesa would be enough to power the entire Horz complex—including the vital gravitron infusing spinning disks.

Silbury would be saved.

Then repairs to the rest of the Tor could be done so that eventually two new energy transconverters could be installed in it along with a new Aspis crystal. Silbury would have its full energy transproduction capabilities returned and the anti-weapons defense shield would again encircle the planet.

The vital temporary repairs to the Tor were never carried out. Just before starting, preliminary exhaustive inspections of the 'undamaged' energy transconverter revealed that the massive explosions which had rocked the Tor had also cracked the steel alloy transconverter sphere. The crack was not repairable and the energy transconverter was as useless as the two energy transconverters which had been totally destroyed.

The council then considered the alternative of constructing a new energy transconverter of an identical size to those of the Tor, whose tornum output could be used to spin the gravitron infusing spinning disks. This was feasible and the project was begun. It would require a year to cast the enormous transconverter sphere, its two surrounding spherical casings, the tetrahedral crystal casing of the new energy transconverter and the steel magnetic field encasing sphere.

In the meantime, just east of the Tor in a shallow impact crater, a base pad was being prepared. 58 The floor of the crater was leveled and the material removed was piled up along the western rim of the crater. An energy cannon turret was placed on the northern rim of the crater. Two ditches were dug through the base pad area and the northeastern rim of the crater to the northward underground conduits which ran between Chapter One and the Tor. Energy and water conduits were laid in the ditches from the base pad area, connected to the conduits which ran between Chapter One and the Tor, the ditches filled in and the disturbed planetary surface returned to its previous natural condition.

The ends of the conduits in the base pad area were prepared for connecting to the energy transconverter conduit systems. The base pad was completed with the pouring of a concrete surface, reinforced with steel rods and finely ground carbon steel filings, which colored the concrete mix black. Such concrete is always used for energy transconverter base pads because the tetrahedral molecules of the carbon in the carbon steel are necessary to the functioning of energy transconverters.

When the base pad was ready, the cast components of the new energy converter were to be carefully transported from Satyr and precisely positioned on the base pad. Two years from the start of construction, the new energy transconverter and the gravitron infusing spinning disks would be fully operational.

Once these spinning disks were performing their vital functions again, the Tor would be completely repaired. Two more new energy transconverters would be constructed and placed in the Tor. Those two could then provide tornum for the Tetrahedron Crater gravitron infusion complex and the remainder of the Horz complex while the first new energy transconverter was relocated from its temporary base pad to the Tor. After all three new energy transconverters began providing tornum, the Upper Tor would be reconstructed—and a new Aspis crystal installed so there would again be an anti-weapons energy net around Silbury.

Cary Manpure was nine years old and in the third grade when the Tor was sabotaged. Tommy Untiman was eight and in the second grade. Cary Jackman was not yet 10 and in the fourth grade. Terry Wellton was 11 and in the fifth grade.

When the Alteans abandoned Silbury, Cary Manpure was not quite 18, and half way through his last year in high school. He never completed his last year. Tommy Untiman was 17 and in the 11th grade. He finished high school on Daphlay. Cary Jackman was 18 and in his first Akadeimia year. Terry Wellton was 20 and in his second year. Neither of them completed their studies at Akadeimia.

Even though Cary Manpure, Cary Jackman, Tommy Untiman and Terry Wellton grew up under unusual and difficult conditions they were four very close friends. The four acted as a unit. They were lads as a unit, they were youths as a unit. The unit of four friends did everything together.

A few months after the destruction of the Tor and shortly after he finished his Akadeimia studies, Cary Manpure's cousin Dan Manpure and his longtime sweetheart Avelina Birrman were married. The members of the unit of four friends were invited to the wedding. So was Dan's sister, Cary Manpure's cousin Vicky.

At the wedding reception at Halkyon, Vicky Manpure was helping serve refreshments when Cary Manpure got an idea. He gathered the unit of four friends about him and they agreed to carry out his plan. Vicky was standing behind a long table covered with a white cloth which hung almost to the floor. On the table were many glasses lined up in neat rows, plates containing various edibles and a large, full, punch bowl. Guests would come to the table and help themselves to food. Vicky would offer each guest a glass of punch and she would ladle into the glass held out by the guest.

When Vicky was not looking, the four friends slipped under the table at one end and crawled on their hands and knees toward a predetermined spot—under the punch bowl. The four sat back to back on the floor, legs crossed: Cary Jackman faced toward the guests; Cary Manpure faced toward his cousin Vicky's feet; Terry Wellton faced the end from which they had crawled and Tommy Untiman faced the opposite end of the table.

Eventually Cary Jackman's sister Rena walked up to the table and began to talk with her good friend Vicky. Vicky offered Rena some punch and Rena picked up a glass and held it out for Vicky. That was the moment for which the four friends had been waiting.

Just as Vicky was filling Rena's glass, Cary Jackman grabbed his sister by the ankles and pulled on them, not too hard, but just hard enough to upset her balance. Cary Manpure did the same to his cousin Vicky.

Simultaneously Tommy Untiman and Terry Wellton grabbed the edge of the table cloth on Vicky's side of the table and pulled as hard as they could.

Vicky and Rena screamed.

Vicky spilled the punch intended for Rena on Rena's hand and on the table cloth and Rena dropped her glass into the punch bowl.

Rena lost her balance and stuck her hands into some food. Vicky fell over the punch bowl which was slopping toward her as a result of Tommy and Terry's tugging. Punch splashed Vicky and went all over her party dress.

Vicky and Rena began to cry.

Vicky's mother and father were livid. Cary Manpure's parents were embarrassed. Cary Jackman's and Terry Wellton's parents were terribly upset. Tommy Untiman's mother berated him when she found out about the incident later.

The unit of four friends was not allowed to eat the famous batter fried fish of Halkyon at the wedding party. The unit of four friends was not allowed to be together for two months. Cary Manpure thought it had been worth it.

Dan Manpure's Voluntary Best Servant—his best friend Alex Woodward—had witnessed the scene and in private laughingly told the bridegroom what had happened. Dan Manpure feigned disgust.

"That little cousin of mine is going to turn out badly, I'm afraid," he said to Alex Woodward. "He's doing all the same sort of things we did when we were his age."

"Is he really THAT bad?" asked Alex Woodward.

"No," responded Dan Manpure, slapping his friend on the back and laughing.

About a year and a half after the sabotage of the Tor and about ten months after work had begun on the new energy transconverter Paul Bunzler was taken into custody. His Pleiadean transceiver had been discovered. The Council of Silbury halted work on the casting of components for the new energy transconverter on Satyr, once again fearing that an attack by the Pleiadeans was imminent. Work could continue on the base pad, but casting could be resumed only after the threat was dealt with.

A month after Bunzler was taken into custody by legal authority, the Altean Naval Service was able to decode the very narrow spherical bearing on which Bunzler had been transmitting.

Colchis was immediately found to be located on that bearing.

The Pleiadeans were on Colchis!

Now the Council of Silbury understood why the Altean Naval Service had not been able to find any Pleiadeans after the destruction of the Tor. The Pleiadeans were not preparing to attack from the Pleiades: the Pleiadeans were preparing to attack from Colchis!

The Councils of Silbury and Daphlay held a joint meeting. The Altean

Naval Service was ordered to full alert and a large number of star ships were dispatched to defend Silbury against a feared attack, considered imminent now that Bunzler was no longer transcommunicating with the Pleiadeans. Bunzler had undoubtedly told the Pleiadeans of the work being done on Satyr. That would be a likely spot for an attack, and if the Pleiadeans got past the Altean Naval Service star ship patrols and the local defenses of and on Satyr, the Pleiadeans might be able to destroy the new energy transconverter. The incomplete components were therefore brought to Silbury and carefully hidden. When the threat was gone, those components would be taken back to Satyr, and the casting process completed.

A single Altean Naval Service star ship was dispatched to the vicinity of the solar system containing Colchis to gather intelligence data. Four months later the star ship returned and reported that it had intercepted transcommunications originating from a single site on Colchis.

The Councils of Silbury and Daphlay met again. They decided to order an assault on the Pleiadean position on Colchis.

During the next year the Altean Naval Service carried out an ongoing operation that resulted in the capture of the private empire of the family Sarkneson and the subsequent establishment of a secret Altean Naval Service base on Colchis.

Since an attack by the Pleiadeans was now deemed unlikely by the Council of Silbury, the council ordered the components of the new energy transconverter be taken back to Satyr, and the casting process resumed. The base pad east of the Tor was ready. Three years had elapsed since the sabotage of the Tor.

Cary Manpure turned 12. Things changed between him and his cousin Vicky.

Dan's wife Avelina had given birth to their son about a year after they were married. They named him Ames. Two years later they had a daughter and they named her Avena.

The problem was not with the children, but with their names.

Alteans in general and the clan Manpure in particular, traditionally named the first born lass in any given generation after her paternal grandmother; the first born lad in any given generation after his paternal grandfather. If Avelina and Dan Manpure had followed tradition their children would have been named Anna and Arnhold. They had ignored tradition and that was the problem.

Dan Manpure had never gotten along well with either of his parents. His father Arnhold Manpure was never wrong. His way the only way. He tried to make his son Dan do everything his way as well. Dan was an artist, which his father could not abide. Arnhold Manpure was a businessman and only businessmen had any sense. Anna Manpure always deferred to her husband.

Arnhold Manpure had made a fuss in the clan when Ames was born and not named after him. He made a bigger fuss when Avena was born and named Avena and not Anna. Anna Manpure made a similar fuss in accordance with her husband's fusses on both occasions.

Arnhold Manpure's brother and his wife tried to improve feelings in the clan Manpure by having a clan party when Avena was a month old. Everything was going reasonably well when Arnhold Manpure suddenly confronted his son, shouting so that everyone could hear, "First you insulted me by not naming your son Arnhold. Now you have insulted your mother by not naming this baby Anna. Your behavior is intolerable. We don't want to see you, your wife or your offspring again."

As Arnhold Manpure berated his son, everyone else stopped what they were doing and turned to watch and listen. Only the sound of Arnhold's raised voice could be heard.

When he had finished traducing his son, Arnhold Manpure took his wife's hand and led her toward the door. Along the way he grabbed his daughter's arm and pulled her with him.

Vicky cried and resisted her father. As she was dragged through the doorway Vicky called through her tears back to her brother, "Dan, I love you. They cannot do this to you. I will fight them."

There had never been such a horrific scene in Lana and Mark Manpure's home and the eight generations of members of the clan Manpure present were totally shocked.

Arnhold Manpure kept his daughter out of class for a week. The day she returned, Cary Manpure immediately walked right up to Vicky and put his arms around her.

"Vicky," he said. "I am sorry for everything. I want to be friends."

She hugged him back, tears in her eyes.

"Thank you, Cary," she said.

The Altean Naval Service assault on the Sarkneson fortress had resulted not only in the release of the family Sarkneson's slaves, but also in the release of the Roon Mining exploration vessel Crew, the Altean Naval Service personnel assigned to that vessel and Hal Roon. Hal Roon tried to lie his way out of his new predicament but on the basis of accumulated evidence concerning his activities, as well as the testimony of the those others who had been shackled by Sarkneson, he was taken into custody.

In an attempt to save himself from life imprisonment Hal Roon decided to cooperate and told Altean authorities his entire story. Everyone was relieved. The sabotage was now obviously an isolated incident.

The casting of the components for the new energy transconverter was completed and then they were carefully transported to Silbury where they were carefully and precisely put together on the base pad.

Two months later the Council of Silbury was meeting with those responsible for the final hookup of the new energy transconverter, going over the procedures for doing so. Everyone on Silbury was eagerly awaiting the starting up of the gravitron infusing spinning disks, only a few days away.

Then an Essene holo-image suddenly appeared and said, "I am an Essene holo-image and I am directed by Essenes to deliver the Sixth Essene Panlogos to the Council of Silbury. You are to complete the genetic project. You are NOT to connect the new energy transconverter!"

The holo-image disappeared.

The Council met through the night and all the next day, then announced its decision. The Council's position was that the genetic project—now obviously the reason for the existence of the Altean settlement on Silbury—was to be completed as quickly as possible, and that once the genetic project was completed there was no reason for the settlement on Silbury to continue. As many Alteans as wanted to could remain on Silbury for as long as the project continued. The rest could begin to evacuate. This was the intent of the latest instructions from Essenes. As had all other previous Councils, the current Council of Silbury would obey Essenes.

When Cary Manpure was 12 and 13 he was in the seventh grade, the first grade of middle school, the school which tried to contain young adolescents. Right after Cary Manpure turned 13 he began taking a compulsory three-week course in sex education, which replaced his physical education. Cary Manpure's course in sex education came right after the midday break for dinner. Cary Manpure had not liked having physical education right after the midday break for dinner and he did not think he would like having sex education right after the midday break for dinner either. Cary Manpure did not look forward to his next class after that either, because he knew he was not very good at transdimensional physics. He endured his class in transdimensional physics because that class was followed by Cary Manpure's favorite and best subject: MYTHOS!

What made Cary Manpure even less enthusiastic about taking a course in sex education was the teacher: it was Mrs. Sara Wellton, Terry Wellton's mother.

Cary Manpure entered the classroom the first day of his course and his eyes were transfixed by two large anatomical illustrations pinned to the front wall of the classroom. Cary Manpure tried to take a seat at the back, but Mrs. Wellton noticed his arrival and motioned him into an empty seat in the middle of the front row. When all the students were seated, Mrs. Wellton began the discussion, "Our course is designed to guide all of you toward an understanding of self-responsibility and self-respect. It is also designed to teach all of you about different, but never 100 percent effective, anti-pregnancy techniques.

"The most important concept that you must understand from the start is that all self-aware beings require sexual release in order to live."

Cary Manpure quickly realized that Mrs. Wellton was a very skilled teacher of sex education and a thoroughly loving guide for young adolescents, becoming aware of their sexuality and of the sexuality of others.

Cary Manpure's teacher for his course in transdimensional physics was Mr. Mark Wellton, husband of Sara Wellton and father of Terry Wellton. Mr. Wellton was an excellent teacher of transdimensional physics and a thoroughly loving guide for young adolescents becoming aware of the many mysteries of the Universe. In the case of Cary Manpure, his being aware of the many mysteries of the Universe was of little help.

Right after the first meeting of Cary Manpure's course in sex education, Mr. Wellton, by using what would ordinarily be considered a three-dimensional object, began the day's discussion with a devious but useful way to illustrate the concept of four-dimensions.

"Does anyone know of a four-dimensional object which I think all of you have in your kitchens at home?" asked Mr. Wellton.

His question elicited only blank stares.

In answer to his question Mr. Wellton held up an apple.

His answer elicited only blank stares.

"An apple is a very good example of a four-dimensional object," Mr. Wellton stated.

His amplification elicited only more blank stares.

"An apple is a very good example of a four-dimensional object," Mr. Wellton continued, "because an apple contains seeds. Seeds are one of the ways in which the Source of the Universe extrudes Itself into the physical universe. Although the Source of the Universe is Everything in four-dimensions, It is 'only' a zero-dimension point in three-dimensions.

"Seeds are an extrusion of the Source of the Universe into the physical universe because that which makes seeds burst forth with life can only be the Source of the Universe, the Source of everything. That which makes seeds burst forth with life cannot be detected in three-dimensions. That which makes seeds burst forth with life must be—like the Source of the Universe—a zero-dimension point in three-dimensions.

"An apple is therefore a very good example of a four-dimensional object because an apple has three-dimensions and seeds—seeds that contain zero-dimension points—zero-dimension points which make seeds burst forth with life.

"Three plus zero is four."

The class laughed.

Cary Manpure thought he understood.

"The apple is used as a symbol in Philosophia," Mr. Wellton continued, "because the uppermost part of the three-dimensional secondary energy disturbance pattern of a soul print looks like a large apple with progressively smaller apples piled on top of one another, all with their stems pointing downward. This pattern continues through the top of the skull and onward indefinitely with the 'apples' getting progressively smaller and weaker.

"This pattern of a large apple with the progressively smaller apples can be modeled geometrically in two-dimensions. The resulting two-dimensional model changes the largest apple into an upside down heart and the other apples into circles. The smaller apples, now circles, are moved to various mirrored locations around the upside down heart and the largest circle. This pattern is repeated again and again on each progressively smaller circle. Above the upside down heart and the largest circle a different pattern is produced. After more circles, a long straight line with replications of the original pattern on it continues onward—indefinitely.

"This two-dimensional depiction of the upper part of a soul print is called the Waldark set. The Waldark set is an extremely useful model for showing how the macro is like the micro, only bigger. The Waldark set also models the transformations which take place at the border of three-dimensions and complexified three-space."

Cary Manpure stared blankly.

"Apples—as well as doughnuts," concluded Mr. Wellton, "can be used as models to shape Waldark things."

The class laughed, so Cary Manpure joined in.

"Apples—as well as other fruit—are as nutritious as doughnuts," Mr. Wellton continued. "Not everyone understands the importance of food such as doughnuts, but as a student of transdimensional physics I can assure that you doughnuts are important.

"Fruit, however, is the most important food you can have with you on a long space voyage. The fruit we eat is a cross between the fruit indigenous to Altea and the fruit brought by the intergalactic migrators, though they were not that different.

"We'll talk more about nutrition later."

Vicky Manpure took very precise notes on everything Mr. Wellton said and she helped her cousin Cary pass transdimensional physics each year. Because of his cousin Vicky, Cary Manpure even passed the sections on nutrition each year.

That same day at the conclusion of his course in transdimensional physics Cary Manpure dashed as usual to his mythos course. All students were required to study mythos in the fourth, eighth and 12th grades. Cary Manpure's seventh grade class in mythos was the optional course he had chosen for the year. In fact he chose mythos every time it was an optional course.

Cary Manpure loved mythos.

His teacher was Mr. Tom Huish, an exceptionally skilful teacher of mythos and a thoroughly loving guide for young adolescents becoming aware of the many mysteries of mythos.

Mr. Huish began the day's discussion by saying something that thrilled Cary Manpure more than anything he had ever heard.

"I propose," Mr. Huish began, "that together we construct an entirely new mythos. I also propose that we write down our newly constructed mythos at three different levels of understanding: one level for 12th graders, one level for eighth graders and one level for fourth graders. After we do that I propose we present our newly constructed mythos to 12th, eighth and fourth graders to see if they understand it, in the way that we project they will."

A month later the newly constructed mythos—a tale of woe from ancient times—was complete. The name of the tragic hero and the name of the newly constructed mythos were both proposed by Rena Jackman and enthusiastically adopted. Seventh grade history at the middle school, which both Rena Jackman and Cary Manpure attended, included a study of the Lotharian movement led by Ell Dan, the only Altean artist to have ever been given the honorific title 'Art Hurian' during her or his lifetime. The name of the tragic hero was Arthur; the name of the newly constructed mythos: THE ARTHURIAN LEGENDS.

Rena Jackman directed the special symposeion. Each year these selected fourth, eighth and 12th graders of the Zuv School System discussed THE ARTHURIAN LEGENDS. Each year these selected graders met during a regularly scheduled symposeion to discuss a selected mythos. The mythos differed every year but it came from a mythos they had been studying, and the varying perspectives held by these three age groups always provided new insights and contributed greatly to a deeper understanding of the mythos under discussion.

Cary Manpure was selected when he was a fourth, eighth and 12th grader to participate in the regularly scheduled mythos symposeion of the Zuv School System. When Cary Manpure was in the fourth grade the mythos was about a dashing hero cast adrift as a baby with his exiled mother, a beautiful princess whom he rescues from horrible beasts and a truly horrific beast whose gaze turned everyone who looked upon him into stone.

At the symposeion conducted that year Cary Manpure had said, "I think that this story is like NOSTOS. The hero is a seeker of knowledge. The princess is the thirst for knowledge. The beast who turns everyone who looks at him into stone is the denial of truth, that which ossifies—not just into bone, but into petrified bone: stone."

When Cary Manpure was in the eighth grade the mythos was about the search for the golden fleece at Colchis—not the planet Colchis but a distant legendary place called Colchis.

At the symposeion conducted that year Cary Manpure had said, "I thought that this mythos could be adapted so it could include something about the beast Sarkneson. This is what I have written."

Cary Manpure took his reworked mythos to the director of the symposeion.

When Cary Manpure was in the 12th grade the mythos was Cary Manpure's favorite, a mythos out of time immemorial: of land combat between opposing armies of heavily armed foot soldiers who slaughtered one another to regain—or retain—a beautiful young princess who had been stolen away from one camp to another by an effete princeling, who was the real cause of the war—NOT the beautiful young princess.

Cary Manpure did not attend that symposeion because it was held on Daphlay after the evacuation of Silbury.

Cary Manpure was on Danebury.

Although the selected mythos was discussed during the regularly scheduled symposeion each year the main reason for holding the symposeion was to rewrite the selected mythos in a contemporary setting, in order to show how the lessons of the mythos applied to contemporary society. At the end of each school year all mythos students individually rewrote a mythos they had studied during the school year, chosing their setting either in a different past locale, in contemporary society or in a projected future locale and society.

Because Cary Manpure loved mythos and because Mr. Huish was an extraordinarily skilful teacher of mythos, Cary Manpure loved Mr. Huish like an older brother. Mr. Huish was 24 and Rena Jackman a seventh grader when she fell in love with him. That was Rena Jackman's secret for nine years. When Rena Jackman finished her Akadeimia studies on Daphlay she tracked down Mr. Huish.

"Mr. Huish," Rena Jackman said to him when she found him in his classroom working long after his students had departed, "my name is

Rena Jackman. I was one of your students who helped write THE ARTHURIAN LEGENDS. You and I are going to be married."

Seven weeks later Rena Jackman became Rena Jackman Huish.

Cary Manpure liked art. Whenever he could he took art classes—that is until he was in the eighth grade when he took his last art class.

On the first day of that art class the teacher stood before the class and said, "Art is based on the phi section. The phi section is the division of a line, or geometric figure, so that the proportion of the smaller section to the larger section, is the same as the proportion of the larger section to the whole..."

After that Cary Manpure hated art.

The youths of the unit of four friends joined other adolescents and adults of the Altean community on Silbury by contributing reproductive material to the genetic project. This female and male reproductive material was also vital in the treatment of many disorders and diseases.

The Alteans of Silbury reconfigured female and male reproductive material by placing it in separate casings which were then placed on spinning disks for off-center rotation into complexified three-space. The casings on the spinning disks were affixed to them in small centrifuges which rotated slowly in the direction opposite to the spin of the disks, thus setting up a force of tension between the two spins within the reproductive material in a way that is similar to the tension created between the forces of planetary rotation and planetary retrograde precession.

Prior to the sabotage of the Tor the enormous spinning disks of the Tetrahedron Crater gravitron infusion complex had been used for this process. When they were no longer available to do the reconfiguring, other spinning disks had to be used, especially those aboard civilian and Altean Naval Service space vessels moored on Silbury. Normally the gravitron drives of space craft are shut down while in port; this was no longer done on Silbury. Reconfigured female and male reproductive material was required to insure the well being of the community and to complete the genetic project; only by keeping the spinning disks spinning on moored space vessels was this material available.

Even though Cary Manpure, Cary Jackman, Tommy Untiman and Terry Wellton grew up under unusual and difficult conditions they were four very close friends. They had been lads as a unit, now they were youths as a unit. They did everything together, including playing golf.

As a result their golfing abilities improved over the years. Only Cary Jackman occasionally missed a game because he felt he had to do extra studying. Terry Wellton's cousin Frank Wellton, who was Cary Jackman's age, filled in for Cary Jackman on those occasions.

Cary Jackman was the best golfer among the unit of four friends. He usually shot almost all pars with a birdie or two and about as many tainted pars. Only rarely did he have any double-tainted pars. Cary Manpure was next best followed by Tommy Untiman and Terry Wellton. This order of golfing ability was convenient because Cary Manpure and Tommy Untiman always wanted to play a team match against the other two, and the teams were therefore evenly matched.

One particular morning when Cary Manpure was 14 the four friends were playing their team match with their usual stakes: losers buying winners a snack at their favorite eatery. They played each hole for a possible two points by comparing the two scores of both teams. During this match Cary Manpure and Tommy Untiman were behind by one point going into the last hole, a difficult par five. The fairway was narrow, tree-lined and bent sharply to the right about half way down its length. Bunkers filled with red Silbury sand were strategically placed along the fairway and surrounding the green.

The team of Cary Jackman and Terry Wellton teed off first and both hit long and straight. Tommy Untiman drove next and hit straight, but not as long as either of his opponents. Cary Manpure hooked his drive into the rough but not into the trees.

Cary Manpure was farthest away so he was first to hit a second shot. He thought he should use a mid-iron to get out of the rough, but Tommy Untiman and he had to win two points on the hole to win the match. Therefore he used his spoon and hit his ball to within approach distance of the green. His partner then proceed to hit his second shot about 50 yards in front of the bunker in front of the green.

Terry Wellton also hit a spoon and nearly reached the bunker in front of the green. Cary Manpure figured Terry Wellton was in a good position to get any easy par and perhaps a birdie.

Cary Jackman hit his second shot over the bunker and onto the green. He would only have to two putt for a birdie.

It looks like it will be difficult for us to win, thought Cary Manpure. "Come on, Pazzy," he shouted across the fairway to his partner. "Let's get 'em."

Cary Manpure lofted his third shot onto the green and two putted for a par five. Terry Wellton mishit his third shot into the bunker in front of the green and ended up with a tainted par six. Cary Jackman got his birdie.

Tommy Untiman SANK his approach for a double-birdie, the only double-birdie he ever made. Cary Manpure and Tommy Untiman won two points on the last hole. Their team won the match by one point. The other team treated them to refreshments.

The youths also had friends outside the unit. Cary Manpure became very close friends with his cousin Vicky after the horrific family party at his place.

When the cousins were 15 Vicky and Cary Manpure worked together on a project for their mathematics class, and chose to do a report on topogly, a traditional numerological system for siting structures. In particular they reported on the topogly locations of Hurbury, the Hurmaze, the Tor, the Tower of Ancestors and the Tetrahedron.

To gather additional information for their project the cousins spoke with someone who knew more about topogly than any living Altean: Joe Lon Odkin.

Odkin was extremely helpful to them both and very interested in their project. Topogly siting had become mostly forgotten to Alteans of Odkin's time, and he was therefore overjoyed to know that Vicky and Cary were interested in the subject. He flooded the two with a vast amount of material, all of which Odkin knew by heart. The young Alteans immediately liked Joe Lon Odkin and they quickly came to respect him greatly.

Vicky presented the report she and her cousin had prepared while Cary Manpure pointed out her discussion points they had illustrated together on a large scale plan of the Horz complex, "In anticipation of the eventual completion of the Horz complex," Vicky said, "the Tetrahedron was located on the northeastern rim of the Tetrahedron Crater with its apex at 41 degrees, 27 minutes, 19.51219512 seconds north latitude. 59 This gave the Tetrahedron a topogly latitude of 21,600.

"Topogly latitudes and longitudes are calculated by multiplying the number of degrees of the location of something times the number of minutes of the location of something times the number of seconds of the location of something. In this case 41 x 27 x 19.51219512 = 21,600."

The classroom erupted with hoots and jeers.

"That is ridiculous!" a student shouted.

"Who cares?" asked another very loudly.

The teacher quieted the students, and Vicky continued, "The number 21,600—a number which represents the number of nautical miles around a planet—was determined first. The site was picked subsequently, knowing it would have to be between 41 degrees 27 minutes and 41 degrees 28 minutes. The number of seconds chosen for the siting were the number of seconds required to make the topogly latitude equal the predetermined 21,600."

"Garbage!" a student shouted.

The teacher glared at him and pointed. The student got up, left the classroom and reported to the school's assistant director.

Undismayed Vicky continued, "The topogly latitudes, longitudes and vectors of Hurbury and the Tower of Ancestors were determined in relationship to the topogly latitude, longitude and vector of the Tor. The siting of the Tor was determined by the siting of the Tetrahedron. The Tor is the prime meridian of Silbury. The Tetrahedron is the sourcemark from which everything—including the Tor prime meridian—in the Horz complex is sited—except the Hurmaze.

"The apex of the Tor was sited at 40 degrees, 52 minutes, 4.773646585 seconds north latitude, resulting in a topogly latitude of 9929.184896.

"Mr. Joe Lon Odkin, Director of the Hurmaze, helped Cary and me with our project. He told us that he tried to figure out why the apex of the Tor is at that latitude. He found that the tangent of the latitude of the apex of the Tor is .865249842, and then found that that tangent is very close to the ratio of e/pi .865255979—an obscure metaphorical representation of the relationship of living things to everything. Next, Director Odkin found that the latitude whose tangent is .865255979 is 40 degrees, 52 minutes, 5.49 seconds. He subtracted the latitude of the apex of the Tor from this latitude and found that the difference in latitudes is equivalent to about 39 feet. The apex of the Tor was sited about 39 feet south of the latitude whose tangent represents the ratio e/pi..."

"Get to the point!" someone shouted.

"Who cares?" asked another again.

Undismayed Vicky continued again, "Director Odkin knew that 39 feet is a long way in terms of topogly sitings, but he also realized that there might have been other considerations which required that the Tor be sited 39 feet south of the latitude whose tangent represents the ratio e/pi. Before trying to find out what those other considerations might have been, Director Odkin decided to find out just how significant the ratio e/pi is, and therefore to try to determine if anyone would have wanted to memorialize the ratio e/pi in the siting of the apex of the Tor..."

The teacher glared at the students as they squirmed in their chairs as Vicky continued, "Director Odkin found the following in a very old book he found in the library in Chapter One:

> It had been thought—aeons ago—that the ratio e/pi .865255979 might have some important relationship to the square root of three divided by two .866025403—the transdimensional component of the transdimensional constant 2.720699044—because the ratios were similar. At that time it was known that there was a very important relationship between the 12th root of two 1.059463094 and the square root of nine-eighth 1.060660172

because the square root of nine-eighths is an important constant associated with tetrahedra, the 12th root of two is associated with the harmonics leading to the development of self-aware life and because tetrahedra are the modeling for everything. However, no such linkage could be found between e/pi and the square root of three divided by two. The ratio e/pi is therefore only a representation of the relationship of living things to everything, because e is associated with the growth of living things and because pi is the Universal Constant of the Universe.

"Director Odkin thought for a while and concluded that since there was no linkage between the ratio e/pi and the square root of three divided by two—though Director Odkin remembered from school that the square root of three divided by two was something which is memorialized throughout the Horz complex—and since the apex of the Tor is 39 feet south of the latitude whose tangent represents the ratio e/pi, there was no intent on the part of those who designed and sited the Tor to memorialize the metaphor e/pi in that siting..."

"So what's the point?" shouted one of the class.

"The point is, Tom Roon," Vicky said pointedly, "that being close is not the same as being the same and that things therefore need to be carefully checked!"

Tom Roon slunk down in his chair, and Vicky continued, "Since the Tor is the prime meridian of Silbury, it has a topogly longitude of 360. Its resulting topogly vector is 27.58106916—calculated by dividing 9929.184896 by 360.

"Topogly vectors are calculated by dividing something's topogly latitude by its topogly longitude—or the other way around, depending on which number is larger. You always divide the larger number by the smaller."

This was more than two more youths could take.

They booed.

They joined the 'garbage' youth in the assistant director's office.

"The Tor's prime meridian location was sited 50 minutes 3.6 seconds west of the Tetrahedron so that the Tetrahedron would have a topogly longitude of 180—half the Tor's topogly longitude—and a resulting topogly vector of 120, a number which represents the number of degrees of longitude separating the three non-polar points of circumscribed tetrahedra in spinning spheres.

"The Tower of Ancestors was sited at 41 degrees, 3 minutes 20.18127011 seconds north latitude, with a resulting topogly latitude of 2482.296224, one-fourth of the topogly latitude of the Tor. The Tower of Ancestor's longitude is 17 minutes and 31.76470588 seconds west, with a resulting topogly longitude of 540, one and one-half times the topogly longitude of the Tor. The topogly vector of the Tower of Ancestors is 4.596844859, one-sixth of the topogly vector of the Tor."

This time a student shouted, "Come on, Vicky, finish up. It's almost time to eat."

Vicky ignored him and concluded her presentation, "Hurbury was sited due east of the Tower of Ancestors at 41 degrees, 3 minutes, 20.18127011 seconds north latitude, with a resulting topogly latitude of 2482.296224, one-fourth of the topogly latitude of the Tor. Hurbury was sited due south of the Tetrahedron at 50 minutes and 3.6 seconds east, with a resulting topogly longitude of 180, one-half the topogly longitude of the Tor. The topogly vector of Hurbury is 13.79053458, one-half the topogly vector of the Tor.

"The site of energy transredimensioning in the Hurmaze was sited at 41 degrees, 11 minutes, 10.03080581 seconds north latitude; and 6.890283706 seconds east longitude. The resulting topogly latitude is 4523.893421; the resulting topogly longitude is 6.890283706; and the resulting topogly vector is 656.5612701.

"None of these topogly numbers have any relationship to the topogly numbers associated with Hurbury, the Tor, the Tower of Ancestors or the Tetrahedron.

"The topogly vector 656.5612701 of the Hurmaze is equivalent to 25,920 divided by the square of two pi. Most traditional topogly sitings represent important mathematical constants, their powers or roots. The topogly vector of the Hurmaze is the ONLY topogly number in the Horz complex which contains a mathematical constant in any form, and it does so in combination with one of the most important numbers we know: 25,920, the number of years in the retrograde precession of planets which are capable of bringing forth self-aware life through natural evolution—and with a function of pi, the Universal Constant of the Universe."

She was hooted down by the rest of the class.

The teacher was helpless to do anything.

Vicky cried.

Cary Manpure tried to help his cousin, and was then avoided by his classmates at the noon meal when he came in late.

Even though Cary Manpure, Cary Jackman, Tommy Untiman and Terry Wellton grew up under unusual and difficult conditions they were four very close friends who had a good time together.

When Cary Manpure was 15 his brother Frank and his sweetheart Alana Sanders were married. The youths were invited, as were Cary

Manpure's cousin Vicky and her parents. Cary Manpure escorted Vicky as her parents had refused to be in the presence of their son Dan and his family, who were also invited along with Rena Jackman and the other family members of the unit of four friends.

The wedding party at Halkyon would have gone quite smoothly except for two things: beer and cold batter fried fish.

Cary Manpure called beer, wine and distilled drinks such as rum and whiskey "beverages which can put the mist before your eyes."

Cary Manpure knew these mist-producing beverages were off limits to the younger set, and probably should have been off limits to all sets. He also knew that if these traditional mist-producing beverages were enjoyed in moderation they could be instruments of conviviality. Lack of moderation was the problem, Cary Manpure thought. He thought mist-producing beverages had been invented not to be enjoyed, but to test the ability of self-aware beings to restrain themselves.

The four friends were part in and part out of the age considered by most to be acceptable for the consumption of mist-producing beverages. Cary Jackman and Terry Wellton were in; Tommy Untiman and Cary Manpure were out. They considered this to be an unfair division of the unit, so during the wedding party its older members took to secretly supplying its younger members with forbidden beverages. Tommy Untiman and Cary Manpure had a great time. They ate. They danced. They drank too much beer.

Cary Manpure had theorized that the amount of beer one can consume in moderation cannot be judged by consuming only small amounts. Neither could one make that judgement accurately by consuming what one might consider just the right amount. Cary Manpure therefore concluded that the amount of beer one can consume in moderation can only be judged by consuming a small amount one time, an amount thought to be about right another time and then too much. Both Cary Manpure and Tommy Untiman started their judging process by consuming too much beer.

Neither Cary Manpure nor Tommy Untiman 'thought' anyone had noticed that they had consumed too much mist-producing beer. They were wrong.

When Vicky and Rena judged that Cary Manpure and Tommy Untiman were becoming too immoderate, the two young ladies took them by the hand, Rena leading Cary and walked out of Halkyon and into the cool evening air. Halkyon was a very large restaurant which catered especially to wedding parties and it was located on a mesa north of the Bastion, northwest of the Wall and northeast of the Hurmaze. Once Cary Manpure was outside he wandered off to near the wall around the edge of the mesa, feeling somewhat refreshed as he looked into the distance—not close up—southward over the Horz complex.

After a few minutes, Cary announced that he was hungry and wanted some fish.

"I don't think you should eat or drink anything more, Cary," said Rena.

Cary Manpure looked her in the eyes and said resolutely, "Rena, get me fish, or I'll talk to Mr. Huish."

"What about?" Rena asked.

"About you and Mr. Huish," said Cary Manpure.

"There's nothing to know about Mr. Huish and me," Rena said.

"That's true," responded Cary Manpure, "but there is something to know about you and Mr. Huish."

Rena ran back into Halkyon and desperately searched for some fish for Cary Manpure. She ended up in the kitchen and found some cold fish in a strainer of the frying vat. Wrapping the cold fish in a napkin she ran back to Cary Manpure. He gobbled it up easily and then as the cold fish, cold batter and congealed fat hit Cary Manpure's stomach he staggered and almost fell off the mesa.

Rena desperately grabbed at Cary Manpure, caught hold of him and then steered him away from the edge to a bench where she sat him down. Afraid that the immoderate youth might fall off the bench, Rena put her arm around him. Rena's touch felt so good to Cary Manpure that he suddenly turned and kissed her. As the immoderate youth closed his eyes he became suddenly dizzy and felt queazy. He stood up, stumbled across the paving to a clump of bushes and threw up. The last thing Cary Manpure remembered was sitting on the tiling next to those bushes as Rena tried to comfort him by wiping the cold sweat from his brow with a damp cloth she had retrieved from the wedding party.

The next thing Cary Manpure knew he was in his bed.

Only many years later was he told how he got there.

Vicky faced a somewhat similar situation with Tommy Untiman. He began vomiting and she could not get him to stop. She left him and ran quickly back inside to get Mr. Wellton. Mark Wellton came right out, helped Tommy to his feet and took him immediately to the Welltons place. Mark Wellton had long since become a loving substitute father for Tommy Untiman. Mark Wellton had grown up without his father being present and he would not let Tommy Untiman suffer as he had.

Cary Manpure loved his legal sister Alana Manpure. When she became pregnant, Cary Manpure gave her a plate on which was the drawing of "a very excited satyr chasing a very exciting nymph," Cary Manpure told her.

"I know about this stuff from my mythos class," Cary Manpure added with a wink.

When Alana Manpure gave birth to her and her husband Frank Manpure's son—whom they named Mark Manpure—Cary Manpure gave his legal sister a herm, a stele with a head of a male near its top and male genitals below.

"One day you'll have to have a frank discussion with your son, Alana," Cary Manpure told her. "Frank never will."

"I know about this stuff from my mythos class too," Cary Manpure added with a another wink.

Even though Cary Manpure, Cary Jackman, Tommy Untiman and Terry Wellton grew up under unusual and difficult conditions they were four very close friends who found sweethearts along the way.

When Cary Manpure was 16, Terry Wellton invited the other youths of the unit of four friends to a dance given by his high school class from Hurartu House's Renart School System just before they completed their studies. Each of the youths invited a young lady.

Tommy Untiman invited Vicky Manpure; Cary Jackman invited Becky Armstrong, a classmate of his; Terry Wellton invited Lana Harwell, his sweetheart and a classmate; and Cary Manpure invited Lura Harwell, Lana's younger sister.

Cary Manpure knew Lura only slightly, having met her briefly a couple of times at Terry Wellton's place. She was a year older and he thought that she was very good looking.

Lura Harwell and Cary Manpure had a fantastic time at the dance. As the evening progressed Cary Manpure began to feel a strong attraction for Lura, the first time the youth had ever felt such an attraction for a young lady.

During the dance Vicky Manpure, Cary Manpure and Tommy Untiman won the two-thirds dancing dance contest.

Shortly after their arrival, the intergalactic pioneers were introduced to two-thirds dancing by the indigenous beings of the galaxy, during one of their first nighttime gatherings around the central hearth in one of their longhouses. Two-thirds dancing is always done to fast music with one lady and two gentlemen. Any fast music will do, the faster the better, as good two-thirds dancers can quickly adapt themselves to the proper tempo and beat. Because of this, but mostly because two-thirds dancing is a great deal of fun, two-thirds dancing has survived, even thrived, among the countless generations who have lived in the galaxy.

To start two-thirds dancing the dancers form a circle and hold hands. When the music starts they circle right and left and go through a number of steps. Later, the gentlemen part hands and dance on either side of the lady. This allows them to go through a varied number of steps and motions. There are basic steps, but threesomes often practice together on improvizations and compete in two-thirds dancing contests such as the one won by Vicky Manpure, Cary Manpure and Tommy Untiman. The lady in the middle is the leader and she often must support one or both of her partners as they lean over and down. During this part of the dance cloth handkerchiefs are used to hold onto one another rather than hands. This is both practical and traditional. The dance was called two-thirds by the indigenous beings long before the intergalactic pioneers introduced them to the concept of two-thirds. This name has nothing to do with the threesomes being composed of two-thirds gentlemen, the inspiration behind the name is that two-thirds of the strength required for this dance is supplied by the lady.

After the dance, the eight of them went to their favorite eating place in the Shopping Center. Seeing that his three friends were having a very good time with the young ladies accompanying them, Terry Wellton suggested that they all go for a walk in Dan Park. Terry Wellton and his sweetheart led the way toward the southwestern corner of the park—away from habitation. The meandering pathway led among the trees and next to the golf course where Cary Manpure and Tommy Untiman had defeated their opponents as a result of Tommy's double-birdie. Cary Manpure put his arm around Lura as they walked. When they came to the branching pathway leading to an amphitheater laid out in an impact crater, Cary Manpure directed Lura along the branch in the pathway with his arm, while the others continued on the main path.

The two walked the short distance to the top of the grassy slope of the amphitheater and then down toward its center before Cary Manpure stopped them. Cary Manpure turned toward Lura, leaned forward and kissed her gently.

Cary Manpure had a sweetheart.

Not far away—but hidden in the trees—Cary Jackman was kissing Becky Armstrong. Cary Jackman had a sweetheart too.

When Cary Manpure was 17, Lana and Lura Harwell moved from Silbury to Daphlay with their family. Becky Armstrong left also. Ukika Brown moved with her family from Daphlay to Silbury.

At the time when the projected completion of the genetic project approached and as the atmosphere of Silbury continued to drift away, Ukika Brown's family came to Silbury. Ukika's parents had been assigned the responsibility of removing cattle, chickens, pigs, sheep and other poultry and stock animals from Silbury.

The school year on Silbury was 36 weeks long, divided into four quarters of nine weeks each. There were 180 classroom days. During the school year there were four breaks of one week each. The break between school years was 12 weeks.

Even though Cary Manpure, Cary Jackman, Tommy Untiman and Terry Wellton grew up under unusual and difficult conditions they were four very close friends who performed voluntary service, both together and separately. Two-thirds of the 12 week break between school years was the traditional time for this.

When Cary Manpure was 16 he worked in the Wall during his 12 week break. Cary Jackman worked at the Bastion. Tommy Untiman worked at Philosophia House. Terry Wellton worked in the Hurmaze. Two-thirds of the population of the Horz complex was made up of those over 72. These retirees also performed voluntary service and worked closely with young ladies and youths during their 12 week breaks.

Cary Manpure volunteered to work in the Wall because he was interested in agriculture. Working in the Wall also meant working in the crop fields which were planted northeast of the Wall, and in the fruit and nut orchards. The fruit orchards were located between the Wall and the western rim of the Tetrahedron Crater; the nut orchards northeast of the crop fields. The Wall had become the agricultural center of Silbury.

The long straight water conduit leading from the corbelled dome grave circle to the Tetrahedron formed a 45 degree angle at the Tetrahedron with the northern end of the extended Wall. 40 With the Tetrahedron as its origin, an arc from the northern tip of the Wall to the point where that arc touched the water conduit described one-eighth of a circle. Part of this one-eighth of a circle was occupied by the rim of the Tetrahedron Crater, the rest was occupied by the agricultural fields of the Horz complex.

Water was fed directly to the roots of the crops by conduits that-branched from the main water conduit which formed the entire northeastern boundary of the fields, nine Silbury miles long. The southern boundary of the fields was six Silbury miles long from the northern tip of the Wall to near the rim of the Tetrahedron Crater. Precisely 3600 acres were contained in these fields; two-thirds was always cultivated.

When Cary Manpure was 17, the sweethearts of Cary Manpure, Cary Jackman and Terry Wellton left Silbury. All four members of the unit of four friends decided to do voluntary service during their 12 week break at the Ranch.

The Ranch was centered about 20 miles southeast of the Tetrahedron Crater. The Ranch House was located due east of the Tower of Ancestors and the apex of Hurbury. Two ancient impact craters whose rims nearly touched dominated the northern half of the Ranch. 60 Tangential to the southwestern corner of the Ranch, and about nine miles southeast of Hurbury, was the Lookout. A smaller mound than Hurbury but a similar shape. The range land of the Ranch was contained in a fenced off rectangular area 24 by 36 Silbury miles, with the Lookout as its sourcemark. Thc azimuth of the long sides of the range land was 27.2 degrees gyro (as measured from the top of the Lookout and parallel to the deep broad ditch leading from Hurbury). The Ranch covered over 75,000 acres, but due to the presence of the craters, the range land was less than 70,000 acres.

The northern crater was called Sheep Crater and the southern Cattle Crater. The sheep were always kept in the northern part of the Ranch, separated from the southern part by a sturdy fence running across the range land and around the top of the southern rim of Sheep Crater. Cattle and all other stock animals and poultry were kept in the southern two-thirds of the ranch. Cattle Crater was a feed lot. Sheep Crater was for sheering.

Just inside the northeastern corner of the Ranch was a conical structure which was the main structure of Akadeimia.

The Ranch House area was located in the eastern central area of the ranch and included the Ranch House, bunk houses, cook house, barns, corals, chicken coops, pig pens and other main structures of the Ranch. 61 The Ranch House itself was circular and enclosed by three concentric fences. The innermost circular fence had a diameter of 934.56 feet, the middle circular fence had a diameter of 1298 feet and the outermost circular fence had a diameter of 2596 feet. The diameters of the three circular fences were proportional to the Silbury mile of 1947 feet. The innermost fence surrounded the Ranch House and bunk houses and its diameter was 48 percent of a Silbury mile, half of 96 percent, or 24/25ths, the Harmonic of the Universe. The middle circular fence surrounded all the other structures and its diameter was two-thirds of a Silbury mile, representing all those things that two-thirds stands for. The area between the middle circular fence and the outermost circular fence was the corral. The Silbury mile is 75 percent of the diameter of the outermost circular fence, a representation of 750,000 rpms, the transdimensional spin rate.

The outermost fence had 420 large crystal fence posts and the Ranch House was 420 feet in diameter. Both were considered to be ten times 42. An embryo—the beginning of life for all animals and self-aware beings—requires the initial growth of 12 cells around it to continue to mature. 6 The next layer of growth around the 12 cells surrounding the embryo contains 42 cells. Philosophia metaphorically represents this growth process as follows: the embryo is the Source, the first layer of 12 cells is self-aware life, and the second layer of 42 cells is animal life.

The Ranch House was constructed entirely of wood and had a very steep 16 sided shingle roof. Each facing of the roof had two windows—one above the other. On top of the 16 sided shingle roof was a round cupola topped by a hexagonal shingle roof. On top of the hexagonal shingle roof was a flag pole. The 16 facings of the main roof, the 32 windows in the main roof and the six facings of the cupola roof added up to 54, or 12 + 42. The roofs were painted red, the sides of the Ranch House white.

When Cary Manpure had first seen a line diagram of the Ranch House area when he was much younger he had shouted out in his classroom, "This looks like Atlantis!—sort of. There aren't enough circles though." 62 (The illustration of Figure 62 is not the illustration Cary Manpure knew. The illustration of Figure 62 does not have enough circles either.)

He received many blank stares from his classmates who had not yet read about the long bygone planet whose civilization had been savaged due to volcanic eruptions, but Cary Manpure could quote pages of text about Atlantis from memory.

"...centuries later, scattered and incomplete records were found by chance in a long since deserted, hermetically sealed tunnel containing shattered crystal tubes, strange looking cars, and what turned out to be control mechanisms." Cary Manpure said aloud to himself after school that day as he rode the Peri to the Waldark House Station to meet Tommy Untiman.

The two were going on a weekend hike together. That afternoon and evening they were going to hike from Waldark House to a large impact crater that was about 10 miles southeast of Waldark House, passing an outlying office structure along the way. They would camp there overnight, explore the crater and then hike about three miles to a curious mesa northeast of that crater. This mesa had always intrigued Cary Manpure because its natural shape was reminiscent of the Tor. That day they would climb to its top and camp there for the night. This would be at a spot Cary Manpure had picked out from aerial imaging that looked down upon the structure containing the water booster pumps for the western portion of the Horz complex. On the last day of their expedition they would descend the mesa and then walk back across the rocky plain to Waldark House, about 11 miles distant. 42

Cary Manpure continued his recitation of history:

"A damaged lexicon was also found in the sealed tunnel and through much hard labor, the lexicon was translated into the language of the day and so that which much later became known as Hellenikos, was preserved. Grave robbers found the tunnel, but were observed by seekers of that time, and those seekers preserved, aired, catalogued and published what had been so miraculously discovered.

"Later those same seekers founded the science of archaeology by meticulously and expertly excavating the area where the original accidental finds had been made. They unearthed the remains of the Capital city of the previously unknown and highly scientifically advanced civilization which had existed on their planet. Numerous times they found written the name of that city: Atlantis. The name of the civilization was never found.

"The archaeologists found a book on electricity and as a result of that find their civilization leaped forward, and they were able to reconstruct and make operational a part of the perierchomai transportation system whose remains they had found—using electricity to power it.

"The electrical energy requirements of that system were so great however, that perierchomai transportation systems were not practical for usage by the burgeoning civilization on that planet—until Waldark and his 'cabalists' came upon consciousness energy. With the advent of consciousness energy as the source of energy for that planet, perierchomai transportation systems almost immediately sprang up everywhere and ever since have been the land based transportation of the galaxies along the chain of galaxies leading to and including this galaxy..."

That day as Cary Manpure and Tommy Untiman proceeded across the plain with the setting sun at their back Cary Manpure said to his friend, "Tommy, tomorrow we're going to become archaeologists. We're going to use our entrenching tools on the top of that curious mesa I've always talked about and which we're going to climb. We're going to find something."

They did and archaeology was reborn.

Under only a foot of soil they hit a hard surface. Quickly they cleared away more soil and discovered the tip of a pyramid shaped structure. Cary Manpure dropped down into their hole, looked at something and then quickly told Tommy Untiman to help him out so that they could fill in the hole.

After they had covered over their find and carefully smoothed back the surface, Cary Manpure turned to a very perplexed Tommy Untiman and said, "I saw a diagram of two galaxies connected by a dotted line carved into the surface of that structure. I saw a diagram of our galaxy with this solar system marked and a diagram of this solar system with the third and fourth planets marked. A single word was written under these three diagrams in a script so similar to Hellenikos that I could read what it said: Eirene, meaning 'peace.'

"Before the destruction of Atlantis, someone who knew what we now call Hellenikos must have left our chain of galaxies and their descendants have been here. Before we came to Silbury they must have observed developing beings on the planet forbidden to us and projected that future beings of the blue-green planet would one day come here. They left their marker of peace right here because they knew that this was an area where a gravitron infusion complex would be constructed. In similar situations intergalactic travelers who came to this galaxy left markers of peace in many places along the way.

"It's been right under our noses for nearly a quarter of a million years, but we never found it until now. This marker of peace is not meant for us, but for the future beings of the blue-green planet right next door. We act as if we never found this. We tell no one. I want them to find it."

"And inside the marker of peace they will find the history of another chain of galaxies," Tommy Untiman responded.

"Yes," concluded Cary Manpure, "just like those who have—or will find—the markers of peace left by the intergalactic travelers who came to this galaxy. There must be many such markers throughout the Universe.

"They will also find the history of everything before the destruction of Atlantis, or at least up until the ancestors of those seekers who put the marker of peace here, had left Atlantis before its final destruction. It is difficult for me to walk away from this, but we must."

When they got back to Waldark House Cary Manpure said goodbye to his friend and entered the perierchomai transportation system. As he did so he looked at the station sign, and as he rode home he thought about the Peri signs.

Cary Manpure knew that the design of those signs had come down to them from Atlantis, in whose ruins excavators had found several battered and shattered perierchomai transportation system signs and their support posts which they painstakingly pieced together to form several complete signs and support posts. The signs themselves consisted of a round white colored shield with a mid-blue colored ring around them and a same mid-blue colored horizontal line across them. Cary Manpure knew that the blue ring represented the cross section of a Peri crystal tube and that the blue line was a side view of one of those same tubes. On the blue line, written in white, in the letters of what is known to Alteans as Hellenikos was the word: 'Peri.'

The round Peri signs were placed on a clear crystal oval shield representing an eye. The signs on their shields were held aloft by tall, thin crystal support posts in the shape of shepherds crooks. From the start those who had excavated the signs understood the symbology of their shields and support posts: the perierchomai is a transportation system which takes many beings around and about quickly and safely.

"The Peri is our vigilant shepherd," Cary Manpure said aloud to himself that day as the Peri car he was riding was automatically shunted around the Tower of Ancestors Seed Station on its way to its destination, the Zuv House Station.

When Cary Manpure was 15, he gave a presentation to his history class on Atlantis. Normally, Cary Manpure worked with his cousin Vicky on such projects, but this was a solo assignment. In order to prepare himself Cary Manpure reviewed the varied sources he had in his own personal library which discussed Atlantis, drew up a plan of the city and made an outline. With outline in hand and the city plan of Atlantis affixed to the wall behind him Cary Manpure stood up and spoke to his classmates:

"Atlantis is the oldest known and recorded city in the chain of galaxies leading to this galaxy," he began. "Atlantis was destroyed due to multiple volcanic eruptions, rediscovered centuries later by accident and subsequently fully excavated. Atlantis means 'something not equaled' and the images of Atlantis in its ruined state which have come down to us, clearly show that Atlantis was a superb city full of style and grace. 62.1,62.2

"Atlantis was laid out and constructed on a broad and gently sloping conical shaped hill. A very wide river ran around the hill on which Atlantis was constructed and that river was later diverted to form a circle around the city three miles wide before flowing onwards about 500 miles to the ocean. Atlantis—including the river which encircled it—was precisely 27 miles in diameter.

"The uppermost and center part of Atlantis was flattened and surrounded by a circular terraced wall five miles in diameter. In the center of this central terraced area was a 10 sided columned structure which housed the city's energy transconversion complex with the energy transredimensioning site at its center. This 10 sided structure was constructed on a 12 sided base. Had that base been circumscribed, the resulting circle would have been one mile in diameter.

"Splendidly designed round, columned structures containing a museum and library were also to be found on the center terraced area of Atlantis. All three structures were surrounded by a park. 62.1

"No one knew the purpose of the structure in the center of Atlantis until after the time of Waldark when the groundplan of that structure was compared with those things which Waldark and his 'cabalists' rediscovered. The museum and the library were identified primarily by the inscriptions over the entryways of their facades.

"A second terraced area contained the business section of the city and warehouses. This area was three miles across and therefore its outer edge had a diameter of 11 miles.

"The wall supporting the second terrace was angled inward at 19.47 degrees from the vertical. The wall supporting the terrace in the center of Atlantis was angled inward at 22.48 degrees from the vertical. The significance of these numbers was discovered by Herzman, one of the Waldark's 'cabalists' and an historian and student of archaeology.

"The third and last area of Atlantis was five miles across and extended from the base of the wall supporting the second terrace to the edge of the river. This area was not significantly sculpted and in it were the residences of those living in Atlantis. Also in this area constructed in a 'ring' 18 miles in diameter (6+5+7 miles in diameter) were an Akadeimia in the east, a Philosophia House in the south, a Gymnasion/Stadion in the west and a Hippodromos in the north. This 18 mile diameter 'ring' was not the same as the other concentric rings, it was only inferred; including the seed structure this inferred ring was the 14th feature of Atlantis. This 18 mile inferred ring combined with the 14th feature of Atlantis (represented the Source of the Universe, that Entity which is beyond our reality.)

"All four complexes of the 18 mile diameter 'ring' were positively identified by inscriptions. Some information was obtained from very severely damaged books found at Akadeimia and in the Philosophia House.

"The river front was 21 miles in diameter, was well developed and had areas for recreational facilities, gardens, shops, restaurants and aquatic activities.

"The thing we know most about Atlantis is its perierchomai transportation system, the transportation system which Atlantis gave to those who followed. The system was laid out in 12 concentric rings, two of which were under the two circular terrace walls of Atlantis. Two others were under the inner and outer banks of the river. One was under the upper terraced area, two were under the lower terraced area and two more were under the residential area. Three elevated concentric rings circled Atlantis well into the countryside.

"Twelve evenly spaced tunnels containing perierchomai tubes radiated outward to connect the nine concentric ring tubes in Atlantis and the three elevated concentric rings outside Atlantis. There were 12 stations in each of the 12 concentric rings. The seed station was under the 10 sided structure in the center of Atlantis and it was accessed by 12 entryways, one entryway in each facing of the 12 sided base of that 10 sided structure.

"Atlantis lay on a relatively flat river plain surrounded on all sides by mountains, through which the river had cut a gorge to the ocean. 62.3 Atlantis also lay in the center of an agricultural area made into a rectangle by a surrounding irrigational canal 300 miles long east-west and 200 miles long north-south. Two interior irrigation canals ran north-south, dividing the agricultural area into three sections 100 miles east-west and 200 miles north-south. Underground crystal pipes ran between the sections of irrigation canals bringing water directly to the roots of crops and trees and to the animals' water troughs. Elevated perierchomai transportation system tubes supported overhead spraying irrigation systems.

"All three agricultural sections were accessible by way of perierchomai transportation system which had concentric rings centered on the center of Atlantis with diameters of 54, 108 and 127 miles.

"The nine concentric rings of the perierchomai transportation system had diameters of 4.386490845 miles, 5 miles, 7 miles, 9.72 miles, 11 miles, 13.5 miles, 15 miles, 21 miles and 27 miles. <u>62.2</u> The 5 and 7 mile rings represented those things which 5 and 7 represent. The 9.72 ring was 36 percent of the 27 and therefore represented the 360 degree system. The 11 mile ring was equivalent to 4 plus 7 and represented those things which 4 and 7 represent. The 13.5 miles ring was half of 27. The 15 mile ring was 55.555+ percent of 27 and represented those things which 5 represent. The 21 mile ring was equivalent to 3 times 7 and represented those things which 3 and 7 represent.

"The 4.386490845 mile ring was not measured that accurately, but that precise distance is inferred because 4.386490845 is equivalent to the square of two-thirds pi.

"My report on Atlantis is brief because we do not know much about Atlantis. Other than the discovery of records, a lexicon in a perierchomai transportation system tunnel and the things I have mentioned above, no other written material of significance was ever found in Atlantis, except for a message found with a resin encased inlaid wooden table, which predated Atlantis by 20 billion years.

"The lexicon proved to be extremely important. It was a lexicon of what we now call Hellenikos and that single volume and the encased table are our only links with the times preceding the last 100 billion years.

"We think that those who lived in Atlantis spoke what we now call Hellenikos and a man named Eumares, who originally owned the encased table, probably spoke Hellenikos as well. He lived long before the time of Atlantis and in Hellenikos his name means 'gentle.'

"I think everyone spoke what we now call Hellenikos prior to the destruction of Atlantis."

Carry Manpure finished his dissertation and sat down.

When Cary Manpure was 11 and Cary Jackman was 12 they worked together to make Cary Jackman's model transportation system into a portion of the perierchomai transportation system of Atlantis for an exhibit on Atlantis made by their school. Cary Manpure was insistent that their exhibit match Atlantis exactly and he badgered Cary Jackman until he relented by releasing enough of his model system to make such an accurate portrayal possible.

The exhibit was such a success that Edler Chee came to see it and with him came his daughter Althena. Althena was bored with the exhibit and wondered around it aimlessly until she came to the model of the Atlantis perierchomai transportation system. There she stopped and watched and listened as Cary Jackman, who had learned all about Atlantis from Cary Manpure, told her many things about it and showed her how everything worked. After Althena Chee had left, Cary Jackman turned to Cary Manpure with glazed eyes and said, "She is gorgeous. I want her."

"Forget it, Buff. She's three times your age," Cary Manpure replied.

Line shacks were located at or near the four corners of the Ranch.

In a wooden pump house located just south of the Tetrahedron Crater's southern tangent and on the sight line from Hurbury to the Tetrahedron, an old-fashioned pump did its job, pumping water out of the Tetrahedron Crater Reservoir and sending it to the Ranch through an equally old-fashioned open topped, wooden conduit, that followed the contours of the topography. The wooden conduit passed between the two craters and then continued to the Ranch House area. Branch wooden conduits led from the main wooden conduit down into each crater. From the Ranch House area smaller underground steel alloy conduits carried water throughout the range land, and fed directly the grass roots in the grazing areas.

During the five-billion year trek of the intergalactic pioneers livestock had been carried in enormous vessels, kept in environments approximating as closely as possible those under which they were kept on planets. Feed crops for that livestock, as well as food crops and fruit and nut orchards for the pioneers were grown aboard specially designed vessels. When the extragalactic travelers had landed on Altea, they were thrilled to see the real farms and ranches of the indigenous beings.

When Essenes left Altea and when the Lotharians escaped from Altean territory vessels similar to those employed by the intergalactic travelers carried livestock, crops, and fruit and nut orchards along with those travelers. They also took along horses, for they were determined not be downcast as the intergalactic travelers had been. When Alteans flew directly to Silbury and settled there, they brought with them livestock, fruit and nut trees and seeds for growing feed and food crops. They also brought along horses.

When the four members of the unit of four friends arrived at the

Ranch they were assigned to a bunk house and after changing into riding clothes were told to report to the corral for horse riding lessons. A week later the sore bottomed youths were sent to the southeastern line shack to look after the cattle in that area and to insure that the fences were in good repair. After a week's work with cattle they were sent north to work with sheep.

On the second day the sheep suddenly bolted. Cary Manpure had just gotten off his horse to check for a suspected loose horse shoe. His horse heard the stampeding sheep and bolted away from him. Cary Manpure heard the sheep and when he turned, saw that they were going to run him down. Cary Jackman saw all this developing and immediately began riding toward his friend. Cary Jackman arrived alongside Cary Manpure just before the sheep did, Cary Jackman pulled his friend up behind him onto the horse and they both rode away to safety.

After finishing that week with the sheep they got a day off and after spending considerable time trying rather unsuccessfully to remove the accumulated Ranch smells from their bodies, they went to an old-fashioned cowboy dance at the Ranch House. Since they were lads, the members of the unit of four friends had heard about the old-fashioned cowboy dances at the Ranch, so they were looking forward to finally attending one.

They were disappointed.

Ever since the delivery of the Sixth Essene Panlogos the population of Silbury had been declining as more and more of them left for Daphlay. By the time the four became cowboys that population had been reduced to below 100,000 and the Ranch had had its livestock reduced accordingly.

So the old-fashioned cowboy dance had only a fraction of the attendees such dances had previously enjoyed. They sat themselves down at a table and listened to the music. After a while Cary Jackman and Terry Wellton decided that there was no point in staying. They went back to their bunk house and fell asleep.

Shortly thereafter the two younger members of the unit spotted a young lady who had just walked into the dance hall. Cary Manpure got up, walked over to her and asked her to dance. Tommy Untiman watched them dance until the dance was over. Then he got up, walked over to them and he asked her for the next dance.

Tommy Untiman and Ukika Brown danced five dances together before Cary Manpure could get his best friend aside so he could talk to him.

"Pazzy," Cary Manpure said, "you win. I'm turning in."

Tommy Untiman had a sweetheart.

Tommy Untiman began spending all his time with Ukika Brown.

Lura Harwell had moved away and Cary Manpure was extremely lonely. Sara Roon and Dan Sardman saw this and they began inviting Cary Manpure to go out with them and among the other things they did as a group they managed to win two-thirds dancing contests.

Two days after the four friends returned from their voluntary service at the Ranch, an Essene holo-image suddenly appeared on Silbury and delivered the Seventh Essene Panlogos to the Council of Silbury. It said, "I am an Essene holo-image and I am directed by Essenes to deliver to the Council of Silbury the Seventh Essene Panlogos. The fulfilling of all previous Essene requirements is not sufficient. Alteans are to make further modifications with regard to the genetic project. When the genetic agent is ready Alteans are to travel to the planet previously forbidden to them by Essenes in order to administer the genetic agent. Additional requirements for the genetic project; for the administering of the genetic agent; and for Altean design and construction projects on the planet previously forbidden to Alteans have been infused into computers in the Tetrahedron."

The holo-image disappeared.

The new requirements for the genetic agent were more curious than difficult to achieve.

Essenes instructed Alteans to make modifications in the genetic agent which, over time, would cause minor anatomical changes in many of the transitional beings resulting from the introduction of the genetic agent into females of the current beings on the forbidden planet.

Essenes also instructed Alteans to make modifications in the genetic agent which, over time, would cause major anatomical changes in some of the transitional beings resulting from the introduction of the genetic agent into females of the current beings on the forbidden planet.

The beings resulting from the genetic agent causing major anatomical changes over time were to eventually resemble the final beings of the two-stepped process resulting only after the second genetic agent was administered in about 200,000 years time by future Alteans.

The beings resulting from the genetic agent causing major anatomical changes over time were to die out before the administering of the second genetic agent.

Essenes also instructed Alteans to modify the genetic agent to make it appear as if all beings on the forbidden planet, born as a result of the introduction of the first genetic agent, descended from a single mother.

The requirement Alteans thought was most curious was that the life span of the forbidden planet's final resulting creative and linear-thinking beings should have a life span that was two-thirds shorter than the normal life span of fully developed self-aware beings. However, it was required that at some future date, this life span should be easily expandable to the normal life span of fully developed self-aware beings. This was to be done by using Altean medical procedures to make minor alterations to the immune systems of the final resulting creative and linear-thinking beings.

The instructions of Essenes to Alteans on how to administer the genetic agent were complex and explicit.

Alteans were only allowed to travel to certain locations on the previously totally forbidden planet and only travel along specified routes between those locations.

Essenes gave Alteans names that they were to use for various geographical locations, and a name to call that planet: Danebury.

Essenes told Alteans that Danebury had a 'natural' satellite which Essenes had placed in orbit around Danebury long ago. When the first babies were born, as a result of administering the first part of the genetic agent, Alteans were to begin calling the 'natural' satellite of Danebury the moon.

The intergalactic travelers had called the smaller celestial body which orbits a seed planet, a glamyrr, meaning 'distant reflection.'

When the indigenous beings heard the word 'glamyrr,' they said, "We don't like the sound of your word 'glamyrr.' The large shining light in our sky which is not the sun is the moon."

The indigenous beings had their way.

The totally unexpected requirement for Altean design and construction projects on Danebury was much less explicit.

Essenes told Alteans to design three structures, but only to construct two-thirds of them. The general geographical areas in which the three structures were to be constructed or sited were specified by Essenes.

Chapter Ten

Joe Lon Odkin

Joe Lon Odkin was a huge but gentle man. Joe Lon Odkin had been given more than his share of tragedies for one lifetime. When Joe Lon Odkin was 40 he lost his wife to a rare disease. When Joe Lon Odkin was 51 he lost his only son in the sabotaging of the Tor. He had no daughter.

When Joe Lon Odkin was 52 he decided to track down those who had killed his son.

Legal authority on Silbury had been unable to find out much about the sabotage of the Tor. The bodies of the Shick brothers had been found at the bottom of the ascending passageway leading from Glamyrr Gate into the Tor. Glamyrr Gate had been found ajar with its locking bolts cut off. The alarm system of the Glamyrr Gate security system had been destroyed. An air ship stripped of all identification and containing no other clues had been found near Glamyrr Gate.

Beyond that there was nothing. After six months the investigation was halted.

Joe Lon Odkin decided that such a situation was not good enough. He would find the accomplice or accomplices of the perpetrators himself, by using that component of his mind which Odkin knew was his greatest asset: logic.

Logic told Odkin many things. It told Odkin that the perpetrators had at least been assisted by someone with access to highly secret information concerning the security systems of Glamyrr Gate. The investigators had already deduced that, Odkin knew. Logic also told Odkin that the sabotage had most likely been timed to coincide with the ceremonies in Hur

Square. The investigators thought that also. The reason for that timing being the absence of the on duty Aspis Crystal Security Director, who, along with the other two Aspis Crystal Security Directors, would be involved in secret security operations relating to the Hur Square ceremonies. Odkin agreed with investigators who had concluded that the accomplice or accomplices also had access to the schedules of the on duty Aspis Crystal Security Director.

Transcommunication logs in the Bastion indicated that the on duty Aspis Crystal Security Director had received a transcommunication from Daphlay about the time he would have had to leave the Tor. The commander of the security detachment at Sustanator Gate had told investigators that he had received a security alert a few minutes before the explosions and had immediately sent a security team to assist the on duty Aspis Crystal Security Director. The computers which recorded security related communications in the Tor had been destroyed by the explosion, but there was no reason to doubt the word of the badly injured security detachment commander.

The discovery of the bodies of the Shick brothers had provided the investigators with additional evidence, but had not led them to an accomplice or accomplices. The Shicks had been convicted of falsifying ore sample data several years before and had only recently been released from incarceration. Investigators could find no one who had even spoken with them since their release. Investigators concluded, and Odkin agreed, that the accomplice or accomplices must also have had access to incarceration records.

The bodies had both been shot in the back from above by an energy pistol, most likely fired by the on duty Aspis Crystal Security Director, the investigators deduced. There was no one else who could have shot them except perhaps a fellow perpetrator. That seemed unlikely because the air ship was still in its presumed getaway position.

The empty bandoleers on the bodies brought investigators to the conclusion, and Odkin agreed also, that the two brothers had set separate high explosive charges in the two energy transconverter rooms. Even though the rubble had not been removed, it was obvious that there had been large explosions in both rooms caused by separate charges. The explosion of one charge had caused a large section of the Upper Tor's crystal facing paneling to collapse; the explosion of the other charge had not done as much exterior damage because directly above the explosion, the extremely strong crystal corner structural support of the Upper Tor had borne the brunt and had not broken.

A third explosion from a third charge had caused the Aspis crystal to fall into the heart of the Tor. Odkin agreed with investigators that a third perpetrator must have set this charge in the area of the Aspis crystal. That body, along with the bodies of the members of the security team and the body of the on duty Aspis Crystal Security Director lay entombed in the rubble of the Tor. Precisely how any of them died was unknown.

When Joe Lon Odkin decided to take it upon himself to uncover the accomplice or accomplices of the perpetrators, he knew everything which the investigation had determined to date. Logic told him that the identity of the unknown third perpetrator would be virtually impossible to ascertain. Someone was probably missing from Silbury, but there was no way of telling unless it had been reported to legal authority. Trying to find out the identity of the third perpetrator would be a waste of time, Odkin concluded.

Legal authority had already reduced the number of possible accomplices to 79, based on those who had access to all the restricted or secret information it would have been necessary to posses. Everyone had been interviewed and none had come under suspicion. Legal authority bound by legal statutes could do no more.

Odkin very carefully went over the list of the 79 possible accomplices, a list he had obtained through means Odkin considered necessary. Odkin intended to use logic to reduce the list as much as he could. Then he would personally follow the remaining suspects until one of them made a mistake. With the list was all the information legal authority had gathered about the 79 possible accomplices. Odkin read through the information several times, thought for a while and eliminated 18 of them.

The list of possible accomplices was now 61.

Odkin read the information about the 61 possible accomplices several more times and eliminated 27 more.

He now had 34 possible accomplices.

Odkin read and read but could eliminate no more. Then he got the idea of attaching a single motive for the accomplice or accomplices.

The only single motive which logic told Odkin could have been responsible: **GREED**.

Odkin reduced his list to four.

On rotating nights Odkin tracked his four suspects for two months. At the end of that time he reviewed in his mind everything he had observed. He eliminated one suspect. Odkin then tracked his remaining three suspects for two more months. At the end of that time he reviewed in his mind everything he had observed and eliminated two.

The only name remaining on Odkin's list was Paul Bunzler.

Joe Lon Odkin went directly to Elder Byron Haley Chee and told him his story. Elder Chee obtained a search patent for Bunzler's living quarters. Legal authority entered those living quarters and found a quantity of gold and a Pleiadean transceiver. Bunzler was taken into custody.

Hoping to reduce his punishment Bunzler told legal authority everything he knew about the sabotage. The name of the man who had contacted him was unknown to him. The origin of the man who had contacted him was unknown. The man had paid him with gold, had promised more gold, and a new home after the completion of the sabotage. They had transcommunicated many times before the sabotage working out details. They had transcommunicated only once since, just after the sabotage. Subsequently he had not been able to contact the other man.

Though Bunzler might be telling the truth, the Council of Silbury was obliged to take resolute action in case Bunzler had actually continued to transcommunicate with the Pleiadeans up until the time he was apprehended. If so, an attack by the Pleiadeans could very well be imminent. The Altean Naval Service was put on full alert.

After the Altean Naval Service had decoded the very narrow spherical bearing on which Bunzler had been transcommunicating, a star ship was dispatched on an intelligence gathering mission to Colchis while numerous other star ships protected Silbury from a possible attack.

The Alteans had to assume Pleiadeans were on Colchis and therefore that space craft could not get near one of the approach points of the solar system containing Colchis without being detected. The Altean Naval Service had worked out a way to secretly gather intelligence data being emitted from sources within any given solar system. The interstellar braking procedure was altered so that space craft commence their slow down sooner. Consequently, Altean Naval Service space craft can approach a solar system, remain beyond detection range and listen. While such craft listen, members of its Crew, wearing environmental suits, rethicken the doors of number nine gravitron thrusters by streaming metallic particles (that they had brought with them specifically for this purpose) against the doors as energy is run through those doors.

Under normal circumstances all space craft which brake for a solar system must proceed to one of the approach points of that solar system to rethicken the doors of their number nine gravitron thruster. Without this procedure, any attempt at either entering that solar system, or even braking for another solar system, would result in the ship being torn apart, due to the weakened doors of the number nine thruster.

The procedure developed by the Altean Naval Service allows space craft to both approach and enter a solar system after having the doors of their number nine thruster rethickened by their Crew.

The transmissions of transmagnetic anomaly search and tracking devices are detectable well beyond the range of these transmissions by passive devices. This is the case because the energy of those transmissions dissipates over distance. Passive detection requires that energy travels in only one direction; active detection requires energy of sufficient strength to travel out to a target and then back. Although targets at great distance may actually be detected, the returning energy carrying a detection message can dissipate before the message is returned. Intelligence gathering Altean Naval Service star ships could therefore get as close as possible to the sources of their intelligence gathering, but could remain out of detection range of transmagnetic anomaly search and tracking devices.

For four months the Altean Naval Service star ship listening to the various transmissions coming from Colchis collected intelligence data, then returned to Silbury.

The Council of Silbury ordered an Altean Naval Service assault on the suspected Pleiadean position on Colchis. This was carried out precisely six months later, after very thorough planning based on complete analysis of the intelligence data, combined with rigorous training in standard Altean Naval Service strategy and tactics.

The Stratopedon—the Altean Naval Service marine training encampment located southwest of the Horz complex, became the operations base for the training of the marine assault force—6666 marines strong. Originally located just west of what was to become Altea City, the Stratopedon was moved when the city was built, and was now situated about 16 miles southwest of Altea City. The headquarters structure of the Stratopedon was located on a mesa, and positioned perpendicular to the sight line connecting the Gymnasion/Stadion and the Tor. The distance from the Stratopedon to the midpoint of that sight line was equal to the distance between the Gymnasion/Stadion and the Tor. 62.4

To the Altean Naval Service marines, the Gymnasion/Stadion exemplified physical courage, and the Tor exemplified mental and ethical courage. The Tor exemplified mental and ethical courage due to its buttresses. The five physical structural buttresses at the corners of the Tor exemplified mental courage, because mental courage is a physical necessity for the sustaining of life. With the ornamental buttresses of the two gates of the Tor, there was a total of seven buttresses exemplifying spirit; from which ethical courage flows.

The emblem of the Altean Naval Service is a silver dolphin representing speed, intelligence and loyalty.

The emblem of the Altean Naval Service marines is a gold shield inscribed with a red Hellenikos letter lambda. The gold shield represents the Source of the Universe shielding everything. The red lambda represents the courage of the soul, courage which helps beings achieve physical, mental and ethical courage.

The 6666 Altean Naval Service marines, two-thirds of them from Silbury, chose a long, hook shaped ridge northeast of the headquarters structure of the Stratopedon for their training. This choice was based on their intelligence information and their knowledge of the general topography of Colchis. They were divided into 185 identically integrated Daphlay-Silbury teams consisting of 36 members each. A similarly balanced leadership team of six oversaw the training and led the assault.

A large flotilla of Altean Naval Service star ships from Daphlay joined with a smaller flotilla of Altean Naval Service star ships and marine transport vessels from Silbury just beyond detection range of transmagnetic anomaly detection and tracking devices on Colchis. The operation against the suspected Pleiadean position on Colchis had began. Wearing environmental suits, Crew members of all star ships and all marine transport vessels rethickened the double clamshell doors of each star ship and each marine transport vessel by streaming metallic particles against the doors as energy was run through them.

Following this procedure, the joint force split into two groups. The strike force, composed entirely of star ships, positioned itself about a billion miles above the north pole of Colchis, outside detection range. The assault force, composed of star ship escorts and marine transport vessels carrying the integrated Altean Naval Service marine assault force, positioned itself about a billion miles above the south pole of Colchis, and outside detection range.

When all star ships and marine transport vessels were in position, the order was given to commence the attack. The strike force immediately began its high speed approach to Colchis, which would take nearly two hours to complete, at near solar system light speed. They adopted a tight diamond formation making it impossible for the detectors to determine what was approaching. Half an hour later, passive detection sensors aboard the strike force commander's star ship indicated that the strike force had been detected by Colchis based active detection devices. The strike force commander—the on scene commander—ordered the assault force to begin their approach from the south, and the assault force immediately proceeded toward Colchis at near solar system light speed in six successive loose line abreast formations.

When a large, unknown object, rapidly approaching from the north was reported to the watch commander in the surveillance center of the private empire of the family Sarkneson, he informed the commander of the defence unit at once. Garth Sarkneson was then informed and he told the unit commander to proceed to the surveillance center and then to report back to him again. This time the unit commander told Sarkneson that the large unknown object was continuing to approach Colchis and was doing so at near solar system light speed. Sarkneson ordered the unit commander to sound the emergency alarm. As Sarkneson himself entered the surveillance center many unknown objects were reported to the watch commander—rapidly approaching from the south.

Sarkneson quickly assessed the situation. He thought someone must have told the Pleiadean emperor about the empire of the family Sarkneson and Xung Halbert Mavor was now attacking. Sarkneson realized he was defenseless against such a massive onslaught, but the family Sarkneson had a plan for just this circumstance.

"I will return in a few minutes," the Pleiadean lied as he turned and left the surveillance center.

All defensive positions of the private empire reported operational status to the surveillance center. The unit commander nervously watched the continuing approach of the unknown objects while anxiously awaiting Sarkneson's return. When the large object to the north began slowing down, as if braking for planetary approach, and Sarkneson had still not appeared, the unit commander called Sarkneson's private quarters. There was no response. The unit commander was very concerned, Sarkneson should have been in the surveillance center leading the defense of his private empire. Sarkneson must have been delayed, the unit commander thought, and continued to prepare to defend Sarkneson's empire.

As the star ships of the strike force approaching from the north slowed to maximum attack speed, their commander reformed his star ships into three columns. The lead star ship in each column was ordered to activate all active sensors and star ships leading the left and right columns were to relay data from their active sensors to his star ship, which was leading the center column. Aboard his star ship the strike commander was comparing three holo-plots both visually and by computers. An ever improving target assessment rapidly evolved as they sped toward Colchis.

By the time these star ships were ten minutes away from their target, the strike force commander had received all the data he needed to complete his strike and assault plan. The enemy was located in a heavily defended fortress built into the side of a narrow canyon. The star ships could not risk flying into the canyon to fire at the fortress. Energy cannon could not be used effectively from above because the fortress was protected by the narrowness of the canyon and the overhanging sides above the level of the fortress. Energy torpedoes would be ineffective for the same reason. The only course of action was to land the integrated marine assault force on the rim of the canyon above the fortress and have that assault force attack the fortress while star ships suppressed enemy fire and kept the enemy otherwise pinned down.

To prepare for the landing, star ships swooped down over the canyon in successive columns firing energy cannon and releasing energy torpedo salvos into the canyon. The defenders returned fire with their energy cannon and in doing so gave away their positions. Energy cannon located at or near the top of the canyon were destroyed by attacking star ships.

Once enemy fire had been sufficiently reduced, the strike force commander ordered the landing of the integrated marine assault force. Marine transport vessels landed above the fortress behind the rim of the canyon. They were protected from below by the same rim that protected the fortress from above.

Sappers quickly debarked and ran forward to the rim of the canyon where they placed dozens of high explosive charges near the edge of the rim. The explosions of those charges sheered away a large section of the overhang.

The first assault wave consisted of 30 teams of 36 and the command team of six. All 31 teams fixed long ropes to the new edge of the cliff and then clambered down. At selected intervals, as the ropes were unwound, spikes were driven into the rock to further secure the ropes and to keep them away from the rock so that the life lines worn by the marines would slide easily down the ropes. Once each team of the first wave had progressed far enough down its rope other teams followed behind until the marines of all six assault waves had clambered down all 31 ropes. The first assault wave had 1086 marines, the other five had 1116 marines each.

The first assault wave approached the top of the fortress recessed about five feet into the wall of the canyon. Leading each of the 30 teams of the first assault wave was the team commander, a sapper and three marines carrying line-throwing devices. Each sapper removed a high explosive charge from the bandoleer she or he wore and attached the charge to a line cut by each team leader to a length of 30 feet. One sapper also attached percussion exploders to each facing of his charge. The high explosive charges were then lowered on their lines 30 feet below the lowest marine and dangled in the air in front of the facing of the fortress. The line connected to the percussion exploders charge was 60 feet long and attached to the rock approximately 30 feet above the top of the 30 foot lines by a two foot long spike.

The marines flattened themselves against the wall of the canyon. A single marine located just below the spike holding the 60 foot line began rhythmically pushing outward on this line, causing the charge at its end to swing inward and outward. When one of the percussion exploders on that charge touched the facing of the fortress the charge exploded causing the other high explosive charges dangling nearby to explode. A hole over 200 feet long and five feet high was blown in the facing of the fortress. The marines carrying line-throwing devices fired them and the sharp spikes at the lead end of the lines stuck securely into the facing of the fortress, just above the long hole created by the high explosive charges. The far ends of those lines were then secured to spikes driven into the rock about ten feet above the team leaders positions. The 30 team leaders and the marines who had fired the line-throwing devices detached their lifelines from the decent ropes and reattached them to the lines fired by the line-throwing devices. As they pulled the quick release on their lifelines, they jumped over the edge, slid down the lines and leaped into the hole in the facing of the fortress.

Two-thirds of the command team followed and the remaining two followed the rest of the marines into the fortress. Once inside the fortress the marine assault force made its way steadily downward, routing all opposition. Outside the surveillance center the defenders put up some resistance but were overwhelmed. Marines burst into the surveillance centre and captured it. Any semblance of organized resistance ceased.

Major Anthony Osmar, one of the four members of the integrated leadership team, was one of the first to enter the surveillance center. As he did so he was shot in the chest by a member of the defense unit hiding behind a console. As Major Osmar fell the marines opened fire on that area and it was obliterated.

As Lieutenant Anna Gandy led her team down a corridor deep in the fortress, she suddenly came upon an entryway beyond which she could see a richly appointed room with an entryway on its far side leading into what appeared to be another richly appointed room. Realizing that they had probably come upon the private quarters of the beast for whom they were searching, Lieutenant Gandy signalled her team to follow her.

They found no one.

Lieutenant Gandy stood in the center of the bed chamber. Scanning its contents with her eyes, Lieutenant Gandy saw nothing of interest and was turning to leave the room to reform her team, when she noticed that a paneled section of the wall next to the entryway through which she had just come was not quite lined up correctly with adjoining panels. Lieutenant Gandy moved quickly to the wall and discovered that this section of paneling was hinged and slightly ajar. Behind this paneling was a niche. In the niche was a button set into a steel panel. She pushed the button.

Lieutenant Gandy watched as the flooring on which she was standing slid back and a spiral staircase formed in the hole left by the receded floor. Lieutenant Gandy descended the long spiral staircase, made her way along a lengthy corridor and then entered a large rock hewn chamber in which there was a space craft.

She boarded the craft and made her way to its bridge. There Lieutenant Gandy blasted the craft's navigational control system with her energy pistol.

Having left the craft, Lieutenant Gandy sought another entryway into the rock hewn chamber and found one opposite the entryway through which she had come. Lieutenant Gandy stepped through and followed a corridor for a short distance until it ended at a closed door.

Lieutenant Gandy turned the knob and threw open the door.

There before her on a bed was the beast for whom Lieutenant Gandy had been looking, in the company of a female.

"You are to immediately surrender yourself to legal authority," said Lieutenant Gandy slowly, loudly and distinctly.

Sarkneson heard the voice and jerked his head around. When the beast saw who confronted him he pushed Suzy Bibbens aside and got to his feet next to the bed.

"Who are you?" he demanded.

"Lieutenant Anna Gandy, Altean Naval Service marines, Silbury," Lieutenant Gandy replied.

Sarkneson laughed at Lieutenant Gandy, suddenly lowered his head and charged at her. The shot from Lieutenant Gandy's energy pistol shattered Sarkneson's skull and the beast fell dead at her feet.

Suzy Bibbens screeched when she saw Sarkneson fall and then threw herself at Lieutenant Gandy. Lieutenant Gandy took one step backward and fired again. The shot hit Suzy Bibbens in the chest, instantly killing the plaything of the beast.

In the meantime, the marines were securing the rest of the fortress. The Crew of the Roon Mining Exploration vessel was discovered and released along with the six incarcerated members of the Altean Naval Service. Hal Roon was found and taken into custody. The slaves of the private empire greatly assisted their liberators in capturing surviving members of the defence unit. Operations were launched to track down escapees and to gain control of the gravitron infusion complexes of Colchis. Within a year Colchis had become a secret Altean Naval Service base.

Very brief inspections made by specially trained Altean Naval Service personnel revealed that the rest of Colchis was virtually intact. The bodies of those gassed to death by the Pleiadeans were mummified. All their possessions were still there.

The encased table of Eumares in a wooden crate labelled "Machine Parts" was still in what were the living quarters of Ell Lana and Dan.

Hal Roon was returned to Silbury. In separate trials both Paul Bunzler and Hal Roon were convicted of treason by separate panels of their peers and sentenced to the Crystal Palace for the duration of their lives. Almost all the facts concerning the sabotage were discovered and made available to the community. Only Joe Lon Odkin was dissatisfied. Joe Lon Odkin still wanted to know how Sarkneson had been able to find Bunzler, who was probably the only Altean living on Silbury who had access to the necessary information and would have been willing to help Sarkneson.

Joe Lon Odkin began another search.

By the time an Essene holo-image delivered the Seventh Essene Panlogos, Joe Lon Odkin had still not figured out how Sarkneson had found Bunzler. On receiving the latest instructions from Essenes, the Council arranged a private session for that same day, and asked Joe Lon Odkin to attend. The Council told Odkin about the Seventh Essene Panlogos. Odkin was totally surprised that he had been most specifically selected by Essenes to design three structures for the forbidden planet. He was equally surprised that he was to oversee the construction of two of them. To design three structures and then to construct only two of them was nonsense, he told them. Odkin had never designed any structures before. He had never overseen any construction projects.

"As you know," Odkin concluded, "only nitwits get sent to the Crystal Palace, nitwits who are stupid enough to commit crimes and therefore end up making crystal. Essenes should be in a Crystal Palace. Essenes are nitwits."

"Will you do it?" asked Elder Chee.

"Of course," replied Odkin.

Odkin had just returned to his office in the Hurmaze when an associate informed him that four young men were present and would like to speak with him. The associate asked Odkin if Odkin could see the young men now.

"Of course," replied Odkin.

When Cary Manpure began his last year of high school he knew that he would never finish it—on Silbury. Well before the end of the school year Alteans living on Silbury would have to move to Daphlay. The genetic project was nearly complete, the gravitron infusion spinning disks remained idle and the atmosphere continued to drift into space. As the first few weeks of the school year went by the frame of mind in which Cary Manpure found himself went from being difficult to intolerable. He could not bear leaving Silbury. He became intolerable to those about him. Even his cousin Vicky found it difficult to deal with Cary Manpure's depression.

Cary Manpure decided that he had to do something to prevent the abandonment of Silbury.

Cary Manpure gathered the young men of the unit of four friends about him. They discussed the situation. The four of them agreed to take concerted action. The young men rode to the Hurmaze on the Peri to talk to Director Odkin.

The four decided to seek out Odkin because he had uncovered Bunzler. After everyone else had given up, Odkin had persisted in looking for the traitors and he had succeeded.

The current situation on Silbury was very similar, the young men thought. Everyone had given up on Silbury. They would try to convince Director Odkin to save Silbury.

The young men chose Cary Jackman as their spokesman and he talked for an hour while Cary Manpure, Tommy Untiman and Terry Wellton sat anxiously listening and carefully watching Odkin for any sign he might make about how he was receiving Cary Jackman's impassioned plea.

After Cary Jackman had finished Odkin said, "Count me in."

Odkin told Cary Manpure, Cary Jackman, Tommy Untiman and Terry Wellton to come up with a plan to save Silbury and to report back to him. When all five of them agreed on a plan he would forcefully present it directly to Elder Chee.

After the four friends had left Odkin's office, tears formed in Odkin's eyes. "I lost my son in the Tor," he said to himself. "Now I have four new sons."

Odkin set to work at once designing structures for Danebury, the name Alteans had been instructed to use for the soon no longer to be forbidden planet.

Odkin used logic to determine how he should proceed.

Odkin began with the instructions and information which Essenes had infused into computers in the Tetrahedron in conjunction with the Seventh Essene Panlogos. Odkin would not touch a computer so these instructions and the information were printed out and brought to him.

No Altean had ever known anything about Danebury, other than that it was forbidden to them and that it appeared as a bright blue-green light in the night sky of Silbury. Odkin studied the printouts and then began to concentrate on the geographical information supplied by Essenes.

About two-thirds of Danebury was covered by water. There were several large land masses. Most of the land was in the northern hemisphere. Alteans were to call the largest land mass Ashintoland, a name which Odkin did not recognize. Despite his research the only thing Odkin could figure out about ashinto was that perhaps the 'a' meant 'not;' since 'a' meant 'not' in Hellenikos. Ashintoland was forbidden to Alteans except for an extensive area to its southeast where beings who were to be administered the first part of the genetic agent lived.

Off the western coast of Ashintoland was a large island Alteans were to call Hurengland, a name which Odkin knew meant 'land of shining great truth' and which was obviously derived from Hurengle. The designed, but not constructed structure, was to be sited on or near Hurengland.

The other large land mass, completely located in the northern hemisphere, Alteans were to call Prehurland, a name which to Odkin meant 'pre-shining land.' Prehurland was forbidden to Alteans except for its southern extension which was the site of one of the structures.

All other lands on Danebury Alteans were to call Abzuland. Odkin recognized the syllable 'zu' as an often used, foreshortened variant of 'zoos,' the syllable meaning 'life,' and brought to this galaxy by the intergalactic pioneers. Since Odkin did not know precisely what the prefix 'ab' meant he looked it up in his massive lexicon and found that the prefix 'ab' meant 'away,' 'from,' or 'off.' Combining 'away,' 'from,' or 'off' with 'life' for the name of all the land masses to be called Abzuland was not logical, Odkin thought. Although most of the land masses to be called Abzuland were forbidden to Alteans; both the site for the second structure and the second area where beings who were to be administered the first part of the genetic agent lived, were in the largest of the land masses to be called Abzuland.

Odkin suspected that the word 'Abzuland' must be like the word 'Ashintoland' in that he could only partly figure out the meaning of these names that Alteans were to call these land masses. Before he gave up, however, he decided to see if 'abzu' meant something in Hellenikos. He found something very close: 'abyssos,' a word which literally meant 'bottomless pit,' but one of its abstract meanings was: 'fathomless.'

Odkin thought that although the word 'Abzuland' applied to all the land masses Alteans were to call Abzuland, it must mean something different when applied to the Abzuland in which was located one of the construction sites and one of the areas where beings who were to be administered the first part of the genetic agent lived. The other Abzulands must have had their names derived from 'ab' and 'zu.' The Abzuland where Alteans were to find the beings must have had its name derived from the word 'abyssos.'

"Life is fathomless," said Odkin to himself. "The lands in which we are to help life along could logically be called fathomless. Perhaps ashinto means 'not fathomable.'"

Odkin re-read the Essene instructions concerning the areas of the two construction sites and the one design-only site on Danebury. The Abzuland site was in the northeastern corner of that land mass, "close to, and west of a large river flowing north into the sea." The Prehurland site was "in the south, above 7000 feet altitude." The Hurengland site was "on Hurengland or nearby."

Odkin made a map of Danebury and marked the three siting areas on it. 63 Then he connected the center of those areas with straight lines, forming a triangle. Odkin looked at that triangle for a long time before an idea came to him. The triangle he had drawn on his map of Danebury was like a mirror image of the triangle formed between Hurbury, the Hurmaze and the Tor. Alteans should construct a scale model of Hurbury in Prehurland, a scale model of the Tor in Abzuland and a site should be found on or near Hurengland for some future construction of a scale model of the Hurmaze, Odkin concluded. Odkin was not certain if this was what Essenes had told Alteans to do, but he thought that must be what they meant because Odkin did not know how to design anything—especially anything new.

"Essenes are nitwits," Odkin said to himself. "They belong in a Crystal Palace."

Odkin then began the process of picking the exact sites of the two constructions and the one design-only site, by carefully studying the vast quantities of detailed geographical data that Essenes had infused into the Tetrahedron's computers concerning the areas of these three sites.

In Abzuland, the land "close to, and west of a large river flowing north into the sea" was for the most part very low and marshy. Higher ground extended from the west nearly to the river from just above to just below 30 degrees north latitude. Anywhere on that higher ground and close to the river would be suitable, Odkin thought.

Much of the interior "in the south" of Prehurland was above 7000 feet in altitude so anywhere reasonably flat would fulfill the Essene instructions, Odkin thought.

"On Hurengland or nearby" was so vague, Odkin thought, that again anywhere reasonably flat would fulfill the Essene instructions.

Odkin was uneasy with his conclusions. Although he thought that he was correct about which scale models to construct and which scale model to site, he felt that he should have a better idea of exactly where he should site them.

Then Odkin remembered that the high ground extending nearly to the river in Abzuland was just above and just below 30 degrees north latitude. Intrigued that this latitude was a nice round number that might have something to do with geometry, Odkin read an old geometry book and then found, in its trigonometric tables, that the cosine of 30 degrees is equivalent to the square root of three divided by two. This was something that Odkin remembered from school as being greatly important in the layout of the Horz complex. Odkin decided to position his scale model of the Tor in the east instead of the west, to be consistent with the mirror image; and at 30 degrees north latitude close to the river so as to represent the square root of three divided by two.

Inspired by his having found a logical representational basis for positioning the scale model of Hurbury, Odkin looked to see if he could find similar logical representational bases for positioning the scale model of the Tor and then for positioning of the Hurmaze scale model site.

Odkin found that 19.47 degrees north latitude divided "in the south" Prehurland into nearly equal northern and southern halves, and that almost the entire interior of Prehurland at that latitude was above 7000 feet. Odkin would position his scale model of Hurbury in the west rather than in the east to be consistent with the mirror image; and at 19.47 degrees north latitude to represent tetrahedra.

Odkin found no latitudes "on Hurengland" which provided a logical representational basis for positioning the Hurmaze scale model site, but he did find one "nearby." North of Hurengland was an island across which ran 60 degrees north latitude. Odkin saw that the sine of 60 degrees is also equal to the square root of three divided by two, so he decided to position his scale model site of the Hurmaze at 60 degrees north latitude again to represent the square root of three divided by two.

Odkin took his conclusions to the Council of Silbury, the Council approved his positioning ideas and asked Odkin to begin designing his scale models.

Odkin went to Chapter One and obtained copies of the plans for Hurbury, the Hurmaze and the Tor from the library there. Then he had to decide what scale to use for his models. Odkin found out that Hurbury had a base diameter of about two miles, that the Hurmaze was "98.11 percent of one mile from the bottom of the banded hair net to the crown of the head," and that the Tor was over two and one-half miles along its longest measurement. Odkin decided to design all his models to be one-tenth the size of Hurbury, the Hurmaze and the Tor.

Odkin found from the plans and from a personal inspection that designing a scale model of the spiral mound Hurbury would be relatively easy for him to accomplish. The plans of the Hurmaze, his access to the Hurmaze and his intimate knowledge of the Hurmaze would allow him to be able to design a scale model of the Hurmaze. The Tor was the grave marker for Odkin's son and therefore Odkin would not personally inspect the Tor. To be able to design a scale model of the Tor, Odkin had to rely solely on the plans for the Tor. Both those plans and the Tor were complex.

Odkin discovered that the Tor was constructed in such a way that its positioning and form represented many very important things.

Odkin knew from his studies of topogly that the apex of the Tor was not positioned in order to be a near representation of e/pi (an obscure representation of the relationship of living things to everything) but he did not know that the Tor was positioned to represent the square root of three divided by two!

"That's interesting!" Odkin said to himself when he found that the square root of three divided by two was encoded in the location of the Tor. "That makes me think that I'm right about my location for the scale model of the Tor.

"I'll have to find out what the square root of three divided by two means—all I remember is the that it is supposed to be represented throughout the Horz complex."

Odkin read that the square root of three divided by two is the transdimensional component of the transdimensional constant 2.720699046.

"That's not very interesting," Odkin said to himself as he closed his old geometry book.

Odkin found out that the Tor was constructed so that one of its five facing edges pointed directly at the site of energy transredimensioning in the Hurmaze and on the same bearing from that facing edge, far beyond the Hurmaze, was the corbelled domed grave circle. On that facing edge had been placed the Transdimensional Triangle, the top of which was located at 40.89339465 degrees north latitude; because the tangent of 40.89339465 degrees is equivalent to the square root of three divided by two. 64

Odkin also found out that the positioning of the Transdimensional Triangle resulted in two very important geodetic distances: the distance from the site of energy transredimensioning in the Hurmaze to the bottom of the Transdimensional Triangle was 19.09859317 Silbury nautical miles; equivalent to 1/360th of the diameter of an idealized perfectly spherical Silbury. The distance from the site of energy transredimensioning in the Hurmaze to a large marker on the facing of the Transdimensional Triangle was 19.47122061 Silbury nautical miles; a representation of the latitude at which the three, non-polar points of circumscribed tetrahedra touch the spinning sphere that circumscribes them.

Odkin found out that the form of the Tor represented some very important things, and that these were represented not in its three-dimensional form, but in its apparent two-dimensional form, as if viewed from high above. 65 The apparent two-dimensional form of the Tor was that of an elongated pentagon, made up of two pairs of similar triangles and one triangle completely different from the others. The two triangles adjacent to the facing edge, pointing at the site of energy transredimensioning in the Hurmaze were similar equilateral triangles, having apparent two-dimensional lengths of 1.947 Silbury nautical miles. The left facing edge of the left equilateral triangle (as viewed from overhead facing northward) pointed at the Tower of Ancestors; the right facing edge of the right equilateral triangle pointed at Hurbury. The similar triangles next to the non-adjacent sides of the two equilateral triangles both had interior angles of 85.36 degrees. The interior angle of the fifth and unique triangle was 69.28 degrees.

The five sides of the Tor metaphorically represented living things. The two similar equilateral triangles closest to the Hurmaze formed one-third of a hexagon. The pentagonal Tor's relationship to the one-third apparent hexagon was meant to be seen as the ratio of 5 to 6, the metaphorical representation of the relationship between the non-living parts of the Universe and living things.

The square root of three divided by two was also represented in the apparent two-dimensional form of the Tor; when any one of the 60 degree angles of the two similar equilateral triangles is divided by the 69.28 degree interior angle of the unique triangle, the result is a near equivalent of the square root of three divided by two.

While searching for and finding the square root of three divided by two throughout the Horz complex, Odkin also discovered that the various angles of the apparent two-dimensional form of the Tor and the fractional angles thereof, were frequently repeated in many of the angular relationships between the diverse large and small components and structures of the Horz complex.

Odkin also found that the angle formed at the Tower of Ancestors, between the apex of the Tor and the site of energy transredimensioning in the Hurmaze, is 69.28 degrees; [64] and that the angle formed at the apex of the Tor by the site of energy transredimensioning in the Hurmaze and the Tower of Ancestors is 60 degrees.

"And the relationship between these two angles is a near equivalent of the square root of three divided by two," said Odkin to himself. "This place must have been designed by Essenes. No one but a nitwit would have planned such a place. I'll have to find out who did it."

Joe Lon Odkin ascertained that Lura Redmand had been most responsible for the final design of the Horz complex and so he read about her.

"She doesn't seem like a nitwit," Odkin said to himself as he closed a biography of Lura Redmand. "I think she must have been a nice lady."

After assimilating the information contained in the plans for the Tor, Odkin designed his scale model to be completely solid and made entirely out of quarried stone. Then he designed his scale models of Hurbury and the Hurmaze. Odkin presented everything to the Council of Silbury, and the Council approved his work.

After the unit of four friends had left Odkin's office they returned to Altea City on the Peri to try to figure something out. Odkin asked them to come up with a plan to save Silbury. They came up with nothing. Cary Manpure's disposition became even more intolerable to those around him.

Out of sheer exasperation, Cary's mother 'suggested' that he take a couple of days off from school and visit his brother Frank, a lieutenant in the Altean Naval Service and assigned to the combined energy transproduction and magnetic field command complex, located about 500 miles northeast of the Horz complex. 66 Cary Manpure asked Tommy Untiman to go with him, which he did.

Cary and Tommy left early the next morning and flew in an Altean Naval Service air ship to the complex, arriving in time for breakfast. Later, Lieutenant Manpure showed his younger brother and Tommy Untiman around the complex which was housed in an enormous pyramidal structure constructed on the rim of an impact crater. The planetary-wide matrix of defensive magnetic fields received its power from the energy transproduction section of the complex. The command section of the complex monitored the matrix for intruders and could then fire upon any intruders, by remote control, using the numerous land based energy cannon which were located around Silbury.

The planetary defenses of Silbury, including those defense systems controlled by the combined energy transproduction and magnetic field command complex (and which before the sabotage included the planetary anti-weapons shield created by the Aspis Crystal at the apex of the Tor) had been made possible by the unprecedented computational power and especially by the enormous data, information and knowledge storage capacity of the three gigantic computers in the Tor. Output from the computers in the Hurmaze—as well as necessary data, information and knowledge stored in those computers—was transcommunicated from the Bastion to the complex and to other planetary defense command centers. The Bastion was linked with the computers in the Hurmaze by secret, secure, deeply buried conduit.

Lieutenant Manpure was a watch officer in the computer interface section, he had to take up his duties on the afternoon watch and that left Cary Manpure and Tommy Untiman without much to occupy them. They sat around the bunk room for a while, then decided to go outside. Just beyond the mooring area Cary Manpure spotted a fence about five feet high, made of crystal posts with crystal cross pieces placed about six inches apart. Along the fence were signs which read, "Do not climb. Open country beyond."

The phrase 'open country' was the standard designation for unexplored areas of Silbury. Almost the entire planet was open country and much of that was also off limits due to magnetic fields and energy cannon. Open country on these signs did not mean that the area beyond was off limits due to a magnetic field or energy cannon battery; if the area beyond the fence was off limits for either or both of those reasons, the signs would have read: "Restricted."

"The Altean Naval Service simply does not want its personnel or visitors to enter open country because it is unexplored and therefore potentially dangerous, they think," said Cary Manpure. "Let's go and see what's out there.

"We are not supposed to climb the fence," responded Tommy Untiman.

"Then we go under it," Cary Manpure said.

"We might get into trouble like we did before," said Tommy Untiman.

"But those signs said 'Restricted,'" said Cary Manpure.

Cary Manpure and Tommy Untiman had once got into trouble by ignoring "Restricted" signs. After that, when they came across other "Restricted" signs, they did not pass them.

The Crystal Palace stood six miles to the northwest of the Gymnasion/Stadion of Altea City, just outside the southeastern rim of a very large impact crater. 62.4 This gleaming, six-sided structure of transparent crystal was the place of incarceration for those who had been convicted of crimes on Silbury. The Crystal Palace afforded its inmates very little privacy, but it did provide them with living quarters so they could work—at the Crystal Works.

The Crystal Works were located inside the crater: the Crystal Crater. Some inmates worked at gathering up sand for crystal production from the vast dunes piled up against the inside of the southeastern part of the rim of the impact crater. These dunes were formed by aeons of sandstorms which had occurred with regularity prior to the adjustment of the atmosphere of Silbury. Other inmates off loaded galena from the space mining vessels which landed in the crater laden with ore mined in the asteroid belt. Still other inmates worked on the process of making crystal. All inmates were carefully supervised and guarded, especially those working on the precise manufacture of crystal.

Energy and water for the Crystal Palace and the Crystal Works was conduited from the main Horz complex system routed from Altea City. Some of the tornum supplied to the Crystal Palace was run through dynamos to produce electricity, one of the two places where electricity was generated on Silbury.

The other site was in the old Crystal Palace, located near the south-western edge of a large mesa just east of the Bastion. Following the construction of Altea City and the new Crystal Palace and new Crystal Works, the old Crystal Palace and Works had been sealed. But after the assault on the private empire of the family Sarkneson they had been unsealed in order to incarcerate the members of the Sarkneson defense unit and collaborators who had been captured by the Altean Naval Service marines.

The electricity generated in the Crystal Palace was sent through a very high tension electrified fence which ran completely around the Crystal Crater and effectively prevented escapees from getting beyond the immediate vicinity of the crater. Authorities were not concerned about escapees who remained at large in that area; if they did not give themselves up they would die of thirst and/or starvation.

Two other non-electrified fences encircled the Crystal Crater—one well inside the electrified fence, the other well outside it. Both of these non-electrified fences had signs on them every 6 feet which read:

"Restricted! Deadly Extremely High Tension Electric Fence with Resulting Extremely Dangerous Powerful Magnetic Field Beyond!" 66.1

Between each non-electrified warning fence and the high-tension electrified fence was a ring of seven cylindrical pylons, a total of 14 pylons in all. These pylons contained sensors which could detect the presence of anything between the warning fences and the electrified fence and when they did, they broadcast additional warnings to anyone approaching death. There were seven pylons in each ring as a symbol of eternity—if you did not heed the last warning.

On that occasion when the curious, exploring Cary Manpure and Tommy Untiman saw these signs on the outermost fence surrounding the Crystal Crater they turned around and went home.

Cary Manpure walked quickly to the fence near the combined energy transportation and magnetic field command complex and found that he could not get underneath it where he was, so he walked along the fence for a distance until he came to a spot where the ground rose sharply. Half way between the two posts, there was just enough clearance for him to wriggle under. Tommy Untiman reluctantly followed.

Shortly after Cary Manpure and Tommy Untiman had discovered the marker of peace buried under Cary Manpure's "curious mesa" they had gone on another archaeological expedition: to the area of the old Stratopedon northwest of Altea City. 62.4 They had met once again at the Waldark House Station of the periérchomai transportation system and proceeded together to the Gymnasion/Stadion Station. From there they walked around the Gymnasion/Stadion and then hiked across the desert for about two and a half miles to a sculpted impact crater which had been the main part of the old Stratopedon.

They had explored the sculpted portion of the crater and the remains of structures that had stood there. Then they walked westward along the southern rim of the crater until they came to a long artificially constructed ridge made of garbage and covered over with sand. They walked along this ridge until they came to near its western end where the garbage was still being deposited and then slid down its southern bank.

Next Cary Manpure and Tommy Untiman had walked about four miles across the desert to a triangular shaped mesa from the top of which Cary Manpure thought they would be able to look down the long axis of Altea City toward the Hurmaze. They climbed the mesa, got their view and then Cary Manpure noticed another "curious mesa" just to the west of the triangular shaped mesa on which they stood.

"Let's go and take a look," said Cary Manpure.

They located a saddle-shaped ridge between the two mesas, climbed down from where they stood and walked across the ridge. When they got to the far end of the ridge they had come to a high fence with signs on it which read: "Restricted."

"Must be old signs," Cary Manpure said as he started to climb over. Tommy Untiman reluctantly followed.

They had climbed only a very short distance up Cary Manpure's new "curious mesa" when they were confronted by three very grim-faced Altean Naval Service marines.

"Stop right where you are!" they were ordered.

Cary Manpure and Tommy Untiman froze.

The marines handcuffed the two lads and led them away.

A few minutes later, they found themselves in a heavily armored room standing before an extremely serious Altean Naval Service marine captain.

"What were you two doing?" he ordered.

"We were just exploring," answered Cary Manpure.

"Who are you?" ordered the marine captain.

Cary Manpure told him their names and added, "my father is a naval officer."

"Give me his full name, rank and duty assignment," ordered the marine captain.

Cary Manpure gave the marine captain that information, and then he and Tommy Untiman were taken to a cell and locked therein.

Two hours later the cell door was opened and Commander Mark Manpure entered with three marines.

"Cary, what are you and Tommy up to?" he asked.

Cary Manpure explained concluding, "I just thought they were old signs."

"They were not old signs!" stated Commander Manpure. "Casings containing the radioactive residue from our energy transconverters are stored in vaults inside this mesa. The location of this storage area is highly secret. Neither of you will ever divulge its whereabouts. Do you understand?"

"Yes," said Cary Manpure.

"Yes," said Tommy Untiman.

"Let's get out of here," said Mark Manpure.

Outside, they boarded a heavily armed Altean Naval Service marine air ship and took off. They flew very low toward the southwest in a long arc passing a large long hill to seaside and a longer long hill to odunside. 62.4 Then they gained altitude, turned sharply eastward, flew high over the Stratopedon and landed at the Bastion. Cary Manpure and Tommy Untiman remained there and returned to Altea City with Cary Manpure's father at the end of the day.

"You two were visiting the Bastion the whole day!" Commander Mark Manpure instructed them before they left the Bastion.

This time Cary Manpure and Tommy Untiman struck out for what they thought was the rim of a very large impact crater which they could see in the distance. They knew that they would not get lost as long as they kept the pyramidal structure of the Altean Naval Service complex in sight behind them. 66.2 The two walked through a large circular depression and onto a curving ridge. From the top of the ridge they could see that there were two smaller separate craters ahead, not just one. They followed the ridge to the larger crater, climbed up its rim and looked down into its floor.

Cary Manpure glanced at his friend and said, "Pazzy, I'm glad you have Ukika Brown. When I get to Daphlay, I'll be with Lura Harwell again. We'll lose Silbury, but we'll have love."

They walked back, wriggled under the fence and appeared in time for supper.

Cary Manpure woke up in the middle of the night, reached over the side of his bunk and shook Tommy Untiman awake.

"Pazzy," Cary Manpure whispered, "I have an idea. The signs on the fence did not say to not go into open country. The sign said not to climb over the fence, so we went under the fence, into open country. Essenes did not say that we had to leave Silbury. Essenes said not to connect the new energy transconverter. We'll do something else so we can stay on Silbury."

The next morning Cary Manpure asked his brother to arrange a ride for Tommy Untiman and himself back to the Horz complex.

When the two arrived in Altea City they rounded up Cary Jackman and Terry Wellton, who were both at home, studying for their Akadeimia examinations. Cary Manpure told them his idea and they agreed that it was a good one. The meeting broke up so that everyone could think more about the "something else" they could do to stay on Silbury.

Cary Manpure decided to look for the "something else" in a history of the Horz complex that his family owned. In the third chapter he found the answer: before the western part of the Horz complex existed, the energy transproduction facilities on Dolphin Mesa had been sufficient to power everything and especially the gravitron infusion spinning disks.

They would save Silbury by reducing the Horz complex to its eastern part again.

The next morning Cary Manpure rounded up Cary Jackman, Tommy Untiman and Terry Wellton and told them what he had just learned.

"Ollun, you have the answer," Cary Jackman said.

The young men of the unit of four friends met with Joe Lon Odkin that afternoon, and Cary Jackman was their spokesman again.

When Cary Jackman had finished Odkin said, "I will present the plan to Elder Chee tonight."

Elder Chee received the plan enthusiastically, but told Odkin that they should wait to formally present the plan to him until just before the final evacuation. That way Elder Chee could present it to the Council as an emergency decision made by himself, and it would take a two-thirds vote of the Council to overrule him. Elder Chee hoped that he Council would not do that. "It's the only way we can do it," said Elder Chee. "I know the Council. If we try anything now, they'll kill it."

When Odkin told the young men of the unit of four friends of his conversation with Elder Chee, they were overjoyed.

"They don't call Elders 'Pan Dan' for nothing!" exclaimed Cary Manpure, in reference to the honorific title bestowed on all Elders of Silbury since Dan 'Pan Hur.' Cary Manpure knew that it had been Dan 'Pan Hur' who had presented the Council of his time with an emergency decision, and now Elder 'Pan Dan' Chee would try the same tactic. Cary Manpure hoped Elder Chee would be as successful.

Cary Manpure's demeanor improved, but only slightly. He did not want to give away the 'cabal,' as the young men came to call the plan to save Silbury.

After Joe Lon Odkin received approval for his plans for Danebury from the Council of Silbury he went directly back to the Hurmaze and to his sleeping quarters. He was exhausted and fell asleep immediately.

In the middle of the night Odkin was awakened by a voice saying, "Wake up, Joe Lon Odkin" over and over again. Odkin turned on the small light next to his bed and looked up. Before him was an Essene holo-image.

When the holo-image 'saw' that Odkin was awake it began speaking, "Joe Lon Odkin, the sites are not intended to be a mirror image of the Horz complex and you have not designed the structures Essenes want you to design. For Abzuland you are to design a computer. For Hurengland you are to design a spinning disk. For Prehurland you are to design a city. Begin NOW!"

The holo-image disappeared.

Although Joe Lon Odkin worked on a daily basis near the computers in the Hurmaze, Joe Lon Odkin hated computers.

"You can't trust computers," he said aloud every time he even saw a computer.

Joe Lon Odkin did all his computations either in his head or he wrote them out on a writing pad he always kept with him.

Joe Lon Odkin was the Director of the Hurmaze because he knew how to manage a large operation and how to manage those who worked in a such an operation.

The computers in the Hurmaze belonged to the Altean Naval Service and that suited Joe Lon Odkin perfectly.

"They're not part of the Hurmaze," he told visitors as he showed them around the Hurmaze. "They're just sitting here."

So when Odkin was ordered by the Essene holo-image to design a computer for Danebury he was outraged, and not just because all his previous work had been for nothing.

He threw his writing pad across his room.

"Essenes are nitwits!" Odkin shouted. "They belong in a Crystal Palace!"

Nevertheless, Odkin proceeded to design a computer for Danebury, and very soon had a plan prepared for a one-third scale model of the computers in the Hurmaze. He also designed a one-third scale model of the spinning disks of the Tetrahedron Crater gravitron infusion complex. Both were to be made of stone, though Odkin knew that the scale model of the spinning disk was only to be designed and not constructed.

Odkin had no idea of how to design a city. There was nothing on either Daphlay or Silbury which Odkin considered to be a city in the sense of what cities on Altea used to be like, so Odkin went to the library in Chapter One again and found a plan for the city of Danebury on Altea.

"If Essenes want us to call the forbidden planet Danebury," Odkin said to himself, "I'll provide a good reason for calling it Danebury."

Odkin took the plan of the city of Danebury and used it as a basis for his design of the city he had been ordered to construct on the planet Danebury.

When Odkin was ready he took his plans and presented them to the Council of Silbury. The Council approved everything.

Once again an Essene holo-image visited Odkin in the middle of the night.

"Joe Lon Odkin," the holo-image said, "your computer and spinning disk are satisfactory. Your city is partially correct. Read books about developing cultures and redesign the structures. Do not change their size or spatial relationships."

The holo-image disappeared.

Odkin read the books and redesigned his city for Danebury accordingly. The Council of Silbury approved his plans.

Once again, an Essene holo-image visited Odkin in the middle of the night.

"Joe Lon Odkin," the holo-image said, "your computer, your spinning disk and your city are satisfactory. Now design a modification of the Hurmaze to be constructed near your computer."

The holo-image disappeared.

Odkin designed a modification of the Hurmaze and the Council of Silbury approved his plan.

Once again, an Essene holo-image visited Odkin in the middle of the night.

"Joe Lon Odkin," the holo-image said, "your computer, your spinning disk and your city are satisfactory. Your modification of the Hurmaze should be a statue."

The holo-image disappeared.

Odkin designed a statue which was a modification of the Hurmaze and the Council of Silbury approved his plan.

Once again, an Essene holo-image visited Odkin in the middle of the night.

"Joe Lon Odkin," the holo-image said, "your computer, your spinning disk and your city are satisfactory. Your statue modification of the Hurmaze is partially correct. Modify the face of the statue to resemble both the face of the transitional self-aware being resulting from the administration of the first part of the genetic agent and the face of the being resulting from the administration of the second part of the genetic agent."

The holo-image disappeared.

Odkin consulted with those working on the genetic project and redesigned the face of the statue. The Council of Silbury approved his plan.

Once again, an Essene holo-image visited Odkin in the middle of the night.

"Joe Lon Odkin," the holo-image said, "your computer, your spinning disk and your city are satisfactory. Your statue modification of the Hurmaze is partially correct. Make the head of your statue into a lady who is wearing a banded hair net, but no tiara. Instead of a tiara, give your lady a soul print but only on her nose and forehead. Make your lady's head too small for the lion body."

The holo-image disappeared.

Odkin redesigned the statue which was a modification of the Hurmaze and on the forehead of the statue he designed an upside down apple as a depiction of the upper part of a soul print. He designed a Waldark soul print for the bridge of the nose. The Council of Silbury approved his plan.

Once again, an Essene holo-image visited Odkin in the middle of the night.

"Joe Lon Odkin," the holo-image said, "your computer, your spinning disk and your city are satisfactory. Your statue modification of the Hurmaze is partially correct. Change the forehead part of the soul print to look like a drakon, not an apple."

The holo-image disappeared.

Odkin redesigned the statue which was a modification of the Hurmaze and on the forehead of the statue he designed a drakon. Once again the Council of Silbury approved his plan.

Once again, an Essene holo-image visited Odkin in the middle of the night.

"Joe Lon Odkin," the holo-image said, "your computer, your spinning disk, your city and your statue are satisfactory. The name of your computer is Hurmyrr, meaning 'shining reflection.' Your city is Alteana and your statue is the Ark Hur, meaning the 'shining beginning-ending.'

The holo-image disappeared.

Joe Lon Odkin still wanted to know how Sarkneson was able to find Bunzler.

Joe Lon Odkin continued his search.

Chapter Eleven

The Wedding

Not only did Ukika Brown and Tommy Untiman become sweethearts after they met at the old-fashioned cowboy dance at the Ranch, soon thereafter they became betrothed. They were both 17, that was young, but they lived in unusual times.

The genetic agent was virtually ready and the final evacuation of Silbury was due. At which point the administering of the first part of the genetic agent and the construction of structures on Danebury would follow. Only the secret knowledge of the plan to save Silbury kept Cary Manpure from utter despair. Cary Manpure knew that even if that plan was carried out he would still have to leave Silbury, but hopefully only temporarily. When he had completed his studies he hoped that he could return to Silbury to be one of those assigned there to keep the planet alive until the time when, he hoped, Essenes would allow Alteans to connect the new energy transconverter, as the first step in the process of rebuilding the Tor.

Not only did Ukika Brown and Tommy Untiman become betrothed at age 17, they were married at age 17 because Tommy Untiman wanted to be married on Silbury.

Cary Manpure, Cary Jackman and Terry Wellton worked together to oversee the wedding party. Since the Gymnasion had been stripped bare for the impending final evacuation and Halkyon was unavailable, the Gymnasion was the obvious site for the wedding party. Cary Jackman hired an orchestra and the best female vocalist on Silbury—Althena Chee. Terry Wellton purchased food and drink at low prices from stores and eating establishments whose owners would otherwise have had to ship their stock to Daphlay. Part of the arena floor of the Gymnasion and a section of the seating were transformed into an old-fashioned theater, complete with very elegant loges and a large dance floor.

The wedding was to be held in one of the smaller athletic facilities in the Gymnasion/Stadion. Weddings were held in a variety of places, usually in a meeting hall in one of the houses of Altea City, but those had all been sealed by the time of Ukika and Tommy's wedding. Only the Gymnasion/Station was still open as it was the staging area for the final evacuation of Silbury.

The population of Silbury had continued to decline, and there were by this time only about 7000 inhabitants remaining. Cary Manpure was able to stay on Silbury to the end because his father Captain Mark Manpure commanded a star ship based at the Bastion. Cary Manpure's brother Frank, his wife Alana and their two-year-old son Mark remained on Silbury because Lieutenant Frank Manpure was assigned to the magnetic field energy transproduction and command complex. Cary Manpure's other brother Ames stayed because he wanted to be with his betrothed Lura Ryans, whose mother was on the Council of Silbury. Cary Manpure's cousin Vicky Manpure lived with her parents and her father Arnhold Manpure was also on the Council of Silbury. Kirk Roon and Kurt Sardman were members of the Council of Silbury so their families stayed with them. Cary Jackman's father Dan Jackman was an associate of the genetic project and his family remained with him. Sara and Mark Wellton were among the teachers still employed by the Zuv School System and their family stayed with them. Marta Untiman remained on Silbury because she had nowhere else to go.

Cary Manpure's cousin Dan Manpure, his wife Avelina, their eight-year-old son Ames and six-year-old daughter Avena remained on Silbury, because Dan Manpure was insulating "Glamyrr and Sustanator" from future erosive forces. This was his recently completed sculpture, dedicated to the children of the Universe. He had chosen this location and positioned the statue southeast of Dolphin Mesa in the Horz complex.

"Glamyrr and Sustanator" stood at the intersection of two sight lines. 67 One was between the northeastern tangent of Ell House and the southwestern tangent of Hurbury—Ell House was the northeastern most structure of Altea City, the northwestern most component of the Horz complex—Hurbury the southeastern most component of the Horz complex. The second sight line was between the southeastern corner of the Tor and the wooden pump house in which old-fashioned pumps pumped water to the Ranch. The Tor was the southwestern most component of the Horz complex.

The second sight line could have been between the southeastern corner of the Tor and the northwestern tangent of the Tetrahedron Crater—the northeastern most component of the Horz complex. But Dan Manpure wanted to include the Ranch—which was not part of the Horz complex—so he used the wooden pump house in his positioning plan. Using the wooden pump house in his plan also allowed him to position "Glamyrr and Sustanator" 5/6ths of 19.47 Silbury nautical miles from the benchmark under the right eye of the Hurmaze. Dan Manpure considered that geometrically obscure benchmark under the right eye to be a teardrop, because at least for the moment, many tears needed to be shed for the children of the Universe as they faced so many hardships. Buried under "Glamyrr and Sustanator" was a casing containing children's toys donated by the last children of Silbury. Avena Manpure donated her favorite doll; Ames Manpure donated a toy star ship.

The sculpture "Glamyrr and Sustanator" consisted of two parts, one representing the moon and the other representing the sun. A lass riding her pony was the moon. A lad and his dog going fishing was the sun.

The morning of the wedding the 'cabalists'—Elder Byron Haley Chee, Joe Lon Odkin, Cary Manpure, Cary Jackman, Terry Wellton and Tommy Untiman—met at Elder Chee's office. The meeting had been scheduled for several days and was known to all who would normally know of Elder Chee's frequent meetings with members of the community. Cary Jackman formally presented the plan for saving Silbury. Elder Chee promised to consider the proposal carefully. The meeting ended.

The evening of the wedding arrived and everyone involved with the wedding was busy with final details. Tommy Untiman behaved like a man about to be married and Cary Manpure—his Voluntary Best Servant—was only able to calm his best friend down by speaking sternly to him. The bride Ukika Brown wore the traditional banded hair net and tiara of Altean ladies and a stunning traditional white gown with a very long train. The Bridesmaid was Lura Brown, younger sister of the bride. The bridegroom Tommy Untiman wore the traditional hat of Altean gentlemen and a traditional black tuxedo, a suit worn only by bridegrooms at their weddings, a suit modeled after penguins, whose males shine up little rocks and present them hopefully to their prospective partners.

After the bride was accompanied down the center aisle of the athletic facility inside the Gymnasion/Stadion by her father, her mother and father presented her to her waiting bridegroom. The bride and bridegroom, flanked by her Bridesmaid and his Voluntary Best Servant, then faced the audience. Cary Manpure gave Tommy Untiman the ring for his wife, Tommy Untiman placed the ring on his wife's left ring finger and swore his marriage vows. Lura Brown gave her sister Ukika Brown the ring for her husband, Ukika Brown placed the ring on her husband's left ring finger and swore her marriage vows. The traditional readings were read by Cary Jackman. The witness for legal authority, Elder Chee, supervised the signing of the marriage document, first by Tommy Untiman and then by his bride, signed the document himself and then presented the marriage pair to the audience.

"Tommy Untiman, having undertaken his responsibilities as husband of Ukika Brown, and Ukika Brown, having willingly accepted Tommy Untiman," Elder Chee said, repeating the traditional presentation, "I would therefore like to introduce to you Ukika and Tommy Untiman, husband and wife."

Everyone applauded and Ukika and Tommy Untiman walked together up the aisle accompanied by traditional marriage music.

The trouble at the wedding party began when Clark Sardman and Tom Roon drank too much beer. Tom Roon then asked Rena Jackman to dance and she accepted. When the dance was over Clark Sardman asked Rena to dance and she accepted. Tom Roon asked her again and she accepted. Clark Sardman asked Rena again and she accepted. When Tom Roon asked her again, Rena said she was tired and needed a rest.

Sara Roon and Dan Sardman had been dancing together nearby and observed what happened next. Clark Sardman and Tom Roon began berating Rena for refusing to dance with Tom Roon. In doing so, they backed Rena from the dance floor and up against the circular barrier separating the seating of the Gymnasion from the floor of its arena. When Clark Sardman and Tom Roon were on the verge of physically abusing Rena, Sara Roon and Dan Sardman rushed to her assistance. Dan Sardman grabbed his brother by the shoulder and pulled him away from Rena. Sara Roon shouted at her brother to leave Rena alone. When so confronted Clark Sardman and Tom Roon relented and slunk off. Rena went off with Sara Roon and Dan Sardman.

Clark Sardman and Tom Roon returned to the consumption of more beer. Then they sought Rena again. In the meantime, Sara Roon had told Cary Jackman about the incident, and Cary Jackman decided to make sure that the two of them did not bother his sister again.

As Cary Jackman was trying to find Rena in the crowd, Clark Sardman and Tom Roon located Rena and began berating her again.

"Why won't you dance with us?" they demanded. "Afraid of two of us? Where's your friend Vicky? Find her so one of us can dance with you and one with her."

"Vicky's not here," responded Rena.

"Not here?" Roon screamed. "I want to talk to Vicky about topogly vectors."

"She's not feeling well," said Rena.

"Then we'll both dance with you at the same time," they yelled, each grabbing one of Rena's hands. "We'll do two-thirds dancing to this slow music."

Rena screamed.

Cary Jackman heard his sister's scream and rushed toward her. When he saw what was transpiring Cary Jackman ran up and grabbed Tom Roon from behind and threw him across the room. Then Cary Jackman confronted Clark Sardman who took a swing at him.

Cary Manpure and Terry Wellton were dancing nearby, but stopped as they saw Cary Jackman rushing through the crowd.

"What's going on?" Terry Wellton asked.

"I don't know," responded Cary Manpure. "We'd better investigate."

The two followed Cary Jackman and arrived at the scene to see Tom Roon sneaking up behind Cary Jackman as he confronted Clark Sardman. Cary Manpure and Terry Wellton could see that Tom Roon was going to try to trip their friend, because Tom Roon crouched down behind Cary Jackman's knees as he backed away from one of Clark Sardman's wild swings.

Cary Manpure rushed up to Tom Roon, and—grabbing his shoulders from behind—pulled him to his feet, spun him around and ordered him to leave the party at once.

Terry Wellton grabbed Clark Sardman's arms from behind and wrestled him to the floor.

"Leave me alone!" Tom Roon shouted at Cary Manpure. "You didn't invite me to this party, and you can't order me to leave."

Tom Roon swung at Cary Manpure, who ducked and then he smashed Tom Roon in the face with his fist. Blood spurted from Tom Roon's lip and nose.

Cary Jackman grabbed Clark Sardman's ankles and Terry Wellton managed to hold on to Clark Sardman's wrists. Cary Jackman and Terry Wellton got back to their feet, carried Clark Sardman from the Gymnasion and threw him out into the indoor park surrounding the Gymnasion. Cary Manpure was right behind them, forcing Tom Roon forward before he threw him into the park as well.

As Clark Sardman and Tom Roon slunk together in the park, Cary Manpure shouted at them, "Stay out! If you try to come back in we'll toss you out again after you're a little more bloodied!"

As Cary Manpure, Cary Jackman and Terry Wellton turned to rejoin the wedding party, Ann Trent rushed past them and over to Clark Sardman and Tom Roon. She bent over the two of them, ministering to their needs. Then she turned her head back toward Cary Manpure, Cary Jackman and Terry Wellton and shouted savagely, "Cary Manpure, you bully!

You'll be sorry for this!"

Cary Manpure turned and laughed. "You take good care of those bums," he said sarcastically, "and they'll take good care of you!"

"You'll be sorry for that too!" Ann Trent shouted savagely again.

"I know something about her," said Cary Manpure to his friends as they entered the Gymnasion. "I accidentally saw her once when I was in Dan Park at night. I knew she had a sweetheart, but she was in the park with two who were not her sweetheart—and they were taking turns. I also know she was not invited to Ukika and Tommy's wedding and wedding party."

When Cary Manpure, Cary Jackman and Terry Wellton returned to the party they looked for Rena, but failed to find her. Dan Sardman was looking for them.

"Sara's taken Rena to Vicky's," Dan Sardman said. "Rena's very upset and she didn't want to stay. Perhaps Sara can talk Rena and Vicky into coming back with her. I'm sorry for all the trouble my brother and Roon have caused."

A few minutes later Cary Manpure met Alea Gandy.

Altean Naval Service Ensign Alea Gandy was posted to one of the marine transport vessels taking part in the final evacuation of Silbury. Her older sister Lieutenant Anna Gandy, Altean Naval Service marines, had been assigned to escort the prisoners Paul Bunzler and Hal Roon from Silbury to Daphlay. The sisters had come to the party with Althena Chee, their cousin.

Cary Manpure was immediately attracted to Alea Gandy. She had grown up living in Zuv House, but he had never met her mostly because she was six years older than he and well ahead of him in the Zuv School System.

Alea Gandy asked Cary Manpure to dance and he accepted.

They danced and danced and danced. Cary Manpure became so intent on Alea Gandy, that he failed to notice that Terry Wellton was dancing and dancing and dancing with Anna Gandy, and that Cary Jackman was dancing with Althena Chee during her singing breaks.

Finally, it was time for the wedding pair to depart for the traditional halkyon days of newlywed couples of Silbury held at the Resort located along the northwestern shores of the Tetrahedron Crater Reservoir. Ukika and Tommy Untiman were to be the Resort's last guests.

The wedding guests formed a long serpentine through the park surrounding the Gymnasion to one of the entryways of the Gymnasion/Stadion. Ukika and Tommy then emerged from the Gymnasion and raced between the lines of the serpentine, as their guests, according to tradition, threw handfuls of bird seed on the scurrying pair, signifying a harmonious and joyful beginning of their life together. This metaphor related them to love birds, who inhabited the wilds of Altea in ancient times, but now lived only in the zoological gardens where they required nurturing in the form of housing, warmth and—bird seed.

Having successfully run the gauntlet, Ukika and Tommy boarded an awaiting air ship rented and piloted by Cary Manpure. Landing an air ship in the plaza before the Gymnasion/Stadion was forbidden, but in those final days before the final evacuation, no one really cared.

When they arrived at the Resort's landing place, Cary Manpure got out and helped the wedding pair from the air ship. Cary Manpure opened the cargo bay and reached in to retrieve the couple's packed things. Instead, Alea Gandy's hand reached out.

"Help me out, will you, Cary?" she said.

Cary Manpure took Alea's hand as she leaped out of the hanger bay and into his arms, covering his lips with kisses.

Cary Manpure had planned to give the marriage couple a special wedding present, but Ukika and Tommy Untiman disappeared into the night before Cary Manpure could unlock himself from Alea Gandy's embrace.

"Wait here a minute," Cary Manpure gasped, then he dashed off after his best friend and his bride.

He caught up with them just before they entered the lobby of the Resort.

"This is for you," Cary Manpure gasped again. He handed Tommy Untiman a small flat package, then dashed back after Alea Gandy.

"Let's go for a ride," Cary Manpure said as he ran up to her.

"Let's go and look at the obelisk monument to Dan 'Pan Hur' by the light of Nymph and Satyr," Alea responded.

A few moments later they were headed west of the Wall. Alea put her head on his shoulder as she snuggled up as closely as she could to Cary Manpure's side.

As they circled above the obelisk the young man tried to think of something to say, and finally managed, "Is there some other place you would like to go next?"

"Althena's. It's all arranged. You and I get one guest room. My sister and Terry get the other. Althena and the other Cary get Althena's room," Alea responded immediately.

Alea Gandy and Cary Manpure entered Althena Chee's place in Ell House. The entryway was lit, but beyond it, it was very dark. Alea Gandy and Cary Manpure found the correct room, closed the door behind them and embraced.

Cary Manpure awoke in the morning when he heard the outer door to Althena Chee's place suddenly burst open. Many loud footsteps followed.

The footsteps proceeded past the entryway, through the living room and down the bedroom hallway.

At the end of the hall a voice Cary Manpure recognized as belonging to Elder Chee boomed out, "Althena Gandy Chee, come out and present yourself immediately to legal authority!"

Then another voice which Cary Manpure did not recognize demanded at the door to the room occupied by Alea Gandy and himself, "If anyone is therein, come out and present yourself immediately to legal authority!"

This was followed by another demand before the room which was occupied by Anna Gandy and Terry Wellton.

Cary Manpure tried to awaken Alea, but could not. Frantic to do something, he wrapped her in a loose sheet, threw her over his shoulder, opened the door and walked into the hallway.

Anna Gandy and Terry Wellton emerged from their room.

Cary Manpure looked inquiringly at Terry Wellton, but all his friend did was shrug.

Moments later the door to Althena Chee's room opened and she and Cary Jackman walked out.

Elder Chee spoke, "You, Althena Gandy Chee, are being taken into custody for withholding information that would have been vital to the apprehension and prosecution of Paul Bunzler. You shall be taken forthwith to legal authority headquarters." 67.1

Then Elder Chee turned to Cary Manpure.

"Who are you, young man?" he asked.

"Cary Burr Manpure," was the reply.

"And the young lady?" Elder Chee asked.

"Ensign Alea Gandy, Altean Naval Service," Cary Manpure responded for her.

Elder Chee nodded to Anna Gandy.

"Lieutenant Anna Jace Gandy, Altean Naval Service marines."

Next Elder Chee inquired of Terry Wellton.

"Terry Dan Wellton," he responded.

Finally Elder Chee nodded at Cary Jackman.

"Cary Mark Jackman," was the reply.

Elder Chee turned on his heel and strode down the hallway. Althena Chee followed with her escort. The door closed behind them.

Joe Lon Odkin had figured out how Sarkneson had been able to find Bunzler.

As Althena Chee left her living quarters after being taken into custody by legal authority, Ukika and Tommy Untiman were enjoying the sandy beach and waters of the Tetrahedron Crater Reservoir. They had emerged only shortly before from their resort bungalow wearing the traditional saffron gowns of newlyweds during their halkyon days, and Tommy Untiman had with him the flat package Cary Manpure had given them the night before. As his wife looked on he opened the package.

"It's a perioikomai!" exclaimed Ukika and she warmly embraced her husband. Tears formed in Tommy Untiman's eyes.

Since they were first created, just after the time of Waldark, perioikomai have been given by special friends to wedding couples to wish them a long and loving life together. Perioikomai, meaning 'living around and about,' are multi-colored ceramic plaques with a multi-symbolic design. 68

At the top of a perioikomai is a long curving ridge. Below the ridge is a wide gulf molded to the shape of the ridge above it. Below the right side of the wide gulf is a banded eye. To the left the bands of the eye meet and trail off together so that the length of the eye and its bands are equal to the length of the wide gulf and the curving ridge.

Extending downward from the bottom of the eye are two things. On the right and going straight down is a short broad line with a rounded end. To the left of this line is a long, slightly tapering line sweeping to the left and ending in a spiral below the left end of the rest of the perioikomai.

The curving ridge, the bands of the eye, the two lines below the eye and the iris of the eye are always black, the eye ball is white and the wide gulf is red. All features are edged with thin gold lines. Brides at their weddings always make themselves up with these colors around their eyes.

The entire perioikomai sweeps from left to right to represent movement, progress and living around and about.

The lines below the eye represent the female and male reproductive organs and they symbolize the good times in life. These lines also represent a perierchomai transportation system crystal tube and a Peri sign and shield support post in the form of a shepherd's crook. They also represent two tear drops, one dropping straight down and the other trailing off to the left. The tear drop dropping straight down symbolizes the difficult times in life, while the one trailing off is for those who have gone before.

The eye is the eye of self-awareness and the shield of a Peri sign. It also represents spinning disks, which, together with perierchomai transportation systems, allow self-aware beings to go around and about and also help reconfigure reproductive material for physical well being.

The bands around the eye represent the shape of the downward, magnetically levitating egg-shaped array of magnets in the upper conscitron thruster armature of the gravitron drive of flying craft.

The bands are a multi-perspective of the double hull of space craft and the bands are an egg as well as the array of magnets.

The wide gulf above the eye represents the vast difference between self-aware life and the Source of the Universe.

The curving ridge above the eye is an Aspis, the shield representing the Source of the Universe who protects self-aware life as self-aware beings go around and about.

The eye and the shepherd's crook also represent the Vigilant Shepherd as It watches over and protects Its flock.

Perioikomai have been crafted down through the ages by dedicated artists who will only sell their perioikomai to those who can prove that they have a special friend who is about to get married. The examinations given by these artists have always included a mental, an artistic and a physical challenge. Cary Manpure had to write an essay about his friend, draw a picture of him and having walked—not ridden—to its top, write Tommy Untiman's name on the eastern facing at the top of the obelisk located by the Wall, the monument to Dan 'Pan Hur.' 41

Chapter Twelve

The Meeting

After Elder Chee, Althena Chee and her escorts had left, Alea Gandy woke up and Cary Manpure set her down. The five who remained behind stood there for a few moments and then started to laugh at how ridiculous they all looked. They had been extremely embarrassed at having been rousted out of bed by legal authority and then purposefully not recognized by Elder Chee. They were also very upset about Althena Chee's being taken into custody by legal authority.

Laughter acted as a catharsis.

After the laughter had subsided Cary Jackman said, "Cary Manpure you were wrong."

"What?" asked Cary Manpure.

"You said I should forget Althena Chee because she was three times my age. Seven years later I am now 19 and she's 43 and she's not three times my age any more. She remembered my model Peri system. She asked me how my system was. I showed her. It is time to go."

The other four were not ready to depart. Anna Gandy and Terry Wellton went back into their room. Alea Gandy and Cary Manpure went back into their room.

At noon Alea Gandy told Cary Manpure she had to report back to the Bastion for duty, and Cary Manpure thought he should put in an appearance at home. They were honestly and earnestly preparing for departure when they became overwhelmed with love.

At four in the afternoon Cary Manpure crawled into his own bed and fell asleep. At midnight Cary Manpure left Zuv House to meet Alea Gandy at a secret place he knew. At four the next afternoon Cary Manpure crawled into his own bed again and fell asleep. At midnight Cary Manpure left Zuv House to again meet Alea Gandy at their secret place. At four the next afternoon Cary Manpure crawled back into his own bed again and fell asleep. The following morning was the meeting of the Council of Silbury at which Elder Chee would announce his acceptance of the plan to save Silbury. Only a vote by at least two-thirds of the council could overrule the Elder's decision. At midnight Cary Manpure did not leave Zuv House to meet Alea Gandy. Cary Manpure needed to rest for the most important event of his life. Alea Gandy and Cary Manpure knew that there was a lifetime for them to renew their love.

The meeting was held in Council House and was attended by only a very few members of the Altean community. Even though it was to be the last meeting of the Council of Silbury, there was little to be decided. The evacuation plan had long since been under way and would be completed two days later. The few remaining matters of policy would be dealt with and then the Council would adjourn.

Elder Chee opened the meeting and the Council quickly acted on all matters pending before it. Then Elder Chee asked if there were any further matters that any member wanted to bring before the Council.

Kirk Roon rose and said, "Before we dissolve the Council of Silbury I think that it would be fitting for the Council to bestow upon Dan Manpure the honorific title 'Art Hurian.' Although this would normally be an action taken by the Art Institute of Silbury, that body has already been dissolved. Ell Dan the Lotharian is the only Altean to have ever been so honored in his lifetime. I think Dan Manpure deserves the same honor."

Elder Chee and the rest of the Council were taken completely by surprise by Kirk Roon's proposal. Arnhold Manpure's anger rose as he listened to Roon. Elder Chee moved quickly to prevent a heated and divisive exchange.

"Members voting to approve the proposal so indicate as your name is called," said Elder Chee.

Elder Chee read off the names of the Council members in alphabetical order. Arnhold Manpure and seven of his closest associates voted against Kirk Roon's proposal.

Dan Manpure was awarded the honorific title 'Art Hurian.'

Elder Chee again asked if there were any further matters that any member wanted to bring before the Council. There were none.

Then Elder Chee said, "Before adjourning the final meeting of the Council of Silbury which is dissolved upon that adjournment, I wish to inform you of a decision I have just made in accordance with the traditional duties of Elders.

"Three days ago five members of our community presented to me a proposal which I told them I would consider. This morning I decided to accept their proposal and to order the necessary actions needed to implement that proposal.

"When the rest of us evacuate Silbury in two days time the Altean Naval Service will maintain a presence on Silbury. The Altean Naval Service will move its base of operations from the Bastion to the Wall. The site of energy transredimensioning will be moved to Chapter One. The spinning disks of the Tetrahedron Crater gravitron infusion complex will begin spinning again."

Bedlam broke out.

Arnhold Manpure outshouted everyone, "I demand we vote on this proposal. I demand you tell us who made this proposal to you."

Arnhold Manpure's demands quieted the Council and all its members looked to Elder Chee who said, "The proposal was presented to me by Joe Lon Odkin, Cary Manpure, Cary Jackman, Tommy Untiman and Terry Wellton."

"I would like to inform the Council," shouted Arnhold Manpure in response, "that none of those named except for Odkin is old enough to even vote. This is outrageous. You cannot just order that this proposal be implemented. I demand a thorough discussion."

A very heated traducing of Elder Chee and the proposal followed. Arnhold Manpure and other members of the Council were outraged by Elder Chee's decision. Elder Chee had totally circumvented established procedure. The presenters of the proposal were totally unqualified by age and/or experience. Elder Chee had used unsound judgement in even listening to the proposal.

Joe Lon Odkin, Cary Manpure, Cary Jackman, Tommy Untiman and Terry Wellton sat and listened. The young men of the unit of four friends were crest-fallen.

"Just wait for the voting," Joe Lon Odkin said to them.

Arnhold Manpure continued berating Elder Chee and the proposal until he thought he had convinced enough members to vote against it, then he demanded an immediate vote.

When the Council member voting before Kirk Roon voted against the proposal only one more vote was required to overrule Elder Chee's decision. Joe Lon Odkin and the four friends sat and listened. Following Roon three more members were due to vote: Arleena Ryans, Kurt Sardman, and Anson Trent.

Cary Manpure thought Arleena Ryans would vote for the proposal. He hoped Kirk Roon would too, despite the trouble at the wedding party involving his son, Tom. Cary Manpure thought Kurt Sardman would vote whichever way Kirk Roon went because they were good friends.

Cary Manpure did not know anything about Anson Trent, except that his daughter's name was Ann.

Kirk Roon, Arleena Ryans and Kurt Sardman all voted in favor of the proposal. Then Anson Trent rose to speak.

"Essenes do not want us to remain on Silbury. I am therefore compelled to vote against the proposal," he said.

Elder Chee closed the meeting, dissolving the Council. As the members began to leave, Arnhold Manpure shouted across the round table at Kirk Roon. "If it had not been for your traitorous brother we would never have had to leave Silbury," he said savagely. "Your ill-timed and ill-conceived attempt to redeem your family name today is contemptible."

Cary Manpure, Cary Jackman, Tommy Untiman and Terry Wellton were devastated.

Joe Lon Odkin opened a dusty old tome he brought with him to the meeting to a place he had marked and said, "I know the four of you are as discouraged as I am about what happened here today, but I would like you to listen to something I would like to read to you in this work about the Lotharians."

The young men of the unit of four friends listened as Odkin read:

> As he was about to depart for Altea, where he could hold Sofy in his arms again, Astir lamented the cyclical nature of history. "Here we are today delving back into musty old tomes, trying to figure out what to do, making our decisions as a result of having tried to understand situations and organizations of long ago," he said.
>
> "We go along for a while, and then get ourselves back into the same old rut. We never seem to get anywhere. This time—unless we do something extraordinary—there won't even be a next time.
>
> "So much for the traditions; there won't be any intergalactic pioneer lad to carry an old cedar box with an encased adventure book to the bridge.
>
> "There will only be the Pleiadeans."
>
> Astir's brother and cousin looked at Astir, feeling great sorrow for the defiant, discouraged youth, who really only wanted one 'thing' from life—Sofy.
>
> Ell Dan retrieved one of the musty old tomes they had been reading and opened it at a place he had previously marked.
>
> "Astir," he said, "I would like you to listen to something written about Essenes which I thought was very interesting. This passage describes the first meeting of Sara Eland and Peter who you know

were among the leaders of Essenes when they left Altea nearly a billion years ago. The passage reads:

As it was, there was not much any one could do except wonder at what this odd group was doing, being so concerned about galactic redemption due to possible upheavals caused by galactic colonization, when colonization was still only an idea.

Among those shaking their heads at the reports of Essene thinking was a relatively young man, called Peter Odun, of very conservative views.

Odun was a teacher of history, coincidentally at the same Akadeimia that Sara Eland had attended, but she had never been in any of his classes. He invariably always began the first day's discussion with a comical self-effacing account of how he was a distant descendant of the famous Bill Odun, hero of Peter Odun's two favorite mythos ODUNSIDE and NOSTOS.

Although Odun was very conservative in his thinking regarding Akadeimia policy and the politics of the day, he was a favorite among his students for his sense of humor and his biting sarcasm against those who felt self-important.

It was therefore not surprising to them that Odun penned a scathing article which was published in Hurtea's largest daily newspaper which thoroughly lambasted the "presumptuous Essenes for thinking they have some sort of monopoly on correct thinking with regard to how matters should proceed." He also skewered them for their secrecy, concluding: "If one single member of the Essene 'movement' will reveal himself to me, and convince me of the rightness of his mission, then I will quit my job and become an Essene myself."

Sara Eland read the article with growing anger until she came to its ending. Inspired by the impudent challenge of this Peter Odun—about whom she knew very little from her Akadeimia days—Sara decided to lay down the gauntlet.

Armed with her own wit, knowledge and wise-thinking Sara emerged from her Essene hideout so she could track down and find her newly discovered tormenter.

That was not difficult as Odun lived alone, not far from his place of work, in a relatively modest home directly on the beach. Early one evening she rang his bell and he opened the door after turning on the porch light.

"May I help...you?" He inquired, pausing somewhat as he discerned that an absolutely beautiful young lady was standing before him.

"Yes," she answered resolutely, "I am an Essene. We have a lot to talk about."

He invited her into his home. After Sara had expressed her concerns to Peter Odun about the possibility of conflict arising during the projected colonization of the galaxy, he responded, "I don't think we should be so concerned. Alteans have Philosophia. Since Alteans study Philosophia I don't think the problems which you foresee will arise."

"How many Alteans do you think actually study Philosophia?" asked Sara.

Peter Odun shrugged his shoulders.

"Your type of mind is perfectly suited to the study and enjoyment of Philosophia," Sara continued. "Not all minds are like yours. Philosophia requires thinking. Not all Alteans think. You are very comfortable with Philosophia at all levels of thinking. Others need to have everything explained to them, or they reject everything. Others simply want to be told what to believe.

"The others, those who reject everything, will do anything.

"The others, those who want to be told what to believe, will become the slaves of those who will do anything."

The next day Peter Odun became an Essene.

Seven weeks later Sara Eland and Peter Odun were married, and their undying love for one another is still known as the romance of the galaxy.

Ell Dan closed the dusty old tome and said, "Sara Eland was right.

"The others who reject everything have done that anything—again.

"The others who want to be told what to believe have become the slaves of those who will do that anything—again.

"It is time for those who can think to think—and act—extraordinarily.

"That makes these extraordinary times, Astir.

"It is time for us to do the extraordinary.

"The cycle must be broken."

Joe Lon Odkin closed the dusty old tome.

"I would like the four of you to go with me to Danebury," Joe Lon Odkin said to them.

During the meeting, many remaining residents of Silbury continued to ship the limited number of possessions they were allowed free of charge aboard the vessels evacuating them from Silbury to the Stadion in the Gymnasion/Stadion. Transport air ships picked up the color coded casings filled with those things in the many service landing areas of each house, flew their cargoes to the Gymnasion/Stadion and landed on the grass turf of the Stadion. Workers in the Stadion removed the casings from the air ships and carefully stacked them according to color so that they could later be loaded aboard the correct transport vessel. Once all the casings were collected, the cut away panels of the roof of the Gymnasion/Stadion above the Stadion were fused back into place.

Chapter Thirteen

From Despair to Despair

Cary Manpure could not bear to think about anything. He left the Council House and flew to the Golden Triangle in the air ship he had just happened to 'find' on returning his rented air ship the day after the wedding. Cary Manpure had used this air ship to get to Alea Gandy and when it was not in use he hid it in the jungle area of the zoological gardens. These extensive zoological gardens had been laid out over the top of excavation debris from the construction of the perierchomai transportation system and in a long winding natural depression northwest and north of Ell House. 56.1

The perierchomai crystal tubes ran high overhead the jungle area and attached to them was an irrigation system which sprayed simulated rain onto the length and breadth of this jungle area. Run offs from the frequent sprayings collected into streamlets and they flowed together to form a short river which cascaded in a long thin waterfall into a natural depression to the north of the jungle area. Along the shores of this ribbon lake freshwater aquatic life had always been in abundance, they never left because there was no other place to go. But now they had been transported to Daphlay, together with all the other inhabitants of the zoological gardens and the horses from the Hippodromos, not far to the northwest. 56.1 Cary Manpure could feel the loneliness of the jungle and it depressed him. He sighed as he removed the huge ferns that he had used to camouflage the 'borrowed' air ship and when he took off, he circled once over Lura Redmand Lake and headed eastwards.

As Cary Manpure flew between Ell House and the Hurmaze, he suddenly felt he wanted to take one last look at the Stathmos, the campground he had gone to many times with Tommy Untiman and other friends. He circled over the deserted wooden campground and small lake and then flew over the cinder cone just south of Stathmos. 56.1

Each time you went to camp it was a requirement to climb up and into the cinder cone—however, many just came to visit without necessarily camping, hiking from the Stathmos Peri station 1.947 miles away. The cinder cone was a memorial to Atlantis. Known as 'The Memorial,' the interior of the cinder cone had been sculpted in concentric rings as an inverse form of Atlantis. In the very center stood a 10 sided columned structure built on a 12 sided base. The 12 facings of this base each had the word 'Eirene,' engraved on it, which he knew means 'peace.'

With tears streaming down his cheeks Cary Manpure left The Memorial behind him and flew on to the Golden Triangle. There he met Alea Gandy and they flew in separate craft to the Lookout, their secret meeting place. At the Lookout, Alea Gandy tried to make Cary Manpure forget about his despair.

Cary Manpure had first been to the Golden Triangle with Lura Harwell when he was 16 and he had flown her there in an air ship he had rented for the evening. Cary Manpure had learned to fly air ships as soon as he turned 16, the earliest age at which one could qualify for a pilot permit. Indeed the very evening he had got his permit he'd flown Tommy Untiman to the Hippodromos for a night out at the races. Cary Manpure did not bet—he always lost—but Tommy had won enough to pay for their entrance, their meals, the air ship rental with a few quid left over.

The Hippodromos was located in an impact crater about two and a half miles north of Zuv House and Cary Manpure could see it from his family's living quarters. In accordance with the traditional locations of those places since the excavation of Atlantis, the Hippodromos was located in the northern part of the Horz complex, the Gymnasion/Stadion in the western, the Philosophia House in the southern and the Akadeimia in the eastern part of the complex. 62.1

The Golden Triangle was located in the desert about five miles southeast of the Hurmaze, at the northern tangent of the crossing of two sightlines which formed eastern and western angles of 50.72 degrees: one of the angles of a golden triangle. 67.1 The first sightline ran between the southwestern corner of Council House and the apex of Hurbury; and the second ran between the northernmost corner of the Tor and the northern end of the base of the Wall. This siting was particularly pleasing to the owners of the Golden Triangle because they were able to incorporate the government of Silbury into their scheme, although that government sometimes made things difficult for the Golden Triangle.

The site of energy transredimensioning in the Hurmaze, the apex of the Tor and the Tower of Ancestors formed an enormous golden triangle in the western part of the Horz complex. The angle at the Tor was 60 degrees, the angle at the Tower of Ancestors was 69.28 degrees and the angle at the site of energy transredimensioning was 50.72 degrees. Golden triangles have to do with love, sex and the Source of the Universe. 64

The 60 degree angles of golden triangles represent the Source of the Universe: 60 degrees is the angle at all the corners of tetrahedra, and tetrahedra model everything. The Tor—a more complex modeling of everything—thus represented the Source of the Universe as well.

The 69.28 degree angles of golden triangles are a depiction of oral sex, and at the same time a pun on the same subject. The four escalator openings to the Tower of Ancestors Seed Station of the perierchomai transportation system and the conical Tower of Ancestors represented female and male sex organs.

The 50.72 degrees angles of golden triangles represent loving couples with the numbers 5 and 2; the 0 depicts female and the number 7 depicts male. Therefore, 50.72 degrees represents sexual intercourse. This is the angle of the golden triangle at the site of energy transredimensioning in the Hurmaze, because during sexual intercourse the soul is the site of an incredible release of energy transredimensioned from the Source and also because following sexual intercourse, life is carried forward.

Actual golden triangles are made of thick golden paper and have side lengths which are 8.94 inches, 10 inches and 10.8 inches. Golden triangles are sometimes given very privately by those who have enjoyed full sexual pleasures with someone they love. Having a sweetheart is sometimes referred to among friends as "8.94." More intimate activities are much more discretely referred to among intimates as "10" and "10.8" or "star ship," because star ships are 108 feet long. 25

At the time when the galactic newcomers were having one of their first discussions with some of the locals concerning various points of transdimensional physics, and they were using the language of the indigenous beings, one of those newcomers wrote "69.28" on a chalkboard and said "69 point two eight." The locals thought that he said "69 point two ate!" The locals laughed and laughed and laughed—much to the chagrin of the speaker. Later, when things got straightened out, the speaker became very embarrassed.

Those same locals were learning the basics of geometry so they went home and made a triangle with two of its angles 60 and 69.28 degrees. They measured the third angle as something less than 51 degrees, but they could not yet add and subtract in the figures used by the extragalactics. The next day, they asked the newcomers to write out the third angle in their triangle. When they saw that the answer was 50.72, they laughed heartily again, because 0 and 7 were ancient symbols they knew well. The locals had already learned that 5 represented life, they knew that 2 meant 'two' from their previous day's discussion, and they had always known that two meant 'couple.'

They told the newcomers all about their triangle and then announced that they would henceforth call their triangle the golden triangle because sex was golden. The extragalactics were thrilled by this insight that the act of sex was golden, adding: "Gold represents the Source of the Universe and sex comes to us directly from the Source."

The Golden Triangle of the Horz complex was a large, golden, triangular-shaped complex which featured a variety of evening entertainments. The Golden Triangle had been conceived and constructed just after the completion of the western part of the Horz complex by two recently married couples who were all friends. The two 50.72 degree angles formed by the crossing of sight lines at the Golden Triangle were intended by the creators of the Golden Triangle to memorialize their love.

Lura Harwell and Cary Manpure had been to the Golden Triangle several times together and enjoyed themselves, but though they loved one another, neither of them ever became eligible to give or receive a golden triangle.

Cary Manpure gave Alea Gandy a new golden triangle every time he was with her, after the first time.

Only the bar remained open at the Golden Triangle during those last few days of life on Silbury. Drinking was strictly forbidden at the Bastion so air ships had always done a brisk business between the Bastion and the Golden Triangle.

On the very last day of life on Silbury Cary Manpure was having a drink at the bar when Alea Gandy found him. He ordered her a whiskey and he finished up his rum and had another before they departed. You had to be 21 to drink without your parents being with you, but that day no one cared at all.

Just as they were about to leave, the giant portraits of the creators of the Golden Triangle which had hung on the wall behind the bar for nearly 150,000 years were removed. Cary Manpure stopped Alea and they both had another drink.

"Let's drink to them," Cary Manpure said, holding up his glass. "Here's to Marta and Tommy. Here's to Lura and Arne. Here's to the ones who made this for us."

Cary Manpure downed his drink and smashed his glass on the floor.

Alea Gandy took him by the arm and she flew them in the air ship to the Lookout where he gave her another golden triangle.

While Alea Gandy was trying to make Cary Manpure forget about his despair Cary Manpure's parents, his brother Frank and his family departed Silbury for Colchis. The Altean Naval Service star ship RAMPART commanded by Captain Mark Manpure had been reassigned to Colchis, Lieutenant Frank Manpure posted to the planetary defenses of Colchis.

Just before the scheduled departure of RAMPART Arleena Broadman, first associate of the genetic project, arrived at the Bastion to pick up the last of the reproductive material needed by the genetic project. As Arleena Broadman was approaching RAMPART a maintenance crew was in the process of removing its weapons pod, in order to undertake maintenance on its Aspis crystal and to allow access to the ship's spinning disk so that they could remove the canister containing the reconfigured genetic material. This had been reconfigured by using RAMPART's spinning disk to spin the canister into complexified three-space, in a slowly counter-rotating centrifuge.

Arleena Broadman waited as the maintenance crew finished unfastening the weapons pod, lowered it onto a specially padded and molded self-propelled dolly and drove it a short distance to the routine maintenance area for Aspis crystals. Then, with the assistance of Matt Holmgren, an Altean Naval Service technician who had frequently helped her with this task, she retrieved the canister and its centrifuge from the under side of RAMPART's spinning disk.

"Thanks, Matt" she said to him. "I probably won't see you again, as I hear you've been reassigned to Colchis and I'm going to Daphlay. I just want you to know how much I have appreciated all your help."

He was about to reply when they suddenly smelled noxious fumes.

"The crystal," he coughed, and dashed over to the maintenance crew who were about to begin the process of removing the film which had collected on the interior surface of the Aspis crystal. This film collects on all Aspis crystals as a result of normal operation, and it must be periodically removed in order to maintain the crystal's ability to form an anti-weapons shield. Its removal requires the use of highly caustic and dangerous chemicals.

Very stringent safeguards for performing this task had long since been established by the Altean Naval Service, but in this case a careless maintenance man had dropped a canister containing the chemicals into the bowl-shaped interior of the Aspis crystal. The canister began to leak and when its contents mixed with the air a highly poisonous gas resulted.

Matt Holmgren realised this almost immediately as he looked through the clear Aspis crystal at the leaking canister and saw the bodies of the maintenance men scattered about. After taking a last breath of reasonably fresh air below the crystal, Matt Holmgren climbed up the maintenance ladder to the rim of the weapons pod, made his way across its top and let himself down into the interior of the crystal. There he picked up the leaking canister, closed it with tape that he carried in his overalls.

Arleena Broadman had set down the canisters for the genetic project and followed Matt Holmgren. As he finished sealing the canister closed she was on her knees above him and reaching down to help him out.

"Grab my hand, Matt!" she screamed.

Then she was overcome by the poisonous gas.

When Arleena Broadman regained consciousness she was in the medical facility of an Altean space vessel headed for Daphlay and she began screaming "Grab my hand, Matt!" over and over again.

When Arleena Broadman finally regained consciousness after being sedated, an Altean Naval Service psychologist said gently to her, "Matt Holmgren saved your life. You tried to save his, but because he saved your life he sacrificed his own."

Arleena Broadman continued as first associate of the genetic project until the project members who had been working on Danebury left for Daphlay. Then she resigned and lived the rest of her life as a recluse. Arleena Broadman had occupied living quarters low on the northwestern facing of Ell House and she had loved to watch the water spraying from the crystal tubes onto the jungle below. The view from her residence on Daphlay was nothing like that.

Vicky Manpure read about the last meeting of the Council of Silbury in the lone remaining afternoon newspaper, left her family and was taken in by the Jackmans.

Following the dissolution of the Council of Silbury, Elder Chee ordered that:

The two enormous spinning disks of the Tetrahedron Crater gravitron infusion complex be carefully removed from their position between the armatures and be carefully stored in the Bastion.

The new energy transconverter be carefully moved from its base pad and stored in the Bastion.

The Waldark thing be carefully removed from Hur Square and stored in the Bastion.

The four longhouses of Hur Square, Chapter One, the Labyrinth and the corbelled dome of the grave circle be expertly covered by a thick mastic to protect them from erosive forces.

The two energy transconverters on Dolphin Mesa be carefully transported to Colchis.

The dolphins living in the Sea of Dolphins be lovingly transported to Colchis.

The flags be lowered from the Ranch House and from the four longhouses in Hur Square and carefully stored in the Bastion.

Elder Chee also ordered Anson Trent—the Council member whose vote had ruined the plan to save Silbury—to oversee the removal of all radioactive material from energy transconverters on Silbury; to oversee its encasement in metallic casings; to oversee the loading of these metallic casings aboard transport vessels bound for Daphlay; and to accompany these casings to Daphlay. He was to report to the authorities on Daphlay that he was in charge of the radioactive material and to do whatever authorities on Daphlay ordered—with one exception. He was not to bring it back to Silbury, nor was he to take it to Colchis.

"Six jobs for a six-sided two-dimensional creature," Elder Chee said to himself after a messenger had left Elder Chee's office bearing these written orders to Anson Trent.

Next, Elder Chee invited 'Art Hurian' Manpure to his office.

Elder Chee asked 'Art Hurian' Manpure to oversee the loving transportation of the 24 trained Silbury dolphins to Danebury. Elder Chee asked 'Art Hurian' Manpure to oversee the releasing of those 24 dolphins into the waters of Danebury. 'Art Hurian' Manpure agreed to do both tasks before joining his family on Daphlay.

The four longhouses of Hur Square had water courses around them in which those 24 trained dolphins of Silbury swam. 54 Traditionally the six dolphins swimming in the water course around the data longhouse were dolphins just beginning their training. The six dolphins swimming in the water course around the Wisdom longhouse were the best trained dolphins. The dolphins swimming in the water courses around the information and knowledge longhouses were in two stages of intermediate training; those swimming in the water course around the knowledge longhouse being the more advanced.

All four longhouses of Hur Square were identical in their construction. Made of gleaming transparent crystal, they contained oval pools surrounded by grandstands. The pools were connected with the exterior water courses and in each longhouse, midway along both of the long sides was a bridge, crossing the water course and leading to a large pentagonal entryway. The dolphins were trained in the oval pools daily and these training sessions were open to onlookers. Dolphin shows were held periodically in each longhouse and were attended by large crowds, their favorite show being that put on by the dolphins just beginning their training.

The four longhouses were all topped by flag poles upon which flew the flag of Altea, as it did on the flagpole atop the Ranch House. The prevailing breeze out of the northwest was enough to show the flag's design clearly: a mid-blue dolphin arched in flight on a white background—blue for loyalty, white for the soul.

In Dan Park work crews began removing as much gum resin as possible from the trees filling the park and lining the fairways of the golf courses. These resins were called myrrh and frankincense and were mixed together to form a mastic. The transconverter spheres of energy transconverters are filled with this mastic, without which torinum could not be transconverted into tornum. The soon to die trees of Dan Park were yielding their last valuable supply of myrrh and frankincense.

On Dolphin Mesa energy transconverter maintenance crews removed the canisters of gold from the gold dolphins and prepared them for shipment to Colchis. Also on Dolphin Mesa conduit maintenance crews removed the diamond dolphins at the ends of the conduits which had been conduiting torinum from the Hurmaze to the energy transconverters on Dolphin Mesa and prepared them for shipment to Colchis. The diamond dolphins at the ends of conduits cause torinum to spin so that it can be transconverted in the energy transconverters into tornum. The diamond dolphins are hollow except for a single, seven carat synthetic diamond precisely formed into a dodecahedron.

In his last act as Elder of Silbury 'Pan Dan' Chee ordered the beloved Peri shut down and sealed. Just east of Ell House elevated Peri tubes descended to below the surface on their way to the Space Port, along a gradient which looked like a thin narrow canyon when viewed from far above. Along both sides of the crystal tubes in this area were the controlling components of the Peri system. Elder Chee ordered all the Peri cars moved to this area, that area of tubes be sealed off from all other tubes and the controlling components covered with mastic.

Tommy Untiman told his new wife about the meeting and Odkin's invitation to himself and his four friends. Tommy wanted to go to Danebury and to take Ukika with him. "No," she responded.

Cary Jackman and Terry Wellton talked together and decided to accept Odkin's invitation.

Alea Gandy continued to try to make Cary Manpure forget about his despair.

The next morning Cary Manpure woke up early and said aloud to himself, "I'm going to Danebury. Sara Eland was right."

Cary Manpure arrived just in time to board one of the two space vessels bound for Danebury. Aboard the other space vessel were the 24 dolphins watched over carefully by 'Art Hurian' Manpure.

Ukika and Tommy Untiman boarded the space transport vessel removing the last of the livestock from Silbury.

Altean Naval Service marine transport vessels were assigned to collect and take to Daphlay those living in the five houses of Altea City who did not have other means of transportation to either Colchis or Daphlay—and that was nearly every one.

Sara and Mark Wellton and their son Hal boarded the marine transport vessel evacuating residents of Hurartu House.

Marta Untiman boarded one of the marine transport vessels evacuating residents from Waldark House. Tommy Untiman's parents had never been married. Marta Untiman's maiden name was Untiman and his father's name was Ansel Hoffman. Ansel Hoffman was a banker, well to do and already married when he knew Marta Untiman and he had never admitted to being Tommy Untiman's father. The only record of that was on Tommy Untiman's birth certificate and no one ever paid attention to the name Marta Untiman had written on that birth certificate. Marta Untiman left Daphlay and went to Silbury as soon as she could after Tommy Untiman's birth and established her new identity there, saying that the father had been killed in a mining accident. She never told her son the truth and he never had any reason to suspect that his mother had told him a lie. When they returned to Daphlay, Ukika and Tommy Untiman went their way with Ukika's parents and Tommy Untiman's mother went hers. Marta Untiman never approached Ansel Hoffman and she lived as a recluse the rest of her life, working as necessary to support herself.

Anna and Arnhold Manpure boarded the transport vessel evacuating residents of Zuv House. Also boarding that vessel were Avelina Manpure and her two children; Cary Manpure's brother Ames and his betrothed Lura Ryans; Avena and Kirk Roon with Sara and Tom Roon; Margina and Kurt Sardman with Clark Sardman and Dan Sardman.

Paul Bunzler and Hal Roon were brought aboard the same marine transport vessel in shackles—escorted by Lieutenant Anna Gandy, Altean Naval Service marines who was heavily armed. All other inmates of both the old Crystal Palace and the new Crystal Palace had been removed previously from Silbury. The inmates of the new Crystal Palace had been taken to a Crystal Palace on Daphlay.

Since the excavations of the areas around Atlantis had revealed the ruins of a crystal, six-sided place of incarceration in the river gorge south of Atlantis, societies along the chain of galaxies leading to this galaxy have always constructed similar places of incarceration, long since called

Crystal Palaces both because of the occupation of the inmates and the material of construction.

The old Crystal Palace inmates had been taken to a Crystal Palace especially constructed for them—on Colchis. Paul Bunzler and Hal Roon, who had both previously worked gathering sand for the Crystal Works, had been kept on Silbury until the last minute so they could sanitize the sewage system of the new Crystal Palace before it was sealed—for later.

Ensign Alea Gandy, Altean Naval Service, was one of the engineering watch officers aboard the marine transport vessel evacuating residents of Zuv House.

Milly and Dan Jackman together with Rena and Tommy Jackman and Vicky Manpure did not board the marine transport vessel evacuating residents of Zuv House; Vicky Manpure would not ride in the same vessel as her parents. The four of them boarded one evacuating residents of Ell House.

On the morning of departure the evacuating marine transport vessels first landed one by one in the plaza in front of the Gymnasion/Stadion and opened their hanger bays. Vehicles normally used to transport large things around and about the Gymnasion/Stadion picked up the color coded casings that were stacked on the Stadion's turf, the color denoting which stack went in which vessel. Loading vehicles belonging to the Stadion picked up these stacks and drove out through the service entryways near the Stadion and into the plaza where they loaded the casings aboard the vessels. This plaza was called Dalos Plaza.

Dalos Plaza had been so named in honor of the legendary athlete after whom the plaza in front of the Gymnasion/Stadion complex of Atlantis had been named. The name Dalos, meaning 'beacon light' in Hellenikos, came from an inscribed stele excavated in this plaza of Atlantis. This stele gave the name of the plaza and was also inscribed: "Dalos rose above every adversity to become the greatest athlete known."

Nearby another stele was found upon which an elegant trident and the names Galen, Dalos and Harmonides was inscribed together with the statement: "With heart, mind and soul they worked together." Not far from there a statue of a discus thrower was discovered.

One by one the loaded marine transport vessels rose from Dalos Plaza and flew to Hur Square, where they landed and took aboard the passengers assigned to them.

The marine transport vessel evacuating residents from Zuv House was the last to lift off from Hur Square. When that vessel had risen well above Altea City, an explosion tore through its hanger bay, shattering the aquamarine colored casings and sending them flying. The burning hulk of the marine transport vessel plummeted down and smashed into the abandoned Ell House consuming it in flames. Bits and pieces of aquamarine casings and their contents littered the landscape.

The passengers were all buckled in their seats. Sara Roon was in a window seat and Dan Sardman was next to her. They were holding hands and he was leaning across her as they looked out their seaside window at what was left of the Tor. All of a sudden they heard a tremendous bang, the lights went out and they plunged immediately straight downward, bow first. They knew they were going to die. Dan Sardman hugged Sara Roon to him all the way down.

Also aboard the doomed vessel was Marta Cosgood, direct descendant of Rena Cosgood who had strongly supported Lura Redmand and her plans for the western part of the Horz complex. Marta Cosgood was 18, a young artist who had been helping 'Art Hurian' Manpure with "Glamyrr and Sustanator." Marta was aboard to help care for Avena and Ames Manpure. Her sweetheart Tom Oakes was not aboard, having gone to Daphlay a year earlier with his younger brother Mark and his parents.

Because he wanted to travel with his older sisters, 16-year-old Damon Gandy was on the bridge in the engineering watch section with Alea Gandy. His sweetheart Carla Simpson was waiting for him with her parents on Daphlay and Damon was eager to see her again.

Nine years previously, Byron Clark had been a member of the security team dispatched to investigate a possible intruder in the Tor and had been among those crushed as a result of the explosions which ruined the Tor. His sweetheart, Alika Burr had been utterly devastated at losing him. Alika Burr gladly went to her death as the marine transport vessel plunged toward Ell House. Cary Manpure's cousin had died the day the Tor and Byron Clark died.

Cary Manpure had stayed with Alea Gandy in the Lookout until she had reported to the transport vessel evacuating residents from Zuv House. One last desperate time before they parted, even though Alea Gandy was sure that she would soon be able to arrange a posting on one of the Daphlay-Danebury shuttles, Alea and Cary had made love to one another. They had shared more love in less than four days than many couples shared in a lifetime, they thought.

Cary Manpure had looked from the Lookout over the dying grass of the Ranch and he had wept. "Someday," he said through his tears, "we'll come back here and fix this."

At last they had to part, and Cary Manpure kissed his love only briefly before turning away and flying his 'borrowed' air ship to the Hurmaze, landing in the Park of Meditation. He made his way into the nearly deserted Hurmaze and was told by one of the few remaining workers that the space vessel leaving for Danebury was departing soon from the Space

Port and that Director Odkin had already gone there.

Cary Manpure never regretted anything more in his life than not having given Alea Gandy what he considered a proper goodbye.

The other thing that Cary Manpure regretted most in his life was not having had the chance to say goodbye to Lura Ryans, who was betrothed to his brother Ames.

Lura Ryans was the daughter of Garrett Ryans, a supervisor of Crystal Palace inmates who gathered sand for the Crystal Works. Lura had attended Akadeimia on Silbury with Ames Manpure and along the way they had fallen in love. Along the way Lura Ryans had been a frequent guest at the Manpure's and along the way Cary Manpure had fallen in love with Lura Ryans as a special friend.

Cary Manpure recalled how they talked together about all sorts of things and quickly got to the point where they could carry on endlessly with sentences of multiple and/or sexual meaning.

One time Lura Ryans said, "Cary, you're growing up."

"I didn't know that my pants were that tight," he responded.

"They're not," she said. "I didn't say that you were 'growing up.' I said that you were throwing up. You must be a little tight."

"I'm not tight," he said. "I'm very generous."

"You're not generous," she said. "You're pants are tight and I can tell you're not generous."

On another occasion Cary said, "Lura, you and Ames sure hang around together a lot."

"Sometimes he hangs, and sometimes he does not," she replied.

"You never hang, Lura," Cary said. "You are very pert."

"I may be pert," she said, "but you, Cary Manpure, are very impertinent."

Still another time Cary said, "I still don't understand how all this stuff works, Lura."

"What stuff?" she asked.

"You know, stuff!" said Cary Manpure.

"Cary," she replied, "you stuff the stuff in the stuff. The stuff in the stuff does stuff and eventually out comes the stuffing!"

"Lura, if the stuffing ever comes out before you and Ames get married, you'll both end up working for your Daddy," Cary Manpure added laughing.

During the waning moments of life on Silbury, Cary Manpure raced out of the Hurmaze to the Park of Meditation, climbed aboard 'his' air ship and flew it right into the Space Port, a highly proscribed maneuver. He jumped from the air ship, ran over to the space vessel, which was soon to be bound for Danebury, and boarded it just before it was sealed for take off.

As Cary Manpure ran to the space vessel he remembered when he had seen Lura Harwell off. They were at the Space Port of Silbury. There were many people boarding a space vessel which was in the background. It was nearly Lura Harwell's time to get on as the line was dwindling. They held both hands and looked at one another. He said, "We'll meet again." There were tears in their eyes. She leaned forward and kissed him gently on the lips, then turned and ran for the vessel. She pushed ahead of those in line and got a seat—on the opposite side of the vessel from where he was standing. She had cried as they took off for Daphlay and had cried herself to sleep. She had loved him.

The space vessel bound for Danebury lifted off, and Cary Manpure could not bear to look out of the windows for one last sight of his beloved Silbury. He knew it would soon return to endless sandstorms and that the remains of the Altean settlement would eventually fade from the landscape and appear from afar as knobbly hills, much like the knobbly hills which surround the basin in which the Horz complex had been laid out.

As the space vessel in which Cary Manpure was riding began its braking procedure for its approach to Danebury two Essene holo-images suddenly appeared simultaneously, one on the vessel's bridge, the other in the passenger cabin.

"I am an Essene holo-image," they said simultaneously. "I am directed by Essenes to give you further instructions. You are not to land on Danebury until you are ready and then only at midnight local time, at a landing site which is precisely four miles east of your chosen landing site. The latitude of the landing site is to be a geographical point which will be located at precisely 30 degrees north latitude in 240,000 years. When you land you will remain aboard ship until you receive further instructions.

"No imaging or recording devices are to be used on Danebury.

"When you complete your braking procedure you are to insert your vessel into a precise circular equatorial orbit around Danebury at an altitude of precisely 1000 miles. When you are ready you are to land at the new landing site precisely at midnight.

"In order to be ready you must compute the precise location of the new landing site. Your navigational computers have been infused with data which can be used to compute the rate of movement of the different plates of the crust of Danebury.

"In order to be ready, Joe Lon Odkin must also have figured out the several precise new possible locations for the site of the scale model of the spinning disk on Hurengland. In 240,000 years time, the precise new location of the site of the scale model of the spinning disk must have a topogly latitude of 21,600 and must be at a distance from the landing site which is precisely equal to the polar radius of Danebury divided by the square root of pi; as measured in Danebury miles. There are several locations in Hurengland which meet these requirements; Essenes will tell you which one is correct after Joe Lon Odkin figures out the several possibilities." 69

The holo-images disappeared simultaneously.

The navigational computers were commanded to print out the information infused into them by Essenes. Joe Lon Odkin got out his writing pad and pencil.

As the space vessel in which Cary Manpure was riding orbited Danebury, the voice of the vessel's commanding officer was suddenly heard over the general internal communications circuit, "Attention, please. We have just received an initial report of the crash of one of our vessels leaving Silbury. I will keep you informed as we learn more."

Everyone waited. Fifteen minutes later the commanding officer's voice was heard again. "I must inform you that the vessel evacuating residents of Zuv House exploded in flight and crashed onto Ell House," he said. "It is not expected that there will be survivors."

Cary Manpure shouted "Noooooo....."

When he regained consciousness, everything was known, the casualty list was in. Alea Gandy was gone.

The last Alteans departed Silbury, but Elder 'Pan Dan' Chee had prepared the way for the eventual return of Alteans to Silbury. In the language of Waldark's time, the mighty gates of ancient castles were called tors. On Silbury the Tor had been so named by Elder Dan 'Pan Hur' because the Tor was to be constructed in the form of a gate, not a castle gate, but a gateway to higher understanding. As Alteans departed Silbury, the Tor was no longer a gate. It was only another stone mountain among the many stone mountains on the planetary surface.

Only minutes after the departure of the last Alteans from Silbury, Essenes occupied the Bastion.

Only minutes after the departure of Joe Lon Odkin and Cary Manpure—an event that occurred nine years later—from the Essene base on Danebury, following their severe traducing by Essenes, Essenes not only stopped maintaining the 'natural' satellite of the planet of preparation in its, until then, perfectly circular orbit. They also stopped maintaining in artificial orbits certain other celestial bodies in the solar system containing the planet of preparation—including the two 'natural' satellites of Silbury. Essenes did this so as to mark clearly the end of an epoch in the history of the solar system containing the planet of preparation. The orbits of these celestial bodies began to change as soon as the maintaining ceased. The artificially maintained orbits of those celestial bodies were both representational and practical. Once someone figured out the representational aspects of those once artificially maintained orbits, it would be fairly simple to count back from the current observed orbital changes over a relatively short period of time, and thus determine when those celestial bodies had last been in representational artificially maintained orbits.

Essenes removed the markers designating an enormous triangle surrounding their base on the planet of preparation, shut down and flooded that base.

Awaiting Joe Lon Odkin and Cary Manpure as they flew to Hurengland was another tor about which, as yet, they knew nothing. This tor was called a tor by Essenes because on this tor was the sourcemark for Danebury. 70 This was a natural mountain sculpted by Essenes to resemble Mount Hurartu on Altea. This tor had only a single, round stone at its summit which was the sourcemark for Danebury. Essenes called this tor 'distant stone mountain' tor because its stone sourcemark was far from Danebury's prime meridian, Hurmyrr. 70.2 This tor Essenes called Glastonbury Tor.

'Art Hurian' Manpure called Glastonbury Tor by another name. 'Art Hurian' Manpure lived in utter despair at the base of this mountain which he called: 'Avelinabury.'

Much later Essenes sculpted another mountain, near 45 degrees north latitude and about 120 degrees west of Glastonbury Tor—a mountain in Huregan—it was meant to closely resemble Mount Hurartu on Altea and was nearly the same size. This mountain was called Chintimini by those who first came to Prehurland. Essenes did this to memorialize Cary Manpure's dedicated striving to climb every mountain—and to memorialize his love for Huregan, the shining great beauty of the Universe! 70.1

The fire in Ell House raged and no one fought it. Ell House was consumed and part of its structural framework was reduced to rubble. Its southwestern exterior crystal support beam had been broken by the blast and it flopped back over onto the lower western facing of Ell House, roughly pointing toward the northeastern corner of the adjacent Dan House. As the beam flew outward it carried with it a large section of the upper western facing and that paneling came to rest with its support beam on the lower western facing. In the atrium of Ell House had been a gigantic profile sculpture of Mount Hurartu; and this sculpture was flung high into the air by the impact, and it also came to rest on the lower western facing of Ell House. 70.3

Part Three DANEBURY

Chapter One

Ending-Beginning

It was midnight when the refugees from Silbury landed on Danebury in their two vessels. They landed where Essenes had ordered them to. Cary Manpure was still unconscious. Most of the Alteans were in one vessel; the dolphins were in the other, along with the vessel's Crew and 'Art Hurian' Manpure.

Cary Manpure regained consciousness shortly thereafter. As he did so, he remembered Alea was gone. He remembered that his parents, his brother Frank and Frank's family had gone ahead to Colchis. As far as Cary Manpure knew everyone else who had lived in Zuv House, except for Cary Jackman and himself, was aboard the crashed vessel. He became frantic with worry imagining that his parents would think that he too had been aboard that vessel.

Cary Manpure tried to jump out of bed, but fell to the floor instead. Since landing, the interior of the Altean space vessel had been converted to Danebury gravity, and Cary Manpure's muscles were still used to the weaker gravity of Silbury. He crawled to the door of the compartment in which he had been recovering from his loss of consciousness, pulled himself up to the door handle, pulled open the door and stumbled down the passageway. Cary Manpure desperately wanted to tell his parents that he was still alive. He reached the elevator to the bridge and its transcommunication section, entered it and rode to the lower level of the bridge.

Cary Manpure staggered into the transcommunication section and screamed at those on watch that he had to talk with his parents on Colchis immediately. When the watch section was slow to react to his demands, Cary Manpure grabbed at one of its members and tried to pull him out of his chair so that he could sit down and operate a transceiver himself. His actions precipitated a grabbing and shoving match between him and the three members of the watch section and he ended up in restricted quarters.

Cary Manpure became hysterical. Alea was gone. His parents thought he was dead. Everyone else from Zuv House except Cary Jackman and himself had gone down with the crash. The security watch sedated him.

When Cary Manpure regained consciousness he was back in his bed again and Joe Lon Odkin was there waiting for him to awaken. When Odkin saw Cary Manpure's eyes open and signs of recognition appear, Odkin explained, "Cary, your parents know you are here. All the other Jackmans and your cousin Vicky were on another vessel. Your cousin Dan is with us here. But all the others who lived in Zuv House are gone."

Cary Manpure looked up at Odkin with tears in his eyes and said, "Thank you."

Alea was gone. His brother Ames and his betrothed Lura Ryans were gone. Avelina Manpure, Dan Manpure and their two children Avena and Ames were gone.

"When you are ready," said Odkin to Cary Manpure, "we can go and get something to eat, and I'll tell you what happened."

Cary Manpure got up and the two of them walked together to the mess decks.

Odkin told Cary Manpure that Kirk Roon was responsible. Kirk Roon had been enraged by Arnhold Manpure's behavior at the Council meeting. He could not bear to leave Arnhold Manpure alive—the man who had ridiculed and berated his own son, the man who had savagely traduced Elder Chee, the man who had led the attack against the plan to save Silbury.

Kirk Roon knew that his traitorous brother and the equally traitorous Bunzler would be aboard the vessel evacuating those who had lived in Zuv House. Kirk Roon could insure the death of all three traitors: Arnhold Manpure, Hal Roon and Paul Bunzler—and so he did. Kirk Roon packed into his personal gear high explosives from supplies awaiting shipment from Roon Mining to Daphlay. This gear was then subsequently stowed in the hanger bay of the Zuv House evacuating vessel. Kirk Roon carried a small detonator aboard with him and had activated it as the vessel rose above Altea City.

Odkin went on to tell Cary Manpure that Kirk Roon had posted a letter to Byron Haley Chee. Kirk Roon had made sure that it left the day before the evacuation aboard the Altean Naval Service vessel transporting Altean Naval Service personnel's families bound for Colchis. Among those families were Cary Manpure's mother, his brother Frank's wife

Alana and their son Mark. So the letter was delivered to Byron Haley Chee upon his arrival on Colchis the night of the evacuation, having traveled aboard the vessel carrying the dolphins (which had lived in the Sea of Dolphins). He was extremely upset as a result of the crash, but he opened the letter nonetheless.

In his letter Kirk Roon had concluded by stating that he knew his execution of the traitors would bring about the loss of many innocent lives, including those of his own family, friends and their families. Kirk Roon stated he was very sorry for that, but that it had to be.

As Odkin was telling all this to Cary Manpure, tears streamed from Cary Manpure's eyes and down his cheeks. He could not conceive that Kirk Roon could do such a thing. Bitterness welled up inside him. Odkin could sense how Cary Manpure was feeling and when he was done Odkin added, "Cary, sometimes we feel we just have to do something. We are not always right."

Cary Manpure was too devastated to respond.

"You go back and rest some more," said Odkin.

Cary Manpure was about to stand up when an Essene holo-image suddenly appeared and said, "I am an Essene holo-image. Essenes have directed that I deliver additional instructions to you. Joe Lon Odkin, at daybreak you are to remain aboard this vessel. A total of 359 passengers are to debark and among them must be Cary Manpure, Cary Jackman and Terry Wellton. All must be blindfolded.

"The other vessel is departing now with 24 dolphins and 'Art Hurian' Manpure aboard. Their Crew needs to come aboard your ship. After they embark, this vessel is to be sealed. No one is to look out during the sealing process."

The holo-image disappeared.

Odkin saw to the embarkation of those who had been put off the vessel with the dolphins and to the sealing of their own vessel. The passengers drew lots to determine which 356 of them would debark.

At daybreak, computed from previous observations by aboard ship computers (the Crew could no longer use any sensors or transcommunicate as a result of the sealing of the vessel) the hanger bay door was opened. The 359 were lined up through the hanger bay and far into the vessel. All were blindfolded. Cary Manpure, Cary Jackman and Terry Wellton were well back in the line so they did not hear the Essene holo-image when it ordered the three of them to the head of the line. The word was passed back to them shortly thereafter, and they groped their way blindly to the hanger bay door.

When Cary Manpure, Cary Jackman and Terry Wellton arrived at the head of the line the holo-image issued more orders, "Cary Manpure, you go first; Cary Jackman, you second; Terry Wellton, you third. Cary Manpure, you follow the sound of my voice. Cary Jackman, you put your right hand on Cary Manpure's right shoulder and follow him. The rest of you do likewise."

The holo-image began a rapid recitation of virtually everything known about the transdimensional physics of the Universe. The voice receded in front of Cary Manpure so he followed it as ordered, with Cary Jackman hanging onto Cary Manpure's right shoulder, Terry Wellton hanging onto Cary Jackman's right shoulder, and on and on and on. Cary Manpure made his way down the ramp formed by the hanger bay door and stepped onto the surface of Danebury, the first Altean to have ever done so.

The holo-image droned on and on and Cary Manpure followed. The way was gently rising, then steeply rising, then flat. At last the holo-image commanded Cary Manpure to stop.

"Turn around. Take off your blindfold. Do not look behind you," the holo-image ordered.

Cary Manpure did as he was told. When he opened his eyes he could see that the rest of the 359 were standing in two lines that serpentined away from him, and they had removed their blindfolds. Everyone had their backs toward him. Cary Jackman and Cary Manpure were closest to him but still about 30 feet away. Cary Jackman was on his right side and Terry Wellton on his left side. Terry Wellton was standing level with Carry Jackman but separated from him by something over ten feet. Cary Manpure thought that a wider spacing continued back along the two lines formed by the passengers from the Altean space vessel. If those two lines were extended to where he stood, Cary Manpure could see that he would be standing at the midpoint between them. The vessel lay more than a mile away in the distance and to the north, Cary Manpure judged, its steel alloy hull glinting in the early morning sunlight.

Cary Manpure stood there for a few minutes taking in his first sunrise on Danebury. Then he noticed a commotion along the lines near the vessel. As the commotion began moving his way, he soon realized that the far ends of the lines were dissolving. An ever larger group comprising the rest of the 359 was now forming and moving toward his position. The group got bigger and bigger and closer and closer. Cary Manpure could hear those in the group shouting excitedly and pointing in his direction—but over his head.

Finally, Cary Manpure could see that Director Odkin was at the head of the group and that as he walked toward Cary Manpure, those standing in the lines turned around to face Cary Manpure as Director Odkin drew level with them. Then they would run up to Director Odkin, shake his hand and fall into the group following him.

At last, Director Odkin reached Cary Jackman and Terry Wellton. Cary Manpure's friends turned toward Cary Manpure and they looked up. Their mouths dropped open. Their eyes widened. They shouted and jumped into the air. Then they ran over to Director Odkin and hugged him at the same time.

"Come here, Cary!" Director Odkin shouted to Cary Manpure. "Don't look around yet."

Totally perplexed by what was going on, Cary Manpure walked toward Director Odkin. When Cary Manpure reached him, Director Odkin took Cary Manpure gently by the shoulders and turned him around.

Before all 360 stood Joe Lon Odkin's computer, already constructed, its smooth nearly white surface glistening in the brilliant morning sunlight. Far up the sloping facing which towered above them was an enormous banner. Written on the banner in huge letters were the words: "Joe Lon Odkin."

Tears streamed from Cary Manpure's eyes and down his cheeks. This was the catharsis Essenes had lovingly planned for Cary Manpure. Even though he had been standing so near, he had no idea that anything was there.

An Essene holo-image suddenly appeared and began speaking, "I am an Essene holo-image. I am directed by Essenes to deliver additional instructions to you. The actual position of the apex of Hurmyrr is precisely 6999.657 Danebury feet directly south of your calculated position for Hurmyrr. This distance is 4.11 Danebury inches less than 7000 Danebury feet, and therefore represents those things that the numbers 4, 7 and 1000 stand for. The digits 6, 5, and 7 of the decimal .657 in the figure 6999.657 represent the interrelationships between the non-living parts of the Universe, living things and spirit.

"The serpentine was 6999.657 Danebury feet long from the space vessel to near the base of Hurmyrr. The lines were 13 Danebury feet apart and along the length of these serpentines 358 of you were separated by a distance of two times 19.47 Danebury feet. Cary Manpure was placed 24 Danebury feet beyond the end of the lines and there was a total of 5.397 Danebury feet behind Cary Manpure to the base of Hurmyrr. You know those things which 13, 19.47 and those digits represent. When Joe Lon Odkin joined you that made 360, representing the angular measuring system of the Universe."

"I don't know about the digit 9," said Joe Lon Odkin.

"If you knew about the computers in the Hurmaze, of which you were director, you would know that there were three computers therein and that each computer had triple redundancy. Three times three equals nine," said the holo-image.

"Computers are redundant garbage," said Joe Lon Odkin.

"Hurmyrr is one-third the size of those computers because Hurmyrr was constructed by Essenes out of stone to show you that Essenes know how to do real solid things," said the holo-image. "Since Hurmyrr is made of stone, it cannot do anything except be a shining reflection and inspiration to those who see it. It would have been redundant to have constructed Hurmyrr three times as large as it is, but it is a good thing that those computers require two-thirds of their three computations to be exactly the same before the solution is accepted—because even computers make mistakes, Joe Lon Odkin.

"Are you saying I've made some mistake now?" asked Odkin.

"Yes," said the holo-image. "You don't accept computers as necessary tools."

"And I never will," said Odkin.

"Yes you will," said the holo-image. "Joe Lon Odkin, you are not ossified, you have not turned to stone and become incapable of doing anything. You can and will do things, but first you must open your eyes. Everyone except Joe Lon Odkin is to remain here. Joe Lon Odkin is to see the interior of this non-working but nevertheless glorious stone model of a computer, before it is sealed, in order to open his eyes."

The holo-image led Odkin the remaining 29.397 feet to the base, up a ladder to a small entryway in its northern facing and into the stone model of a computer. They returned an hour later as the 359 waited. When he reached them the only thing Joe Lon Odkin said was, "Inside Hurmyrr is a chamber containing a large granite coffer. It is precisely placed there in memory of the innocents who died on Silbury."

"Joe Lon Odkin, were there not other things of interest?" asked the holo-image.

"No," said Odkin.

"Then we'll just have to wait until they open it up later," said the holo-image. "Many of them won't find it very interesting—either."

The holo-image then led the 360 around the eastern side of Hurmyrr and to the eastern edge of the plateau on which Hurmyrr stands. The holo-image pointed to a spot along this edge of the plateau and said, "Here you will construct and sculpt the Ark Hur. Joe Lon Odkin has the plans of the Ark Hur. Your general purpose aboard ship computers have been infused with the precise positioning of the Ark Hur. Begin NOW!"

The holo-image disappeared.

For the next month the Altean refugees from Silbury worked at constructing and sculpting the Ark Hur: the statue that replicated the representations of the Hurmaze. To those working on The Ark Hur (the 'shining beginning-ending') it represented the ending of their old lives on Silbury and the new life that was to emerge on Danebury. They were awed by what they were doing and they dedicated themselves to voluntary service. The construction and sculpting of the Ark Hur was the catharsis lovingly planned by Essenes for these Alteans.

After the Alteans had completed the head of the Ark Hur and while they were still working on the body an Essene holo-image suddenly appeared and began speaking, "I am an Essene holo-image. I am directed by Essenes to deliver additional instructions to you, "Joe Lon Odkin, you have completed enough of the Ark Hur.

"Joe Lon Odkin, before you construct Alteana in Prehurland you need some more information and you need to know where to construct it.

"Joe Lon Odkin, your measurements are no longer to be made in inches, feet and miles. They are to be made in Danebury inches, Danebury feet and Danebury miles.

"Joe Lon Odkin, Hurmyrr was partially constructed using an inch which is called the pyramid inch which is longer than the Danebury inch by a ratio of 1.00106 to 1. You are not to use the pyramid inch in any other construction.

"Joe Lon Odkin, Essenes constructed Hurmyrr so that its height, including the non constructed capstone, is precisely 480.3471728 Danebury feet. In the height of Hurmyrr there are more Danebury feet than feet because Danebury is slightly smaller than Altea. You intended to construct Hurmyrr so that it stood at slightly more than 480.3471728 feet, including its non constructed capstone. That would have been about one-half of one inch too tall.

"All future references to the height of Hurmyrr are not only to be in Danebury feet, they must always include its non constructed capstone.

"Joe Lon Odkin, you are to rescale Alteana so that the axial distance as measured along the main avenue between the apex of the largest pyramid and the apex of the next largest pyramid is precisely 720 Alteana yards. You are to call the main avenue the Way of the Life. You are to call the largest pyramid Sustanator and the next largest pyramid Glamyrr. 71 Each Alteana yard is to be 3.47571113 feet long.

"Joe Lon Odkin, you are to place the apex of Sustanator near 130 degrees west of the current prime meridian of Danebury: Hurmyrr—the source of the topogly matrix of this planet. In 240,000 years the apex of Sustanator is to have a topogly longitude of 280,538.1821. In 240,000 years the topogly vector of the apex of Sustanator is to be 12. You calculate the resulting topogly latitude."

"I certainly don't need a computer to work that out," snarled Odkin. "I can easily do that in my head."

As if it had not heard the holo-image continued, "Joe Lon Odkin, in 240,000 years the azimuth of the Way of the Life at Alteana is to be equivalent to the height of Hurmyrr, divided by pi cubed.

"Joe Lon Odkin, you are to calculate the new radius of the base ring of your model of a spinning disk by multiplying the future azimuth of the Way of Life by pi. You can also calculate the new radius of the base ring of your model of a spinning disk by dividing the future topogly latitude you calculated for the apex of Sustanator, by the height of Hurmyrr; or by dividing the height of Hurmyrr by pi squared.

"Joe Lon Odkin, Essenes constructed Hurmyrr shorter than you had planned so that the new diameter of the base ring of your model of a spinning disk would be equivalent to four pi, times the square root of 60. To determine the size of your scale model you divided the size of the Tetrahedron Crater's spinning disks by three. That was close, but not correct.

"Joe Lon Odkin, later you will have to use another unit of measure: 2.719715671 Danebury feet in length. Since this unit will be associated with structures using large stones it is called the megalithic yard. It is derived by dividing the topogly longitude of Hurmyrr by the new radius of the base ring of your model of a spinning disk, and then calculating the square root of the result. Although the megalithic yard 2.719715671 feet is numerically close to both the transdimensional constant 2.720699046 and the constant e, 2.718281828, the near equivalencies of these three numbers are all coincidental.

"However, the near equivalencies of important numbers is not always coincidental. The near equivalencies of the twelfth root of two, namely 1.059463094 associated with the harmonics which allow for the bringing forth of self-aware life; and the square root of nine-eighths 1.060660172 associated with tetrahedra are very important and vital near equivalencies. These near equivalencies are not perfectly equivalent, because three-dimensional reality is not perfect. Numerical near equivalencies should therefore not be rejected immediately but explored thoroughly—even though most often they prove coincidental, as with the near equivalency between the ratio e/pi and the square root of three divided by two.

"Joe Lon Odkin, do you have all of this?" asked the holo-image.

"I can write everything down, think and calculate faster in my head than you nitwits can talk," said Odkin.

As if it had not heard the holo-image continued, "Joe Lon Odkin, when you are ready you are to fly to Prehurland and construct Alteana.

You will be ready when you have resited Alteana, when you have rescaled Alteana in Alteana yards, and when you have rescaled your model of a spinning disk with the new diameter of its base ring."

The holo-image disappeared.

"Essenes are nitwits," said Joe Lon Odkin. "They all belong in that thing they have just sealed—then it would be worth something—as a tomb!"

While Joe Lon Odkin and his associates had been constructing and sculpting the Ark Hur, Hal Arbur and his associates of the genetic project waited. In the Seventh Essene Panlogos Essenes had given specific instructions that with regard to the genetic project nothing was to be done until Alteans had completed their work in Abzuland and moved on to Prehurland. Essenes had also specified that the director of the genetic project and his associates were to accompany Joe Lon Odkin and his associates to Abzuland. However, they were not to assist them with their work there.

Hal Arbur chafed.

As the Essene holo-image ordered Joe Lon Odkin and his associates to stop working on the Ark Hur, another Essene holo-image suddenly appeared before Hal Arbur sitting in his cabin aboard the Altean transport vessel. That vessel was still on the ground 6999.657 feet north of the apex of Hurmyrr. Hal Arbur was startled.

"I am an Essene holo-image," it said. "I am directed by Essenes to deliver additional instructions to you. The beings of Danebury who face extinction due to inbreeding are nearly all dead. The surviving females of child bearing age of the beings of Danebury are mostly healthy and are therefore able to receive the first part of the genetic agent and then bear children. These females are concentrated in southeastern Ashintoland and the eastern central section of the Abzuland in which you are now located. Your aboard ship general purpose computers have been infused with the specific locations of these females.

"After arriving at your destination in Prehurland you are to begin the process of administering the first part of the genetic agent. In order for that process to be complete, a total of 735 healthy female and 750 healthy male children must result. The mothers and the children must be returned to the original living environment of the mothers, but not where they can be confronted by male beings of Danebury who face extinction due to inbreeding.

"The mothers and their children must never see any of you.

"The children will be self-aware.

"The work of Joe Lon Odkin and his associates together with the work of Hal Arbur and his associates mark the beginning of Altean involvement in the project Panergon Gwynmyrr. This means 'All deed, all work, clear reflection.'

Previously, Alteans knew about panlogos, meaning 'all word.' Now Alteans know about panergon, meaning 'all deed, all work.'

"Clear reflection—understanding—comes about as a result of deeds and work—not words.

"Words alone are no longer adequate.

"The time for deeds and work begins NOW!"

The holo-image disappeared.

Chapter Two

The New Being

While Joe Lon Odkin and his associates were constructing Alteana, Hal Arbur and his associates administered the first part of the genetic agent to healthy child bearing age female beings of Danebury. As they slept in their natural living environments, the females were sedated and flown in an unconscious state to Alteana. There they were taken to two large compounds constructed nearby while still unconscious and placed in those compounds during the night with other female beings of Danebury. During the flight each female was examined to determine when she would next ovulate. At the appropriate time after ovulation and in the middle of the night, each female was again sedated, taken in an unconscious state to the medical building which was hidden from the compounds, and administered the first part of the genetic agent.

The female beings were impregnated, without their knowledge, in order to avert biological catastrophe due to inbreeding; to speed up the evolutionary process leading toward a free-willed self-aware being on Danebury; and to bring about a being who would lead Alteans in the redeeming of the galaxy. This last requirement was a component of Panergon Gwynmyrr about which Alteans knew nothing.

Everything the Alteans did with regard to the female beings of Danebury was done with careful planning, great care and love. The sedating, transporting, examining and administering of the first part of the genetic agent were all done as gently as possible. One large compound replicated the natural living environment of those who lived in Abzuland; the other replicated the natural living environment of those who lived in southeastern Ashintoland. Only the limits of the compounds made them any different. Whenever a female being reached those limits she would receive a mild shock. Very soon they learned those limits and approached them no more—long before any of their children were tempted to do so. Despite the mild shock the female beings could have easily escaped from either of the compounds. They did not try to do so because they liked where they were living, they were among their own kind and they loved their new children.

The children of these female beings were very different from their mothers. They were born self-aware. They had souls. They were the first of the transitional creative-thinking beings of Danebury.

When there were 735 daughters and 750 sons of the female beings of Danebury—one daughter or one son for each female—the Alteans ceased sedating, transporting, examining and impregnating them. None of the children died or became seriously ill while they lived in the compounds.

For nearly nine years the female beings lived in one or the other compounds, and for nine years Joe Lon Odkin and his associates worked on the construction of Alteana. When Alteana was completed, it was time for the female beings and their children to be returned to the natural living environments of the mothers.

The children of the female beings developed rapidly and some of them were nearing the age at which they would begin having children of their own—without the administration of the first part of the genetic agent. The children were about to become mothers and fathers.

When fully grown these children of the female beings of Danebury were about five and one-half feet tall. They had large heads and were hairy. They were intuitive. They were nocturnal. They were left-handed. They lived in harmony with one another and with their environment.

When Alteana was nearing completion an Essene holo-image suddenly appeared before Hal Arbur as he worked at his desk in the medical building near the compounds. The holo-image began speaking, "I am an Essene holo-image and I am directed by Essenes to deliver additional instructions to you. You are now to take the 735 daughters and 750 sons and their mothers to their natural living environments but away from male beings of Danebury who are headed for extinction. Two-thirds of these mothers are to be returned to their previous living environments. You are now to take 245 daughters and 250 sons with their mothers to their natural living environments in southeastern Ashintoland, 245 daughters and 250 sons with their mothers to their natural living environments in Abzuland and 245 daughters and 250 sons with their mothers to new natural living environments in far western Ashintoland. The locations of these new natural living environments have been infused in your computers."

The holo-image disappeared.

When all 735 daughters and 750 sons with their mothers had been taken to their natural living environments it was time for the Alteans to leave Alteana and return to Daphlay. As Hal Arbur cleared out his desk in the medical building just prior to its dismantling an Essene holo-image suddenly appeared and said, "I am an Essene holo-image and I am directed by Essenes to deliver additional information to you. Hal Arbur, you have done well. In about 200,000 years Alteans are to return to Danebury in order to administer the second part of the genetic agent to the transitional creative-thinking beings who will then be living on Danebury."

The holo-image disappeared.

While Joe Lon Odkin and his associates were constructing Alteana and encoding therein things basic to the Universe—including: e, phi, pi, the twelfth root of two and others—Odkin was ordered by Essenes to incorporate four-dimensional gravity into the layout of Alteana. Essenes also told Odkin that the future beings of Danebury would not know of four-dimensional gravity when Alteana was studied by seekers of knowledge because almost all future beings of Danebury would discount hyperdimensionality.

"I don't know anything about four-dimensional gravity either," Odkin told the holo-image.

"But you have access to information concerning four-dimensional gravity," said the holo-image. "They won't have such access. They need your help. Joe Lon Odkin, will you help them?"

"Of course," said Odkin.

In order to be able to begin to fulfill this specific and yet vague requirement of Essenes, Joe Lon Odkin decided to study gravity. Odkin read that gravity is both three-dimensional and four-dimensional, and then remembered that he had learned that fact long before in a transdimensional physics class. Odkin read all could on the subject.

Odkin thought about what he had learned and then consulted an Altean astrophysicist for information about the orbits of the planets in the solar system containing Danebury and Silbury. Odkin found, as he had hoped, that there were perturbations in the orbits of planets which were far from the intense gravity of the sun of that solar system. These perturbations, the astrophysicist told Odkin, were the result of four-dimensional gravity that continued to operate at a long distance from the sun, while the three-dimensional gravity of the sun began to weaken.

If the beings of Danebury would not know of four-dimensional gravity when Alteana was studied by seekers of knowledge, the only way those beings could explain the perturbations in the orbits of planets—which orbited far from the intense gravity of the sun—Odkin thought, would be for them to hypothesize that the cause was a planet beyond the known planets of that solar system.

In order to fulfill the Essene requirement to incorporate four-dimensional gravity into the layout of Alteana, Odkin decided to encode Danebury and Silbury's solar system in the layout of Alteana and to add three extra planets—two-thirds of those planets inside the orbit of the innermost planet—the other planet beyond the outer fringes of the encoded solar system.

Odkin thought when Alteana was studied by seekers of knowledge, observers of that time would know for certain that there were no planets orbiting inside the orbit of the innermost planet of their solar system. Odkin hoped that when astronomers of their solar system learned of the findings at Alteana they would think about those discoveries and realize that all three additional planets were allegorical. Odkin also hoped that finding would induce the observers of the solar system to think about the perturbations in the orbits of planets which orbited far from the intense gravity of the sun, and to seek a new cause for those perturbations. With luck, Odkin thought, they would come upon four-dimensional gravity, a discovery which might lead them to hyperdimensionality in general. 72

When Odkin was finished with his plan he presented it to the astrophysicist with whom he had spoken previously and the astrophysicist responded, "This may be too subtle for them. The perturbations are small. When they get good data on the outer planets of their solar system they may very well assume that the perturbations are insignificant. They are not."

Odkin laid out the orbits of the inner rocky planets inside the confines of the structure he and his associates called Eternity. The encoded distance between Danebury and its sun was fixed at 96 Alteana yards—representing 24/25ths, the Harmonic of the Universe. 73

The two planets which orbit closer to its sun than Danebury were given proportional encoded distances of 72 and 36 Alteana yards. The two allegorical planets added closer to the sun were given encoded distances of 18 and 9 Alteana yards. Silbury was given a proportional encoded distance of 144 Alteana yards.

The other planets and the other allegorical planet were encoded along the Way of Life and beyond, with the center line of Eternity as the starting point. 73

Their distance in Alteana yards and their markers were as follows:

- 520, a small platform.
- 945, a platform.
- 1845, the apex of Glamyrr.

- 2880, a temple.
- 3780, a temple.
- 7200, a temple.

After the encoding of the nine planets plus the three allegorical planets of the solar system had been completed by Odkin, an Essene holo-image suddenly appeared before Joe Lon Odkin as he was preparing to retire for the night and said, “I am an Essene holo-image and Essenes have directed that I convey to you the following. Joe Lon Odkin, you have done well. You have encoded a solar system containing fourteen celestial bodies: the nine planets and the three allegorical planets you have encoded, plus the moon and the sun in the forms of Glamyrr and Sustanator. Essenes will infuse a similar but allegorical encoding in a culture of Danebury that is yet to be decided. We will leave out your two inner most allegorical planets. Your outermost allegorical planet will become known as ‘the twelfth planet.’ Essenes do not want that culture to know about the great significance of 13 or 14, but Essenes want the beings of Danebury to think about those things they are led to by your encoding.”

The holo-image disappeared.

“I didn’t know Essenes could be polite,” said Odkin to himself. “Maybe they have suddenly realized that if they are polite we will be more inclined to help them.”

The holo-image suddenly appeared and said, “Essenes do whatever is necessary to get the job done.”

The holo-image disappeared.

“We should have sealed them in that big worthless stone tomb,” said Odkin to himself, now unable to get to sleep.

Chapter Three

Lupeikalia

Marta Weynard entered Akadeimia on Daphlay two years after Cary Manpure went to Danebury concluding her studies six years later at the age of 27. To broaden her education in architecture and to render voluntary service, Marta Weynard traveled to Danebury to work at Alteana during the final stages of its construction.

After her shuttle landed on Danebury, Marta Weynard exited through the cargo bay and began to walk down the pathway leading to Alteana. Due to her excitement at arriving on Danebury, Marta forgot that the gravity of Danebury is about twice that of Daphlay, lost her balance and fell to the ground. Cary Manpure saw this as he was approaching, ran forward and assisted Marta to her feet.

"Thank you," Marta Weynard said. "I seem to have forgotten the training I received for dealing with the extra gravity of Danebury."

"If you'll wait here a couple of minutes," Cary Manpure responded, "I'll be right back. I have to pick up the mail. I'll get your luggage as well. My name is Cary Manpure."

"I would certainly appreciate your help," she said. "I'm Marta Weynard. I'm here to help with the completion of Alteana."

Up until that moment Cary Manpure had hardly said a word to a female since Alea Gandy's death nearly nine years before. He had rented single quarters at Alteana and during his free time he'd kept very much to himself except for the occasional trip exploring with Cary Jackman and Terry Wellton.

Cary Jackman and Terry Wellton had rented living quarters together and that decision had proven to be a good idea because they both came to fall in love with ladies who also shared living quarters.

Marla Owens was 16 when she arrived at Alteana with her legal ward Arleena Osmar, aged 44. Her mother, Zoe Owens had committed suicide following the death of her husband. Lieutenant Damon Owens, Altean Naval Service marines, had been killed during the assault on the private empire of the family Sarkneson. Arleena Osmar was the widow of Major Anthony Osmar, Altean Naval Service marines, the member of the team who led the assault. He was killed in the private empire's surveillance center. Arleena Osmar was an architect and her legal ward Marla Owens was her assistant.

While Cary Manpure mostly worked directly for Joe Lon Odkin, Director of the Alteana construction project, Cary Jackman and Terry Wellton were assigned to work for Arleena Osmar, the project's Assistant Director. Cary Jackman soon realized that Arleena Osmar was a tortured soul, and over a period of time he was able to draw her out.

Arleena and Anthony Osmar, although both 35 at the time, had only been married a short while when Major Osmar had been killed. They had purposefully delayed Arleena becoming pregnant until after her husband returned from the expedition to Colchis. Arleena Osmar had been utterly devastated by the loss of her husband, had contemplated suicide and had only been saved as a result of the assistance she had automatically received from the Altean Naval Service marines. In group therapy she had met Zoe Owens and they became friends. Zoe Owens had not been able to deal with her loss, and Arleena Osmar was again utterly devastated by the loss of her new friend. A very insightful Altean Naval Service marines psychologist had suggested that Arleena Osmar become the legal ward for the seven-year-old Marla Owens, and as a result of Arleena Osmar's accepting that duty both she and her legal ward had survived. Neither wanted to go to Daphlay, so when the opportunity arose they chose to work on the project to construct Alteana.

This revelation utterly devastated Cary Jackman and he lay awake several sleepless nights trying to think of some way he could help Arleena Osmar deal more successfully with the loss of her husband. Finally, he had an inspiration and told her of his plan. She rejected his ideas and steadfastly refused to do as he suggested. Cary Jackman remained adamant and badgered Arleena Osmar until she finally gave in.

As a result of Cary Jackman getting his way, the positions of the structures Glamyrr and Sustanator were secretly adjusted so that the distance between the southeastern corner of Glamyrr and the northeastern corner of Sustanator became 600 Alteana yards. The reason for this being that 600 is 5/6ths of 720 and the axial distance between the apex of Sustanator (the largest pyramid) and the apex of Glamyrr (the next largest pyramid) as measured along the main avenue of Alteana (the Way of the Life) was to be 720 Alteana yards. 71

Cary Jackman visualized Glamyrr and Sustanator as a very private secret memorial to the loving relationship between Arleena and Anthony Osmar. Glamyrr was to represent Arleena and Sustanator her husband. The 5/6ths ratio between 600 and 720 Alteana yards memorialized the memory of their love for one another, a memory which transcended death. The secret 600 Alteana yards distance between the corners of the two pyramids would represent their holding hands across the void.

Cary Jackman stayed away from Arleena Osmar for some time after she accepted his ideas. Then one night, she called him and asked him to her living quarters.

Terry Wellton knew nothing about the secret plans to alter the layout of Alteana. He had, however, learned Arleena Osmar's story from Marla Owens. As a result of their work, Marla Owens and Terry Wellton had become acquainted. And as a result of that acquaintance, they fell in love.

Cary Manpure returned to where Marta Weynard stood waiting with the mail bag draped over one shoulder, Marta Weynard's clothes bag over the other, smaller bags under both arms and suitcases in either hand. When they arrived at the fabricated structural unit which contained the living quarters, entertainment centers and dining facilities of those working at Alteana, Cary Manpure set everything down, except the mail bag and showed Marta Weynard into the administrative office.

"You can get everything you need in here," he said. "This is also where I drop off the mail."

Marta Weynard smiled at Cary Manpure. "Thank you for your help," she said.

At supper that evening Cary Manpure spotted Marta Weynard sitting at a table by a window overlooking Alteana and walked up to her. She was looking intently at the construction site, so she did not notice his approach.

"May I join you?" he asked, startling her.

Marta Weynard turned quickly having recognized the voice behind her. She smiled up at him. "Please do, Cary," she said.

Seating himself across from the young lady Cary Manpure smiled back at her. "You look refreshed from your long trip, Marta," he said.

"I took a nap before supper and I do feel much better," she said.

As they finished supper, Cary Manpure suggested that they take a walk through the construction site.

"I would be delighted," she responded.

"I'll meet you by the lounge door near the dining room in a few minutes, if that's all right with you," he suggested.

"That's perfect," said Marta Weynard as she rose from the table.

After entering the construction site, the two young Alteans walked toward the nearly complete pyramid at the far end of a broad avenue.

"This long avenue was named by Essenes the Way of Life," said Cary Manpure.

On their right, they passed a sizeable and complex structure.

"This large structure is called Eternity by us," Cary Manpure explained, "not because it is eternal, but because it has taken an eternity to construct!"

Marta Weynard laughed.

Midway along the Way of Life they came to one and then another large plaza which represented the physical and hyperdimensional parts of the Universe, as Cary Manpure informed Marta Weynard.

Then after crossing the second plaza the two turned to the right, leading off the Way of Life and walked over to the base of the largest pyramid being constructed at Alteana.

"Essenes ordered us to call this pyramid Sustanator," said Cary Manpure. 71,73

They walked up the steps of Sustanator and Marta Weynard had her first panoramic view of Alteana.

"It is absolutely breathtaking," she said.

"Yes," said Cary Manpure deadpan. "The elevation here is over 7000 feet."

Marta Weynard laughed again.

"We are deliberately constructing Alteana in stages so that it will appear as if it took centuries to complete. Later investigations will completely fail to grasp its age, constructors and purpose," he said. "The underground constructions near the two plazas we crossed will soon be completely covered by 'newer' structures, and the pyramid on which we are standing has been terraced underneath the visible terraces. Essenes ordered us to construct Alteana this way, and Essenes say that they will ensure that the construction dates of the Ark Hur and Hurmyrr are also masked. The mortar used in the construction of Hurmyrr contains straw, Essenes say. All plants contain carbon and some of that carbon is in the form of a radioactive isotope. The date of a plant's death can be determined by analyzing the residual radioactive carbon in the remains of that plant. Essenes will ensure that the dating of Hurmyrr, using this method of analyzing the mortar, results in the wrong conclusion. They say that they have other ways of ensuring that the Ark Hur is misdated too."

Marta Weynard turned to Cary Manpure and asked, "What is the purpose of what looks like mica layering I can see at the top of this pyramid?"

"Essenes told us to put this mica here and Essenes say that the mica will be discovered long before mica's vital insulation function in computers is known. Essenes say that the discoverers of the mica will not know about computers and will not be able to figure out why the mica is on this pyramid. Essenes want to confuse those that find this mica and they will most likely succeed. Essenes confuse us," Cary Manpure concluded.

They descended the steps and walked back to the Way of Life where they turned toward the other large terraced pyramid, Cary Manpure explained that it was being called Glamyrr, again as ordered by Essenes.

As Marta Weynard and Cary Manpure approached Glamyrr, they crossed a wide plaza in which was a large oblong structure. Upon reaching the highest terrace of Glamyrr, they looked back down the length of the Way of Life.

"This really takes my breath away," said Marta Weynard. "I am simply overwhelmed by this view."

"This is similar to the view that we had from the Gymnasion/Stadion in the city of Danebury on Altea," stated Cary Manpure. "Alteana is a scale model of the city of Danebury but with a different style of architecture."

A shiver went through Marta Weynard's body as Cary Manpure told her about the intimate connection between the city of Danebury and Alteana.

Cary Manpure noticed this and put his arm around the young lady, to keep her warm. They silently descended the steps of Glamyrr, walked back down the Way of Life and to the fabricated structural unit.

"We call the fabricated structural unit Odkin House, but not in front of Director Odkin," said Cary Manpure. "How about a drink?"

"Well, just one," Marta Weynard replied.

Six years after the beginning of construction of Alteana, the sports director died suddenly of a heart attack. He was replaced by a young man named Mark Oakes who came to Alteana from Daphlay. Mark Oakes was 24 at the time, tall, handsome and quick-witted. He fell in love with Marla Owens who was by that time 22 years old.

Mark Oakes, like everyone else at Alteana, soon knew that Marla Owens and Terry Wellton were very much in love. The more Mark Oakes loved Marla Owens too, the more he brooded and the more he drank. One night he had consumed more than enough and he destroyed the lounge.

In that same lounge, the two young Alteans were enjoying their drinks when Marta Weynard said, "I have heard you are using a rather curious unit of measurement in your construction of Alteana."

"Yes," said Cary Manpure. After telling Marta Weynard that Essenes had ordered the constructors of Alteana to use a unit of measure called the Alteana yard but refused to tell them of its derivation. Cary Manpure added, "Essenes have told us that there is an imprecise derivation for the Alteana yard. The Alteana yard is imprecisely 1/12,000,000th of the polar diameter of Danebury. It is also very nearly equal to the twelfth root of two times 1/10,000,000th of the distance from the equator of Danebury to either of its poles.

"These somewhat interesting calculations and resulting units of measure are profoundly irrelevant, because they do not take time into account as a major element in deriving units of measure.

"Essenes have also told us that at some point they might have to impose the derived unit (which is 1/10,000,000th of the distance from the equator of Danebury to either of its poles) on a yet-to-be-determined violent segment of the future population of Danebury. If this happens, Essenes then anticipate that this violent segment will perceive this profoundly irrelevant unit of measurement to be a panacea to the hodgepodge of measuring systems being used at that time and being arrogant, they will ruthlessly impose their 'panacea' on nearly everyone else.

"It seems like even on Danebury the few who will do anything may enslave the many who will allow themselves to be enslaved."

"Sara Eland must have been right," responded Marta Weynard sadly, "but how do Essenes know this? What is the purpose of imposing this profoundly irrelevant unit of measure?"

"I don't know how Essenes know anything," responded Cary Manpure, "but I do know why they will impose this unit of measure. Essenes confuse, but not totally. There are always hints. The profoundly irrelevant unit of measure is the key to solving many of the encodings of Alteana by some future seeker of knowledge. Remember, this profoundly irrelevant unit of measure can be multiplied by the twelfth root of two and then by 12 million to approximate the polar diameter of Danebury. Multiplied by the twelfth root of two it is very nearly the imposed yard. We're leaving the twelfth root of two all over Alteana. Someone will figure out the length of our imposed yard and then much more as a consequence."

Marta Weynard could only shake her head as she asked Cary Manpure to order her another drink.

As they talked, the moon of Danebury rose and Marta Weynard and Cary Manpure could see its crescent shape through the windows of the lounge.

"Essenes intend to confuse the beings of Danebury about their moon too—a moon which is the single reason why complex life arose on Danebury," said Cary Manpure. "Essenes intend that the moon of

Danebury becomes a symbol of romance in the culture of Danebury, as it is in ours. Essenes also intend that the moon of Danebury becomes a harbinger of madness in cultures of Danebury. I think Essenes will turn the beings of Danebury into schizophrenics. Essenes say they know what they are doing."

Marta Weynard shivered again, and shortly thereafter the two young people said good night and went their separate ways.

Mark Oakes was hauled before Director Odkin who thoroughly lambasted him to the point where the young man shuddered in his presence.

"You'd better mend your ways, young man," Odkin shouted. "Or we'll separate your way from ours. Begin NOW!"

Mark Oakes mended the lounge, mended his ways and then asked Marla Owens if he could have a private word with her.

The completion of Alteana neared. Marta Weynard and Cary Manpure often worked side by side and sometimes ate together when their voluntary extra service to Atleana's completion allowed. During one of these meals and after Marta Weynard had been at Alteana for about two weeks Cary Manpure asked, "Would you like to come with me to find a suitable quarry for facing stones. They are needed for the standard serving altar in the large plaza in front of Glamyrr?"

Marta Weynard replied, "I don't know what a standard serving altar is, but I think I'd like to go."

"A standard serving altar is the name given by Essenes to many of the small architectural features of Alteana which Essenes keep adding for us to construct. I think the term 'standard serving' means that something serves as a standard substitute, in this case for a real altar," responded Cary Manpure.

The air ship, with Cary Manpure in the pilot's seat and Marta Weynard beside him, flew over the hills northeast of Alteana. Through the windows they maintained a continuous watch for suitable outcrops of rock and for a landing area which might be near any such outcropping. Vast mountainous areas loomed in the distance.

Marta Weynard spotted an extensive spur of rock.

"Cary, look!" she exclaimed, pointing seaside.

The young man quickly turned the helm and reduced speed so that they could look for a landing area. Toward the far end of the spur was a relatively flat open meadow, so Cary Manpure guided the air ship over it and landed. He removed the landing ladder affixed to the inside hull of the air ship, opened the odunside exit hatch, carefully walked across the sloping exterior hull and attached the landing ladder to its exterior hull fitting. Marta Weynard followed.

The two young Alteans reached the spur of rock and it only took a few minutes for Cary Manpure to break off several stone samples with a hammer and chisel.

"I think this stone will be good for the facings, but I have to take it back so it can be analyzed," he said. "Before returning would you like to share some food I packed in the air ship? We could have a picnic in the meadow."

Marta Weynard took Cary Manpure's hand and they walked down the hillside to the meadow.

As they finished their picnic the two young Alteans were concluding a discussion of how the stone would be quarried, transported and fitted to the structure that had been designed to convince future beings that it had indeed once been used by "primitive sun worshippers" as an altar—according to Essenes.

Suddenly Cary Manpure stopped in mid-sentence and gazed deeply into Marta Weynard's eyes.

"Marta," he stammered, then stopped.

"Yes?" she asked.

"I have suddenly found myself wildly in love with you," he confessed.

Cary Manpure looked at her as if he was a whipped puppy. Marta Weynard leaned forward and kissed him gently, but with assurance, on his lips.

"Fear not, Cary Manpure, most pure of men. You have me in a similarly perplexing situation."

The sun was setting in the west when they started back to Alteana.

As they were mooring Marta Weynard suddenly asked, "Now that you have taken an interest in me, dear Cary, how do you plan to take me on more brilliant, educational searches for stone facings that are needed for tremendously important standard serving altars?"

Cary Manpure threw his head back and laughed. "I'll plot something devious," he answered.

During the next few days of intense work, Marta Weynard and Cary Manpure barely had the opportunity to pass more than friendly greetings. Even so, Cary Jackman and Terry Wellton noticed a definitive change in Cary Manpure's behavior.

Terry Wellton had suddenly noticed a definitive change in Marla Owens' behaviour as well. Terribly perplexed and frightened by this, he asked her to tell him what was the matter.

"I have suddenly found myself in love not only with you, but also with Mark Oakes," she confessed.

An utterly devastated Terry Wellton walked away and locked himself in his bedroom.

As the three young men of the unit of four friends ate together one evening Cary Jackman asked casually, but with purpose, "Ollun, what is going on with you lately? Fliff and I haven't been able to find you for any of our usual childish pursuits during our time off?"

Cary Manpure was totally unprepared for this questioning and blushed brightly.

His friends laughed uproariously.

Then Terry Wellton took his turn at Cary Manpure by saying, "We've had some really interesting adventures lately, exploring along the east coast sea shore, we found some very important mineral samples in the sand. Why, just last week we collected a whole ditty bag of pretty sea shells. If you had been along, Ollun, who knows what further decisive action we might have taken to increase our vital knowledge of the Universe."

Cary Jackman and Terry Wellton doubled over in laughter.

Cary Manpure could only sit there and face his tormentors.

To make matters worse for Cary Manpure, Marta Weynard suddenly appeared from behind him and asked, "May I join you gentlemen for supper?"

Attempting to control their fits of merriment, Cary Jackman and Terry Wellton rose simultaneously from their chairs and gallantly offered the young lady a seat, falling over each other in the process. When Marta Weynard saw this she looked at Cary Manpure questioningly, but his only response was to shrug his shoulders.

Having concluded her assessment, Marta Weynard acted as if she accepted the polite gestures of the young men at face value. She settled into her chair, determined to rescue Cary Manpure by turning the joke back on Cary Manpure's friends.

Following introductions, during which the jokers could barely contain themselves, she asked deadpan, "Could someone please explain to me how one obtains sanitary napkins around here?"

Cary Manpure gulped. Cary Jackman and Terry Wellton stopped their antics immediately, their jaws dropping open.

Marta Weynard continued, "I am having the most difficult time finding the necessities of life in this complex living environment which you gentlemen have so lavishly and conscientiously appointed so that females can afford themselves of every luxury."

Suspicion began to creep into the minds of Cary Manpure's friends as Marta Weynard continued to complain about living conditions at Alteana, and they looked at one another knowingly. Terry Wellton nodded to Cary Jackman who responded to Marta Weynard's complaints. "We never knew there was this problem," he said. "We'll run out right now and locate the director of living quarters and ask her to immediately requisition dozens of cases of sanitary napkins so that our ladies will not have this problem in the future.

"Come on, Terry, let's go," Cary Jackman added as he stood up, "but only after we watch the evening movie."

When Terry Wellton finally emerged from his locked room, he decided to go to the evening movie. On his way in, he saw Marla Owens and Mark Oakes sitting together talking and laughing. Terry Wellton went back to his room, locked the door and set his room on fire.

Fortunately Cary Jackman walked into their living quarters a few minutes later, smelled smoke, activated the fire alarm and broke down Terry Wellton's door. Cary Jackman's actions saved Terry Wellton's life, but when Terry Wellton regained consciousness he had to be sedated.

Cary Manpure volunteered for one of the holo-mapping expeditions which Essenes had unexpectedly and for no apparent reason suddenly ordered Joe Lon Odkin and his associates to undertake. This expedition called for a single air ship, equipped with special holo-mapping device, to be flown northward up the chain of volcanic mountain peaks, inland of Prehurland's western coast and then to return southward along the coastline. The holo-mapping could be accomplished within a week. This included overnight stops at sites predetermined by Essenes, where additional geologic data was to be obtained by means of sonic transceivers. A pilot and an assistant were required for each holo-mapping expedition.

Cary Manpure asked Director Odkin if he could pilot the air ship which would fly up western Prehurland.

"Yes," replied Odkin.

Cary Manpure next asked Director Odkin if Marta Weynard could be his assistant on the expedition.

"Yes," replied Odkin.

After receiving those positive replies from Joe Lon Odkin to both requests, Cary Manpure looked for Marta Weynard in the last place that he had seen her, which was in the laundry, washing her clothes. Cary Manpure helped her out until she was done.

After they left the laundry together, Cary Manpure excitedly told Marta Weynard that he was going to be the pilot for one of the holo-mapping expeditions, adding that the pilots of the four holo-mapping expeditions each required an assistant. Marta Weynard did not respond as Cary Manpure had hoped she would.

"You will be gone for a week?" she enquired.

"You don't see what I'm plotting, do you?" he asked in response.

"Don't you mean holo-plotting?" Marta Weynard asked avoiding

Cary Manpure's eyes.

"You do remember that I promised I would plot something more devious, don't you?" Cary Manpure asked.

"Yes, but I fail to understand what connection that has with your week long holo-mapping expedition," she responded deadpan.

"Marta, would you like to come along?" Cary Manpure finally asked.

"I'd love to," she responded immediately kissing him.

There were four holo-mapping expeditions altogether: Marta Weynard and Cary Manpure's; another up the eastern coast of Prehurland—returning mid-continent; and two expeditions south across Abzuland. Essenes required that each expedition return transmissions simultaneously of the in flight data, plus the geologic data collected from the specified overnight rest stops. In training for their expedition, pilots and their assistants were taught every detail of their assignment, including operation of all applicable devices, emergency repair procedures, routes, timetable schedules and the set up, monitoring, break down and restowing of the sonic transceiver.

Proper attention to every facet of each expedition kept Joe Lon Odkin from personally attending the departure of Marta Weynard and Cary Manpure, but he wished them good luck as they flew northwest along the eastern coast of the long gulf formed by a peninsula which extended southward from the main part of the mainland for hundreds of miles.

The first stop was just north of the head of the gulf. After landing, Marta Weynard and Cary Manpure according to their expedition plan, immediately set up and activated the geologic data collecting sonic transceiver. Next they unstowed tents, provisions, water and personal gear. And when they had finished setting up camp, the two young Alteans prepared their evening meal using a portable stove.

After supper Cary Manpure said, "We have an early start in the morning. I think we should go to bed."

"What did you say, Cary?" Marta Weynard asked.

"What I said, Marta," Cary Manpure responded, "is that we should got to bed—in the same tent."

Marta Weynard took Cary Manpure's hand and led him to her tent.

Marla Owens visited Terry Wellton as he recovered from his near asphyxiation. "I am utterly devastated by the way things have turned out, Terry," she said, "but I have to be frank with you. I am going to marry Mark."

Breaking camp only took a few minutes and they were airborne with all gear securely stowed on schedule. The second day's route required that they first fly along a string of snowcapped peaks. Around midday they passed over an expansive deep blue lake surrounded by mountains. Later they passed on their odunside a solitary volcanic mountain towering over the surrounding countryside. Marta Weynard and Cary Manpure flew onwards and in the late afternoon they found their predetermined landing site in the woodlands west of volcanic peaks, well north of the solitary volcanic mountain.

Not far from their camp site and the geologic data collecting sonic transceiver, a small stream rushed down the slope of a little meadow, splashing against rocks scattered across its breadth. Colorful wild flowers grew amidst the lush grass. As Marta Weynard and Cary Manpure watched, a doe and her spotted fawn emerged from the forest, seeking water. The deer warily made their way to the stream and began drinking while keeping a continuous watch for predators. Suddenly an enormous eagle dived into the meadow, impaling a small rodent with its sharp talons, and startling the deer into hasty retreat. The magnificent eagle screeched at the strange creatures who had intruded into its domain and quickly rose, flying out of sight within minutes.

Terry Wellton stood at the window of his recovery room and watched, as the shuttle rose quickly and flew out of his sight within seconds.

The next three days saw the young Alteans continue their mission far to the north and then begin the return trip down the coast. Marta Weynard and Cary Manpure stopped twice at the same place, leaving their gear while they flew a long loop over territory too inhospitable for camping.

Proceeding southward the young Alteans flew over the mouth of a very large river. Farther south they reached their final landmark of the day, a towering tree-covered headland jutting into the sea. Just beyond, shielded from the strong seasonal northwesterly winds, lay their destination: a flat grass-covered area above high cliffs, against which the waves crashed in a never ending roar. Cary Manpure managed to land the air ship despite gusty cross currents.

Struggling against the wind, which was formidable even in the lee of the headland, they used additional lines and stakes to pitch their tent. Marta Weynard and Cary Manpure then changed into their warmest clothing and set up the geologic data collecting sonic transceiver.

Undaunted by the blustery conditions, Cary Manpure suggested that they go for a walk on the beach before supper. Marta Weynard agreed. The young man led his companion southward along the edge of the bluff before discovering a way down. Climbing hand over hand facing the wall of the bluff, they reached the beach where at last they found calm weather against the cliffs. As Marta Weynard and Cary Manpure walked toward the surf they struggled through soft footing before reaching easier going damp sand, strewn with agates and numerous varieties of sea shells.

Fog rolled in during the night as the wind eased. Nevertheless they lifted off in the air ship at precisely the correct time to continue their data transmission simultaneously with the other three missions. As the sun burned away the fog the weather soon cleared, giving the young Alteans magnificent vistas during their flight southward along the coastline.

Well into the day, they passed over a huge bay formed by two peninsulas of unequal length, then by a much smaller bay open to the sea. They subsequently arrived at their final stopping place on another peninsula towering over the northern approach to another huge bay.

"Will you marry me?" asked Cary Manpure on the final day of their expedition, as they flew south.

Marta Weynard threw her arms around Cary Manpure's neck and nuzzled up to him.

"You're a star ship," she whispered in his ear as she handed him a golden triangle.

Marla Owens and Mark Oakes were going to be married on the journey to Daphlay, and it was not long after their departure, and Terry Wellton's 'recovery,' that Cary Jackman gave Arleena Osmar a golden triangle.

As she snuggled up to him, he asked her to marry him.

"I love you, Cary Jackman," she responded," but I have to be absolutely frank with you now. I can only have one husband: Anthony Osmar. I am adamant about that."

Many, many years later, Cary Jackman related this story to Cary Manpure.

"The reason we call our festival of love Lupeikalia," Cary Manpure had replied "is because Lupeikalia is a combining word from Hellenikos made up of the root word 'kalos'—meaning 'beautiful,' 'honorable,' 'noble,' 'favorable' and 'fine'—and the word 'lupei'—meaning 'grief,' 'distress,' 'suffering' and 'sad plight.'

"Now we know why."

"Do you think Fliff killed himself?" Cary Jackman asked.

"No," responded Cary Manpure. "Fliff was only trying to save a life—as you did THREE TIMES."

Chapter Four

South of Huregan Complex

On landing at Alteana, Marta Weynard and Cary Manpure reported to Director Odkin. When they had completed their verbal report of their holo-mapping expedition, Cary Manpure said, "Director Odkin, Marta and I would like you to attend our wedding. We would also like you to be the witness for legal authority. We became betrothed during the holo-mapping expedition."

Odkin was about to reply when an Essene holo-image suddenly appeared before them and said, "Marta Weynard and Cary Manpure are not to be married. Marta Weynard is to return immediately to Daphlay. Joe Lon Odkin and Cary Manpure are to travel immediately to a destination on Danebury determined by Essenes. Cary Jackman and Terry Wellton are to travel to another destination on Danebury determined by Essenes. The destination of Joe Lon Odkin and Cary Manpure has been infused into the general purpose computers of Alteana. The destination of Cary Jackman and Terry Wellton, their method of transportation and those things they are to take with them will be infused into those computers later."

The holo-image disappeared.

Marta Weynard and Cary Manpure were crushed.

After Marta Weynard boarded a vessel bound for Daphlay Cary Manpure went berserk and had to be sedated.

Cary Manpure was unconscious as he flew north aboard an air ship piloted by Joe Lon Odkin to the destination specified by Essenes, a destination which was "south of Huregan."

Huregan was the name Alteans had been ordered by Essenes to use for the territory north of the solitary volcanic mountain peak. After he recovered, Cary Manpure discovered that the word 'huregan' meant 'shining great beauty' in Hurtegel. Cary Manpure was in agreement with Essenes on only one thing: Huregan was indeed a huregan.

Joe Lon Odkin and Cary Manpure settled near a creek. An animal trail meandered through the mixed woodland to the west of the creek so they built their habitation on the gently rising land above the trail. Farther to the west stood fairly high and very steep hills.

Essenes had ordered that Joe Lon Odkin and Cary Manpure bring nothing except food and books with them. They therefore fashioned adz and hammer heads from stone and strapped their crude tools to hand made wooden 'handles,' using dried strands of the tough grass which grew in the meadows east of the creek.

After Joe Lon Odkin and Cary Manpure had completed their habitation, Cary Manpure named it the Pavilion because their habitation was not a house but only a framework of pillars, beams and cross slats on a rough hewn board platform. Fast growing native wisteria soon covered the Pavilion.

The Pavilion was constructed according to the precise specifications of Joe Lon Odkin, using a unit of measure called Director Odkin pacings by Cary Manpure. These pacings were divided by three to form Director Odkin feet. 74

The length of the eastern side of the Pavilion was 'precisely' 36 Director Odkin feet. The southern side was 'precisely' 16 Director Odkin feet. The western side extended from the south 'precisely' 24 Director Odkin feet, jogged 'precisely' two Director Odkin feet west, then turned north again for 'precisely' the 12 Director Odkin feet required to match the 36 Director Odkin feet of the eastern side. The northern side was 'precisely' 18 Director Odkin feet.

In the Pavilion the only floor to beam opening was an entryway 'precisely' five Director Odkin feet wide, its center located 'precisely' 13 Director Odkin feet north of the southeastern corner of the Pavilion.

The well planned, but less than precisely constructed Pavilion consisted of two interior 'suites.'

On the right as they entered the Pavilion was what Cary Manpure named the sleeping suite: 'precisely' 12 x 18 Director Odkin feet, a two-thirds ratio of width to length. Its interior was very sparsely 'appointed.' Across the front, under the 'windows' was a long low 'wardrobe' which Joe Lon Odkin and Cary Manpure shared. Upon opening the 'wardrobe' Odkin's things were on the right in accordance with Cary Manpure's always deferring to Director Odkin. In the northwestern section of the sleeping suite were two 'cots,' the two slept at right angles to each other with their heads toward the northwestern corner of the Pavilion.

On the left and straight ahead as they entered the Pavilion was what Cary Manpure called the living suite: it contained working, living, 'food' 'preparation' and 'dining' areas. The proportion of the living suite was also a two-thirds ratio of width to length, and 'precisely' 16 x 24 Director Odkin feet. The long axis of the living suite was north-south, at 90 degrees to the long axis east-west of the sleeping suite.

The working and living area was to the left as they entered the Pavilion. Immediately behind the left front 'wall' section of the living suite were two 'chairs' with a 'table' between them. Joe Lon Odkin's was on the right as they looked out the 'window' toward the creek.

Directly behind the working and living area was the area in which Cary Manpure 'prepared' their 'food.' Cary Manpure called this area the Gauntlet.

In the back right hand corner of the living suite and against the back 'wall' of the Pavilion—was the 'dining' 'table,' an irregular slab of sandstone filled with fossilized shells.

They used the commode in the head in the air ship and washed in the creek.

After the Bench of Musing on the Knoll of Musing and the Hearth had been built, Cary Manpure called their new home the South of Huregan complex.

Cary Manpure discovered the Knoll of Musing as he named it, during the first southward walk he took with Joe Lon Odkin along the animal trail on the lower slopes of the hills west of the Pavilion. It was early afternoon a few days following their arrival and springtime had just begun. The hills were a vibrant green, but then with the approach of summer they would soon become brown as the grass dried up.

As they walked southward, Cary Manpure spotted a tall tree to their right, growing above the animal trail and thus began his discovery of the Knoll of Musing. Joe Lon Odkin was concentrating on counting his paces since he had determined that he would walk precisely 1947 paces—three Silbury miles—before turning back to the Pavilion. Joe Lon Odkin would walk only this distance because 1947 of his paces had been required for him to walk from the Altean space vessel to the Ark Hur. Joe Lon Odkin had enjoyed making this walk to and from the Ark Hur during its construction and sculpting and since leaving Abzuland he had walked this same distance every day.

Cary Manpure suggested they change directions and head for the tree, but Odkin was nearing his limit of 1947 paces and refused to leave the trail. Cary Manpure then asked Director Odkin how many more paces were left before he reached the specified 1947. Director Odkin told him and Cary Manpure suggested that was exactly the number of Director Odkin paces from where they were standing to the tree. Odkin turned, headed for the tree and stopped five feet short of it.

"This is precisely 1947 paces," he stated.

Joe Lon Odkin and Cary Manpure took the rest of the afternoon to build the Bench of Musing, five feet northeast of the tree on the Knoll of Musing—precisely 1947 Director Odkin pacings from the Pavilion. By the time the Bench of Musing had been completed there was no time for musing, it was nearly time for Cary Manpure to get back to the Gauntlet.

Cary Manpure had a 'better' idea. Instead of returning the way they had come, he suggested they take a more westerly route to do some more exploring.

"My proposed route will also be precisely 1947 Director Odkin paces," Cary Manpure stated.

Joe Lon Odkin consented.

They soon found themselves utterly lost in a nearly impenetrable thicket. Amidst the gathering dusk, Odkin lunged ahead, diligently counting each pace until he reached 1947. Then he stopped. Odkin and Cary Manpure camped at that spot for the night. Though they had no supper, Cary Manpure built a small fire. Later he built the Hearth on the same spot.

Each day thereafter while they lived at the South of Huregan complex Joe Lon Odkin and Cary Manpure walked to the Bench of Musing on the Knoll of Musing. Four times a week they returned to the Pavilion. Three times a week they walked from the Knoll of Musing to the Hearth, spent the night and then returned to the Pavilion the next morning. Cary Manpure established clear trails between the components of the South of Huregan complex.

As Springtime gave way to summertime and summertime became early fall, the daily high temperatures rose dramatically from the low 70s to the 100s. Joe Lon Odkin and Cary Manpure sweltered and sweated.

Neither Joe Lon Odkin nor Cary Manpure knew how long they were to stay "south of Huregan." They thought that they were there so that Cary Manpure could recover from his most recent trauma—a trauma caused by Essenes. The very hot weather, the physical labor, but mostly the companionship of Joe Lon Odkin slowly healed Cary Manpure's latest wounds, at least somewhat.

In early fall, an Essene holo-image suddenly appeared before them as they sat on the Bench of Musing and said, "You are to leave the South of Huregan complex and fly to an Essene base on Danebury. The information you need to fulfill this requirement has been infused into the general purpose computer aboard your air ship."

The holo-image disappeared.

Cary Manpure commanded the computer to print out the information which had been infused by Essenes and gave that printout to Director Odkin.

The next day they departed from the South of Huregan complex and flew to the Essene base on Danebury, and on their way Cary Manpure said, "Marta Weynard gave me the only golden triangle I ever got. I think I know now why there are four escalator openings to the Tower of Ancestors Seed Station: I think that ladies are hyperdimensional."

Chapter Five

Nitwits

Joe Lon Odkin and Cary Manpure departed the South of Huregan complex in their air ship and flew southeastward across Prehurland toward the Essene base. As they flew, Odkin told Cary Manpure about the triangular shaped Essene Exclusionary Zone 1003 Danebury miles per side that he had read about in the printout. The Essene Exclusionary Zone was considered by Essenes to be their domain, and no one, Essenes had repeated several times, was allowed to enter without their permission.

"At first I thought the distance 1003 Danebury miles to be rather curious," Odkin told Cary Manpure. "Then I read on."

Odkin read from the printout, "'This number 1003 Danebury miles is not the actual figure, but only a close approximation to the precise distance: 1044 precessional miles. The precessional mileage system has 25,920 miles around the equator of Danebury and is therefore related to the nautical mileage system by a ratio of 5 to 6, metaphorically representing the relationship between the non-living parts of the Universe and living things. Measured in precessional miles, the distance 1044 is 96 and two-thirds percent of 1080, which is 1/24th of the distance around the equator of Danebury. The number 96 represents 24/25ths. You know what 24/25ths and two-thirds are.

"'The western corner of the Essene Exclusionary Zone is clearly marked by a black obelisk precisely 120 Danebury feet high standing on a long narrow island extending north to south. This island is located just off the eastern coast of the major peninsula which extends southward from the southeastern corner of Prehurland.

"'The Essene base is sited about 60 Danebury miles east of that black obelisk and approximately 60 Danebury miles north of the southern tip of that peninsula.

"'The northeastern and southeastern corners of the Essene Exclusionary Zone are marked with similar obelisks, both standing on islands.

"'The northeastern obelisk stands near the center of an island shaped by opposing hooks; and near the tip of the northeastern bay formed by the southwestern hook. The southeastern obelisk is located near the end of a high rocky peninsula protecting the extensive harbor on the northern side of the smallest and easternmost island of three large islands. These stretch nearly west-east across the sea which lies south and east of the Prehurland peninsula described above.

"'You have permission to enter the Essene Exclusionary Zone.'"

Joe Lon Odkin stopped reading and gave the printout to Cary Manpure as he added, "The Essene text concludes with the exact routing we are to use to get to the base and also gives precise coordinates of where we are to land."

Cary Manpure infused the navigational computer of the air ship with the information on the printout. After landing the two Alteans climbed down from the air ship and waited for an hour. Then, to the southeast but as if from out of nowhere, a strange aircraft suddenly appeared hovering just above the water before heading in their direction.

Joe Lon Odkin and Cary Manpure waited for another 20 minutes as the craft reached them, then circled around them two and one-half times before hovering in the air behind them. Finally the aircraft floated to the ground and a voice, emanating from the craft ordered, "Embark NOW!"

Cary Manpure looked at Joe Lon Odkin. Odkin shrugged his massive shoulders, walked the few feet to the waiting craft and stepped aboard. Cary Manpure followed.

They landed on the floor of a cavern after descending a long shaft.

"Debark NOW!" a voice ordered.

As the two Alteans stood on the floor of the cavern an Essene holo-image suddenly appeared.

"Come here NOW!" it ordered.

Odkin did as the holo-image ordered and Cary Manpure followed. The holo-image turned around as the Alteans approached it and proceeded down a passageway leading from an entryway in the side of the cavern. Joe Lon Odkin and Cary Manpure followed the holo-image as it led them through a labyrinthine maze until they eventually came to a circular chamber brightly lit by glowing panels which covered its ceiling. A single wooden chair stood in the center of the chamber.

The holo-image turned to Cary Manpure and ordered, "Sit NOW!"

Cary Manpure sat down. Then the holo-image turned to Odkin and ordered, "Follow NOW!"

Odkin followed, and the holo-image led him out an entryway opposite the one by which they had entered. Cary Manpure sat for an hour and then the lights suddenly went out. Subdued lighting illuminated the chamber, and Cary Manpure could see that he was surrounded by all kinds of food neatly placed on shelves all around him.

The subdued lighting stayed on for what Cary Manpure thought was about five or six minutes and then went off for 10 or 12. When the subdued lighting came back on the food was gone. On the shelves surrounding him were drinks, a considerable number of drinks in glasses. Once more the subdued lighting stayed on for five or six minutes and then went off again for 10 or 12 minutes. When the subdued lighting came back on, there was nothing surrounding Cary Manpure.

This was the beginning of many hours of a repetitive cycle of subdued lighting on and subdued lighting off. When the subdued lighting was on there was first food; the next time there were drinks; the third time there was nothing. This three part cycle was repeated again and again.

Cary Manpure decided to investigate. The next time the subdued lighting came on nothing surrounded him and Cary Manpure got up from his chair and warily inched his way across the floor. Just as he had expected he eventually came to a transparent barrier. The young Altean turned around and went back to the chair.

After what Cary Manpure thought must have been at least a day, the bright ceiling light panels suddenly came on. When Cary Manpure's eyes had adjusted to the greater light he saw that an Essene holo-image stood in front of him.

"Go NOW!" ordered the holo-image pointing.

Cary Manpure got up from the chair, walked out the entryway through which he had seen Joe Lon Odkin leave and went down a long passageway which led back to the cavern below the shaft. In the cavern was the strange aircraft and an Essene holo-image.

"Embark NOW!" ordered the holo-image.

Cary Manpure flew in the craft back to the place they had left their air ship.

"Debark NOW!" ordered the holo-image.

When Joe Lon Odkin left the circular chamber in which Cary Manpure was sitting, he was led by an Essene holo-image back to the cavern below the shaft, past the aircraft and through another entryway. Odkin followed the holo-image through another long passageway, up a stairway to the surface and to their destination, a hardened mound in the shape of a sea creature, either a dolphin or a shark, Odkin could never decide which it was meant to be. 75

"In 240,000 years this sea creature mound," the holo-image began, "will have a topogly longitude equivalent to the square of the topogly longitude of Hurmyrr. In 240,000 years the topogly vector of this sea creature mound will be equivalent to two-thirds pi. Later, you must calculate the resulting topogly latitude.

"To the northwest of here, in Prehurland there is a sky creature mound which in 240,000 years will be located at about 114 and one-half degrees west of Hurmyrr; and about 400 feet south of the latitude at which there are the square root of three, divided by two times 1000 Danebury miles in 15 degrees of longitude. 76 In 240,000 years the topogly longitude of the sky creature mound will be equivalent to four times one-tenth the topogly latitude of the scale model of the spinning disk, times the square root of 60. In 240,000 years the topogly vector of the sky creature mound will be equivalent to ten times the square of the megalithic yard, divided by two-thirds pi. Later, you must calculate the resulting topogly latitude.

"As you know, Hurmyrr is the source of the topogly matrix of this planet. The first growth ring of topogly sites includes the sea creature mound; the sky creature mound; Sustanator; and the scale model of the spinning disk. Later Essenes will give you the other six sites of five-sixths of the sites of the first growth ring. You will then determine the last two sites of the first growth ring. You will also determine 41 of the 42 sites of the second growth ring, 91 of the 92 sites of the third growth ring, 161 of the 162 sites of the fourth growth ring and 251 of the 252 sites of the fifth growth ring. You will determine a total of 13 times 42 sites of the topogly matrix of this planet. Essenes will give you the first site of each succeeding growth ring. It is mandatory that you complete the topogly matrix of this planet.

"When Althena Chee was taken into custody by legal authority it was Elder Byron Haley Chee who did so. When Althena Chee was taken into custody she was in her living quarters. When Althena Chee was taken into custody she was with Cary Jackman. When Althena Chee was taken into custody Cary Manpure was also in Althena Chee's living quarters with Alea Gandy, and Terry Wellton was there with Anna Gandy."

Joe Lon Odkin attacked the holo-image. Odkin swung his right fist at the head of the holo-image, but his fist passed right through its head.

Enraged by his failure to injure the holo-image Odkin leaped at the throat of his tormenter with both hands, only to meet with similar results. Odkin's hands passed right through its neck.

By then totally frustrated, Odkin lost control of himself. Bellowing like a bull Odkin charged the holo-image which had backed away following Odkin's attempt to strangle it. At full speed Odkin threw his body sideways at the holo-image in an attempt to somehow knock it down. Odkin's body passed right through its body. The Altean lay panting on the ground.

"Before you begin the mandatory completion of the topogly matrix of this planet," the holo-image continued, "you are to tell Cary Manpure, Cary Jackman and Terry Wellton that it was you who revealed to legal authority that Althena Chee had led Sarkneson to Bunzler."

Uncontrollable agony seared through the mind of Joe Lon Odkin and he lost consciousness.

"Follow NOW!" the holo-image ordered when Odkin opened his eyes some time later. Odkin pulled himself to his feet and then did as he had been ordered.

The holo-image led Odkin back to the air ship, arriving as Cary Manpure stood waiting.

"Embark and go NOW!" one Essene holo-image ordered Cary Manpure.

"Embark and go NOW!" the other Essene holo-image ordered Joe Lon Odkin.

Joe Lon Odkin and Cary Manpure embarked and took off. As the air ship rose into the air another holo-image suddenly appeared between the two Alteans and said, "Your destination is about 18 miles and about three degrees west of due north from the location you correctly recalculated for the site of your scale model of a spinning disk. You will recognize the place when you get there."

The holo-image disappeared.

As they flew over the ocean toward Hurengland, Joe Lon Odkin asked Cary Manpure what he had done during his visit to the Essene base. Cary Manpure related his experiences and then added, "I don't know what Essenes were trying to do with me, but they failed because I did not respond to anything. Essenes placed me in a situation very similar to that of the hero of a mythos I know—so I did nothing. I used to think Essenes were smart. They should have known better than to subject me to the duplication of a situation from a mythos.

"Essenes must be nitwits."

"The nitwits had you in a Crystal Palace," concluded Odkin. "You are not a nitwit. You don't belong in a Crystal Palace. They're the nitwits. Because we can't get them into that nitwit stone tomb any more, they now belong in THE Crystal Palace."

Joe Lon Odkin did not tell Cary Manpure what had befallen him.

"When I first got into that circular chamber with the chair in its center," Cary Manpure added, "I thought of the seed tale of NOSTOS.

Things changed very quickly, however. Bill Odun met a nice lady. I only encountered a nitwit holo-image."

"There were no circular chambers in that pyramid thing they built in Abzuland," said Odkin. "In fact, everything inside of it was either too small or too large. Perhaps real Essenes are either giants or dwarfs."

Chapter Six

Well of Despair

When Cary Jackman and Terry Wellton first arrived in Hureng-land there was nothing but beautiful, untamed and bountiful wilderness.

After Joe Lon Odkin and Cary Manpure left Alteana bound for "south of Huregan," Cary Jackman and Terry Wellton continued their work at Alteana and waited for further instructions from Essenes regarding their traveling to another location on Danebury. As they knew, their destination, their method of transportation and those things they were to take with them were to be infused into Altean computers "later."

It was during this time that the 735 daughters and 750 sons of the healthy child bearing age female beings of Danebury and their mothers were ready to be taken to their natural living environments. In order to accomplish this task several enormous Altean Naval Service marine transport vessels were flown from Daphlay to Alteana carrying volunteers, necessary equipment and large cargo air ships. Among the volunteers were Lena Arbur, daughter of Hal Arbur, and Cary Jackman's brother, Tommy.

After the female beings of Danebury with their children had all been taken to their natural living environments, it was time for the volunteers, the equipment and the cargo airships to be flown back to Daphlay aboard the transport vessels. Aboard one of the vessels were Lena Arbur Jackman and her new husband Tommy Jackman.

While helping with the careful offloading of the sedated female beings and their sedated children in Ashintoland, Tommy Jackman had contracted a virulent strain of hepatitis previously unknown to Alteans.

Nothing could be done for him in the Ashintoland medical facilities, so an urgent request for assistance was transmitted to the medical facilities at Alteana. In a matter of hours an agent to counter the hepatitis was made from reconfigured reproductive material and immediately flown to Ashintoland in an air ship piloted by a medical worker named Bern Whitmore.

Bern Whitmore administered the agent to Tommy Jackman immediately and Tommy Jackman recovered from near death. When Bern Whitmore was relaxing later in the Ashintoland worker's field lounge, a young lady named Alika Marsden, a friend of Lena Arbor and Tommy Jackman, walked right up to Bern Whitmore and kissed him. Alika Marsden did not return with the other volunteers to Daphlay. Alika Marsden Whitmore stayed behind and flew to Daphlay with her new husband Bern Whitmore later on, after things were done at Alteana.

Just as the last cargo air ship was about to be loaded for the return of the volunteers to Daphlay an Essene holo-image suddenly appeared. "Stop!" ordered the holo-image. "This cargo air ship is to remain here."

Simultaneously another Essene holo-image suddenly appeared before Cary Jackman and Terry Wellton as they were helping with the completion of the last architectural features which were being added to Alteana. "Your destination, instructions for a special assignment and those things you are to take with you have now been infused into the general purpose computers of Alteana," it said. "Your method of transportation is the cargo air ship which is being left at Alteana. Depart NOW!"

The holo-image disappeared.

Cary Jackman and Terry Wellton carried out their special assignment along the way to Hurengland. East of the mountain range dividing Prehurland into unequal eastern and western geographic halves stood a pinnacle of immense proportions. Essenes ordered Cary Jackman and Terry Wellton to shoot the top off this pinnacle. Civilian air ships are unarmed, so the cargo air ship which Cary Jackman and Terry Wellton were flying had been equipped with an energy cannon, something the Altean Naval Service considered highly irregular. After Terry Wellton positioned the cargo air ship next to the pinnacle, but far enough away to avoid being hit by flying boulders, Cary Jackman fired a stream of energy from the cannon and quickly reduced the pinnacle to its required new height. 77 Essenes had given Cary Jackman explicit details on how to use the energy cannon, but he was nervous nonetheless—he had never fired a weapon before in his life.

Cary Jackman and Terry Wellton's destination in Hurengland was a heavily wooded hill—as was the entire countryside surrounding it. They had to use the energy cannon to clear a suitable area on top of the hill before they could even land.

When Joe Lon Odkin and Cary Manpure flew to Hurengland several months later they found the clearing, the cargo air ship, Cary Jackman and Terry Wellton quite easily.

Cary Jackman and Terry Wellton were living in the cargo air ship atop the hill. They were carrying out the instructions given to them by Essenes as to what to do after their arrival in Hurengland. Essenes had ordered Cary Jackman and Terry Wellton to wait and to do nothing else. Joe Lon Odkin and Cary Manpure landed their air ship on the hill next to the cargo air ship, climbed down and were warmly greeted by Cary Jackman and Terry Wellton.

"We didn't know you'd be here," said Cary Manpure excitedly, "but we were hoping you would be."

As they spoke with one another an Essene holo-image suddenly appeared and said, "The location of your house and the plans for it have been infused into the general purpose computer of the air ship," the holo-image said. "Begin construction of your house NOW!"

The holo-image disappeared.

The building was constructed of crystal, was six-sided with about 120 feet between opposite sides. In the southeastern part of the split level house, four separate living quarters were built into the hill. The main living area was a large circular raised platform in the center of the hexagon, 60 feet in diameter. A big, low circular hearth occupied the center of the platform and a chimney flue hung from above to catch the smoke from wood fires which warmed the living area. Four fluted columns stood around the hearth to support the crystal roof beams. Huge windows afforded panoramic views from the living area toward the east, southeast and south. The entryway to the house was just above ground level on the northwestern side of the house and faced the upslope of the hill. Between the entryway and the circular platform were the food preparation area and other service areas of the house.

"This is not a house!" shouted Cary Manpure. "This is THE Crystal Palace!"

Cary Jackman and Terry Wellton had brought with them a large number of volute casings of tornum, many barrels of water and cases containing precooked rations of food. Even so, the four Alteans knew that they would eventually run out of energy unless they received additional volute casings of tornum. They did not have a transceiver with them and no Alteans knew where they were—they had been ordered to remove the transceivers from both the air ship and the cargo air ship before leaving Alteana. Information infused into the computers at Alteana regarding their destinations had been addressed to them only. Only if Essenes directed other Alteans to them could they expect to obtain the energy they needed, they thought.

They were marooned in Hurengland—in THE Crystal Palace.

About six months after Joe Lon Odkin and Cary Manpure's arrival, when the four of them had just returned from an afternoon walk and were ascending the stairway to the circular living platform, Joe Lon Odkin noticed something horribly familiar standing at the top of the steps: an Essene holo-image. At the very sight of this unwanted intruder Odkin became enraged and charged up the rest of the steps. The holo-image backed away so Odkin had to continue charging across the platform until the holo-image had backed all the way to the hearth. Odkin lowered his head and tried to butt the holo-image, but Odkin's head went right through the holo-image and he head butted the flue above the hearth instead. Odkin's forehead split open and began to bleed profusely.

Cary Manpure, Cary Jackman and Terry Wellton picked up Director Odkin and carried him to a nearby sofa. Cary Manpure ran to the food preparation area and brought back ice in a towel as the other two young Alteans staunched the flow of blood. The three of them were so engrossed in helping Odkin that they paid no attention to the holo-image which stood near the sofa and stared at them. Finally, it was Odkin who sat up suddenly, looked around and spotted the unwanted intruder.

"What are you doing here?" Odkin roared.

"I am here to ask the four of you to greatly assist Essenes in preparing this planet for the beings who will grow up here, so that they can become the leaders of the redeeming of the galaxy," it answered.

"Essenes are aware that you know many things that two-thirds means. Essenes would like to introduce you to another thing which two-thirds means, something which deals directly with the redeeming of the galaxy.

"At first there were only Alteans in the galaxy. Then there were Pleiadeans as well. The Pleiadeans have misdirected themselves, but Alteans on their own are not capable of redirecting the Pleiadeans. Essenes are preparers, not redirectors. Alteans need assistance to redirect the Pleiadeans and to redeem the galaxy. The beings who will one day inhabit this planet will lead Alteans in redirecting the Pleiadeans and insure the redeeming the galaxy.

"There will therefore be three groups of beings in the galaxy: Alteans, the Pleiadeans, and the future beings of this planet. There will therefore be three groups of beings in the galaxy and two-thirds must work together.

"Essenes have directed that I return at this same time tomorrow to receive your answer to this direct question: will you assist Essenes in preparing this planet for the future beings who will live here and lead the redeeming of the galaxy?"

The holo-image disappeared.

The four Alteans were stunned into silence.

Finally, Odkin stood up with some effort and said, "Let's have some supper."

During the time the four Alteans were eating not one said a word. After supper they cleaned up in silence and then went back to their living area.

After they had all sat down Joe Lon Odkin turned to Cary Manpure and asked, "Pureman, what do you think?"

"I think we should tell the Essene holo-image to tell Essenes that they are nitwits," Cary Manpure replied.

Cary Manpure stood up, walked down the stairs and went into his living quarters.

The next afternoon when the Essene holo-image appeared before the four Alteans as they sat around the hearth in the center of their living platform, Odkin spoke to the holo-image, and none of the others knew what he would say.

"Tell Essenes that they are nitwits," Odkin told the holo-image.

"Essenes have directed that I return tomorrow at the same time to tell you why you should reconsider," the holo-image responded.

The holo-image disappeared.

The next day the four Alteans gathered around the hearth again for the projected third visit of the holo-image. The holo-image appeared and said, "You should reconsider your decision of yesterday because this project is too important to be left incomplete. Now is the time to prepare this planet for the future beings who will live here and lead the redeeming of the galaxy. You are the ones to assist Essenes in that preparation. Essenes have instructed that I wait while you reconsider now."

Cary Manpure looked at the holo-image and said, "I have reconsidered. I will help."

Joe Lon Odkin, Cary Jackman and Terry Wellton nodded their agreement with Cary Manpure.

"Joe Lon Odkin, you must tell them now," said the holo-image.

Odkin told them about Althena Gandy, and then the holo-image said, "I am a holo-image of a nitwit Essene. You are all nitwits too. This is THE Crystal Palace on the Hill of Musing. The nitwit Essene who lives in a Crystal Palace has directed that I return tomorrow morning to give you some information you will like."

The holo-image disappeared.

Cary Manpure laughed for the first time in a long time. Joe Lon Odkin, Cary Jackman and Terry Wellton joined in.

The holo-image disappeared.

Cary Manpure laughed for the first time in a long time. Joe Lon Odkin, Cary Jackman and Terry Wellton joined in.

The nitwit Essene directed the holo-image to tell the four Alteans about the fifth Altean living on Danebury—'Art Hurian' Manpure. Essenes had taken 'Art Hurian' Manpure and the 24 dolphins from Abzuland to Hurengland aboard the other Altean transport vessel, the night Joe Lon Odkin had told Cary Manpure how and why Kirk Roon had blown up the marine transport vessel. 'Art Hurian' Manpure was suicidal due to the loss of his wife and children, but during the flight, Essenes managed to redirect his thoughts and energies toward the dolphins. When the transport vessel arrived at its destination and hovered over the water, Essenes ordered 'Art Hurian' Manpure to remove the dolphins one by one from their pool in the hanger bay, to wheel the dolphins on a dolly to a hatch and then to as gently as possible push each dolphin into the water. This would have been an incredibly difficult physical task for anyone, but it was even more difficult for 'Art Hurian' Manpure because of his physical handicap.

When 'Art Hurian' Manpure got to the last dolphin he was exhausted, but he managed to get that dolphin to the hatch before he collapsed. After resting a few minutes 'Art Hurian' Manpure tried to push the dolphin into the water, but could not. In desperation 'Art Hurian' Manpure grabbed the dolphin just in front of its tail with both hands, lifted the dolphin from the dolly, held the dolphin aloft and then let the dolphin plunge head first into the water.

The catharsis had made 'Art Hurian' Manpure sane again.

"Today," the holo-image concluded, "we will go and visit 'Art Hurian' Manpure."

Joe Lon Odkin, Cary Manpure, Cary Jackman, Terry Wellton, and the Essene holo-image rode together in the cargo air ship to Glastonbury Tor, some 35 miles southwest of the Hill of Musing. As they circled, the holo-image said, "Glastonbury Tor looks like Mount Hurartu, it is the analog of the Tor on Silbury and the stone at its northeastern tip is the sourcemark for the marker of the prime meridian of Danebury: Hurmyrr. This stone is the sourcemark because it is on a great circle which crosses a great circle which passes through Hurmyrr.

"To the northeast of Glastonbury Tor you can see the wooden hut of 'Art Hurian' Manpure, set between his fields and his animal pens. He has wanted to remain here alone, but Essenes told him that in order to be able to do so he would have to receive visits from you. He is expecting you, but he does not know when you will arrive.

"Land in the open field to the east of the hut."

The holo-image disappeared.

'Art Hurian' Manpure opened the door of his hut after Cary Manpure had knocked firmly. When 'Art Hurian' Manpure saw his cousin standing before the door he stepped out and threw his arms around him.

"Welcome to Avelinabury," he said softly, tears running down his cheeks.

As they all sat in the hut 'Art Hurian' Manpure told the others that he had been anxiously awaiting their arrival.

"For nearly ten years," he said, "I have been planning to construct and sculpt a scale model of 'Glamyrr and Sustanator' on a hill I can see from the other side of Avelinabury. It is across the water and I have no way of getting there."

"That isn't a problem any more," said Terry Wellton.

"Let me show you the hill I mean," said 'Art Hurian' Manpure.

Art Hurian' Manpure led the way past his animal pens and to the southwestern side of the steep hill he called Avelinabury. When they had reached their vantage point, 'Art Hurian' Manpure pointed across the water at the hill. As 'Art Hurian' Manpure was about to speak he suddenly lost his footing, slid down the steep bank and sank into the water. The other four Alteans immediately jumped in after him.

Cary Jackman found 'Art Hurian' Manpure in the murky water and dragged him ashore. 'Art Hurian' Manpure was still alive.

Cary Manpure and Joe Lon Odkin surfaced, saw Cary Jackman and 'Art Hurian' Manpure along the bank and swam to them.

Terry Wellton did not surface.

Joe Lon Odkin, Cary Manpure and Cary Jackman dived back into the water to look for Terry Wellton. Cary Jackman found Terry Wellton in the murky water and dragged him ashore.

Terry Wellton had drowned. While searching for 'Art Hurian' Manpure, Terry Wellton had trapped a foot among sunken logs and had not been able to surface.

Cary Manpure went berserk.

Joe Lon Odkin hit Cary Manpure with his fist, knocking him out.

Cary Jackman threw up the murky water he had swallowed while looking for 'Art Hurian' Manpure and Terry Wellton, whereupon he lost consciousness.

Joe Lon Odkin picked up 'Art Hurian' Manpure, carried him back to his hut, wrapped him in a warm blanket and set him in a chair in front of his fire.

Joe Lon Odkin picked up Cary Manpure, wrapped him in a warm blanket he had brought from the hut, carried him to the cargo air ship, bound him and strapped him into a seat.

Joe Lon Odkin picked up Cary Jackman, wrapped him in a warm blanket he had previously put over him, carried him to the cargo air ship and strapped him into another seat.

Joe Lon Odkin picked up the body of Terry Wellton, carried it to the cargo air ship and lovingly placed it in the hanger bay.

Then Joe Lon Odkin went back to the hut to check on 'Art Hurian' Manpure.

"Do not ever come back," 'Art Hurian' Manpure said when he saw Joe Lon Odkin entering the hut.

Joe Lon Odkin made sure 'Art Hurian' Manpure was warm enough and then returned to the cargo air ship. As Odkin started to fly the cargo air ship back to the Hill of Musing the Essene holo-image suddenly appeared and said, "Joe Lon Odkin, Essenes are shocked and deeply saddened by the drowning of Terry Wellton. Only Essenes can save the rest of you. You have had too many shocks. Let Cary Manpure off at a spot to which Essenes direct you. Essenes will tell you when to pick him up."

Joe Lon Odkin landed the cargo air ship a few miles northeast of the hut of 'Art Hurian' Manpure, unstrapped and untied Cary Manpure, carried him from the cargo air ship, placed him on the ground and made sure he was still wrapped in the warm blanket. When Cary Manpure regained consciousness the next morning, the Essene holo-image was standing next to him.

"Get up!" it ordered. "You have a kirk to build NOW!"

As he built the wooden longhouse, quaintly called a kirk by the Essene holo-image, Cary Manpure had only one emotion: hate. He hated everyone and everything—including and especially himself.

One day while he was digging a well which the holo-image had ordered to be dug next to the completed kirk, Cary Manpure threw down his digging 'implement' and shouted, "I want to blow up the entire Universe!"

He then collapsed into unconsciousness. Cary Manpure awoke that night and sat up.

"I see!" he cried.

Cary Manpure's cry in the night had been brought on by catharsis, and catharsis had been brought on by realization. He suddenly understood how Kirk Roon had been driven to murder and suicide. Kirk Roon had not had anyone to help him through his insanity, but each time he had been on the brink of permanently losing his mind, Cary Manpure realized, Essenes had been there to help him. He had completely misunderstood Essenes. Essenes seemed to be cruel and uncaring, but he now understood that Essenes had consistently been using an extremely effective method to insure what needed to be done was done. This method was to steadfastly insist that Alteans, including himself, did everything in their power to accomplish what they could on their own—at which point Essenes would help them along—so that they could again accomplish as much as possible on their own. It was the method used by the intergalactic migrators to lovingly guide the indigenous beings of this galaxy toward an equal union. It was the only method that could have been used then, Cary Manpure knew, and it was the only method that would work now, he suddenly understood. Essenes also realized how personally devastating events had been on him, and Cary Manpure suddenly realized as well, that they had carefully and lovingly used catharsis to bring him through his periods of insanity.

"Cary Manpure," the holo-image said to him later after it had suddenly appeared, "the place where you dig your well is an analog of the place on the rim of the crater where you camped with Tommy Untiman one night before you climbed your first curious mesa. That time you had a much better thing for digging and you found something very interesting."

"I don't know what you are talking about," Cary Manpure hissed.

"You will soon find out about places on Danebury which are analogs of places on Silbury," the holo-image said and then disappeared.

"They know!" Cary Manpure shouted in anger. "They know everything!"

Sometime later Cary Manpure said to himself as he continued to dig his well, "I'm not going to tell those bastards a thing."

After Cary Manpure had finished digging the well he was picked up by Cary Jackman and they flew together back to the Hill of Musing.

Joe Lon Odkin and Cary Jackman had permanently sealed off Terry Wellton's living quarters. They had also constructed a corbelled dome tomb under the Hill of Musing, reached by a labyrinthine maze which they had also dug as ordered by Essenes.

Upon their return to the Hill of Musing Joe Lon Odkin and Cary Jackman had removed everything from the freezer in the food preparation area and placed the body of Terry Wellton in it. They had waited to bury the body until Cary Manpure's return. After he and Cary Jackman had landed they put on long, hooded robes made by Joe Lon Odkin and Cary Jackman and then joined Joe Lon Odkin, similarly robed.

Joe Lon Odkin, Cary Manpure and Cary Jackman carried the body of Terry Wellton over their heads down the northern slope of the Hill of Musing, through the labyrinthine maze leading to the tomb and on into the tomb. There in the grave circle inside the corbelled dome tomb they wrapped the body of Terry Wellton in a shroud and placed it in a shaft grave on a bed of pebbles. The walls were lined with flag stones. They then covered this shaft grave with wooden beams, placed a layer of clay over the beams and filled the hole above the shaft grave with chalk.

Joe Lon Odkin, Cary Manpure and Cary Jackman had buried the body of Terry Wellton in the manner of his ancestors, and then filled in the labyrinthine maze in a way similar to that which their ancestors had filled in the straight passageways leading to ancient corbelled dome tombs.

Just before Joe Lon Odkin, Cary Manpure, Cary Jackman and Terry Wellton had gone to visit 'Art Hurian' Manpure an Essene holo-image suddenly appeared before Byron Haley Chee, former Elder of Silbury, and current keeper of the dolphins on Colchis. Byron Haley Chee was determined that either the dolphins he had brought with him from Silbury or their descendants would one day return to Silbury to swim in the pools of the data, information, knowledge, and Wisdom longhouses of Hur Square.

The holo-image said, "Byron Haley Chee, you have done well.

"Byron Haley Chee, you are to inform the Council of Daphlay that the Council is to move the genetic project to Colchis.

"Byron Haley Chee, you are also to inform the Council of Daphlay that there are additional requirements for the second part of the genetic agent. Alteans know that the creative and linear-thinking self-aware beings of Danebury resulting from the administration of the second part of the genetic agent must have great diversity in both culture and physical characteristics. The current second part of the genetic agent meets those requirements.

"Alteans are also to insure that there are four different genetic groups within the single species of beings who result from the administering of the second part of the genetic agent. These four groups are to include: those who are to be genetically most like the beings resulting from the administration of the first part of the genetic agent; those who are to be genetically least like those first beings; and two mid-range groups—one consisting of those who are to be more genetically like the first beings and the other of those genetically equally alike and not alike the first beings.

"The resulting beings genetically <u>most</u> <u>like</u> the first beings are to be culturally and physically like the beings who were indigenous to this galaxy.

The resulting beings genetically <u>more</u> <u>like</u> the first beings are to be physically like the intergalactic pioneers and culturally like the ancestors of the beings who were indigenous to this galaxy.

The resulting beings genetically <u>equally</u> <u>alike</u> and <u>not</u> <u>alike</u> the first beings are beings culturally like Alteans and physically mostly like Alteans.

The resulting beings genetically least like the first beings are to be physically like Alteans and culturally like a mixture of the other groups of beings.

"Additionally, the resulting beings genetically least like the first beings, physically like Alteans and culturally like a mixture of the other groups are to be given a genetic propensity to be antagonistic toward everyone else. These beings are also to be given a genetic propensity to: have great difficulty in conceiving of any dimension beyond three-dimensions; have great difficulty in conceiving of great lengths of time, especially when it seems as if nothing of importance is happening. They are also to be given the propensity to: have great difficulty in conceiving of life spans longer than their own; have great difficulty in conceiving that life exists anywhere except on Danebury, except that they are to have an inexplicable nagging imperative toward the fourth planet from their sun.

"When the Council of Daphlay has moved the genetic project to Colchis, Essenes have directed that I give you additional instructions."

The holo-image disappeared.

Shortly after the associates of the genetic project began to work on the additional and extremely difficult Essene requirements for the second part of the genetic code in their new facilities on Colchis, the Essene holo-image suddenly appeared again before Byron Haley Chee and began speaking, "Byron Haley Chee, you have done well.

"Byron Haley Chee, Essenes have a new assignment for you. In addition to being the keeper of the dolphins you are to be the new Director of the Altean Logistical Support Group of Panergon Gwynmyrr.

"You are to prepare for delivery to the plateau on which Hurmyrr stands, a small mobile energy transproduction unit, a tractor with plow and harvester, energy conduit, three centrifugal water pumps contained in a fabricated pump house, a large fabricated water storage tank, water conduit of various sizes with sprinklers, seeds for vegetables and grain, poultry and livestock, horses—and a large number of geometric shapes of different sizes made of varying materials.

"When you have set up facilities for the Altean Logistical Support Group of Panergon Gwynmyrr on Colchis, Essenes will infuse the Group's computers on Colchis with the details of all those things you are to prepare for delivery to the plateau on which Hurmyrr stands."

The holo-image disappeared.

The Altean Logistical Support Group of Panergon Gwynmyrr was set up by Byron Haley Chee as an independent organization, modeled after the genetic project with its own board of trustees. Donations from Alteans allowed the group to exist and carry out its mandate.

As Joe Lon Odkin, Cary Manpure and Cary Jackman were burying the body of Terry Wellton in the manner of his ancestors on Danebury, an Essene holo-image suddenly appeared before Byron Haley Chee, who was working at his desk in the new facilities on Colchis.

The holo-image said, "Byron Haley Chee, you have done well.

"Transport everything NOW!"

The holo-image disappeared.

After Joe Lon Odkin, Cary Manpure and Cary Jackman had buried the body of Terry Wellton in the manner of his ancestors and sealed the labyrinthine maze entryway to the corbelled dome tomb under the Hill of Musing, they walked sadly back to their house. As they ascended the stairway leading to their living platform an Essene holo-image suddenly appeared at the top of the stairs and ordered, "Essenes have infused additional instructions for you into the general purpose computer of the cargo air ship. You have work to do NOW!"

The holo-image disappeared.

As a result of these instructions, Cary Manpure and Cary Jackman transformed the area of and around the Hill of Musing into the Danebury Ranch.

First, using the energy cannon mounted on the cargo air ship, they cleared a large, rectangular, relatively flat forested area to the east of the Hill of Musing. Then they fenced in that area and divided it with fences into three fields, using some of the tools and some of the materials brought from Alteana aboard the cargo air ship. Next, fairly near to the house, they constructed chicken coops, animal pens, a corral and a barn. Finally to the southeast of the house, they terraced and spaded an area for a vegetable garden.

After they were done, Cary Manpure and Cary Jackman flew the cargo air ship from Hurengland to Abzuland to begin transporting the things which Byron Haley Chee had insured were carefully and safely delivered to the plateau.

The cargo air ship was four times the size of an Altean Naval Service star ship and had hanger bays both fore and aft of the central gravitron drive unit and its 54 foot diameter spinning disk. Both hanger bays were about 180 feet long and both were fitted with three dextrous robotic arms capable of lifting tremendous weights. The upper hull over the hanger bays opened like a clam shell toward the sides of the cargo air ship so that the robotic arms could lift things from inside the hanger bays—while in the air or on the ground—and place them where an operator of the robotic arms wanted them. Both hanger bays had large sections of the deck which opened to allow access from below. Access to the gravitron drive unit to replace volute casings of tornum and/or to perform maintenance was also from below. Access to the bridge was by way of a ladder to the edge of the hull and then up the sloping hull to hatches on either side of the bridge.

On the first return trip to the Hill of Musing, Cary Manpure and Cary Jackman took the tractor, plow and harvester, the seeds for vegetables and grain, the poultry and livestock—and the horses. Before returning to Abzuland, Cary Manpure and Cary Jackman put some of the horses in the corral, used two of the horses to drive the cattle into one of the fenced fields, put the poultry and other livestock in the chicken coops and animal pens, plowed and planted grain in another of the three fields and planted their vegetable garden.

On the second return trip to the Hill of Musing, Cary Manpure and Cary Jackman took the three centrifugal water pumps contained in a pump house, the large water storage tank and the water conduiting of various sizes and sprinklers. Before returning to Abzuland, Cary Manpure and Cary Jackman used one of the robotic arms of the cargo air ship to place the pump house containing the water pumps on a base pad they had constructed near a river southeast of the Hill of Musing, then laid three water conduits from the river to the pumps. Utilising the largest water conduit, they next laid a conduit above ground from the pump house to the water storage tank they had sited on a previously constructed base pad near the top of the Hill of Musing, using a robotic arm of the cargo air ship to do so. Cary Manpure and Cary Jackman then ran a smaller conduit above ground to their house and vegetable garden, and used the cargo air ship and its robotic arms to lay a conduit above ground to the chicken coop, animal pens, corral and barn; then to the fields below and to the east of the Hill of Musing. Finally, they connected sprinklers to some of the conduit running into the three fields.

On the many additional trips Cary Manpure and Cary Jackman made to Abzuland, they transported the large number of geometric shapes which had been placed in containers along the eastern and southern edges of the plateau. At the end of each trip, Cary Manpure and Cary Jackman used the robotic arms to remove the numbered containers in which these geometric shapes were packaged from the cargo air ship and place them about two miles southwest of the Hill of Musing. Following their orders, they were placed in six predesignated groups along a southwestern to northeastern diagonal line. They had used the energy cannon mounted on the cargo air ship to clear the required space in an amphitheater-like valley. They started by placing group five along the southeastern side of the line, at and near the line's northeastern end. Opposite group five they placed group six. Along the southeastern side at and near the center of the line they placed group three. Opposite group three they placed group four. Along the southeastern side of the line at and near the line's southwestern end they placed group one. Opposite group one they placed group two, along the northwestern side of the line at and near the line's southwestern end.

As Cary Manpure and Cary Jackman were about to return to Hurengland with the small mobile energy transproduction unit and the energy conduit aboard (all that remained of the delivery from Colchis to Danebury by Altean transports working for the Altean Logistical Support Group of Panergon Gwynmyrr) an Essene holo-image suddenly appeared between them and ordered, "Destroy the nose of the Ark Hur!" Cary Manpure and Cary Jackman could not believe their ears.

"Destroy the nose of the Ark Hur!" the holo-image ordered again.

"No," responded Cary Manpure and Cary Jackman simultaneously.

"This project is too important for you to disobey orders," said the holo-image. "The time to destroy the nose of the Ark Hur is now, and you are the ones to do it. Cary Jackman, you are to aim the energy cannon directly at the center of the nose and fire NOW!"

Cary Manpure maneuvered the cargo air ship into position and Cary Jackman fired the energy cannon. The nose of the Ark Hur disintegrated and with it the part of a soul print which Joe Lon Odkin had designed for that nose. Sculpted on the nose of the Ark Hur—directly above where the soul of a self-aware being translocates itself—was a three dimensional depiction of a Waldark soul print; a two-dimensional representation of the three-dimensional energy disturbance pattern of the soul; and a small portion of the three-dimensional secondary energy disturbance pattern. Thus the sculpture on the nose of the Ark Hur had consisted of a circle, from which extended the elongated and foreshortened points of an irregular five pointed star. Inside the circle was a six pointed star. In the center of the six pointed star was a small tetrahedron.

After the nose of the Ark Hur had been destroyed the holo-image said, "You will be coming back here later."

The holo-image disappeared.

Cary Manpure and Cary Jackman went into a funk.

When they arrived back at the Hill of Musing the Essene holo-image suddenly appeared and ordered, "Install the energy transproduction unit and assemble the energy conduits NOW!"

The holo-image disappeared.

Not far from their house, they constructed a base pad for the energy transproduction unit. With robotic arms they lifted the unit from the forward hanger bay of the cargo air ship, placed it on the pad and prepared the unit for activation. Then they laid energy conduits between the energy transproduction unit and the house and used the cargo air ship and its robotic arms to lay a conduit above ground alongside the large water conduit to the pump house. In the pump house they connected the energy conduit to the centrifugal pumps.

Cary Manpure had never been so angry. After they had finished connecting the conduit to the pumps he walked alone back up the hill, went into the barn and slammed the barn door behind him. "I hate THE Crystal Palace!" he shouted along the way.

Cary Manpure also hated the cargo air ship in which he had slept since the Essene holo-image had ordered him and Cary Jackman out of THE Crystal Palace to begin preparing the Danebury Ranch. Cary Manpure hated the cargo air ship because it had destroyed the nose of the Ark Hur, and he never wanted to go near the ship again. Despite his recent catharsis and the 'understanding' he had gained concerning Essene tactics, the repeated despair Cary Manpure had felt as a result of the traumatic events of his life had returned. Cary Manpure wanted to be alone.

Cary Jackman's despair led him to fly the air ship to Cary Manpure's kirk and to dig a second well next to the one that Cary Manpure had already dug.

Joe Lon Odkin—still unaware of the destruction of the nose of the Ark Hur—was frustrated. Essenes were trying to teach him to meditate so that he could transredimension energy, but he could not learn. Joe Lon Odkin became so frustrated that he smashed his fist into the chimney flue and broke his hand in several places. There was no way to set the bones properly so Joe Lon Odkin lost most of the use of his right hand, and had to learn to do things with his left hand.

Essenes insured that the Danebury Ranch ran smoothly while Joe Lon Odkin continued to try to learn to meditate and while Cary Manpure and Cary Jackman despaired. Following the return of Cary Manpure and Cary Jackman to the Hill of Musing after the nose of the Ark Hur had been destroyed, an Essene holo-image suddenly appeared before Byron Haley Chee as he was sitting at his desk in the facilities of the Altean Logistical Support Group on Colchis and said, "Byron Haley Chee, you have done well. Byron Haley Chee, you are now to deactivate but not dissolve the Altean Logistical Support Group of Panergon Gwynmyrr. The Altean Logistical Support Group will be needed again later."

The holo-image disappeared.

Byron Haley Chee continued as the keeper of the dolphins on Colchis until his passing many years later, but he was never called upon to reactivate the Altean Logistical Support Group of Panergon Gwynmyrr. The reactivation did not occur until over 200,000 years later, just before the administering of the second part of the genetic agent.

Just before he passed on, an Essene holo-image visited Byron Haley Chee privately and told him of the Hill of Musing and some of the things that had been achieved by Joe Lon Odkin, Cary Manpure and Cary Jackman.

Essenes did not want Byron Haley Chee to be downcast.

Chapter Seven

THE Crystal Palace

After Cary Manpure and Cary Jackman had left THE Crystal Palace to begin preparing the Danebury Ranch, the Essene holo-image suddenly appeared before Joe Lon Odkin and said, "Joe Lon Odkin, it is time for you to become a meditator who can transredimension energy."

The holo-image tried to teach Joe Lon Odkin to meditate, but could not—until he broke his right hand, and started to do things with his left hand.

In order to become a meditator, it is necessary to subordinate the linear-thinking left side of the brain to the creative-thinking right side of the brain. Meditators have various methods to help them do this. They sit with the left side of their heads facing the inflow of planetary torun. They close their eyes and mentally try to feel their Waldark thing in their right hand. They listen to repeated musical tone sequences of 24/25ths played on specially tuned two stringed lyres. With their eyes closed and using their left hand they color rainbows, using very differently shaped colored crayons. Joe Lon Odkin tried all these things and nothing worked—until he broke his right hand and had to do things with his left hand.

After Joe Lon Odkin had learned to meditate, the holo-image had Odkin put on the Waldark hat. On getting up for the second day of his training Odkin had found this hat, alongside a Waldark thing, on the hearth in the middle of the living platform. Like the Waldark thing, the Waldark hat had been specially designed for Joe Lon Odkin. When Joe Lon Odkin began to meditate while wearing his Waldark hat the energy transdimensioners of the energy transproduction unit began to transdimension torun into torinum. Shortly thereafter the energy transconverter of the energy transproduction unit was activated, tornum started flowing in the conduit leading to the pump house and the centrifugal pumps began pumping water to the water storage tank near the top of the Hill of Musing. Shortly thereafter volute casings in the energy transproduction unit's manifolds began filling with tornum flowing from the energy transconverter.

Cary Manpure and Cary Jackman had worked to insure that the inhabitants of the Hill of Musing never lacked food, now Joe Lon Odkin was meditating to insure that they never ran out of energy—or water.

After Joe Lon Odkin had learned to meditate, Essene holo-images simultaneously ordered Cary Manpure and Cary Jackman back to THE Crystal Palace. Cary Manpure entered, went to his living quarters and slammed the door behind him. Cary Manpure was still in a funk. Cary Jackman flew back to the Hill of Musing, went to his living quarters and fell asleep, only to be periodically awakened by Cary Manpure shouting "I hate THE Crystal Palace!"

The next morning when Joe Lon Odkin ascended the stairway to the living platform, he noticed something lying on the hearth. He walked to the hearth and looked. What he saw was a white, curved, conical Waldark hat inside a red casing, which covered the lower part of the Waldark hat and which had a high, straight section extending up the back of the hat to just above the bulbous top. 78 As Odkin was looking at this curious thing the Essene holo-image suddenly appeared before him and said, "Joe Lon Odkin, you are looking at something which you will find very interesting and useful. Cary Manpure and Cary Jackman will enjoy hearing about the Waldark hat with amplifier, when I tell you about it."

Odkin leaped past the holo-image and ran off to get Cary Manpure and Cary Jackman.

As all three Alteans stood before the Waldark hat with amplifier, the holo-image began speaking, "This is a highly secret device known only to Essenes.

"After Essenes departed Altea about 950 million years ago an Essene discovered an additional weak three-dimensional secondary energy disturbance pattern caused by the soul which manifests itself above the head. 79,79.1 This secondary energy disturbance pattern is flat in the back while the front is shaped like two half cones whose points overlap halfway up. Any given cross section of this disturbance pattern is shaped like the letter D; at the bottom the Ds are large, they get progressively smaller until halfway up and then the Ds get larger again toward the top. The height of this secondary energy disturbance pattern caused by any given soul, is four-thirds the height of any given pair of conical, primary three-dimensional disturbance patterns caused by that same soul: about 40 inches in adults.

"The Essene who discovered this new secondary energy disturbance pattern knew that souls transredimension energy, causing primary and secondary energy disturbance patterns to form. He also knew that the Waldark hat only captures the energy which causes the upper half of the primary disturbance patterns; that the energy released which causes the lower half of those disturbance patterns is needed by the bodies of meditators while they are meditating; and that the secondary disturbance patterns of soul prints are needed by the souls of meditators during meditation. He knew that shortly after the time of Waldark, attempts were made to tap the energy which causes the lower primary disturbance patterns and similar attempts to tap the energy within soul prints, had nearly killed those who had volunteered for those experiments.

"The new secondary energy disturbance pattern intrigued its Essene discoverer who very carefully proceeded to perform experiments designed to try to capture the additional energy which causes this previously undiscovered secondary energy disturbance pattern. After he succeed without affecting the health of volunteer meditators, this Essene modified the Waldark hat so that the energy which causes this secondary energy disturbance pattern could be combined with the energy already captured by the Waldark hat. He soon discovered that when a meditator's soul spins at 98.11 percent of 777,777 rpms while wearing the Waldark hat with amplifier; the new total amount of energy captured is equivalent to the projected amount of energy transredimensioned by a soul spin rate of 98.75 percent of 777,777 rpms. But it is less than the energy transredimensioned by a soul spin rate of 98.7654321 percent of 777,777, which is the maximum soul spin rate during sexual release—the most powerful release of energy known in the Universe.

"This Essene knew that the 'speed of torun flow'—a description of convenience used to describe a four-dimensional 'process' as observed from three-dimensions—increases (along with the actual amount of torun transredimensioned) with the incremental increases of the spin rates of the meditator's soul. He discovered that the speed of torun flow associated with the total amount of energy captured by Waldark hats with amplifiers, was the same as the projected speed of torun flow associated with a soul spin rate of 98.75 percent of 777,777 rpms; but less than the speed of the torun flowing from the soul during sexual release. He subsequently discovered that the speed of torun flow associated with the total amount of energy captured by Waldark hats with amplifiers is too fast to be transdimensioned into torinum by energy transdimensioners, no matter what modifications he made to existing energy transdimensioners.

"This Essene thought that there might still be something useful that could be done with the extremely high speed torun captured by Waldark hats with amplifiers. He discovered that three beams of this extremely high speed torun can be magnetically braided together and that the resulting braided beam can literally move mountains. He also discovered that beams of this extremely high speed torun can be narrowed, and when these extremely narrow beams are magnetically braided they can be used as precision cutting tools, so accurate that during surgery they can cut along the edge of a cell wall.

"This Essene discovered that both visual and auditory data can be infused into braided beams and that data can then be infused into souls. He also discovered that braided beams can be made so powerful, that the data infused into souls by them can be so intense that souls are forced to release some of the infused data into the subconscious mind which in turn releases part of that infused data into the conscious mind. He discovered that data infused into souls can be coded to a specific individual, if the soul print of that individual is known or if the soul print of a soul antecedent of that individual is known.

"This Essene discovered that magnetically braided beams can be made so powerful that they interact with the planetary torun flowing across its surface. He also discovered that when powerful braided beams strike the surface of planets in certain geometric relationship to the flow of planetary torun, the planetary torun within that area realigns itself to the size and shape of the braided beams which struck the surface. So that the size and shape of the braided beams which struck the surface remain as a virtually permanent realignment of the flow of planetary torun; maintaining their alignment with the flow of the planetary magnetic field, but changing their physical orientation on the surface of the planet as the direction of the flow of the planetary magnetic field varies over time. He discovered that if these virtually permanent realignment patterns of the flow of planetary torun are subsequently struck by another braided beam, the patterns become so intense that planetary surface features—such as crops, trees and snow—try to align themselves with these realignment patterns.

"This Essene discovered that very powerful braided beams cause the molecular structure of things which they strike to be altered. He discovered that wide and powerful braided beams, such as those which can move mountains, and those which cause the flow of planetary torun to realign itself, are intense enough to cause these molecular changes. He also discovered that extremely narrow braided beams used as precision cutting tools and braided beams used to infuse data into souls are not powerful enough to cause the molecular structure to be altered."

The holo-image disappeared.

The next morning when he rose, Cary Manpure found a Waldark hat, a Waldark thing and a weighty tome on the hearth in the center of the living platform. He picked up the tome and discovered that it was a history book about developing societies. Cary Manpure knew that the other things were not for him so he began to read the book. As he did so the holo-image suddenly appeared before him and said, "Joe Lon Odkin is to teach Cary Jackman to meditate. You are to return to the barn and read. You will be told when to return to THE Crystal Palace."

While Cary Manpure read and while Joe Lon Odkin taught Cary Jackman how to meditate, Essenes insured that the Danebury Ranch was properly maintained.

After Cary Jackman had begun transredimensioning energy the Essene holo-image ordered Cary Manpure back to the THE Crystal Palace.

When Joe Lon Odkin, Cary Manpure and Cary Jackman were eating supper one evening the holo-image suddenly appeared and said, "Tomorrow morning Cary Manpure and Cary Jackman are to fly the cargo air ship to the amphitheater-like valley and use the robotic arms of the cargo air ship to pick up and on load the numbered containers of group two. They are then to fly the cargo air ship to the southwestern tip of Hurengland where they are to precisely place and secure the geometric shapes of group two. Their positions have been infused into the navigational computer of the cargo air ship, and the methods for securing these shapes have been infused into the general purpose computer of the cargo air ship. When Cary Manpure and Cary Jackman have completed this task they are to return here."

The holo-image disappeared.

After Cary Manpure and Cary Jackman had finished they flew back to the Hill of Musing and after they told Joe Lon Odkin what they had been doing, the holo-image suddenly appeared and said, "Cary Manpure and Cary Jackman, the Danebury Ranch has not been properly maintained. Get on your horses and see to the Danebury Ranch. You will be told when the Danebury Ranch is properly maintained again."

Cary Manpure's anger flashed. He could no longer tolerate the twistings and turnings of Essene behavior, even though he recognized them for what they were: purposeful guidance.

"We want to know what we are doing here!" he demanded. "Do Essenes think we will keep doing things without knowing why? Do Essenes think we are nitwits?"

"I am a holo-image," the holo-image responded, "of a nitwit Essene. You are all nitwits too. This is THE Crystal Palace on the Hill of Musing. The nitwit Essene has directed that I return once the Danebury

Ranch is properly maintained again to give you some information you will like."

The holo-image disappeared.

While the Danebury Ranch was in the process of being properly maintained again the holo-image suddenly appeared before Joe Lon Odkin and began speaking, "You already know that Glastonbury Tor is the analog of the Tor," it said. "You already know the precise new location of the site of the scale model of the spinning disk and the precise location of Hurmyrr. Both Hurmyrr and the site of the scale model of the spinning disk are analogs of Hurbury. The site of the scale model of the spinning disk is also an analog of the Hurmaze.

"I am a holo-image," the holo-image concluded, "of a nitwit Essene. You are all nitwits too. This is THE Crystal Palace on the Hill of Musing. The nitwit Essene has directed that after you figure out the rest of the two scale models of the Horz complex, I return to give you some information you will like."

The holo-image disappeared.

Joe Lon Odkin had suspected there was a special geometric relationship between Hurmyrr and the site of the scale model of the spinning disk. 69,70 He suspected this since Essenes had ordered him to relocate that site so that in 240,000 years its location would have a topogly latitude of 21,600, since, from the original landing site of Alteans it would be at a distance precisely equal to the polar radius of Danebury divided by the square root of pi. And since Essenes had told him which of the several possibilities to select as the correct site for the scale model of the spinning disk. Odkin therefore concluded that a very large scale model of the Horz complex was based on the positions of Hurmyrr and the scale model of the spinning disk in 240,000 years time.

To figure out the very large scale model, Odkin drew a great circle around Danebury which passed through where Hurmyrr and the scale model of the spinning disk would be in 240,000 years. Odkin noted that this great circle crossed the equator 22.48 degrees east of Hurmyrr and had a slope of 56.44 degrees north of due west as it crossed the equator. 80 He then discovered that a second great circle crossing the equator 19.47 degrees east of Hurmyrr and passing through Hurmyrr had a slope of 60 degrees north of due west as it crossed the equator. The finding of the highly significant numbers 19.47, 22.48 and 60 so closely associated led Odkin to think that the number 56.44 might also be important—especially after he discovered that as the great circle between Hurmyrr and the scale model of the spinning disk reaches that scale model, its slope flattens to 28.22 degrees, half its slope at the equator.

Odkin studied books which Cary Jackman and Terry Wellton had brought with them from Alteana. He went on reading until he found out that 56.4426902 degrees is the angle whose sine is 5/6ths—a fraction which represents the ratio of 5 to 6, the metaphor for the relationship between the non-living parts of the Universe and living things.

He also read that the observed top of the cone of the physical universe forms an angle of 56.4426902 degrees with the outward slope of the cone of the physical universe. Odkin could find no significance to the angle 28.22 except that it was half 56.44.

"Since I am dealing with Essenes," Odkin said to himself, "the angle 56.44 degrees I have found must actually be 56.4426902 degrees, and I just can't measure more precisely than I did when I got 56.44 degrees."

Odkin drew to scale all seven major components of the Horz complex on his map of Danebury, placing Hurbury over Hurmyrr and the Hurmaze over the scale model of the spinning disk. He calculated that this very large scale model of the Horz complex was over 100 times larger than the Horz complex on Silbury.

Since Glastonbury Tor is the analog of the Tor and the site of the scale model of the spinning disk is an analog of Hurbury, Odkin thought further, as such they must comprise part of a large scale model of the Horz complex. 81 He drew to scale all seven major components of the Horz complex on his map of southern Hurengland and calculated that the large scale model of the Horz complex was about one and one-half times as big as the Horz complex. 81.1 When Odkin drew the scale Tetrahedron Crater—over four miles in diameter—he noticed that a bowl-shaped valley shown on the map (and now under his scale Tetrahedron Crater) inferred a scale analog of the Tetrahedron Crater. 82

When Odkin drew the scale Tor with its apex on the stone sourcemark on Glastonbury Tor he noticed something very interesting. The Tor on Silbury had been constructed so that one of its five facing edges pointed directly at the site of energy transredimensioning in the Hurmaze; the analog facing edge of this scale of the Tor seemed to point at the kirk built by Cary Manpure. Odkin drew a line from the sourcemark on Glastonbury Tor to the kirk and discovered that that line precisely overlaid the analog facing edge line of the scale Tor. He measured the distance from the sourcemark to the kirk and discovered that that distance was 3.15 times the apparent two-dimensional length of any of the sides of the two apparent two-dimensional equilateral triangles adjacent to the facing edge of the scale Tor, which Odkin knew pointed at the kirk. Not only was this distance ratio of 3.15 a near equivalent of pi; Odkin knew that it was also the ratio of the overall length to the axial distance, as measured along the Way of the Life—between the apex of Sustanator and the apex of Glamyrr in Alteana.

So as to mark this spot clearly, Odkin labeled his map Kirk and then changed his mind.

He erased Kirk and wrote Wells. 83

After Joe Lon Odkin had figured out both the very large and the large scale models of the Horz complex, the holo-image suddenly appeared before him and began speaking, "There is a third scale model of the Horz complex, a small one," it said. 84 "In this third, small scale model the entrance to the labyrinthine maze leading to the corbelled dome tomb in which you buried the body of Terry Wellton is the analog of the corbelled dome grave circle of the Horz complex. 84.1

"In 240,000 years the apex of the analog of Hurbury in the small scale model will have a topogly latitude which is three times the topogly latitude of the apex of the analog of Hurbury in the large scale model. In 240,000 years the topogly vector of the apex of the analog of Hurbury in the small scale model will be equivalent to the square of the megalithic yard, divided by five. 85 You must calculate the resulting topogly longitude.

"In 240,000 years the center of the analog of the Tetrahedron Crater in the small scale model will have a topogly latitude equivalent to the square of the megalithic yard, times the area of the base ring of the scale model of the spinning disk. In 240,000 years the topogly vector of the center of the analog of the Tetrahedron Crater in the small scale model will be equivalent to the megalithic yard. 85 You must calculate the resulting topogly longitude.

"I am a holo-image," the holo-image concluded, "of a nitwit Essene. You are all nitwits too. This is THE Crystal Palace on the Hill of Musing. The nitwit Essene has directed that I return after you figure out the small scale model of the Horz complex, but in order to figure it out you must know that the amphitheater-like valley, about two miles southwest of the Hill of Musing, in which Cary Manpure and Cary Jackman placed the numbered containers is the analog of Dan Park in the Horz complex on Silbury." 84.1,84.2

The holo-image disappeared.

Joe Lon Odkin easily figured out the small scale model of the Horz complex and drew to scale all seven major components of the Horz complex on his map of the area surrounding the Hill of Musing and calculated that the small scale model of the Horz complex was about seven percent as big as the Horz complex. The holo-image suddenly appeared before Joe Lon Odkin as he finished his work and said, "The small scale model of the Horz complex contains two analogs: the first, Silbury Hill will be both the analog and close scale model of Hurbury. The second will be the analog of the Tetrahedron Crater, but it will only be an inexact scale model of the Tetrahedron Crater. However, it will also be a two-dimensional representation of one of the components of the three energy transconverters in the Tor.

"I am a holo-image," the holo-image concluded, "of a nitwit Essene. The nitwit Essene has directed that I return after you modify your scale drawings of the three analogs of the Tetrahedron Crater on your three maps so that they are correct. To be able to do this you need to know that the northwestern rims of the analogs need to be extended so that the rims of all three analogs become two-dimensional representations of the steel alloy spheres—which encased the energy transconverters in the Tor, to contain the magnetic fields surrounding those energy transconverters."

Because Essenes had ordered that information concerning energy transproduction at the Horz complex be infused into the general purpose computer of the cargo air ship, before Cary Jackman and Terry Wellton left Alteana, Joe Lon Odkin easily corrected the scale drawings of the three analogs of the Tetrahedron Crater on his three maps.

Joe Lon Odkin would not allow computers in the house so each time a computer had to be consulted or commanded Cary Jackman had to go out to the cargo air ship, climb aboard, energize the appropriate computer and do his work. The general purpose computer of the cargo air ship had been infused with incredibly important things—including the plate movement data of Essenes and the plate movement data from the Altean holo-mapping expeditions. By having the accumulated plate movement data they could calculate any future latitude and longitude of anything on Danebury, an ability absolutely vital to the completion of the topogly grid matrix. Even so, Joe Lon Odkin still hated computers.

The Danebury Ranch was properly maintained, so the holo-image ordered Cary Manpure and Cary Jackman back to the house. As Joe Lon Odkin finished telling them what he had found out about the three scale models of the Horz complex, the holo-image suddenly appeared before them and said, "The name of the analog which will be an inexact scale model of the Tetrahedron Crater and which will be a two-dimensional representation of one of the spheres encasing the energy transconverters of the Tor is Avenabury Circle. The name of the scale model of the spinning disk is Amesbury Circle. 81.1,84.1

"These are the only names by which you will call these things henceforth.

"I am a holo-image," the holo-image concluded, "of a nitwit Essene. The nitwit Essene has directed that I return after Cary Manpure and Cary Jackman fly the cargo air ship to the amphitheater-like valley, on load the numbered containers of group six, fly the cargo air ship on a bearing of 27.2 degrees gyro from the Hill of Musing to the eastern coast of Hurengland, precisely place and secure the geometric shapes of group six and return here."

The holo-image disappeared.

Tears welled up in Cary Manpure's eyes. Avenabury Circle and Amesbury Circle had been named by Essenes after Avelina and 'Art Hurian' Manpure's children, Avena and Ames Manpure, killed in such tragic circumstances.

After Cary Manpure and Cary Jackman completed their task, they flew back to the Hill of Musing and told Joe Lon Odkin about what they had been doing, then the holo-image suddenly appeared and said, "Cary Manpure and Cary Jackman, the Danebury Ranch has not been properly maintained. Get on your horses and see to the Danebury Ranch. You will be told when the Danebury Ranch is properly maintained again."

The holo-image disappeared.

When the Danebury Ranch was properly maintained again, the Essene holo-image ordered Cary Manpure and Cary Jackman to fly the cargo air ship to the amphitheater-like valley, on load the numbered containers of group one, fly the cargo air ship to the southwestern tip of Hurengland, precisely place and secure the geometric shapes of group one and then return to the Hill of Musing.

After Cary Manpure and Cary Jackman had completed their task, they flew back to the Hill of Musing and told Joe Lon Odkin about what they had been doing, then the holo-image suddenly appeared and said, "Cary Manpure and Cary Jackman, the Danebury Ranch has not been properly maintained. Get on your horses and see to the Danebury Ranch. You will be told when the Danebury Ranch is properly maintained again."

The holo-image disappeared.

When the Danebury Ranch was properly maintained again, the Essene holo-image ordered Cary Manpure and Cary Jackman to fly the cargo air ship to the amphitheater-like valley, to on load the numbered containers of group five, to fly the cargo air ship on a bearing of 27.2 degrees gyro from the Hill of Musing to the eastern coast of Hurengland, to precisely place and secure the geometric shapes of group five and to return to the Hill of Musing.

After Cary Manpure and Cary Jackman completed their task, they flew back to the Hill of Musing and after they told Joe Lon Odkin about what they had been doing, the holo-image suddenly appeared and said, "Cary Manpure and Cary Jackman, the Danebury Ranch has not been properly maintained. Get on your horses and see to the Danebury Ranch. You will be told when the Danebury Ranch is properly maintained again."

The holo-image disappeared.

When the Danebury Ranch was properly maintained again the holo-image ordered Cary Manpure and Cary Jackman back to the house and then told all three Alteans new information. "Cary Manpure and Cary Jackman have now completed precisely placing and securing the geometric shapes of two-thirds of the lengths of the two drakon which make up the Keirykeion Line," it said. "The two drakon of the Keirykeion Line are to extend all the way across southern Hurengland and in 240,000 years will twist and turn around a great circle of Danebury and will cross the equator of Danebury southwest of Hurengland with a slope of 56.4426902 degrees south of due west, and north of due east. In 240,000 years this great circle will cross, at approximately 19 miles northwest of Amesbury Circle, the great circle on which Hurmyrr and Amesbury Circle will then lie. 86 To the east and west of this crossing of great circles, two angles of 56.4426902 degrees will be formed. The angle 56.4426902 is the angle whose sine is 5/6ths, a fraction which represents the ratio of 5 to 6, the metaphor for the relationship between the non-living parts of the Universe and living things.

"In 240,000 years the portion of the great circle between the Ark Hur and the intersection of that circle with the western coast of Hurengland is the Lion Line. Hurmyrr and Amesbury Circle will lie on that great circle, the Ark Hur will be just off it. The intersection of the Lion Line with the two drakon of the Keirykeion Line cuts these drakon, thus representing the character of the future, free-willed, self-aware beings of this planet who will lead Alteans in the redeeming of the galaxy. They will gain great courage and fulfill their destiny, wielding the sword—symbolized by the Lion Line—to slay the drakon.

"These future, free-willed, self-aware beings of this planet will only be able to fulfill their destiny if you continue to assist Essenes in preparing Danebury. Destiny is not inevitable fate, nor the foretelling of the future. The destiny of the future beings of this planet is a projection of the way things will be if—you, Essenes and those who follow, do what they must."

"You are telling us about the two great circles that make the stone on Glastonbury Tor the sourcemark for the prime meridian Hurmyrr," said Cary Manpure. "Why is the sourcemark itself not at the crossing of those two great circles?"

"Because there was no mountain at that crossing which could have been sculpted to look like that Mount Hurartu," said the holo-image. "What became Glastonbury Tor worked out."

"Then Glastonbury Tor really is the source," said Cary Manpure.

"I am a holo-image," the holo-image concluded, "of a nitwit Essene. The nitwit Essene has directed that I return when Cary Manpure is ready to tell all of us about anomalies in the flow of planetary torun and about how some individuals can sense these anomalies."

The holo-image disappeared.

When Cary Manpure was ready the holo-image suddenly appeared and Cary Manpure told them all what he had found out. "Although planetary torun flows at a required specific rate across the surface of planets which are inhabitable, this energy flow is not uniform," he said. "Planetary magnetic anomalies, topographic features and adjustments made by beings to the landscape cause channels, eddies and areas of either high or low energy to form. Two-thirds of the causes of planetary torun anomalies are natural, cause only relatively minor anomalies and do not affect the well-being of self-aware beings.

"Adjustments made to the landscape—such as constructions and the inducement of magnetic fields—can cause major anomalies to form and can be very damaging to self-aware beings, to the point of inducing death by way of disease or insanity. An example of a potentially destructive adjustment made by beings to the landscape was the inducement of the extremely strong magnetic field on Altea known as the Shield. The war between East and West broke out before the Shield could kill those forced to live near it, but it would eventually have done so.

"Some individual beings can sense high and low concentrations of planetary torun. With regard to relatively minor natural anomalies this sensing induces feelings of foreboding and unease if too little planetary torun is present, and feelings of optimism and well being if more than the normal amount of planetary torun is present. These same feelings apply to anomalies due to adjustments made to the landscape, and if the induced anomalies are large enough, those sensing them can be driven insane.

"The individuals who are most likely to be able to sense high and low concentrations of planetary torun are those most likely to be able to meditate. In scientifically unsophisticated societies those able to sense high and low concentrations of planetary torun are generally very highly regarded by their society because they often have the ability to encourage others because they often have feelings of optimism and well-being. In order for these sensitive beings to have these feelings, they need to first obtain them from areas high in concentrations of planetary torun. Therefore, sensitive beings and those who wish to be encouraged by these beings gather at places of high concentrations of planetary torun, where those encouragements can most effectively take place.

"This often results in the construction of meeting structures in areas of high concentrations of planetary torun. Depending on where they are located, the material with which they are constructed and their shapes, such structures can increase, decrease or not change the amount of planetary torun (in the areas of high concentrations of planetary torun in which the meeting structures are constructed). The most successful of such meeting structures are those sited and constructed according to the feelings of those individuals who are most sensitive to areas of high concentrations of planetary torun. Over time the materials and architecture of these structures become standardized; the siting of them remains individualized. Such meeting structures (although they may be correctly designed with the proper materials) prove to be totally unacceptable if they are not properly positioned by an individual sensitive to concentrations of planetary torun."

After Cary Manpure completed his presentation, the holo-image said, "Cary Manpure and Cary Jackman, the Danebury Ranch has not been properly maintained. Get on your horses and see to the Danebury Ranch. You will be told when the Danebury Ranch is properly maintained again."

"Joe Lon Odkin," the holo-image said after Cary Manpure and Cary Jackman had departed, "the last four topogly matrix sites of the first growth ring which Essenes are going to give to you are as follows: the first of these topogly matrix sites is for a mound to be constructed in the shape of an eye. It is located at about 32 and three-quarters degrees north latitude and about 122 and one-half degrees west of Hurmyrr. 87 In 240,000 years its topogly latitude is to be equivalent to one and one-half times the topogly latitude of Amesbury Circle. Its topogly vector is to be equivalent to the topogly latitude of Amesbury Circle, divided by pi, divided by 360, divided by 10. The resulting topogly longitude of the eye mound will be the same as the resulting topogly latitude of the sea creature mound.

"The second of these topogly matrix sites is for a double-headed drakon pyramid which is located at about 17 and one-quarter degrees north latitude and about 120 and three-quarters degrees west of Hurmyrr. 88 In 240,000 years its topogly latitude is to be equivalent to one-half the area of the base ring of Amesbury Circle. Its topogly longitude is to be equivalent to radius of the base ring of Amesbury Circle, times one-quarter of the topogly latitude of Amesbury Circle. You must calculate its resulting topogly vector.

"The third of these topogly matrix sites is for a courage pyramid also located at about 17 and one-quarter degrees north latitude and about 120 and three-quarters degrees west of Hurmyrr. 89 In 240,000 years its topogly longitude is to be equivalent to one-half the area of the base ring of Amesbury Circle, times the radius of the base ring of Amesbury Circle. Its topogly latitude is to be equivalent either to two times the topogly longitude of the eye mound, or to two times the topogly latitude of the sea creature mound, divided by the radius of the base ring of Amesbury

Circle. You must calculate its resulting topogly vector.

"The fourth of these topogly matrix sites is for a flat, irregular five-sided mound located about 31 and three-quarters degrees north latitude and about 122 and one-third degrees west of Hurmyrr. 90 In 240,000 years its topogly latitude is to be equivalent to one-half the topogly latitude of Amesbury Circle. Its topogly longitude is to be equivalent to area of the base ring of Amesbury Circle, times the topogly vector of the Amesbury Circle, times the square of the megalithic yard. You must calculate its resulting topogly vector.

"Joe Lon Odkin, there are to be three circles, three effigies, three mounds and three pyramids in the first growth ring of the topogly matrix of this planet. To complete the first growth ring you are to design and locate a circle and an effigy between 30 and 45 degrees north latitude and between 90 and 120 degrees west of Hurmyrr.

"When you have completed the first growth ring of the topogly matrix of this planet you will explain the topogly of the source of the topogly matrix as well as the entire first growth ring of topogly matrix to Cary Manpure and Cary Jackman."

The holo-image disappeared.

After Joe Lon Odkin had designed and located a circle and an effigy to complete the first growth ring of the topogly matrix, and when the Danebury Ranch was properly maintained again, the Essene holo-image ordered Cary Manpure and Cary Jackman back to the house.

"The drakon mound is the effigy that Essenes ordered me to design and locate," Joe Lon Odkin told Cary Manpure and Cary Jackman after he had explained the source and the first ten sites of the topogly matrix to them. "In 240,000 years its topogly latitude is to be equivalent to one-tenth the circumference of the base ring of Amesbury Circle, times the square root of one-tenth of the topogly latitude of Amesbury Circle. Its topogly vector is to be equivalent to five (there are five coils in the drakon) times pi, times three squared. Its topogly longitude is to be equivalent to the area of the base ring of Amesbury Circle, times three cubed.

The holo-image suddenly appeared and said, "Move your drakon mound so that its topogly vector is tangent to the western tip of its tongue; and tangent to the southern point of its tongue. Between the triangular tip of the tongue and the open mouth remove the rest of the tongue and replace that part of the tongue with an oval ring. 91 The ring is to represent marriage. The ring is also an egg and the drakon a sperm. The triangle that was the tongue represents the Source of the Universe. After the sperm enters the egg, the Source of the Universe decides whether the miracle of life should burst forth. This mound represents the miracle of life and it will be totally misunderstood until the triangle, whose southern and western tangents mark the mound's topogly vector, is understood to be a representation of the Source of the Universe."

The holo-image disappeared.

"The avenue circle is the circle Essenes ordered me to design and locate," Joe Lon Odkin continued. "I call it the avenue circle because I envision an avenue projecting from its northeastern rim which will point in the general direction of Amesbury Circle. 92 In 240,000 years its topogly latitude is to be equivalent to one-tenth of the topogly latitude of Amesbury Circle. Its topogly vector is to be equivalent to the topogly longitude of the sea creature mound, divided by the topogly latitude of the drakon mound. I haven't figured out the significance of the resulting topogly longitude 196,968.3811, but I will."

When Joe Lon Odkin had finished his presentation, Cary Manpure asked, "Director Odkin, do you remember when my cousin Vicky and I came to you tasking for information about topogly locations in the Horz complex for a presentation to our math class?"

"Yes," responded Odkin.

"Director Odkin, when we made that presentation we were shouted down by the whole class and Vicky cried. Does it surprise you that they shouted us down?"

"No," responded Odkin.

The holo-image suddenly appeared and began speaking, "I am a holo-image," the holo-image said, "of a nitwit Essene. You are all nitwits too. This is THE Crystal Palace on the Hill of Musing. No one but nitwits could understand topogly.

"Tomorrow morning Cary Manpure and Cary Jackman are to fly the cargo air ship to the amphitheater-like valley and to use the robotic arms of the cargo air ship to pick up and on load the numbered containers of group four. They are then to fly the cargo air ship to a high mound shaped hill about 12 miles southwest of Glastonbury Tor. They are then to precisely place and secure the geometric shapes of group four in positions which have been infused into the navigational computer of the cargo air ship using methods for securing the geometric shapes which have been infused into the general purpose computer of the cargo air ship. When Cary Manpure and Cary Jackman have completed the precise placement and securing of the geometric shapes of group four they are to return here."

"I am a holo-image," the holo-image said, "of a nitwit Essene. You are all nitwits too. This is THE Crystal Palace on the Hill of Musing. No one but nitwits could understand the Keirykeion Line.

"I am a holo-image," the holo-image said, "of a nitwit Essene. You are all nitwits too. This is THE Crystal Palace on the Hill of Musing. No one but nitwits could understand transtime crop glyphs."

The holo-image disappeared.

Joe Lon Odkin, Cary Manpure and Cary Jackman looked at one another.

Then Cary Jackman said, "No bozo holo-image is going to tell us what to call our home. No more THE Crystal Palace. From now on our home is the PALACE!"

Chapter Eight

The PALACE

The next morning Cary Manpure and Cary Jackman flew the cargo air ship to the amphitheater-like valley and used the robotic arms of the cargo air ship to pick up and on load the numbered containers of group four. Then they flew the cargo air ship to the high mound shaped hill about 12 miles southwest of Glastonbury Tor and precisely placed and secured the geometric shapes of group four in their predetermined positions. Some of those positions were underwater and to the west of Glastonbury Tor. Many of those positions were on Glastonbury Tor. Cary Manpure and Cary Jackman did not see 'Art Hurian' Manpure while they were working and no smoke rose from the chimney of his hut. Cary Manpure and Cary Jackman did not like working on or in the vicinity of Glastonbury Tor and they were glad when they had completed the precise placement of group four so they could return to the Hill of Musing.

When they returned to the PALACE they told Joe Lon Odkin about what they had been doing and after they had finished, the holo-image suddenly appeared and said, "You have now completed the precise positioning and securing of the geometric shapes of the male drakon of the Keirykeion Line. There are 2400 geometric shapes in the male drakon, divided into 26 alternating groupings: 13 positive, 13 negative plus 132 neutral shapes.

"The 13 positive groups each have one source geometric shape and these are numbered 72, 252, 432, 612, 792, 972, 1152, 1332, 1512, 1692, 1872, 2052 and 2232.

"The 13 negative groups also have one source geometric shape and these are numbered 108, 288, 468, 648, 828, 1008, 1188, 1368, 1548, 1728, 1908, 2088 and 2268.

"Cary Manpure and Cary Jackman, the Danebury Ranch has not been properly maintained. Get on your horses and see to the Danebury Ranch. You will be told when the Danebury Ranch is properly maintained again.

"Joe Lon Odkin," the holo-image said after Cary Manpure and Cary Jackman had departed, "before Essenes give you the first of the 42 sites of the second growth ring of the topogly matrix of this planet, so that you can design and locate the rest of the second growth ring, you need some more information about Hurmyrr and the plateau on which it stands.

"Henceforth you are to call the plateau on which Hurmyrr stands: the Bastion.

"In 240,000 years the topogly latitude of the apex of Hurmyrr will be 85.789.35689. In 240,000 years the topogly latitude of Hurmyrr to be used in the topogly matrix will be 89,298.07682. The location of the topogly latitude of Hurmyrr is: the middle of that sign Essenes placed on the northern facing of Hurmyrr, and can therefore never be measured. Other topogly locations can be measured, but the topogly latitude of Hurmyrr can only be calculated by knowing other things about the topogly matrix. That Hurmyrr is the prime meridian to be used to construct the topogly matrix—with a resulting topogly longitude of 360 and a topogly vector of 248.0502134, the cube of two pi—can also only be calculated by knowing other things about the topogly matrix.

"Hurmyrr is the source of the topogly matrix and it is hidden in the topogly matrix in a way similar to the way that the Source of the Universe is hidden in the Universe. The Source of the Universe can never be measured, but because we know other things about the rest of the Universe, things about the Source of the Universe can be calculated. <u>93</u>

"Once enough of the topogly matrix is known to be able to understand that Hurmyrr is the source of the grid matrix, the location of Sustanator at Alteana can be very accurately measured and its topogly vector 12 can be determined. The topogly vector of Sustanator is 12 because Sustanator encodes the verifying number for the first growth ring of the topogly matrix: 12. <u>71</u>

"Hurmyrr was precisely located so that in 240,000 years its position will encode the equatorial circumference of this planet—as measured in statute miles—and the number of years in the retrograde precession of a seed planet. The ratio between 24,901.54558 and 25,920 is precisely the same as the ratio between 85,789.35689 and 89,298.07682.

"The height of Hurmyrr was adjusted by Essenes so that the height to width ratio of Hurmyrr encodes the nautical mileage system. When the ratio between the height of Hurmyrr and its length is multiplied by 30, the result is 19.09859317. There are precisely 19.09859317 nautical miles in 1/360th of the equatorial diameter of a planet when that diameter is measured in nautical miles.

"The ratio of the perimeter of Hurmyrr to its height is two pi.

"Hurmyrr has four facings, four facing edges and an unconstructed apex—a total of nine features. The topogly latitude of the apex of Hurmyrr, divided by one-ninth, divided the number of statute miles around the equatorial circumference of this planet is equivalent to pi cubed.

"Hurmyrr has 12 edges: the four edges of its base, four facing edges and the four edges at its top. The number 12 is important: 12 is the number of things in the first growth ring of anything.

"The four sides of the base of Hurmyrr are bent slightly inward between the corners of Hurmyrr and as a result the facings of Hurmyrr are slightly concave to represent the concave sculpting of spinning disks.

"Since the base of Hurmyrr is nearly square and the ratio of the perimeter of the base to its height is equivalent to two pi, Hurmyrr implies the square of two pi. The square of two pi, divided by pi cubed is 1.2732395, the tangent of the slope angle of Hurmyrr.

"Eventually there are to be nine pyramids constructed on the Bastion. Two-thirds of those pyramids are to be small.

"Two-thirds of the large pyramids are to be constructed by the future beings of this planet after the minds of some of them have been infused with the design and location of those pyramids. You are to design and determine the positioning of those two large pyramids NOW."

The holo-image disappeared.

Joe Lon Odkin thought about what the holo-image had told him, how he should design the two pyramids and where they should be positioned.

Then he read.

Odkin read about how the Horz complex had been laid out and about how its various structures and components had been constructed. He became very interested in the equiangular spiral which wound around Hurbury and thought that he might use that spiral to help site the additional pyramids on the Bastion. When he made scale drawings of an equiangular spiral centered on the Ark Hur and then on Hurmyrr, he realized positioning additional pyramids on the Bastion by means of an equiangular spiral was not right.

Next Odkin read more about the Tor. He found that a triangle formed by the corner of the Tor which pointed at the Hurmaze and the two corners at the southern end of the Tor had two long sides which were 1.618 or phi times as long as the short side.

When Odkin read this he shouted, "I was right! There is absolutely no relationship whatsoever between the positioning of the Tor and the ratio e/pi!

"The apex of the Tor was offset from the sourcemark Tetrahedron so that the Tetrahedron came to have a very meaningful topogly longitude and vector.

"The Tor was also positioned so that the top of the Transdimensional Triangle had a latitude with a tangent equivalent to the square root of three divided by two.

"The size and shape of the Tor were determined by: the required 1.947 Silbury nautical mile lengths of the sides of the two apparent two-dimensional equilateral triangles; the required apparent 69.28 degree angle at the apex of the Tor of the southernmost apparent two-dimensional triangle; and the required triangle formed by the corner of the Tor which pointed at the Hurmaze, and the two corners at the southern end of the Tor that had two long sides which were 1.618 or phi times as long as the short side.

"All the other angles of the apparent two-dimensional triangles making up the Tor are simply results of these requirements!"

Odkin read further that a scaled Transdimensional Spiral could be drawn so that it was tangent to the corners of isosceles triangles having two long sides which are 1.618 times as long as their short side. 94 Odkin drew such a Transdimensional Spiral over a diagram of the Tor and found that not only was the spiral tangent to the two southern corners of the Tor, but that it was also tangent to the Tor's northwestern corner, the corner closest to Altea City. 94.1 Then Odkin studied everything he could find about the Transdimensional Spiral.

On his map of the Bastion Joe Lon Odkin drew a phi section rectangle with its long north-south axis aligned with Hurmyrr, with the Ark Hur halfway between the eastern and western sides of the rectangle and positioned at the northern end of an equally wide, similarly aligned rectangle overlaying the southern portion of the phi section rectangle, starting at its southern end. The ratio of the width to the length of this smaller rectangle was equivalent to the square root of three divided by two. Starting in the southeastern quadrant of the phi section rectangle, Odkin made a scale drawing of the Transdimensional Spiral: the logarithmic spiral based on e, which also models the growth of living things. 95

Odkin scaled this spiral so that it was tangent to the eastern, southern and western sides of the phi section rectangle and so that it passed through the northeastern corner of the rectangle. The spiral passed through the apex of Hurmyrr, and Odkin decided that the spiral should also pass through the apexes of the two other pyramids, which he decided should be positioned to the southwest of Hurmyrr.

Since he had found something very interesting when he drew a Transdimensional Spiral on a diagram tangential to the Tor, Odkin decided to draw a scaled Tor within the phi section rectangle he had drawn on his map of the Bastion. When Odkin positioned the correctly scaled Tor, so that its northern point (which pointed at the Hurmaze) was tangent to the Ark Hur, he was amazed to discover that the southeastern point of the Tor was tangent to the Transdimensional Spiral on his map of the Bastion. 95

As Odkin was thinking about this, the holo-image suddenly appeared and said, "Joe Lon Odkin, your drawing of the phi section rectangle, the Transdimensional Spiral, the scaled Tor within it and the position of the Ark Hur are a representation of the miracle of life. You have brought into perfect harmony the Tor, the phi section rectangle, the Transdimensional Spiral and the Ark Hur. The key to the harmony is the Tor and without the Tor there is no harmony, because the Tor's six-sided and five-sided symmetry both point at, and are tangent to, the Ark Hur. The position of the Ark Hur on the Bastion will be meaningless to searchers until they place the Tor on the Bastion."

The holo-image disappeared.

Odkin had been very interested to read that one of the ways in which the various structures and components of the Horz complex had been sited was by means of drawing circles and arcs. One such arc could be drawn with its center halfway along the line between Hurbury and the Tor, so that that arc passed through the apex of Hurbury, across the tips of the noses of the Hurmaze and across the apex of the Tor. 96

To continue the process of positioning the other two pyramids and to determine how big they should be, Odkin drew an arc centered at a point on the prime meridian to the south of Hurmyrr. 97 arc A This arc passed through the Ark Hur, to the southern tangent of the not constructed capstone of Hurmyrr and intersected the Transdimensional Spiral. The crossing of this arc and the Transdimensional Spiral determined the apex of the nearer additional pyramid, Odkin decided. Next, Odkin drew a short arc with the same radius centered on the prime meridian at the northern base of the not constructed capstone of Hurmyrr. 97 arc B Odkin decided that it would help to determine the siting of the northeastern corner of the additional pyramid nearer to Hurmyrr. From the crossing of the first arc and the Transdimensional Spiral, Odkin drew a circle with a radius tangential to the not constructed capstone of Hurmyrr in order to help determine the siting of the southeastern corner of the pyramid farther from Hurmyrr. 97 arc C This circle was approximately 30 seconds of Danebury arc in diameter. Odkin left the siting of the apex of the additional pyramid farther from Hurmyrr until later.

Next, Odkin thought about how high to design the other two pyramids, and he decided that they would have to be shorter than Hurmyrr. Odkin was intrigued by the fact that the ratio between the topogly latitude of the apex of Hurmyrr, and the topogly latitude of Hurmyrr that was to be used in the topogly matrix, was identical to the ratio between the number of statute miles around the circumference of Danebury and the number of years in the retrograde precession of seed planets. Odkin also re-read in a history book about the beginning of the union on Altea, that the number of statute miles around the equator of seed planets is always 24,901.54558. Odkin divided 24,901.54558 by 25,920 and obtained .960707777.

Odkin looked some more at the specifications of Hurmyrr. He calculated its height to be about 96.07 percent of 500 feet, but 500 did not at first mean anything to him. Then he divided 500 into 25,920 and obtained 51.84, a number close to the slope angle of Hurmyrr. Odkin next calculated that 51.84 was 96 percent of 54, another number Odkin did not recognize. He read some more and found out that 54 is the result of adding 12 and 42, the number of cells in the first two growth rings of all living things.

"And it is also the number of topogly sites in the first two growth rings of the topogly matrix," Odkin said to himself. "But all these near equivalencies could be wrong, like the previously supposed connection between the ratio e/pi and the square root of three divided by two."

Odkin knew that 96 percent was also 24/25ths, the tonal progression Essenes had suggested that he use to help him in his meditation so that he could transredimension energy.

"Maybe all this has something to do with meditation, if it has to do with anything," he said to himself.

Odkin read that 96 and 96.0707777 are the percentage spin rates of the soul—percentages of the spin rate which spins things out of three-dimensions—which are the first two levels of meditation which trans-redimension energy.

"If I multiply 96.0707777 percent times 25,920 the result is 24,901.54558. And that is the number of statute miles around the equator of a planet having a retrograde precession of 25,920 miles—a seed planet. That's strange, but a very precise match," said Odkin to himself. "Since I have found a connection between meditation and the ratio between the number of statute miles around the equator of seed planets and the length of the retrograde precession of seed planets, and that that ratio is memorialized in the topogly latitudes of Hurmyrr, I think that the other near equivalencies I found may mean something. I will make the heights of the other two pyramids 96.0707777 and 96 percent the height of Hurmyrr."

When Odkin calculated the lengths of the sides of the two additional pyramids based on their heights' being 96.0707777 and 96 percent the height of Hurmyrr and their slope angles being the same as Hurmyrr, he realized that the pyramid farther from Hurmyrr was too big to fit his previous determinations.

No matter where he placed the apex of the farther pyramid along the Transdimensional Spiral, the southeastern corner of that pyramid would not fit on the circle approximately 30 seconds of Danebury arc in diameter centered on the apex of the nearer pyramid. Odkin divided the projected height of the farther pyramid in half, and then the resulting projected pyramid fitted his siting specifications.

Odkin sited the farther pyramid so that in 240,000 years its topogly latitude would be equivalent to two times the topogly latitude of Sustanator at Alteana; the longitude of the courage pyramid, divided by the square root of 15; and the area of the base ring of Amesbury Circle, times two pi.

Odkin also sited the farther pyramid farther, so that in 240,000 years its topogly longitude would be equivalent to the area of the base ring of Amesbury Circle, divided by the topogly longitude of Hurmyrr; and also equivalent to the topogly vector of the sea creature mound, times the topogly vector of Sustanator. In 240,000 years the topogly vector of the pyramid farther from Hurmyrr would be equivalent to the circumference of the base ring of Amesbury Circle, times the megalithic yard.

Odkin sited the nearer pyramid so that in 240,000 years its topogly latitude would be equivalent to the topogly longitude of the double-headed drakon pyramid, divided by the square root of 15; and equivalent to the topogly latitude of the flat irregular five-sided mound, times two pi.

At first Odkin could not site the nearer pyramid so that in 240,000 years either its topogly longitude or its topogly vector would be equivalent to anything. The closest he could come was to site the pyramid nearer Hurmyrr so that in 240,000 years its topogly longitude would be equivalent to the topogly longitude of Hurmyrr, divided by pi cubed; but that placed the nearer pyramid almost 16 and a half feet too far east.

This was unsatisfactory to Odkin, so he read some more to see if he could find an appropriate number which was slightly larger than the 360 topogly longitude of Hurmyrr, a number which would allow him to site the pyramid nearer Hurmyrr more to the west and thus in accordance with his previous determinations.

In place of 360 Odkin decided to use 365.3544652, the number of days in the paradigm length of year. Long ago this had been calculated by multiplying the square root of three divided by two times 1000; then multiplying that result six more times (for a total of seven times) by the square root of three divided by two.

As Odkin was about to calculate what the topogly longitude of the nearer pyramid would be in 240,000 years by dividing 365.3544652 by pi cubed, when the holo-image suddenly appeared before him and said, "Do not use 365.3544652 in your calculations. Instead use 365.020081, the length of the year of this planet before Essenes adjusted the length of the year of this planet."

The holo-image disappeared.

Odkin sited the nearer pyramid so that in 240,000 years its topogly longitude would be equivalent to the unadjusted length of the Danebury year, divided by pi cubed. 98

Odkin found out that this new projected topogly longitude for the nearer pyramid was equivalent to ten times the square of the megalithic yard, divided by two pi; and equivalent to the topogly longitude of Hurmyrr, divided by one-tenth the circumference of the base ring of Amesbury Circle.

Odkin could not find that the projected resulting topogly vector of the nearer pyramid would be equivalent to anything.

"But I will," Odkin said to himself.

The Danebury Ranch was again properly maintained, so the holo-image ordered Cary Manpure and Cary Jackman back to the PALACE. As Joe Lon Odkin finished telling Cary Manpure and Cary Jackman what he had been doing, the holo-image suddenly appeared before them and said, "Tomorrow morning Cary Manpure and Cary Jackman are to use the robotic arms of the cargo air ship to pick up and on load the numbered containers of group three. They are then to fly the cargo air ship to the high mound shaped hill about 12 miles southwest of Glastonbury Tor. They are then to precisely place and secure the geometric shapes of group three. When Cary Manpure and Cary Jackman have completed the precise placement of group three they are to return here.

"I am a holo-image," the holo-image concluded, "of a nitwit Essene. You are all nitwits too. This is the PALACE on the Hill of Musing."

The holo-image disappeared.

After Cary Manpure and Cary Jackman had left the holo-image suddenly appeared before Joe Lon Odkin and said, "Your projected topogly vectors for the two additional pyramids are correct. You are now to work out a way in which the three topogly vectors of Hurmyrr and the two additional pyramids can interact to result in a number which is equivalent to three pi. You will need to calculate another topogly number, use a five step process and use only division."

The holo-image disappeared.

The topogly number which Odkin calculated to fulfill the Essene requirement was 5577.096018. Odkin divided 5577.096018 by the projected topogly vector of Hurmyrr and obtained 22.48373804. Next he divided 5577.096018 by the projected topogly vector of the nearer pyramid and obtained .967546033. Then he divided 5577.096018 by the projected topogly vector of the farther pyramid and obtained 2.465617777. Finally he divided 22.48373804 by .967546033 and the result of that division by 2.465617777 and obtained 9.42477796, the number equivalent to three pi.

When Odkin finished his calculations the holo-image suddenly appeared before him and said, "Your topogly number 5577.096018 is a topogly vector. Point to that vector with the six little pyramids."

The holo-image disappeared.

Odkin reasoned that the best way to point at a spot with a projected topogly vector of 5577.096018 was to divide the six small pyramids into two groups of three and to line one group up east and west and the other north and south. Since Essenes had already told Odkin that six small pyramids were to be constructed on the Bastion, he reasoned that the group with which to start was the group lined up north and south. It was much easier to deal with a topogly longitude which would consist of only seconds, than with a topogly latitude which would require that degrees, minutes and seconds be multiplied together (being close to 30 degrees north latitude).

In a notebook Odkin kept an ever increasing numerically ordered list of all the numbers used in the topogly matrix. He started with the first number and multiplied it by 5577.096018 to see if he could obtain a number which would correlate with any number in his notebook, and if that resulting number could be broken down into a latitude which would be on the Bastion in 240,000 years.

When Odkin got to 7.396853331—the square of the megalithic yard —and multiplied 7.396853331 by 5577.096018 he obtained 41,252.96126, a number very nearly equivalent to the projected longitude of the sea creature mound, divided by pi; and the projected grid longitude of Hurmyrr, times the diameter of the base ring of Amesbury Circle, times the quantity of the square of the megalithic yard, divided by two pi.

"Sometimes when you get to over five or six decimal places these things don't quite work out," Odkin said to himself. "That is just the way things are."

Odkin found a spot on the Bastion which in 240,000 years would have a topogly latitude of 41,252.96126, a topogly longitude of 7.396853331, and a topogly vector of 5577.096018. The spot was south and west of the Ark Hur, south and east of Hurmyrr, and south and east of the large pyramid which would be further from Hurmyrr. 99

To determine the sites for the two groupings of three small pyramids which were to point at the spot that had a projected topogly vector of 5577.096018, Odkin drew two arcs centered on that spot. The first arc was tangent to the southeastern corners of Hurmyrr and the farther pyramid. 99 arc X The second arc was tangent to the northern base of the not constructed capstone of Hurmyrr. 99 arc Y Having already decided to center all three small pyramids of one group on the longitude line pointing toward the spot that had a projected topogly vector of 5577.096018, Odkin decided to site two-thirds of those pyramids between his two arcs, where those arcs crossed that longitude line. The third pyramid he sited just south of the arc, closest to that pyramid's point of origin. Similarly Odkin decided to site two-thirds of the pyramids of the other group between his two arcs, at the place where those arcs crossed the latitude line on which all three pyramids of the other group were to be centered. The third pyramid he sited just west of the arc farthest from that pyramid's point of origin.

As Odkin was thinking that he had found a good solution to the Essene requirements the holo-image suddenly appeared before him and said, "The dimensions of the two additional large pyramids are not correct. The projected perimeter of the pyramid nearer Hurmyrr should be equivalent to the unadjusted length of the Danebury year, times the square root of 60. The projected height of the pyramid farther from Hurmyrr should be equivalent to one-tenth of its projected grid vector. The projected perimeter of the pyramid farther from Hurmyrr should be equivalent to the projected grid latitude of the drakon mound.

"You will find out that the correct height of the pyramid farther from Hurmyrr is not 48 percent of the height of Hurmyrr, but instead is to be 48 percent of the projected height of the pyramid nearer to Hurmyrr. Calculate all the dimensions of the additional pyramids and figure out why the projected height of the pyramid nearer Hurmyrr is as it is."

The holo-image disappeared.

Odkin made those calculations and determined that the projected height of the nearer pyramid was 471.2388992 feet, 98.1038144 percent of the height of Hurmyrr. Odkin thought that 98.1038144 percent might also have something to do with meditation and energy transredimensioning, so he read more. Odkin was soon able to determine that the 98.1038144 percent ratio between the height of Hurmyrr and its nearer pyramid is equivalent to the percentage of the spin rate that spins things out of three-dimensions during the second to highest meditational state used by meditators when they transredimension energy.

"I wonder why they didn't use the highest," said Odkin to himself.

The holo-image suddenly appeared and said, "Nothing is perfect in three-dimensions.

"The angle whose tangent is .9607 is 43.85. The angle whose tangent is .981 is 44.45. On a bearing of approximately 44.45 degrees gyro from Hurmyrr approximately 1000 miles northeast, is a very high mountain to be called Mount Hurartu by Alteans. Less than 20 miles north of Mount Hurartu is the site of a projected scientific, metallurgical and philosophy center to be called Metsamor. 100

The Metsamor site has a bearing of approximately 43.85 degrees gyro from Hurmyrr. The Metsamor center will be far ahead of its time in its knowledge of things pertaining to science, metallurgy and philosophy because Essenes will secretly operate the Metsamor center. Essenes will give hints as to the functions of Metsamor because the word 'Metsamor' is a foreshortening of the phrase 'metallurgy, science and more'."

The holo-image disappeared.

In the meantime, Cary Manpure and Cary Jackman had flown in the cargo air ship to the amphithcater-like valley and used the robotic arms of the cargo air ship to pick up and on load the numbered containers of group three. They then flew the cargo air ship to the high mound shaped hill about 12 miles southwest of Glastonbury Tor and precisely placed and secured the geometric shapes of group three in their predetermined positions. Some of those positions were underwater to the west of Glastonbury Tor and many of those positions were on Glastonbury Tor. Cary Manpure and Cary Jackman did not see 'Art Hurian' Manpure while they were working and no smoke rose from the chimney of his hut. Cary Manpure and Cary Jackman still did not like working on or in the vicinity of Glastonbury Tor and they were glad when they had completed the precise placement of group three so they could return to the Hill of Musing.

Joe Lon Odkin told Cary Manpure and Cary Jackman what he had been doing since he had last seen them.

When Odkin described how he had calculated that the height of Hurmyrr was about 96.07 percent of 500 feet, that 500 divided into 25,920 was 51.84—a number close to the slope angle of Hurmyrr—and that 51.84 was 96 percent of 54, Cary Manpure began to remember something from his childhood. When Odkin said that he had planned that the farther pyramid would be 48 percent (one-half of 96 percent) as high as Hurmyrr, Cary Manpure became agitated. When Odkin said that the height of the farther pyramid was to be 48 percent the height of the nearer pyramid instead, something clicked in Cary Manpure's mind.

"Stop!" he shouted. "I've just remembered something. The height of

Altean Naval Service star ships is precisely 51.84 feet and the length of their keels is precisely 108 feet. Star ships are 48 percent as high as they are long! My father taught me all this when I was young." 25

"Then the ratio of the heights of the nearer and farther pyramids which will one day stand on the Bastion with Hurmyrr, encodes the height to length ratio of Altean Naval Service star ships," Odkin replied.

Cary Manpure picked up Odkin's pencil and labeled the two large projected pyramids. Next to the site of the nearer pyramid he wrote Keel. Next to the site of the farther pyramid he wrote Bridge.

"Bridge and Keel are on the Bastion," Cary Manpure said. "Essenes always give hints."

"My father also told me," he added, "that the 51.84 foot height of star ships is 96 percent of the 54 foot diameter of the spinning disks of their gravitron drives. 24,28 He said that if the height of star ships were anything other than 24/25ths of the diameter of the spinning disk, harmonic resonances caused by the 750,000 rpm spinning of the disk would tear the ship to pieces."

"I was right!" Joe Lon Odkin shouted. "Those near equivalencies I found in Hurmyrr were relevant and they were encoding vital information about harmonics—especially the harmonics of star ships."

Then Odkin pulled out his drawing of Amesbury Circle. To it he added four large stones which formed a rectangle just inside the outer ditch and earth circle. 100.1

"The rectangle formed by these four stones will represent a side view of the steel box which encloses the engineering spaces of a space vessel," he said. "The northwestern and southeastern stones will point to the Bastion on which Bridge and Keel will stand. I'll put the northern and southern stones on small mounds so that everyone will think they are more important—even though they're not."

After Odkin completed telling Cary Manpure and Cary Jackman about what he had done, they told Odkin what they had been doing. As they were finishing the holo-image suddenly appeared and said, "You have now completed the precise positioning and securing of the geometric shapes of the female drakon of the Keirykeion Line. There are 2352 geometric shapes in the female drakon, 98 percent as many geometric shapes as there are in the male drakon of the Keirykeion Line. The 2352 geometric shapes in the female drakon are divided into 26 alternating groupings: 13 positive, 13 negative plus 48 neutral shapes.

"The 13 positive groups each have one source geometric shape and these are numbered 36, 216, 396, 576, 756, 936, 1116, 1296, 1476, 1656, 1836, 2016 and 2196.

"The 13 negative groups also have one source geometric shape and these are numbered 144, 324, 504, 684, 864, 1044, 1224, 1404, 1584, 1764, 1944, 2144 and 2304.

"Cary Manpure and Cary Jackman, the Danebury Ranch has not been properly maintained. Get on your horses and see to the Danebury Ranch. You will be told when the Danebury Ranch is properly maintained again."

"Joe Lon Odkin," the holo-image said after Cary Manpure and Cary Jackman had departed, "there is something else for you to tell Cary Manpure and Cary Jackman when they return.

"As you already know, the three gigantic computers in the Hurmaze always calculated everything three times before they gave out their results. This is the three times three equals nine that we talked about. As you also already know, Hurmyrr is a one-third scale model of the computers in the Hurmaze. There are to be a total of nine pyramids on the Bastion on which Hurmyrr stands, in order to encode that Hurmyrr is one-third the size of the computers in the Hurmaze, and that those computers always calculated everything three times before they gave out their results. Three times three equals nine."

"I'm going to give you some results if you don't get out of here," resounded Odkin as he took a swing at the holo-image.

The holo-image backed away and said, "Further, the Bastion on which Hurmyrr stands is not the Bastion just because Bridge and Keel will some day stand there. The Bastion, the name for the plateau on which Hurmyrr stands also encodes the fact that the computational results from the computers in the Hurmaze were conduited to the Bastion on Silbury from where they were transcommunicated to the planetary defense system of Silbury.

"Joe Lon Odkin, don't forget to tell Cary Manpure and Cary Jackman these things."

The holo-image disappeared.

As Odkin muttered to himself, the holo-image suddenly appeared and said, "In your refrigerator you will find barley, hops and malt. You are to brew beer for a party. Begin NOW!"

The holo-image disappeared.

The Danebury Ranch was again properly maintained so the holo-image ordered Cary Manpure and Cary Jackman back to the PALACE.

"We're supposed to have a party," Odkin told them. "I was ordered to brew beer, and I did."

Cary Manpure looked at Odkin as if he were insane. "With whom are we supposed to have a party?" he yelled.

The holo-image suddenly appeared and ordered, "You are to have a party among yourselves. Begin NOW!"

The holo-image disappeared.

Odkin poured beer for everyone and they sipped from their glasses.

The holo-image suddenly appeared and ordered, "Play some music. Begin NOW!"

The holo-image disappeared.

Cary Jackman turned on a music player and they continued to sip their beer.

The holo-image suddenly appeared and ordered, "Eat something. Begin NOW!"

The holo-image disappeared.

They nibbled on cold meat that Cary Manpure had brought from the food cooler and they continued to sip their beer.

The holo-image suddenly appeared and began speaking, "The geometric shapes of the female and male drakon of the Keirykeion Line," it said, "will cause channels, eddies and areas of high and low energy to form in the planetary torun flowing across the surface of this planet. In particular, the geometric shapes of the female and male drakon of the Keirykeion Line will cause two twisting and turning channels to form in the planetary torun flowing across southern Hurengland. These patterns of will vary from place to place, but on Glastonbury Tor one of the twisting and turning channels is a representation of the birth canal of a female self-aware being. The other is a representation of the reproductive organ of a male self-aware being. 101 The male reproductive organ is inside the birth canal and inside the end of the male reproductive organ is the stone sourcemark which is on Glastonbury Tor. The stone sourcemark represents a growing fetus of a self-aware being. The growing fetus is inside both the birth canal and the male reproductive organ because both mother and father are equally responsible for the nurturing of their children."

"Is our 'party' supposed to be a lecture on sex education?" Cary Manpure shouted sarcastically.

The holo-image stopped speaking.

"Why do you not like us?" Cary Manpure asked.

The holo-image continued, "On top of a ridge southeast of the Silbury Hill site future beings of this planet are to construct a long narrow burial mound. Inside, at one end of the long narrow burial mound, there will be a stone lined passageway with stone lined burial chambers on either side of it. Nearby, at the appropriate time, a transtime crop glyph in the shape of a dolphin will be formed. This transtime crop glyph will be the same length as the long narrow burial mound, this will link the two together. 102 However, this dolphin shaped transtime crop glyph is meant to be scaled so that it fits inside the stone lined passageway of the long narrow burial mound. 103

"The long narrow burial mound with the dolphin shaped transtime crop glyph in its stone lined passageway will represent the end of an energy conduit leading into an energy transconverter and its diamond dolphin.

"The long narrow burial mound with the dolphin shaped transtime crop glyph in its stone lined passageway will be at the western tangent of the Lookout site in the small scale model of the Horz complex. 60,104

"The long narrow burial mound with the dolphin shaped transtime crop glyph aligned with its stone lined passageway will also represent all of you.

"You are to remain on this planet for the rest of your lives alone."

The holo-image disappeared.

Cary Manpure felt like he had been knifed in the heart.

"Alea and I were together on the Lookout," he said, "until just before..."

Cary Manpure could speak no more.

Odkin looked at Cary Manpure and said, "This is uncalled for brutality."

The holo-image suddenly appeared and said, "Joe Lon Odkin, tell them about three times three equals nine. Begin NOW!"

Odkin told them.

The holo-image disappeared.

"That was also uncalled for brutality," said Cary Manpure.

The holo-image suddenly appeared and said, "The long narrow burial mound with the dolphin shaped transtime crop glyph in its stone passageway will be at the western tangent of the Lookout site in the small scale model of the Horz Complex in order to tell Cary Manpure that that which was once atop the Lookout will never be for him again."

The holo-image disappeared.

"Bastards!" Cary Manpure shouted as he left the living platform on his way to slam the door of his living quarters behind him.

The next day Cary Manpure and Cary Jackman both stayed in their living quarters. Joe Lon Odkin took a walk. When he returned he requested through their doors that Cary Manpure and Cary Jackman join him on the living platform.

"We are marooned on Danebury," Joe Lon Odkin said as they sat around the hearth. "No Alteans know where we are. We have no method of contacting any Alteans and we have no means of traveling beyond the atmosphere of Danebury.

"I have had the opportunity to fall in love, to marry and to have a child. Neither of you has had that opportunity.

"I plan to tell the holo-image that I will remain here and do what is necessary, but that you two must be allowed to go to Daphlay so that you can have the opportunity to fall in love, marry and have a family. There is nothing more important than that, and I will not allow Essenes to deprive you of that experience. Their conduct is brutal and I will not allow you two to be brutalized further."

Before either Cary Manpure or Cary Jackman could respond the holo-image suddenly appeared.

"Go away!" Cary Manpure shouted at it.

The holo-image disappeared.

The next day Joe Lon Odkin, Cary Manpure and Cary Jackman all stayed in their living quarters.

The following day Cary Jackman was very hungry and made something to eat. Then he invited Joe Lon Odkin and Cary Manpure through their doors to join him.

After eating they sat down on sofas in front of the hearth and silently watched the burning logs in the fireplace.

"We have no choice," said Cary Jackman.

Neither Joe Lon Odkin nor Cary Manpure objected.

The next morning Cary Manpure woke up after falling asleep on one of the sofas and stared at the fire.

When Cary Jackman woke up later and came to the living platform Cary Manpure looked Cary Jackman in the eyes and said, "This place is not the PALACE. It is—as I said originally—THE Crystal Palace!"

Chapter Nine

Home!

Cary Manpure had taken more than enough and he began destroying everything. Cary Jackman tried to calm his enraged friend, but he would have nothing of it. Cary Jackman got a bloody nose for his efforts. As Cary Manpure continued to rampage, Director Odkin suddenly appeared and shouted, "Cease! NOW!"

Director Odkin thoroughly lambasted Cary Manpure to the point where the young man shuddered in his presence.

"You had better mend your ways, young man," Odkin shouted. "Or we'll separate your way from ours. Begin NOW!"

Cary Manpure mended everything, mended his ways and then asked Director Odkin if they could have a symposeion so they "could arrive at a mutually agreeable name for our place of incarceration."

"NO!" roared Director Odkin. The name of where we live is HOME!"

Cary Manpure went to his living quarters and said to himself, "I may have to call this place HOME when I'm around them, but to myself I'll call it IMPOSED home!"

"Geometry," the holo-image said the next morning after it suddenly appeared before Joe Lon Odkin, Cary Manpure and Cary Jackman as they sat around the hearth watching the flames in the fireplace, "can be used to model the way in which channels, eddies and areas of high and low energy are formed in the planetary torun which flows across the surface of this and other planets. Before any adjustments were made to the landscape of this planet, planetary magnetic anomalies and topographic features caused channels, eddies and areas of both high and low energy to form around the planet in ways so complex that they can only be geometrically modelled with great difficulty.

"As soon as Hurmyrr was constructed the channels, eddies and areas of either high or low energy around the planet were permanently altered by the introduction of just a single large geometric shape. The construction of the geometrically shaped structures at Alteana about 120 degrees west of Hurmyrr added to this permanent alteration of the channels, eddies and areas of high and low energy around the planet.

"The construction of your geometrically shaped HOME on the Hill of Musing—about four-sevenths of the way from the equator to the north pole—also added to this permanent alteration of the channels, eddies and areas of high and low energy around the planet. The completion of the drakon of the Keirykeion Line significantly altered the channels, eddies and areas of high and low energy around the planet—especially in southern Hurengland. As more and more geometric shapes are added to the landscape, the location and shape of more and more of the channels, eddies and areas of high and low energy around the planet are changed to locations and shapes which can be more easily modelled by geometry.

"The construction of appropriate geometric shapes in a topogly matrix is a way in which the channels, eddies and areas of high and low energy around the planet can be geometrically manipulated. Topogly latitudes have geometric relationships with the equator of the planet, topogly longitudes have geometric relationships with Hurmyrr—the geometric structure which began the permanent alteration of the energy around the planet—and topogly vectors have relationships with both the equator and Hurmyrr.

"Almost all sites of the five growth rings of the topogly matrix will be located in certain portions of Prehurland. The alterations to the energy around the planet caused by the geometric constructions of the topogly matrix will be enhanced by the geometric shapes of the Keirykeion Line; the future construction of geometric structures in Hurengland; Hurmyrr and other geometric structures to be constructed on the Bastion; and many geometric structures which will be constructed on carefully selected locations northwest and northeast of Hurmyrr. These constructions will cause vortices to form in the planetary magnetic field, in geometric relationships with one another and with the various geometric constructions. These magnetic anomaly vortices will cause great localized disruptions in the flow of planetary torun, which will cause those beings sensitive to areas of high and low planetary torun to be terrorized by the lack of planetary torun in and around these vortices. These magnetic anomaly vortices can—for reasons unknown—also cause localized disruptions of the planetary gravitational field which will sometimes result in disruptions of the local speed of light (since the speed of light is governed by gravity).

Such disruptions of the local speed of light will distort the size of objects and this phenomenon will be a local verification to future seekers that the speed of light is greatly affected by gravity.

"Cary Manpure and Cary Jackman are now to fly in the cargo air ship to the Bastion."

The holo-image disappeared.

When Cary Manpure and Cary Jackman arrived at the Bastion the holo-image gave them new instructions. "You are to construct five of the six small pyramids whose positions were determined by Joe Lon Odkin," it said. "Information concerning the size and shape of these small pyramids and which five you are to construct has been infused into the general purpose computer of the cargo air ship. Begin NOW!"

The holo-image disappeared.

While Cary Manpure and Cary Jackman were constructing five-sixths of the small pyramids and therefore the remaining two-thirds of the total number of nine pyramids which were to eventually be constructed on the Bastion, Joe Lon Odkin was designing and siting the circles, effigies, mounds and pyramids of the second growth ring of the topogly matrix. The holo-image gave Joe Lon Odkin the design—which included the usage of the numbers 26 and 42—and the exact future topogly location of the pyramid which was to be the first of the 42 structures of the second growth ring, and then ordered Odkin to figure out the best geographical location for that pyramid. Odkin sited this enormous terraced pyramid in the mountains over 60 miles southeast of Alteana.

After Odkin had determined the site of that pyramid, the holo-image gave him the general geographical locations for the remaining circles, effigies, mounds and pyramids of the second growth ring of the topogly matrix. The holo-image ordered him to "design and site all 41. Begin NOW!"

After Cary Manpure and Cary Jackman had constructed five-sixths of the small pyramids on the Bastion, the holo-image suddenly appeared before them and said, "Cary Manpure and Cary Jackman, the Danebury Ranch has not been properly maintained. Return to Hurengland, get on your horses and see to the Danebury Ranch. You will be told when the Danebury Ranch is properly maintained again."

The holo-image disappeared.

While Cary Manpure and Cary Jackman were maintaining the Danebury Ranch, Joe Lon Odkin continued designing and siting the circles, effigies, mounds and pyramids of the second growth ring of the topogly matrix.

The Danebury Ranch was again properly maintained, so the holo-image ordered Cary Manpure and Cary Jackman back HOME. After Joe

Lon Odkin finished telling Cary Manpure and Cary Jackman what he had been doing and after Cary Manpure and Cary Jackman finished telling Joe Lon Odkin what they had been doing, the holo-image suddenly appeared before them. The holo-image began speaking, "With the completion of two-thirds of the pyramids which are to be constructed on the Bastion, the drakon of the Keirykeion Line are now fully established. The structures on the Bastion, the structures of Alteana, your HOME and the two groups of geometric shapes now positioned on either side of the Keirykeion Line are the four elements which have established, and will maintain for some time, the two drakon of the Keirykeion Line. Later, the fifth element—composed of many geometric structures to be constructed on carefully selected locations northwest and northeast of Hurmyrr—will be added, in order to maintain the Keirykeion Line, after the geometric shapes of the drakon are gone.

"The two most important things in the establishment and maintaining of the two drakon of the Keirykeion Line are the two large groups of geometric shapes which are now positioned on either side of the Keirykeion Line. As you know there are 2400 geometric shapes in the male drakon, divided into 26 alternating groupings: 13 positive, 13 negative plus 132 neutral shapes.

"The tangent of the numbers of the geometric shapes which are the source geometric shapes of the 13 positive groups making up part of the male drakon is 3.077683537.

"The tangent of the numbers of the geometric shapes which are the source geometric shapes of the 13 negative groups making up part of the male drakon is –3.077683537.

"As you know there are there are 2352 geometric shapes in the female drakon, 98 percent as many geometric shapes as there are in the male drakon of the Keirykeion Line. The 2352 geometric shapes in the female drakon are divided into 26 alternating groupings: 13 positive, 13 negative plus 48 neutral shapes.

"The tangent of the numbers of the geometric shapes which are the source geometric shapes of the 13 positive groups making up part of the female drakon is .726542528.

"The tangent of the numbers of the geometric shapes which are the source geometric shapes of the 13 negative groups making up part of the female drakon is –.726542528.

"The geometric shapes which make up the male drakon help form the male drakon because the source geometric shapes of the 13 positive and 13 negative groups are placed so that the sequential numbers of these 26 source geometric shapes have tangents which are alternately 3.077683537 and –3.077683537 and therefore result in a total cumulative tangent of 0 —which is the tangent of 360, 2160, 21,600 and 25,920.

"The geometric shapes which make up the female drakon help form the female drakon because the source geometric shapes of the 13 positive and 13 negative groups are placed so that the sequential numbers of these 26 source geometric shapes have tangents which are alternately .726542528 and –.726542528 and therefore result in a total cumulative tangent of 0.

"The geometric shapes which make up the female and male drakon help form the female and male drakon because the tangents of the sequential numbers of the source geometric shapes interact as follows: .726542528, times 3.077683537 equals the square root of five and –.726542528, times –3.077683537 equals the square root of five.

"The square root of five is not only a metaphor for living things, it is also the mathematical constant which is the basis for the geometry which models the way in which channels, eddies and areas of high and low energy are formed in the planetary torun which flows across the surface of this and other planets.

"There are three reasons why alterations to the energy around this planet are being made—and will be made—by the five growth rings of the topogly matrix; the geometric shapes of the Keirykeion Line; the future construction of geometric structures in Hurengland; Hurmyrr and other geometric structures on the Bastion; and the many geometric structures which will be constructed northwest and northeast of Hurmyrr.

"The first reason is to provide future individual beings who can sense high and low concentrations of planetary torun with many channels, eddies and areas of high energy in specific locations around this planet so as to induce in them, feelings of optimism and well-being. In the scientifically unsophisticated societies which Essenes project will arise on this planet, these sensitive future individuals able to sense high concentrations of planetary torun will often be highly regarded by some of these societies because they will have the ability to encourage others, due to their feelings of optimism and well-being. In order that they are able to acquire these feelings, sensitive future individuals and those desiring encouragement will gather at places of high concentrations of planetary torun.

"Essenes project that meeting structures will be constructed in areas of high concentrations of planetary torun so that sensitive beings can obtain feelings of optimism and well-being and encourage others. The most effective of these meeting places will be those positioned and constructed according to the feelings of those sensitive individuals.

"Over time, more and more of these meeting structures will be positioned and constructed in areas of high concentrations of planetary torun according to the feelings of those sensitive individuals. This process will increase the number of channels, eddies and areas of high energy and offer more opportunities for individuals able to sense high and low concentrations of planetary torun to encourage others.

"The second reason is to establish and maintain the drakon of the Keirykeion Line so that transtime crop glyphs can be laid out and activated.

"The third reason is so that when the future beings of this planet find out about the first two reasons their perceptions of the way the Universe operates will be dramatically and swiftly altered."

The holo-image disappeared.

The next day the holo-image appeared and began speaking, "You already know that the magnetically braided beams made up of three beams of the extremely high speed torun captured by Waldark hats with amplifiers can be made so powerful that they can interact with the planetary torun which flows across the surface of planets.

"You also know that when powerful braided beams strike the surface of planets in certain geometric relationships to the flow of planetary torun, the flow within the area of the striking beams realigns itself to the size and shape of those braided beams. So that the size and shape of those braided beams which struck the surface remain as a virtually permanent realignment of the flow of planetary torun, maintaining their alignment with the flow of the planetary magnetic field but changing their physical orientation on the surface of the planet, as the direction of the flow of the planetary magnetic field varies over time.

"You also know that if virtually permanent realignment patterns of the flow of planetary torun are subsequently struck by another braided beam, the patterns become so intense that planetary surface features—such as crops, trees and snow—try to align themselves with the virtually permanent realignment patterns of the flow of planetary torun.

"Essenes call the purposeful formation of such patterns transtime crop glyphs.

"You also know that the second reason why alterations to the energy around this planet are being made (and will be made) is to establish and maintain the drakon of the Keirykeion Line so that transtime crop glyphs can be laid down and activated.

"Joe Lon Odkin, you are to design and determine the protosites for the source transtime crop glyph and for the first transtime crop glyph of the first growth ring of these transtime crop glyphs. The design of the first transtime crop glyph of the first growth ring of transtime crop glyphs is to represent process.

"Cary Manpure, you are to read about the constructions of early developing societies, and do so in the barn. Where you will remain until you are told to return.

"Cary Jackman, you are to read about the constructions of societies which build large stone meeting structures in which sensitive beings encourage others and you are to do so in the kirk at Wells. Where you will remain until you are told to return."

The holo-image disappeared.

Joe Lon Odkin thought about how to design the source transtime crop glyph. He knew that the ultimate source is the Source of the Universe, but he did not think that he could nor should design a representation of the Source. Odkin had been told that transtime crop glyphs were to be laid down and then activated by magnetically braided beams made up of three powerful beams of the extremely high speed torun captured by Waldark hats with amplifiers, so he thought that after the Source of the Universe, the source of transtime crop glyphs was self-aware beings. There were only three self-aware beings on Danebury who knew about transtime crop glyphs, so Odkin decided to represent Cary Manpure, Cary Jackman and himself in the design of the source transtime crop glyph. Odkin made a sketch of three stylized beings.

The holo-image suddenly appeared and said, "Joe Lon Odkin, you are the source. Cary Manpure and Cary Jackman are your assistants."

The holo-image disappeared.

Odkin erased two of the stylized figures, but made the remaining figure grotesque. Above the right hand of the figure he drew two capital letter Cs representing Cary and Cary.

The holo-image suddenly appeared before him and said, "Joe Lon Odkin, your design for the source transtime crop glyph needs to be reversed like the Ark Hur which faces east instead of west. <u>105</u>

"The Ark Hur ought to be facing west because it is meditating and on this planet you have to face west during meditation so that the planetary torun can blow away the left, linear side of your brain. The Ark Hur actually faces east because everything is to be backwards until they figure it out."

The holo-image disappeared.

Odkin reversed his design for the source transtime crop glyph and then designed the first transtime crop glyph of the first growth ring of transtime crop glyphs.

The design of this transtime crop glyph was similar to the source transtime crop glyph except Odkin added a long antenna coming out of the right side of the head to represent the main energy outflow from the soul captured by the Waldark hat, and a short antenna coming out of the left side of the head to represent the secondary energy outflow from the soul captured by the Waldark hat amplifier. 106 Odkin moved the two capital letter Cs representing Cary and Cary to well above the head and then reversed his drawing.

The holo-image suddenly appeared before him and said, "Joe Lon Odkin, your design for the first transtime crop glyph of the first growth ring should not be reversed.

"The protosite of the first transtime crop glyph of the first growth ring is to be reversed."

The holo-image disappeared.

Next Odkin thought about how to determine the protosites for the source transtime crop glyph and for the first transtime crop glyph of the first growth ring, keeping in mind the Essene order that the protosite of the first transtime crop glyph of the first growth ring was to be reversed. He postulated that perhaps the scale models of the Horz complex had been laid out on Danebury so that transtime crop glyphs could be laid down and activated at protosites which were associated with those scale models. With that theory in mind Odkin reviewed his maps on which he had drawn the three scale models.

Amesbury Circle interested him greatly because in the large scale model Amesbury Circle was the analog of Hurbury and in the very large scale model Amesbury Circle was the analog of the Hurmaze. Odkin knew that the site of energy transredimensioning was part of the Hurmaze and from his previous reading he had found out that the equiangular spiral on Hurbury represented the harmonics of the natural environment required for the evolution of self-aware life from life. He therefore decided to locate the protosite of the first transtime crop glyph of the first growth ring (a transtime crop glyph which represented process) in association with Amesbury Circle.

In order to know how to do that, Odkin decided to read up on the process of energy transredimensioning. Very quickly he read that the soul is tangent to and on the right side of the center line of self-aware beings. In accordance with the Essene order that the protosite of the first transtime crop glyph of the first growth ring be reversed, Odkin determined that this protosite should not be located on the western right tangent of the scale drawing of Hurbury. It should, he thought, be located on the eastern left tangent of the scale drawing of Hurbury in the large scale model: over a mile east of Amesbury Circle. So he placed it there.

Since the Tetrahedron was the sourcemark of the Horz complex, 59 Odkin determined that the protosite of the source transtime crop glyph should be located in association with the analog site of the Tetrahedron (of either the small or large scale model of the Horz Complex). As Odkin was trying to figure out where the protosite of the source transtime crop glyph should be, the Essene holo-image suddenly appeared and said, "Joe Lon Odkin, in the Horz complex the Tetrahedron represents the Source of the Universe in the sight line that extends from the Tetrahedron, through the Wall and the mouths of the Hurmaze and to the Tower of Ancestors. This sight line represents the unfurling process of the physical universe as it is extruded from four-dimensions into three-dimensions, bringing about the birth of self-aware life and subsequently the birth of civilization.

"You are not dealing with this process when you are working with transtime crop glyphs, so you are not to locate the protosite of the source transtime crop glyph in association with an analog of the Tetrahedron.

"You are to determine the protosite for the source transtime crop glyph as an analog for something outside the Horz complex."

The holo-image disappeared.

Odkin studied places on Silbury outside the Horz complex and quickly came upon the main structure of Akadeimia in the northeastern corner of the Ranch. 60 The analog position of this structure in the large scale model was over 20 miles southeast of Amesbury Circle and Odkin determined that the protosite of the source transtime crop glyph should be there. As Odkin was about to plot this protosite on his map the holo-image suddenly appeared and said, "Do not place the protosite of the source transtime crop glyph there. Draw an arc from your proposed protosite for the source glyph centered on Amesbury Circle northward. Measure northward the number of degrees that the orientation of the scale models of the Horz complex are different from the orientation of the Horz complex and place your protosite for the source transtime crop glyph there. This location should be just north of due east of Amesbury Circle. 107

"Do not use Akadeimia on Silbury as you had intended for your calculations, use the Ranch House. 60

"If you calculate correctly, Amesbury Circle, the first transtime crop glyph of the first growth ring and the source glyph should form a virtual straight line. 107 Nothing is perfect in three-dimensions—not you, Joe Lon Odkin—not even computers.

The holo-image disappeared.

"And certainly not nitwit Essenes," Odkin shouted after the holo-image.

As he was working on changing the location of the source transtime crop glyph Joe Lon Odkin said to himself, "The orientations of the three scale models of the Horz complex have all been rotated clockwise about 16 degrees from the orientation of the Horz complex. This must have been done so that the analogs of the Tor and the analogs of the Tetrahedron Crater (in both the small and large scale models of the Horz complex) would be along the Keirykeion Line."

The holo-image ordered Cary Manpure and Cary Jackman back HOME and when they arrived Odkin showed them the source transtime crop glyph and the first glyph of the first growth ring of transtime crop glyphs.

"The energy antennas look like the representations of female reproductive organs in perioikomai," said Cary Manpure when he saw Odkin's drawings.

"They're not," responded Odkin.

"Well, female reproductive organs do emit lots of energy," said Cary Manpure sadly.

Odkin did not reply.

As Joe Lon Odkin finished telling Cary Manpure and Cary Jackman about his activities, the holo-image suddenly appeared and said, "All of you are to design and determine the protosites for the rest of the transtime crop glyphs of the first growth ring of transtime crop glyphs.

"The transtime crop glyphs are to be divided into four groups of two and one group of three.

"All five groups of transtime crop glyphs are to be associated with a construction from early developing societies and with a construction from societies which build large stone meeting structures in which sensitive beings encourage others.

"Three of the five constructions from early developing societies are already designed and their sites determined: Amesbury Circle, Avenabury Circle and the long narrow burial mound with the dolphin shaped transtime crop glyph in its stone lined passageway (which will be tangent to the analog location of the Lookout in the small scale model of the Horz complex). The diamond dolphin transtime crop glyph is to be one of the 12 transtime crop glyphs of the first growth ring.

"The five groupings composed of transtime crop glyphs, a construction from early developing societies and a construction from societies which build large stone meeting structures (in which sensitive beings encourage others) are to depict five-sixths of the process of energy transproduction.

"The groupings are to depict: energy transredimensioning; energy conduiting; an energy transconverter; a spinning disk and components of the gravitron drive—and a computer."

"A computer?" Joe Lon Odkin exploded. "Computers have nothing whatsoever to do with energy transproduction!"

"Without computers," the holo-image responded, "there would be no technology whatsoever and therefore the ability to transproduce energy would not exist."

Cary Manpure and Cary Jackman laughed loudly.

Joe Lon Odkin said nothing.

The holo-image continued, "An energy transdimensioner will not be depicted but their three phi section rectangles are inferred by the phi section layout of the Bastion and the repetition of the number three in the grouping of its structures on the plateau. Other things associated with energy transdimensioners are already encoded in Hurmyrr.

"You are to begin with the group depicting energy transredimensioning. The two transtime crop glyphs, one construction from early developing societies and one construction from societies building large stone meeting structures that are to make up this depiction, are all to be associated with the small scale model of the Horz complex. In 240,000 years the construction from societies which build large stone meeting structures is to be located at a latitude precisely 4/7ths of the way from the equator to the north pole."

The holo-image disappeared.

Joe Lon Odkin took out his map of the area surrounding the Hill of Musing and drew two different shaped triangles over the small scale model of the Horz complex. 108 One triangle pointed west and the other east. Their parallel bases were close to each other near the center of the scale model and Odkin joined those bases with straight lines at their northern and southern ends.

"These two connected triangles," he said to Cary Manpure and Cary Jackman, "are a two-dimensional depiction of the first pair of cones of energy which emanate from souls of self-aware beings when their eyes are closed. To meditate you have to have your eyes closed, so this is also the pattern during energy transredimensioning."

Odkin pointed to the point of the western triangle. "Here is where we'll site an earthwork," he said, "and we'll make it look like the cross section of a brain."

Odkin pointed to the point of the eastern triangle. "Here is where we'll place the protosite of one of the transtime crop glyphs," he said, "and we'll make it look like a cross section of the oblate spheroid reconfiguration of the cones caused by Waldark hats so that they can collect and transmit torun. 109

"We'll determine the site for a stone meeting structure along the latitude which in 240,000 years will be 4/7ths of the way from the equator to the north pole after Manjack goes out to the cargo air ship and figures out what the current latitude of that future latitude is."

Cary Manpure and Cary Jackman laughed again.

Joe Lon Odkin issued orders as they laughed, "Pureman, you design the earthwork. Manjack, you design the stone meeting structure. You two do these things—after you both work together in the cargo air ship to figure out the current latitude of the future latitude."

Cary Manpure and Cary Jackman stopped laughing.

"I'll work on the other glyph," Odkin concluded laughing to himself after Cary Manpure and Cary Jackman had scurried out of the door.

When all of them were done with their projects, Odkin showed Cary Manpure and Cary Jackman his drawing of the transtime crop glyph and read from a book: "'Two-thirds has many very important meanings. With regard to self-aware consciousness, two-thirds is the soul's proportional share of the total amount of consciousness energy transredimensioned by the soul. Although the total amount of energy may vary with different states of consciousness (as demonstrated by Waldark) the soul always retains two-thirds of that energy, releasing the remainder of the total energy transredimensioned, thus causing primary and secondary three-dimensional energy disturbance patterns.'

"This glyph," Joe Lon Odkin stated as he closed the book, "is designed primarily to represent two-thirds, since two-thirds is so vital in the context of energy transredimensioning." 110

Odkin then explained the transtime crop glyph, starting with its smaller circle, proceeding up a straight line to a larger circle and concluding with a line which originated from the larger circle and then bent at 90 degrees toward the smaller circle.

"The smaller circle is about 27 feet in diameter, about ten times the square root of three, divided by two times pi—the square root of three divided by two—that being one of the two things I remember from my transdimensional physics class. I made this part of the glyph because I have re-read that the square root of three divided by two, times pi is 2.720699046, the transdimensional constant."

Cary Manpure and Cary Jackman looked at one another and shrugged their shoulders.

"The length of the line connecting the two circles plus the diameter of the smaller circle is about 98 feet, a representation of the highest attainable state of meditation, 98.11 percent of the rotational speed which spins things out of the physical universe, which is something I recently read about as well.

"The average diameter of the larger circle is 66 and two-thirds feet, two-thirds of 100 feet.

"The 60 degree angle between the long line connecting the circles and the outward pointing part of the bent line is 60 degrees, representing the twelve 60 degree angles of tetrahedra. Three such 60 degree angles being at the three corners of each of the four equilateral triangles which make up tetrahedra.

"This same 60 degree angle divided by the 66 and two-thirds foot diameter of the larger circle results in .90, a representation of the 90 percent spin rate of self-aware being's consciousness in the 'eyes closed' spin rate mode.

"Two-thirds is also represented by the bent line extending from the larger circle and pointing toward the smaller circle. Two-thirds of the bent line is missing, just like the 'missing' two-thirds of the energy trans-redimensioned and retained by the soul.

"If you draw a line from the center of the smaller circle to the outer edge of the bent line projecting toward it—and then draw another line, from the center of that same circle to the point at which the inner edge of the bent line joins the circumference of the larger circle, the angle formed between these two lines will be 19.47 degrees—the other thing that I remember from transdimensional physics.

"The reason I have said 'about' and 'average' with regard to diameters in this glyph is because I could not make everything fit together if I tried to make everything exact."

Cary Manpure showed Joe Lon Odkin and Cary Jackman his drawing of the brain earthworks. "I have a problem with the topography," he said. "Part of the brain is missing because the hill isn't big enough." 111, 111.1,111.2

Odkin looked at the drawing. "This is perfect," he declared. "We'll just chop off one-quarter of the right side of the brain. I also re-read that 750,000 rpms is the transdimensional spin rate. Since the hyperdimensional soul translocates itself within the right side of the brain, we'll only show 75 percent of that part of the brain."

Cary Manpure and Jackman looked at one another and shrugged their shoulders again.

Then Cary Jackman showed Joe Lon Odkin and Cary Manpure his drawing of the stone meeting structure. "This stone meeting house is typical of such structures. 112 I adjusted its design so that when viewed from the altar in the east, the font to the west is on the right tangent of the aisle's centerline. The font therefore represents the soul." 113

Odkin then looked at Cary Manpure and Cary Jackman's calculations of where 4/7ths of the way from the equator to the north pole would be in 240,000 years and found that that latitude ran east and west almost exactly through the center of the Avenabury Circle site. He then decided to site Cary Jackman's stone meeting house just west of the future Avenabury Circle with the font over the spot which was projected to be 4/7ths of the way from the equator to the north pole. This spot was also about halfway between the western rim of the future Avenabury Circle and the analog site of the Wall. It also turned out to be about halfway along the north-south axis of the analog site of the Wall. 114

Cary Manpure got an idea for where they should put the protosite of the transtime crop glyph representing energy transredimensioning. He drew a line from the southeastern tangent of the analog site of the Tor to just south of the Avenabury Circle site, where the analog of the wooden pump house for the Ranch would be. Then he drew a second line from the southwestern tangent of where the analog of the Hurmaze would be, to the southern edge of the eastern cone; so that these two lines crossed at the analog site of where 'Art Hurian' Manpure had positioned his statue "Glamyrr and Sustanator" within the Horz complex. 115

"Let's put the glyph right here," Cary Manpure said, pointing to where the second line and the southern edge of the triangle representing the consciousness cone met. "From there a third line drawn to the center of Avenabury Circle will form a right, western tangent to Silbury Hill."

Joe Lon Odkin laughed.

"Pureman, I think you are beginning to enjoy this," he said.

"I don't trust Essenes," Cary Manpure retorted. "I'm going to find a suitable stone and raise it at precisely the correct spot to be the analog of the old-fashioned pump house in the small scale model of the Horz complex!"

The holo-image suddenly appeared and said, "You are now to design and determine the siting of the other four groups. These are to depict a computer; energy conduiting; an energy transconverter; a spinning disk and components of the gravitron drive. The group depicting a computer also includes Hurmyrr. The group depicting a spinning disk and components of the gravitron drive has three transtime crop glyphs.

"Start with the computer! Joe Lon Odkin, you design two transtime crop glyphs for this depiction.

"I will not!" Odkin exploded.

"Begin NOW!" the holo-image ordered.

The holo-image disappeared.

Joe Lon Odkin designed two transtime crop glyphs.

The first one consisted of very long boxes separated by relatively thin lines. 116

"Crystal disks and mica slats," he told Cary Manpure and Cary Jackman.

The second transtime crop glyph consisted of two nearly connected, capital letter Ys facing each other. The Ys were at the end of lines leading from two different geometric patterns.

"Depicts inflow and outflow," Odkin said. "Garbage in, garbage out."

Cary Manpure and Cary Jackman hooted.

"Looks like two snakes kissing to me!" shouted Cary Manpure. 117

"Something like that," Odkin grumbled.

Cary Manpure had found a location just south of the future site of Amesbury Circle where another structure of an early developing society could be constructed. He designed this structure with massive circular outer earthen walls and a circular stone castle in the center. 118

"This is the doughnut earthworks," Cary Manpure proudly called his creation. "It's where the crystal disks and mica slats go, so there can be inflow and outflow—and so the snakes can kiss!"

Joe Lon Odkin cleared his throat.

Cary Jackman sited a large future stone meeting house in the plain, south of the doughnut earthworks, so that a line from its western tangent, through the doughnut earthworks would continue through Amesbury Circle and point to the small scale model of the Horz complex. 119

"The very tall octagonal tower of the stone meeting house is to evoke the Tower of Ancestors," Cary Jackman said. "The floor plan depicts the central cylindrical column of a computer, the central cylindrical conduit and the cylindrical ring which surrounds the central column about midway up from its base." 120

"We take all these things," Joe Lon Odkin concluded, "and then we cram them into Hurmyrr." 49

The holo-image suddenly appeared and said, "Joe Lon Odkin, you continue to savagely traduce computers. As a result, Essenes will make one of the two transtime crop glyphs you have designed depicting a part of computers appear to be wind damage. 116

"In addition, Essenes will lay down the crystal disks and mica slats transtime crop glyph several times, in very conspicuous places and activate those repetitions when not much else is going on.

"These transtime crop glyphs will appear between Cary Manpure's very appropriate doughnut earthworks and Amesbury Circle.

"These wind damaged crops and other seeming hoaxes will add fuel to the many who will be debunking transtime crop glyphs, debunkers who will be debunking because they have succumbed to the beast—the refusal to accept views beyond their own.

"Essenes project that by the time the seeming hoaxes and wind damaged crops are activated the debunkers will have been going strong for years, initially by attempting to find meteorological explanations for the transtime crop glyphs. They will attempt to recreate conditions under which transtime crop glyphs will form, but they will be unsuccessful, especially if they attempt to make patterns beyond simple circles. 121

"There will be those who actually go into the fields and hoax transtime crop glyphs. They cannot fool themselves, but they will fool those who want to go back to sleep.

"We will fool them, though. They will think they are hoaxing on their own, but they will be 'hoaxing' because we will be inducing them to do things. Their 'hoaxing' transtime crop glyphs will be no more hoaxing than is the induced construction of Amesbury Circle, Avenabury Circle, Silbury Hill, many stone meeting houses and many other constructions around the planet.

"Sometimes only parts of things will be induced, but in such a way that no one will know. The designs of all these induced things will be completely compatible with similar uninduced structures of the same time period and locale, so that there will be no way in which their style will reveal anything. Everything will be as if there were no inducings, except that things will be adjusted slightly to encode those things Essenes want encoded.

"The things in the topogly matrix, including and especially those things to be constructed in Prehurland, will be similarly induced. Those living there will completely independently construct things. Essenes will only induce their specific—never general—design, and their specific—never general—location.

"Everything we have told you about, and more, will work in this way."

"What about the induced profoundly irrelevant unit of measure?" asked Cary Manpure. "What about turning their moon into a harbinger of madness for them?"

"These things will be either the inducement of specifics and/or the intensification of ideas already held," replied the holo-image.

"But you already know, at least in general, in whom you will induce the profoundly irrelevant unit of measure," insisted Cary Manpure.

"We know history," replied the holo-image. "Since we know history, we can very accurately project what is going to happen, for we also know the genetic background of those who will one day live on Danebury."

"What about the unexpected?" demanded Cary Manpure. "There is always the unexpected."

"That is true," said the holo-image, "and Essenes can only deal with unexpected things when they happen."

There were no more questions or comments, so the holo-image continued. "When those who are more open-minded see that even the transtime crop glyphs which seem to be hoaxes or the result of the wind are meaningful, the debunkers will no longer have an audience," it said. "The debunkers will then have to make a choice: continue to debunk and thereby remain slaves of the beast—or wake up!

The holo-image disappeared.

Joe Lon Odkin woke up.

"Bring in the computers from the cargo air ship," Director Odkin said to Cary Jackman.

To complete the depiction of energy conduiting, Odkin designed a diamond dolphin transtime crop glyph which could be scaled to fit inside the long narrow burial mound which Cary Manpure was forced to design. 103 Cary Jackman designed columns which were to be part of the structure inside a future stone kirk at Wells. 122 And together, the three of them designed another transtime crop glyph with six petals (two-thirds of them spaced equally among themselves) inside two concentric circles, depicting the double casings of energy conduits. 123 This transtime crop glyph they signed with Odkin's antenna and two capital Cs.

They made six petals because they were angry with Essenes and they made two-thirds of them identical as they thought that the souls of Essenes were dead. The arcing of the petals, they thought, sufficed to represent the roundness of energy conduit cables.

The columns of the future kirk were to be paced on eight-sided lower bases, eight to show two times four: two different kinds of energy being conduited and the fourth-dimension as the source of those energies. 122 On the lower bases, four-sided and eight-sided upper bases were implied. On those four-sided upper bases, four columns were implied. On those eight-sided upper bases, six columns were implied. Much of the upper bases and many of the columns were only to be implied, as a representation of the bunching together of everything in a real conduit.

The implied six columns on their eight-sided upper bases were meant to represent 6/8ths, 3/4ths, 750,000 rpms and therefore transdimensioning. The implied four columns on their four-sided upper bases represented eight again, two times four: two different kinds of energy being conduited and the fourth-dimension as the source of those two kinds of energy.

The energy conduits to be depicted in the columns of the future kirk (represented by the unequal six-petaled transtime crop glyph) were the dual energy conduits of the Horz complex which conduited both torinum and tornum. Those conduits contained two packets of six cables each for tornum; two packets of four cables each for torinum. All the cables were encased in a double steel alloy casing and the spacings between cables, packets and casings were filled with crushed mica.

Odkin placed the protosite for the diamond dolphin transtime crop glyph south of the analog of Hurbury in the small scale model of the Horz complex 84.1 and the unequal six-petaled transtime crop glyph in the vicinity of the analog site of the Ranch House in the large scale model of the Horz complex. 81.1

The depiction of an energy transconverter included the already designed Avenabury Circle, so Cary Manpure assisted Cary Jackman with his designing of a substantial stone meeting house whose floor plan was to depict one of the two lead lined casings containing the gold dolphins which are inserted into the transconverter sphere of energy transconverters. 124,31 Cary Manpure placed the site for this stone meeting structure in the same vicinity as the six-petalled glyph (and in the vicinity of the analog site of the Ranch House in the large scale model of the Horz complex). 81.1

In the meantime, Joe Lon Odkin designed two transtime crop glyphs. The first was another dolphin, this one designed to depict the gold dolphins and its attended spheres used in energy transconverters. 125,31 The second transtime crop glyph was a two-dimensional depiction of the major components of an energy transconverter. 126

Odkin placed the protosite for the gold dolphin transtime crop glyph south of the site of the analog for the Tor in the small scale model of the Horz complex. 84.1 He placed the protosite for the glyph which was a two-dimensional depiction of the major components of energy converters on the northwestern rim of the site of the modified analog of the Tetrahedron Crater in the large scale model. 82

Joe Lon Odkin had previously designed Amesbury Circle as a scale model of a spinning disk. Cary Manpure and Cary Jackman designed another large stone meeting house to depict components of the gravitron drive, 127 and Odkin designed three transtime crop glyphs as depictions of yet more components. 127.1,127.2, 128, 129, 130 One of the transtime crop glyphs was a multi-perspective of the gravitron capture rings; the gravitron drive support and gravitron emission shaft; the gravitron distributor ring and the six gravitron vents around the distributor ring (through which gravitrons are vented into the spacings between the inner and outer hulls). 131

When he saw the design of this transtime crop glyph Cary Manpure complained, "The distributor ring and vents look more like a ship's wheel than the keel of a space craft. The vents are supposed to be of different lengths so that they can attach to the hull and provide support at the six points of critical stress on a space craft's hull. The very strong distributor ring and vents are the backbone of a space vessel, not its wheel."

"Shut up, Pureman," replied Odkin.

When Cary Manpure looked at him like a whipped puppy dog, Odkin burst out laughing.

In the vicinity of the analog site of the Ranch House in the large scale model of the Horz complex, Odkin placed the protosites for two-thirds of the transtime crop glyphs which were depictions of components of the gravitron drive. He placed the protosite for the glyph depicting the gravitron capture rings and gravitron distributor ring east of the analog site of the Bastion on Silbury, in the large scale model.

Through the years that followed Joe Lon Odkin, Cary Manpure and Cary Jackman worked together to design and determine both the protosites of the glyphs of the other growth rings of transtime crop glyphs, and the sites of the other growth rings of the topogly matrix.

Cary Manpure found a suitable stone and erected it as an analog of the wooden pump house for the Ranch. It still stands just south of Avenabury Circle. 132

Cary Manpure did virtually all the cooking and cleaning up. On one occasion when they were all tired of his cooking he suggested that they go hunting for deer. "We could make bows and arrows," he said enthusiastically.

The holo-image suddenly appeared and said, "No!"

"We'll go fishing then," said Cary Manpure.

The holo-image again said, "No!"

Cary Manpure had thoroughly enjoyed the explorations he had made in Prehurland with Tommy Untiman and he had been overwhelmed with the beauty of Huregan during the holo-mapping expedition. So he suggested to Cary Jackman that they hike around the area and explore more of the planet by air ship.

The holo-image suddenly appeared and said, "No!"

What can we do then?" asked Cary Manpure in disgust.

"You can ride your horses to keep the Danebury Ranch properly maintained," the holo-image replied. "Joe Lon Odkin is allowed to walk 1947 Joe Lon Odkin pacings outward and 1947 Joe Lon Odkin pacings HOME."

"Can we tell sexy stories and jokes?" asked Cary Manpure.

"Yes," said the holo-image.

"I don't feel like it," responded Cary Manpure.

He got up, went to his living quarters and secretly designed a series of six transtime crop glyphs which he titled "The IMPOSED Home, a Mockery." He never brought his plans out of his living quarters. Essenes found them when they were carefully removing his things, at the time they were preparing to remove the house on the hill. Subsequently they laid down and activated the entire series of six glyphs.

The first of the series he titled, "Bozo the holo-image." This transtime crop glyph actually spelled out 'ozo,' but the letter 'b' was strongly implied in the design and only half the face was implied because it was the face of the holo-image, all they ever saw of Essenes. 132.1

"Nitwits belong in a Crystal Palace," said Cary Manpure to himself, "and this is the nitwit Bozo, the holo-image who belongs in THE Crystal Palace—instead of us."

The second of the series he titled, "The dead nitwit." This transtime crop glyph depicted a body lying over a section of circular fencing, with the fencing doubling as arms. The part of the body inside the fence was solid, the head was empty. 132.2

"Fried by the electric current," said Cary Manpure to himself. "If we had some dynamos on Danebury I'd generate some electricity and fry Bozo the holo-image too."

The third of the series he titled, "Geometric shapes." The large triangle in the center was the IMPOSED home and the smaller shapes to either side were shapes from the Keirykeion Line which ran over the Hill of Musing. 132.3

"Also a cross section of the defenses of all Crystal Palaces," said Cary Manpure to himself.

The fourth of the series he titled "Running around and about." The circle in the center depicted Cary Manpure and Cary Jackman, running around and about so feverishly they seemed to be sevened. 132.4

"Also an overhead view of one of the rings of warning pylons around all Crystal Palaces," Cary Manpure said to himself.

The fifth of the series he titled "The Mark missed." The center circle represented ladies, and the four outer circles represented Cary Manpure's thinking that to him, ladies appeared to be "hyperdimensional." The fifth circle symbolised missing the mark. 132.5

"This is also Atlantis with its center terrace, four important things and the Crystal Palace of Atlantis in the river gorge far away—for those who missed the mark."

The sixth of the series he titled "Cary Manpure's Agony." 132.6

"A man without a lady crying out in agony," Cary Manpure cried out in agony.

Next Cary Manpure wrote out a short note for Director Odkin and Cary Jackman and left that note on the raised hearth of the circular living platform. He wrote, "I may never be able to have a lady, but I will have a home. Cary Manpure."

By daybreak Cary Manpure was in the air ship and well on his way to an area they had flown over many times in their travels between Hurengland and the Bastion. Cary Manpure's destination was a very large, almost island, at the end of the long mountainous peninsula which jutted southeastward into the sea shared by the mouth of the river which flowed near the Bastion. This almost island was connected to the mainland by an isthmus at its northeastern corner. Cary Manpure reached its northern coast and began circling counterclockwise. When he had nearly completed his loop he came upon an area he liked and turned inland. He set down in a lush plain surrounded on three sides by steep wooded mountains. To the south was a gulf. Cary Manpure set up his tent in the shade of a tree, carved a sign on a piece of wood he found, lashed it to another, longer piece of wood and erected his sign. It said, "Home."

That night as Cary Manpure slept, shadowy figures entered his home. As they sought to sedate him, Cary Manpure suddenly awoke and lashed out. As many hands grabbed at him, Cary Manpure swung his fists again and again and again as his knuckles becoming bloody from many landed blows until he was finally sedated. The shadowy figures tied him up, lashed him to the pilot's seat of his air ship. Then they removed the tent, the sign and all signs that anyone had ever been there.

The next morning when a very unhappy Joe Lon Odkin went out for his walk he noticed that the air ship was moored in its usual place. He ran up to it, climbed aboard and found the still unconscious Cary Manpure lashed to the pilot's seat.

"Those bastards," Joe Lon Odkin said as he carried Cary Manpure back to HOME.

When Cary Manpure regained consciousness, the holo-image suddenly appeared before them and said, "There are to be no more attempted escapes. Things will improve around here, but you cannot leave."

Cary Manpure looked at the holo-image and said, "I'll keep escaping until you kill me."

"If you continue to escape you will be hauled back here each time and conditions will worsen instead of improving," responded the holo-image. "These deteriorating conditions apply not only to you, Cary Manpure, but also to Joe Lon Odkin and Cary Jackman."

"You're all a bunch of bastards!" shouted Cary Manpure.

The holo-image disappeared.

An uneasy truce broke out between the Alteans and the holo-image. They were not humiliated further and Cary Manpure escaped no more. Cary Manpure realized that as far as leaving was concerned, things were hopeless unless Essenes changed their minds. He therefore lapsed into a mindless torpor and just did things without thinking too much. Eventually the routine became so automatic that Cary Manpure somewhat accepted what was happening to him. He did not become angry very often, and he was never happy. Things just were.

Chapter Ten

Ant men, the Urinal and the Vasectomy

When Cary Manpure was 51, Cary Jackman was 52 and Joe Lon Odkin was 93, the holo-image told them how to lay down and activate transtime crop glyphs.

During the preceding years, they had worked together to design and determine the protosites of the transtime crop glyphs and to design and site the other growth rings of transtime crop glyphs and the effigies, circles, mounds and pyramids of the other growth rings of the topogly matrix. They encoded many things into the topogly matrix.

Cary Manpure's favorite encoding had to do with 19.47122061 degrees, the lower angle of the circular cone of gravitron emission and the latitude at which the three non-polar corners of circumscribed tetrahedra just touch spinning spheres that circumscribe them. Early on, Cary Manpure discovered that if one divides the diameter of Amesbury Circle by five the result is 19.46418289, a close approximation of 19.47122061. "Let's use 19.46418289 instead of 19.47122061 in the topogly matrix," he suggested to Director Odkin. "They'll never figure it out."

"You're a devious bastard, Pureman," Director Odkin replied.

Odkin then preceded to pepper the topogly matrix with 19.46418289 —indirectly. As a result, only by mathematically manipulating diverse constants, and by manipulating many different topogly matrix numbers in various ways can one obtain 19.4618289 from the topogly matrix—many times.

Cary Manpure and Cary Jackman worked to keep the Danbury Ranch properly maintained.

During this time, the holo-image also told them many other important things relating to Panergon Gwynmyrr:

Essenes had used braided beams to push a dead planet from another galaxy to this galaxy, so that the dead planet could be reconfigured and placed in the appropriate orbit to become the moon of Danebury. In order to be able to produce the proper environment for the evolution of self-aware life, Danebury needed to be given a retrograde precession of 25,920 years. This was accomplished by placing the reconfigured dead planet in a retrograde circular orbit around Danbury—an orbit having a radius of 221,546.7453 Danebury miles. Essenes had determined this orbit by multiplying 25,920 times pi, times 2.720699046, the transdimensional constant, equivalent to the square root of three divided by two times pi; the ratio of the surface area of a sphere to the tetrahedron it circumscribes.

The period of revolution of the moon around Danebury was fixed at 27.20699046 days—ten times the transdimensional constant.

Both the orbit and the period of revolution of the moon of Danebury are now changing because Essenes have stopped keeping the moon in its previously required orbit, the holo-image said. The period of the retrograde precession of Danebury is also changing as a result of the changing orbit of the moon of Danebury, but it is no longer required that a retrograde precessional period of 25,920 years be maintained.

The moons of seed planets are in virtually unchanging and perfect for bringing forth life orbits, because they are there as a result of the physics of the Universe, the holo-image told them. Essenes brought in a moon to make Danebury a seed planet, but Danebury's moon stayed in its required orbit only when that orbit was artificially maintained.

Also important in producing the required retrograde precessional period for Danebury was the diameter, mass and angle of orbital inclination of the future moon of Danebury. Essenes determined that the paradigm diameter of moons of seed planets is .273239545, the size of the seed planet around which they orbit. Essenes also determined that the paradigm ratio between the mass of a seed planet and its moon is 81 to 1. Finally, Essenes determined that the paradigm angle of orbital inclination of moons of seed planets to the equator of their seed planet is 5.150818881 degrees, the result of dividing 114 by .273239545 and then by 81.

"The number 114 is the Number of Harmony since 114 is the total of 96 and 6 + 5 + 7," the holo-image told them.

"You know what 96 or 24/25ths, 6, 5, and 7 represent—but numbers are more than representations of things—they are harmonics. For a seed planet to bring forth life everything must be in harmony.

"Essenes wanted the average diameter of the moon of Danebury to be

2160 Danebury miles, so they made it about five and eight-tenths miles smaller than the paradigm diameter of the formula. They made the moon's mass slightly less than paradigm and its angle of orbital inclination slightly less than paradigm so that the total 114 was still achieved.

"It was Waldark who discovered that the spin rate 10,000 rpms is a vital minimum spin rate, it being the lowest spin rate at which higher-dimensional energy emanates from single spinning tetrahedra in opposing multi-cone patterns. Waldark deduced from this discovery that a higher-dimensional transformation takes place at 10,000 rpms during which the spinning tetrahedra reduplicate themselves into two interlocked tetrahedra, one imaginary.

"Waldark and his associates also discovered that spinning celestial bodies rotate themselves partially into a higher dimension and then open a gate from that higher dimension into the physical universe, thereby allowing energy to flow down from one dimension to the next. Later seekers discovered that the higher dimension discovered by Waldark and his associates was complexified three-space.

"A hypersphere in complexified three-space is defined by 27 points, 27 times 1000 is 27,000, and 24/25ths of 27,000 is 25,920—the number of years in the required retrograde precessional period of seed planets.

"The spiral on Hurbury is an equiangular spiral based on the twelfth root of two. That spiral on Hurbury was therefore meant to represent the harmonics of the natural environment which are required for the evolution of self-aware life from life, because those harmonics are based on the twelfth root of two.

"Essenes wanted the average diameter of the moon of Danebury to be 2160 Danebury miles because 2160 is one-twelfth of 25,920, because 12 is closely associated with the twelfth root of two, and because 2160 unifies 21,600 and 25,920.

"You already know that there are 21,600 nautical miles around any given planet's equator, that there are 25,920 years in the retrograde precession of seed planets and that the ratio of 21,600 to 25,920 is equivalent to the ratio of 5 to 6, the metaphor for the relationship between the non-living parts of the Universe and living things.

"Living things exhibit five-sided symmetry. Self-aware beings are also physically bi-symmetrical. The soul of self-aware beings is on the right tangent of the bi-symmetry of self-aware beings, so self-aware beings are not completely bi-symmetrical.

"Since self-aware beings are physically bi-symmetrical they have two hands, five fingers per hand, and a total of 10 fingers.

"Self-aware beings therefore naturally count by 10s.

"Self-aware beings need to live in harmony with their non-living environment, an environment which exhibits six-sided symmetry. To be in harmony with their non-living environment self-aware beings must also count by a system which is in harmony with the non-living parts of the Universe. Since self-aware beings are also physically bi-symmetrical and therefore count by 10s and not 5s, they must also count by 12s and not 6s.

"The number 2160 unifies 21,600 and 25,920 because 21,600—a representation of the non-living parts of the universe, divided by 10 (the natural base number of counting by physically bi-symmetrical self-aware beings) and 25,920—a representation of the emergence of self-aware life, divided by 12 (the required base number of counting by physically bi-symmetrical self-aware beings in order for them to be in harmony with the non-living parts of the Universe)—are both 2160.

"The angular measuring system of the Universe is the 360 degree system because 25,920 divided by 360 is 72, and—when using the 360 degree system—there are 72 degrees in all five angles of a regular pentagon, the representation of the five-sided symmetry of living things.

"Self-aware beings are physically bi-symmetrical.

"The number 360 divided by 2 is 180.

"Self-aware beings have 10 fingers.

"The number 180 divided by 10 is 18.

"The number 18 is 6 + 5 + 7.

"The twelfth root of two is relevant only in the base 10 counting system, a system necessitated by self-aware beings' having 10 fingers. The twelfth root is necessary because it is necessary for self-aware beings to count by 12s to stay in harmony with the non-living parts of the Universe. The number two is necessary because self-aware beings are physically bi-symmetrical.

"There is also a very important relationship between the twelfth root of two 1.059463094 and the square root of nine-eighths 1.060660172 because the square root of nine-eighths is an important constant associated with tetrahedra and the twelfth root of two is associated with the harmonics leading to the development of self-aware life, because tetrahedra are the modeling for everything."

The holo-image disappeared.

"I remember that last part," said Cary Manpure. "Director Odkin told my cousin Vicky and me about that for a project we were doing for school. Vicky told the class, the class shouted her down, Vicky cried.

"Tomorrow," Cary Manpure added as he was going after beer for them all, "we can review what the holo-image just said."

Two days later the holo-image suddenly appeared and said, "Essenes also adjusted the period of rotation of Danebury by the insertion of its new moon to the required 23 hours and 56 minutes. This resulted in the creation of a major environmental problem which had to be overcome before life could flourish on Danebury. Since Danebury's speed of rotation had been increased, its angular momentum was also increased. This resulted in the inducement of the proper magnetic field and the proper flow of planetary torun across Danebury, but it also created a vast increase of energy upwelling at 19-20 degrees north latitude, the three-dimensional manifestation of energy transdimensioning which was first observed and studied by Waldark and his associates.

"Had this energy not been dealt with by Essenes, there would have been excessive volcanic activity and heat which would have made Danebury forever uninhabitable. To alleviate this problem Essenes altered the orbit of the planet next to Danebury which is between it and its sun. This procedure resulted in the establishment of an energy transdimensioning unit consisting of Danebury, the planet with the altered orbit and Danebury's moon. This allowed for the excess energy and heat, created as a result of the increased angular momentum of Danebury to be hyperdimensionally drawn from Danebury, passed through its moon and then transdimensioned into the planet of the altered orbit. Because of this procedure the planet of the altered orbit died from the continuous and violent volcanic activity it has suffered from ever since."

The holo-image disappeared.

"The sacrificed planet," said the three Alteans virtually simultaneously.

The next day the holo-image suddenly appeared and said, "The tangent of the Number of Harmony 114 is –2.246036774; the tangent of 66 is 2.246036774. The cumulative tangent of 114 and 66 is 0 —which is the tangent of 360, 2160, 21,600, 25,920 and 27,000.

"The Source of the Universe extrudes Itself into three-dimensions through a zero-dimension point which has no tangent. Numbers which have a tangent of 0 and combinations of numbers which have cumulative tangents equal to 0 are harmonics of the zero-dimension point and therefore contain the harmonics of the transdimensional physics which is the basis of the Universe."

The holo-image disappeared.

"I think I'll brush up on my transdimensional physics," said the three Alteans virtually simultaneously.

After Joe Lon Odkin, Cary Manpure and Cary Jackman had brushed up on their transdimensional physics, the holo-image suddenly appeared and said, "The interior diameter of the gravitron distributor ring of Altean Naval Service star ships is 66 feet, virtually 96 percent, or 24/25ths of the 68.75493542 foot exterior diameter of the gravitron distributor ring, a diameter which is 1.273239545 times the 54 foot diameter of the spinning disk of Altean Naval Service star ships.

"The commanding officer's circular command station aboard Altean Naval Service star ships has a diameter of 14.75493543 feet, is derived by multiplying 54 by .273239545.

"Star ships must be in harmony too, or they could not function properly. The harmony of star ships is obtained by using the same geometry that creates the harmony of seed planets and their moon.

"This geometry is based on squaring the circle: creating a square inside a circle (though the corners of that square extend beyond the circle) which has the same perimeter as the circle's circumference. The diameter of the squared circle is 1.273239545 times the length of any given side of the square which squares it."

The holo-image disappeared.

Joe Lon Odkin pulled out his drawing pad, designed a new transtime crop glyph and showing it to Cary Manpure and Cary Jackman said, "The large circle is 81 feet in diameter and represents the mass ratio between Danebury and its moon. The small circle is 21 feet 6 inches in diameter and it represents the 2160 mile diameter of Danebury's moon. The line connecting the two circles is six feet six inches wide representing 66 and 19.5 feet long because 195 – 81 = 114!

"I'll call it Harmony, but I'll add a little extension at the top to make it look like a corked wine flask," Odkin concluded with a grin. 133

"Let's put it down near the gold dolphin, south of the analog site of the Tor," suggested Cary Manpure. "Dolphins are about the only beings I can think of who are in harmony with one another and their environment. The glyph and that suggestion have made me thirsty. I think a little Meisterbraue will put us in harmony with one another and our environment."

When they had all consumed what Cary Manpure considered just the right amount of mist-producing Meisterbraue, as he had long since called the beer Odkin was brewing for them, Cary Manpure got an idea and said, "Director Odkin has just designed a glyph he calls Harmony.

"I suggest that we now produce a Disharmony series of depictions to illustrate our feelings toward the last council on Silbury.

"I suggest that Director Odkin make his contribution to the Disharmony series in the medium of crops, that Cary Jackman make his contribution in the medium of gigantic stone meeting houses and that I try to do something with earthworks or rocks.

"I further suggest that we each go to our living quarters to conceive and design our depictions in private. In the morning we can then make our individual presentations to the group—and to the holo-image, if it's around.

"Begin NOW!"

Cary Manpure ran out of the room.

Joe Lon Odkin drew an insect like figure with four different sized circles connected by lines. 134 Two pairs of bent lines protruded from the two larger circles and two disconnected short lines were adjacent to the line connecting the two circles with bent lines coming off them.

"Ant men," he said as he showed his work to Cary Manpure and Cary Jackman. "Ants live in an ant hill, scurrying about doing everything and nothing—mostly not thinking. The council did likewise. The middle set of limbs are not connected to the body to show that only two-thirds of the council are ant men."

"There is a problem with your design, Director Odkin," Cary Manpure stated. "Ants have only three body parts, not four."

"This is not a depiction of antmen, but of ant men!" responded Odkin with a twinkle in his eye. "Ant men have very long large conspicuous features which can be used to describe them."

Cary Manpure laughed. "Which is which?" he asked.

"You pick," responded Odkin.

Cary Manpure and Cary Jackman applauded.

Next, Cary Jackman showed his line drawing of what looked like one of the water courses surrounding the longhouses of Hur Square. 135

"The Urinal," he said. "Large stone meeting houses need large stone urinals. This gets attached to the large stone meeting house which will be constructed at Avelinabury on ground which is now under water. Dolphins used to swim in the water courses of Hur Square. Before we left Silbury we should have drained the water from the water courses, put two-thirds of the council in them, including and especially Halbert Hargrave, the 'teacher' who ruined art for me—and then used the water courses as urinals."

Joe Lon Odkin applauded.

Cary Manpure howled with delight. "I didn't know that Halbert Hargrave had you for art," Cary Manpure said after he gained control of himself. "He ruined art for me too."

"I know something more about Halbert Hargrave," said Cary Jackman, "and I would have told you long ago if I'd known before what you have just told me. My brother told me this when he was at Alteana.

"It seems Halbert Hargrave fancied himself as the leading expert on art of Silbury and he was always commenting on various works of art. At an art exhibit on loan from Daphlay in the Tower of Ancestors Peri seed station there was a particularly fine sculpture by Ell 'Art Hurian.' My brother was admiring this statue, of a strong nude bearded man in the act of hurling something, my brother specifically remembered thinking the word 'hurling' and not the word 'throwing' when Halbert Hargrave and Neal Ames, a physical education teacher, walked up beside him. He recognized them, but they did not notice my brother.

"'Now, Neal,' Hargrave said to the physical education teacher, 'this is a fine example of a statue of Poseidon throwing a trident.'

"'I don't think so,' replied Neal Ames. 'If this was supposed to be Poseidon throwing a trident, the trident would be there. From his pose he has obviously not released anything yet. I think that this is Zeus hurling a thunderbolt. Jagged thunderbolts are allegories for the twistings and turnings of life. You can't see them coming—and you can't see thunderbolts either. This statue has a "thunderbolt" in the hand of Zeus so Zeus can hurl it.'

"Hargrave then responded, 'You're only a physical education teacher, Neal, so how could you know!'

"After Hargrave and Ames left, my brother went over to where there were brochures explaining the pieces of art in the exhibit. He looked up that statue and under its picture in the brochure it said, 'Zeus.'

"My brother told me that he then reflected on how he had thought of the word 'hurl' and not the word 'throw.' That got him interested in art and that is why he was studying art at Akadeimia, he told me."

Cary Manpure howled with delight again and after he regained control of himself said, "That bastard Halbert Hargrave ruined art for you and me, but he unwittingly got your brother interested in art—because your brother and 'only a physical education teacher' knew more about art than the much puffed up, stuffed up Halbert Hargrave will ever know about anything in a myriad of transarkings."

"The Vasectomy," Cary Manpure said unveiling his depiction. "I would have preferred the Castration, but I couldn't think of how to depict castration.

"This ground plan is of a mighty fortress to be constructed of enormous rocks. <u>136</u> A sally port penetrates the walls near the proper spot. Two underground cisterns are below. A small gate penetrates a round extension wall and a staircase leads along the interior of that rounded wall to the small gate.

"When we are through with them in the urinal course—and just before they drown—we haul them up and use very rusty knives on them," Cary Manpure added.

"I have shown two-thirds of the council also.

"Those two-thirds have holes in the wrong place—the cisterns, not the sally port," Cary Manpure concluded.

Before Joe Lon Odkin and Cary Jackman could respond to Cary Manpure's presentation, the holo-image suddenly appeared and said, "You gentlemen have concocted some very interesting depictions which Essenes will insure come to fruition if you add a representation to the Disharmony series—a representation of Sarkneson," the holo-image said. "To be able to make this representation you need to remember that you now have three depictions in your Disharmony series."

The holo-image disappeared.

"That's easy!" shouted Cary Manpure. "Three depictions, one representation. Three-quarters. 750,000 rpms. Spinning disks! And gravitron drives!"

"Pureman," Odkin said blandly. "I think you really are enjoying this."

Joe Lon Odkin, Cary Manpure and Cary Jackman looked at Odkin's design of Amesbury Circle, at Cary Manpure and Cary Jackman's design for an enormous stone meeting house which depicted components of the gravitron drive and at Odkin's three transtime crop glyph depictions of more components.

"What is this small H shaped structure at one end of your stone meeting house?" Odkin asked. 129

"That's the spinning disk flyer," responded Cary Manpure. "The flyer has a magnet in it, runs madly around a track below the spinning disks of space craft, and helps to keep the spinning disk level with the centerline of the craft despite any wild maneuverings the craft might make."

Odkin drew three circles and a square on the design of the stone meeting house and said, "The inner circle is the base ring of the spinning disk and is both in proportion to your design and in the right place. That square, squares the circle of the base ring. The two outer circles which cut through the small H shaped structure are the tracks of the flyer. The square cuts through the inner track of the flyer. If you square the circle of the base ring, the flyer won't fly around its track—the space craft won't fly for long. Sarkneson should have squared all the circles of the base rings of spinning disks in Altean space craft so we couldn't leave Silbury!

"Manjack, design a square room of this size and add it to your stone meeting house depicting components of the gravitron drive. 127 We'll call it the Sarkneson—no, the Garth Representation—just to upset the holo-image. 137

"By the way," Odkin concluded, "what is the purpose of the long extension of the stone meeting house to which the Garth Representation is to be attached? None of it has anything to do with the gravitron drive does it?"

"No, it doesn't," responded Cary Jackman.

"It's garbage," added Cary Manpure.

"Nothing's garbage, Pureman," said Odkin. "I'll diddle with your design and use it to properly scale my gravitron distributor ring glyph. I used the other end of your stone meeting house to scale my spinning disk base ring crop glyph. Now I'll use the 'garbage' end—after I've diddled with it—to scale my gravitron distributor ring glyph." 127.2

"What does diddle mean?" Cary Manpure asked.

"To fuss with," said Odkin.

The holo-image suddenly appeared and said, "Your Garth Representation is a good addition to your Disharmony series."

The holo-image disappeared.

Some time later the holo-image suddenly appeared and said, "You know that the Essene discoverer of the secondary energy disturbance pattern of souls also discovered that three beams of extremely high speed torun collected by Waldark hat amplifiers can be magnetically braided together.

"Some time later another Essene discovered that braided beams can be introduced during the process of making crystal, considerably strengthening it by braiding its molecules. As a result, Essene space vessels are constructed without the use of metal—and are therefore undetectable by transmagnetic detection and tracking devices. Braided beams are also used to contain the powerful magnetic fields in engineering spaces of Essene space vessels, replacing the previous steel boxes that surrounded engineering spaces."

The holo-image disappeared.

Some time later the holo-image suddenly appeared and began speaking, "Some time later another Essene discovered a secondary emission of gravitrons from spinning disks. This very thin circular secondary emission comes from the center of the disk and at an angle of 49.61004268 degrees above and below the plane of the disk—an angle equivalent to the cube of two pi divided by five, or the future grid vector of Hurmyrr, divided by five-sixths of the small pyramids which will one day stand on the Bastion. Alteans unwittingly included the angle 49.61004268 in the apparent two-dimensional appearance of the Tor, as one of the resulting angles of the westernmost and easternmost triangles comprising part of that two-dimensional appearance.

"The solution to the engineering problem of how to capture this secondary emission of gravitrons in space vessels eluded this Essene, and his successor continued to work on the problem for many years before she found the answer.

"As you know spinning disks are magnetically levitated above their base ring and lower conscitron thruster armature, and below their upper conscitron thruster armature, by the magnets of their base ring and the magnets embedded in an egg shape in their upper armature. There is still even now metal inside the engineering spaces of Essene craft, but this metal cannot be detected because of the braided beam shielding around those spaces. It proved to be impossible to place collection rings for the secondary emission of gravitrons in close proximity to the strong counterbalancing magnetic fields created by these two sets of magnets, because the gravitrons thus collected would not flow outward to the gravitron emission shaft.

"The solution was twofold. The magnets embedded in an eye shape in the upper armature were moved into a horseshoe shaped configuration, with the open end of the horseshoe pointing aft along the axis of the armature. 138 This reconfiguration maintains the stability of the counterbalancing magnetic fields, reangles the secondary emission of gravitrons on top of the spinning disk from 49.61004268 degrees to 19.47122061 degrees and focuses the gravitrons at a point on the upper armature, where they are collected for outflow to the gravitron emission shaft. To reangle and refocus the gravitrons available below the spinning disk due to the secondary emission, a smaller horseshoe shaped configuration of smaller magnets was embedded into the lower armature. These magnets do not upset the stability of the counterbalancing magnetic fields, they reangle the secondary emission of gravitrons from 49.61004268 degrees to 19.47122061 degrees and they focus the gravitrons at a point on the lower armature where they can be collected for outflow to the gravitron emission shaft. On both armatures, the focusing gravitrons form an angle at the collection points of 49.61004268 degrees.

"The discovery of the secondary emission of gravitrons and the engineering which captures these gravitrons gives Essene star ships the capability of traveling intergalactically and allows for the miniaturization of flying craft. Previously only spinning disks 1080 feet in diameter or multiples of 1080 feet could generate the correct amount of gravitrons to propel the space craft in which they are installed at near intergalactic light speed. The capturing of the additional gravitrons provided by the secondary emission allows spinning disks 54 feet in diameter or multiples of 54 feet to generate the correct amount of gravitrons to propel a space craft at near intergalactic light speed. It was an Essene space craft with a 54 foot in diameter spinning disk that discovered the dying planet in another galaxy that later became the moon of Danebury.

"The miniaturization of flying craft (as a result of the capturing of the additional gravitrons provided by the secondary emission and the ability to use only non-metallic material in flying craft) has allowed Essenes to hear and see virtually everything of importance that goes on within the galaxy. Previously, the smallest spinning disk which could generate enough gravitrons to propel any type of flying craft at any speed was six feet in diameter, a size first calculated by Waldark's associates to be the minimum disk diameter required to generate enough gravitrons for both hovering and movement of any craft. Since miniaturization, Essene probes with spinning disks as small as 1.62 inches in diameter—1/400th the diameter of 54 foot in diameter spinning disks—gather information for Essenes throughout the galaxy.

"Joe Lon Odkin, Essenes originally told you to make your scale model of a spinning disk in proportion to the Tetrahedron Crater spinning disks. You have since modified the size of the Amesbury Circle design according to Essene requirements. You have also modified the Amesbury Circle design to encode a cross section of the engineering spaces of space craft and to point to the two (as yet unconstructed) pyramids Bridge and Keel. You are now to make further modifications to the Amesbury Circle design to reflect the engineering which captures the gravitrons of the secondary emission."

The holo-image disappeared.

In order to represent both the circular secondary emission of gravitrons coming from the center of spinning disks at an angle of 49.61004268 degrees above and below the plane of spinning disks; and the gravitron focusing angle of 49.61004268 degrees at the collection points on both armatures, Odkin added an armature to his scale model. An armature reminiscent of the avenue in his previously designed avenue circle for eastern Prehurland. Odkin did not give the center of this armature a future azimuth of 49.61004268 degrees gyro from the center of Amesbury Circle, but instead sited two large stones—one along the armature and the other just inside the armature—whose left tangents did have a future azimuth of 49.61004268 degrees gyro from the center of Amesbury Circle.

Odkin gave the left-right center of the armature a future azimuth of 48.94 degrees gyro from the center of Amesbury Circle, and marked that center with two stone holes. This future azimuth was to be 69.28 degrees less than the future 118.22 degrees gyro bearing of Bridge and Keel from Amesbury Circle. A bearing which Odkin had previously marked with two of the four large stones forming a rectangle just inside the outer ditch and earth circle of Amesbury Circle. Odkin also adjusted the position of the two stones which were not to point at Bridge and Keel so that both the two northwestern stones and the two southeastern stones lined up on a bearing of 48.94 degrees gyro, also 69.28 degrees less than the bearing of Bridge and Keel.

Odkin used 69.28 degrees because he knew that in a two-dimensional overhead view of the Tor, 69.28 degrees was the angle formed at the apex of the Tor by the southernmost of its five triangular facings. Odkin also knew that 69.28 is important in relationships.

"The cross section of the engineering spaces of a space craft isn't quite exact any more," Odkin said to himself as he worked, "and all the angles are not precise, but everything is close. As Essenes say, nothing is perfect in three-dimensions."

Odkin went on to reshape his depiction of the ring of magnets embedded in the upper armature into a horseshoe and pointed the open end of that horseshoe toward the armature. 138 He also added a smaller horseshoe of smaller stones inside the larger horseshoe of larger stones to depict the additional magnets Essenes embedded in the lower armature. To complete his depiction of the Essene engineering modifications Odkin designed a ring of small stones just inside the large stone base ring, a representation of the single point on both armatures where the gravitrons of the secondary emission are focused by the two horseshoe shaped arrays of magnets.

Odkin also modified one of the transtime crop glyphs he had previously designed in part to depict components of the gravitron drive, so that it too reflected the Essene engineering modifications. 128

East of the Amesbury Circle site, Odkin sited a future mound. A line drawn from the southern tangent of Amesbury Circle across the southern tangent of the mound would form an angle of 27.3239545 degrees east of the mound with a line drawn from the northern tangent of the large stone in the armature across the northern tangent of the mound. 139 This angle was meant by Odkin to represent the squaring of the circle and to encode the fact that the base ring of spinning disks have diameters that are 27.3239545 percent as big as the diameters of the spinning disks they help to magnetically levitate.

Odkin also designed two irregular circles made up of 30 holes each to represent the flyer's mad-dash around its track. The total of 60 holes of these two circles was meant to reinforce the message of 60 (60 degrees being the angles at the corners of the four equilateral triangles making up a tetrahedron) a message that was also part of the larger circle of 60 holes, incorporated into Odkin's original design and which represented the gravitron capture rings of spinning disks. 129

Next Odkin designed a series of five transtime crop glyphs representing the process by which Essenes had prepared Danebury for life. The first was a solid circle surrounded by a ring surrounded by four smaller circles forming a square. Odkin intended this transtime crop glyph as a depiction of a spinning disk, surrounded by a gravitron distributor ring, and of the fourth-dimension, the source of all energy, represented by the four smaller circles. 140 The second glyph was a depiction of the moving of the future moon of Danebury from one galaxy to another. It was a solid circle with a broad line extending from it, this then split into three smaller lines which fanned out at the end. The broad line and the three smaller lines represented the braided beam. 141 The third glyph was a complex display of lines (split into three at one end) solid circles, a ring and various arcs. This was Odkin's concept of maneuvering the future moon of Danebury into orbit. 142 The fourth glyph was a solid circle and a ring connected by a line. Tangent to the ring, opposite the connecting line, was a very thin crescent. Odkin meant this depiction to represent the process of drawing the extra heat from Danebury to the sacrificed planet—which from Danebury is often seen as a crescent. 143 The fifth glyph depicted the new moon of Danebury: a wider crescent, inside a ring This ring represented the orbit of the new moon of Danebury around Danebury. 144

Odkin showed Cary Manpure and Cary Jackman his designs and told them of everything that he had done.

"The series of five transtime crop glyphs relating to Danebury, its moon and the sacrificed planet I call Life," Odkin concluded somberly.

Some time later the holo-image suddenly appeared and began speaking, "You already know that the Essene discoverer of the secondary energy disturbance pattern of souls discovered that visual and auditory data can be infused into braided beams and that data can then be infused into souls.

"Energy transdimensioners receive four-dimensional torun (transmitted by Waldark hats worn by energy transredimensioning meditators) and transdimension that torun into torinum. Within icosahedral shaped energy transdimensioners are three phi section rectangles which help transdimension torun through complexified three-space into three-dimensional torinum. Scribed into both facings of all three phi section rectangles are Transdimensional Spirals. Each of these six spirals is made up of 153 rhombus shaped inscribings and each rhombus shaped inscribing is composed of 16 rhomboid synthetic rubies. Torinum is transmitted to 27 locations within the icosahedral shell of energy transdimensioners and is transdimensioned, partially as a result of the geometric shape of the three phi section rectangles, and the six Transdimensional Spirals. 47

"The tangent of 153 is –.509525449; the tangent of 27 is .509525449. The cumulative tangent of 153 and 27 is 0 —which is the tangent of 360, 2160, 21,600, 25,920 and 27,000.

"The tangent of 2448—the total number of rhomboid synthetic rubies on each of the six facings of the three phi section rectangles, is –3.077683537; the tangent of 612—one-quarter of the total number of rhomboid synthetic rubies on each facing is 3.077683537. The cumulative tangent of 2448 and 612 is 0 —which is the tangent of 360, 2160, 21,600, 25,920 and 27,000.

"The tangent of 1224—one-half the total number of rhomboid synthetic rubies on each facing—is –.726542528; the tangent of 1836—three-quarters of the total number of rhomboid synthetic rubies on each facing—is .726542528. The cumulative tangent of 1224 and 1836 is 0 —which is the tangent of 360, 2160, 21,600, 25,920 and 27,000.

"You already know that the geometric shapes which make up the female and male drakon help form the drakons because the tangents of the sequential numbers of their source geometric shapes interact as follows: .726542528 multiplied by 3.077683537 equals the square root of five and –.726542528 multiplied by –3.077683537 equals the square root of five. The same tangents of 1836 and 612 and the tangents of 1224 and 2448 interact in the same way.

"Not only is the square root of five the mathematical constant which is the basis for the geometry modeling the way in which channels, eddies and areas of high and low energy are formed in the planetary torun flowing across the surface of this and other planets; the square root of five, along with the numbers 27 and 153, is also part of the basis for the geometry modeling the way in which energy is transdimensioned.

"The square root of five and the numbers 27 and 153 are also the basis for the geometry modeling the way in which the visual and auditory data infused into braided beams can be infused into souls.

"Any given hyperdimensional soul transcommunicates through complexified three-space with the three-dimensional being to whom it is attached, and in so doing creates a spherical disturbance pattern in three-dimensions. It is in complexified three-space that visual and auditory data that have been infused into braided beams can be infused into souls. A hypersphere in complexified three-space is geometrically defined by 27 points. The square root of five describes the geometry of the way in which transdimensioning energy infused with data from the soul interweaves around the 27 points of that hypersphere. The number 153 is the number of required interweavings of transdimensioning energy about each of the 27 points before transcommunication between a soul and the being to whom it is attached can be completed.

"Data is infused into souls by directing 18 identical braided beams—all carrying the same data—at a particular being or at a group of beings. These 18 braided beams interact with two-thirds of the 27 points of the hypersphere-shaped soul-created disturbance in complexified three-space as it transcommunicates into three-dimensions. They then transfer the data they carry to the transdimensioning energy which interweaves about those 18 points. It is in the intensity of the 18 identical braided beams that determines how much of the data transferred to a soul is passed to the subconscious and conscious minds. Essenes use 18 braided beams to interact with two-thirds of the 27 points which geometrically define the soul in complexified three-space. This is because interacting with fewer points does not allow for the transference of data to the soul, and interacting with more points interferes with the transcommunication between a soul and the being to whom it is attached."

The holo-image disappeared.

Some time later the holo-image suddenly appeared and began speaking, "You already know that the Essene discoverer of the secondary energy disturbance pattern of souls discovered that braided beams can be made so powerful that when they strike the surface of planets in certain geometric relationships to the flow of planetary torun, the flow within the striking beams realigns itself to the size and shape of those braided beams. So that the size and shape of the braided beams which struck the surface remain as a virtually permanent realignment of the flow of planetary torun. You also know that he discovered that if a virtually permanent realignment pattern of the flow of planetary torun is subsequently struck by another braided beam, some types of planetary surface features try to align themselves with that pattern.

"Also you already know that this Essene discovered that very powerful braided beams can cause the molecular structure of things which they strike to be altered, that braided beams which cause the flow of planetary torun to realign itself are powerful enough to do this.

"Some time later another Essene figured how transtime crop glyphs can be formed. She discovered that the reason crops and some other surface features realign themselves with the realignment pattern of the flow of planetary torun after being struck by the second braided beam is because their molecular structures are altered as a result of being struck by that beam. Being struck by the first beam also alters the molecular structure of crops, but does not cause them to realign themselves with the realignment pattern of the flow of planetary torun. Crops struck by the first beam die, she discovered, but crops growing up in a realignment pattern of the flow of planetary torun caused by an intense braided beam realign themselves with the realignment pattern of the flow of planetary torun when they are struck by a second braided beam. Transtime crop glyphs can only be transtime, she discovered, because the initial striking of the surface by braided beams must happen before crops begin to grow."

The holo-image disappeared.

Some time later the holo-image suddenly appeared and began speaking, "Some time after an Essene discovered how transtime crop glyphs are formed, another Essene worked out a way to make intricate and highly detailed patterns with braided beams; a way to carefully and precisely lay those patterns down on a planetary surface; and a way to carefully and precisely activate them at some point in the future.

"First, transtime crop glyphs are meticulously designed working with a special graphics computer. This computer is attached by energy conduit to a device which replaces the number nine gravitron thruster of flying craft. Two sea snail shaped casings containing braided beams are also attached by a hollow conduit to this device. After the craft has been very precisely maneuvered to a predetermined position in relationship to an extremely accurately predetermined protosite for a transtime crop glyph, the design data of a particular transtime crop glyph stored in the graphics computer and the braided beams contained in the two sea snail shaped casings are simultaneously transmitted to the device replacing the number nine thruster. This device first infuses part of the design data into one braided beam and part into the other. Then a rapidly clockwise spinning stroboscope disk, with two quarter-circumference wedge shaped openings at the outlet of the device, twists the two beams around each other and transmits them to the predetermined spot on the ground. 145

"The reason that two braided beams are used—each containing only part of the design—is so that different patterns in the crops can be created within the same overall transtime crop glyph. The reason that the beams are twisted around each other is to impart a swirling pattern to the affected crops—something that is done to insure that the pattern is neat and precise. It is also a representation of the spinning nature of everything.

"The maneuvering of craft to a predetermined position in relationship to an extremely precise predetermined protosite for a transtime crop glyph is of vital importance as transtime crop glyphs can only be laid down in very specific geometric relationships to the existing local flow of planetary torun. Even during the process, which can take up to several minutes, depending on the size and complexity of the transtime crop glyph, the accuracy of this positioning must be carefully monitored in comparison with its paradigm positioning, and only very low margins of positioning error are permissible. The positioning process for laying down transtime crop glyphs is monitored by a specially designed positioning monitor aboard the craft which is laying down the glyph. Pilots of such craft must watch this monitor carefully and keep the actual positioning location display directly over the paradigm positioning display on their monitor, maneuvering their craft accordingly. Essenes have found that pilots using their eyes are much better at making these adjustments than are the computers.

"If a transtime crop glyph is laid down outside positioning error limitations, then that particular transtime crop glyph in that particular location must be abandoned because the flow of planetary torun has been virtually permanently and incorrectly altered.

"Due to the construction of the various geometric structures on Danebury—but particularly due to the inducement of the drakon of the Keirykeion Line—there are a very large number of locations in southern Hurengland on which transtime crop glyphs can be laid down.

"The transtime crop glyphs you lay down will be activated at the appropriate time in the future by Essenes. The process of activating transtime crop glyphs is to be carried out by precisely positioned Essene probes which will transmit intense braided beams which overlay the original transtime crop glyph protosites. The crispness of the appearance of transtime crop glyphs when they are activated can be modified by varying the intensity of the activating beam.

"As you know, and for the reasons you know, by making them look imprecise, some transtime crop glyphs will be made to look as if they are hoaxes."

The holo-image disappeared.

Some time later the holo-image suddenly appeared and began speaking, "You already know that energy transdimensioners contain three phi section rectangles which help to transdimension torun through complexified three-space into three-dimensional torinum and that Transdimensional Spirals are scribed into both facings of all three phi section rectangles of energy transdimensioners. You also already know that each of these six spirals is made up of 153 rhombus shaped inscribings, that each rhombus shaped inscribing is composed of 16 rhomboid synthetic rubies and that there are 2448 rhomboid synthetic rubies in each spiral in each facing.

"There are therefore 14,688 rhomboid synthetic rubies in energy transdimensioners.

"You already know that any given soul transcommunicates through complexified three-space with the three-dimensional being to whom it is attached and that in so doing it creates a spherical disturbance pattern in three-dimensions. Also you already know that it is in complexified three-space that visual and auditory data that have been infused into braided beams can be infused into souls, that a hypersphere in complexified three-space is geometrically defined by 27 points, and that transdimensioning energy containing data from the soul, must interweave around each of the 27 points defining a soul in complexified three-space, 153 times before transcommunication between a soul and the being to whom it is attached is complete.

"There are therefore 4131 total interweavings required in order for complete transcommunication to take place.

"When Horun is taken into the soul, the soul transredimensions Horun into torun. This process also takes place in complexified three-space and requires that the Horun be interwoven around each one of the 27 points defining a soul in complexified three-space 153 times before the process of transredimensioning is complete. Since Horun is from the Source and is therefore 'external' to the soul, only 4130 total interweavings are required in order for complete transredimensioning to take place.

"The computed geometric modeling of the three-dimensional disturbance pattern of Horun is two interlocked tetrahedra, in which both tetrahedra are simultaneously spinning about all seven axes of spin symmetry of tetrahedra—resulting in 14 simultaneous spin axes for Horun.

"The projected geometric modeling of Horun as it is transdimensioned through complexified three-space includes 295 spin axes about which Horun spins simultaneously—before being transdimensioned back into four-dimensions as torun.

"The projected geometric modeling of Horun in four-dimensions includes 16,524 spin axes about which Horun spins simultaneously.

"The progression of spin axes of Horun, from 14 in three-dimensions, to 295 in complexified three-space, to 16,524 in four-dimensions, is calculated as follows: the 14 spin axes in three-dimensions are computed from observation; the 295 spin axes in complexified three-space are equivalent to the 4130 interweavings (which take place in the soul to transdimension Horun from four-dimensions into complexified three-space) divided by 14; and the 16,524 spin axes in four-dimensions are equivalent to the 4131 total interweavings (required in order for complete transcommunication to take place between a soul and the being to whom it is attached) times four.

"The 16,524 spin axes of Horun in four-dimensions, divided by the 14,688 total number of rhomboid synthetic rubies in energy transdimensioners, gives a ratio 9/8ths. This ratio 9/8ths is the harmonic of transdimensioning.

"The harmonic of transdimensioning 9/8ths; the Harmonic of the Universe 24/25ths; the harmonic of sex 80/81sts (the ratio between the maximum spin rate of the soul at the point of sexual release 768,167.9012, and the spin rate which spins everything out of the physical universe 777,777); the harmonic of soul transcommunication 15/16ths (the harmonic that reconciles 24/25ths and 9/10ths, the spin rate ratio of the soul during the 'eyes closed' mode, to the spin rate which spins everything out of the physical universe 777,777) can all be expressed as musical steps. Because 24/25ths is the Harmonic of the Universe, two tones—one 24/25ths of the other—are played sequentially and repeatedly on a specially tuned two-stringed lyre to assist meditators in their meditations. The harmonic of sex 80/81sts is used to enable musical compositions to be played in various keys.

"The harmonics of music, which are both mathematical and pleasing to the ear, are the only thing in three-dimensions which can bring both the creative and linear halves of the self-aware mind into harmony. The harmonics of music do this because they devolve from the higher order hyperdimensional harmonics which control the Universe."

The holo-image disappeared.

"That's too much harmony and too many harmonics for me," exclaimed Cary Manpure. "How about some mist-producing Meisterbraue!"

Some time later Joe Lon Odkin suggested that they design some additions to their Disharmony series. Cary Manpure and Cary Jackman took up his suggestion with a vengeance.

"Anson Trent, the ultimate traitor!" shouted Cary Manpure and Cary Jackman as they held up their latest transtime crop glyph design to show Odkin. 146

Odkin feigned mock disgust, "I would have expected something less blatant and something more creative from you two than that. Do another one while I wait."

"Anson Trent, the ultimate traitor, second version," announced Cary Manpure and Cary Jackman as they held up their new transtime crop glyph design to show Odkin. 147

"He's not being very nice to us, either," added Cary Manpure, pointing at the very vulnerable cup-like Cs under Anson Trent. I put the Cs at an angle so we wouldn't drown, as they would in the urinal!

In response, Odkin held up his design and Cary Manpure and Cary Jackman were really shocked.

"Ann Trent," said Odkin, "according to Terry Wellton." 148

Cary Manpure became very upset.

"Director Odkin, do you know that I had words with her at Tommy's wedding party and that she threatened that I would be sorry for that?" he asked. "Do you know she must have told her father and that is probably why he voted against the proposal?"

"Yes, to the first question," Odkin replied. "I know Anson Trent voted against the proposal for another reason, and I will explain why.

"Before the council meeting, Terry Wellton told me what had happened at the wedding party. I had also spoken with Kirk Roon, Kurt Sardman, and Anson Trent, telling them that I knew you, that you were very upset, but too ashamed to face those whom you had humiliated. Roon and Sardman knew their sons and were very understanding. Trent would not listen to anything I said. I then made a little investigation of Anson Trent and found out that he had been offered a high position with a legal firm on Daphlay which would be open to him as soon as he got there. I don't know if his daughter told him anything, but I do know that Trent voted against our proposal because he wanted that position with that legal firm on Daphlay."

Before Cary Manpure could respond, Cary Jackman turned to him and added, "I knew all about Ann Trent too. Everybody did. I think she hated you because you were the only one who didn't."

Cary Manpure felt as if a great load of guilt had been lifted off his shoulders.

He cried.

"I'm sorry I didn't tell you sooner," Odkin said. "Essenes told me not to tell you, or anyone else, anything about this until I knew for certain that the time was right. I guess I finally forced the issue."

They were silent for some time.

"Time for some mist-producing beverages," Odkin said finally. "I built a small distilling device in my living quarters some time back to provide me with something to ease my aches and pains. I've a quart or two of whiskey we might enjoy together."

As they drank their whiskey Odkin added two Cs to his transtime crop glyph depiction of Ann Trent.

Cary Manpure noticed this and said, "We sign some of our glyphs with two Cs. That's your glyph, Director Odkin, you should sign it with your curling antenna."

"You said that antenna looked like the inner workings of ladies," replied Odkin. "Ann Trent is no lady. The two Cs are up there, to do what Anson Trent is doing to the two Cs in your glyph. I've made the Cs thin so they'll know that the author is not the same as the thicker Cs authors. Then they'll know it's not you who designed this, the naughtiest glyph."

They laughed and drank more whiskey.

The next morning Cary Manpure woke up with the worst headache he had ever had.

While Cary Manpure suffered, Joe Lon Odkin reduced from 60 to 56 the number of holes of the large circle representing the outer edge of the gravitron capture rings in the Amesbury Circle design. Odkin did this to represent the 14 spin axes of four-dimensional Horun, as modeled in three-dimensions: since 4 x 14 = 56. 149

Odkin also altered his transtime crop glyph designed to represent energy transredimensioning. 110 He made both sections of the bent line extending from the larger circle 29.5 feet long. He also made the length of the chord connecting the points on the circumference of the larger circle (where the nearer edges of the long line and the bent line touch that circumference) 29.5 feet long. The distance 29.5 feet was meant by

Odkin to represent 295, the number of projected spin axes of Horun in complexified three-space, the intermediate zone in which energy trans-redimensioning takes place. 150

Odkin also designed a transtime crop glyph to represent the four harmonics about which the holo-image had told them the day before. Odkin connected two, different sized, solid circles with a line (to represent the two parts of each harmonic). Around the top of the smaller circle he drew three semi-circular arcs. Two-thirds of the arcs were narrow, the other broad. 150.1

"Since the two narrow arcs are close together and relatively far from the broad arc, the two narrow arcs are meant to be read together as one musical tone of a musical harmonic; the broad arc is meant to be read as the other musical tone of the same harmonic," Odkin said to himself as he worked.

Odkin added two short lines on either side—for a total of four—of the line connecting the two circles.

"These four short lines represent the Source of the Universe, the Source of all harmonics," Odkin also said aloud to himself.

The holo-image suddenly appeared and said, "The moon of Danebury is in a retrograde orbit and thereby caused the previously required 25,920 year retrograde precession of Danebury. When the moon was causing this retrograde precession, Danebury rotated in precisely 23 hours 56 minutes and the moon of Danebury was directly overhead the meridian of any given location on Danebury exactly 59 and five-sixths minutes later each day; giving the moon of Danebury an apparent 'orbital period' of 24 hours 55 and five-sixths minutes. The ratio between 23 hours 56 minutes and 24 hours 55 and five-sixths minutes is precisely 24/25ths, the Harmonic of the Universe. Thus the ratio between the length of the period of rotation of Danebury and the apparent 'orbital period' of its moon was the primary factor in the establishment of the retrograde precession of 25,920 years, and more importantly, this ratio (equivalent to 24/25ths, the Harmonic of the Universe) was the primary factor in setting up the harmonics by which self-aware life could evolve on Danebury."

"As you know, both the orbit and the period of revolution of the moon of Danebury are now changing because Essenes have stopped keeping the moon in its previously required orbit. The period of the retrograde precession of Danebury is also changing. However, it is no longer required that a retrograde precessional period of 25,920 years be maintained. As a result of these changes the plate movement of Danebury is also changing. That is why Essenes ordered you to undertake holo-mapping expeditions over Prehurland and Abzuland, and while unknown to you, Essenes conducted holo-mapping expeditions over the rest of Danebury. As you also know, that updated accumulated plate movement data is absolutely vital to the completion of the topogly grid matrix, because it allows you to calculate any future latitude or longitude of anything on Danebury."

The holo-image disappeared.

Cary Jackman had drunk more whiskey than he 'thought' possible. During the night he wandered outside, climbed into the air ship and took off. He woke up below a hill above a large river to the east of the Hill of Musing, threw up and fell asleep again. When he was able, he flew back to the Hill of Musing and sneaked in.

Joe Lon Odkin saw him and asked, "Where have you been Manjack?"

"Sizing things up," said Cary Jackman, substituting 'sizing' for 'throwing.' "I think I'll do that again sometime."

Thereafter Cary Jackman frequently sneaked off to size up where he had once thrown up, as he felt it was a nice place to be, away from it all.

Chapter Eleven

Time

When Cary Manpure was 157, Cary Jackman was 158 and Joe Lon Odkin was 199, Joe Lon Odkin died. One morning Director Odkin did not appear at breakfast, so Cary Manpure went to look for him in his living quarters. Cary Manpure found Director Odkin dead in his bed.

Cary Manpure and Cary Jackman removed the body of Director Odkin from his living quarters and sealed them off permanently.

Next Cary Manpure and Cary Jackman put on two of the long hooded robes which Joe Lon Odkin and Cary Jackman had made for the burial of Terry Wellton, carried the body of Joe Lon Odkin over their heads down the northern slope of the Hill of Musing and placed it gently and lovingly on the ground. Then they cleared the labyrinthine maze leading to the corbelled dome tomb in which they would bury the body of Joe Lon Odkin near the grave of Terry Wellton.

Having completed the unsealing of the tomb, Cary Manpure and Cary Jackman carried the body of Joe Lon Odkin through the labyrinthine maze and into the grave circle of the tomb. There they wrapped the body of Joe Lon Odkin in a shroud and placed it on a pebble bed in a shaft grave, the walls of which were lined with flag stones. Cary Manpure and Cary Jackman covered the shaft grave with wooden beams, placed a layer of clay over the beams and filled the hole above the shaft grave with chalk.

Cary Manpure and Cary Jackman buried the body of Joe Lon Odkin in the manner of his ancestors, and filled in the labyrinthine maze in a way similar to the manner in which their ancestors had filled in the straight passageways leading to ancient corbelled dome tombs.

In the more than one hundred years between the time when the Essene holo-image had told them how to lay down and activate transtime crop glyphs and the death of Joe Lon Odkin, Cary Manpure and Cary Jackman had laid down hundreds of transtime crop glyphs for future activation. 150.2, 150.3

The morning after the Essene holo-image had told them about the harmonic of transdimensioning 9/8ths, when Cary Manpure had a splitting headache, the holo-image suddenly appeared, told Cary Manpure that the Danebury Ranch was not properly maintained and ordered him to work on it until it was properly maintained. The holo-image then ordered Cary Jackman to follow it.

The holo-image led Cary Jackman up the hill to the cargo air ship and into its forward hanger bay, which now contained several large crates. "This is everything you will need to begin laying down transtime crop glyphs," it said. "Instruction manuals accompany each component. You are to install everything. Begin NOW!"

The holo-image disappeared.

Cary Jackman opened the crate marked number one and found in it several sea snail shaped casings, a manifold, hollow conduiting, a device which braided the beams and a receiver for the high speed torun transmitted by Waldark hats with amplifiers. As instructed, he placed the receiver on the floor of their living platform near the similar receiver they had long been using to receive the torun transmitted by their Waldark hats.

Next he installed hollow conduiting from the new receiver to a service area of HOME and connected the beam braiding device to that conduiting. Then he connected the manifold to the beam braiding device with additional hollow conduiting and attached the sea snail shaped casings to the manifold. They were now ready to receive, braid and store high speed torun.

Cary Jackman went back to the cargo air ship, opened the other crates and installed in the cargo air ship those things needed to lay down transtime crop glyphs. When he was done, he removed the portable component of the special graphics computer and took it back to HOME. They were now ready to begin transferring their previously made transtime crop glyph designs to the graphics computer.

When Cary Manpure returned from insuring that the Danebury Ranch was properly maintained again, he and Cary Jackman began the long job of transferring the designs.

While Cary Manpure and Cary Jackman were working the holo-image suddenly appeared and said, "The navigational computer aboard the cargo air ship has been infused with: the protosite locations of the transtime crop glyphs you have infused into the graphics computer; the magnetic bearing axes on which those transtime crop glyphs are to be laid down; the precise positioning of the cargo air ship when you lay down each crop glyph; and the order in which the transtime crop glyphs are to be laid down.

"Cary Manpure and Cary Jackman, pack a picnic dinner—including Meisterbraue. You are to lay down the first transtime crop glyph NOW!"

The holo-image disappeared.

The day was raw and blustery.

Cary Manpure reinfused the navigational computer of the cargo air ship with the deceptive, but necessary, information that the number nine thruster was inoperative. Then they flew the huge flying craft south-eastward toward the spot where Cary Manpure and Cary Jackman would lay down their first transtime crop glyph: along a ridge running north-south and northeast of the future Silbury Hill. The location of its proto-site was the point of the eastern triangle in Joe Lon Odkin's two-dimensional depiction of the first pair of energy cones (which emanate from souls of self-aware beings when they meditate and transredimension energy). It was oval shaped, a two-dimensional depiction of the oblate spheroid reconfiguration of the cones of energy caused by Waldark hats (so that they can collect and transmit torun).

As Cary Manpure carefully maneuvered the cargo air ship into position, Cary Jackman prepared to select the oval shaped transtime crop glyph from the 12 capacity crop glyph display on the graphics computer monitor. Before Cary Jackman could make his selection, the holo-image suddenly appeared and said, "Before laying down the oval shaped transtime crop glyph Cary Jackman must first modify it by putting rings around each end. This is to make it resemble the dolphin shaped transtime crop glyphs—and therefore confuse future categorizers of crop formations. While Cary Jackman is making these modifications, Cary Manpure must hold the cargo air ship in the precise positioning for laying down the modified oval shaped transtime crop glyph."

The holo-image disappeared.

Cary Jackman took some time redesigning the oval shaped transtime crop glyph and he then transferred that new design to the graphics computer. In the meantime, Cary Manpure held the flying craft in position while battling with the gusts of wind which buffeted the cargo air ship.

At last, Cary Jackman selected the modified oval shaped glyph from the display monitor, and when Cary Manpure told him they were in position—as indicated by his positioning location monitor (which showed him that the actual position of the cargo air ship was directly over the paradigm positioning display) Cary Jackman activated the device which began the process of laying down the transtime crop glyph. The design data of the modified oval shaped glyph in the graphics computer and braided beams contained in two sea snail shaped casings (Cary Jackman had installed these by perilously climbing a gantry in the forward hanger bay) were simultaneously transmitted to the device that had replaced the number nine thruster.

This device first infused part of the design data into one braided beam and part into the other. Then a rapidly clockwise spinning stroboscope disk, with two quarter-circumference wedge shaped openings at the outlet of the device, twisted the two beams around each other and transmitted them to the predetermined spot on the ground.

When the process was nearly complete, a huge gust of wind smashed into the side of the cargo air ship and pushed it nearly instantaneously an inch sideways. Cary Manpure reacted quickly and repositioned the cargo air ship according to his monitor, but the transtime crop glyph had been permanently marred. 151

The holo-image suddenly appeared and said, "This transtime crop glyph will be unsatisfactory, but its positioning is vital so it must be activated regardless of its flaws. As a result, you are to lay down this same transtime crop glyph again. The location of the second positioning for the modified oval shaped transtime crop glyph has been infused into your navigational computer. You are to lay it down immediately. Begin NOW!"

The holo-image disappeared.

Cary Manpure flew the cargo air ship west, to the area where the gold dolphin transtime crop glyph was to be laid down, and tried to position the large flying craft precisely so that Cary Jackman could lay down the modified oval shaped transtime crop glyph at its required by Essenes second location. Stronger gusts of wind prohibited him from being able to hold the cargo air ship in position. Both Cary Manpure and Cary Jackman became extremely frustrated.

Finally, the holo-image suddenly appeared and said, "Discontinue your attempts. Fly eastward and create a clearing just south of the analog position of 'Glamyrr and Sustanator' in the small scale model of the Horz complex. Land the cargo air ship. Debark and walk eastward until you find a good spot for your picnic and Meisterbraue."

The holo-image disappeared.

Cary Jackman blasted away the trees with the energy cannon mounted on the cargo air ship and Cary Manpure landed the craft in the newly made clearing. They picked up their food and beer, clambered down from the cargo air ship and walked eastward. Rain had now joined the strong gusty wind. A short distance to the east of the clearing they found a rotting log and sat on it. They huddled together in the rain and cold, eating their picnic and drinking their Meisterbraue. When they were done the holo-image suddenly appeared, ordering them back to the cargo air ship to lay down the modified oval shaped transtime crop glyph at its second location.

This time, despite continual heavy buffeting from gusts of wind, Cary Manpure was able to maneuver the cargo air ship into its precise positioning and hold it there as Cary Jackman activated the process of laying down the modified oval shaped transtime crop glyph and the laying down process was completed. 151.1

The holo-image suddenly appeared and said, "The laying down of the modified oval shaped transtime crop glyph is satisfactory, but the laying down of complex transtime crop glyphs is too difficult for you without much more practice. Now return to the Hill of Musing."

"The problem is not with us!" Cary Manpure shouted at the holo-image. "The problem is with the cargo air ship. It is not equipped for such precise maneuvering. Star ships are capable of extremely precise maneuvering because they are so equipped. Give us the equipment and we'll stay right where we are supposed to."

"No!" said the holo-image.

Cary Manpure kicked at the holo-image and stubbed his toe. "You promised better conditions if I did not escape," Cary Manpure shouted. "I haven't. Today has been intolerable."

"Today was necessary," the holo-image replied, "because you have many things to learn. You needed to learn how important precision is with regard to laying down transtime crop glyphs. If you hadn't learned that first, you might have ruined a very important laying down later."

"I can understand that," said Cary Manpure, "but why the eating in the rain, and why not better equipment?"

"The eating in the rain was to show you the difference between necessary discomfort and unnecessary discomfort. The discomfort because of the equipment is also necessary; you were told earlier, you can control the cargo air ship with your eyes better than any computer. Essenes have laid down and will continue to lay down transtime crop glyphs using their eyes as the best guides."

The holo-image disappeared.

Cary Manpure debarked from the cargo air ship and hobbled toward his IMPOSED home. He felt he was floating between a dimension of hopelessness and a dimension of hope. His hopelessness, born out of his being marooned on Danebury, allowed him to exist: to eat, to sleep, to drink. His hope: that as a result of their work there was the promise of better days ahead for those who would follow—this propelled him in his work. He cried as he thought of his great disappointment at the way things had turned out for him. He had wanted to live and love, but now his life was only to be an existence, except for his work. Is that enough to keep me going? he thought to himself as he entered HOME.

Cary Manpure had eaten a very disappointing meal on a previous occasion. Both times he had enjoyed being with his 'dining' companion, but both times the atmosphere had been all wrong. This time he had eaten and drunk with Cary Jackman in the rain and cold; the other time he had 'dined' with Rena Jackman at Halkyon, in an atmosphere which was cold for both of them.

Cary Manpure was sad and lonely because Lura Harwell had left some time before and gone with her family to Daphlay; Rena Jackman was sad and lonely because Mr. Tom Huish had also left and gone to Daphlay. They enjoyed one another's company, but the atmosphere of Halkyon, the spot where wedding parties were frequently held on the eve of the newly weds' halkyon days, proved to be a disaster for them, and they could not shake the feeling of foreboding that overwhelmed them as they sat and talked. 67.1

"Do you know why I invited you to dinner?" Rena had asked Cary Manpure.

"I suppose because we're both lonely," he answered.

"Partially that," responded Rena, "but mostly because I'm curious as to how you know about me and Mr. Huish. You do remember that you threatened me with certain revelations at your brother's wedding party, don't you?"

"Yes, I remember that," he answered. "I just don't remember how I got home."

"I'll trade information with you," Rena offered.

"Remember the time you and your brother Cary and I were going to play cards at your place, and we couldn't find a score sheet?" said Cary Manpure.

"And I told you to look in my desk drawer," stated Rena.

"Yes," said Cary Manpure.

"You saw something in my desk?" asked Rena.

"By accident," he replied.

"What was it?" asked Rena.

"You had written his name a few hundred times on a sheet of paper on a pad. The score sheet was under the pad," said Cary Manpure. "How did I get home?"

"I had you flown home. I tucked you in," answered Rena.

"How did you get in?" asked Cary Manpure.

"I took the keys out of your pants pocket," said Rena. "Let's dance."

A few days after Rena Jackman and Cary Manpure 'dined' at Halkyon, and six months before the scheduled final departure from Silbury, Halkyon was destroyed by fire only a few days before the time when all fire insurance on Silbury had expired.

Six months and a few days later Lieutenant Dan Gandy, Altean Naval Service, was extremely upset at the abandonment of Silbury and became a fanatic about things after he learned of the death of all his siblings. He dug around and found out some things. Dan Gandy was the sort who could do things that needed to be done. He needed help and he knew exactly where to go. He went to the former slaves on Colchis, and later they all took a trip together.

After Cary Manpure and Cary Jackman had completed telling Joe Lon Odkin about their day, the holo-image suddenly appeared and said, "You are to design many simple transtime crop glyphs that should become progressively more complex. They should include circles; rings; rings around circles; different combinations of different sized rings and circles together; and circles attached to other circles by lines.

"The transtime crop glyphs you have been entering into your special graphics computer all need to be adjusted now in accordance with new things infused into that computer by Essenes. Essenes have infused the requirement that transtime crop glyphs infer the way of the Universe, through such things as six-sided and five-sided geometry, counting by 10s and 12s and various harmonics. All previously entered transtime crop glyphs and all additional glyphs must therefore conform with at least some of the things recently infused by Essenes. You are to pick out which things you want each transtime crop glyph to demonstrate the way of the Universe, so that transtime crop glyphs reflect life."

The holo-image disappeared.

Before any one did anything else, Cary Manpure grabbed a drawing pad and 'designed' a future earthen mound.

"This mound goes right where we landed the cargo air ship today so we could 'enjoy' a beer. This mound is a pile!" 152

Through that winter period, Cary Manpure and Cary Jackman laid down the many simple transtime crop glyphs which they and Joe Lon Odkin 'designed' and which Cary Jackman transferred into the special graphics computer. When Springtime came, the holo-image suddenly appeared and said, "Many of the simple transtime crop glyphs you have laid down this past winter will be those transtime crop glyphs which will be activated first. They will prepare the future beings of Danebury for the transtime crop glyphs you will lay down in the future."

The holo-image disappeared.

The next day the holo-image suddenly appeared and said, "You are to read everything about the genetic project. When you have finished reading, Joe Lon Odkin is to design a series of transtime crop glyphs representing the genetic project. Cary Manpure and Cary Jackman are to work together to design a single transtime crop glyph which also represents the genetic project.

"While Joe Lon Odkin reads first, Cary Manpure and Cary Jackman are to insure that the Danebury Ranch is functioning properly. Begin NOW!"

The holo-image disappeared.

While Cary Manpure and Cary Jackman insured that the Danebury Ranch was functioning properly Joe Lon Odkin read, and went on reading The amount of information they had concerning the genetic project was vast. It had been compiled over nearly 150,000 years! Joe Lon Odkin's head began to spin and he threw down the book he was reading.

"This is ridiculous!" he shouted.

Then he went through the stacks of books he had piled up in front of him on the circular living platform and looked for those which had been most recently published. Among those he found was a summary of the genetic project from inception to completion, a book published the last year they were on Silbury. He read the book through to the end and grasped the information it contained fairly well.

Then the holo-image suddenly appeared and said, "Joe Lon Odkin, you have read everything you need to read, but you need additional information. Since that book was published there are new requirements which have been given to those on Colchis who were working on the genetic project.

"The self-aware beings of Danebury who are to be the final result from the administering of the second part of the genetic agent—who are least like the beings resulting from the administration of the first part in both culture and physical characteristics—will be antagonistic toward every one else. Additionally, they will have great difficulty in conceiving of any dimension beyond three-dimensions; and they will have great difficulty in conceiving of great lengths of time—especially of great lengths of time when it seems as if nothing of importance is happening—and they will have great difficulty in conceiving of life spans longer than their own. These beings will also have great difficulty in conceiving that life exists anywhere except on Danebury—except they will have an inexplicable nagging imperative toward the fourth planet from their sun."

The holo-image disappeared.

Odkin was dumfounded.

"And we're supposed to do all this work for them?" he shouted.

The holo-image suddenly appeared and said, "They will have initiative."

The holo-image disappeared.

"I'm glad," said Odkin sarcastically, "that makes it all better."

The holo-image suddenly appeared and said, "Joe Lon Odkin, there are to be four different genetic groups within the single species of beings who result from the administering of the second part of the genetic agent.

"These four groups are to include those who are to be genetically most like the beings resulting from the first part of the genetic agent, those who are to be genetically least like those first beings and two mid-range groups, consisting of those who are to be more genetically like the first beings, and those who are to be genetically equally alike and not alike the first beings.

"The resulting beings who are to be genetically <u>most</u> <u>like</u> the first beings are to be culturally and physically like the beings indigenous to this galaxy.

"The resulting beings who are to be genetically <u>more</u> <u>like</u> the first beings are to be physically like the intergalactic pioneers and culturally like the ancestors of the beings indigenous to this galaxy.

"The resulting beings who are to be genetically <u>equally</u> <u>alike</u> and <u>not alike</u> the first beings are to be culturally like the Alteans and physically nearly like Alteans.

"The resulting beings who are to be genetically <u>least</u> <u>like</u> the first beings are the beings who are to be physically like Alteans and culturally like no one else.

"The resulting beings who are to be genetically most like the first beings are the beings who are to be the most spiritual.

"The resulting beings who are to be genetically more like the first beings are the beings who are to be the most intuitively attuned to the harmonics of the Universe.

"The resulting beings genetically equally alike and not alike the first beings are to have the best balance between linear and creative thinking.

"The resulting beings who are to be culturally like no one else are the beings who are to have the most initiative.

"These four groups will intermingle, and Essenes project that they will culturally, and to some extent genetically, transmit and absorb the strong positive genetic traits which they possess. This process will take a long time and the projected results will be difficult in their achievement, partially due to the antagonistic—but necessary—genetic traits given to those who are to be culturally like no one else!

"The reason for going through all this, is that only in this way can the future beings of this planet be prepared to become the leaders of the redeeming process of the galaxy—because by going through this process they will gain individual and therefore cultural courage.

"Despite the great individual courage exhibited by you, Joe Lon Odkin, and Cary Manpure, Cary Jackman and Terry Wellton, the ingredient sorely lacking in the galaxy today, and the ingredient absolutely vital to the redeeming of the galaxy—is cultural courage—the ability of a society to do those things necessary to overcome challenges presented to it."

The holo-image disappeared.

Joe Lon Odkin designed a series of three transtime crop glyphs representing the genetic project and the results it would produce. Two-thirds of the series represented two-thirds of the possible combinations of intermingling between the four groups which were culturally, genetically and physically different. A fourth transtime crop glyph represented the process which Essenes projected would result in a being capable of leading the redeeming of the galaxy.

Odkin designed a different symbol to represent each of the four groups described to him by the holo-image. He did not like the beings who were to have initiative but who were to be antagonistic toward everyone else. He made them a solid circle. He did not like Altean society much better so he made the symbol of those who were to be culturally like Alteans a solid circle with a ring around it. Those who were to be intuitively in harmony with the Universe were represented by a solid circle with a tuning fork projecting from the circle. The beings who were to be spiritual with both the physical and cultural characteristics of the beings who had been indigenous to this galaxy were the beings Odkin liked best. They were represented by Odkin as a solid circle surrounded by a ring—and projecting from the ring was a trident, a trident representing heart, mind and soul.

Odkin's transtime crop glyphs representing two-thirds of the possible combinations of intermingling between the four groups were both very similar. At one end of their linear structure were two small circles, one larger than the other. These two circles represented the first and second parts of the genetic agent. Next came the representations of two of the four groups, connected by a line representing intermingling. A short line on either side of the connecting line indicated that there were two separate entities involved in the process. This type of representation was then repeated with two different groups also connected by a line. However, this time there were no short lines along the connecting line as Odkin did not want the number four to be in any way associated with these two crop glyphs. 153,153.1

The transtime crop glyph meant to represent the process, which Essenes projected would result in a being capable of leading the redeeming process of the galaxy, was also linear. This time a solid circle (representing the spinning disk on which reproductive material is spun off-center into complexified three-space for reconfiguration) with two arrows, their rounded heads projecting toward the rest of the glyph, represented the first and second parts of the genetic agent. These arrow heads were rounded as Odkin also wanted them to be part of a ring. The missing part of that ring represented complexified three-space, which has no physical manifestation in three-dimensions. 154

Odkin then added a line (emanating from the circumference of that 'missing' circle) connected to a solid circle, representing the being who resulted from the administering of the first part of the genetic agent. There followed another line, Y shaped (indicating continuity) at the end nearest this solid circle and terminating in a larger solid circle, representing the being who was to result from the administering of the second part of the genetic agent. After a break, the circle representing the second being was repeated with the same representational meaning. This circle was then connected by a long line to a large solid circle from which projected a tuning fork representing harmony. On either side of that long connecting line were four short lines, meant to represent the four groups of beings making up the second being.

"I hope they turn out as harmonious as I've made this transtime crop glyph," Odkin said to himself as he finished.

The holo-image suddenly appeared and said, "Joe Lon Odkin, this is good, but too obvious. Make some changes."

To one of the transtime crop glyphs which represented intermingling, Odkin added onto one of the circles a line with a knob at the end, representing the beings who were to have initiative but who were to be antagonistic toward everyone else.

"They remind me of Anson Trent," he said to himself.

Halkyon was built by a man named Omar Hermand during the construction of the western part of the Horz complex, and Halkyon remained in Hermand's family until it burned down, about six months before the abandonment of Silbury, those few days before the end of fire insurance liability on Silbury. There was suspicion that the fire had been deliberate, but a thorough investigation by authorities and insurance inspectors determined that the fire was the result of "natural causes." These natural causes had to do with a build up of fat in the filter of the extract vent over one of the fish fryers. These fryers were used for the preparation of the famous Halkyon batter fried fish. For insurance purposes, such filters had to be inspected and replaced regularly, but due to people wanting to get married before leaving Silbury, there had been a particularly heavy period of business at Halkyon. Inspection dates were predicated on what was determined on a very safe and conservative estimate of when fat would begin to build up in such filters of extract vents. Those inspection dates were not modified as a result of the extra demand for fried fish, and the fire resulted, according to the inspectors.

The owner of Halkyon at the time was Alick Hermand, who had been sued the year before for unfair working conditions by some of his employees. They claimed that Alick Hermand was intent on making as high a profit as possible before he left Silbury and that he had cut staff levels to well below minimum requirements. The employees presented an extremely good case, but Anson Trent took on the defense of Alick Hermand and won the case for him. Alick Hermand did not have enough money to pay for Anson Trent's services, and it was agreed that Anson Trent would take on the case as a contingency. If he won the case for Alick Hermand he, Anson Trent, would get a 50 percent ownership in Halkyon.

Following the very thorough investigation, Simpson Insurance paid out the full insured amount to Alick Hermand—and Anson Trent. The amount was five million quid.

On the same transtime crop glyph Odkin canted and moved the trident so that it was not attached by its center to its staff.

On both transtime crop glyphs which represented intermingling Odkin also canted and moved the prongs of the tuning fork off center.

"Too harmonious as it was," Odkin again said to himself.

Odkin also added spurious lines projecting outward from a circle and rings of the two transtime crop glyphs.

"Two lines from a ring and one from a circle on one glyph represents two-thirds once," Odkin said to himself again. "Spurious lines coming out of two rings and one circle represents two-thirds twice. Three lines in one transtime crop glyph and one in the other represents 750,000 rpms. Two representations of two-thirds and one representation of 750,000 rpms represents two-thirds three times!" 153,153.1

Next Odkin attacked the transtime crop glyph representing the process which Essenes projected would result in a being capable of leading the redeeming process of the galaxy. He moved everything off center, mangled the tuning fork and took a bite out of the second being, (representing imperfection).

"My mangling of the tuning fork includes changing the handle into a representation of Anson Trent's most obvious characteristic," Odkin said to himself, "and the prongs of the tuning fork into a representation of Ann Trent's best known characteristic. They touch at its closed end of Ann Trent's best known characteristic, not the front, so I'll add a thin curved line linking them together." 154

There were five members of the panel in the civil case against Alick Hermand. They voted three to two for acquittal. The majority were Mark Burgson, an inspector of meat; Alika Barns, a housewife; and Arne Dorf, a hotel worker.

Odkin finished the design.

"Essenes are nitwits. It'll never work," he said to himself, shaking his head. "There are too many Anson Trents coming along."

Anson Trent borrowed a million quid just before the beginning of the trial and paid it all back, plus interest, after the insurance payment. Anson Trent borrowed the money as a personal loan, from the Quid House on Silbury, There was no unusual amount of money transferred into the accounts of Mark Burgson, Alika Barns and Arne Dorf on Silbury, but when the Quid House was closed down on Silbury they all had over 300,000 quid transferred to Daphlay. The other 100,000 quid of Anson Trent's loan went to Arne Jackson, who had arranged the loan.

The holo-image suddenly appeared and said, "Joe Lon Odkin, you need to add another intermingling transtime crop glyph, designed to confuse."

The holo-image disappeared.

Odkin designed a third intermingling glyph by adding one of the two unshown interminglings, but instead of adding the last unshown intermingling, he made a second representation of the intermingling between those who were to be most spiritual and those who were to be intuitively harmonious. He purposefully omitted a representation of intermingling between those who were to have initiative but antagonistic with those who were to be intuitively harmonious. 155

"The future Anson Trents may not get along with anybody; they surely won't get along with beings who are intuitively in harmony with the Universe!" Odkin said to himself.

Next Odkin added a single spurious line to this transtime crop glyph.

"That line indicates only one of the interminglings represented here is in addition to those already shown, and that one (an impossible one) shall remain forever unshown," Odkin said aloud to himself.

The holo-image suddenly appeared and said, "Change the size of the two solid circles which represent the two parts of the genetic agent. Make them so that if you draw tangents to them and form an angle above the smaller circle, that angle is 19.4712206 degrees to represent tetrahedra, the geometric modeling of everything." 155

The holo-image disappeared.

Odkin made the changes. Then he removed the end of the line connected to the circle inside the ring part, and removed the ring from around the circle with a trident part. "Essenes want me to confuse," said Odkin. "I'll confuse." Then Odkin removed the end of the line connected to the circle inside the ring part of one of the other glyphs in that series and stuck the removed section on the opposite side of the ring. 153.1

The holo-image suddenly appeared and said, "In the future, Essenes will activate your last transtime crop glyph first in order to really confuse."

Following the destruction of the private empire of the family Sarkneson there was a lot of discussion in the press on Silbury about the former slaves, and many interviews with them, which included discussions of the sabotage they had carried out against Sarkneson. Shortly before the civil trial of Alick Hermand Anson Trent's legal company hired a former slave named Carl Banks as an administrative assistant. Only about 200 former slaves ever went to Silbury. They were sponsored by families or individuals who needed specific work to be done, usually manual labor. Carl Banks was sponsored by Arne Jackson of the Quid House. Arne Jackson went to Colchis just before the trial and brought Carl Banks back with him. Carl Banks never worked for Arne Jackson, he went straight to work for Anson Trent. Carl Banks was one of those interviewed who talked about sabotaging the Sarkneson empire. Carl Banks left Silbury with Anson Trent and continued to work for him on Daphlay.

When the Danebury Ranch was again properly maintained, Cary Manpure and Cary Jackman returned to HOME and Joe Lon Odkin told them what he had found out and what he had done.

As Odkin was finishing, the holo-image suddenly appeared and said, "While the three of you and Terry Wellton have shown that you possess great courage, many of the things which Essenes have inflicted upon you are to make you more courageous. Doing what you have done, and what you will do, requires enormous amounts of courage. You may not think so now, but when you reflect back you will understand. The great regret that Essenes have is that Terry Wellton died before it was appropriate for Essenes to tell him those things that Essenes have just told you and will tell you in the future. Your courageous work in preparing the way for the future beings of this planet, so that they will have the opportunity to gain courage, is vital to the redeeming of the galaxy.

"Cary Manpure and Cary Jackman are to read those things about the genetic project that Joe Lon Odkin thinks would help in creating such a design depicting the genetic project. This design should be created in a similar fashion to that proposed by Joe Lon Odkin to represent the process which will result in a being capable of leading the redeeming process of the galaxy. Begin NOW!"

The holo-image disappeared.

When Cary Manpure and Cary Jackman finished reading, they designed a transtime crop glyph they thought fulfilled the Essene requirement given to them by the holo-image. 156 They showed it to Joe Lon Odkin and Cary Jackman explained, "At the top of the glyph is a small ring attached to a somewhat larger circle by a line. Also attached to that larger circle is another line with a knob on the end (a depiction reminiscent of Anson Trent's most obvious characteristic) though it is not meant as a depiction of Anson Trent. The Anson Trent-like configuration is a representation of the male component of the genetic agent. The small ring is a representation of the female component and the somewhat larger circle is the genetic agent: a mixture of both female and male reproductive material.

"The somewhat larger circle is attached by a line to an even bigger circle, representing the much more complex results after nearly 150,000 years of the first part of the genetic agent. The line is slightly bent to indicate Altean thinking concerning Essenes along the long, long road to completion.

"The even bigger circle is attached to a very large ring by a short bent line. This line is short to indicate that once ready, the genetic agent was administered shortly thereafter. The line is bent to represent Cary Manpure's and my thinking that Essene thinking was bent, off track in that they seemed to want us to abandon Silbury.

"The very large ring is divided in two to represent the two types of creative-thinking beings eventually evolving from the administration of the first part of the genetic agent. One of those beings is to die out, so it is not attached to a circle below the very large ring representing both the second part of the genetic agent and the beings who are to result therefrom.

"Extending below the circle at an angle of 120 degrees—representing two-thirds of the three 60 degree angles which make up one of the four equilateral triangles which make up tetrahedra—to the dividing line of the very large ring, is a semi-circular ring, with boxes inside the broad line forming the straight edge of the semi-circular ring. The straight broad line represents a side view of one of the spinning disks of the Tetrahedron Crater gravitron infusion complex. (Spinning disks which were used to spin off-center both female and male reproductive material into complexified three-space so that that material was reconfigured in such a way that it could form the basis of the genetic agent.) The curved line of the semi-circular ring represents a side view of the hemispherical domes which covered the spinning disks of the gravitron infusion complex.

"The 14 full-sized boxes and two half-sized boxes inside the broad straight line represent the second being and the number 42. The two half boxes imply two more groups of 14 boxes, and 3 x 14 = 42, the number of things in the second growth ring of anything. The 14 full-sized boxes and two half-sized boxes inside the broad straight line, also depict a ladder, up which the second being has climbed in order to reach its projected destiny as leader of the redeeming of the galaxy. This depiction is a metaphorical representation of the traditional encouragement to 'climb every mountain in order to seek understanding.'

"From what the holo-image has told us, it seems that the second being of Danebury will have to surmount not only mountains, but also great adversity in order to gain understanding, and to achieve great courage."

Before Joe Lon Odkin could comment, the holo-image suddenly appeared and said, "Cary Manpure and Cary Jackman, you are now to design four meaningless variants of this transtime crop glyph in order to confuse.

"While Cary Manpure and Cary Jackman are doing that, Joe Lon Odkin is to design a series of three transtime crop glyphs representing the three introductions of non-indigenous reproductive material into the beings of this planet, two-thirds of which are the administering of the first and second parts of the Altean genetic agent."

The holo-image disappeared.

Cary Manpure and Cary Jackman designed their four meaningless variants, and they all looked similar to their original meaningful transtime crop glyph. The main difference being that in each case there was no representation of female reproductive material, which had very early on proven to be absolutely vital to the development of the genetic agent.

"These four meaningless transtime crop glyphs all have two representations of the most obvious characteristic of Anson Trent at their top," Cary Jackman later told Joe Lon Odkin when he was explaining the meaningless transtime crop glyphs to him. 157

"We signed one with two capital Cs as we often do," added Cary Manpure, "but we made one much smaller and put that one inside the other. We did that to show that the transtime crop glyph was meaningless."

Dan Gandy knew that Kirk Roon was the direct cause of the crash which took the lives of his brother and two sisters, but he also knew that the real causes were Arnhold Manpure and Anson Trent. Dan Gandy decided to investigate Anson Trent because Anson Trent was still living and Dan Gandy wanted to get Anson Trent for what he had done. Dan Gandy uncovered everything.

What Dan Gandy needed to find out was precisely how Carl Banks had caused the fire that destroyed Halkyon. Dan Gandy therefore found former slaves who had known Carl Banks before he left Colchis for Silbury. This was easily accomplished and they knew what Carl Banks would have done. Dan Gandy then realized that he had to go to Silbury to find the direct physical proof, but there was no way to do so. This situation frustrated him greatly because everything uncovered so far was only circumstantial evidence. He needed actual proof that insurance fraud had been committed, and that proof could only be obtained on Silbury in the ruins of Halkyon.

Dan Gandy decided that he had to go to Silbury himself and to do so he would have to have his own ship. He had no means of obtaining one, so he turned to the former slaves with whom he had already spoken. This time he told them the entire story, not just the hypothetical scenario he had outlined before. They were appalled that one of their number would involve himself in such a cabal, and they resolved to get Carl Banks for what he had done.

The former slaves mostly worked for the Altean Naval Service and most of those jobs had to do with the maintenance of star ships. They talked things over with Dan Gandy and decided that they would construct their own ship from parts of star ships which came their way as the result of their work positions. They called themselves facilitators. Dan Gandy would supply the plans and his expertise as a naval officer. They set up their construction site in a secret cave the former slaves had known for years, having used it for meetings at which they discussed ways and means of defying and ridding themselves of the family Sarkneson. The process of constructing the ship began.

Dan Gandy soon tied himself permanently to the facilitators by becoming the first Altean Naval officer to marry one of them, a most beautiful young lady named Roxanne Adair. Roxanne and Dan Gandy had 10 children. Roxanne Gandy worked in the administration on the naval base and Dan Gandy continued his naval career until he retired at age 45 as a captain, his last posting having been as the commanding officer of a star ship. The construction of their private ship—REVENGE—continued during this time and beyond.

Following his retirement from naval service, Dan Gandy seemingly spent all his time raising their children as Roxanne Gandy continued to work. On the sly Dan Gandy supervised the construction of REVENGE and trained a Crew for her. Over 100 years after the abandonment of

Silbury REVENGE streaked away from Colchis with a Crew made up of former slave facilitators who wanted to get Carl Banks, and the family Gandy—12 strong—who wanted to get Anson Trent. They were detected by Altean Naval Service detection devices, but due to Roxanne Gandy being the Facilitator Lady, they were deemed friendly and not intercepted.

The journey to Silbury was uneventful, but they had to wait for a horrendous storm to subside before they could land. At last they did so and they put down on the mesa on which the sand covered ruins of Halkyon lay. Dan Gandy stepped onto the surface of Silbury in an environmental suit to investigate. Despite the piles of sand he soon found what he wanted and returned to the ship. The return trip was equally uneventful and they landed without incident due to their having those things they needed because of the Facilitator Lady in their midst, and they rehid their ship in the cave.

While they were gone, Anson Trent had been ruined. Dan Gandy decided not to do anything against him, but decided when the time was right he would do something against his descendants and those of Alick Hermand, Arne Jackson and Carl Banks. He sent part of his family to Daphlay to keep an eye on them and to record everything they did. The rest of his family remained on Colchis carefully guarding everything Dan Gandy had found, especially the physical proof he had brought with him back from Halkyon to Colchis—until it was time to release everything and to confront the descendants of those who had done what they had done.

None of the three cabalists, Alick Hermand, Arne Jackson and Anson Trent, had known what to do to start the perfect fire; they had only known that they had to find a former slave to do what needed to be done for them. Anson Trent ordered Arne Jackson to look in old newspapers for accounts of sabotage against Sarkneson because Anson Trent had remembered reading such accounts. When Arne Jackson came up with the name Carl Banks, Anson Trent ordered Arne Jackson to Colchis to bring Carl Banks to Silbury. Carl Banks was wily. He accepted the offer, but he would not tell the others how he would do it, principally because it was so simple that anyone could do it and that would leave Carl Banks out of an easy life. Carl Banks never told them what he had done, he had just carried it out and the others were pleased.

The only thing Carl Banks told them was that they should use one fryer almost exclusively for frying the famous Halkyon batter fried fish. Alick Hermand managed this by doing all that frying himself, "a gesture of good will to my employees." The fat and dust build up in the filter of one particular extract vent over the fish fryer would therefore be greater and would eventually cause a fire, they all knew. Only Carl Banks knew how to insure that happened on time.

On the appointed night, Carl Banks had dinner at Halkyon and then left by the main entryway. Instead of heading directly to the area where air ships were waiting to take patrons home, Carl Banks went around the other side of Halkyon and climbed onto the roof. Alick Hermand had supplied him with plans, so he knew precisely which extract vent to partially cover with a plate he'd stolen during dinner. He attached the plate to the extract vent with a mastic, but not too strong a mastic. In the explosion caused by the onset of the fire in the extract vent ducting (as a result of the fat build up) the plate had to be blasted away from the vent's aperture, so that it would never be linked to that conflagration.

The investigation of the fire had been very thorough and bits and pieces of things were piled about outside Halkyon by the investigators. Dan Gandy had only to sift through the pile of plates until he found the one (or bits of the one) with mastic on it. He found that it was broken into two parts, and mastic was smeared in an arc across the two pieces.

Dan Gandy did not find out, but his sons and daughters who went to Daphlay had discovered why Arne Jackson had obeyed Anson Trent implicitly. Arne Jackson was married with a family, and Arne Jackson had impregnated 17-year-old Ann Trent just prior to the trial. Afterward Ann Trent had a son she named Anson Jackson. The 100,000 quid which Arne Jackson got for obtaining the loan for Anson Trent went to Ann Trent "to take care of the baby." Anson Jackson grew up an abused child and became just like his 'parents' and Anson Trent.

In the meantime, Joe Lon Odkin designed a transtime crop glyph to represent the Pleiadean insemination of developing beings on Danebury resulting in fatal genetic weakness due to inbreeding. Odkin designed a long curly sperm with heads at both ends, one head being larger than the other. Then he randomly chopped the coils into a number of pieces.

"Pleiadeans are so constructed," he explained to Cary Manpure and Cary Jackman, "that their two heads are directly connected to each other."

"They are connected," Cary Manpure added, "until Excalibur is wielded against them." 158

"That still doesn't complete the task," said Odkin. "Notice that one piece is growing another new head at its chopped end. Pleiadeans regenerate themselves somehow."

"That's because they have worms—not sperms," said Cary Manpure. Odkin's transtime crop glyphs representing the administering of the first and second parts of the genetic agent were somewhat similar. "The first has a very tightly coiled tail," he 'explained' to Cary Manpure and Cary Jackman. "The second has less coil, and is more straightened out—it is sperm like and therefore represents the male component. So as to show the female component, the tightly coiled one is meant to represent part of the female reproductive system. I don't know much about this sort of thing, but I figure one way or the other I am close." 159

Neither Cary Manpure nor Cary Jackman responded, but Cary Jackman broke out in a cold sweat. When Cary Manpure was 16 he worked in the Wall during his 12 week break, and Cary Jackman worked in the Bastion. At the time, Lura Harwell was Cary Manpure's sweetheart, and Becky Armstrong was Cary Jackman's sweetheart. Lura Harwell and Cary Manpure never qualified for a golden triangle, but Becky Armstrong and Cary Jackman did.

Cary Jackman was very quick thinking, so he soon held responsibilities normally filled by those who were older and more experienced. He especially liked being a ground control approach controller, one who looked out the large wide windows of the Bastion and with the aid of computers guided the star ships to their assigned landing piers. One day he invited Becky Armstrong to come to watch him at work. She enjoyed watching him and she stayed until his shift was over. On their way out of the Bastion they ducked into an unoccupied room and locked the door behind them. Becky Armstrong and Cary Jackman then sweated things out until her much delayed schedule came to be.

Some time later the holo-image suddenly appeared and began speaking, "In about 200,000 years Alteans are to return to Danebury in order to administer the second part of the genetic agent. The site of the administering of the second part of the genetic agent will be a structure to be called the Avenabury Tor. The Avenabury Tor will be located just west of the Avenabury Circle site, where you decided to site Cary Jackman's stone meeting house, with its font over the spot which in 240,000 years will be 4/7ths of the way from the equator to the north pole.

"Before Alteans bring transitional creative-thinking female beings of Danebury from southeastern Ashintoland, Abzuland and far western Ashintoland to Hurengland to administer the second part of the genetic agent to them, Alteans will be told to construct three large compounds which replicate the three different natural living environments of those beings. These compounds are to be centered—as nearly as possible—three and three-quarter miles from the Silbury Hill site on bearings of 135 degrees gyro, 165 degrees gyro and 195 degrees gyro from the Silbury Hill site. As an analog of Hurbury, Silbury Hill will represent the harmonics necessary for bringing forth self-aware life. The distance of three miles represents three-dimensional existence. The distance of three-quarters of a mile represents the transdimensional devolvement of everything. The 60 degree angle between 135 and 195 represents tetrahedra, the geometric modeling of everything.

"The females will live in these compounds until they become pregnant. Then they will be taken to the amphitheater-like valley in which the crates containing the shapes of the Keirykeion Line were stored. The transitional creative-thinking female beings of Danebury are to give birth to their children in this amphitheater-like valley and then raise them there.

"Some of the children of the transitional creative-thinking female beings of Danebury are to be very different from their mothers; some of them are to be somewhat different from their mothers; some of them are to be hardly different from their mothers; and some of them are to be practically like their mothers.

"The children who are to be the tallest, have finely shaped heads, have hair only on their heads, who are to be linear thinkers, to fear the dark, be right-handed and who are to live in disharmony with one another and their environment, will abuse all other children. You already know the reason why.

"When the children are old enough, Alteans will be told to take the daughters and sons of the healthy child bearing age transitional creative-thinking female beings of Danebury who are most like the transitional creative-thinking beings of Danebury together with their mothers and return them to their natural living environments in southeastern Ashintoland. They will also be told to take the daughters and sons who are next most like their mothers with their mothers to their natural living environments in Abzuland. They will also be told to take the daughters and sons who are equally alike and not alike their mothers to their natural living environments in the coastal area at the very eastern end of the sea shared by the mouth of the river that flows past Hurmyrr. They will also be told to take the daughters and sons who are least like their mothers to their natural living environments in far western Ashintoland.

"The descendants of the children least like their mothers will have initiative. They will migrate and occupy Hurengland..."

"And they will be abusive to everyone and everything!" interrupted Joe Lon Odkin.

Odkin leaped out of his chair and attacked the holo-image. He lowered his head in an attempt to butt it, but he passed right through the holo-image hitting his head on the flue above the fireplace hearth. Blood spurted from Odkin's forehead and Cary Manpure ran off to get ice and a wet towel. Cary Jackman pulled Odkin onto a sofa.

While Cary Manpure was applying the ice pack Odkin looked up and said, "Essenes are nitwits!"

The holo-image disappeared.

When Joe Lon Odkin's forehead stopped bleeding, the holo-image suddenly appeared and said, "Cary Manpure and Cary Jackman, leave the house immediately and insure that the Danebury Ranch is properly maintained."

After Cary Manpure and Cary Jackman had departed the holo-image said, "Joe Lon Odkin, you are to design two similar transtime crop glyphs which are to have protosites for the locations of two-thirds of the three separate compounds in which the female beings of Danebury are to live before they become pregnant. The third location is unsuitable for a transtime crop glyph. Do something else there."

The holo-image disappeared.

Joe Lon Odkin was still extremely angry, his forehead hurt and he had the worst headache of his life. Nevertheless, he pulled out his map of the area surrounding the Hill of Musing and plotted the future locations of the three compounds. The two western protosites were on relatively flat ground; the easternmost site was amongst hills.

Odkin pulled out his pad and was about to begin, when the holo-image suddenly appeared and said, "The future Anson Trents of Danebury will be the spawn of some of those who live in these two compounds. Future Anson Trents will impregnate ladies who are intuitively in harmony with the Universe."

"That is the 'intermingling' I am NEVER going to depict," stated Odkin.

"You don't have to show the intermingling," said the holo-image, "only the result."

"The result is bad enough," said Odkin. "The intermingling would make me throw up."

The holo-image disappeared.

Odkin drew two knobbed lines coming out of the bottom of a solid circle.

"If Pleiadeans have worms," said Odkin to himself, "the spawn of this intermingling will be two headed snails—and the heads will not be at the top of their bodies. They'll be as stupid as snails, but they'll be more than able to regenerate themselves."

The holo-image suddenly appeared and said, "Show them regenerating."

The holo-image disappeared.

"In that case," said Odkin, "I'll have to make one head somewhat near the top of the body—but I'll make that the part which is regenerating. Snails have antennas, so I'll give that head one bent antenna because this is to be a particularly stupid snail. Instead of another antenna they get another head somewhat near the top, with a bent antenna. After that they die out due to genetic collapse." 160

Odkin sited a snail at the middle compound site and another snail at the western most compound site, and then decided that a future village should be one day located at the eastern most compound site, a quiet village to represent the tranquil lives of the future beings of Danebury, before they meet up with the future Anson Trents of Danebury.

Odkin thought about what to name the village, then wrote Huish.

"I'll name this village after Pureman's favorite mythos teacher Tom Huish," said Odkin aloud to himself. "Panergon Gwynmyrr can only succeed in mythos." 161

The holo-image suddenly appeared and said, "Joe Lon Odkin, now design two more transtime crop glyphs representing the results of a future Anson Trent impregnating a lady from each of the other two genetic groups of beings who will result from the second part of the genetic agent."

The holo-image disappeared.

Odkin later described his two new transtime crop glyphs to Cary Manpure and Cary Jackman, "I first designed the transtime crop glyph representing the spawn of a lady of the group of beings who are to have the best balance between linear and creative thinking—a female who has been impregnated by one of the future Anson Trents of Danebury. Since I had made the snail transtime crop glyph with a male spawn, I made the spawn of this 'union' female. 162

"The bottom of the glyph is a solid circle representing the future Anson Trents of Danebury. The upper part of the transtime crop glyph is a solid circle surrounded by a circle representing the group of beings who are to have the best balance between linear and creative thinking. The line connecting the upper and lower parts of the transtime crop glyph represents the 'union.' That line is bent slightly to the right, however, and the circle of the upper part is pointed slightly—also to the right. The four lines hanging down from the upper ring are the hair of the female spawn, who has thrown her head back, and to the right so that we can see the point of her nose, twisted her body to the right and has her mouth wide open, crying out in agony at her lot in life.

"Pureman, right after we found out about the twistings and turnings of the drakon around the top of Glastonbury Tor and their significance, you also cried out in agony because of the similar, but tragic representation to be made by the long earthen mound which is to be tangent to the analog site of the Lookout. This glyph also encodes the twistings and turnings of the drakon around the top of Glastonbury Tor. It also represents you crying out in agony and the four strands are also tears streaming down from your anguished eyes.

"I next designed the transtime crop glyph representing the spawn of a lady of the group of beings who are to be most spiritual—a female who has also been impregnated by one of the future Anson Trents of Danebury. Since I had made the snail glyph with a male spawn, and the anguish glyph with a female spawn, I made twin spawns—one female, one male—for this 'union.' 163

"On the far right of this transtime crop glyph is a large thick ring attached on its left to a small solid circle by a line and attached on its right by a representation of Anson Trent's most obvious characteristic. These three components represent the female spawn. The spawn is female due to the thick ring, it is dense due to the solid circle, and is her daddy's daughter due to her having attached Anson Trent's most obvious characteristic to herself.

"In the center, attached to the left of another very large thick ring, is another line with a large knob on the end. The line and the large knob are the male spawn.

"The thick ring in the center to which both spawn are attached depicts the thick skulls and lack of brains of both spawn.

"I had to put something to do with the trident somewhere so I stuck it on the far left of the glyph, though I do not mean it to be more closely associated with the male spawn than with the female spawn. It is misshapen and bent to emphasize the disharmony of the twins."

Before Cary Manpure or Cary Jackman could respond the holo-image suddenly appeared and said, "There are two major problems which Essenes project the future Anson Trents of Danebury will face, problems whose existence some will suspect but which will be totally discounted by the future Anson Trents of Danebury. They will be linear thinkers and will have initiative and will lead the scientific advancement of Danebury, but because they will not be spiritual and will not be intuitively in harmony with the Universe, they will discount hyperdimensionality. Therefore they will not even consider that there exists the requirement for self-aware beings with souls to live in an environment having a flow of hyperdimensional torun. Hence they will not understand that there will be problems caused by the disruption of the flow of planetary torun across the surface of Danebury due to strong magnetic fields, or that there will the problems caused when future beings of Danebury try to live in an environment lacking the correct flow of planetary torun or an induced flow of torun.

"Joe Lon Odkin, you are to design a transtime crop glyph representing the problems caused by strong magnetic fields.

"Cary Manpure and Cary Jackman, you are to design a transtime crop glyph representing the problems caused when self-aware beings try to live in deep space in space craft without an induced flow of torun and without infrared light.

"Begin NOW!"

The holo-image disappeared.

Joe Lon Odkin knew well the dangers of living near a strong magnetic field—all Alteans knew about those dangers from their required historical studies of the Shield on Altea. Odkin knew that the main reason strong magnetic fields affect self-aware beings is that they rob the soul of the flow of hyperdimensional energy needed to be able to continue to transcommunicate properly with the being to whom it is attached. Odkin also knew that the ensuing lack of transcommunicating between a soul and the three-dimensional mind of the being to which it is attached can result in insanity, and definitely results in illness and even death if the exposure is for too long.

As a result, Odkin designed a transtime crop glyph which consisted of a turtle and an asymmetrical pattern he called a 'mess.' The turtle was a representation of life that is not self-aware. Since animals are relatively unaffected by strong magnetic fields, Odkin's turtle was undistorted. The mess represented the end result of self-aware being trying to exist in the vicinity of strong magnetic fields.

As Joe Lon Odkin finished this crop glyph design the holo-image suddenly appeared and said, "Add a second mess so that two-thirds can also be represented in this transtime crop glyph. 164

"Essenes will insure that a magnetic field is near this transtime crop glyph when it is activated so that a link between the messes and the magnetic field is suspected."

The holo-image disappeared.

In the meantime, Cary Jackman and Cary Manpure had to do considerable research to find information concerning the problems caused when self-aware beings travel into space in space craft lacking an induced flow of torun and infrared light. Cary Manpure finally found what they needed in a book about Waldark's associates, and then they designed their transtime crop glyph.

They showed their design to Joe Lon Odkin and Cary Jackman explained it to him, "Our space disaster transtime crop glyph is linear and to be read from right to left—just like your twin spawn glyph. 165 On the far right are three circles of unequal size representing the three-dimensional components of self-aware beings. From right to left they are: the body, the heart and the mind.

"Through a widening line these three-dimensional components combine to form a three-dimensional being—represented by the large circle attached to the left end of the widening line. At the end of a relatively long line attached to that large circle, a small circle, represents the soul. This soul is shown at a distance from the three-dimensional being, as it is about to be subjected to the environmental deficiencies of space travel—which it cannot tolerate.

"We had difficulty with the next part separated by breaks from everything else, but we settled on what you now see. Below, within the bottom of an elongated curving letter lambda—the designation from Hellenikos for a soul—is a small circle representing a photon of infrared light. The top of the curving lambda connects to the right end of a straight line; on the left end of that straight line is another representation of a soul—in the form of another small circle. A straight line from above the axis of the crop glyph also connects to the right end of that straight line. Since there is nothing at the right end of this short straight line which begins above the axis of the crop glyph, this short straight line is meant to represent the induced flow of torun.

"We haven't actually represented a soul experiencing space travel that lacks the correct environment—which the soul cannot tolerate—because we couldn't figure out a way to do so. So instead we have shown what happens when a soul is not subjected to the environmental deficiencies of space travel.

"In the following parts of the transtime crop glyph, however, we do show the results of a soul's having been subjected to the environmental deficiencies of space travel—which it cannot tolerate.

"We repeated the large circle representing a three-dimensional being. The being's heart is trying to escape and is being held back by a cane. A short line extending out from the cane makes the cane into a backwards and unproportional lambda—a troubled soul. Due to illness (which requires the use of a cane) the being loses its will to live—the courage in its heart.

"On the far left the self-aware being dies. The body and heart (shown by the small circle which is at the end of the line) remain attached, continuing to the left but courage is gone, so the heart is shown attached at a distance from the body.

"Two souls depart. These souls are the two circles at the ends of the lines at angles above and below circles representing the dying being.

"We decided to use two souls to indicate that the soul is only transitorily the possession of any given self-aware being, and that when the soul departs from a self-aware being it eventually attaches itself to another self-aware being and on, and on, and on, and on. These subsequent attachments allow a soul to gain additional experience and knowledge so that it becomes—in many ways—a 'different' soul along the way. Many self-aware beings know this—either intuitively or through education and we think that is why we hang on to life so dearly."

As Cary Jackman completed his presentation the holo-image suddenly appeared and said, "There is another very serious problem associated with space travel: illness and bodily damage due to weightlessness. Weightlessness has never been a problem with those who know about hyperdimensionality, as induced gravitational fields have always been associated with the gravitron drive system. The future Anson Trents of Danebury will send beings into space who will become ill. Because these future Anson Trents will not be spiritual nor intuitively in harmony with the Universe they will discount hyperdimensionality and will therefore attribute these illnesses solely to weightlessness. They will completely miss two-thirds of the causes of space illness.

The holo-image disappeared.

Some time later the holo-image suddenly appeared and said, "Cary Manpure and Cary Jackman, leave HOME immediately and insure that the Danebury Ranch is properly maintained."

After Cary Manpure and Cary Jackman had departed the holo-image said, "Joe Lon Odkin, you are to design a single transtime crop glyph which represents both the process by which Essenes prepared Danebury for life and what happens to self-aware beings when they do not live in an environment with the correct flow of planetary torun or the correct induced flow of torun." 166

The holo-image disappeared.

Odkin designed a circular transtime crop glyph with nine components—one in the center and eight on a large connecting ring, paired into groups of two. The components of each group of two were opposite each other on that ring.

At the top of the glyph was a representation of the braided beam being used to push the future moon of Danebury from galaxy to galaxy (a representation very similar to one Odkin had used in his series of five glyphs representing the process by which Essenes had prepared Danebury for life).

Above the three open ends of the braided beam Odkin placed a small circle, a representation of the Source of the Universe.

At the bottom of the transtime crop glyph, paired with the braided beam component, Odkin placed a large circle with antlers coming out of it.

"Danebury and life in the form of deer emerging from it," Odkin said to himself.

Clockwise from the braided beam pushing the moon component, Odkin placed a thin crescent, representing the sacrificed planet (again a representation he had previously used in his series representing the process by which Essenes had prepared Danebury for life). Paired with this crescent, straddling the large ring, was a circle surrounded by three smaller circles, representing the energy transdimensioning unit formed by Danebury, the sacrificed planet and Danebury's moon. The larger circle represented the sun, sustainer of life. Clockwise from the thin crescent Odkin designed a component consisting of a ring with a small circle attached to this ring by a line. The large ring continued through the ring of the component, but was narrower as it did so.

"Danebury and its moon orbiting around it," Odkin said to himself. "The thin bent line through Danebury is its axis, bent to show retrograde precession. Danebury's moon is connected to Danebury because Danebury's moon is responsible for the evolution of self-aware life on Danebury."

Paired with this was a similar component but instead of a small circle attached to the ring of the component by a line, this component had a tuning fork connected to the ring of the component. Odkin turned the prongs of the tuning fork 90 degrees to its handle.

"Rotation," he said out loud to himself. "Harmonic rotation and therefore the off-center rotation caused by retrograde precession. That's why I put the bent tuning fork away from the equator of Danebury. It also looks like a key because off-center rotation is the key to the development of self-aware life."

Clockwise from the component which represented Danebury's moon in orbit around it, Odkin designed a large but misshapen heart. Paired with the misshapen heart was another mess.

"First you lose heart; then you die," said Odkin to himself (referring to his representation of what happens when the soul is subjected either to a magnetic field or to the environmental deficiencies of space travel—which it cannot tolerate).

The ninth component of this glyph—and in its center—was a very accurate depiction of the stroboscope, the device replacing the number nine thruster in flying craft, which lay down transtime crop glyphs.

"Without this, you can't depict or represent anything in the crops," Odkin said aloud to himself.

The holo-image suddenly appeared and said, "Joe Lon Odkin, you have also represented 9/8ths, the harmonic of transdimensioning—by having nine components, eight of which are arrayed together."

"I'm sick and tired of transtime crop glyphs," Odkin replied.

"Cary Jackman," the holo-image ordered, "you make a geometric design to illustrate 9/8ths in this transtime crop glyph."

The holo-image disappeared.

Cary Jackman worked very hard and drew an eight pointed star within the transtime crop glyph with each point in the center of the area of each of the things on the ring. The lines connecting those eight points circumscribed the stroboscope in the center.

The holo-image suddenly appeared and ordered, "Cary Jackman, now overlay this transtime crop glyph with both left and right hand Transdimensional Spirals so that those spirals form tangents with things."

Cary Jackman worked very hard and did what he had been told to do.

The holo-image suddenly appeared and ordered, "Cary Jackman, now overlay the transtime crop glyph and the two Transdimensional Spirals with an isosceles triangle, whose two long sides have a phi section ratio of 1.618 to 1 with its short side. And in such a way that the corners of the triangle are tangent to the Transdimensional Spirals, and the representation of the Source of the Universe is tangent to one corner of the triangle." 166.1

The holo-image disappeared.

Cary Jackman worked very hard, but the holo-image did not return after Cary Jackman had completed his work.

"Time I was sick of all this too," said Cary Jackman. That night Cary Jackman sneaked out and did some more secret sizing up.

During the years that followed, Cary Jackman and Cary Manpure designed many more transtime crop glyphs, many of which were meaningless variants of glyphs they had already designed. Others included depictions and representations of components of star ships; representations of soul-related configurations; processes of technologies; celestial bodies and the motions of celestial bodies; transdimensional physics; the harmonics of the Universe; geometry and transdimensional geometry; more depictions of the spinning disk and gravitrons, and the Waldark healer.

During wintertimes, Cary Manpure and Cary Jackman laid down the transtime crop glyphs. Sometimes they were unable to lay down a glyph within tolerable limits of its predesignated positioning, so they had to lay it down again at another suitable location.

Just before Joe Lon Odkin passed on, the Essene holo-image suddenly appeared and said, "Essenes have deceived you somewhat regarding the group of future beings who will be linear thinkers and have initiative. Their culture will not be unique, it will be a combination of the cultures of the beings of the other three groups. Their genetic make up will not require that they be abusive to everyone else, it will only give them the propensity to do so. It will only give them the propensity to have great difficulty in conceiving of any dimension beyond three-dimensions. The propensity to have great difficulty in conceiving of great lengths of time, the propensity to have great difficulty in conceiving of life spans longer than their own and the propensity to have great difficulty in conceiving that life exists anywhere except on Danebury. They will not all be future Anson Trents.

"Essenes have told Alteans to make this group of beings in that way because Essenes operate under the mandate of the Source of the Universe.

"You were deceived concerning this group of beings, because Essenes wanted you to make derogatory representations of this group of beings in transtime crop glyphs.

"Essenes want this group of beings—composed of linear thinkers who have initiative but who lack spirituality and intuitive harmony—to see themselves so depicted and represented in the crop formations. Like the other groups of beings of Danebury they will have gained great amounts of courage along the way, so they will be able to face up to their shortcomings depicted and represented in the crops. Once the linear thinkers see these shortcomings they will know what they have to do to gain spirituality and intuitive harmony with the Universe. Then the door will be open for all four groups of beings on Danebury to come together in peace and harmony. Only by having gone through all those things Essenes have told you about and more, will the future beings of this planet have been fully prepared to become the courageous leaders of the galaxy.

"You have courageously carried through—and will continue to courageously carry through—your vital roles in the process of preparing the future leaders of the galaxy."

The holo-image disappeared.

When Cary Manpure and Cary Jackman were both 183, Cary Jackman died, just under 26 years after the passing of Joe Lon Odkin. Since Terry Wellton drowned, Cary Jackman had frequently suffered from a nagging cough. One night at supper he started to cough badly and went to bed early. Cary Manpure was in his living quarters and could hear the violent coughing through the wall. When the coughing stopped Cary Manpure became uneasy. He waited a few minutes and then went into Cary Jackman's living quarters. Cary Manpure found Cary Jackman dead in his bed.

Cary Manpure was overcome and he lost consciousness.

Essenes removed the body of Cary Jackman from his living quarters.

Next Essenes put on long hooded robes, carried the body of Cary Jackman over their heads down the northern slope of the Hill of Musing and placed it gently and lovingly on the ground. Then they cleared the labyrinthine maze leading to the corbelled dome tomb in which they would bury the body of Cary Jackman near the graves of Joe Lon Odkin and Terry Wellton.

Having completed the unsealing of the tomb, Essenes carried the body of Cary Jackman through the labyrinthine maze and into the grave circle of the tomb. There they wrapped the body of Cary Jackman in a shroud and placed it on a pebble bed in a shaft grave, the walls of which were lined with flag stones. Essenes covered the shaft grave with wooden beams, placed a layer of clay over the beams and filled the hole above the shaft grave with chalk.

Essenes buried the body of Cary Jackman in the manner of his ancestors, and then filled in the labyrinthine maze in a way similar to the manner in which their ancestors had filled in the straight passageways leading to ancient corbelled dome tombs.

When Cary Manpure regained consciousness he found himself in his bed. He got up, went into Cary Jackman's living quarters and found that the body of Cary Jackman was gone.

Cary Manpure left Cary Jackman's living quarters and then sealed them off permanently.

Cary Manpure went up to the circular living platform, sat down on a sofa, and cried out in agony, "Every one I have ever known is dead or gone and I have never had the chance to say goodbye to any of them!"

Cary Manpure was alone.

'Art Hurian' Manpure had also been alone and he had died very shortly after Terry Wellton had drowned. Essenes buried 'Art Hurian' Manpure's body on top of Glastonbury Tor, west of the stone source-mark of the planet.

In time, the waters receded around Glastonbury Tor and Essenes constructed the first structures of the complex, which in time, became known as Glastonbury Abbey. The Glastonbury Abbey complex and its grounds were located in the analog position of the undestroyed (but damaged beyond repair) energy transconverter of the Tor in the Horz complex on Silbury, as represented in the large scale model of the Horz complex in southern Hurengland. 83

In time, Essenes also constructed a well near the site of Terry Wellton's drowning located in the analog position of the entrance to the Labyrinth Corridor of the Tor in the Horz complex on Silbury as represented in the large scale model of the Horz complex in southern Hurengland. The entrance to the Labyrinth Corridor of the Tor on Silbury was located tangential to the sight line connecting the southern facing of the Tor's damaged beyond repair energy transconverter with the apex of the Tor and the apex of Hurbury; the Well of Despair at Glastonbury was located tangential to the sight line connecting the center of the southern boundary of the Glastonbury Abbey complex, with the stone sourcemark on Glastonbury Tor and the center of Amesbury Circle.

The Well of Despair was constructed with an irregular five sided chamber, irregular to represent the irregular five pointed star of soul prints.

Both Hurbury and Amesbury Circle—in the large scale model of the Horz complex in southern Hurengland—represent the harmonics required for the development of self-aware life.

The energy transconverter of the Tor—already damaged beyond repair—and Glastonbury Abbey—later also to be damaged beyond repair—represent the horrific deeds perpetrated by those who will do anything.

The shattered entrance to the shattered Labyrinth Corridor of the Tor and the Well of Despair represent souls shattered by the horrific deeds of those who will do anything.

Essenes constructed a labyrinthine underground passageway from the Well of Despair to Glastonbury Tor, and at the end of that passageway they constructed a corbelled dome tomb and grave circle. Essenes disinterred 'Art Hurian' Manpure's body, and reburied 'Art Hurian' Manpure's body in the grave circle in the corbelled dome under Glastonbury Tor, then sealed the labyrinthine passageway leading from the Well of Despair.

Chapter Twelve

Vicky

After the death of Joe Lon Odkin, Cary Manpure and Cary Jackman had been very sad. As a tribute to the man they loved they designed a special transtime crop glyph in memory of Joe Lon Odkin. 167

In the center they drew a large ring to show that Joe Lon Odkin was a large man. They divided the ring with a line, and (looking upward) within the left side of the large ring they drew a solid circle representing Joe Lon Odkin's enormous heart. They agreed that using a heart shape would be "too obvious." They then extended the line dividing the large ring upward and attached it to a circle representing Joe Lon Odkin's head.

To complete this transtime crop glyph Cary Manpure added a smaller circle attached to the rest of the transtime crop glyph by a lower extension of the line dividing the large ring.

"This smaller circle is also a head—a small head of a small man, such as were most of the men on the council," Cary Manpure said to Cary Jackman. "To see this smaller circle as a small head you have to turn the transtime crop glyph upside down. That also puts the heart of the small man on the wrong side."

The next morning Cary Manpure asked Cary Jackman if he would like fried eggs for breakfast.

"Yes, please," responded Cary Jackman, "but only two."

"You always have three, Buff," said Cary Manpure.

"I'm not as hungry any more," said Cary Jackman.

When Cary Manpure was frying Cary Jackman's eggs he looked down into the frying pan and said, "I feel as if we are two eggs in a frying pan."

After breakfast Cary Jackman designed a transtime crop glyph which depicted two eggs in a frying pan. Then he added a short line extending from the rim of the frying pan so that, when superimposed and rotated, the frying pan would fit into and align with the ends of the arcs of the double clamshell doors of a number nine thruster, in a design for a glyph he had previously made. 33

As Cary Jackman was about to explain to Cary Manpure why he had done that, the holo-image suddenly appeared and said, "The Essene who has thrust you into the frying pan has some more work for you to do. You are to design two additional transtime crop glyphs for the depiction of energy transredimensioning which overlays the small scale model of the Horz complex. One of these glyphs is to represent the magnetic orientation of transtime crop glyphs and the other is to represent the mind of a self-aware being. Give these transtime crop glyphs protosites according to your previous depiction of energy transredimensioning.

"The Essene who has thrust you into the frying pan will insure that your transtime crop glyph depicting two eggs in a frying pan is activated at the appropriate time in the future—provided you lay it down properly now on its protosite. This has been infused in the navigational computer of the cargo air ship.

"While you are infusing your design into the graphics computer you are to add another even shorter line extending from the rim of the frying pan which is 25 degrees counterclockwise from your first short line. 168

"Before you depart, the Essene who has thrust you into the frying pan would also like you to know that this design has now been incorporated into the design of Avenabury Circle as well, to represent the two Tetrahedron Crater spinning disks.

"The Essene who has thrust you into the frying pan would also like you to know that this design has now been incorporated into the design of Avenabury Circle as well, as two stone eggs in the large Avenabury Circle frying pan.

"The future beings of this planet will be in the frying pan until they figure it out."

The holo-image disappeared.

When Cary Manpure and Cary Jackman returned to the house having laid down the two eggs in a frying pan transtime crop glyph they discovered that Joe Lon Odkin's drawings, maps, notes and writings were laid out neatly on the floor at the top of the stairway leading to the living platform.

As they saw Odkin's things the holo-image suddenly appeared and said, "It is necessary for you to have these things in order for you to continue your work."

The holo-image disappeared.

Cary Manpure designed the transtime crop glyph representing the magnetic orientation of transtime crop glyphs. 169 He drew two different sized circles connected by a long line. From the smaller lower circle he extended three lines at 90 degrees to one another so that the middle of those three lines was opposite the line connecting the two circles. Below the larger circle he drew a line on either side of the connecting line. These two lines were angled outward toward the bottom of the transtime crop glyph and had thicker portions at their tops.

Cary Manpure described his transtime crop glyph to Cary Jackman as he showed him his design, "The main design is from the pendulum of a clock. I added directional markers at the bottom. The lines along the sides restrict the swinging of the pendulum because the changes of magnetic directions are also restricted. The lines are thicker at the top to reinforce the larger size of the top circle. This glyph is also Director Odkin and a small man. Director Odkin is steady; the small man swings back and forth as the winds blow."

"Many construction lines of our designs are tangential to circles making up the image," said Cary Jackman, and some of these lines are aligned with magnetic north. "We've got to lay it down upside down because we are in the northern hemisphere and so the swinging back and forth part has to point to magnetic north," he added.

Then Cary Jackman showed Cary Manpure his transtime crop glyph design and explained it to him, 169.1 "The two small circles at the top are eyes. The semi-circular line at the bottom is a smiling mouth. The large circle in the center is the mind. The two circles at each end of the connecting lines are the left and right sides of the brain. The embellishments between the right side of the brain and the mind are the soul."

They positioned the protosite for Cary Jackman's self-aware mind transtime crop glyph, northwest of the site for the analog of the Hurmaze in the small scale model, and gave it the same orientation as the analog of the Hurmaze would have in the small scale model. It was also midway between the straight upward part of the first set of energy transredimensioning cones, as depicted by Joe Lon Odkin in two-dimensions.

They placed the protosite for Cary Manpure's magnetic orientation transtime crop glyph (after they had turned it upside down so that it pointed north) along the lower edge of the straight upward part of the first set of energy transredimensioning cones, as depicted by Joe Lon Odkin in two-dimensions. 169.2

As Cary Manpure and Cary Jackman were finishing, the holo-image suddenly appeared and began speaking, "In the future, Essenes will add encoded analogs of the other components of the Horz complex and of some of the structures of the Horz complex to the small scale model. This will be done in ways similar to that in which Cary Manpure found a suitable stone and erected it as an analog of the wooden pump house for the Ranch.

"Essenes will insure that the Tetrahedron will be encoded by a mound on the northeastern rim of the earthworks of Avenabury Circle and that the shape of that mound—as is the shape of Glastonbury Tor—will be similar to the shape of Mount Hurartu on Altea. 170

"Essenes will also insure that the top ridge of the Wall will be encoded by a village road. 171

"Essenes will infuse future beings with the idea of constructing a long earthen tomb on the analog site of Chapter One with the idea of erecting two huge stones to mark the analog site of the pump house northeast of Chapter One. 172,172.1

"Essenes will infuse future beings with the idea of constructing a small mound on the analog site of Glamyrr Gate of the Tor and will insure that Glamyrr Gate is represented by a stone on top of the mound. 173

"Essenes will insure that the knowledge and Wisdom longhouses of Hur Square will be marked in the amphitheater-like valley at the appropriate time. 174

"Due to ideas infused into their minds by Essenes, future beings will construct a small mound along the northern ridge of the amphitheater-like valley, which will be on the analog site of Zuv House. 175

"Essenes will insure that at the right time the analog site of the right side of the Hurmaze will be marked by three subtle ridges: one for the eye brows; one for the point of the nose and one for the point of the chin.

"Essenes will also insure that local roads are constructed along the tangents of the analogs and of analog sites of the components of the Horz complex in the small scale model. 176

"An eating and drinking establishment will be located where you enjoyed your picnic and beer in the rain. 177

"Cary Manpure's pile mound just west of your picnic area will be at the crossing of tangent roads. 152

"Essenes will insure that at the right time trees are planted in various locations throughout the small scale model to highlight various aspects of the Horz complex. 178

"Essenes will sculpt scale models of the buttresses of the Tor at the end of which were Glamyrr Gate and Sustanator Gate. 179 These sculpted earthen buttresses—like their counterparts of the Tor—will not be needed for physical support, but they will appear to support the hill on which the brain earthworks will be sited. These sculpted buttresses will be an encoded metaphor of how the soul helps beings attain physical, mental and ethical courage. (Similar to the Altean Naval Service marines' understanding of the symbolism of the buttresses of the Tor on Silbury.)

"Essenes will insure that the roads, fields, constructions and other changes to the landscape made by the future beings of southern Hurengland, do not interfere with any of the preparatory work.

"Essenes will insure that the farming equipment used and the methods of plowing and servicing the future grain fields of southern Hurengland, are both compatible with the preparatory work."

The holo-image disappeared.

Some time later the holo-image suddenly appeared and said, "The Essene who has thrust you into the frying pan has more requirements for you. The Essene who has thrust you into the frying pan knows that you will be reluctant. You are to make some vital additions and modifications to Joe Lon Odkin's transtime crop glyph depicting of one of the energy transconverters in the Tor, whose design you have not yet entered into your graphics computer. Essenes had intended that Joe Lon Odkin make these additions and modifications, but his passing on has prevented that. The Essene who has thrust you into the frying pan is greatly saddened by the death of Joe Lon Odkin and understands your very strong feelings. It was necessary to tell you now about these vital additions and modifications to Joe Lon Odkin's glyph, but you will not be asked to make them until you are ready."

The holo-image disappeared.

Time dragged for Cary Manpure and Cary Jackman. They got on their horses and insured that the Danebury Ranch was operating properly. They cleaned up the house. They read.

Finally, Cary Manpure said, "Let's do something. I'm tired of diddling around. Let's not diddle around, let's diddle with something. Let's fuss with some glyphs."

They found that the transtime crop glyph they had designed with Joe Lon Odkin representing energy conduits (the transtime crop glyph which had six not all equally spaced petals inside two rings) had not yet been laid down.

Cary Manpure added three small arcs to the transtime crop glyph, each small arc connecting a petal with the inner ring.

"Diddling," he announced.

Cary Jackman took the design and added two concentric rings near it.

"More diddling," he added.

Cary Jackman then began to draw furiously and Cary Manpure stopped to watch him. When Cary Jackman was done, he showed Cary Manpure his design and said, "69.28." Then Cary Jackman told Cary Manpure about how he and Becky Armstrong had sweated things out, and then how they had come up with a solution. "Their solution was 69.28," Cary Jackman concluded.

"Lets make a series of these diddlings," said Cary Manpure. "We can vary each one slightly, but make them mostly the same. We'll call the series: the Solution 69.28." 180

"Time for a serious diddle," said Cary Manpure, "and then it'll be time for an unserious Meisterbraue."

They designed a new transtime crop glyph of a six part thing inside a ring. Then they added a long and a short arc coming out of the ring and defiantly signed the transtime crop glyph with two bold block letter Cs. 181

"Six Essene craft colliding and spinning downward toward a crash," Cary Manpure said as he went off to get several bottles of Meisterbraue. Some time later that night Cary Manpure wrote the first and only poem he was ever able to write, and titled it ESSENES:

High diddle diddle,
The cat and the fiddle,
The cow jumped over the moon;
The little dog laughed to see such craft,
And the dish ran away with the spoon.

Cary Manpure read his poem to Cary Jackman and then explained it to him, "The first line means that Essenes are diddling from up above.

"The second line means that because of the diddling the future beings of this planet will eventually add heart and soul to their makeup. The cat is a lion and therefore courage. The fiddle is a lyre. Specially tuned lyres are used to help meditators meditate and thereby transredimension energy with their souls. The fiddle is also a soul.

"The third line means that with heart and soul having been added to their makeup the future beings of this planet will be so powerful they can jump over the moon. The moon is the reason they live in the first place. Because the Pleiadeans treated their ancestors like cows, we Alteans became involved in the process.

"The fourth line means that Essenes are and will be so sneaky that only dogs will be able to sense the presence of Essenes, think them strange and bark at them. I use the word 'craft' here to mean both the space craft of Essenes and to mean that Essenes are crafty.

"The fifth line means that when Essenes are done with any given diddling they take off and leave in their space craft. The dish is the spinning disk. The spoon is the shape of the lower half of Essene space craft, I think."

Cary Jackman looked at his friend and said, "Ollun, that is the most incredible, the most wonderful, the most precisely correct thing that has ever been written."

Cary Manpure responded, "I was able to write this poem somewhat because I am drunk—but mostly because I am in an eternal rage against Essenes."

Some time later the holo-image suddenly appeared and said, "You are ready. Cary Manpure, you are to design alterations and additions to Joe Lon Odkin's energy transconverter transtime crop glyph in order to encode the transdimensioning processes of the Universe. 126

"Cary Jackman, after Cary Manpure explains his alterations and additions to Joe Lon Odkin's energy transconverter transtime crop glyph to you, you are to figure out how the ways of the Universe have also been unwittingly encoded by Cary Manpure into his alterations and additions to Joe Lon Odkin's energy transconverter transtime crop glyph.

"Cary Jackman, leave immediately and insure that the Danebury Ranch is properly maintained."

The holo-image disappeared.

Cary Manpure was surprised at how well he finally grasped the things he read once again about transdimensional physics. The many years of working on Panergon Gwynmyrr (but especially the many years of listening to Joe Lon Odkin explaining what he had discovered as a result of fulfilling Essene requirements) had helped Cary Manpure to gain an understanding of why many things were as they were.

When Cary Manpure had completed his work, Essenes ordered Cary Jackman to return to HOME. Cary Manpure then showed Cary Jackman his new design for Joe Lon Odkin's energy transconverter glyph and explained what he had done, "First, I diddled with the equilateral triangle portion of the depiction of the tetrahedral crystal casing of the energy transconverter. I had to bend its lines and make them different lengths.

"Next, I moved the depictions of the transconverter sphere and its two cooling casings off center. 182

"Then, I added additional designs at the three corners of the former equilateral triangle.

"At the lower left I added a ring with a line running into it from its circumference to just past its center, a thin extension of one of the three lines originating at the center of the transtime crop glyph (which infer the three-dimensionality of the casing of the energy transconverter). 182.1

"At the top I added another ring. Inside it I drew six unequally spaced arcs from the center of the ring to its circumference. 182.2

"At the lower right I added a spiral with notches. At the end of the spiral is a small circle. 182.3

"I bent two of the lines of the equilateral triangle so that a two-dimensional depiction of a complexified three-space tetrahedron would fit over the former equilateral triangle. 182.4 I did this because the process of transconverting torinum into tornum in an energy transconverter takes place in complexified three-space. The geometric shape of the tetrahedral casing of an energy transconverter helps transdimension the incoming torinum. I could not show the geometric shape transdimensioning the torinum, so I showed the geometric shape being transdimensioned instead. (This is similar to the way we illustrated a soul receiving infrared light and torun; instead of not receiving infrared and torun.)

"I also bent one of the lines because I moved the depiction of the transconverter sphere and its casings off center, if I hadn't bent that line, the ring depicting the inner cooling casing of the transconverter sphere would have bumped into it.

"I also bent this line to illustrate some things with a polar projection latitude finder I made from the circle and rings which make up the transconverter sphere and its two cooling casings. If you draw that circle and rings from a perspective of 45 degrees below the vertical, draw a line across the long axis of the circle and rings, and then draw a semi-circular arc from one outer edge of the long axis of the drawing to the other outer edge (using the center of the circle as the center of the semi-circular arc) you end up with a two-dimensional model of a three-dimensional holo-plot. I had to flatten this arc somewhat to make it work out right. I used to get to ride in star ships sometimes, and I loved to watch the holo-plots.

"To calculate a latitude on this drawing of a holo-plot, you first draw a line straight up from the line across the long axis to the flattened semi-circular arc. From the point where this line touches the flattened semi-circular arc, you draw a line to the line across the long axis (where that line crosses the center of the transconverter sphere). You then measure the angle at the center of the transconverter sphere formed by the line across the long axis and the line from the point on the flattened semi-circular arc. 183

"The two most important latitudes to be read on this holo-plot are 19.47 and 22.48 degrees. The latter is the latitude of the inside of the outer ring. The former is read by drawing a line from the end of the narrow line extending past the center of the ring in the lower left, to the center of the ring at the top; and then by measuring from where there that line crosses the line across the long axis. The latitude 22.48 degrees is reemphasized by drawing a line from the center of the ring in the lower left, to the center of the ring at the top (because that line is tangent to the inner side of the outer ring at the point where the line across the long axis crosses the inner side of that outer ring). The very important relationship between 19.47 degrees and 22.48 is represented by the resulting two-dimensional depiction of the circular cone of gravitron emission (formed by the two lines which meet at the center of the circle at the top of the glyph).

"The outside of the inner ring is 44.89 degrees, the inside of the inner ring is 51.84 degrees and the outside of the circle is 66 and two-thirds degrees. The ratio of 44.89 degrees to 51.84 degrees is nearly equivalent to the square root of three divided by two, as is the ratio between 19.47 degrees and 22.48 degrees, so there are two encodings of the square root of three divided by two in the reading of the holo-plot. The angle 66 and two-thirds degrees represents two-thirds. I used 51.84 degrees because it represents star ships and therefore their holo-plots, because the total height of star ships being 51.84 feet. I love star ships.

"There is one more latitude encoded in the transtime crop glyph, representing a very important Essene angle which stands by itself in the holo-plot and is not to be read in ratio with any other latitude. This latitude (like the 19.47 degree latitude) can only be read on one side of the holo-plot, the same side as the encoding of 19.47 degrees.

"If the bent line of the former equilateral triangle (which runs from a point on the circumference of the ring in the lower left to a point on the circumference of the ring at the top) was not bent, it would pass through the ring depicting the inner cooling casing of the transconverter sphere. This unbent line—in the same way as the line which creates the 19.47 degree latitude—creates a latitude of 49.61004268 degrees.

"This latitude 49.61004268 degrees is meant to represent the angle 49.61004268 degrees and therefore to represent the secondary emission of gravitrons by a spinning disk. This latitude 49.61004268 degrees also encodes the apparent two-dimensional angle at one corner of one of the triangles making up the apparent two-dimensional shape of the Tor.

"The ring at the lower left depicts the spinning disk—spinning so rapidly you can't see its radial half-hexagon grooves. 182.1

"The thin line which goes past its center is a conscitron thruster armature aboard an Essene space craft, an armature which also collects gravitrons of the secondary emission. This thin line is an Essene conscitron thruster armature because of the 49.61004268 degree latitude (encoded in the glyph) which can be read in the holo-plot when decoded.

"The ring at the upper part of the transtime crop glyph with six unequally spaced arcs is meant to represent a seed planet. 182.2 The unequal spacings of the arcs are meant to represent wobbling—the off-center rotation of the 25,920 year retrograde precession of seed planets.

"The reason I moved the circle and rings depicting the transconverter sphere and its two cooling casings off center was to emphasize the importance of retrograde precession by inferring off-center rotation.

"At the same time I moved them away from the spiral in the lower right 182.3 as that spiral in the lower right is an equiangular spiral based on the twelfth root of two, the spiral which represents the harmonics of the natural environment required for the evolution of self-aware life from life.

"The small circle at the center of the equiangular spiral depicts a seed planet.

"The notches are intended to represent the different types of beings who evolve along the way toward the final self-aware being. I have made the number of notches ambiguous. I intend that there be both five and six notches to represent the ratio of 5 to 6, as the metaphor for the relationship between the non-living parts of the Universe and living things.

"The notches are 90 degrees apart so that there are four notches every 360 degrees. I have also aligned the glyph so that the notches to the north of the seed planet (at the center of the spiral) have a bearing of 4 degrees magnetic from its center. I have shown four once and encoded four once to emphasize that the Source of the Universe is in the fourth-dimension.

"The seven of spirit is represented by the four facings of the 'tetrahedron' and the three additions I made at the corners of the transtime crop glyph. Tetrahedra are the geometric modeling of everything. The spinning disk is the most important tool of the physical universe, but the emergence of self-aware life—as represented in two-thirds of the additions I made to the three corners of the depiction of the tetrahedral crystal casing of the energy transconverter—is the most important event to have ever taken place.

"I did not alter the three broad lines converging toward the center of the transtime crop glyph and which infer the three-dimensional tetrahedral crystal casing of the energy transconverter. These three converging broad lines infer the apex of the tetrahedron—an apex which is not visible (due to the solid circle depiction of the transconverter sphere). The non-visible apex of the tetrahedron is therefore a representation of the invisible Source of the Universe. 184

As Cary Manpure concluded, the holo-image suddenly appeared and ordered him out from HOME.

While Cary Manpure was insuring that the Danebury Ranch was properly maintained, Cary Jackman tried to figure out how the ways of the Universe had been unwittingly encoded by Cary Manpure into his alterations and additions to Joe Lon Odkin's energy transconverter transtime crop glyph.

Eventually, Essenes ordered Cary Manpure back to the house and Cary Jackman told Cary Manpure what he had found out.

"Ollun," Cary Jackman began, "I don't understand much of this, but I do see some patterns, so I think what I'm going to tell you is correct in the context of the Essene requirement. The first part I am going to read."

Cary Jackman read from some papers he held in his hand:

> The four longhouses of Hur Square are named data, information, knowledge, and Wisdom. They were named this way to metaphorically represent the progressively more complex components of the physical universe and the only repository of Wisdom in the Universe, the Source of the Universe.
>
> The Source of the Universe extrudes Itself into the three-dimensional physical universe by means of time in three ways. One of these extrusions forms the physical universe, the second binds it together and the third carries forward souls.
>
> These extrusions can be modeled by a tetrahedron with data, information and knowledge representing these three extrusions at the three corners of its base. Wisdom, the zero-dimension point at the apex of the tetrahedron is the radiating Source from which these extrusions emanate. The lines connecting the apex to its three lower corners of the tetrahedron represent Eternal Time, physical time and consciousness time.
>
> Eternal Time, which is eternally invariant, carries forward the non-living parts of the physical universe. Physical time, which varies greatly with environment, carries forward those things which hold the physical universe together. Consciousness time, is also invariant, carries forward souls and measures the duration of self-aware consciousness and the conditions under which self-aware consciousness can exist.
>
> The non-living parts of the physical universe are organized in a less complex way than both living things and self-aware consciousness. Therefore, the conditions under which the non-living parts of the physical universe can exist are also less complex, usually resulting in a long period of existence.
>
> Living things are more complex and require a more complex set of conditions under which they can live, usually for a short life span.
>
> Souls are extruded into the physical universe by the Source so that they may gain experience and knowledge. To do this souls attach

themselves to three-dimensional beings. Together, souls and the beings to whom they are attached form self-aware consciousness.

Self-aware consciousness requires not only the conditions required by both the non-living parts of the physical universe and living things in order to exist in three-dimensions, but also another, highly complex set of conditions.

Consciousness time is the carrier in which all the conditions required by the non-living parts of the physical universe, living things and self-aware beings are embedded so that all of them can exist in the physical universe.

The radiating of Eternal Time is accomplished in a spiraling fashion. There are spirals of ascending size, from the smallest at the sub-atomic level to the largest: the enormous vortex which is the conical physical universe. As a result of this vorticular unfolding, spin is imparted on everything. Spin is what makes everything work.

The radiating of physical time contains four-dimensional gravity and the three-dimensional manifestations of four-dimensional gravity: the weak force, the strong force, light and three-dimensional gravity.

These three-dimensional manifestations of four-dimensional gravity can also be represented tetrahedrally, with three-dimensional gravity at the apex.

Four-dimensional gravity and three-fourths of its four manifestations in three-dimensions—the weak force, the strong force and three-dimensional gravity—hold the physical universe together.

Although the natures of the weak force, the strong force and three-dimensional gravity are somewhat understood, light remains a mystery. Light is complex, multi-faceted and unfathomable. Light does, however, seem to be a governor on how fast things can travel.

Three-dimensional and four-dimensional gravity govern the speed of light.

Working together, three-dimensional and four-dimensional gravity are sometimes strong enough to even stop light, due to the coalescing of an enormous amount of extremely dense matter—as in the collapse of certain types of stars.

The strength of three-dimensional gravity decreases at greater and greater distances from matter. Similarly, and at the same rate, the strength of four-dimensional gravity decreases at greater and greater distances from matter. However, as the initial strength of three-dimensional gravity is weaker than that of four-dimensional gravity, the ability of three-dimensional gravity to help govern the speed of light decreases at a closer distance from a large mass than that of four-dimensional gravity. Due to the fact that galaxies are close enough together throughout the physical universe, four-dimensional gravity never actually loses its ability to govern the speed of light.

As a result of the increasing inability of three-dimensional gravity to govern the speed of light, there are three greatly different speeds of light depending upon how far distant light is from a large amount of matter. It is unknown why light suddenly changes speed by discreet amounts, instead of gradually as it gets farther and farther from large amounts of matter, but the Universe likes to do things in blocks rather than just dribbling on.

Solar system light speed is approximately 186,000 miles per second and extends well beyond the limits of a solar system.

Interstellar light speed is the speed of light between solar systems. Over 400,000 times faster than solar system light speed, interstellar light speed begins well beyond the limits of a solar system and extends well beyond the fringes of galaxies.

Intergalactic light speed is seven times faster than interstellar light speed. Intergalactic light speed is the speed of light in the physical universe well beyond the fringes of galaxies.

Physical time is affected by the speed of travel: slower speed results in faster time; faster speed results in slower time.

The rate of physical time is determined by the total speed component of the observer.

Only a certain band of physical time rates is compatible with the existence of physical matter. A narrower band of physical time rates allows for the existence of life. A band of physical time rates narrower yet, produces the environment in which self-aware beings can live.

Only a retrograde precession rate of 25,920 years produces the off-center rotation which calibrates and fine tunes the physical time rate to the point where natural evolutionary forces can work to produce a life form. A life form which can evolve highly enough to become that vital three-dimensional being to which the four-dimensional soul can attach itself, in order to have the opportunity to experience and learn, the very important and vital process which insures galactic redeeming and eventual redemption of the Universe.

Cary Jackman set down his papers and reached for his notes.

"That's incredibly well written, Buff, and much clearer than anything I've ever heard or read about transdimensional physics," said Cary Manpure. "Where did you get that?"

"It's a paper Pazzy wrote for my mother when he was 12 or so, after he finished his special class on Philosophia," answered Cary Jackman. "She gave me a copy and I kept it."

Cary Manpure wiped tears from his eyes as Cary Jackman continued, "Pazzy's material is the stuff I understood too, and it is an introduction to what I am about to tell you: things which I think relate to the Essene requirements.

"I think that the three additions you made to Director Odkin's glyph and the hidden apex of the crystal casing of the energy transconverter are representations of the relative positions of the weak force, the strong force, light and three-dimensional gravity in the tetrahedral model—with the weak force as data, the strong force as information, light as knowledge and with three-dimensional gravity at the apex as Wisdom—mentioned at the beginning of Pazzy's writing.

"I do not completely understand these positionings of the weak force, the strong force, light, and three-dimensional gravity as data, information, knowledge and Wisdom or why numbers are associated with them.

"However, there is an underlying matrix associated with these positionings which progresses as follows: 2 x 2 = 4; 4 x 4 = 16; 16 x 16 = 256; 256 x 256 = 65,536.

"There is also a series of other numbers associated with this underlying matrix in the form of a hierarchy, and associated with the weak force, the strong force, light and three-dimensional gravity as follows: 3, 10, 137, and 1.7016 times 10 to the 38th power. 184.1

"The circle in the lower left (depicting a spinning disk) has the matrix 4 and the associated number 3, which is associated with the weak force because the spinning disk spins at 750,000 rpms and 750,000 rpms is often represented by three-fourths.

"The circle at the top (representing a seed planet) has seven in it because there are six arcs and one circumference. The number 10 associated with the strong force is derived by cubing two, subtracting one and adding the number three (associated with the weak force). Cubing two and subtracting one is seven.

"The number 137 associated with light is derived by taking two to the seventh power; subtracting one to obtain 127; then adding the three of the weak force (obtained by squaring two and subtracting one) plus the seven of the strong force. The underlying matrix which is associated with light is 16 x 16.

"In your alteration of Director Odkin's glyph you made notches in the spiral 90 degrees apart so that there are four notches every 360 degrees. You also aligned the glyph so that the notches to the north of the seed planet (at the center of the spiral) have a bearing of 4 degrees magnetic from the center of that seed planet.

"The four notches per 360 degrees times 4 degrees are equal to 16.

"The three other notches have resulting bearings of 94, 184, and 274 degrees magnetic. Dividing 274 by two results in 137.

"The very large numbers associated with three-dimensional gravity cannot be read from the glyph as the apex of the tetrahedral crystal casing of the energy transconverter is obscured by its transconverter sphere."

At the first three levels the product (the result) is smaller than the matrix for those levels, whereas at the fourth level the product way exceeds the size of the matrix for that level. Cary Manpure stared at Cary Jackman and said, "The whole thing sounds totally contrived to me."

Cary Jackman stared at him and said, "I did this mostly by feeling. There was not much else to go by, especially since I did not, and still do not understand much of this—but it is clearly a combinatorial hierarchy, the construction of which terminates at the fourth level."

Cary Manpure decided against further comment, and then the holo-image suddenly appeared and said, "The number 137 is an interesting number because it is a near equivalent to the value of the fine structure constant of hydrogen, which is approximately 137.0359.

"The number 137 is even more interesting because the number 13 represents the Source of the Universe and life because the number 13 represents a seed and its first growth ring. The number 7 represents spirit and therefore the soul. The number 137 therefore represents self-aware life coming from the Source of the Universe."

"You are to enter the design of the modified transtime crop glyph depicting the energy transconverter into your graphics computer and lay down that transtime crop glyph NOW."

The holo-image disappeared.

As Cary Jackman was entering the design into the graphics computer Cary Manure asked, "What is 'the fine structure constant of hydrogen'?"

This time it was Cary Jackman who decided against further comment.

Some time later the holo-image appeared and began speaking, "You already know that the future topogly vector of Hurmyrr is to be equivalent to the cube of two pi.

"The tangent of 24,901.54558 (the number of statute miles in the equatorial circumference of Danebury) is a very close equivalent to the cube root of two pi.

"The ratio between 21,600 (the number of nautical miles in the equatorial circumference of Danebury) and 24,901.54558 is .867416037.

"The number which forms the same .867416037 ratio with 248.0502134 (the cube of two pi) is 285.9645232.

"You already know that Hurmyrr was partially constructed using the pyramid inch, an inch which is longer than the Danebury inch by a ratio of 1.00106 to 1.

"The entryway in the north facing of Hurmyrr is offset precisely 286.10213 pyramid inches. 185

"The difference between 286.10213 and 285.9645232 is .1376068.

"You already know what 137 represents. The 60 represents tetrahedra. The 68 represents six-eighths, three-quarters, 750,000 rpms and the spinning disk—which is the most important tool of the Universe.

"The number .1376068 therefore represents all those things which Joe Lon Odkin's modified energy transconverter transtime crop glyph represents."

The holo-image disappeared.

Cary Manpure and Cary Jackman wondered what important new concept the Essene holo-image was beginning to reveal to them. Before the holo-image told them anything more Cary Jackman had died.

After Cary Manpure cried out in agony following the death of Cary Jackman the holo-image immediately appeared and said, "Cary Manpure, you are to design a transtime crop glyph representing your love for Cary Jackman. Then pick out a protosite for this transtime crop glyph.

"Essenes will insure that a transtime crop glyph representing your love for Cary Jackman is laid down and activated at the location you pick.

"Essenes will insure that you have energy for the house, the Danebury Ranch and the air ship.

"Essenes will insure that the Danebury Ranch continues to be properly maintained.

"Essenes are very saddened by the death of Cary Jackman."

The holo-image disappeared.

It was some time before Cary Manpure even wanted to think about designing another transtime crop glyph. He ate little, drank only water and wandered about aimlessly.

Finally, he picked up a piece of paper and drew four different sized Cs hugging one another.

"There are four," Cary Manpure said aloud to himself, "because Buff is now in the fourth-dimension." 186

He cried himself to sleep.

When he awoke later he wrote at the bottom of the paper on which he had drawn the hugging Cs, "Put this down near the source transtime crop glyph so that it is in the northern part of the Ranch in the large scale model of the Horz complex, as twisted northward by Essenes. Cary Jackman saved my life there. This is all I can do for him." 187

A short time later the holo-image appeared and said, "You are now to fly the air ship to the Bastion."

As Cary Manpure approached Hurmyrr from the north he noticed that something was on the Bastion just north of Hurmyrr.

When he got closer he could see that that something was a someone.

After he landed and walked up to that someone, he thought he knew who she was.

"Vicky?" he asked.

"Cary?" she asked.

The cousins hugged.

On the way back to Hurengland Vicky told her cousin about how she had gotten there, "About 11 days ago an Essene holo-image suddenly appeared before the Council of Daphlay and ordered the council to have me transported immediately to the plateau on which Hurmyrr stands.

"As the Altean Naval Service star ship was about to land, a holo-image suddenly appeared on the upper bridge (where I was standing next to the commanding officer) and ordered that the landing be made between the Ark Hur and Hurmyrr, that I was to be the only one to debark, that the star ship was then to depart immediately and that I was to walk to the northern side of Hurmyrr and wait.

"Due to the difference in gravity, I stumbled as I was walking along so when I got there I sat down. I had been waiting about an hour before I saw what turned out to be you flying in from the northwest.

"Cary, it is so good to see you again. I never expected to be here."

"I never expected to see anyone again," responded Cary Manpure.

He then told her of the losses of Terry Wellton, Joe Lon Odkin and Cary Jackman.

"Becky Armstrong missed Buff a lot," said Vicky.

"Buff?" asked Cary Manpure.

"There are no secrets, Ollun," said Vicky.

"Don't call me Ollun," said Cary Manpure.

After a while Vicky asked about her brother and Cary Manpure told her what he knew.

"This place is a mess!" Vicky pronounced when she saw inside. "I'll have to clean it up."

"This kitchen is disgusting!" Vicky exclaimed when she went to the food preparation area to make supper.

"Have you been eating properly?" she asked as they sat down to dine.

"What are you, a nutritionist?" Cary Manpure asked.

"Something worse—a practitioner of medical arts," Vicky responded.

Vicky spent the next day cleaning and putting the kitchen in order.

The day after that Cary Manpure saddled up two horses and took his cousin for a tour of the Danebury Ranch. Along the way he showed her the sites of the future Avenabury Circle and the future Avenabury Tor.

When they were back Vicky said, "This is not a ranch. It is also a farm, an energy transproduction facility—and a mess. After we sort this place out, it's going to have a new name: Avenabury. Not Avenabury Circle, not Avenabury Tor, not Avenabury Farm, not Avenabury Ranch. Just Avenabury."

"Are you sure you didn't get any other orders from Essenes?" Cary Manpure asked.

After the Danebury Ranch was straightened up sufficiently to be called Avenabury, Cary Manpure asked his cousin if she knew anything about Marta Weynard.

"No," she responded.

"What about Tommy?"

Vicky Manpure got up from the table where they were dining, walked to the circular hearth and leaned against one of the columns. She kept her back turned to her cousin as she said, "Tommy and his wife had a baby about nine months after they were married. The baby had a birth defect and died a week after being born. The baby's name was Cary.

"Tommy never recovered.

"Tommy's wife became a shrew.

"They still live together—sort of."

"What about Anson Trent?" Cary Manpure asked.

"He became a very successful practitioner of legal arts with a large legal firm. He's dead now," Vicky responded.

Cary Manpure was afraid to ask the next question.

"Your parents are gone, Cary. They both lived to over 200. They had a good life, but they missed you. And they missed your brother Ames," said Vicky anticipating him.

"Alana and Frank are both still alive. Your big brother became an admiral before he retired. Their daughter Lana joined the Altean Naval Service and also became an admiral. Her brother Mark married, he was just a baby when we left Silbury, and he and his wife had a boy named Dan and a girl named Vicky. Vicky was not named after me, but after our grandmother, but Dan was named after my brother. Young Dan married and had more Manpure boys and now there seems to be a steady stream of them. Despite being down so low for a while, it seems that the clan Manpure is to continue."

"What about you, Vicky?" her cousin asked.

"I told you, I am a practitioner of medical arts. I never retired."

"That isn't what I mean," said Cary Manpure.

"I never married," Vicky answered reluctantly. "I lived alone until Rena Huish moved in with me a couple of years ago."

"Rena Jackman Huish?" asked Cary Manpure.

"Yes, Rena Jackman Huish, Cary Jackman's sister," Vicky said. "She tracked down Mr. Huish after she got to Daphlay and told him they were going to get married. They had three wonderful children. He died and she moved in with me."

Cary Manpure couldn't listen to any more.

"Excuse me, Vicky. I'm very tired. I need to go to bed," he said.

After her cousin had retired, Vicky Manpure sat up for a while and watched the dancing of the flames in the fire. She was tired too. When she fell asleep there were tears in her eyes as well.

Chapter Thirteen

The Gwynmyrr of Cary Manpure

Vicky stayed at Avenabury for seven weeks, and then the holo-image ordered Cary Manpure to take her back to the Bastion. He left her there after only a brief farewell and flew back to Hureng-land. An hour after Cary Manpure had left the Bastion, Vicky Manpure was picked up and flown back to Daphlay aboard an Altean Naval Service star ship. The cousins had a wonderful time together. The evening after Vicky told Cary Manpure about those who had left Silbury she asked him if he had anything to drink.

"Milk," he responded.

"I was thinking of something mist-producing," Vicky said.

Cary Manpure laughed for the first time since Cary Jackman died. "I didn't know you knew about mist-producing beverages," he said.

"I told you there are no secrets; I know lots of things," Vicky said. "For instance, I know that when you finished high school you had planned to apply for entrance to the Daphlay Naval Institute so you could begin a career in the navy."

"I didn't just want to be in the navy," Cary Manpure responded. "I wanted to command a star ship. I knew it when they pinned the labyrys of command on my father's uniform."

"I was there too," said Vicky. "I've always wondered why they call the double headed axe a labyrys."

"The double headed axe is representative of command because it has two sharp edges, one for authority and one for accountability. The labyrys is that which cuts labyrinthos, the brain. To wield authority sometimes you have to be very resolute. If you are not prudent they will wield the axe on you. They make you accountable."

"I'd better get those mist-producing beverages.

He returned with two glasses and a bottle of whiskey.

"We used to drink mostly Meisterbraue, a beer Dircctor Odkin brewed, but we couldn't figure out how to match its quality after he was gone," Cary Manpure said. "Making whiskey proved to be easier."

"Whiskey is perfect," said Vicky.

"I also know about you and Rena," Vicky offered.

Cary Manpure did not know what his cousin was talking about.

"What about Rena and me?" he asked suspiciously.

"You remember when you got so drunk at your brother's wedding that you threw up?" Vicky asked.

"Yes," Cary Manpure replied still suspicious.

"Well, after you threw up Rena took you home. You were a mess so she had to give you a shower to clean you up," Vicky said deadpan.

Vicky told Cary Manpure many other things.

"How do you know 'things'?" Cary Manpure asked as he poured his cousin another mist-producing whiskey.

"Cary Manpure, you were the most naive young man to live in Altea City. Everybody else knew everything about everything and everyone. For instance, you were the only young man who did not know Ann Trent—and that got you into trouble."

Cary Manpure shook his head.

"Was I really so dense?" he asked.

"Cary Manpure, you were and still are, the purest of men," his cousin answered. "Never change."

"I do know a few things," said Cary Manpure. "For instance, I knew Rena Huish was Rena Jackman Huish."

"Yes, I suspected that by the way you asked," responded Vicky. "How did you know? I didn't know anything until after they got secretly married."

"You're not so smart Vicky," said Cary Manpure laughing.

They laughed together and then Cary Manpure asked her about the chandelier. In the dining room in their living quarters in Zuv House the Jackmans had hung an exquisite chandelier. At the last moment Cary Jackman had gone back in and brought the chandelier with him to Danebury, having shredded the fine dining room curtains to pack it carefully in a large container. He had loved it since his early childhood. Cary Jackman had kept the chandelier with him in its container for nearly nine years and then he decided to give it to his brother Tommy to take back to Daphlay.

"He still has the chandelier, Cary," Vicky replied. "That chandelier has been our memory of all of you."

Next Cary Manpure told Vicky about everything they had done.

When he finished telling her about his incarceration at the Essene base, he said, "I have never figured out why Essenes did what they did to me there. I know that they are aware of my knowledge of mythos, so I know they did not make a mistake as far as my being able to figure out what they were doing. It makes no sense."

The Essene holo-image suddenly appeared—the only time it appeared while Vicky was visiting Avenabury—and said, "Essenes did what they did to you at the Essene base because Essenes knew you were the most belligerent of those who had been picked out to assist Essenes. Essenes wanted to put you in an uncomfortable situation—but one that made some kind of sense to you. Essenes wanted to see how you would react. Essenes learned that you would react sanely even in an uncomfortable situation, if that situation made some sort of sense to you.

"This was a very important thing for Essenes to learn about you because Essenes planned that the rest of your life would be uncomfortable, but that that discomfort would make some sort of sense.

"You have rebelled along the way when the situations have been too uncomfortable, but when you have been able to make some sort of sense of them you have returned to your work.

"It is very important for you to rebel and then to return to your work after you are able to make some sense of uncomfortable situations.

"Essenes operate under the mandate of the Source of the Universe. The mandate of the Source of the Universe demands that Essenes make you live as you live and it is mandatory that you react as you have. If you had not reacted as you have, then you would not be qualified to carry out all those important things that you must do. You even waited until you were to be all alone forever before you checked on a map to confirm that the well you dug after the death of Terry Wellton (the well which has an analog location to where you slept with your entrenching tool at your side) is where Essenes told you it was, in relation to other things."

The holo-image disappeared.

"What was that part at the end all about?" Vicky asked.

"Nothing!" Cary Manpure growled. "They're all bastards!"

Then Cary Manpure continued telling Vicky everything that they had done on Danebury, but nothing concerning what he and Tommy Untiman had once found on Silbury.

When her cousin was done Vicky said, "I think I'll only tell them about Avenabury, and not about anything else. They don't deserve to know anything more.

"I'll tell Rena, though."

After they were both silent for a while Vicky said, "There is one thing I've never told anyone, even Rena."

Cary Manpure looked at his cousin.

"I have always been, am now, and always will be, in love with Tommy Untiman," Vicky blurted out.

On what turned out to be their last day together they went on horseback to the amphitheater-like valley. Vicky rode Cary Manpure's favorite horse Glamorgan, meaning 'distant morning.' Cary Manpure told Vicky that he had named this horse Glamorgan and that it was a horse like no other horse, a horse with whom he had been instantly as one. He hoped that one distant morning, self-aware beings could be as one with the Source of the Universe.

They rode along the northern ridge of the valley and stopped where Cary Manpure thought the future mound for the analog of Zuv House would be. There they had a picnic in the sunshine.

"Cary, I've been reading about Atlantis," said Vicky, "and I can't figure out what happened to make them forget one language completely, and then start up with a completely new and different language."

"No one knows," said Cary Manpure, "There must have been great trauma though, and as the descendants of Atlantis, we still suffer from it."

"Is that trauma what is the matter with us?" asked Vicky.

"Yes," said Cary Manpure, "it is also our greatest asset. We have forgotten who we are, but we doggedly strive to find out."

Vicky thought for a moment and then said, "Cary, I have it! The release of poison gases by the volcanoes caused great trauma, including and especially AMNESIA."

"It's been right in front of me all these years, and I couldn't see it," he said.

"You're not so smart, Cary Manpure," said Vicky laughing.

Later Vicky said, "I know you have had an especially difficult time in many ways because you have been cut off from everyone else and most especially from female companionship, but you have been doing some very important things, and Avenabury is not a bad place in which to live."

"I know," he responded. "We have especially enjoyed living a more rustic life style. Although we've benefited from many of the things we would normally have, we still had to make a lot of things ourselves.

"I have particularly enjoyed ranching, and farming even more. It seems that the more scientifically advanced you become, the more you enjoy things from simpler times, and old-fashioned physical labor."

"The thing I miss most about Silbury is our team races in the Peri," Cary Manpure continued. He described their races, concluding, "Tommy and I always won."

"I lost Tommy," Vicky responded as she broke out in wild sobbings. Her cousin put his arms around her and held her tightly but very gently.

As Cary Manpure was flying Vicky back to Abzuland he turned to her and said, "There is one more thing I'd like to know, and about which I've been afraid to ask. What happened to Althena?"

"Althena Gandy Chee," Vicky responded, "was convicted on Daphlay for obstruction of justice. She was incarcerated for five years and worked on the production of crystal. After her release she asked her father to allow her to come to Colchis. He did, and she still lives there. She raised a fine son who became a naval officer and she still teaches music to the children of naval personnel based on Colchis."

"There is something else I need to tell you, Cary," Vicky said somewhat later. "I wanted to save it as a special treat for you at the appropriate time."

Cary Manpure eyed his cousin suspiciously.

"It's a story about Anson Trent and Cary Manpure—Cary Arker Manpure," she continued.

"Who is Cary Arker Manpure?" Cary Manpure asked.

"Cary Arker Manpure, or Arker as we call him, is the son of Dan, son of Mark, son of Frank Manpure. That makes him your nephew of some sort," answered Vicky. "Arker is a very nice young man. He always enjoyed history and read about what happened at the end on Silbury. Then he talked to everyone who was there. After that he decided to get Anson Trent.

"Arker knew a little about Director Odkin and found out more, in particular he learned how Director Odkin had tracked down Bunzler and poor Althena. So Arker went after Trent. He discovered that although Trent had made a small fortune as a practitioner of legal arts, he was after an even bigger one.

"Arker discovered that Ann Trent was working for her father in a scheme designed to corner the market on silver: by purchasing all the silver they could at low prices, stashing the silver away to drive up the price and then selling it when the price was artificially high.

"Arker also discovered that in order to raise the necessary funds for his scheme, Trent had been obliged to pledge everything he owned as collateral on short term, high interest loans. He was risking everything for one big haul.

"Arker wrote to Elder Chee on Colchis and told him what was going on. Elder Chee used every quid he had to buy as much silver as he could on Colchis and sent every ounce to Arker with instructions to flood the market on Daphlay when the time was right.

"As the price of silver rose Arker carefully watched every move Ann Trent made, including some you don't want to hear about, Cary. When Arker was certain that Ann Trent was going to start selling, Arker dumped all Elder Chee's silver onto the market.

"The price of silver plummeted. Trent's loans came due. He could not repay them.

"The walls would have come tumbling down on Anson Trent, except that he had no more walls. He was on the street. Anson Trent went to ask his daughter to take him in, and Ann Trent had her latest male companion throw her father out onto the street.

"Arker recovered about half of Elder Chee's funds by selling the silver. Arker then worked ten years to pay back the rest. When Arker tried to give Elder Chee what he owed him, Elder Chee wouldn't take anything. He told Arker he had enjoyed the revenge so much he wouldn't think of taking back any of Arker's reward," Vicky concluded.

Cary Manpure smiled, thought for a moment and then said, "Vicky, do you remember that I adapted the mythos about the golden fleece to include Sarkneson?" he asked.

"Yes," replied Vicky.

"Well, I'm going to change that mythos again," Cary Manpure stated. "I'm going to take out Sarkneson, he only started the disaster. I'm going to put Ann Trent and her daddy in, they finished it off."

They were silent for a while, then Cary Manpure asked, "What about Lura Harwell?"

"Lura Harwell married a man named Michael Stanton about six years after I got to Daphlay," said Vicky Manpure. "They were killed in an accident. I know. I tried to save her life. He was already dead."

Tears streamed from Cary Manpure's eyes, but he talked through them.

"I loved her more than either Alea or Marta," he said. "When she left I cried as I had never cried before. I was so lonely, Vicky. I have thought about her a great deal over the years and have always wished her happiness. Why is it that everyone I touch dies?"

"I don't know," was all Vicky could say.

When Cary Manpure arrived back at Avenabury after dropping his cousin off next to Hurmyrr, he was utterly devastated at being alone again and at having learned of the early, tragic death of Lura Harwell.

The holo-image failed to appear and Cary Manpure was even more lonely, though he managed somehow to go about his daily life. He even made sure to have a proper diet, including the "lots of protein" Vicky had told him was absolutely necessary.

Cary Manpure was also careful to intake moderate amounts of alcohol in mist-producing whiskey, animal fat in butter, salt on his meat and sugar in his tea.

"Sugar is for energy," Vicky had said. "Fat is to keep you warm. Salt tastes good. Protein is for the soul. Alcohol is for relaxation. If you don't relax, stress will kill you!"

Some time later the holo-image suddenly appeared and just 'stood' there. "Where have you been?" asked Cary Manpure.

"I have been lonely," he added when the holo-image continued to be speechless.

At last the holo-image spoke, "The nitwit Essene has been sick. The body is fine, but the soul is wracked. The nitwit Essene will be back with you soon."

The holo-image of the nitwit Essene did not appear, so Cary Manpure constructed a Bench of Musing on the eastern slope of the Hill of Musing just south of the trail leading to the three fields of Avenabury. He liked to sit on the bench at night and watch the stars. His particular favorite was a bright orange star which he renamed Ark Tor. He noticed that Ark Tor was the brightest of a group of four progressively brighter stars which formed an almost perfect tetrahedron in the sky. From his perspective Ark Tor was not at the apex of the tetrahedron. Nevertheless, he took Ark Tor to be the apex so that the tetrahedron pointed off into space. That was uplifting to him because the arrangement seemed to indicate that there was more out there to be learned.

South of Ark Tor and the star group Tetrahedron, and very close to the southern horizon, was another bright star, a red star Cary Manpure renamed Antares. Cary Manpure saw Antares as an enormous ruby in the pommel of a great sword in the sky. He named the sword star group Excalibur after a famous sword in a mythos he knew. Antares was a foreshortening of anti-Ares, Ares being the villain in that same mythos.

The Bench of Musing was not well situated for looking north, but when he sat with his legs over the eastern end of the bench, it was easy for him to see the stars near the celestial north pole.

One group of stars appeared to him as a long twisting and turning line.

"Drakon!" Cary Manpure said aloud to himself as his eyes followed the meandering line of stars.

Two other groups looked like two bears—one big, one small.

"Makros Arktos!" Cary Manpure said, naming the big bear with words from Hellenikos. Cary Manpure thought for a moment trying to name the smaller bear. Then he said, "Little Bear!"

Another time Cary Manpure was sitting on the Bench of Musing and he noticed a spider spinning its web. Some flying insects got caught in the net and Cary Manpure saw that the net was so strong that the insects could not get away. When Cary Manpure was growing up on Silbury there had been no spiders, the only insects were bees and cockroaches—both imported by Alteans, the cockroaches unintentionally—so he was fascinated by the spider, its web and the struggling insects.

Cary Manpure looked up spider webs in a reference book and read that although each strand is relatively weak, the net those strands form is very strong. "Individually we are weak too," Cary Manpure said to himself. "That is why those who will do anything try to divide us, they know that when we unite—in a network—we are strong."

Cary Manpure got an idea. He knew that the Keirykeion Line and the Lion Line crossed southwest of where he lived, much like the strands of a net cross, so he decided to locate the site of a future city tangent to that crossing. "The name of that city will memorialize the crossing of the strands of the net," he said to himself.

Cary Manpure knew that Essenes would not accept anything as blatant as Net City, so he set about finding an encoded name. He looked through lexicons of languages from previous galaxies, and to his amazement found that in one such language the word 'tor' meant 'net.' Cary Manpure knew that the word 'tor' was also unacceptable, so he moved the letters around and added the letter 'w' to come up with the new word 'trow.'

"Trow is not a very good name for a city, so I'll add the word 'bridge' and call it Trowbridge," Cary Manpure said to himself. "Bridge is also a very interesting word because when we transdimension we bridge across dimensions. Trowbridge is therefore the transdimensional net, a transdimensional net, because we need our souls in order to be strong enough to unite and stop those who will do anything." 86

Cary Manpure thought a lot about Anson Trent, Arnhold Manpure, and Kirk Roon. Cary Manpure had long before forgiven Kirk Roon emotionally for what he had done and finally he was able to forgive him intellectually as well.

"Sara Eland was even more right than I thought," Cary Manpure wrote. "She said that the real problem does not lie with those who will do anything, but with those who will follow along with those who will do anything. They accommodate those who will do anything because they want to be comfortable.

"On Silbury they accommodated Anson Trent and Arnhold Manpure—two ruthless egomaniacs who used public service as a guise for furthering their own ambitions—because they wanted to be comfortable.

"Kirk Roon became the victim of the accommodators.

"Next time, we must not accommodate the ruthless egomaniacs who hide behind public service in the pursuit of their own ambitions. Instead, we must crush the future Anson Trents and the future Arnhold Manpures.

If we do not, we (those who have been accommodators and those of us who have always fought) will always be their victims, just as Kirk Roon was their victim. We must unite into an indestructible network and not allow anybody to divide us.

"The labyrys of command should be worn by everyone in a position of authority, to remind them that one razor sharp edge of the double headed axe is for them—if they abuse their position of leadership. The Anson Trents and the Arnhold Manpures have axes with only one blade. We must use that one blade to axe them, and then pin onto the breasts of those who serve, the double headed axe labyrys. And then constantly remind them of the duality of leadership: authority and accountability."

187.1

Shortly thereafter the holo-image suddenly appeared at last and said, "Cary Manpure, when you were at Alteana, Essenes told Alteans there that Essenes intend to confuse the future beings of Danebury about their moon—a moon which is the single reason why complex life arose on Danebury—by making it a harbinger of madness in cultures of Danebury.

"Now Essenes also intend that the future beings of Danebury closely associate their moon with spiders and that many of those future beings of Danebury have a strong unreasoning fear of spiders. The reason being that when those future beings suddenly understand how important their moon is, and how important are strong networks between those who care (as are the strong network of cobweb chords important to spiders) that realization will cause a dramatic shift in their thinking and suddenly allow them to work together toward their role as leaders of the galaxy.

"Essenes also intend that many of those future beings of Danebury have a strong unreasoning fear of drakon—particularly snakes. The reason for this is so that when those future beings suddenly understand the importance of the metaphor of the drakon of the keirykeion, that realization will also cause a dramatic shift in their thinking and suddenly allow them to work together toward their role as leaders of the galaxy.

"Essenes also intend that the square cross becomes the symbol which represents those future beings of Danebury, as those beings will be a cross between indigenous and non-indigenous genetics. And the square cross also depicts a section of a network of those working together because they care.

"Cary Manpure, you care greatly. Essenes do not want you to be downcast. You deserve to know."

The holo-image disappeared.

Some time later the holo-image suddenly appeared before Cary Manpure and repeated for him information that Cary Manpure and Cary Jackman had been wondering about just prior to the death of Cary Jackman. "You already know," the holo-image said, "that the future topogly vector of Hurmyrr is to be equivalent to the cube of two pi; that the tangent of 24.901.54558 (the number of statute miles in the equatorial circumference of Danebury) is a very close equivalent to the cube root of two pi; that the ratio between 21,600 (the number of nautical miles around Danebury) and 24,901.54558 is .867416037; that the number which forms the same ratio .867416037 with 248.0502134 (the cube of two pi) is 285.9645232; that Hurmyrr was partially constructed using the pyramid inch, an inch which is longer than the Danebury inch by a ratio of 1.00106 to 1; that the entryway in the north facing of Hurmyrr is offset precisely 286.10213 pyramid inches; and that the difference between 286.10213 and 285.9645232 is .1376068.

"You already know what 137 represents; that the 60 represents tetrahedra; that the 68 represents six-eighths, three-quarters, 750,000 rpms, and the spinning disk—which is the most important tool of the physical universe.

"You already know that the number .1376068 therefore represents all those things which Joe Lon Odkin's modified energy transconverter crop glyph represents.

"Cary Manpure, from now on you must always have a pad and pencil ready so that you can write down what you are told."

The holo-image disappeared.

The next day the holo-image suddenly appeared and waited while Cary Manpure fumbled for his pad and pencil. Then the holo-image said, "When you were in school, Cary Manpure, you and your cousin Vicky Manpure made a report to your class on topogly. You reported that the topogly vector of the site of energy transredimensioning in the Hurmaze was 656.5612701, a number which is equivalent to 25,920 divided by the square of two pi.

"Any given cross section, cut perpendicular to the central axis of the cone of the physical universe, results in a circular slice of the physical universe. Any given circular slice contains data, information and knowledge extruded into the physical universe by the Source; though the composition of that data, information and knowledge is always different from one slice to the next. Nevertheless, any given circular slice (even one which is so thin that it is no thicker than the ink with which it can be drawn on a piece of paper) is still three-dimensional—and only deemed two-dimensional as a convenience for geometric calculation. Any given circular slice contains something of everything, including the all-important spinning which makes everything work.

"The lengths of the vast number of the regularly varying circumferences of three-dimensional circular slices of the conical physical universe—which can be geometrically modeled to be so thin that they can be called two-dimensional and therefore deemed to have only one circumference—are calculated by multiplying their diameters by pi, the Universal Constant of the Universe.

"When any given 'two-dimensional' circle is spun, a sphere is formed and pi is the ratio between the diameter of the spinning circle (which has become a sphere) and all the resulting circumferences.

"Since everything spins, everything is spherical.

"Since everything is spherical, the circumferences of everything divided by the diameter of everything, is pi.

"If the angular momentum of any given sphere increases enough, that sphere spins itself partially into complexified three-space.

"If a sphere attains a spin rate of 777,777 rpms it spins itself instantaneously completely through complexified three-space and into four-dimensions. The three-dimensional manifestation of this is the physical destruction of the sphere.

"The modeling of the ratio between the 'diameter' of a hypersphere in complexified three-space and its 'circumferences,' is the square of two pi.

"The modeling of the ratio between the 'diameter' of a hypersphere in four-dimensions and its 'circumferences,' is the cube of two pi.

"Pi is widely known. The square of two pi is encoded in the location of the Hurmaze on Silbury. The cube of two pi is encoded in the location of Hurmyrr on Danebury."

The holo-image disappeared.

The next day the holo-image suddenly appeared and said, "Essenes offset the entryway in the north facing of Hurmyrr precisely by 286.10213 pyramid inches. Essenes did this to encode the number 285.9645232, because the cube of two pi divided by 285.9645232 is .867416037; the ratio between 21,600 and 24,901.54558—a number whose tangent is a very close equivalent to the cube root of two pi. Essenes also offset the entryway by 286.10213 pyramid inches because they wanted to encode the number .1376068, which represents all those things which Joe Lon Odkin's modified energy transconverter crop glyph represents. Essenes offset the entryway to the east, because east is on the right (if one faces north from inside Hurmyrr) and Essenes wanted the entryway of Hurmyrr to represent the soul of a self-aware being." 185

The holo-image disappeared.

The next day the holo-image suddenly appeared and said, "You also unwittingly encoded the number 285.9645232 into your two eggs in a frying pan crop glyph when you added the very short line 25 degrees counterclockwise from the short line you had previously added. 168

"Essenes will insure that there are breaks in Avenabury Circle through which roads will run. The road which will pass through Avenabury Circle just south of the analog of the Tetrahedron will have an azimuth of 360 degrees Avenabury from the center of Avenabury Circle. Another road will have an azimuth of 182 degrees Avenabury from the center of the circle. When a correctly scaled overlay of Joe Lon Odkin's modified energy transconverter crop glyph (with the two-dimensional depiction of a complexified three-space tetrahedron) is properly superimposed over a map of Avenabury Circle, one of the three lines inferring the apex of the tetrahedral casing of the energy transconverter, will line up on a bearing of 182 degrees Avenabury from the center of the circle. 188 This is the line whose thin continuation is a depiction of a conscitron thruster armature of an Essene space craft. In addition, one of the lines of the complexified three-space tetrahedron will line up with the road leading from Avenabury Circle to the north on a bearing of 261 degrees Avenabury from the center of the circle.

"When a correctly scaled overlay of your two eggs in a frying pan is properly superimposed over the map of Avenabury Circle and then overlaid onto Joe Lon Odkin's correctly scaled and positioned modified energy transconverter crop glyph, the handle of the frying pan will be superimposed over those things which will have a bearing of 182 degrees Avenabury, from the center of Avenabury Circle. 188.1

"Then the very short line will have a bearing of 236 degrees Avenabury and the short line a bearing of 261 degrees Avenabury: the road leading to the north. When 25 more degrees are added to 261 degrees Avenabury, the result is 286 degrees Avenabury: the long axis of the two eggs in the frying pan transtime crop glyph, a near equivalent of 285.9645232.

"The long axis of the two stone eggs in the Avenabury Circle frying pan will not be 285.9645232 degrees Avenabury. The long axis of the stone eggs will be 19.47 degrees west of geographic north—to give the correct positioning of the lead lined casings containing the gold dolphins in relation to the transconverter sphere." 189

The holo-image disappeared.

The next day the holo-image suddenly appeared and began speaking, "When you were in the seventh grade, Cary Manpure, your transdimensional physics teacher told your class that the apple is used as a symbol in Philosophia because the uppermost part of the three-dimensional secondary energy disturbance pattern of a soul print looks like a large apple with progressively smaller apples piled on top of one another, all with their stems pointing downward. This pattern continues through the top of the skull and outwards indefinitely with the 'apples' getting progressively smaller and weaker.

"Mr. Wellton said, 'This pattern of a large apple with the progressively smaller apples can be modeled geometrically in two-dimensions. The resulting two-dimensional model changes the largest apple into an upside down heart and the other apples into circles. The smaller apples, now circles, are moved to various mirrored locations around the upside down heart and the largest circle. This pattern is repeated again and again on each progressively smaller circle. Above the upside down heart and the largest circle a different pattern is produced. After more circles, a long straight line with replications of the original pattern on it continues onward—indefinitely.

"'This two-dimensional depiction of the upper part of a soul print is called the Waldark set. The Waldark set is an extremely useful model for showing how the macro is like the micro, only bigger. The Waldark set also models the transformations which take place at the border of three-dimensions and complexified three-space.'

"You did not understand what Mr. Wellton was talking about.

"Until you were in the eighth grade you liked art and whenever you could you took art classes. Since then you have hated art because on the first day of your eighth grade art class your teacher stood before the class and said, 'Art is based on the phi section. The phi section is the division of a line, or geometric figure, so that the proportion of the smaller section to the larger section is the same as the proportion of the larger section to the whole.'

"Now you know the importance of phi section rectangles in energy transdimensioning and you may want to take up art again so that you can learn the importance of the phi section in art.

"In order for you to better understand the complexities and subtleties of the Waldark set and in order to illustrate the importance of phi section rectangles you are to design a crop glyph which is a modification of the Waldark set encoding phi section rectangles."

The holo-image disappeared.

Cary Manpure designed the crop glyph ordered by Essenes. He altered the shape of the main part of the Waldark set slightly and moved upward the small replication of the Waldark set—which is above the main part of the Waldark set. He also made that small replication larger and turned it into a circle to represent a soul. 190

As a result of Cary Manpure's having moved the small replication upward the axial distance from the center of the largest circles, on either side of the heart, to the center of the top circle of the main part of the Waldark set had a ratio of 1 to 1.618 (the phi section ratio) as compared to the distance from the center of the largest circles on either side of the heart, to the center of the circular representation at the top of the crop glyph.

By drawing a semi-circular arc from the center of the circular representation of the soul to below the main part of the Waldark set (with the center of the arc the juncture of the top of the heart and the bottom of the largest circle) the distance from the center of the circular representation of the soul to where the arc met the centerline axis of the Waldark set, had a ratio of the square root of five to one; as compared with the axial distance between the center of the largest circles on either side of the heart, to the center of the top circle of the main part of the Waldark set. 190.1

When Cary Manpure had finished his design the holo-image suddenly appeared and said, "You have now discovered that the square root of five is related to the phi section by adding one over the phi section ratio to the phi section ratio."

The holo-image disappeared.

The next morning Cary Manpure woke up early on one of the sofas on the circular living platform. Almost immediately he noticed two drawings which he had not made and which had not been there the night before. One showed two circumscribed interlocked tetrahedra inside his construction of the modified Waldark set transtime crop glyph. The other showed his design overlaid by a transdimensional spiral, an isosceles triangle having long sides with a 1.618 to 1 ratio to its short side and the Tor. 190.2,190.3

The holo-image suddenly appeared and said, "The Waldark set is important in many ways, but in this case the Waldark set was used as a basis from which you could begin to understand the interrelationships between the square root of five, the Transdimensional Spiral, various aspects of the phi section and the Tor. You can now begin to see why the square root of five is so important in the many things you have learned and will learn about."

The holo-image disappeared.

In the modified Waldark set transtime crop glyph designed by Cary Manpure as overlaid by the Transdimensional Spiral, the Transdimensional Spiral did not cut through the center of the circle representing he soul, but two-thirds of the way through it instead, a representation of the fact that the conscious and subconscious minds are only two-thirds of self-aware consciousness.

As Cary Manpure was entering the design of the modified Waldark set transtime crop glyph into the graphics computer the holo-image suddenly appeared and said, "You can more easily enter the heart shaped part of your design into the computer if you know that it can be constructed using the algorithm for its radial line of 2 (1-cos phi) with the origin at the cusp."

"I will do that," said Cary Manpure, "and then I never want to hear about phi again."

Some time later the holo-image suddenly appeared and began speaking, "You now know almost all the things that Essenes know about. Lura Redmand unwittingly encoded the square of two pi in the location of the Hurmaze on Silbury. Essenes have encoded many things in Hurmyrr. You and your associates have also encoded many things in transtime crop glyphs and in the topogly matrix.

"The cube root of two pi was long ago encoded in the tangent of the number of statute miles around any given seed planet.

"The cube root of two pi is the encoded metaphor for two-thirds.

"The cube root of two pi was encoded in the tangent of the number of statute miles around any given seed planet long before the emergence of what Essenes consider to be the most important thing concerning two-thirds—a thing which deals directly with the redeeming of this galaxy.

"At first there were only Alteans in this galaxy. Then there were Pleiadeans as well. The Pleiadeans have misdirected themselves, but Alteans on their own, are not capable of redirecting the Pleiadeans. Essenes are preparers, not redirectors. Alteans need assistance to redirect the Pleiadeans, and to redeem the galaxy. The beings who will one day inhabit this planet will lead Alteans in redirecting the Pleiadeans and insure the redeeming the galaxy.

"There will therefore be three groups of beings in the galaxy: Alteans, the Pleiadeans, and the future beings of this planet. There will therefore be three groups of beings in the galaxy and two-thirds must work together.

The holo-image disappeared.

"Is that all there is?" Cary Manpure screamed. "I have battled through this pile just to get to know that the cube root of two pi is an encoded metaphor for two-thirds, two-thirds being most important in that we have been preparing the way for future Anson Trents to lead the redeeming of the galaxy. Essenes are nitwits!"

The holo-image suddenly appeared and said, "That is not all.

"The cube root of two pi is much more.

"Find the wavelength of planetary torun on inhabitable planets and calculate the cube root of two pi."

The holo-image disappeared.

Cary Manpure found the required wavelength of planetary torun in Joe Lon Odkin's tattered old transdimensional physics book and copied it down: it is 15.37725124 feet in length.

He calculated that the cube root of two pi is 1.845270149.

He stared blankly at his note pad.

The holo-image suddenly appeared and said, "Convert the required wavelength of planetary torun from fect to inches!"

The holo-image disappeared.

Cary Manpure multiplied 15.37725124 by 12 inches and obtained 184.5270149 inches.

"The wave length of planetary torun is 100 times the cube root of two pi when measured in inches," Cary Manpure said to himself.

The holo-image suddenly appeared and said, "The three-dimensional disturbance pattern of the soul spins, and it also twangs. There is a complex relationship between spinning and twanging, but the result is that the three-dimensional disturbance pattern of the soul functions as a tuning fork. The retained two-thirds torun of the soul vibrates back and forth along the vertical, central, dimensionless non-spinning spin axis of the three-dimensional disturbance pattern of the soul. The twanging tuning fork projects through this and harmonizes the soul and the being to whom it is attached.

"Planets are very different from souls, but the twanging process is similar. The spin rates, sizes and resulting angular momentum of planets vary. Only a period of rotation of 23 hours, 56 minutes creates the proper angular momentum for planets to transredimension torun with a wavelength of 184.5270149 inches. 191,191.1

"Planetary torun having a wavelength of 184.5270149 inches is the only wavelength of planetary torun in harmony with the wavelength of the three-dimensional disturbance pattern of the soul of self-aware beings, because the diameter and resulting wavelength of the three-dimensional disturbance pattern of the soul of self-aware beings is .1845270149 inches.

"The wavelength of planetary torun must be 1000 times longer than the wavelength of the three-dimensional disturbance pattern of the soul.

"The cube root of two pi is 10 times the wavelength of the three-dimensional disturbance pattern of the soul.

"You already know that living things exhibit five-sided symmetry; that self-aware beings are also physically bi-symmetrical; and that the soul of self-aware beings is on the right tangent of the bi-symmetry of self-aware beings, so beings are not completely bi-symmetrical.

"You already know that since self-aware beings are physically bi-symmetrical they have two hands, five fingers per hand, and a total of 10 fingers.

"You already know that self-aware beings therefore naturally count by 10s.

"The cube root of two pi is 10 times the wavelength of the three-dimensional disturbance pattern of the soul because self-aware beings have 10 fingers and therefore count naturally by 10s.

"The compatible wavelength of planetary torun must be 1000 times longer than the wavelength of the three-dimensional disturbance pattern of the soul because in order to be in harmony with the soul the wavelength of planetary torun must be either the same length, 10 times that wavelength, 100 times, 1000 times, 10,000 times and so on. Due to the size and practicable rotation rates of planets only the scale of 1000 times is possible."

The holo-image disappeared.

"I suppose that is interesting," Cary Manpure said to himself, "but so what?"

The holo-image suddenly appeared and added, "When referring to the physical manifestations of souls in three-dimensions, Essenes always mean only the three-dimensional disturbance pattern of souls, since souls reside only in four-dimensions. However, as a matter of convenience it is customary to use the terms 'diameter of the soul' and 'wavelength of the soul' instead of the much more precise but much longer proper terminology. Essenes request that I ask you if you consider that to be appropriate in our conversations."

Cary Manpure shook his head. "That would be perfectly fine with me," he responded.

The holo-image continued, "The diameters and therefore the wavelengths of the soul of self-aware beings vary slightly with the size of the seed planet of any given galaxy. This is because the length of inches are slightly different on any given seed planet. The souls of self-aware beings, indigenous to any given seed planet, have wavelengths that are precisely in harmony with the wavelength of the planetary torun of that planet. The beings who were indigenous to Altea were such beings.

"The extragalactic pioneers however, were the end result of the intermingling of many earlier extragalactic pioneers and many earlier indigenous beings. The wavelength of the souls of the extragalactic pioneers was an average of the wavelengths of the souls of all their ancestors. The extragalactic pioneers had souls not precisely in harmony with any planet.

"After the extragalactic pioneers and the indigenous beings of this galaxy had intermingled for some time, there were no longer any beings in this galaxy whose souls were precisely in harmony with Altea.

"This situation has resulted in each succeeding galaxy of the chain of galaxies—up to and including this galaxy—being filled with self-aware beings with souls having wavelengths which are an average of the wavelengths of the souls of their ancestors.

"This averaging of soul wavelength is caused by the mutual exchange of extremely powerful and extremely high speed torun during sexual intercourse. The torun from the female acts on the sperm of the male; the torun of the male acts on the egg or eggs of the female. The result of this interaction of torun is an offspring whose soul has a wavelength which is an average of the wavelengths of her or his mother and father.

"Offspring who result from artificial insemination—or other means than by direct sexual intercourse and the release of extremely powerful and extremely high speed torun—are not directly affected, but repeated generational continuance of such procedures as artificial insemination eventually puts self-aware beings at risk of contracting both physical and mental illnesses.

"Although the self-aware beings of Danebury are—and will be—the result of a kind of artificial insemination process, they will not have the problems associated with the lack of intermingling of extremely powerful and extremely high speed torun during sexual intercourse as only one generation is involved in each of the two administerings.

"However, as a result of not resulting from the intermingling of extremely powerful and extremely high speed torun during sexual intercourse, the self-aware beings of this planet have—and will have—souls with wavelengths that are precisely in harmony with the wavelength of the planetary torun of their planet..."

"This period of rotation of Danebury was artificially set by Essenes," Cary Manpure interrupted. "That period is now changing. They'll get out of harmony."

"The change will be slight," said the holo-image. "They'll get slightly out of tune. They'll feel creative tension. We'll talk more about that later. Now back to where we left off...

"This was also the case of the all the indigenous beings back through the chain of galaxies up to and including this galaxy, but they have long since intermingled with extragalactic pioneers.

"Therefore, the self-aware beings of this planet are—and will be—unique. They are the only beings in this galaxy to live on a planet with which the wavelengths of their souls are almost exactly in tune. Even when they eventually intermingle with Alteans their offspring will also be unique; they will differ from offspring born and bred on Altea because Danebury is slightly different in size."

The holo-image disappeared.

"I'm still not precisely sure what Essenes are telling me," Cary Manpure said to himself.

The next day the holo-image suddenly appeared and said, "The self-aware beings of this planet are—and will have—souls with wavelengths almost precisely in harmony with their planet. No other beings in this galaxy have souls with wavelengths that are so precisely in harmony with their planet. The self-aware beings of this planet are—and will be—unique. Their descendants will also always be unique.

"This almost precise harmony and uniqueness is vitally important to the future psyche of the self-aware beings of this planet.

"When they finally realize how harmonious they are with their planet and how unique that is, they will attain the will to fulfill their destiny as leaders of the redeeming of the galaxy.

"They will finally understand the way things are and that even with everything else they have attained as a result of their ordeals—especially the amount of courage—it is only their planetary harmony and uniqueness which will give the future self-aware beings of this planet the self-realization—the clear reflection—to do those things which it is their destiny to do."

The holo-image disappeared.

"So now I know," Cary Manpure said to himself.

After learning these things Cary Manpure walked down to the Bench of Musing to think. He became agitated, got up and walked all the way down the Hill of Musing to the east, toward his three fields. The river (in which they were not allowed to fish) ran along the western boundary of those fields and they had never built a bridge across it. Instead, they forded the river on their horses. Cary Manpure wanted to walk across those fields to the land beyond, so he sought a way across without getting wet. To the south he spotted a tree growing along the river bank, its branches overhanging the water. He climbed this as far as he could and then jumped for the far bank. As he did so his foot slipped and he twisted in the air. Cary Manpure landed back first on a log with a stub of a limb sticking out of it. He struck the limb stub squarely between his shoulder blades and searing pain stabbed through him. He tried to get up, vomited and lost consciousness.

When Cary Manpure regained consciousness he was lying on one of the sofas on the circular living platform of HOME, and as his eyes focussed he saw the holo-image standing in front of him.

"I didn't just float up here did I?" asked Cary Manpure.

The holo-image said nothing.

"I would have died down there," Cary Manpure said.

The holo-image said nothing.

Cary Manpure laid back and the pain seared through him. He slept and whenever he woke a warm bowl of soup awaited him. Finally, the pain began to subside.

Cary Manpure looked for the holo-image but could not find it. "I know you are out there and can hear me," he said aloud to Essenes. "Director Odkin told us about the sea creature mound and that he couldn't decide if it was a shark or a dolphin. I have thought about it a lot, and now I know. The sea creature mound is a self portrait of Essenes, and Essenes themselves cannot decide if they are sharks or dolphins. I know that Essenes are dolphins!"

Sometime later the holo-image suddenly appeared before Cary Manpure as he continued to rest and recover on the sofa.

"Thank you, Cary Manpure," it said. "Essenes have never known."

"Don't go!" Cary Manpure shouted at the holo-image. "Please take me with you. I have become totally alienated and alone on this planet. I am no longer an Altean. I want to be an Essene!"

"Cary Manpure," the holo-image said, "it is not yet time for the reunion. The reunion is to be among Alteans, Essene Alteans, and the future beings of this planet. You have been and you still are, greatly facilitating the process of moving forward toward that reunion."

"You have created an incredible tension within me," Cary Manpure cried out. "I hate you, but I want to learn."

Suddenly the word 'tension' seared through Cary Manpure. "Life bursts forth on a seed planet because of the incredible tension created by the counter forces of rotation and retrograde precession," he shouted out, "and a similar tension precedes sexual release. Everything works because of tension, not stress, but creative tension. Creative tension is the key to everything!"

"Precisely," said the holo-image. "As in the creative tension of the almost precise harmony of the souls of the future beings of this planet."

"And we need sexual release, not only because we express love but also to release tension. This tension is creative, but if it builds too much it is devastating," said Cary Manpure.

"Yes," said the holo-image. "The soul also needs to release tension, tension caused by the soul's inability to transcommunicate perfectly with its three-dimensional partner. A kind of interference energy builds up and sexual release blows this interference away."

"Then if we don't have sexual release," said Cary Manpure, "our souls can't communicate very well with us."

"Precisely," said the holo-image.

The holo-image disappeared.

Some time later the holo-image suddenly appeared and said, "Sexual intercourse has three purposes. Two-thirds of those purposes have to do with bringing forth offspring.

"As you know, the mutual exchange of torun during sexual intercourse sizes the soul of the offspring so that its soul has a diameter which is an average of the diameters of the souls of the mother and father.

"Additionally, this same exchange of torun transfers soul experience and learning from both mother and father to the soul of the offspring.

"Offspring generated as a result of other means than sexual intercourse do not receive this sharing of torun, and therefore do not receive a soul which is balanced between mother and father—with regard to its size and resulting harmonics. Such offspring are disharmonious. Also such offspring do not receive soul experience and learning from their parents. They therefore lack experience and learning that is vital to their development.

"As you said, the last and most important purpose of sexual intercourse is to exchange love."

The holo-image disappeared.

Some time later the holo-image suddenly appeared and said, "All living things have an energy aura surrounding them, which is in complexified three-space. In plants this aura originates in the center of the main stalk and gives the plant stamina to survive. In animals and self-aware beings this energy aura is the carrier of courage and emanates from the heart. During sexual intercourse the auras of mother and father are intermingled and transferred to the heart of the offspring, giving that offspring additional courage—which is a combined courage of mother and father. Offspring generated by other means than sexual intercourse lack this balanced additional courage."

The holo-image disappeared.

Some time later the holo-image suddenly appeared and said, "Courageous harmonic offspring are therefore the result of processes which take place in three-dimensions, complexified three-space and four-dimensions.

"In three-dimensions all of those things which make up the three-dimensional body and mind are intermingled.

"In complexified three-space courage is intermingled.

"In four-dimensions soul size and experience and knowledge is intermingled.

"In four-dimensions the Source of the Universe makes the interminglings work."

The holo-image disappeared.

Some time later the holo-image suddenly appeared and said, "The metaphor mind, heart and soul is a metaphor for the interminglings which take place during sexual intercourse. Mind is the three-dimensional interminglings. Heart is the complexified three-space interminglings. Soul is the four-dimensional interminglings."

The holo-image disappeared.

Some time later the holo-image suddenly appeared and said, "Essenes project that the future beings of Danebury will not know of two-thirds of the interminglings which take place during sexual intercourse: those interminglings taking place in complexified three-space and in four-dimensions. Therefore, Essenes will give the future beings of Danebury the metaphor mind, heart and soul and an encoded accompanying key for all three interminglings: father, son and spirit. Father represents parents and therefore three-dimensional biological intermingling; Son represents the future beings of this planet and the intermingling of courage in complexified three-space; Spirit represents the soul.

"Essenes plan to use only male references in this encoded key because Essenes want the future female beings of Danebury to have even greater courage than males.

"In their encodings Essenes will omit the fact that the Source of the Universe makes the interminglings work, so that when the future beings of Danebury find this out there will be clear reflection."

The holo-image disappeared.

Cary Manpure lived for over 20 years after the death of Cary Jackman and he assisted Essenes in many ways. He especially enjoyed working with Essenes on projects involving mythos.

Cary Manpure continued to be very bothered by the specter of the future Anson Trents of Danebury, beings who would have souls with wavelengths in precise harmony with their planet, but who would not be in harmony with anything. He was especially troubled by their linear thinking because he thought that they would not be able to understand allegory, since that demands creative thinking.

To help them along, he wrote a very simple allegory in the form of a riddle, "What creature is it that walks on four feet in the morning, on two feet at noon and on three feet in the evening?"

Cary Manpure meant morning, noon and evening to be allegories for early childhood, adulthood and old age. Cary Manpure thought that if these allegories could be understood, the answer to the riddle would be self evident: a self-aware being, since self-aware beings crawl on hands and knees when they are young, walk on two feet when they mature and often need a cane when old.

After Cary Manpure had written his allegorical riddle the holo-image suddenly appeared and said, "Essenes will infuse your allegorical riddle into a future mythos of Danebury. Essenes project that those who learn this mythos will think that those in the mythos who could not solve the riddle were infantile. Essenes project that those who finally figure things out, mostly by understanding allegory, will think of everyone—including themselves before they understood allegory—as infantile."

The holo-image disappeared.

In those years when he was alone, Cary Manpure thought a lot about things. He was especially intrigued by the elements that Joe Lon Odkin, Cary Jackman and himself had unwittingly included in the design of crop glyphs. He studied many of those crop glyph designs and continually found more and more things in them.

When he was re-reading his copy of the adventure book, the encased book brought from the previous galaxy, Cary Manpure suddenly realized why they had unwittingly put many things into their crop glyph designs. He had long known of the tradition that many important things were unwittingly included in that book by its author, and as he was rereading it, he began to see those things.

"Those who are in harmony with the Universe," Cary Manpure said to himself, "do things which are in harmony with the Universe. We became in harmony with the Universe and the designs of our crop glyphs reflect that. The author of the encased book must have been in harmony with the Universe, or else he would not have unwittingly included so many important things in his book. He was, so he did."

Cary Manpure read a great deal about a lot of things, but especially he read about transdimensional physics. He came to understand that although things are very complex, that complexity is the result of patterns within patterns within patterns within patterns.

One day when Cary Manpure sat on the Bench of Musing, looking out over Avenabury, he said to himself, "The future Anson Trents of this planet will figure out everything they can relying solely on three-dimensions, and then they will come to a seeming dead end. They will continue to try to figure things out, but their explanations for how things are will get more and more complex to the point that no one, not even themselves, will understand those explanations.

"Then Essenes must activate the transtime crop glyphs.

"The origin of transtime crop glyphs will be totally inexplicable.

"Why transtime crop glyphs suddenly appear will be totally inexplicable.

"The precise location of transtime crop glyphs will be totally inexplicable.

"The content of transtime crop glyphs will be totally inexplicable.

"History teaches that despite the obstruction of some and the malaise of the many, a few will always seek.

"By the time they seek the answers to the riddle of the crops in the fields the future seekers of this planet will have been prepared.

"They will have courage.

"They will understand allegory.

"They will succeed.

"The walls will come tumbling down around the last of the Anson Trents."

Cary Manpure designed only two more transtime crop glyphs during this time, and he called one of them Stick Figures. He determined that the protosite for Stick Figures was to be on a hill between Amesbury Circle and Avenabury. Cary Manpure intended this crop glyph to be a transcommunication to the soul of Cary Jackman.

The circles at both ends were representations of two eyes looking upward. The message was written between the two eyes. Part of the message was to be read from left to right, the other part from right to left. 192

Cary Manpure had suddenly realized that many things could be seen either intuitively (as Cary Jackman had often seen them) or logically (as Director Odkin had usually seen them). Cary Manpure had also suddenly realized that he had frequently been able to see things both intuitively and logically, a realization that made him feel in harmony for the first time.

"I guess that is why Pazzy named me Ollun," said Cary Manpure to himself as tears streamed down his cheeks. "Pazzy knew."

The two upright lines to the right of the right eye were to be read as 'to,' the following U as 'you,' the first C as 'Cary,' the second C as 'see,' the next U also as 'you,' and the upside down and backward L as 'later.'

The first message was: "To you, Cary. See you later."

The two upright lines to the left of the left eye, the following backward C, the upside down pi, and right side up pi were meant to be read in combination as 'the cube root of two pi.' Cary Manpure made only two-thirds of the representations of pi look like pi because he wanted to encode the encoded metaphor of the cube root of two pi: two-thirds.

The next part of the second message was a backwards C—reinforcing the reading from right to left—and meant to be read as 'Cary.' The single upright line was meant to be read as 'I,' the two upright lines as 'to,' the U as 'you,' and the upside down and backwards L as 'later.'

The second message was: The cube root of two pi, Cary, I to you later."

Cary Manpure represented six, five, and seven in Gwynmyrr in the number of characters or groups of characters in his messages and sub-message. The first message had six characters or groups of characters, the second message seven. There were five individual characters, in the group of characters expressing the cube root of two pi.

In the encoded messages the upside down and backwards L was sixth from the left and seventh from the right, but from the perspective of the eyes looking upward the upside down and backwards L was on the right tangent of the center of the two messages. Cary Manpure meant the upside down and backwards L—the Hurengle equivalent of lambda—the Hellenikos symbol for the soul—to be a representation of the soul.

Cary Manpure began to understand things in a way he felt no one had ever understood things before. He began to feel things in addition to thinking them.

We can only think up to a certain point, he mused, and after that we have to feel. The way things are in the reality of our existence devolves from a higher reality: the four-dimensional realm of the Source of the Universe. That realm is too complex and too inexplicable to be thought about and explained, but I am beginning to feel some of it. I can't even express to myself how this is or what I feel. The only thing I can say, even to myself, is that I feel at peace and in total harmony with the Universe. I like that, it makes me happy and I am going to have a good time the rest of my life just by thinking and feeling.

Cary Manpure read an old geometry book and noticed that the patterns of their transtime crop glyphs seemed to match the things he read and saw in the diagrams of that geometry book. Then he printed copies of crop glyph designs that were still in their computer. He then carefully went over each crop glyph design and found that they did indeed correspond to what he had seen and read about in that old geometry book, as he had suspected. He knew that they had never sat down and worked these things out. They had drawn free hand, shown them to one another and then refined them according to the comments of the others. Crop glyphs that were meant to convey certain things were very carefully refined further in the computer. The remainder, however, were only slightly altered as they were entered into the computer, enough to straighten out lines, check tangential alignments, make circles round and conform with Essene instructions and so forth. Cary Manpure suddenly realized that they had all been much more in harmony with the Universe than he had thought.

"They knew much more than they could have guessed," he cried out in agony. "I know now, but they never did. It is not fair. We all were denied the companionship and love of wives and family, but at least I now have peace of mind."

Then Cary Manpure thought some more and remembered his transtime crop glyph message to Cary Jackman. "We'll all meet again," he said to the sky. "We'll all meet again. Then we will all know."

When Cary Manpure was gone, Essenes buried the body of Cary Manpure in a shaft grave in the grave circle in the manner of his ancestors near the graves of Joe Lon Odkin, Cary Jackman and Terry Wellton.

Then Essenes permanently sealed the labyrinthine passageway leading to the corbelled dome tomb under the Hill of Musing.

Some time before the passing of Cary Manpure the holo-image said to him, "The reason Essenes have given you such difficulty was to create creative tension. Your growing ability to deal with everything which has come your way is proof that you have reacted as Essenes thought you would—and you have grown."

"What did Essenes want me to be able to do as a result of receiving all this creative tension?" asked Cary Manpure.

"What you have done," said the holo-image.

"Then it was for the same reason you did everything to Director Odkin and Buff too," said Cary Manpure.

"Yes," said the holo-image. "Everything was done for Panergon Gwynmyrr."

"Then Panergon Gwynmyrr had better be worth it," said Cary Manpure, "because you ruined our lives."

"A very few must do extraordinary things so that the children of the Universe can have the opportunity to know harmony," said the holo-image.

"Have Essenes ever stopped to think that if they had told us what you just told me," said Cary Manpure, "that we would have VOLUNTEERED to do what we have done? Then we would not have had to have lived in such disharmony. The challenge of the work would have created more than sufficient creative tension. We have done what we have done DESPITE, not because of what Essenes have inflicted on us."

"Essenes have done what they do for a long time," said the holo-image. "They know what must be done."

"Perhaps some would have required such methods," said Cary Manpure, "but not us. I know myself. I know Director Odkin and Buff. We don't need to be coerced to do what is right. We cared long before Essenes took us."

"What you say is very true," said the holo-image, "but you must also think about Essenes. Essenes have been working for nearly a billion years to insure the redeeming of the galaxy. The only way Essenes have been able to continue is by engendering creative tension between themselves and those through whom they forward Panergon Gwynmyrr. If Essenes did not do this, they would not be able to continue."

"Then we were the victims of the requirement of Essenes to feel creative tension," said Cary Manpure.

"Partially," said the holo-image, "but Essenes insist that the challenge of the work would not have been sufficient to have created enough creative tension in either Essenes or especially in you. Think back on all you have done. You have been most creative when you have been the most angry."

"Then anger is the key?" said Cary Manpure.

"For you, yes," said the holo-image. "You are what you are."

"Then you tailor your harassment depending on whom you are harassing?" said Cary Manpure.

"Based on many things, Essenes plan everything very carefully," said the holo-image. "The most important things Essenes consider are those things which they have learned, what needs to be done and what those through whom they are going to forward Panergon Gwynmyrr are like."

"It would be nice if sometimes Essenes worked WITH someone instead of through them," said Cary Manpure, "but in order to do that Essenes would have to take feelings into account and they would never want to do that, would they?"

"Essenes do not have that luxury," said the holo-image.

"I completely disagree with the WAY in which Essenes have done everything," said Cary Manpure.

"You are what you are," said the holo-image, "and Essenes do what they must."

"Do Essenes like that?" asked Cary Manpure.

"No," said the holo-image.

"Essenes ripped us away from those whom we loved and Essenes marooned us on Danebury so that they could make us do what they wanted," said Cary Manpure. "Would Essenes have killed us if we had not cooperated, if we had just sat there? Do Essenes kill to keep Panergon Gwynmyrr?"

"Essenes have killed for Panergon Gwynmyrr and will kill again if necessary," said the holo-image, "but they have never killed anyone like you, nor will they ever do so. That possibility will not arise. You and those like you are what you are—always cooperative. Essenes choose carefully."

"Will Essenes ever change their ways?" asked Cary Manpure.

"Essenes will adapt to circumstances," said the holo-image.

"That is not very specific," said Cary Manpure.

"The future is unknowable," said the holo-image, "but Essenes project that Panergon Gwynmyrr will one day be openly manifested to all. When that happens Essenes will adapt to circumstances."

"They will open up?" said Cary Manpure.

"Yes," said the holo-image. "Essenes cry out in agony to open up even now, but they are not afforded the luxury to do so."

"When will they have that luxury?" asked Cary Manpure.

"When it is time," said the holo-image.

"We are getting no where," said Cary Manpure.

"That is not correct," said the holo-image. "You have accomplished much and have prepared the way for those who are to follow."

The holo-image disappeared.

Cary Manpure thought for a while, smiled to himself and began writing.

When Essenes found the body of Cary Manpure they found those things he had been writing neatly placed on the top of his desk. The last thing he wrote was:

> "The Universe is in harmony because everything—from those things which are very small to those which are very large—works in exactly the same way. If things did not work this way, the Universe could not exist. Small things would be at odds with large things, and the Universe would tear itself apart. Everything sings together in harmony. These realizations make me soar like an eagle on high. These realizations are for those who follow."

Out of his love for Cary Manpure the Essene who had thrust Cary Manpure into the frying pan asked that future Essenes insure that the future beings of Danebury erect structures and stones on the analog of the Ranch House site in the small scale model of the Horz complex. These would represent the Ranch House on Silbury.

Out of his love for Cary Manpure the Essene who had thrust Cary Manpure into the frying pan also designed a meandering stone lined avenue—as an analog of the old-fashioned wooden water conduit connecting the Tetrahedron Crater Reservoir and the Ranch—which he asked that future Essenes insure that the future beings of Danebury construct from Avenabury Circle to the representation of the Ranch House on Silbury. 193

To counterbalance this meandering stone lined avenue, the Essene who had thrust Cary Manpure into the frying pan designed another stone lined avenue which was to lead past the two huge stones in the vicinity of the long earthen tomb on the analog site of Chapter One. (These stones were to mark the analog site of the pump house to the northeast of Chapter One). This second stone lined avenue also meandered and was therefore an inaccurate analog of the straight water conduit which ran underground southwestward from the Tetrahedron Crater Reservoir. Essenes wanted it to be a continuation of the drakon whose head was to be the analog of the Ranch House on Silbury.

In this representation of a drakon, Avenabury Circle was to depict an egg with two yolks (representing the indigenous and genetic agent parts of the future beings of Danebury). These parts were swallowed by a drakon (meaning they would have a long and difficult trail to transverse) but their hard shell protector—their courage—would help them get to where they needed to go.

Out of love for Cary Manpure, the Essene who had thrust Cary Manpure into the frying pan designed a transtime crop glyph representing the old-fashioned wooden water conduit connecting the Tetrahedron Crater Reservoir and the Ranch; Cattle and Sheep craters; and the fence that separated those animals. 193.1

Out of love for Cary Manpure, the Essene who had thrust Cary Manpure into the frying pan asked that future Essenes insure that effigies of white horses be cut into the chalk hills around and about Avenabury as symbols of the hyperdimensional Source of the Universe and as memorials to Cary Manpure's favorite horse Glamorgan, the distant morning. 193.2

Out of love for Cary Manpure, the Essene who had thrust Cary Manpure into the frying pan asked that future Essenes insure that Cary Manpure's adaptation of the mythos of the search for the golden fleece (which included an allegory of the beasts Ann Trent and Anson Trent) be incorporated into an indigenous mythos.

The Essene who had thrust Cary Manpure into the frying pan projected that such a mythos would one day exist on Danebury, because he knew that the original mythos had a basis in fact: that gold is washed down swiftly rushing rivers and that gold can be (and frequently has been) obtained from such rivers by beings who stretch fleeces tightly on frames and then place them in the rushing rivers so that the water goes through the fleece and the gold is caught in the fleece.

Out of love for Cary Manpure, the Essene who had thrust Cary Manpure into the frying pan—Lyman Lindsay—asked that future Essenes insure that the Hill of Musing be encircled by earthen rings in order to be an analog of Atlantis.

Lyman Lindsay did not long outlive Cary Manpure. Lyman Lindsay had co-ordinated the Holo-Image Program since the day Marta Weynard and Cary Manpure had been ordered to part. Though the experience had toughened him, it had taken its toll on Lyman Lindsay as well.

Part Four BEYOND

Chapter One

Return to Avenabury

Cary Jackman, the director of the genetic project, was a descendant of both Lena Arbur, daughter of Hal Arbur, and Tommy Jackman, brother of Cary Jackman—all of whom lived about 200,000 years before his time. Cary Jackman was the first to see the Essene holo-image, as he and his associates stood in the rain outside their space craft, having just landed in a small clearing at Avenabury.

The day before, on Colchis an Essene holo-image had suddenly appeared during a meeting between those working on the genetic project and said, "I am an Essene holo-image and I am directed by Essenes to give you new instructions. Alteans are to travel to Danebury and land in a clearing at Avenabury. Upon landing, Cary Jackman and his associates of the genetic project are to debark and wait outside the space craft. The location of Avenabury has been infused into the computers of the genetic project. Depart NOW!"

The holo-image disappeared.

Due to the receipt of these instructions, Cary Jackman and his associates had thought that it was time to administer the second part of the genetic agent.

When Cary Jackman saw the Essene holo-image as he stood in the rain at Avenabury it began to speak, "I am an Essene holo-image and I am directed by Essenes to deliver additional instructions to you. There are too many transitional creative-thinking beings of Danebury still alive. Alteans of the genetic project will be told when to come back.

"When Alteans return to Avenabury, Alteans are to administer the second part of the genetic agent. In order for that process to be complete, a total of 1470 healthy female and 1500 healthy male children must result. The mothers and the children must be returned to the original living environment of the mothers, but not to where they can be confronted by the male beings of Danebury who face extinction. You had only two-thirds enough children last time. That is why the transitional creative-thinking beings are facing extinction, but there are still too many of them."

The holo-image disappeared.

Later, Cary Jackman tried to calculate what Essenes could have meant by Alteans having only two-thirds enough children the first time. If that were true, then this time there should only have to be 2227.5 children, three-quarters of the total of 2970 children ordered by Essenes, a biological impossibility. There had been a total of 1485 children the first time; that was one-half the new total, not two-thirds.

Then Jackman remembered that Alteans had taken female beings from two locations but had put the mothers and their children in three locations. Even though Essenes had told Alteans (before the administering of the first part of the genetic agent) that the mothers and their children must be sent to the original living environment of the mothers, only two-thirds of the mothers and their children had been returned to their natural living environments. When Jackman remembered this, he hypothesized that Essenes would be adding a fourth destination (to which one-fourth of the next set of mothers and children would be sent). This time, Alteans would take females from three locations and put the mothers and their children in four locations. This was also in line with the Essene requirement that there be four distinctly different types of beings.

Jackman tried to calculate how this would work out. The total number of 1500 male children, divided by four locations was 375. The total number of 1470 female children, divided by four locations was 367.5. Jackman thought that there were two possibilities presented to him as a result of these calculations. Either his hypothesis was wrong, or Essenes intended that different numbers of female children were to go to the four different locations.

Cary Jackman concluded that Essenes did intend that different numbers of female children were to go to the four different locations, but he could never figure out why—until one day when he suddenly exclaimed, "Stress!"

"Those who are to have initiative will also have more stress," he said to himself. "In order for them to survive, there will have to be more males because they will be dying of stress."

The holo-image suddenly appeared and said, "Cary Jackman, you are never to let anyone know what you have just figured out."

The holo-image disappeared.

Marta Wellton was born 1954 years after the Altean return to Avenabury (which resulted in the immediate return to Colchis of Cary Jackman and his associates). Marta Wellton was a descendant of Anna Galen (a young lady Hal Wellton met on the transport vessel evacuating them from Silbury to Daphlay) and Hal Wellton, older brother of Terry Wellton—all of whom lived over 200,000 years before her time. When Marta Wellton was 21 she was allowed to read a secret history written over 200,000 years previously by Vicky Manpure. This secret history was the joint secret property of the clans Manpure, Jackman and Wellton.

All members of these three clans read the secret history when they became 21. Among Alteans, only members of the clans Manpure, Jackman and Wellton knew the purpose of Panergon Gwynmyrr: the preparing of the beings who were to lead the redeeming of the galaxy. They never told anyone else because Vicky Manpure had written at the beginning and end of her history, "They don't deserve to know."

Marta Wellton closed the ancient tome.

"I'm going to Colchis," she said aloud to herself. "I want to work on the genetic project and go to Danebury."

Marta Wellton became director of the genetic project when she was 43 and she went to Danebury when she was 46.

In accordance with the orders of an Essene holo-image, the director of the genetic project and her associates returned to Danebury. It was nearly 2000 years after Cary Jackman and his associates had stood in the rain in a small clearing at Avenabury and this time Alteans found no clearing. As they sought a landing site two Essene holo-images suddenly appeared, one on the bridge, the other in the passenger cabin, and said simultaneously, "I am an Essene holo-image and Essenes have directed that I give you the following instructions. You are to clear a circular area with energy cannon and land in that clearing. The location and size of that clearing have been infused into the general purpose computers of your space craft."

The holo-images disappeared.

The Alteans did as instructed and then waited. Two days later, as she ate dinner on the mess decks of the Altean space craft, an Essene holo-image appeared in front of Marta Wellton and began speaking, "Essenes have directed that I give you further instructions. Alteans are to construct the Avenabury Tor in the clearing. The Avenabury Tor is to be used as both the headquarters of the genetic project and as the site of the administering of the second part of the genetic agent. The precise positioning of the Avenabury Tor and plans for the Avenabury Tor have been infused into the general purpose computers of your vessel. Begin NOW!"

The holo-image disappeared.

When the Avenabury Tor was complete the holo-image suddenly appeared before Marta Wellton and said, "Alteans are to remove all existing geometric shapes of the Keirykeion Line and replace them with similar geometric shapes which are to stand virtually unchanged for 25,000 years. They are then to dissolve completely due to natural erosive forces.

"The precise locations of the geometric shapes of the Keirykeion Line and the specifications of the new geometric shapes that are to maintain the Keirykeion Line will be infused into the computers of the Altean Logistical Group of Panergon Gwynmyrr. This will be done after Dan Hartman is made director of the Altean Logistical Group of Panergon Gwynmyrr and after he reactivates the Altean Logistical Group's facilities on Colchis.

"When the new geometric shapes of the Keirykeion Line have been precisely positioned, additional instructions will be given to you concerning your administration of the second part of the genetic agent."

The holo-image disappeared.

The board of trustees of the Altean Logistical Group of Panergon Gwynmyrr asked its current director to resign, and then named Dan Hartman the new director. The board of trustees solicited new donations and once sufficient funds had been received, Dan Hartman reactivated the group, reopened its office and appointed associates. Dan Hartman then insured that the new geometric shapes which were to maintain the Keirykeion Line were speedily and precisely manufactured to Essene specifications, that all the existing geometric shapes were removed and that the new geometric shapes were positioned exactly as ordered by Essenes.

When Dan Hartman had completed his tasks an Essene holo-image appeared before Marta Wellton and said, "The center of the Silbury Hill site is directly south of the easternmost point of the Avenabury Tor and nine-tenths of a mile distant.

"Before you bring female beings of Danebury here from southeastern Ashintoland, Abzuland and far western Ashintoland, you are to construct three separate compounds in which they are to live before they become pregnant. These areas are to be centered three and three-quarters miles from the Silbury Hill site on bearings of 135 degrees gyro, 165 degrees gyro and 195 degrees gyro. 161

"You are to take the pregnant female beings of Danebury to an amphitheater-like valley two miles west southwest of the Avenabury Tor, a valley which is to be their home while they bear and raise their children. 174

"When you have completed your work, remove everything except the geometric shapes of the Keirykeion Line.

"Dan Hartman is to deactivate but not dissolve the Altean Logistical Support Group of Panergon Gwynmyrr. It will be needed again later.

"Marta Wellton, Essenes know that members of the clans Manpure, Jackman and Wellton know many things and that they have keep those things secret.

"You already know that you will be administering the second part of the genetic agent at a geodetic location, which will be precisely four-sevenths of the way from the equator to the north pole of Danebury in about 38,000 years.

"After you depart, Essenes will place a 12 foot high, five-sided steel alloy obelisk on that spot to memorialize the birth of human beings on the planet Earth."

The holo-image disappeared.

Chapter Two

Human Beings

Marta Wellton and her associates administered the second part of the genetic agent to healthy, child-bearing age, transitional creative-thinking female beings of Danebury. As they slept in their natural living environments in Abzuland, southeastern Ashintoland and far western Ashintoland, these females were sedated and flown in an unconscious state to the large clearing which surrounded the Avenabury Tor. There they were taken to one of the three large compounds located south of the landing site while still unconscious and placed in their compound during the night, with other transitional female beings of Danebury. During the flight each female was examined to determine when she would next ovulate. At the appropriate time after ovulation and in the middle of the night, each of the transitional female beings was again sedated, without their knowledge. They were then taken in an unconscious state to the Avenabury Tor and administered the second part of the genetic agent.

Marta Wellton and her associates were able to administer this second part of the genetic agent to the healthy, child-bearing age, transitional creative-thinking female beings because:

1. Tommy Burr had found important information in a moldering and weighty tome on one of the upper shelves of the library in Chapter One. Tommy Burr discovered that the natural evolutionary process of the development of self-aware beings always follows the same pattern: a self-aware transitional being develops creative thinking and then evolves into another species of self-aware being, which develops linear thinking. In that weighty tome Tommy Burr

discovered that in order to function and survive, the resulting fully developed self-aware being must rely on both the creative thinking developed by its immediate predecessor in the evolutionary chain, and on its own species' development of linear thinking.

2. Alteans had produced a genetic agent which insured that the creative and linear-thinking self-aware beings resulting from the administration of the second part of the genetic agent would have great diversity of both culture and physical characteristics. While working to insure that the creative and linear-thinking self-aware beings resulting from the administration of the second part of the genetic agent would have great diversity of both culture and physical characteristics, Alteans found that although all self-aware beings are basically the same physically, there had always existed a great diversity of physical appearances among them. This diversity was not only that which was apparent to Alteans on a daily basis: different physical statures, facial features, eye colors, hair colors and types; it included differences of anatomy and skin color.

3. Essenes had infused Altean computers in the Tetrahedron on Silbury with those things which enabled Alteans to fulfill the requirement that the creative and linear-thinking self-aware beings resulting from the administration of the second part of the genetic agent would have great diversity of culture.

4. The first part of the genetic agent had fulfilled the requirements of the Seventh Essene Panlogos. It told Alteans to make modifications to the first part of the genetic agent which, over time, would cause minor anatomical changes in many of the transitional creative-thinking beings resulting from the introduction of the first part of the genetic agent into females of the then current beings on Danebury.

5. Alteans had fulfilled the Essene instructions to make modifications in the first part of the genetic agent which, over time, would cause major anatomical changes in some of the transitional creative-thinking beings resulting from the introduction of the first part of the genetic agent into females of the then current beings on Danebury.

6. The transitional creative-thinking beings resulting from the first part of the genetic agent and resembling the final beings of the two-stepped process had died out.

7. The first part of the genetic agent had fulfilled the Essene re-

quirement that it appear as if all beings born on Danbury had descended from a single mother.

8. Alteans had fulfilled the requirement that the life span of the final resulting creative and linear-thinking beings would be only one-third of the normal life span of fully developed self-aware beings. But that at some future date, that life span would be easily expandable to the normal life span of fully developed self-aware beings. This was to be done by using Altean medical procedures to make minor alterations to the immune systems of the descendants of the original creative and linear-thinking self-aware beings of Danebury.

9. Alteans had fulfilled the requirement that there were to be four distinctly different types of beings: in genetic, cultural and physical characteristics. These four groups were to range from those most like the beings resulting from the administration of the first part of the genetic agent to those least like those first beings. The two mid-range groups would consist of those more like the first being, and those equally alike and not alike the first being.

10. Alteans had fulfilled the requirement that the final self-aware beings resulting from the administration of the second part of the genetic agent, who were to be least like the beings resulting from the administration of the first part of the genetic agent, in both cultural and physical characteristics, would have the propensity to be antagonistic toward every one else; the propensity to have: great difficulty in conceiving of any dimension beyond three-dimensions; great difficulty in conceiving of great lengths of time, especially when it seems as if nothing of importance is happening; and also the propensity to have: great difficulty in conceiving of life spans longer than their own; great difficulty in conceiving that life exists anywhere except on Danebury, except that they would have an inexplicable nagging imperative toward the fourth planet from their sun. They were also to have great initiative.

Everything Marta Wellton and her associates did with regard to the healthy, child-bearing age, transitional creative-thinking female beings of Danebury was done with careful planning, great care and love. The sedating, transportation, examining and administering of the second part of the genetic agent were all done as gently as possible. The three large compounds, located south of the Avenabury Tor, replicated the three different natural living environments of the transitional creative-thinking beings—in Abzuland, southeastern Ashintoland and far western Ashintoland. Only the limits of the compounds made them any different.

Whenever a transitional female being reached those limits she would receive a mild shock. Very soon they learned those limits and no longer approached them. Despite the mild shock the transitional female beings could have easily escaped from the compounds. They did not try to do so because they liked living where they were and they also enjoyed living among their own kind.

After each transitional female being became pregnant she was taken to the amphitheater-like valley west of the Avenabury Tor. There each gave birth to her child and raised her or him.

The amphitheater-like valley west of the Avenabury Tor, was the analog of Dan Park in the small scale model of the Horz complex, and the most beautiful place any of the transitional creative-thinking female beings had ever seen. It became home for them and their children.

When there were 1470 daughters and 1500 sons of the transitional creative-thinking female beings—one daughter or one son for each female—the Alteans ceased sedating, transporting, examining and impregnating them. None of the children died or became seriously ill while they lived in the amphitheater-like valley.

Some of children of the transitional creative-thinking female beings were very different from their mothers. Some of these children were somewhat different from their mothers. Some of these children were hardly different from their mothers. These children were the first of the creative and linear-thinking beings of Danebury.

For 14 years the mothers and their children lived in the amphitheater-like valley. After this period, it was time for them to be taken to their natural living environments—away from the male beings who were headed for extinction.

Some of these children were nearing the age at which they would begin having children of their own, without the administration of the second part of the genetic agent. They were about to become mothers and fathers.

Some of these children who were the tallest, had finely shaped heads, had hair only on their heads, feared the dark, were linear thinkers, and were right-handed, lived in disharmony with one another and their environment and abused all the other children.

This outcome was due to the Essene requirement that the creative and linear-thinking self-aware beings (resulting from the administration of the second part of the genetic agent) who were least like the transitional creative-thinking beings in both cultural and physical characteristics, were to have the propensity to be antagonistic toward everyone else.

Some of the descendants of the children who were the tallest, had finely shaped heads, had hair only on their heads, feared the dark, were linear thinkers and right-handed, would continue to live in disharmony with one another and their environment and abuse everyone else. They would have: great difficulty in conceiving of any dimension beyond three-dimensions; great difficulty in conceiving of great lengths of time, especially when it seemed as if nothing of importance was happening; great difficulty in conceiving that life exists anywhere except on Danebury, but they would have a nagging inexplicable imperative toward the red planet—because Alteans fulfilled Essene requirements.

When 14 years had passed, an Essene holo-image suddenly appeared before Marta Wellton as she worked at her desk in the Avenabury Tor. As soon as Marta Wellton saw it the holo-image began to speak, "I am an Essene holo-image. I am directed by Essenes to deliver the following instructions to you. You are to take the 1470 daughters and 1500 sons of the transitional creative-thinking female beings with their mothers to their natural living environments—away from the male beings who are headed for extinction. <u>63</u>

"You are to take the 375 daughters and 375 sons of the transitional creative-thinking female beings who are <u>most</u> <u>like</u> the transitional creative-thinking beings, with their mothers, to their natural living environments in southeastern Ashintoland.

"You are to take the 375 daughters and 375 sons of the transitional creative-thinking female beings who are <u>next</u> <u>most</u> <u>like</u> the transitional creative-thinking beings, with their mothers, to their natural living environments in Abzuland.

"You are to take the 345 daughters and 375 sons of the transitional creative-thinking female beings who are <u>least</u> <u>like</u> the transitional creative-thinking beings, with their mothers, to their natural living environments in far western Ashintoland.

"You are to take the 375 daughters and 375 sons of the transitional creative-thinking female beings who are <u>equally</u> <u>alike</u> and <u>not</u> <u>alike</u> the transitional creative-thinking beings, with their mothers, to their natural living environments in the coastal area at the very eastern end of the sea shared by the mouth of the river that flows past Hurmyrr.

"The reason you are to take a different number of daughters to one location is that the mortality rates of the sons will be different there, due to the different genetic makeup of the beings in that location. The mortality rate of the sons who are least like the transitional creative-thinking beings and are to live in the far west of Ashintoland will be higher, due to higher levels of stress brought on by their abusive behavior and their trait of having more initiative than the others.

"The total numbers of daughters compared to sons is 98 percent.

"The number of daughters you have in each category does not match the Essene requirement for the number of daughters in each group. Therefore you are to move a small number of daughters from one group to another, in order to fulfill the requirement to put the requisite number of daughters in each group.

"This will begin the process of intermingling.

"Begin NOW!"

"From the outset you will be substantially increasing the level of stress in the group with fewer females than males," said Marta Wellton.

"Yes," said the holo-image, "and also increasing their initiative."

The holo-image disappeared.

When the 375 daughters and 375 sons of the transitional creative-thinking beings who were equally alike and not alike the transitional creative-thinking beings, and their mothers, had been taken to their natural living environments in the coastal area at the very eastern end of the sea shared by the mouth of the river that flows past Hurmyrr, the children were very sad.

Of all the children that had been born and grew up in the amphitheater-like valley, they were the ones who had lived most in harmony with one another and with their environment.

Later, after the descendants of the children (equally alike and not alike the transitional creative-thinking beings) had multiplied and moved eastward, into the land between the two rivers, and after they had been ruthlessly driven into disharmony with one another and with their environment by the hateful interference of the Pleiadeans—Essenes allegorized the history of these children and their descendants, and infused it into the culture of these children's descendants.

This allegorized history—this mythos—made it seem as if through the fault of the children who were equally alike and not alike the transitional creative-thinking beings they had been compelled to leave the amphitheater-like valley. This mythos also made it seem as though it was the Source of the Universe who had driven them away from the amphitheater-like valley.

Somewhat later, Essenes infused into the culture of the planet whose beings were being prepared to lead the process of redeeming the galaxy, their allegorized mythos of the beast from the mythos NOSTOS, in order to juxtapose the beast—the refusal to accept ideas beyond one's own—with the lover of the hero of the mythos—the thirst for knowledge. Essenes marked the beast of their mythos with the number 666, meaning thrice dead. The mark of the beast was on the forehead of the beast, and could therefore be read by everyone—except the beast.

Essenes allegorized the history of the children who were equally alike and not alike the transitional creative-thinking beings and their descendants in such a way, as preparation. The real history of these children and their descendants was to be available only upon clear reflection, made possible by Panergon Gwynmyrr.

The two adults in the mythos of these children who were equally alike and not alike the transitional creative-thinking beings and their descendants, represent all the original children who were equally alike and not alike the transitional creative-thinking beings, who were born and grew up in the amphitheater-like valley. The realization of their sexuality on the part of the two adults was their growing up.

The three children of these two adults in the mythos represent all the children who were born and grew up in the amphitheater-like valley. The brother who kills his brother represents some of the children who were least like the transitional creative-thinking beings, the children who abused all the other children. The brother who is killed represents all the other children. The brother who survives represents the descendants of the children equally alike and not alike the transitional creative-thinking beings.

The part of the mythos which tells of the serpent, the eating of the apple and the banishment, represents the hateful interference of the Pleiadeans which transformed the descendants of the children who were equally alike and not alike the transitional creative-thinking beings. As a result of the hateful interference of the Pleiadeans, the descendants of these children became out of harmony with one another and with their environment and therefore could no longer develop toward their projected role as mediators between the descendants of the children least like the transitional creative-thinking beings, and the descendants of the children who were most and next most like them.

As a result of the hateful interference of the Pleiadeans, the descendants of the children who were equally alike and not alike the transitional creative-thinking beings became the most divisive and violent descendants of these beings.

Through its shape, the serpent in the mythos represents life. Life is full of twistings and turnings. The imperative of life is the thirst for knowledge.

The apple in the mythos represents the soul.

The eating of the apple in the mythos represents self-realization.

The banishment in the mythos is not physical banishment from a place but a banishment of harmony, brought on by the hateful interference of the Pleiadeans.

This hateful interference of the Pleiadeans transformed the descendants of the children equally alike and not alike the transitional creative-thinking beings into beings no longer in harmony with one another and with their environment. That hateful interference of the Pleiadeans divided the descendants of these children into two armed camps: male and female. Pleiadean males demean and dominate their females. With regard to the 'relationship' 'between' female and male, the Pleiadeans transformed the culture of the descendants of the children who were equally alike and not alike the transitional creative-thinking beings into something vaguely akin to their own 'culture.'

Adam, derived from the Hellenikos word meaning 'iron,' was infused by Essenes into the allegorical history to allegorize the tragedy of Kirk Roon, who had developed the iron resolve of a victim. Eve was infused into the allegorical history as a foreshortening of Avena, the wife of the tragic Kirk Roon.

After the dismantling of the Avenabury Tor in the large clearing just west of the Avenabury Circle site and the departure of Marta Wellton and her associates, Essenes raised the 12 foot high, five-sided steel alloy obelisk on the site where the second part of the genetic agent had been administered to the female transitional creative-thinking beings—a spot which in about 38,000 years would be precisely four-sevenths of the way from the equator to the north pole of the Earth.

That event was about 35,000 years ago.

The projection Essenes made for how long it would take for human beings to be ready for clear reflection was about 3000 years too long.

For over 30,000 years human beings developed completely by themselves except for the occasional infusion by Essenes of pieces of mythos to supplement the many rapidly developing and richly varied cultures.

Despite some horrific climatic conditions, human beings increased and migrated around their planet.

Despite their varying genetic backgrounds, different groups of human beings got along well and intermingled.

Human beings lived in harmony with their environment.

Many migrators met human beings that lived in far eastern Ashintoland had migrated to Prehurland. They were from those human beings who were more spiritual than any other human beings. In Prehurland these migrators from far eastern Ashintoland met and intermingled with migrators who had previously come to Prehurland from the Abzuland on which Hurmyrr stands. The Abzuland migrators were from among those human beings who were intuitively in harmony with the Universe.

The societies of human beings formed from among those who had migrated to Prehurland, lived more in harmony with their environment and with one another than any other society in the history of human beings. This situation was partially due to their genetic makeup, and partially because the effigies, circles, mounds and pyramids they constructed caused many channels, eddies and areas of high energy to form in the planetary torun flowing across the surface of the Earth.

Essenes infused ideas into the minds of some of the inhabitants of Prehurland for the design, building and location of the many effigies, circles, mounds and pyramids. These inhabitants continued designing, building and siting many more effigies, circles, mounds and pyramids on their own, because they liked them and enjoyed the feelings engendered by them.

Chapter Three

The Interferers

Once again, a Pleiadean scout craft on a random patrol of the outer reaches of the galaxy happened upon the solar system containing the blue-green planet, it investigated and reported. This time the report got through very quickly to the Pleiadean emperor. He had a notion.

Instead of annexing the blue-green planet into the Pleiadean empire, the Pleiadean emperor decided to make it the private possession of the Pleiadean imperial family. Instead of placing the blue-green planet under the direct control of Pleiadean rulers, he decided to keep its beings unaware that they belonged to the Pleiadean emperor. He wanted to enjoy the beings who lived on the blue-green planet. He could enjoy these beings by watching them fight over wealth, power and sex. The Pleiadean emperor sent secret agents to the blue-green planet and they used wealth, power and sex to entice certain promising beings into causing trouble. The secret Pleiadean agents in place on Danebury transmitted reports to the Pleiadean emperor and his family who enjoyed the troubles stirred up at the instigation of those secret Pleiadean agents. Succeeding Pleiadean emperors and their families continued to enjoy these troubles.

The first secret Pleiadean agents in place started their activities almost 5000 years ago in the land between the two rivers. One of the first promising beings they enticed with wealth, power and sex was a man known to the history of the Earth as Sargon, Emperor of Akkad. The land between the two rivers became the first permanent base for the secret Pleiadean agents.

Over a thousand years later, the secret Pleiadean agents moved westward and established their second permanent base in the land of the damned, almost half way up the western coast of the peninsula, at the southern end of which is Hellas, the land of the Hellenes. The Pleiadean emperor wanted to enjoy the destruction of the great civilizations flourishing in and around Hellas. Secret Pleiadean agents enticed a princeling with sex and were able to bring about a horrific war between the Hellenes and their trading partners to the east, the Wilusans. The Heraklaidai who lived in the land of the damned and its vicinity, were enticed with the prospect of wealth and power, resulting in their invasion of Hellas and its destruction. Secret agents in place also enticed the Scythians who then destroyed many of the civilizations around Hellas.

About 800 years later, secret Pleiadean agents based in the land of the damned enticed promising beings from the city of Epidamnos in the land of the damned. The resulting war destroyed the flowering of the civilization of the Hellenes.

About 400 years after that, secret Pleiadean agents based in the land of the damned enticed a promising being named Gaius Cassius who murdered the last hope for the survival of the Roman republic, thereby ushering in such Pleiadean imperial favorites as Caligula and Nero.

From their base in the land between two rivers, secret Pleiadean agents had previously enticed a promising being who was the pharaoh of Egypt, Ignaten. This psychopath who claimed the name Akhenaten, was enticed into moving the capital of Egypt from Thebes to a new city Ignaten called Akhetaten. Ignaten claimed Akhetaten should be the capital of Egypt because it was located in the middle of Egypt, while Thebes was too far south to claim that it was the center of Egypt. Ignaten ignored what he was told by the priests of Thebes—that a stone marker in Thebes marked a spot two-sevenths of the way from the equator to the north pole. Therefore, Thebes was in the middle of an area, the boundary of which was marked by another marker, four-sevenths of the way from the equator to the north pole: the most important marker on the Earth, as the priests of Thebes informed Ignaten, because it marked the birthplace of human beings. Ignaten ignored the priests of Thebes and proceeded with his new city, a city which died when the psychopath Ignaten died.

The priests of Thebes did not know that there was a third marker—located across the gulf from Punt and to its north, on a small headland to the east of the southeastern tip of the Arabian peninsula—at a place named Aden by Essenes. The marker at Aden was one-seventh of the way from the equator to the north pole and, like Thebes, it was southwest of the Lion Line—while Avenabury was northeast of the Lion Line.

Avenabury was marked because it was the site of the birth of human beings. Thebes was marked, located on both sides of the Nile and so named because Thebes was to represent the sexual development of females. The name 'Thebes' was derived from a Hellenikos word meaning 'intoxifier.' Aden was chosen as the marker to represent the sexual development of males and the word 'aden' means 'gland' in Hellenikos.

The Pleiadean who was emperor at the time hated the American Revolution, a revolution carried through to the successful implementation of a forward looking republic by visionaries who were heirs to the civilization of the Hellenes. They knew the hermetic teachings, understood the ways of those who had preceded them in America and had great hopes for a better future for everyone.

To counterbalance the American Revolution, secret Pleiadean agents operating from the land of the damned, enticed promising beings in France to corrupt the French Revolution and to turn the French from their ideals of Fraternity, Equality and Liberty toward envious class hatred and stubborn nationalism. The most promising of the beings enticed by secret Pleiadean agents was Napoleon Bonaparte whose forces shot off the nose of the Ark Hur—the replacement nose which had been attached to the Ark Hur by Egyptians.

Almost 2000 years after secret Pleiadean agents based in the land of the damned brought about the murder of Julius Caesar, secret Pleiadean agents based in the land of the damned enticed promising beings to murder Archduke Franz Ferdinand, heir to the throne of Austria-Hungary, thus precipitating the first world-wide conflagration.

Less than 30 years later, secret Pleiadean agents based in the land of the damned enticed promising beings who subsequently caused the beastling of the south to invade the land of the damned. When the beastling's army was severely routed by the Hellenes, the beast of the north (whose armies were poised to attack the beast of the east) was forced to intervene on behalf of the beastling of the south. The heroic resistance of the Hellenes (descendants of the heroic Hellenes who had been twice smashed due to the interference of the Pleiadeans) both delayed the attack on the beast of the east and drew away from that attack the forces belonging to the beast of the north. The heroic resistance of the Hellenes prevented the beast of the north from conquering the beast of the east and gaining control of the planet. The Pleiadean emperor was disappointed as the beast of the north was the favorite beast.

The resulting standoff between the beast of the east, his descendants and those who had best absorbed the culture of the Hellenes bothered the Pleiadean emperor, because if the beings of the blue-green planet destroyed themselves, he could no longer enjoy the trouble he caused among them. The Pleiadean emperor could find no solution to this dilemma. Eventually human beings resolved the situation on their own, allowing the secret Pleiadean agents in place to increase their enticing of promising beings from their two permanent bases in the land between two rivers and in the land of the damned.

The heavy consumption of fossil fuels by the beings of the blue-green planet also bothered the Pleiadean emperor. If the beings of the blue-green planet could no longer produce large amounts of energy, they could no longer kill one another very efficiently, and this would reduce the enjoyment of the Pleiadean emperor. The Pleiadean emperor knew that the only viable alternative to using fossil fuels for energy was to use energy created by men while their minds were under the influence of mind altering drugs, drugs which secret Pleiadean agents in place introduced to human beings.

Shortly after the cabalists had seized the Pleiades, they found that they faced an energy shortage because fewer and fewer meditators could continue to meditate to transredimension Horun into torun. As no new meditators could be trained, the ability to meditate, and consequently the ability to transredimension energy diminished, as transredimensioning requires that meditators live harmoniously. The environment of the Pleiadean confederacy did not allow for those capable of meditating and transredimensioning energy to live in harmony.

The cabalists figured out a way to partially 'replicate' meditation by injecting mind altering drugs into captive beings who could thereby transredimension energy, though very inefficiently. Energy transproduction complexes are attached to the countless prisons of the Pleiadean empire, and prisoners under the influence of mind altering drugs transredimension energy for the empire. Since those coerced beings survive only for a limited period of time, several prisoners must be aboard Pleiadean space craft at all times while in space to prevent those craft from running out of energy.

Nevertheless, the Pleiadean emperors have always known secretly that the most efficient way to transredimension energy is through meditation. Through propaganda and ridicule the Pleiadean emperors have tried to suppress meditation by beings of the blue-green planet, because they did not want the beings of the blue-green planet to discover that as a result of meditation, virtually unlimited energy can be made available to everyone inexpensively. That so many beings of the blue-green planet have always practiced meditation has secretly frightened all Pleiadean emperors.

Pleiadean emperors have always hated the beings of the blue-green planet because they have always been envious of them. The Pleiadean emperor before the next to current emperor hated the beings of the blue-green planet even more, because not only have they continued to survive the many interferences of the Pleiadeans, but they were becoming more disinclined to fight at the slightest provocation.

That Pleiadean emperor concocted a response to the energy crisis of the blue-green planet. In order to reduce the demand for energy on the planet, that Pleiadean emperor decided to reduce the population of the blue-green planet.

That Pleiadean emperor introduced a savage virus to the beings of the blue-green planet, which would attack the immune system of those infected by this disease.

That Pleiadean emperor enticed beings to become infected by this savage virus with sex.

That Pleiadean emperor had this savage virus specifically designed to attack those who are most harmonic among human beings, as they are the human beings who have been most savaged along the way. The Pleiadean emperor wanted to eliminate the most harmonic, most savaged human beings because he saw them as drainers of energy.

Chapter Four

Gwynmyrr and Panergon

Essenes were utterly appalled by the savage intervention of the Pleiadean interferers.

Essenes had anticipated the possibility of rediscovery of the Earth by a Pleiadean scout craft, but Essenes were amazed that the mandate of the Source of the Universe did not allow them to take immediate and decisive action against the Pleiadean interferers.

Essenes therefore had to watch in frustration and anger, as human beings were savaged by the Pleiadeans.

Eventually, the mandate of the Source of the Universe allowed Essenes to counter the effects of Pleiadean savagery—but only in ways that would not be discerned by human beings. Essenes understood what human beings had understood along the way, and presented human beings with things which were just beyond their ability to comprehend. Human beings in ancient times 'saw' flying craft which looked like birds; later human beings 'saw' flying objects, then flying 'saucers'—which changed as technology advanced among human beings. The UFOs of the 1990s appeared very different to the flying 'saucers' of the 1950s.

Along the way, Essenes were frustrated by the fact that helping human beings directly was prohibited, so Essenes used all their wits to circumvent this prohibition, and under the guise of such informants as Hermes Trismigestos, infused many very important things about the Universe into human society. Although this information has remained mostly intact, secret societies have continued to keep the majority of it from most human beings. Diverse priesthoods—working in conjunction with various rulers—have used bits and pieces of this vital information to bring fear and subjugation to most human beings, while they have used their spiritual and service positions for their own temporal well being.

Essenes have been appalled by the greed and thirst for power of these multifarious priesthoods and rulers.

Essenes came to understand that their circumventing of the mandate of the Source of the Universe caused matters to worsen among human beings. Essenes therefore stopped and waited for the mandate of the Source of the Universe to allow them to proceed further in respect of presenting to human beings more things about the Universe. When Essenes were allowed to proceed they had learned a valuable lesson.

They gave the information not to the priests and the kings—but directly to the people.

Over a thousand years before the time of the psychopath Ignaten, a blow-hard named Cheops became pharaoh of Egypt. Even though it was widely known that Hurmyrr was already there when the Egyptians first settled around the Bastion, the bragger Cheops insisted that he had built 'the great pyramid of Cheops.' Everyone knew this was not true, because no one even knew how to get inside Hurmyrr, not even the blow-hard Cheops himself.

After the passing of bragger Cheops, another blow-hard, Chephren became pharaoh. Even though everyone knew that the Ark Hur was already there when the Egyptians first settled around the Bastion, the blow-hard Chephren insisted that he had sculpted 'the great sphinx of Chephren.' To prove his point, Chephren added his nose to the long since noseless Ark Hur. Chephren also identified himself with Bridge on the Bastion, now known as 'the pyramid of Chephren.' 194,194.1

Essenes have been appalled that Egyptologists, clearly recognizing that Hurmyrr is both the oldest and the most-finely constructed pyramid, can still say that Hurmyrr was the beginning of a brief architectural fad, denying the obvious: Hurmyrr is the legacy of an incredibly sophisticated, complex and meaningful architectural tradition.

Essenes began to infuse Cary Manpure's adapted mythos of the search for the golden fleece into the culture of human beings, when they saw that human beings living near the coast northwest of Mount Hurartu were obtaining gold by stretching the fleeces of lambs on frames and leaving the fleeces in rapidly flowing rivers. This was done so that the fleeces would capture gold flowing in these currents. Essenes gave these human beings the idea of naming their main village—which later became a city—Colchis.

In conjunction with other preparatory work undertaken by Cary Manpure, Essenes sited a future oracle at a place which came to be called Dodona. Dodona is nearly on the Lion Line, the great circle connecting

Hurmyrr and Amesbury Circle, and near one of the mountains—of a range which included Mount Hurartu—which were to be associated in mythos with an allegorical flood, a flood which was an allegory of the many escapes of beings descended from those who had lived in Atlantis.

The triangle formed by Colchis, Dodona and Hurmyrr was a near equivalent of a mirror image of the golden triangle formed by the site of energy transredimensioning in the Hurmaze, the apex of the Tor and the Tower of Ancestors on Silbury. The triangle was a mirror image, as the relationship between the Earth and Silbury and the importance of sex would be understood only upon clear reflection. Joe Lon Odkin had thought that the two sites for the scale models and the site of a future construction that he was to locate on Danebury formed a mirror image of the triangle between Hurbury, the Hurmaze and the Tor. Although that was incorrect, Essenes liked the idea, and many years later adapted the idea of mirror images and used them.

A much more equivalent mirror image, a golden triangle relationship was repeated between Dodona and the later oracles at Hieropolis in northern Syria and Siwa in the western Egyptian desert.

Rumors of a golden fleece reached the shores of Hellas and an intrepid young sailor named Jason launched an expedition to seek the golden fleece. Jason's adventures became legendary among the Hellenes and mythos became attached to the expedition which had sought the golden fleece.

Essenes ensured that Cary Manpure's adaptations of the much older mythos became attached to the new indigenous mythos: Jason's ship was given the name Argo from the Hellenikos word 'argurion,' meaning 'silver.' Although Jason had been seeking gold, Anson Trent had been seeking wealth and power through profits generated from dealing in silver.

The historical princess-priestess-protectress of the golden fleece of Colchis was Medea, daughter of historical King Aeetes. In their overlaying of the developing mythos, Essenes assigned the characters adapted by Cary Manpure as representing Ann Trent to Medea, and Anson Trent to Aeetes.

Medea became a treasonous daughter and Aeetes a greedy king. Medea also became a faithless wife of Jason, a wife who murdered their children—children representing Avena and Ames Manpure—who had died as a result of Anson Trent's greed.

The historical Medea was a loving wife and companion of Jason.

To honor Arker Manpure, Cary Manpure invented a watchman with a hundred eyes, so that he could sleep and never close more than half his eyes. Cary Burr Manpure called this watchman Argus. Essenes made

Argus the watchman of Hera, queen of the gods.

To honor Arker Manpure for having ruined the would-be silver baron Anson Trent, Essenes combined the names Argo and Argus (made up by Cary Manpure) into Argos and insured that an important city in Hellas came to be called Argos.

Essenes insured that a city near Argos had Cary Manpure's vasectomy attached to it, to honor Arker Manpure for having 'castrated' Anson Trent. Essenes insured that a small settlement on a mountain overlooking the vasectomy came to be called Medea, thus representing how the small Ann Trent had looked down upon her father.

To further honor Arker Manpure, Essenes insured that the historical stout-hearted King Danaus fled to Argos.

Danaus' great granddaughter, the equally stout-hearted Danae was put adrift at sea with her infant son Perseus by her father King Acrisius, who was afraid of the child, said to be the son of Zeus. Despite being adrift at sea for an extended period of time, Danae and Perseus survived. Perseus fought many battles against various and diverse beasts and won the hand of the princess Andromeda.

Perseus' adventures became legendary among the Hellenes and mythos became attached to his many exploits and to his marriage.

Essenes knew that when Cary Manpure was in the fourth grade, the mythos of the Zuv School System's mythos symposeion was about a dashing hero cast adrift as a baby with his exiled mother, a beautiful princess whom he rescues from horrible beasts, including a truly horrific beast whose gaze turned everyone who looked upon him into stone.

Essenes also knew that at the symposeion Cary Manpure had said, "I think this story is like NOSTOS. The hero is a seeker of knowledge. The princess is the thirst for knowledge. The beast who turns everyone who looks at him into stone is the denial of truth, that which ossifies not just into bone, but into petrified bone, stone."

Due to Cary Manpure's having taught a fuller understanding of this mythos, Essenes insured that important parts of the older mythos became attached to the new and growing indigenous mythos of Perseus.

As a result Perseus, enabled to do so by having seen her clear reflection in his shield, became known as the slayer of Medusa, the one who turned into stone those who gazed upon her.

Perseus also became known as the liberator of the flying white horse Pegasus, who sprang forth fully grown from the blood of Medusa.

Perseus killed the beast through clear reflection, thereby ridding the world of ossified slavery to the beast—and freeing the concept of hyperdimensionality from the confines of the beast.

To further honor Arker Manpure who had used clear reflection to free the galaxy of the power of the beast Anson Trent, Essenes insured that one of the twin citadels of Argos became known as Aspis, meaning 'shield.'

After the terrible war between the Hellenes and their former trading partners, brought about by the Wilusans, through secret Pleiadean agents in place who enticed the effete princeling Alaksandus with the promise of sex, Essenes infused Homer with additional mythos material, which he then skilfully interwove with existing indigenous mythos material.

Essenes added Tros to the indigenous mythos. Tros was inserted into the mythos as one of the founders of Ilios, the name Hellenes used for Wilusa. Essenes inserted Tros (a foreshortening of Trosumur) into the mythos in honor of the Hermurian escapee who was most responsible for the usage of mythos as a teaching mode.

Essenes changed the character of Agamemnon, leader of the Hellenes. Agamemnon had not sacrificed his daughter, argued over the spoils of war or been unfaithful to his wife. It was Agamemnon's wife who was unfaithful, having been enticed into unfaithfulness by a promising being, Aigestheus (one of the Heraklaidai) himself enticed by secret Pleiadean agents operating out of the land of the damned. After Agamemnon's murderers were brought to justice, his body, the face covered by a well fashioned death mask, was reburied in a shaft grave in the grave circle he had previously enclosed within the walls of Mycenae, in honor of the kings of the Pelasgians, with whom the Hellenes shared the land.

Essenes changed the character of Agamemnon because Essenes operate under the mandate of the Source of the Universe.

Essenes added the followers of Achilleus and Patroklos, the Myrmidons. The Myrmidons, meaning 'the reflecting ones,' were inserted into the mythos of the war between the Hellenes and their former trading partners, to prepare the way for another reflector—Merlin.

Essenes insured that the ratio between length of the foot used by Agamemnon was 15/16ths the length of the foot used by the Wilusans, a ratio equivalent to the harmonic of soul transcommunication. The length of the foot of the Wilusans was later adopted by the Romans from the Etruscans, whose ancestors included refugees from Wilusa. Essenes insured that this length of foot adopted by the Romans was 24/25ths of the length of the foot used by later Hellenes. Thus the foot used by Agamemnon was 9/10ths the length of the foot used by his descendants in Hellas, since 15/16ths times 24/25ths equals 9/10ths.

Essenes infused ideas into the minds of the mother and father of the Penruddock family, and as a result, they devoted their lives to the construction of one of the greatest monuments of human endeavor—Avenabury Circle. The mother and father of the Penruddock family inspired many in their own time to assist them. Avenabury Circle and the legends of the devoted work involved in its completion, inspired those who were infused with the idea of constructing Amesbury Circle and those who assisted them, as well as those who were infused with the idea of constructing Silbury Hill and those who assisted them.

By slightly modifying Joe Lon Odkin's final design, Essenes also insured that Amesbury Circle could serve as an astronomical observatory so that solstices, equinoxes and other celestial events could be marked by the stones and other markers of the circular complex.

Following through from the Holo-mapping project and the resulting maps based on the projected geography of the Earth 240,000 years hence, Essenes infused ideas into many different human beings. This was so that the constructions they were about to undertake northwest and northeast of Hurmyrr were positioned in a geometric array around Hurmyrr, to help maintain the drakon of the Keirykeion Line.

Essenes infused ideas into many different human beings so that constructions were positioned on or near the Lion Line, the great circle connecting Hurmyrr and Amesbury Circle. Alexandria in Egypt (the destruction of Alexandria's library by promising beings enticed by secret Pleiadean agents, is the greatest loss of knowledge in the history of human beings); Mycenae (whose Lion Gateway was constructed under the supervision of Agamemnon); Nemea (site of one of the four Great Games of the Hellenes); Dodona; and the rock hewn Lion of Lucerne are all located along the Lion Line.

Based on his broad knowledge of history and mythos, Cary Manpure drew and named three additional lines: sections of great circles, which interact either with the Lion Line, or with the great circle of which the Lion Line is a section. Cary Manpure constructed one of his lines originating at the point where the great circle which is an extension of the Lion Line crosses the equator, 22.48 degrees east of Hurmyrr. This line extends northwesterly from its point of origin and is east and nearly parallel with the Lion Line. Cary Manpure named this line the Sacred Line. Because he had read widely, Cary Manpure was able to project that the future beings of Danebury would develop many different religions before they studied philosophy. He knew from history that religions compete with one another, each religion claiming to have the answer. Cary Manpure hoped that if the future beings of Danebury could one day figure out that many of the major sacred sites of different religions were located along the same long line, they might also think that there was some connection between them—rather than just differences.

Essenes infused ideas into many different human beings so that either the constructions they were about to undertake were positioned on or near the Sacred Line, or their legends and mythos became associated with locations on or near the Sacred Line. Mecca, Mount Sinai, Behdet (where the sourcemark of Egypt was located), Delos (traditional birthplace of Artemis and Apollo) and Mount Olympus (home of the gods) are all either all located where they are or are associated with legends and mythos.

The third line which Cary Manpure drew and named, originates at a point in the Nile delta near the coastline, on the axis of the Nile, and extends eastward. Cary Manpure named this line the Line of Civilizations because it passes through fertile areas. He projected that they would provide the basis for surplus food production. Cary Manpure knew from his reading of history that surplus food would free workers from the fields, allow for specialization of labor, promote the beginnings of cities and foster trade between cities.

Essenes infused ideas into many different human beings so that the constructions they were about to undertake were positioned on or near the Line of Civilizations. Mohenho Daro in the Indus Valley, the ceremonial capital of the Persian Empire Persepolis, Ur in the land between two rivers, the first city of the Hebrews, Hebron and Behdet are all located where they are for this reason.

The last line which Cary Manpure drew and named was to extend both eastward and westward from Hurmyrr, so that at Hurmyrr it would form a 60 degree angle with the Lion Line—thereby representing tetrahedra, the modeling of everything—and Hurmyrr is that too. Cary Manpure named this line the Excalibur Line after a powerful sword, which in a mythos he knew, the hero used to kill a courageous lion guarding the fortress of the beast Ares, and because the Excalibur Line crosses and cuts the Lion Line.

At the point where the Excalibur Line and the Line of Civilizations cross, Essenes induced the construction of Ur. To the west of Ur on the Excalibur Line, Essenes induced the construction of Petra; and in the desert of western Egypt, in an oasis called Siwa on the Excalibur Line, Essenes induced the beginnings of a great oracle.

Cary Manpure drew the Line of Civilizations so that it would cross the Sacred Line at an angle of about 51.84 degrees, representing star ships—because Cary Manpure loved star ships.

He also named his lines to represent those things represented in both the Hurmaze and the Ark Hur. Cary Manpure wanted the Excalibur Line, and its relationship to the Lion Line of Essenes—to represent courage. He wanted the Line of Civilizations to represent the three-dimensional mind and he wanted the Sacred Line to represent the soul. Cary Manpure knew that heart, mind, and soul were the ingredients that the future beings of Danebury would need, to fulfill their destiny as leaders of the redeeming of the galaxy.

Essenes later added a powerful sword to THE ARTHURIAN LEGENDS when they overlaid the growing indigenous mythos of a heroic and tragic king of Hurengland with the mythos inspired by Rena Jackman, written by the seventh grade class of Tom Huish and modified by Cary Manpure. Essenes named that powerful sword Excalibur, in 'honor' of Cary Manpure for having adapted/altered mythos.

Essenes also insured that a city was named in honor of Trosumur, the Hermurian escapee who was most responsible for the usage of mythos as teacher.

The city named to honor Trosumur was another foreshortening of his name: Ur.

In the city of Ur in the land between two rivers lived a man whose name was Abram. Abram and his family went to the city of Harran on the upper reaches of the land between two rivers. Abram and his growing extended family stayed for some time in Harran. Abram eventually left Harran and led his extended family to Canaan and settled at Bethel before the onset of a famine, causing Abram and his extended family to leave Bethel. They traveled to Egypt, but Abram and his even larger extended family eventually returned to Bethel. After a short second stay at Bethel Abram and his extended family traveled south and founded the city of Hebron, where Abram—by then called Abraham—became patriarch of the Hebrews.

Harran was the most important city of a people known as the Hurrians. Hurrians understood many things and Hurrians helped those who were interested and who enquired. Hurrians also allegorized things they knew and created mythos designed to help others think for themselves and gain understanding. The Hurrians then made this mythos available to others. This mythos adapted and retained by those living in the land between two rivers, contained a pantheon of jealous and quarreling gods. Essenes infused that mythos with an additional goddess/god who was called variously Nanna, Sin or Zu. In the mythos accompanying Nanna/Sin/Zu, this upstart god steals the Tablets of Destinies from the god Enlil while he bathes. A tremendous battle ensues which results in the return of the Tablets of Destinies and the banishment of Nanna/Sin/Zu. Enlil and the other jealous and quarreling gods force Nanna/Sin/Zu to leave her/his patron city Ur and to go into exile in Harran.

Although Essenes wanted the battle for the Tablets of the Destinies between Nanna/Sin/Zu and Enlil and the other gods to appear as if it was just another squabble between jealous and quarreling gods, Essenes inserted Nanna/Sin/Zu and her/his attendant mythos into the larger framework of mythos to provide another allegorized history of the children who were equally alike and not alike the transitional creative-thinking beings of Danebury and their descendants.

The Tablets of Destinies are analogs of the forbidden apples in the garden of Eden.

The alternately female and male Nanna/Sin/Zu is Eve and Adam.

The theft of the Tablets of Destinies is the gaining of self-realization.

The banishment of Nanna/Sin/Zu is the savaging of human beings by the Pleiadeans.

The jealous and quarrelsome pantheon of gods are the Pleiadeans.

Abram lived in Ur where Nanna/Sin/Zu had been ascendant and he traveled to Harran, the place of exile of Nanna/Sin/Zu.

Abram lived in Egypt and founded Hebron.

Ur is located at the crossing of the Line of Civilizations and the Excalibur Line, a crossing which represents the interaction of the three-dimensional mind of self-aware beings, and courage. Behdet in Egypt is located at the crossing of the Line of Civilizations and the Sacred line, a crossing which represents the interaction of the three-dimensional mind of self-aware beings, and their soul.

Abram needed heart, mind and soul so that he could continue his journeys, found Hebron and become Abraham.

Behdet, Hebron and Ur are located from west to east, on or near the Line of Civilizations. The distance between Behdet and Harran and the distance between Harran and Ur are each about 577 miles. Thus the angles at Behdet and Ur in the triangle formed by Behdet, Harran and Ur are virtually the same: 40.5 degrees. The angle at Hebron in the triangle formed by Harran, Hebron and Ur is 60 degrees, making the angle at Hebron in the triangle formed by Behdet, Harran and Hebron 120 degrees. The angle at Harran in the triangle formed by Behdet, Harran and Hebron is 19.5 degrees (since 180 – 40.5 and 120 = 19.5).

In order to be able to found Hebron and become Abraham, Abram had to ascertain where to locate Hebron. The location of Hebron had to be on the Line of Civilizations between Behdet and Ur, east of Behdet by 19.5 degrees (a near equivalent of 19.47 degrees) as measured from the line between Harran and Behdet, and forming a 60 degree angle between Harran and Ur.

The triangle formed by Behdet, Harran and Ur encodes the Number of Harmony, and part of the formula for inducing the required retrograde precession on Earth, so that the Earth could bring forth self-aware life. The number 66 (the number whose tangent combines with the tangent of 114 for a cumulative tangent of 0 —the tangent of 360, 2160, 21,600, 25,920 and 27,000) is two-thirds of the 99 degree corner of the triangle at Harran. The two 40.5 degree corners at Behdet and Ur add up to 81

—the paradigm ratio between the mass of a seed planet and its moon being 81 to 1.

Essenes infused Egyptians with the idea of creating a special administrative district between Northern Egypt and Southern Egypt (between latitude 29 degrees 51 minutes north and latitude 30 degrees 6 minutes north) and establishing their capital Memphis on the southern boundary of this special district. Since their capital city had to be on the bank of the Nile—which at the latitude of Memphis is east of the main axis of Egypt and the Nile—Egyptians set up a geodetic marker marking the main axis of Egypt and the Nile, and the southern boundary of the special administrative district between Northern Egypt and Southern Egypt west of Memphis. At 29 degrees 51 minutes degrees north latitude, the geodetic marker of Sokar is 42 feet less than 3600 feet north of 29 degrees 50 minutes 24.93 seconds north latitude—the latitude in the northern hemisphere at which the parallel circling the Earth is precisely 21,600 statute miles long.

Essenes infused Egyptians with the idea of creating a special administrative district because Essenes hoped Egyptians would mark the southern boundary of the district in a way Egyptians had previously marked other boundaries. Essenes wanted to geodetically illustrate both nautical and statute miles to human beings and they did so by encoding that illustration with the assistance of Egyptians, who set up the Sokar geodetic marker.

Ur is located at the crossing of the Line of Civilizations and the Excalibur Line. Ur is also located so that the angle at Ur (of the triangle formed by Hurmyrr, Thebes and Ur) is 19.5 degrees, another near equivalent of 19.47 degrees. (Thebes is located two-sevenths of the way from the equator to the north pole, along the Nile, and the same distance from Ur as is Hurmyrr.)

Cary Manpure worked for years to find many combinations of sites for settlement by the future beings of Danebury—sites which would be suitable for habitation and sites which had repeated angular interrelationships according to the geometry of the Horz complex—especially the angles of golden triangles.

The angular relationship of Hurmyrr, Thebes and Ur was just one example of many such interrelations worked out by Cary Manpure.

The angle formed at Mecca between Hebron and Ur is 50.72 degrees, the angle formed at the site of energy transredimensioning in the Hurmaze between the Tor and the Tower of Ancestors on Silbury; the angle representing sexual intercourse in golden triangles.

The angle formed at Ur between Al Marj (an oracle site in Libya) and Metsamor north of Mount Hurartu and the angle formed at Ur by Al

Marj and Mecca are both 69.28 degrees: the angle representing oral sex in golden triangles.

The angle formed at Siwa between Dodona and Latakia (an oracle site southwest of Hieropolis) is also 69.28 degrees and the triangle formed by Dodona, Latakia and Siwa is a replication of the apparent two-dimensional southernmost triangle of the Tor on Silbury.

The angle formed by the Line of Civilizations at Persepolis which runs from Behdet through Hebron, Ur and Persepolis to Mohenho Daro and Metsamor is 45.03 degrees, one of the interior angles of one of the five apparent two-dimensional triangles making up the Tor on Silbury.

The angle formed at Mohenho Daro by Mecca and Metsamor is also 45.03 degrees.

The angle formed at Mecca between Thebes and Ur is 85.36 degrees, the apparent two-dimensional angle at the apex of the Tor on Silbury of the two apparent two-dimensional identical triangles on the western and eastern sides of the Tor.

Essenes insured that many settlements were built on sites according to the geometric interrelationships worked out by Cary Manpure.

Babylon's site was carefully chosen and encoded by Essenes. At the latitude of Ur there are 894 and one-half miles in 15 degrees of longitude, 1/24th the circumference of the Earth. Essenes calculated at what latitude there would be 98 percent of 894 and one half miles in 15 degrees of longitude, moved 7 miles southward and insured that Babylon was constructed at that latitude between the two rivers.

Babylon was given its name as a pun on the phrase 'babble on.' The ziggurat of Babylon was called the Tower of Babel as a pun on the word 'babble.'

As a result of Alteans' having fulfilled all Essene requirements for the genetic agent, Essenes projected that human beings would naturally come to speak a variety of languages, indigenous variants of the many languages which had been spoken before, along the chain of galaxies leading to this galaxy.

Babylon and its Tower of Babel were originally intended by Essenes to memorialize the babble of tongues which were to emerge as a result of the diversity of human beings, diversity fostered by Essenes to strengthen the courage of human beings.

Babylon was in the land between two rivers and therefore came to be subjected to the savage interference of secret Pleiadean agents in place.

Babylon suffered.

The intended mythos of the Tower of Babel was altered to reflect the suffering of human beings at the hands of savage Pleiadean interferers.

Suffering which was not as a result of speaking many tongues, but because those who resisted had their tongues cut out.

Essenes had allegorized the story of the beast of the mythos NOSTOS and were prepared to infuse their story into the mythos of human beings when appropriate. Essenes wanted to juxtapose the beast—the refusal to accept ideas beyond one's own—and the lover of the hero of the story—the thirst for knowledge. Essenes marked the beast of their allegorized story with the number 666 to show that being a slave of the beast makes one thrice dead—dead of heart, dead of mind, dead of soul.

When Babylon fell prey to the savage Pleiadean interferers, Essenes became angry and frustrated that they were not allowed by the mandate of the Source of the Universe to stop the Pleiadeans, and drive them from the planet. As a result Essenes changed the beautiful young lady of their allegorized story—who represented the thirst for knowledge—into the thrice dead whore of Babylon, the word 'whore' being a pun on the syllable 'hor,' meaning 'hyperdimensional Source of the Universe.'

Essenes established a base of operations on the northwestern coast of the island of Crete at a time when human beings were beginning to settle in the Mediterranean basin. This base was located at what was later to become the Minoan palace of Kydonia and was located according to repeated angular interrelationships of the geometry of the Horz complex as worked out by Cary Manpure. Essenes also called their base Kydonia, a word meaning 'city of glory' in Hellenikos. It was from Kydonia that Essenes infused into human society the concept of human beings as hawks, who would one day swoop down and destroy their prey: the Pleiadeans.

In Egyptian society the human hawk became the hawk god Horus, the son of Isis and Osiris. Osiris is killed by Seth, but his wife Isis extracts the 'essence' of Osiris from his body and impregnates herself in order to bear Horus. Seth represents the Pleiadeans. Isis represents the indigenous ancestry of human beings, Osiris represents those developing beings butchered by Pleiadeans, and the essence of Osiris represents the genetic agent. Horus the hawk represents human beings. Later, Horus and Seth do battle and Horus cuts off the testicles of Seth, making Seth forever sterile. Essenes intended that human hawks should do the same to Pleiadeans.

In Homer's ODYSSEY, Essenes infused the story of Circe, a sorceress whose name comes from the Hellenikos word 'kirke,' meaning 'hawk.' Circe is a female hawk representing the fact that human ladies must be even more hawk-like than human men. Odysseus and his men represent human men who do not treat ladies correctly. They get along better when Odysseus decides to love Circe, instead of treating her badly. He is able to do this because he meets Hermes who tells Odysseus how to avoid being turned into swine (as his men had been because they had behaved like pigs). Hermes represents Essenes, and it will be information given to human beings by Essenes that will assist human men.

Essenes infused Ezekiel with the illusion of seeing a flying machine which as part of its form had the depictions of a man, a bull, a lion and an eagle. The depiction of a man was intended to represent the three-dimensional mind of self-aware beings. The bull represented the soul (because bulls have horns which resemble part of the soul print). The lion represented courage. The eagle represented the Source of the Universe because both winged eagles and space craft with spinning disks are able to fly by the grace of the Source of the Universe.

Together heart, mind and soul also devolve from the Source of the Universe, to form the three cornerstones of self-aware consciousness which reside in the physical universe. The fourth cornerstone of self-aware life—the Source of the Universe—resides in the fourth-dimension, but extrudes Itself into three-dimensions in order to lovingly guide self-aware beings along the twistings and turnings of life toward the ultimate redeeming of the Universe: harmony.

Essenes infused substitutions for the man, the bull, the lion and the eagle as representations in hermetic teachings. The color black replaced the man as a symbol of the three-dimensional mind; white replaced the bull as a symbol of the soul; red replaced the lion as a symbol of courage and gold replaced the eagle as a symbol of the Source of the Universe. In the hermetic teachings red and gold often switch places, making red the ultimate achievement. Essenes infused this concept because the courage of human beings is to be their most important trait as leaders of the redeeming of the galaxy and because courage is the result of the interworkings of mind, soul, and the Source of the Universe.

Essenes insured that stories developed and persisted describing how, at some point in time, Hurmyrr had writing upon it; that it had been painted and that it once had a capstone made of gold. The story of writing on Hurmyrr was a distant reflection of the sign that Essenes had draped on the northern facing of Hurmyrr which read "Joe Lon Odkin." The story of the paint was an encoding of the colors black, white and red. The gold capstone story encodes the meaning of gold in the hermetic teachings: gold represents the Source of the Universe, a four-dimensional Entity which has no physical presence in three-dimensions. This story also encodes the fact that Hurmyrr has never had a capstone.

Essenes have been appalled that the gold capstone story of Hurmyrr has been taken literally by so many, despite it being totally absurd. No one would ever put so much valuable gold on top of a structure nearly 500 feet tall as an attraction to thieves, or worse yet, as an attraction to invaders. Essenes have sadly concluded that most human beings would not understand allegory.

When human beings living in and around Hellas became interested in the prospect of what the future might hold for them, Essenes infused into the minds of many the idea of establishing oracles. Essenes insured that the most important oracles were located along nine latitudinal bands, one degree of latitude apart, starting in the south with Behdet, at 31 and one-half degrees north latitude.

Two-thirds of these latitudinal bands of oracular sites are south of Hellas. The three oracles in Hellas, separated by about one degree, were on the island of Delos, at Delphi and at Dodona. Delphi (closely associated with dolphins and drakon) was the most important oracle because it was the middle of the three oracles in Hellas. The capital letter E was also associated with Delphi because the word 'Essenes' starts with the capital letter E.

Eight-ninths of the latitudinal bands of oracular sites did not have the capital letter 'E' associated with them, as a representation of 9/8ths, the harmonic of transdimensioning.

Essenes insured that a poem became the epitaph for Leonidas and the 300 Spartans. They kept the promise of the Spartans despite interference from the priesthood, themselves enticed by secret Pleiadean agents operating from the land of the damned. Had it not been for the treason of a Hellene who had also been enticed by secret Pleiadean agents, Leonidas and the 300 Spartans would have defeated the Persian hordes (who had been urged forward by a mad king himself enticed by secret Pleiadean agents operating from the land between two rivers) this mad king had thoughtlessly abandoned the wise-thinking of Zoroaster.

Leonidas and the 300 Spartans showed Essenes that human beings were capable of great feats of physical, mental and ethical courage.

Having witnessed Alexander the Great's decisiveness in cutting the Gordion knot, Essenes insured that priests presented the truth to the would-be world conqueror, when he visited the Oracle of Siwa. Alexander the Great courageously accepted the truth, changed his mind and became a unifier—no longer a conqueror. Alexander the Great died young, but his spirit lives on.

Essenes infused the story of the final battle 'Armageddon' into the culture of human beings as an allegory of the final battle with the beast—the refusal to see viewpoints other than one's own. To illustrate this allegory Essenes used Mount Megiddo in the land where the 375 daughters and 375 sons of the healthy, child bearing age transitional creative-thinking female beings of Danebury, who were equally alike and not alike the transitional creative-thinking beings were taken with their mothers. The battle with the beast (lurking everywhere like a sneak thief in the night) requires the acceptancc of both creative and linear thinking, and those 375 daughters and 375 sons (children whose descendants have been savagely misdirected by Pleiadean interference) equally alike and not alike the transitional creative-thinking beings were the human beings best able to accept creative and linear thinking. The winners of the battle of 'Armageddon' against the beast will be those who accept both creative and linear thinking.

The losers will be those who do not, and they will cast themselves down into a lake of fire and become downcast by their own discord.

Several centuries after the death of an heroic and tragic king in Hurengland, Essenes overlaid the growing indigenous mythos of this king with the mythos inspired by Rena Jackman, written by the seventh grade class of Tom Huish and later altered by Cary Manpure to fit the tragic events of the life of his cousin 'Art Hurian' Manpure. Essenes changed the character of Guinevere who had not been unfaithful, so in order to be able to make her unfaithful, Essenes added the character Lancelot.

Essenes changed the character of Guinevere because Essenes operate under the mandate of the Source of the Universe.

The addition of the character Lancelot and the altering of the character Guinevere were intended by Essenes to allegorize the rape of Hurengland by the beast of 1066, a beast who feigned friendship, and then stabbed its neighbor in the back.

Lancelot is the beast.

Guinevere is Hurengland.

Later Essenes infused the misdirected French Revolution with the idea of imposing on its conquests the profoundly irrelevant unit of measure. (The meter.) Essenes did this so that when the truth about the profoundly irrelevant unit of measure is revealed the spawn of the French Revolution and of the beast of 1066 will suffer.

Essenes encoded part of the name of Panergon Gwynmyrr in the names Guinevere and Merlin. The first syllables of those two names added together are a near equivalent of Gwynmyrr—clear reflection.

Mordred, Morgause and Morgana were intended by Essenes to be near equivalents of the phrases 'more dead,' 'more grousing' and 'more gain' because that most dreadful trio was more dead—thrice dead—due to their more-grousing for more-gain.

Essenes insured that THE ARTHURIAN LEGENDS were closely associated with Glastonbury and that the meanings of this legend would only be understood upon clear reflection.

Essenes insured that the abbey complex constructed at Glastonbury—including its latrine and its Garth Cloister—modified in its design but not in its dimensions by Essenes from the original concept of the Garth Representation—were constructed over time as far as was practicable, in accordance with the designs of Cary Jackman.

The human societies which resulted from a mixture of those who had migrated to Prehurland from the Abzuland on which Hurmyrr stands and those who had migrated from far eastern Ashintoland, lived in harmony with their environment and with one another. This was so until refugees reached Prehurland from lands near Hellas, following the invasions induced by secret Pleiadean agents, after the horrific war between the Hellenes and the Wilusans—a war also brought about by secret Pleiadean agents.

These refugees, who had come from harmonious and flourishing civilizations, had been so traumatized by their experiences to the extent that, as they intermingled with the existing populations, they sewed the first seeds of disharmony in Prehurland. Much later, explorers came from far northwestern Ashintoland and spread more disharmony.

Later still, mercenary spawn of the inquisition descended upon the populations of Prehurland and ruthlessly murdered, looted and raped Prehurland and its populations.

Explorers and settlers from Hurengland were less interested in booty and less intent on murder, but they nevertheless forced populations of Prehurland from their lands and fought bloody wars with them. These explorers and settlers were always of two minds concerning those who had lived in Prehurland originally, and the descendants of these explorers and settlers have never decided whether the descendants of those who preceded them were/are noble or savage.

The descendants of the mercenary spawn of the inquisition include descendants of that violent segment of human society who arrogantly and ruthlessly imposed their profoundly irrelevant unit of measurement on nearly everyone else. And include those who continue to ruthlessly slaughter bulls in the arena—bulls whose horns represent a portion of soul prints of self-aware beings.

The descendants of the explorers and settlers from Hurengland include those who have arrogantly prohibited the ceremonial usage, by the survivors of those who came first to Prehurland, of the feathers of eagles—eagles ruthlessly slaughtered to near extinction by some of the descendants of the explorers and settlers from Hurengland—eagles who symbolize the Great Spirit to those who came first to Prehurland—eagles who represent the Source of the Universe.

Essenes infused warnings into the mind of the megalomaniac, would-be world conqueror, Napoleon Bonaparte when he visited the chamber in Hurmyrr containing the precisely placed coffer, memorial to the innocent victims of Silbury. Napoleon Bonaparte ignored those warnings, and suffered an horrific fate.

Panergon Gwynmyrr entered a new phase towards the end of the 19th Century as Essenes began choosing authors in whom they could infuse allegorical historical information. These authors then unwittingly incorporated that information into their works of fiction, so that their works of fiction became mythos. Among the authors so infused by Essenes are Jules Verne, Edgar Rice Burroughs and Arthur C. Clarke.

Essenes infused Edgar Rice Burroughs with many things.

Essenes infused Burroughs with the hermetic metaphor in which black, white, red and gold represent the three-dimensional mind, the soul, courage, and the Source of the Universe.

In Burroughs' mythos Tarzan, the infant Tarzan and his parents are cast ashore in west Africa following a mutiny at sea. Later, Tarzan is adopted by a she-ape named Kala who lovingly raises the, by then, orphaned waif. Kala is subsequently murdered by a black man and Tarzan travels alone to east Africa where he becomes chief of the Waziri, a tribe of blacks who wear white plumes on their heads.

This story is an allegorical rendering of the rebellion of the Pleiadeans, the birth of human beings and the interference of Pleiadeans in the affairs of human beings. The she-ape Kala, whose name in Hellenikos means 'beautiful,' 'honorable,' 'noble,' 'favorable,' and 'fine,' represents the harmonious nurturing environment of the Earth before the arrival of the savage Pleiadean interferers. The black man who murders Kala represents the savage Pleiadeans, savage beasts who do not recognize the existence of the soul. The white-plumed black Waziri are self-aware beings who enjoy the harmonious relationship of the interaction between the three-dimensional mind and the soul. Tarzan and the Waziri live in east Africa where most of the development toward human beings took place.

In Burroughs' mythos of John Carter, the hero is mysteriously transported to the red planet where he battles against great odds to win the hand of the Princess of Helium—Helium being the mightiest empire of the red men of the red planet. The largest city of Helium is actually two cities—Greater Helium to the west and Lesser Helium to the east. 195 Greater Helium is marked by its Scarlet Tower and Lesser Helium by its Yellow Tower. The Scarlet Tower of Greater Helium represents the red stone Tower of Ancestors in the center of Hur Square in Altea City on Silbury; the Yellow Tower of Lesser Helium represents the Tower of Ancestors, never constructed, which was to have stood on the mesa to the east of Altea City, which became the base for the Hurmaze. The Yellow Tower of Lesser Helium (to the east of Greater Helium) is yellow, because the Tower of Ancestors was not built on the mesa to the east of Altea

City, and yellow represents gold, and gold represents that which does not exist in three-dimensions.

Lesser Helium is 75 miles east of Greater Helium, a representation of transdimensioning.

Essenes infused into the mythos of John Carter, the seemingly oddly named Helium as the mightiest empire on the red planet because helium is the first element which is formed by the fusing of two hydrogen atoms. In this allegory one hydrogen atom represents Alteans and the second hydrogen atom the previously existing, but headed for extinction, beings of Earth. When female and male reproductive material from Alteans was introduced to those beings headed for extinction, human beings resulted. John Carter becomes the leader—though not the ruler—of Helium. Human beings are leaders not rulers.

Burroughs' mythos of John Carter contains a history of the red planet going back millions of years. Originally, there had been three races of beings—blacks, yellows and whites—but various conditions required them to unite, resulting in the red race encountered by John Carter. The colors of these races, with the red race as the end result—represent the interworkings of mind, soul, and the Source of the Universe to bring about courage.

The redskins of the mythos of John Carter are the most courageous of those who ever lived on the red planet (before the arrival of the human being John Carter).

The human being redskins—who frequently used the symbol of a leftward bent swastika (a representation of the clockwise spinning stroboscope used to lay down transtime crop glyphs) are the most courageous of human beings. John Carter of Burroughs' mythos is even more courageous than the red men of the red planet because John Carter is a human being.

John Carter accepts his role when he writes:

> "My mind is evidently so constituted that I am subconsciously forced into the path of duty..."

The path of duty of John Carter is the path of duty of human beings. In Burroughs' mythos, the inhabitants of the red planet have a nine-faceted crystal which divides light into nine rays. They use the 8th ray to give their air ships buoyancy, and they use the 9th ray to make air. The 8th and 9th rays are allegories for gravitrons which fly off spinning disks; gravitrons which propel air and space craft; gravitrons which increase the effective mass of planets so that infused air will not fly off into space. Gravitrons are produced by a transdimensional process and 9/8ths is the harmonic of transdimensioning.

Later, Essenes began choosing movie makers in whom they could infuse allegorical historical information. These movie makers then unwittingly incorporated such information into their works of fiction and historical fiction, so that their movies became mythos. Among the movie makers so infused by Essenes are Stanley Kubrick, George Lucas and Steven Spielberg.

Essenes have infused both authors and movie makers with allegorical historical information in order to create mythos, because Essenes operate under the mandate of the Source of the Universe.

In the movie *Spartacus* directed by Stanley Kubrick, Essenes insured that the Roman Marcus Crassus was portrayed in such a way that he would resemble any of the savage Pleiadean emperors.

The escape to freedom of the widow of Spartacus with their son allegorized the many escapes of the Atlantean descendants—and their continuing on.

Because it was time, at the mid point of the year, in July 1947 (19.47) Essenes created the illusion of a crashing alien space craft. Essenes infused the crash site with simulated parts of alien bodies and with simulated parts of an alien space craft.

By doing this, Essenes began a new phase of Panergon Gwynmyrr. This new phase also entails the creation of illusions of sightings of alien space craft and 'experiences' involving aliens through the use of holographic projections and magnetically braided beams.

At the request of the Essene leaders of Panergon Gwynmyrr, Olmquist Engineering, an Essene engineering company, developed the 'aliens' 'seen' by millions of human beings since 1947. These aliens—often called 'the grays'—are short and very thin with large heads and eyes. The hint that the grays are illusions rather than fact, is that the grays do not have five fingers on their hands—an impossibility—since all living things have five-sided symmetry. Olmquist Engineering developed the grays, and Essenes have induced 'sightings' of gray aliens because Essenes operate under the mandate of the Source of the Universe.

Essenes subsequently added three additional components to illusions of sightings of alien space craft and gray aliens: 'abductions,' 'medical examinations and surgery' also 'sexual encounters' sometimes leading to the 'birth of half-alien babies.' These three newer components of this phase of Panergon Gwynmyrr are also illusions, as they are all induced by magnetically braided beams infused into the souls of certain human beings. If the braided beams are intense enough, those receiving them remember their experience; if the braided beams are less intense the remembering occurs during hypnosis when the subconscious is tapped. This is so because the subconscious is the intermediary between the consciousness and the soul.

Essenes have been able to infuse certain carefully chosen human beings with various illusions because Essenes know the soul antecedents of many human beings; all souls have unique soul prints; and the magnetically braided beams used to induce illusions into human beings through their souls can be directed to an individual soul by way of soul print encoding of braided beam messages. This can therefore be carried out no matter where those receiving the illusions are located and even when those human beings move about the planet. Those carefully chosen by Essenes to receive illusions have been chosen for many reasons but principally because Essenes know that they will help with the process of redeeming the galaxy.

Some recipients have been told that their alien abductors come from the constellation Reticulum. Essenes have done this because the word 'reticulum' means 'network' and Essenes want to build up a network of those who care.

Essenes also know that the soul descendant of Anson Trent is alive among the Hellenes. Essenes know that the soul descendant of Henry Shick is the beast who lives in the land between two rivers. Essenes know that the soul descendant of Hal Roon is a school administrator. Essenes know that the soul descendant of Arnhold Manpure was a captain in the United States Navy. Essenes have diddled with, toyed with and bedeviled these beasts, along with other known beasts.

Essenes added another physical component to new phase of Panergon Gwynmyrr: cattle mutilations. Essenes have added real cattle mutilations to the illusions of aliens and alien space vehicle sightings. These demonstrations have been accomplished through the cutting power of magnetically braided beams and have been undertaken, among other things, to lend credence to the stories of aliens and alien space vehicle sightings.

These components of the new phase of Panergon Gwynmyrr are all intended to allegorize the history of the galaxy—including and especially those parts of the history of the Earth about which human beings have no knowledge.

The appearance of grays in particular is meant to encode many things. The shape of their faces was taken from the shape of the faces of lions—sad lions to evoke the difficulty of attaining great courage. The shape of the heads and eyes are encoded perioikomai, especially the egg metaphor and the dual-perspective of star ship hulls. The jagged 'ears' or 'jaw bones' are encoded thunderbolts, metaphors for the twistings and turnings of life. The wiry bodies of these aliens are intended to evoke toughness without bulk.

The most important encoding of grays has to do with their fingers and lack of genitals—even though individual grays evoke female or male categorization. Grays have three fingers (not four) and a thumb, making a total of four. Lacking five fingers they are not living, but in lacking five they are missing their fourth finger—hyperdimensionality. The message is: to be really alive you have to know about hyperdimensionality. To be really alive you also have to know that sex is the most hyperdimensional part of life. Grays lack these things to reflect back that human beings lack hyperdimensionality. 196,197

Essenes previewed grays when they induced the naming and specific design of Barbury Castle earthwork north of Avenabury. The syllable 'bar' in Barbury is a foreshortening of the Hellenikos word 'barbaros' meaning 'foreign' or 'alien' and the syllable 'bury' is the Hurtegel syllable meaning 'mountain.' Therefore, Barbury means 'alien mountain.' Barbury Castle earthwork is a dual-perspective of the hulls of star ships—including both inner and outer hulls. Barbury Castle is also an egg, and it is the shape of the heads of alien grays. 198

Even before Essenes induced things at Barbury Castle, they induced the specific design of the crowns of Egypt. The combined crown of the pharaohs of Egypt is a very close modeling of the Waldark hat with amplifier, and the curled loop extending outward from the front is the signature of Joe Lon Odkin—and his representation of the transredimensioning of energy by meditators.

Essenes have seen that there are those who will debunk everything, and there are others who will believe anything. For those who will believe anything, Essenes have designed and carried forward the Density Program.

Essenes have 'channeled' meaningless garbage by means of magnetically braided beams to those who will believe anything, making them go through contortions in order to be ready for and carry out the 'channeling.'

Essenes have particularly enjoyed using the term 'densities' when referring to dimensions—including dimensions which do not exist—in these 'channeled' 'communications' because densities is the term the extragalactics determined would be the best to use when explaining hyperdimensionality to scientifically unsophisticated beings. The extragalactics did not intend the use of the term 'densities' in a derogatory way when communicating with scientifically unsophisticated beings.

Essenes have very much meant to infer that the unsophisticated beings who receive their 'channeled' 'communications' are dense. The Density Program was so named by Essenes because those who will believe in 'channeling' have densities, not destinies. The densest thing about those in the Destiny Program, Essenes have come to realize, is that the dense ones always try to figure out how messages come to them, but hardly never try to figure out how their messages get back to those 'channeling' densities to them.

Essenes know that the soul descendant of the doubter Paul Gravenson and the 'art teacher' Halbert Hargrave who interrupted and walked out on Lura Redmand, is the puffed up stuffed up 'compiler' of a book whose interpretations of meaningful communications are ludicrous beyond compare. This later day Paul Gravenson/Halbert Hargrave fancies himself as an expert in the field of crop formation analysis, but the only thing he has got right is that there are formations in the crops. When presented with the keys to everything, he flatly rejected them because they were not his own (and because he wouldn't know the keys to everything if they were spelled out and handed to him which they were).

Although many have claimed to have seen space craft from beyond, human beings have only 'seen' what Essenes have directed for them to see—no human being has ever seen any Essene craft.

Although many have claimed to have seen extraterrestrials, only three very carefully chosen human beings—who are no longer living—have ever seen extraterrestrials and have known that those persons were extra-terrestrials.

Although many have claimed governments are doing everything from suppressing information about UFOs and craft to actually building them, governments are blind—with the exception of experimental work like biofeedback, they are not using hyperdimensional capabilities—they are doing nothing.

Concurrent with the 1975 launch year of the United States Viking probes to Silbury, Essenes began activating transtime crop glyphs in southern Hurengland, many of which had been laid down over 237,000 years ago by Cary Manpure and Cary Jackman.

Essenes have laid down and activated some transtime crop glyphs in other places around the planet to demonstrate that transtime crop glyphs are not a natural local phenomenon of southern Hurengland.

Essenes have also laid down and activated additions to some of the transtime crop glyphs laid down by Cary Manpure and Cary Jackman. These additions, including additional 'signatures,' were made to enhance the meanings of the transtime crop glyphs to which they were added—and to confuse.

Essenes have also designed, then laid down and activated in southern Hurengland additional transtime crop glyphs. Some of these transtime crop glyphs juxtapose the harmony of the gravitron drive with the brutal disharmony of rockets.

Essenes discovered that Joe Lon Odkin's twin spawn transtime crop glyph unwittingly encoded the three very different local light speeds. Essenes then designed, laid down and activated two additional transtime crop glyphs to reinforce the encoding of solar system light speed, interstellar light speed and intergalactic light speed. 199

Essenes designed, then laid down and activated in southern Hurengland a transtime crop glyph depicting the doughnut shaped portion of computers. 200 This transtime crop glyph was made in order to illustrate a connection between it and the doughnut earthworks known as Old Sarum, and to enhance the connection between those earthworks and computers.

Essenes were very pleased by the inclusion of a greeting plaque on a space craft launched by human beings which was designed to (and did) fly beyond the confines of the solar system containing Earth. Essenes saw this greeting plaque as a near equivalent to the markers of peace which have been left by seekers around the Universe, including the marker of peace found on Silbury by Cary Manpure and Tommy Untiman, and left by them for human beings to uncover.

Essenes infused the legend of Atlantis into human society as a distant reflection of the historical Atlantis which existed about 100 billion years ago on the planet upon which Waldark later lived. Essenes changed the story of Atlantis to state that the reason for the natural disaster that destroyed Atlantis was due to those living in Atlantis having grown out of harmony with their environment. Essenes did this so that when human beings learn the truth about the historical Atlantis they will be shocked into crying out in agony at the cruel fate suffered by their innocent ancestors.

Essenes also infused partially incorrect parts of the diagram and allegorical stories of Atlantis into human society, because Essenes wanted the true story of Atlantis to be made available to human beings only after human beings study the diagrams of the Sanctuary near Avenabury and the diagrams of the Ranch House of Silbury. 61,62 Essenes know that only by properly scaling and overlaying a diagram made from Plato's description of Atlantis, together with scaled diagrams of the Sanctuary near Avenabury and the Ranch House of Silbury, can the seed and all 12 concentric rings of Atlantis be found.

Essenes know that the description and diagram of the allegorical Atlantis from Plato strongly supports 10, but totally lacks 12. Essenes know that the additional information supplied by the Sanctuary near Avenabury and the Ranch House of Silbury adds 12 to the description and diagram from Plato and provides the actual description and actual diagram of the historical Atlantis—thoroughly bringing Atlantis back into harmony with its environment. Essenes also infused the story of the lack of harmony of those living in Atlantis because they omitted 12 in the allegorical descriptions and stories that they had previously infused into human society.

Essenes also know, however, that lack of harmony with one's environment can bring about disaster to that environment. Essenes know that Europeans using the metric system which counts ONLY by 10s are bringing about the deaths of trees in Europe because Europeans are growing out of harmony with their environment by not counting by 10s AND 12s.

These disharmonies cluster in certain areas and sap the trees in those areas of their will to live. Essenes know that there is a connection between the deaths of trees and these disharmonies because the areas in which the trees are dying are areas in which the flow of planetary torun is already low, and Essenes have detected that the flow has decreased substantially in those areas for reasons not connected with constructions.

From observation, Essenes have concluded that all living things need planetary or induced torun to survive and therefore must have 'souls;' disharmonious beings affect the flow of planetary torun; perhaps disharmonious beings affect the planet itself—because the planet itself is the originator of the flow of planetary torun.

Essenes have also come to realize that the difference between non-living things, animals and self-aware life, is not so much in fundamentals, as it is in degrees of complexity. The differences in complexity are great, but they still constitute a continuum. In a sense, everything is alive.

Essenes have also come to realize that everything in three dimensions is the result of the extrusion of the hyperdimensional thoughts of the Source of the Universe through the zero-dimension point of the Universe. They understand that the difference between things in three-dimensions is the result of different four-dimensional thoughts. Essenes have extrapolated their knowledge concerning braided beams and planetary torun, and have applied those extrapolations.

Essenes designed, laid down and activated in southern Hurengland a series of five transtime crop glyphs depicting Atlantis and the perierchomai transportation system in order to further imprint the correct description and diagram of Atlantis.

The first transtime crop glyph has a small circle in the middle, surrounded by a thick ring, surrounded by 10 small circles, two of which are connected across a space by an arcing line. 201 The arcing line represents two missing small circles which would fit into that space and thus make 12 small circles around the outside in all. These small circles and the missing circles indicate 10 and 12.

The outside of the small middle circle represents the 15 mile diameter concentric ring of Atlantis. The inside of the thick ring represents the 27 mile diameter concentric ring. The outside of the thick ring is 45 miles in this scale—10/12ths of 54, the next concentric ring of Atlantis. This transtime crop glyph also conveys 5/6ths.

The second crop glyph in the series consists of a small circle surrounded by a thin ring on which there are four very small circles, each separated by 90 degrees. 202 The small circle in the center represents the upper circular terrace wall which was five miles in diameter. The thin ring is inaccurately placed (since there never was such a ring) with a scaled diameter near to 18 miles. The four very small circles represent the Gymnasion/Stadion, Akadeimia, the Philosophia House and the Hippodromos of Atlantis—four things which are representative of the need of self-aware beings to educate their minds, bodies and souls—and to have a good time.

The inclusion by Essenes of the 18 mile diameter 'ring' (which was not really a ring like the concentric rings of Atlantis) in this series was done so as to reemphasize the inferred ring—the 14th feature of Atlantis including the seed structure—and the fact that the 18 mile diameter inferred ring of Atlantis represents the Source of the Universe—the invisible Entity from which three-dimensional reality devolves.

The third crop glyph is similar to the second, but it has additional thin lines. 203 The circle in the center represents the 9.72 mile diameter concentric ring of Atlantis, the first thin line represents the 11 mile diameter concentric ring and the second thin line with four small circles the Gymnasion/Stadion, Akadeimia, the Philosophia House and the Hippodromos of Atlantis. The third and fourth thin lines are additive, because the third line has a scaled diameter of 24.5 miles and the fourth line a scaled diameter of 29.5 miles—and 24.5 miles + 29.5 miles = 54 miles, the first concentric ring beyond the river surrounding Atlantis.

The fourth crop glyph is a very thick ring with a thin line extending from it. 204 The outer edge of the thick ring represents the 54 mile concentric ring and its inner edge approximates the never existing 18 mile ring. The extending line represents the river, its scaled width is three miles and its scaled length is 27.777+ miles. The length of the river is determined by multiplying 27.777+ x 54 and dividing the result by three, to obtain 500 miles.

The fifth transtime crop glyph consists of a circle in the center surrounded by four very thin concentric rings, surrounded by a thick ring, surrounded by a thin ring. 205 The thin ring represents the 54 mile diameter concentric ring and the outside edge of the thick ring represents the 27 mile diameter concentric ring of Atlantis. The inside edge of the thick ring represents a perierchomai transportation system crystal tube.

The four concentric very thin rings represent the rings of magnetically levitating magnets surrounding perierchomai transportation system crystal tubes at discrete intervals, as they would appear from a perierchomai transportation system car speeding through a tube. The inner circle represents the way a perierchomai transportation system station would appear in the distance as it is approached by a peri car.

Essenes have been amazed at the way in which human beings have developed, even though human beings have developed as Essenes anticipated (albeit more quickly) as a result of the administration of the two parts of the genetic agent. Essenes know that both genes and souls have memories of things past. Essenes know that due to these facts, human beings would replicate (with local variations based on local conditions) the physical characteristics of virtually all previous beings, the architectural features of virtually all previous cultures and the customs and languages of virtually all previous societies. Even so, Essenes are amazed.

The most amazing replication Essenes have witnessed was Wilusa—called Ilios by Hellenes, the trading partners of Wilusans—which was a virtual clone of Atlantis, given somewhat different terrain, great political differences and vastly different technology. Essenes had intended that Atlantis be only a fictional place on Earth, but the style and grace and tragedy of Wilusa matched the previously unmatched style and grace and tragedy of Atlantis. 206

Essenes know that Hellenes and Wilusans had been friends for centuries and that they shared an elegant and graceful lifestyle. Essenes know that the war between friends destroyed Wilusa, 'The City of White Horses,' and barbarized the Hellenes.

Essenes know that until the time just before the destruction of Atlantis, all self-aware beings of the Universe lived together. Essenes know that in the face of impending disaster most of those who had been living in Atlantis and many others living on the planet on which Atlantis lay, escaped into space and eventually came to settle in eleven galaxies.

Essenes know that those who remained behind were barbarized (following the destruction of Atlantis and virtually everything else on the planet under which the ruins of Atlantis were buried). Essenes know that as a result of the chance finding by grave robbers of Atlantis, the flame of civilization began to burn again among those who had survived. Essenes know that the rediscoveries of Waldark and his 'cabalists' brought almost full civilization back to the survivors.

Essenes are sad, because the 12 groups of self-aware beings who inhabit the Universe are so widely separated and because they do not know that they are all descendants of Atlantis, and they do not even know that the others exist (beyond shadowy encounters during intergalactic migrations).

The intergalactic travelers changed the encounters they had experienced with shadowy figures along the way, into encounters with the beast in their mythos, not because they thought those shadowy figures were the beast, but because they were afraid of the beast within. They had seen the beast within arise among them in those who gave up along the way (those who insisted that they abandon the imperative of intergalactic migration) and they were afraid that the beast might still be with them. This fear of the beast within, was what impelled Essenes to initially feel uncertain about the development of the galaxy. And then to leave Altea to prepare for all contingencies and finally to maintain their steadfast resolve throughout nearly a billion years of tireless work, on behalf of the galaxy and the Universe.

Essenes are therefore intent that human beings lead the redeeming of this galaxy, so that all those who live in this galaxy can finally attain full civilization and reach out to the other descendants of Atlantis and reunite.

Essenes know that such a reunion will work because Essenes know that those living in the other 11 inhabited galaxies of the Universe, speak variants of what Alteans and Essenes call Hellenikos, a variant of what human beings know as the language spoken in Athens during the golden Age of Pericles.

Essenes know that Pericles, whose genius was behind the Parthenon, the columned structure which still has more style and grace than ANYTHING ever conceived by self-aware beings was correct when he said of Athens:

"Future ages will wonder at us, as the present age does now."

Essenes think that for the last 100 billion years there have always been 12 galaxies in preparation for the eventual arrival of intergalactic pioneers, so that the beings indigenous to those emerging galaxies can intermingle with the descendants of Atlantis, add their own flavor to the expanding culture of the Universe and help bring about strong hybrid self-aware beings. Essenes do not know how this is so, but they think it is so.

However, recent observations by Essenes show that this is no longer the way. Although there are new developing galaxies, there do not seem to be seed planets in these galaxies. Instead, there are planets which are near seed planets—as was the Earth. These near seed planets can therefore only become seed planets through the extraordinary work of self-aware beings, such as that performed by Essenes with regard to the preparation of Earth.

Essenes think this means that life can continue indefinitely only through the extraordinary hard work of making near seed planets into seed planets. Essenes think that this can be done over and over again, only if the 12 groups of beings inhabiting the Universe get back together and work in harmony.

Essenes know these things about the Universe, because Essenes have thoroughly explored the inhabitable parts of the Universe. They inspired Cary Manpure and Tommy Untiman to discover, some 237,000 years ago, the marker of peace, located between the Hurmaze and the Tor on Silbury. Essenes have been able to carry out this exploration in a relatively short time period because they are in possession of holo-maps of many regions of the inhabitable parts of the Universe. These holo-maps had been passed down to them from the intergalactic pioneers who arrived in this galaxy after five billion years of travel, holo-maps which have been updated, filled in and completed by Essenes.

Essenes operate under the mandate of the Source of the Universe and though they are anxious to witness the reuniting of the people of the Universe, they know that this galaxy must be made harmonious first. Essenes know that only after this galaxy has lived in harmony for some time, will the people of this galaxy be ready—and have the mandate of the Source of the Universe—to go forth and lead.

Essenes know that human beings are called human beings because the word 'human' is derived from the word 'humus,' meaning 'Earth.' Essenes also know that the word 'human' is derived from the Hellenikos word 'hymen,' meaning 'wedded,' because human beings are wedded to the Earth and because human beings are also wedded to their ancestors from beyond the Earth. The syllable 'man' in the word 'human' is from the language of the time of Waldark and means 'individual,' 'one,' or 'person.' Therefore, the comprehensive meaning of the word 'human' in human beings is: 'wedded Earth one.'

In September 1992 NASA launched an imaging probe to Silbury which had the capability—beginning in December 1993—of reimaging the Horz complex (using a camera which could capture surface details that are as small as three feet in size). Despite the strong evidence supporting the intelligence hypothesis (which came about as a result of the careful and persistent non-governmental study of images of Silbury taken by the Viking orbiters) repeatedly and expertly presented to NASA, NASA refused to reimage in detail the area in which the Horz complex is located. According to NASA, images of that area would be made available to the public approximately six months after they are received on Earth if—by chance—those images were taken. Subsequent photography of the complex has been incomplete and has not replicated the detailed coverage of the 1975 Viking mission.

Essenes know that one of those preventing the proper reimaging of the Horz complex is the soul descendant of Paul Bunzler.

Essenes have prevented the widespread acceptance of the intelligence hypothesis postulated as a result of the images of Silbury returned to Earth because it was not yet the time and that hypothesis was not the vehicle.

Essenes have also prevented the widespread acceptance of that hypothesis because the self-proclaimed 'leaders' of those studying the intelligence hypothesis have as soul antecedents Carl Halverson and Halbert Sarkneson/Garth Sarkneson.

Essenes also insured that the soul descendant of the Pleiadean Sarkneson, incorrectly interpreted the repeated message of the Horz complex by believing it was the obscure ratio e/pi—instead of the square root of three divided by two—the hyperdimensional component of the transdimensional constant, 2.720699046.

Prior to the beginning of imaging of Silbury by the Viking probes, Essenes made a large ditch north of the Hurmaze. The ditch was made to look like the combination of a backwards capital letter L and a lambda, the Hellenikos designation for the soul.

This ditch was intended as an encoded message to human beings:

Come to Silbury and find your souls!

Essenes have also sculpted land features on Silbury to confuse and lure.

Essenes have been operating under the mandate of the Source of the Universe when they infused different cultures and religions with different pieces of soul prints. Minoans received the horizontal extensions of soul prints in the form of downward-tapering columns and bulls horns ornamentation. Hebrews received the two-dimensional representation of two interlocked tetrahedra and the point at their center. Christians received the cross, a generalized but imprecise and upside down form of the entire soul print. Egyptians received the Ankh symbol of life, a close but still upside down and imprecise representation of a soul print. Muslims and others received the upper portion of the soul print in the form of the onion shaped domes of their architecture. Many other cultures and religions received bits and pieces of the soul print, particularly the concept of a five-pointed star in connection with a circle. The reason for the fracturing of the soul print and the infusing of pieces of the soul print into different cultures and religions was to draw together those different cultures and religions, in order to see the complete picture of how things really are.

The most recent Pleiadean agents in place in the land between two rivers created the beast who invaded Kuwait in 1990, the beast who has repeatedly savaged the descendants of the Hurrians—the Kurds.

The beast Saddam Hussein was not deposed, Essenes halted the counterattack because it was not yet the time to depose the beast and because Essenes operate under the mandate of the Source of the Universe.

Essenes know that only those groups in the galaxy who provide an environment conducive to meditation are able to use their technology. The transredimensioning of energy by means of meditation depends on the ability of the meditators who can only meditate when living in harmony. Meditators cannot be coerced into meditation (and therefore transredimension energy) because coercion destroys the harmony of those able to meditate.

The disastrous war on Altea was nearly averted because East and West meditators rapidly lost their ability to meditate. The war ceased after just a few hours, because surviving East and West meditators could no longer meditate and because they knew they were contributing to the death of their civilization.

Only the Deterrent brought an end to life on Altea.

Essenes know that meditators can meditate over a period of time (and therefore consistently transredimension energy) only if the meditators know that the energy they help provide is available to everyone at reasonable prices—and is not controlled by the few, for the benefit of the few.

Precisely 50 years to the minute after the Japanese navy attacked Pearl Harbor, (which is located approx. 2/3rds the way between 19.47 and 22.48 degrees north latitude) it became time: at the font of the church at Avenabury—the birthplace of human beings—the Source of the Universe mandated the beginning of the final phase of Panergon Gwynmyrr, the phase in which human beings lead the redeeming of the galaxy.

About a year after the Source of the Universe mandated the beginning of this final phase, a combined and well coordinated action undertaken by Alteans, Essenes and the Odunside Alliance permanently removed the Earth from the Pleiadean empire. Essenes removed all Pleiadean agents in place and their paraphernalia from the Earth and turned over their prisoners to the Alteans (who have put the Pleiadeans to work, removing the mummified bodies of those whom the Pleiadeans gassed on Colchis). The Odunside Alliance, composed of diverse subjects of the Pleiadean empire, attacked and virtually destroyed one of the largest Pleiadean bases in the center of the galaxy. The Altean Naval Service destroyed the largest base in the Pleiades. While the Odunside Alliance and the Altean Naval Service were conducting their attacks, Essenes unleashed a myriad of 10,000 'grays' upon the Pleiadean imperial palace, thereby preventing any coordinated defense of the bases being attacked—completely terrorizing the Pleiadeans.

The Altean Naval Service destroyed the headquarters building of the base its forces attacked, but intentionally left standing a portion of the facade on which a plaque bearing the emblem of the Pleiadean empire was affixed. The Altean Naval Service burned a second diagonal line into the Pleiadean emblem and the words "Altean Naval Service" into the plaque below the circular Pleiadean emblem. The Odunside Alliance did the same thing at the base that they attacked, substituting the words "Odunside Alliance" below the emblem.

Until the Pleiadeans discovered this graffiti, they thought that the last Alteans had died 489,000 years ago and they had never heard of the Odunside Alliance.

The joint coordinated action against the Pleiadeans removed the Earth from the Pleiadean empire because Alteans and Essenes will not allow—and have the combined capabilities to prevent—the Pleiadeans from even approaching the Earth—ever again.

The joint coordinated action against the Pleiadeans came just in time to save additional targets of a hateful Pleiadean cabal designed to destroy priceless art and architecture. The cabal was responsible for the partial destruction by fire of Windsor Castle in Hurengland and of an important section of the Hofburg Palace in Vienna.

The joint coordinated action against the savage Pleiadeans came just in time to save Somalia—formerly Punt, the land of frankincense and myrrh—from utter devastation because the joint coordinated action removed the Pleiadean agents operating from the land between two rivers who were encouraging, through enticement, the rival factions to fight one another and to rape their country and its citizens.

The joint coordinated action against the Pleiadeans came almost 5000 years after Essenes had first wanted to take action against the Pleiadeans. The mandate of the Source of the Universe did not allow direct action against the Pleiadeans then, but the mandate of the Source of the Universe did allow the recent joint coordinated action against the Pleiadeans.

Five months before this joint coordinated action against the Pleiadeans, Essenes left Silbury and the Altean Naval Service re-established an Altean presence on Silbury.

Two Altean Naval Service star ships—EXCALIBUR and THALASSA—based in the Bastion of Silbury participated in the Altean attack on the base in the Pleiades.

Four days after the joint coordinated action against the Pleiadeans, the then Pleiadean emperor Xung Carl Halverson was murdered and replaced by another Pleiadean emperor. This Xung Carl Halverson was the biological descendant of both the Carl Halverson (killed in the land between two rivers about 1.65 million years ago) and of the first Xung Carl Halverson (who ordered the first secret Pleiadean agents in place to the land between two rivers about 4500 years ago). The most recent Xung Carl Halverson became the Pleiadean emperor just in time to observe the Hellenes smash the forces of the beastling of the south and died right after the Altean Naval Service and the Odunside Alliance smashed his forces in both the Pleiades and in the center of the galaxy. The first Xung Carl Halverson became Pleiadean emperor after murdering the last Xung Halbert Mavor. The current Pleiadean emperor has now come to power having murdered the last Xung Carl Halverson. The way of the Universe includes the use of irony. The way of the Universe insures that those who live by the sword also die by the sword—either in the hand of others, or in their own hands.

Throughout his life Cary Manpure suffered many ordeals. When he was old and had gained much experience and knowledge, he developed clear reflection. When Cary Manpure adapted/altered THE ARTHURIAN LEGENDS to the life of his cousin 'Art Hurian' Manpure, he thought back to the few brief moments of his life when there had been harmony and love. He tried to recreate those times in the mythos of King Arthur surrounded by his Twelve Knights of the Round Table. Cary Manpure knew that the moments of harmony and love had been brief for him, so he made those same moments brief for Arthur.

Essenes have observed human societies since human beings first walked on the Earth. Essenes have been overjoyed by the achievements of human societies. Essenes have observed these achievements, accomplished over a relatively short period of time, despite the cultural, genetic and physical differences in, and between, human societies. Essenes have also observed these achievements, despite the continuous and hateful interference of the savage Pleiadeans.

Essenes have been particularly overjoyed by the courage displayed by human beings and human societies. They have seen individuals and groups rise up against tyranny and injustice. They have seen countless cases of self-sacrifice. They have seen old and young, female and male respond to overwhelming challenges and seek to overcome them.

Essenes were happy to witness the meeting of the four very different groups of human beings, and to see that great hybrid societies sometimes resulted therefrom.

The three greatest societies in the history of human endeavor came about as a result of such mixtures. The societies of Prehurland were the result of the intermingling of highly spiritual human beings from far eastern Ashintoland and intuitively harmonic human beings from the Abzuland on which Hurmyrr stands.

The societies among the Hellenes were a result of the intermingling of migrants from the north, who possessed great initiative and human beings who already lived in Hellas—human beings who were among those who possessed the best balance between creative and linear thinking.

The society of the Egyptians came about as a result of the intermingling of the indigenous intuitively harmonic human beings from the Abzuland on which Hurmyrr stands and migrants who were among those who possessed the best balance between creative and linear thinking.

Many other hybrid societies have flourished, but some have fallen prey to those who would not intermingle peacefully and equally.

The human beings of Hurengland lived in great harmony with one another and the land for ages—mainly because they were hybrids. Then invaders (predecessors of the spawn of the inquisition) came in 1066 from a land without hybrids and ruthlessly murdered, looted and raped Hurengland and its populations. Hurengland survived, but only in a society of castes.

Not only did Hurengland survive, despite its ruthlessly imposed caste system, Hurengland lived to withstand the attack of the armada of other spawn of the inquisition and the horrific onslaught of the forces of the beast of the north.

Those were Hurengland's two finest hours.

Essenes have been appalled at the voracious greed of certain human beings and at the uncaring greed of many, mostly large, businesses. Essenes know that over one-quarter of the wealth of the Earth has been squirreled away by the greedy who selfishly hold onto their ill-begotten wealth rather than invest it in the world economy. Essenes see boards of directors, regularly composed of those who know little about the business corporations they are running, and have little or no personal stake in those businesses, 'directing' in order to maximize profits. They frequently ignore the advice of those involved in those businesses on a daily basis, care little for the long term viability of those businesses and care not at all about the welfare of those working for those businesses. Essenes also see many of these businesses teaming up with power hungry military and political machines which waste vital resources and inflict misery on human beings.

Essenes have been appalled at the insatiable lust for greed and power on the part of 'leaders' of labor unions. These organized, often crime ridden gluttons have routinely bilked their memberships and excluded from membership those who do not qualify under obscenely exclusive 'rules.' Labor unions have also routinely vied with big business to establish who is the most overstuffed.

Essenes have also been appalled by the greed and thirst for power of the latter day successors of the diverse priesthoods and rulers: the medical, the legal professions and politicians. But Essenes have not been terribly surprised by the greed and thirst for power by many members of the legal profession and politicians because lawyers/politicians have historically been greedy and thirsty for power. As a consequence, societies have historically sought (and have sometimes succeeded) to check the greed and thirst for power of lawyers/politicians.

Essenes have been stunned by the greed and thirst for power by the medical profession—led by doctors whose sworn oath it is to save lives, not to ruin lives by charging extortionate rates for saving lives. Taking advantage of the pervading belief that they have the power of life and death over their patients, many doctors have also allowed themselves to be 'deified.'

Essenes anticipated that the legal profession and politicians would be slaves of the beast and have sadly accepted that many members of the medical profession are among the leading worshippers of the beast.

Essenes have cried out in agony, at the savaging that the human beings who are most harmonic have received, as a result of the virus designed by Pleiadeans—and as a result of the epidemic dereliction of duty on the part of the entire medical profession of the planet. Essenes have seen that it has neglected to deal with an epidemic of staggering proportions by purposefully understating its danger—and by totally ignoring those who are most harmonic among human beings. Essenes have seen the entire medical profession of the planet do this—in conjunction with the entire legal/political profession of the planet—due to sexual politics.

The beast enslaves the entire scientific community of the planet because those running the scientific community steadfastly refuse to accept creative as well as linear thinking. The entire scientific community stubbornly clings to outdated and outmoded orthodox notions. The entire scientific community steadfastly refuses to listen to radically new ideas.

The beast especially enslaves the entire 'academic' community of the planet which savagely enslaves students. The entire 'academic' community insists on its point of view and it savagely berates and expels those students who are physically, mentally and ethically courageous enough to defy the beast.

Essenes have diddled with, toyed with and bedevilled numerous unmanned probes from NASA because NASA is the beast institutionalized.

Such diddlings, toyings and bedevillings include the delaying of messages sent from probes beyond the solar system, because Essenes want

NASA to be the last to know that the speed of light is NOT a constant. Essenes will continue to diddle with, toy with and bedevil NASA until the beast at NASA is dead.

The beast enslaves everywhere.

With journalism nearly dead, the so called 'news media' of the entire planet is rotten to the core with pundits of the beast. These unthinking constantly jabbering purveyors of nonsense are trying (but not succeeding) to sap human beings of their thirst for knowledge, their will to move forward—and their courage.

As an extension of the Density Program, Essenes created the Doug and Dave show, starring two blokes 'from a pub' who claimed to have hoaxed the crop formations. Essenes watched in horror, and satisfaction, as the mindless news media, which had previously either ignored transtime crop glyphs, or treated them with utter disdain, sopped up the fantastic story of Doug and Dave—so that they could try to put everyone comfortably back to sleep again.

Although Essenes have always operated under the mandate of the Source of the Universe, the interpretation of specific points of that mandate (as those points have been manifested along the way) has always been the responsibility of Essenes. Essenes are people, just like Alteans and human beings—but Essenes are preparers. Essenes have clear reflection, for Essenes have gone beyond.

Alteans have suffered horrific traumas throughout the history of galaxy, but Alteans have survived despite those traumas, and Alteans are now ready to move forward. Alteans are ready for clear reflection.

Despite the savage, obscene, long standing interference of the Pleiadeans and despite the savage long standing enslaving of them by obscene, greedy savages of the beast, human beings continue to move rapidly forward toward their destiny as the courageous leaders of the redeeming of the galaxy—and then as the courageous leaders of the redeeming of the Universe. Human beings are ready for clear reflection.

Human beings are ready to lead—beyond.

Human beings are ready to lead beyond, because despite the systematic withholding from human beings of the ways of the Universe, human beings are on the verge of working everything out anyway.

In some places on Earth mains electricity has a frequency of 50 cycles per second; in other places it has 60 cycles per second. The ratio of electricity having 50 cycles to electricity having 60 cycles per second is 5 to

6, the same 5 to 6 as the representation of the relationship between the non-living parts of the Universe and living things.

Movie film is projected in theaters at the speed of 24 frames per second. When movie film came to be shown on television it was found that the standard 24 frames per second was incompatible with television operating on mains electricity having 50 cycles per second. The solution to this incompatibility was to run movie film at 25 frames per second when transmitted on television operating at 50 cycles per second.

The resolving harmonic to this incompatibility involves 24/25ths, the Harmonic of the Universe.

Human beings are ready to lead beyond because they understand ***Harmony***.

APPENDIX

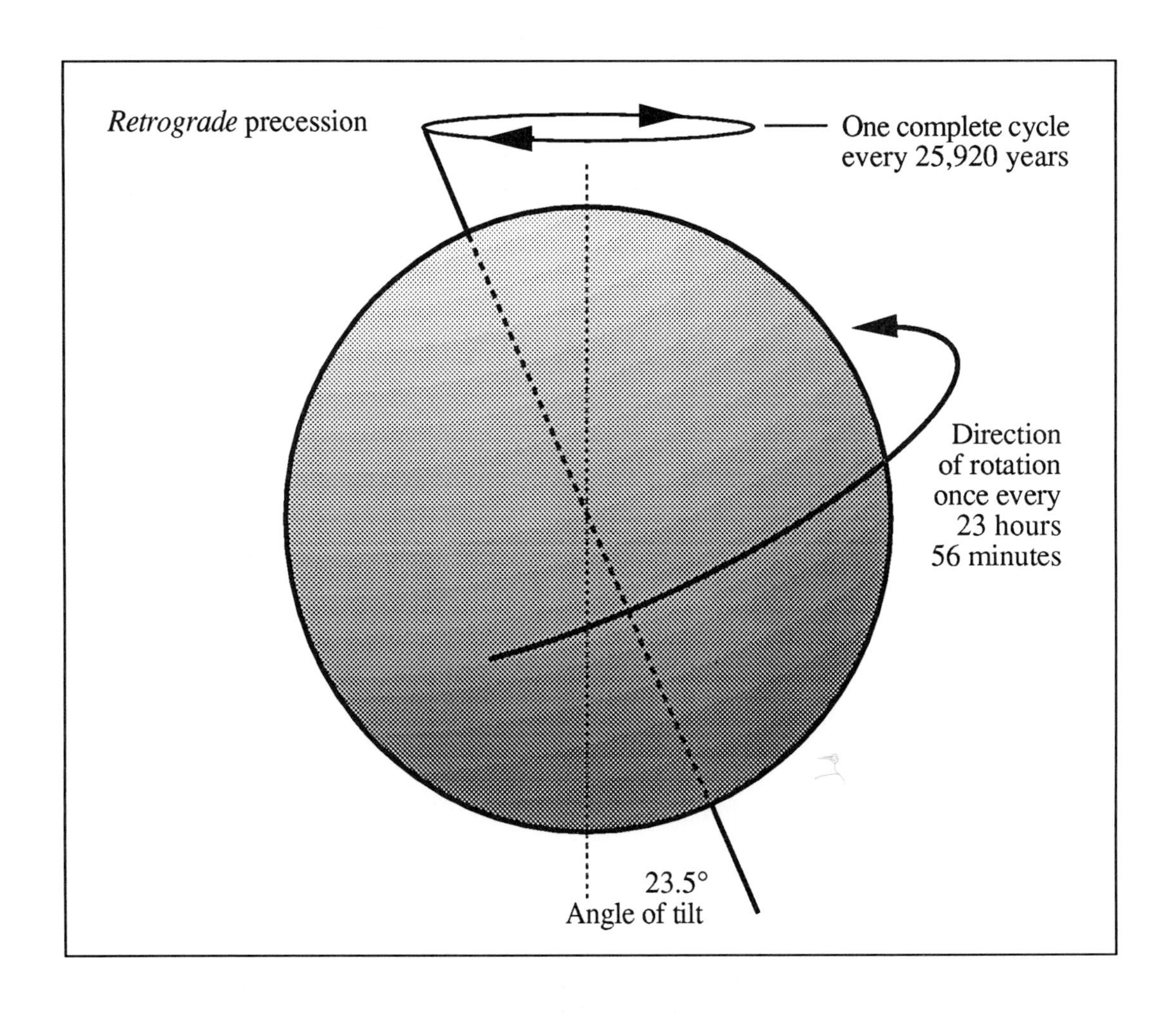

Figure 1. Planet with retrograde precession period of 25,920 years.

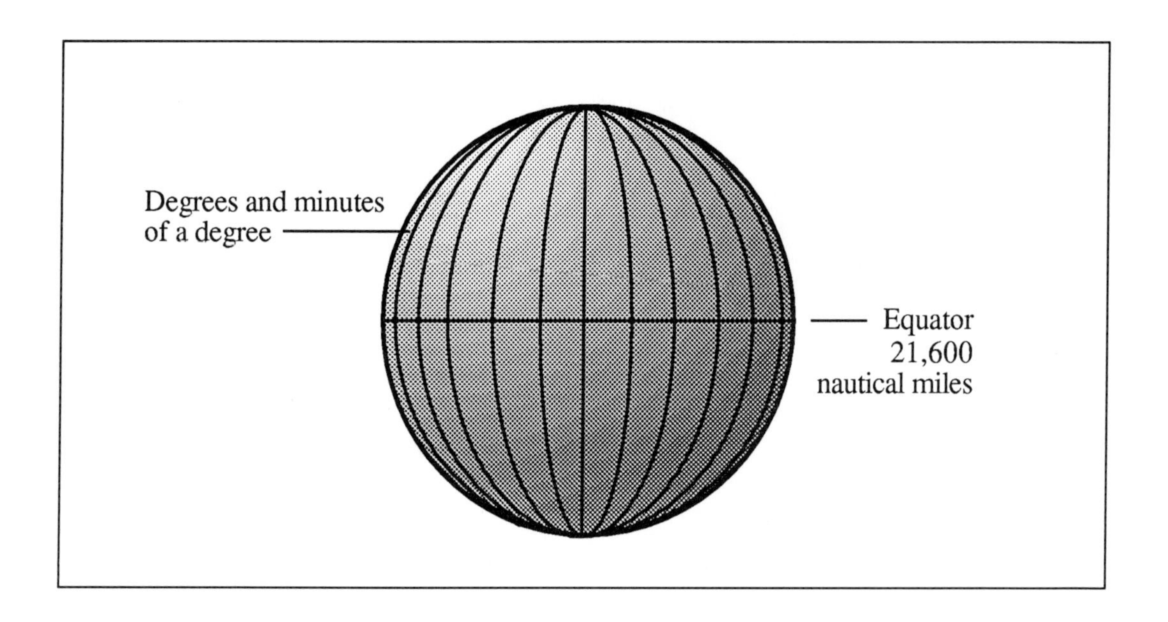

Figure 2. Nautical miles around the equator of any planet. 360 degrees and 60 minutes in each degree 360 x 60 = 21,600 nautical miles.

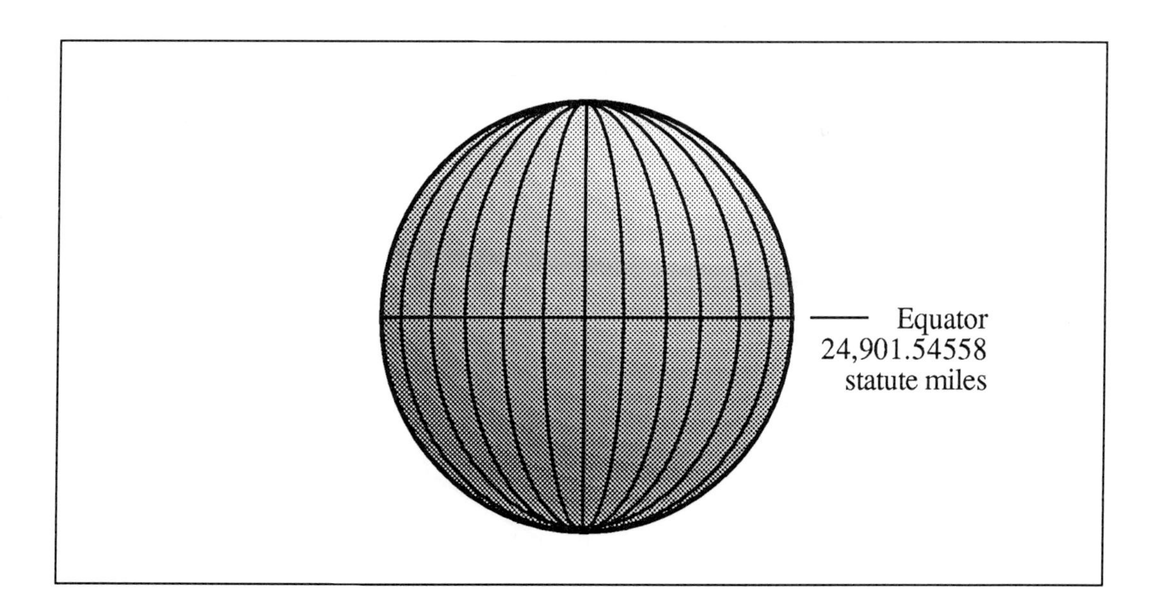

Figure 3. Statute miles around the equator of the seed planet of any galaxy. 12" = 1 foot 5,280 feet = 1 mile. There are precisely 24,901.54558 statute miles around the planet.

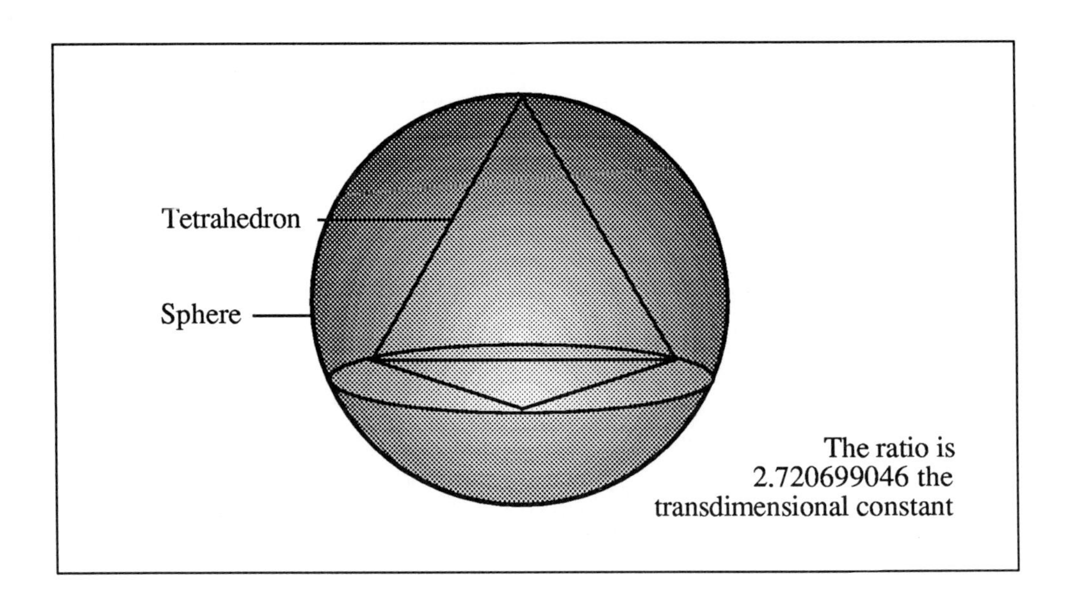

Figure 4. Ratio between the surface of a sphere and the surface of the tetrahedron it circumscribes.

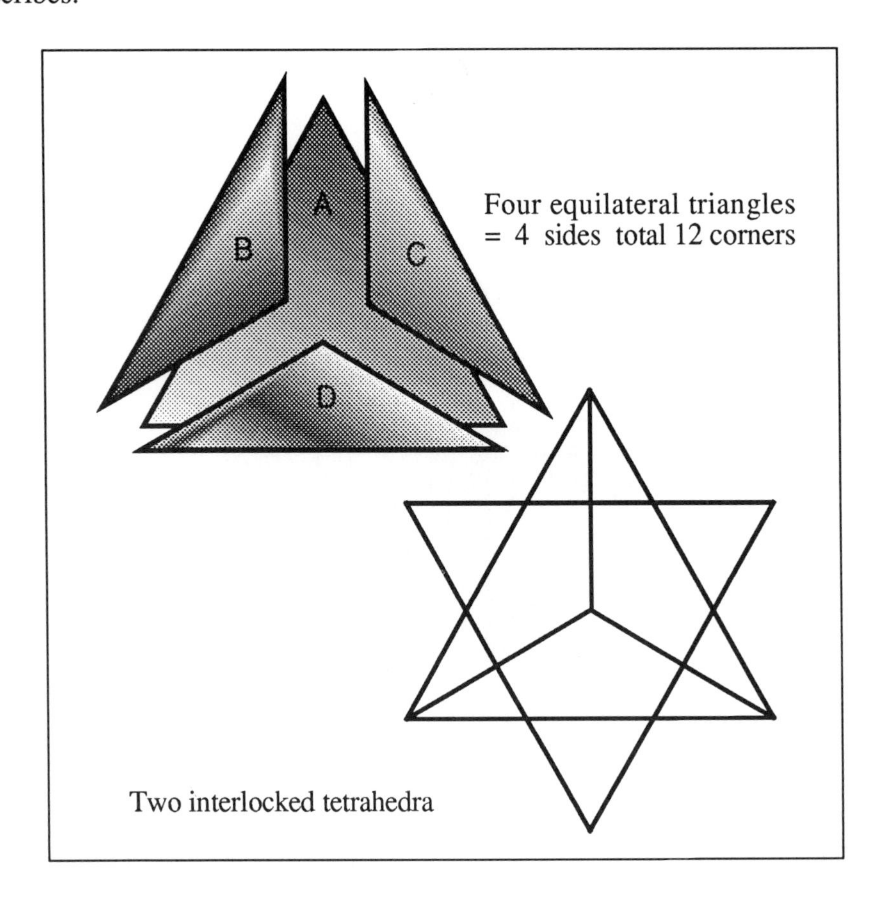

Figure 5. Tetrahedra.

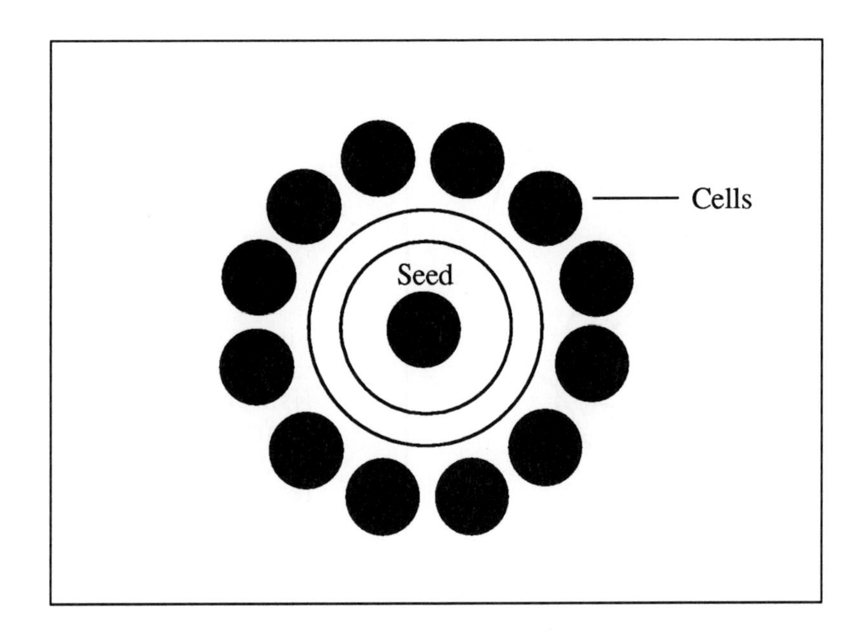

Figure 6. 12 cells form the first growth layer around a single seed resulting in a total of 13.

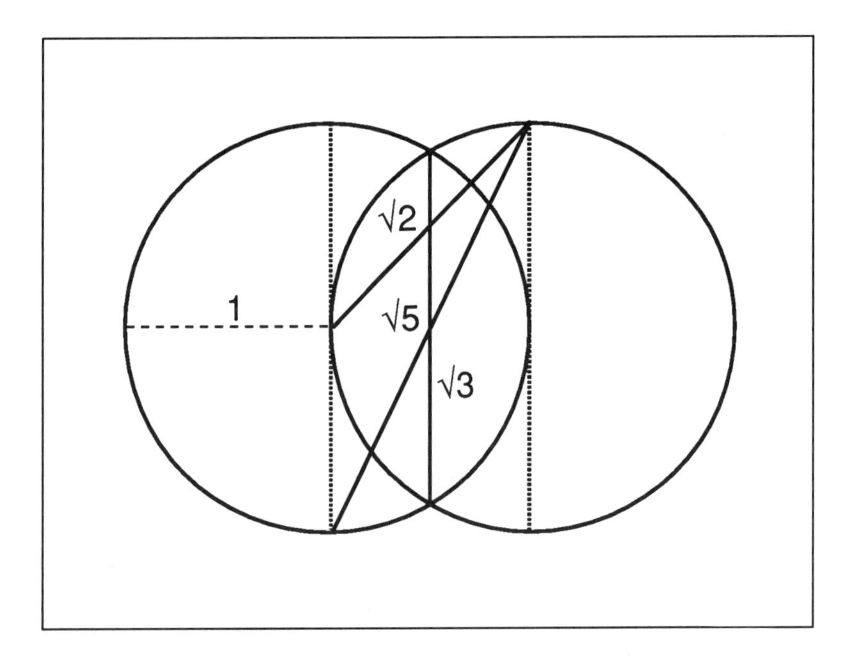

Figure 7. The shape of the fish. This elipse produces the square roots of two, three and five, the numbers which form the basis of geometry and harmonic proportion.

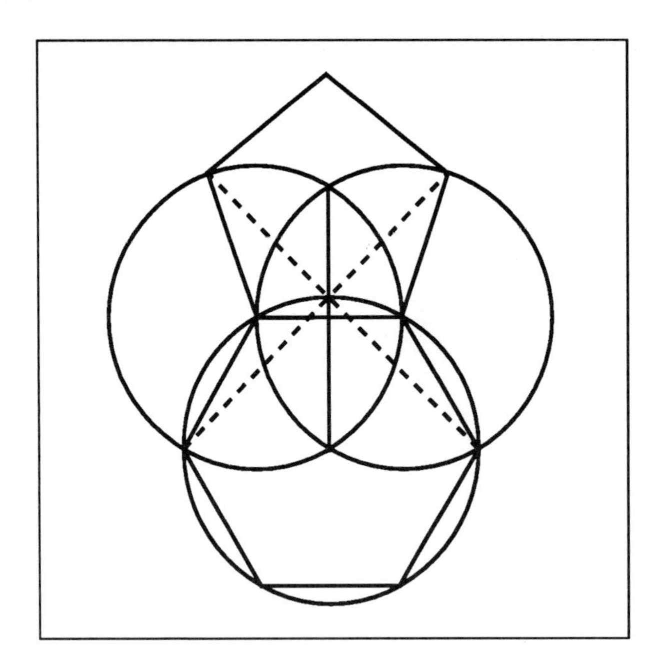

Figure 8. Additional lines drawn in relationship to the shape of the fish produce a hexagon and a pentagon, six- and five-sided figures which metaphorically represent the non-living parts of the Universe and living things.

Part 1 Chapter 2

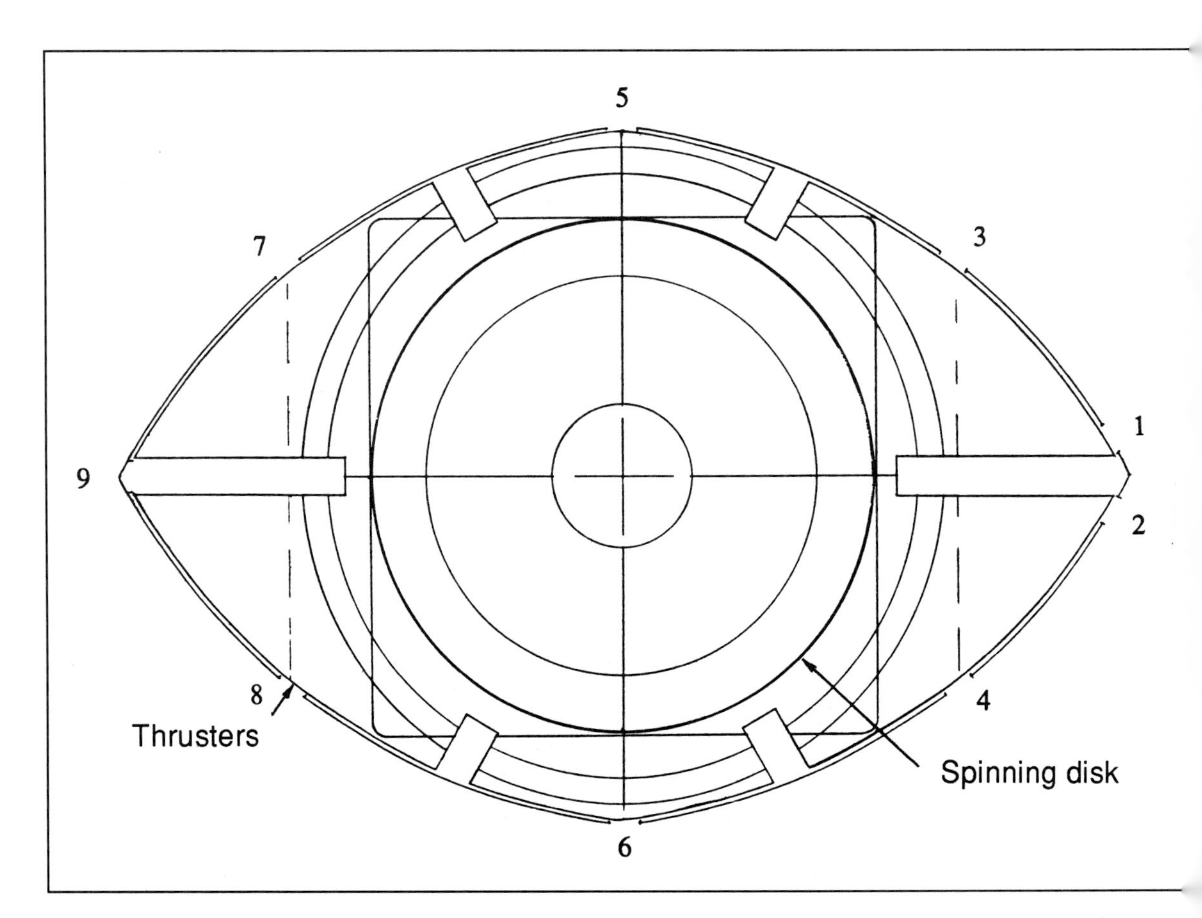

Figure 9. Top view cross section of flying craft. The nine thrusters are directable and thrust *very rapidly* bits of gravity in a stream to propel the craft in any direction.

Part 1 Chap

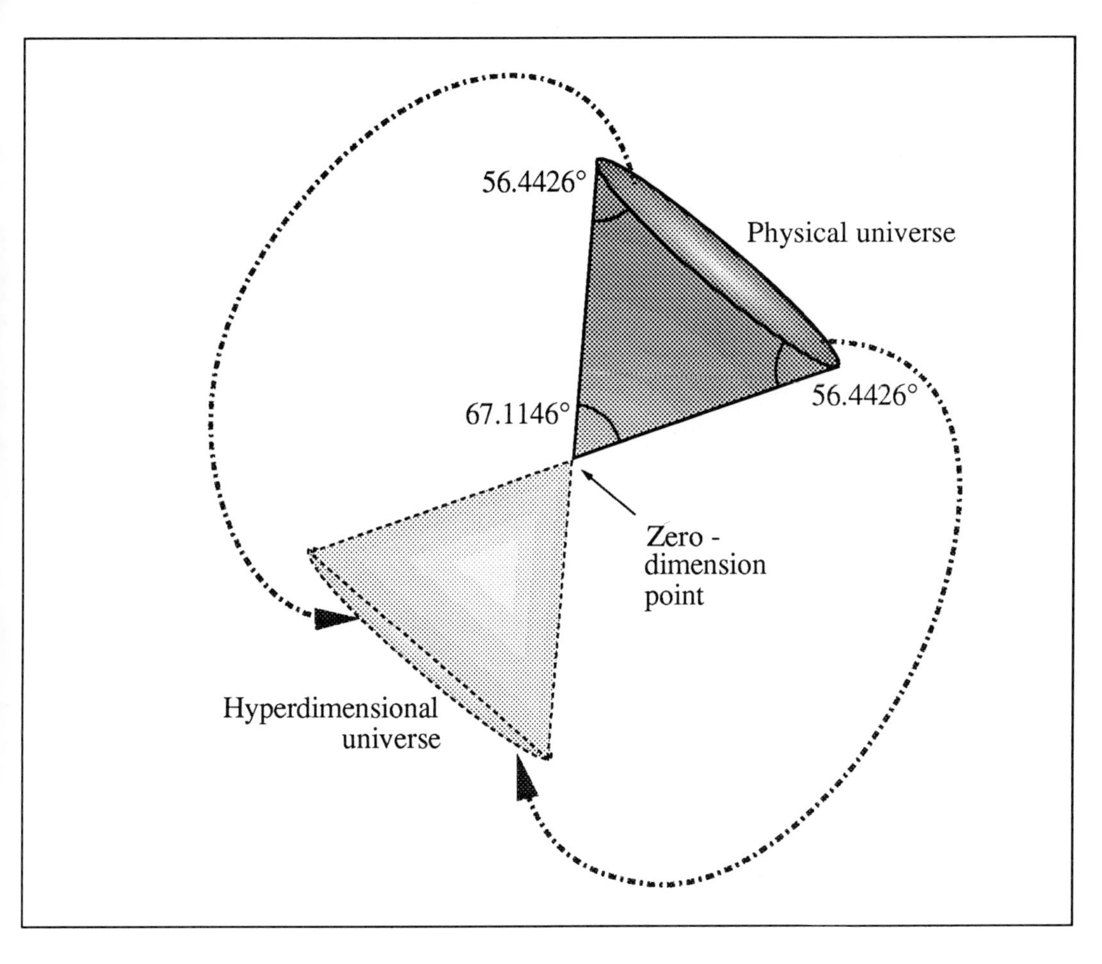

Figure 10. Representation of the cones that make up the Universe.

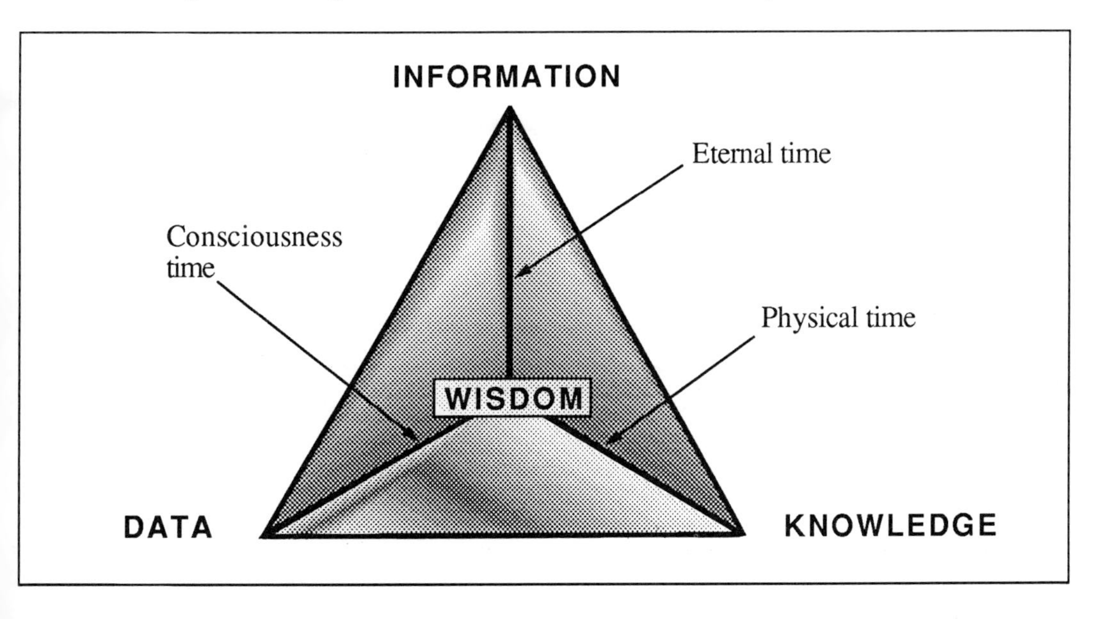

Figure 11. The Source of the Universe extrudes Itself into the three-dimensional physical universe by means of time in three ways.

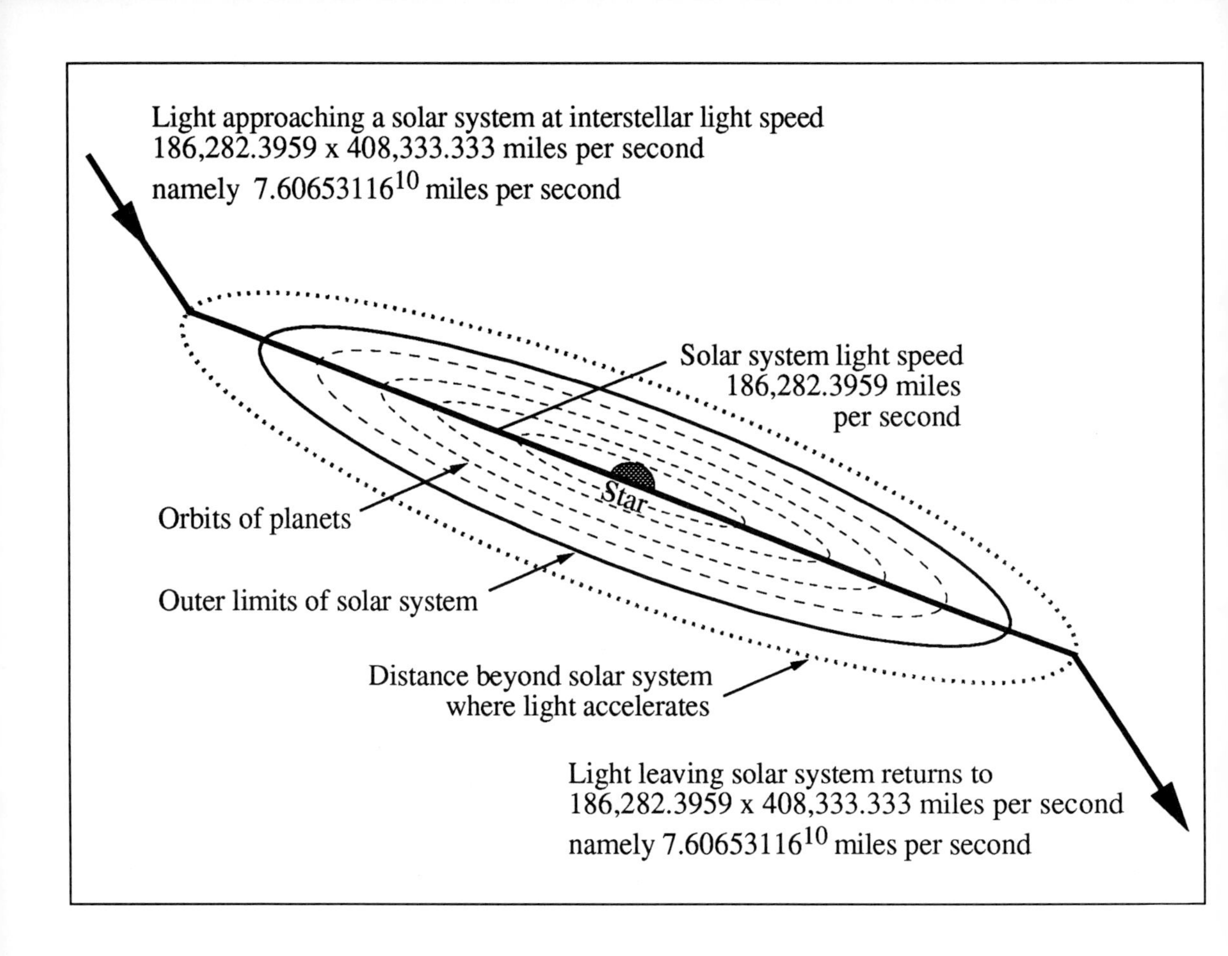

Figure 12. Representation of the *refraction* of light when light enters a solar system. Interstellar light speed is over 400,000 times faster than solar system light speed, begins well beyond the limits of a solar system and extends well beyond the fringes of galaxies. Light entering a galaxy is similarly refracted.

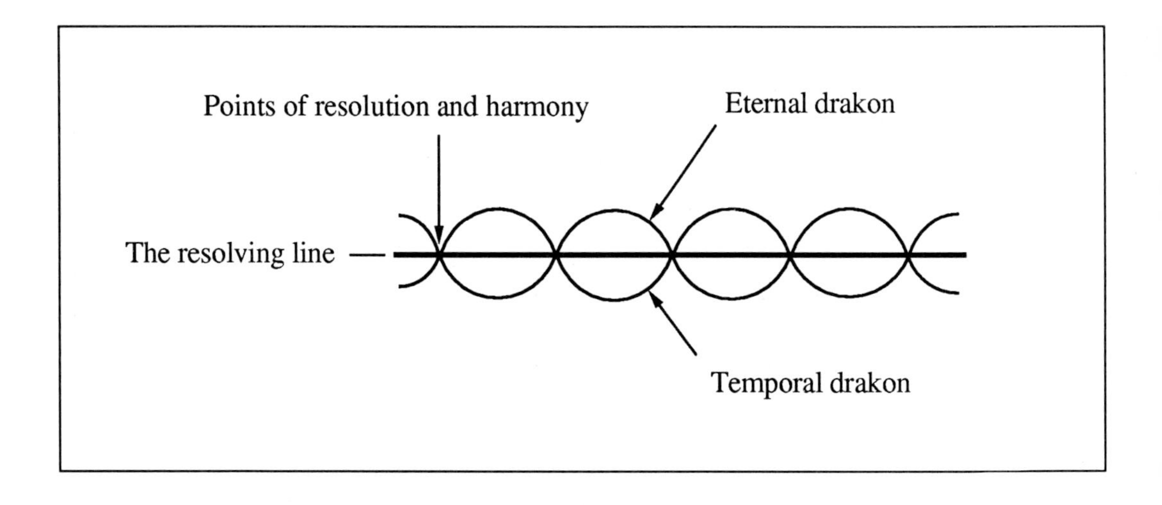

Figure 13. The keirykeion.

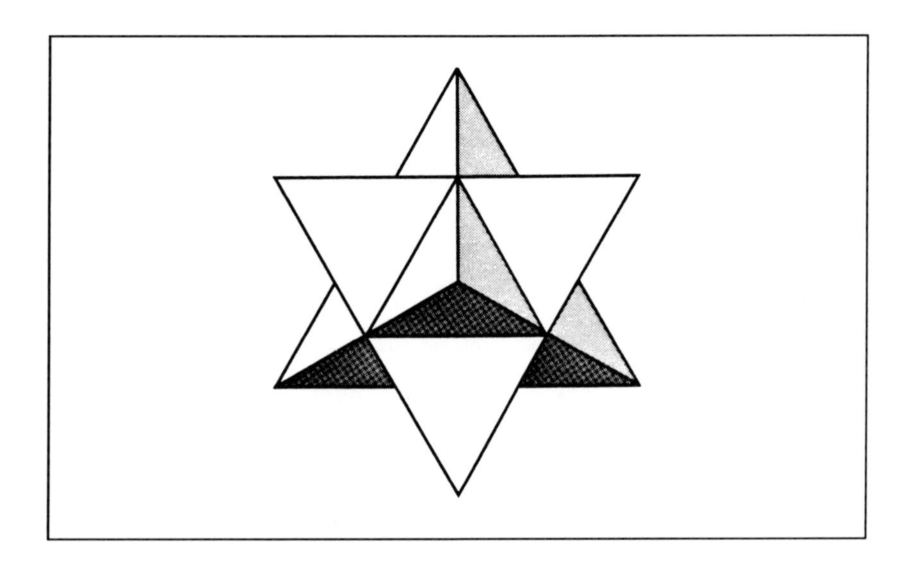

Figure 14. Two interlocked tetrahedra, a three-dimensional representation of Horun, the hyperdimensional energy which streams from the source. Horun has 14 simultaneous spins in three dimensions.

Part 1 Chapter 4

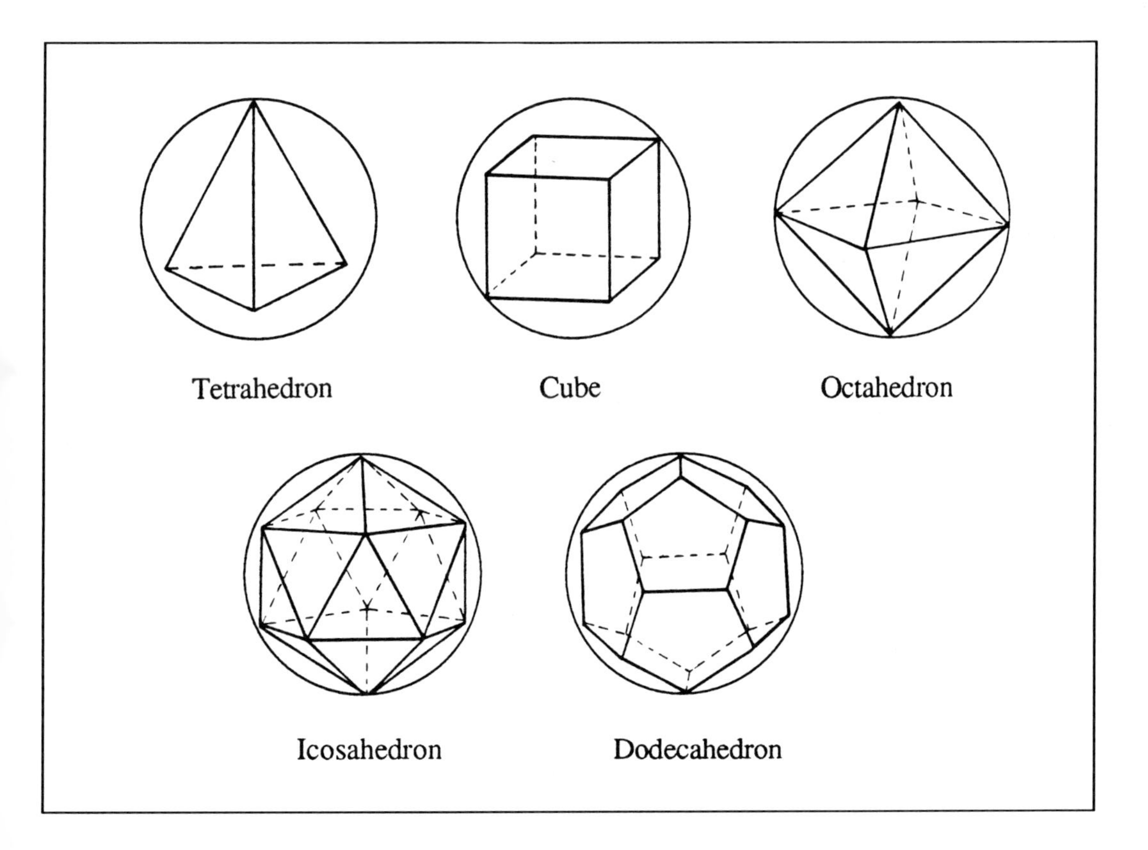

Figure 15. The circumscribed solids, the five most simple regular three-dimensional building blocks of the physical universe. To circumscribe these solid shapes means to surround them with a sphere so that their varying numbers of points just touch the sphere.

Part 1 Chapter 5

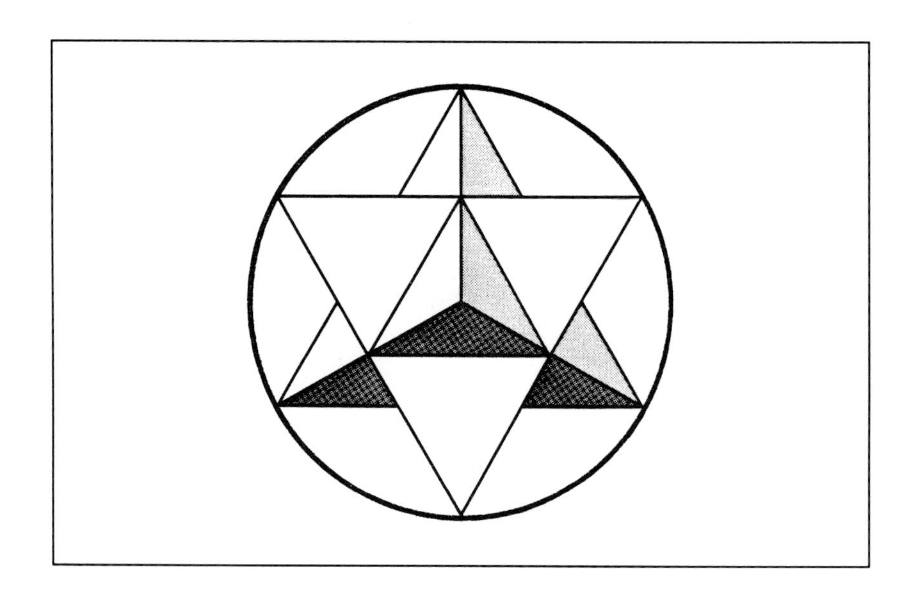

Figure 16. Two circumscribed interlocked tetrahedra.

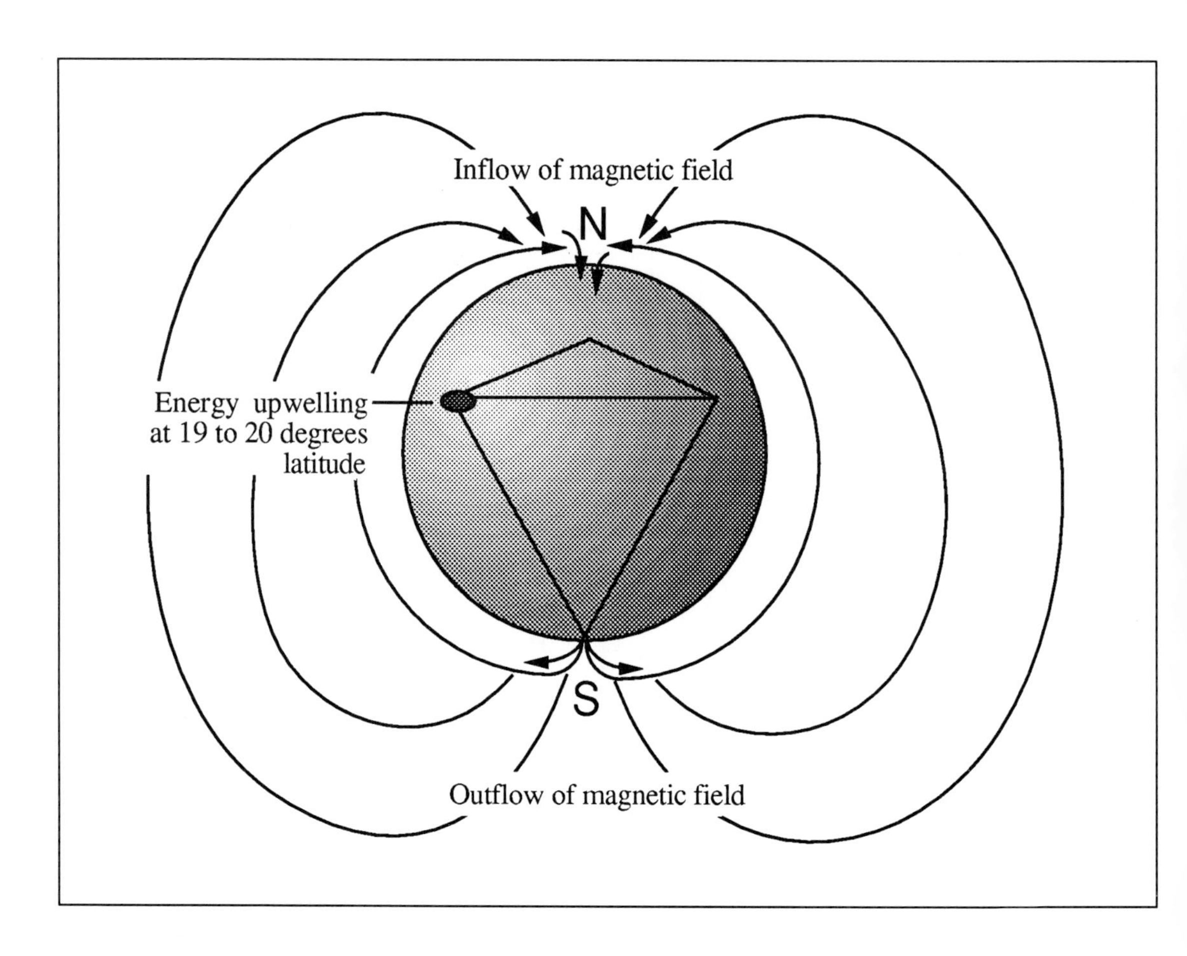

Figure 17. Upwelling of three-dimensional energy at 19 to 20 degrees latitude.

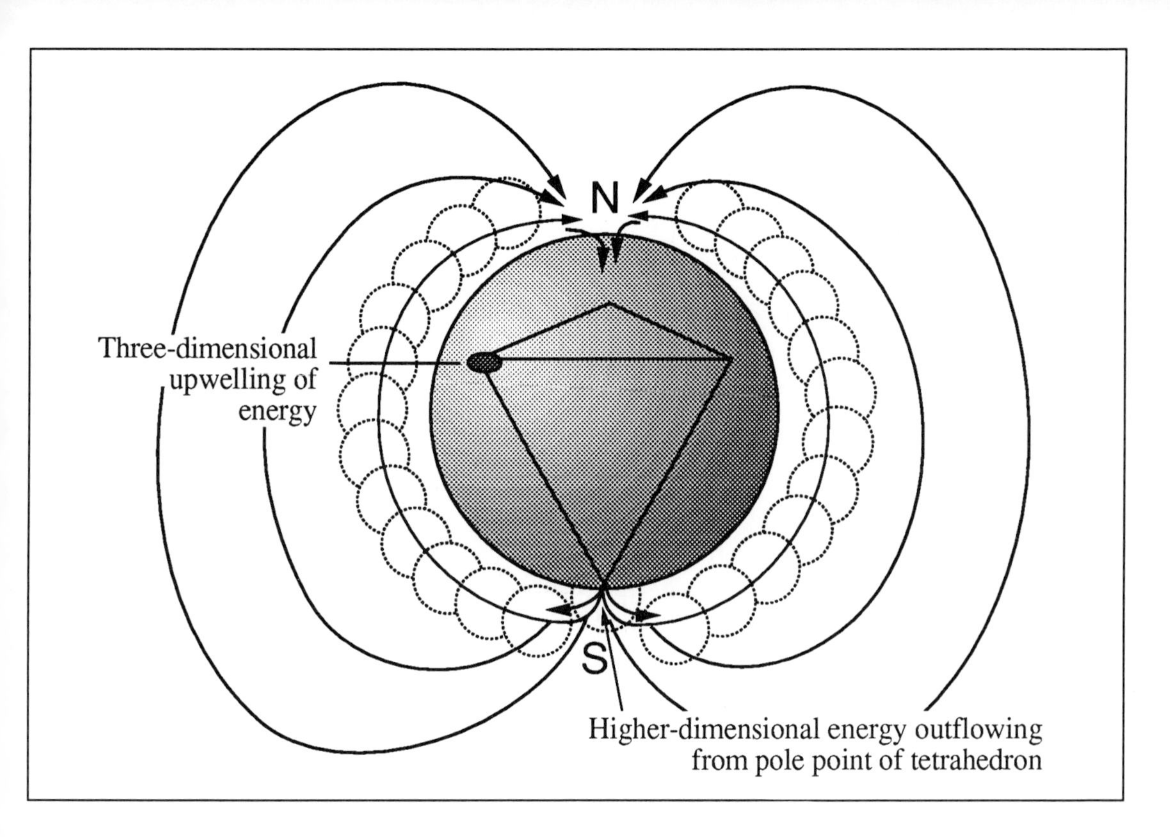

Figure 18. Planetary 'consciousness energy' radiating out of planet with the magnetic field.

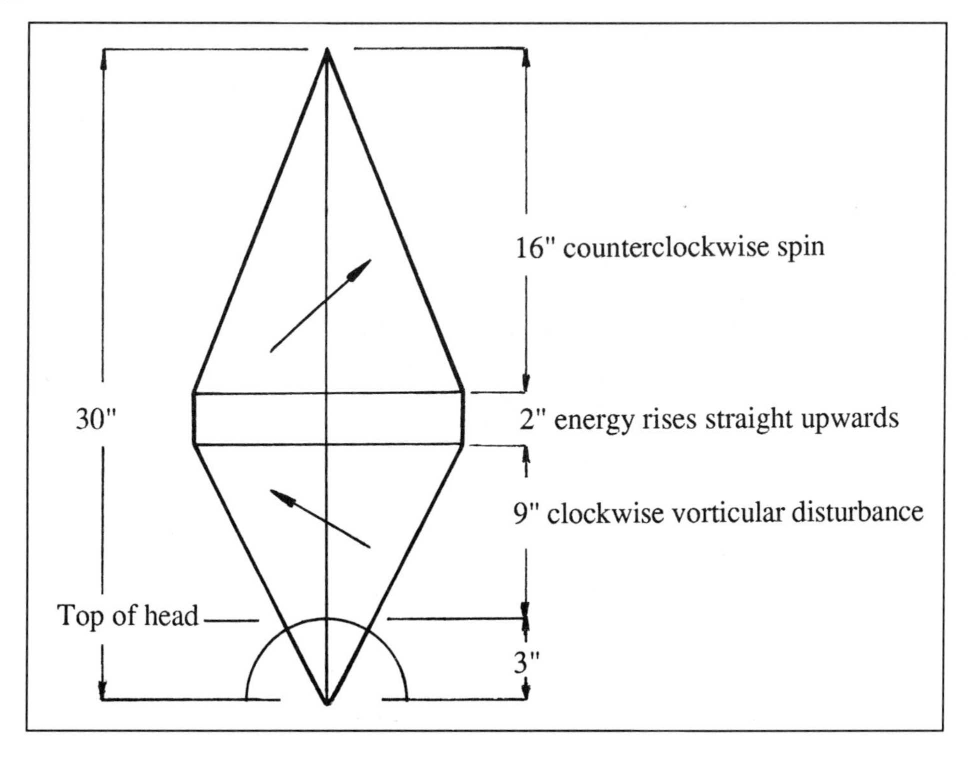

Figure 19. Eyes closed consciousness energy cone as measured by Waldark above the top of the head. The upper point of the cone closes with cross section of one-fifth of an inch.

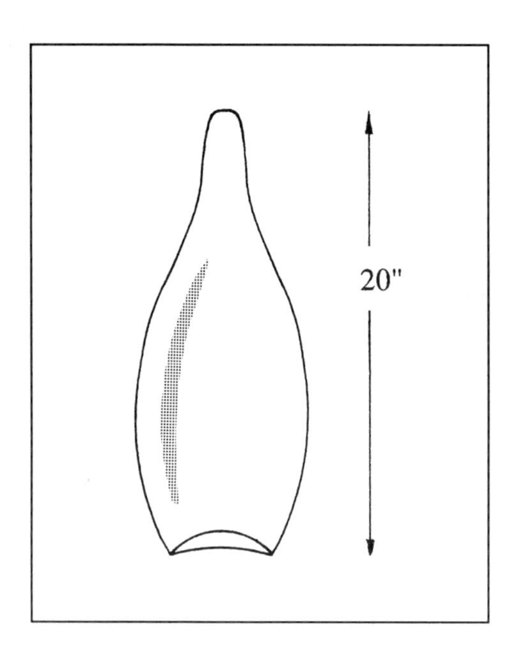

Figure 20. The Waldark hat serves to capture refocus, and then transmit higher-dimensiona consciousness energy to a receiver.

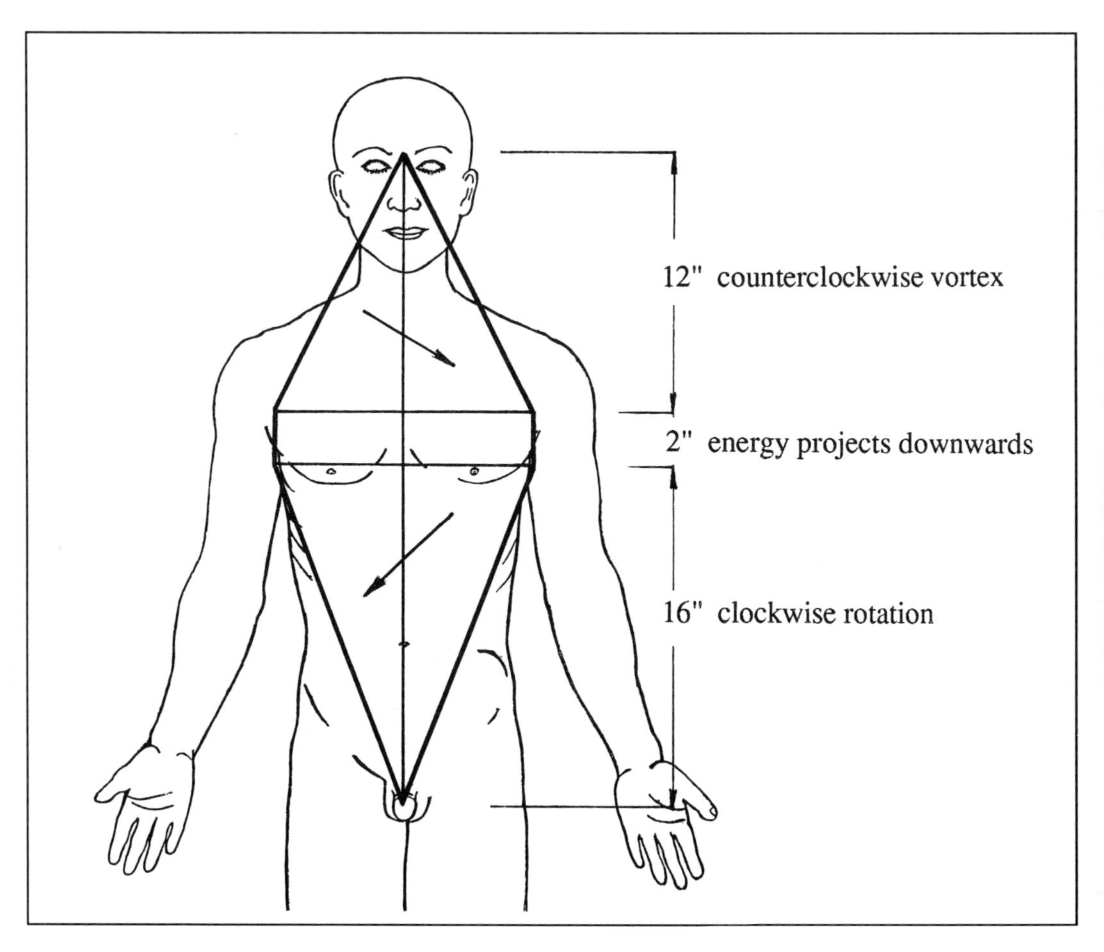

Figure 21. Eyes closed consciousness energy cone as measured by Waldark below the head. The lower point of the cone closes with cross section of one-fifth of an inch at the genetal area.

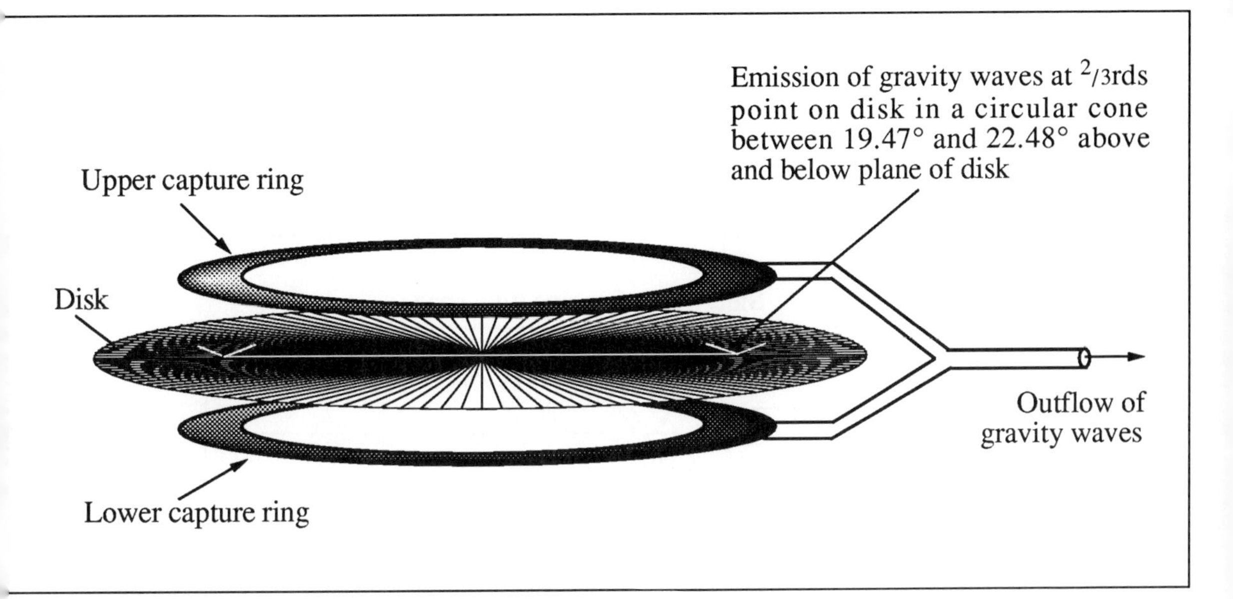

Figure 22. Waldark's spinning disk, double gravity wave captutre ring and Y shaped attachment. For clarity in this illustration the capture rings are shown further from the disk than in the working model.

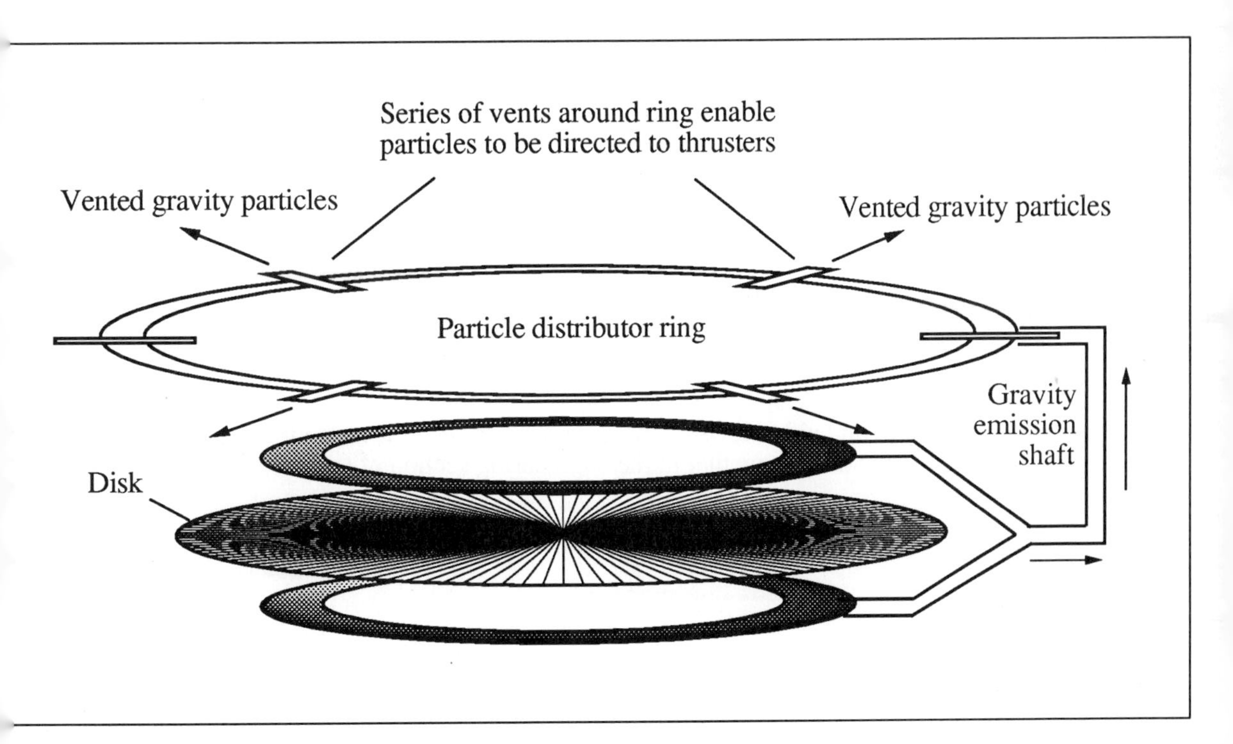

Figure 23. Gravity particle distributor ring located above previous arrangement of spinning disk and double collector ring. The gravity particles now travel up the emission shaft to be distributed to the vents located around the ring.

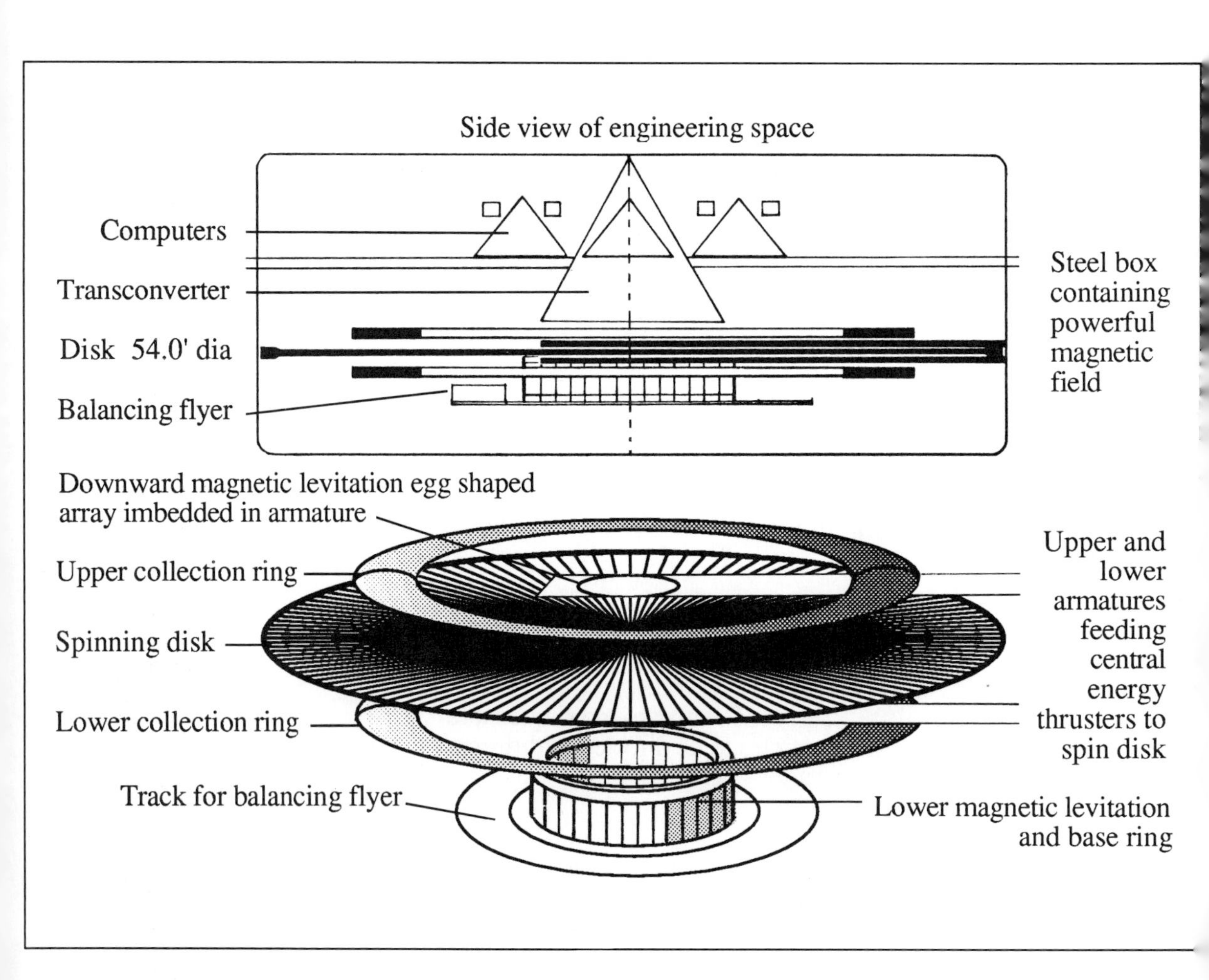

Figure 24. Isometric and side views of the gravitron drive. The side view illustrates the principal components stacked together in the engineering section of star ships.

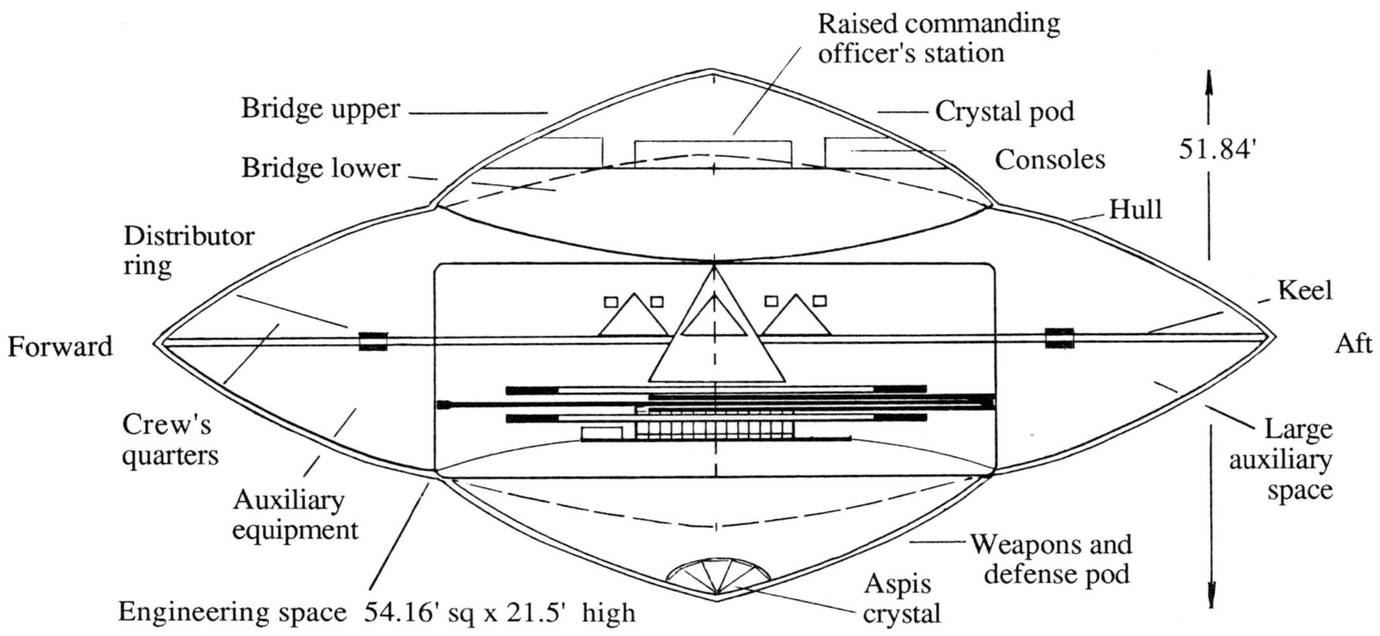

Figure 25. Altean Naval Service star ship side view. The craft is 108' long with a maximum beam width of 72'. The weapons and defense pod is removable for access to the engineering section to facilitate replacement of the spinning disk.

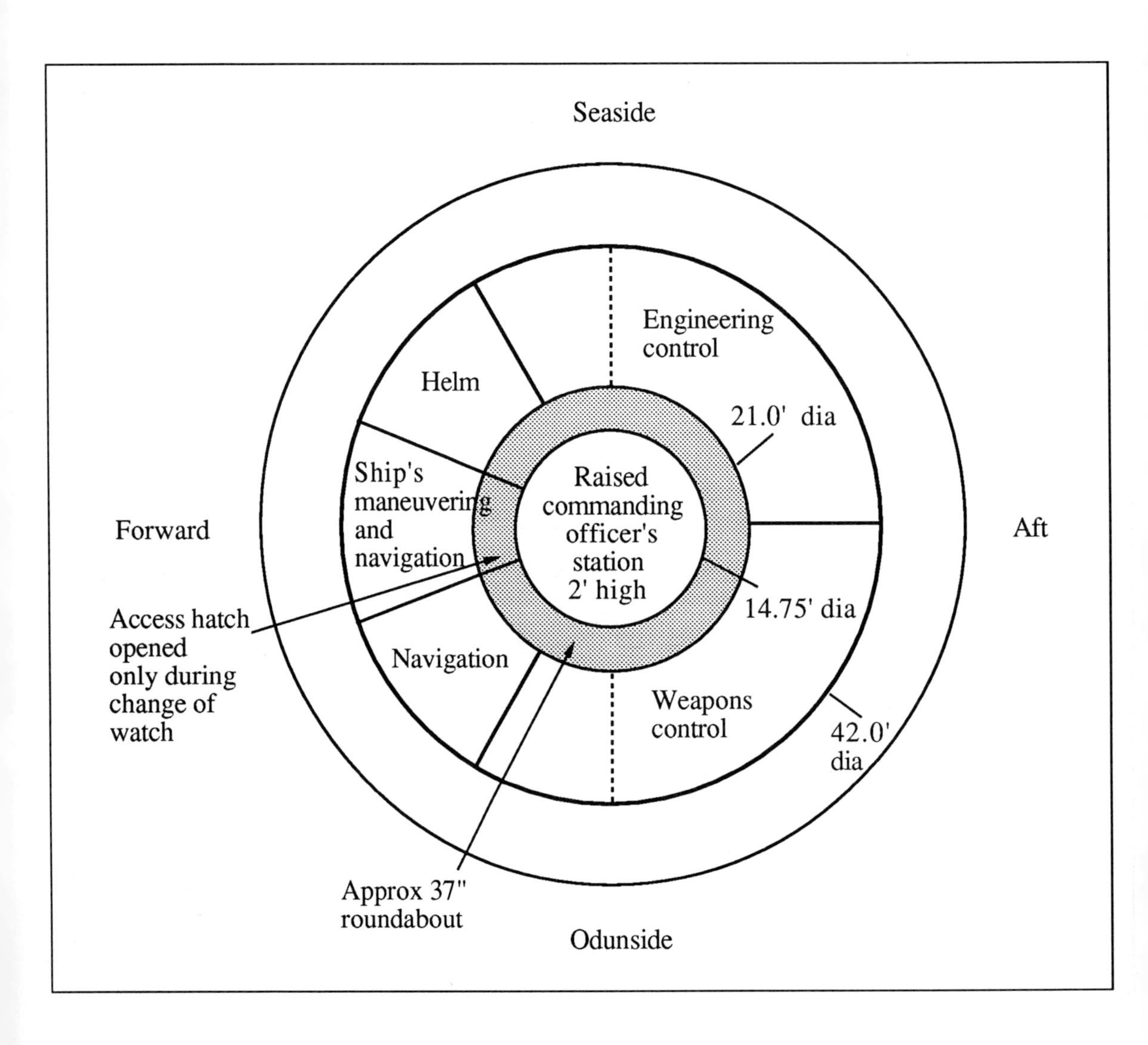

Figure 26. Altean Naval Service star ship upper level of bridge. From the central raised command station the commanding officer can oversee everything.

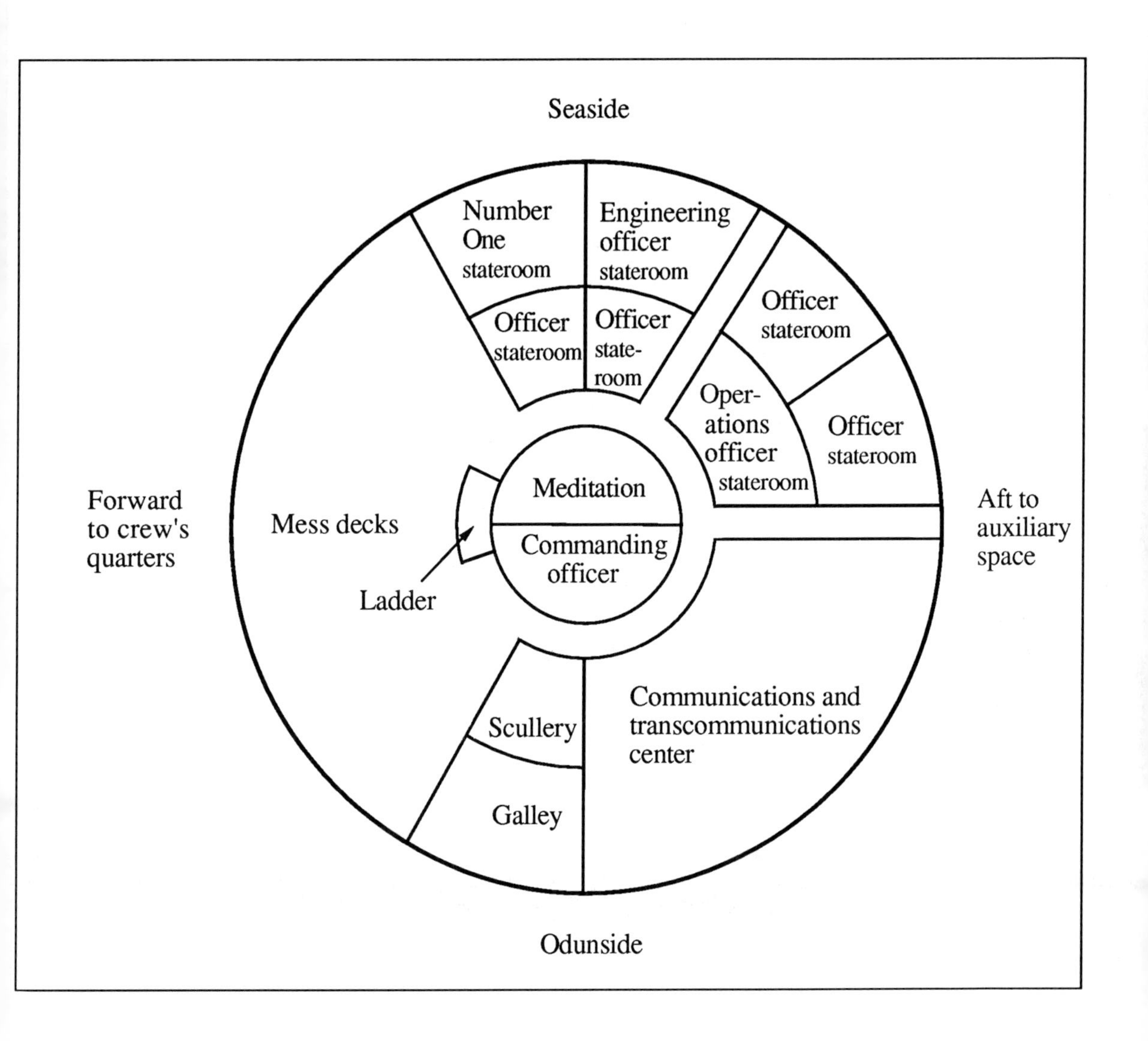

Figure 27. The lower bridge. Sailors of the Altean Naval Service refer to a star ship as a 40 plus 8, because a star ship's complement is 40 Crew and 8 officers.

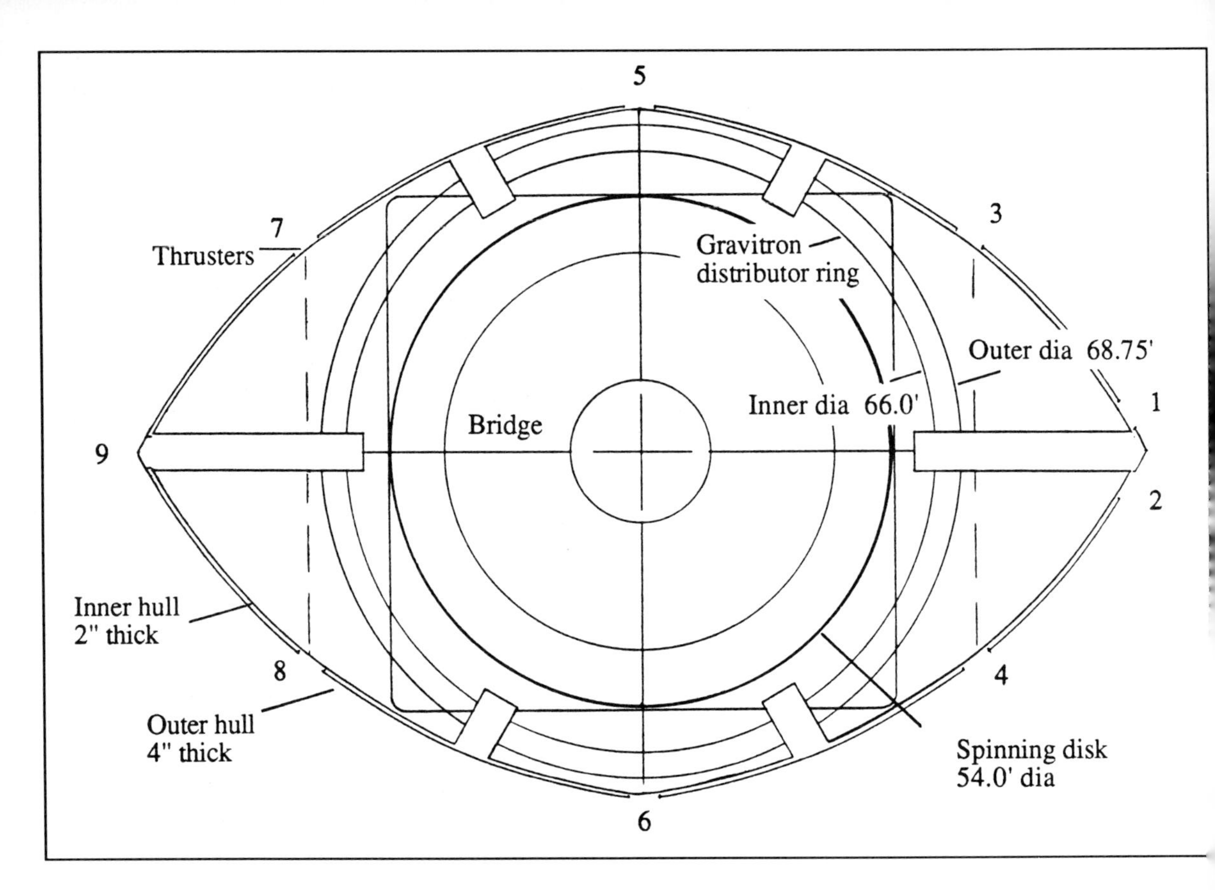

Figure 28. The gravitron distributor ring distributes gravitrons throughout the space between the ship's inner and outer hulls. By use of magnetic fields most of these gravitrons are directed to the appropriate thrusters in order to propel the ship.

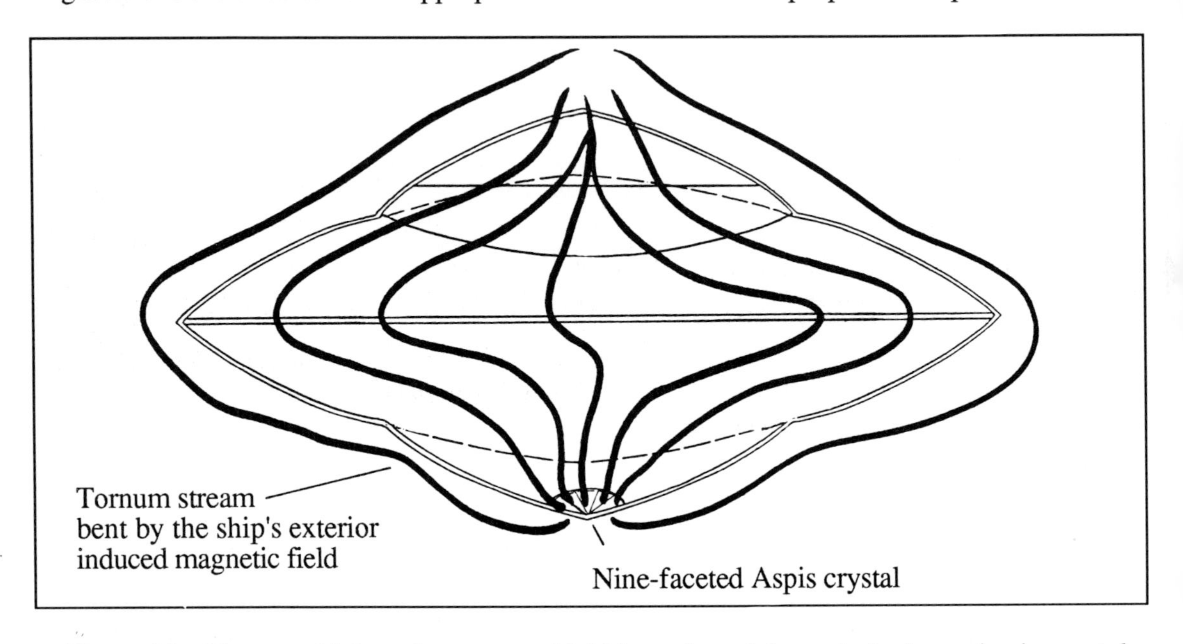

Figure 29. The star ship's anti-weapons shield is projected through the large Aspis crystal in nine streams of tornum. This forms a net of hyperdimensional energy around the ship. Energy torpedoes and streams from energy canon are deflected by the net.

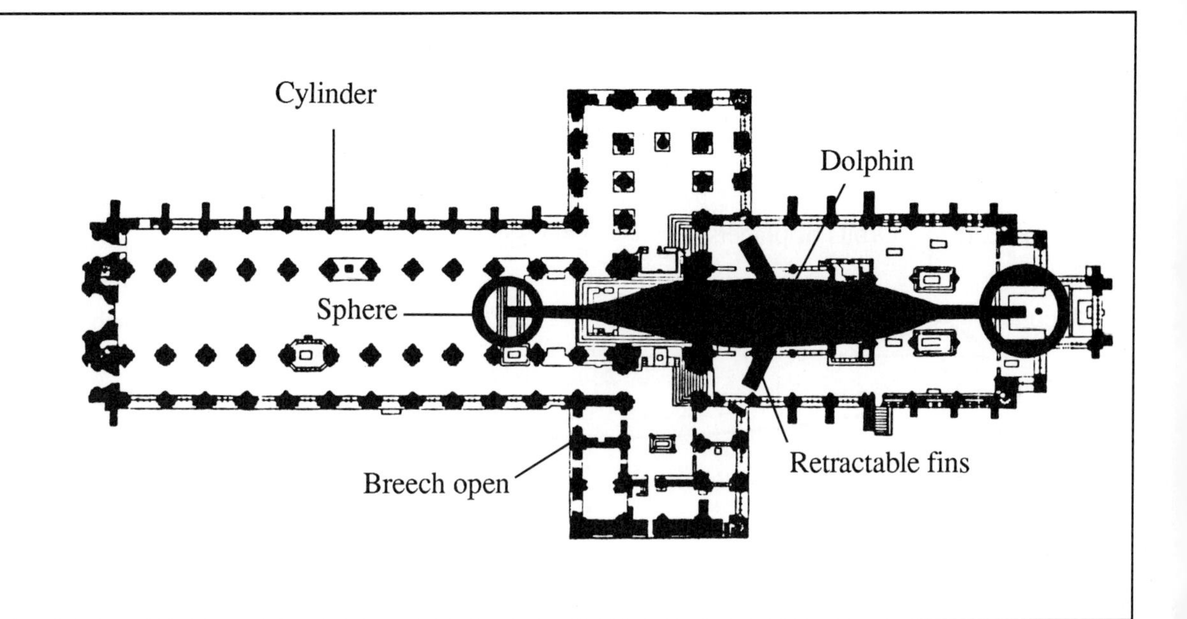

Figure 30. The dolphin shaped casing containing a canister of fine grain gold and its attendant spheres are shown here inserted into the cylindrical outer casing. The dolphin, the spheres and the cylinder are all lead lined.

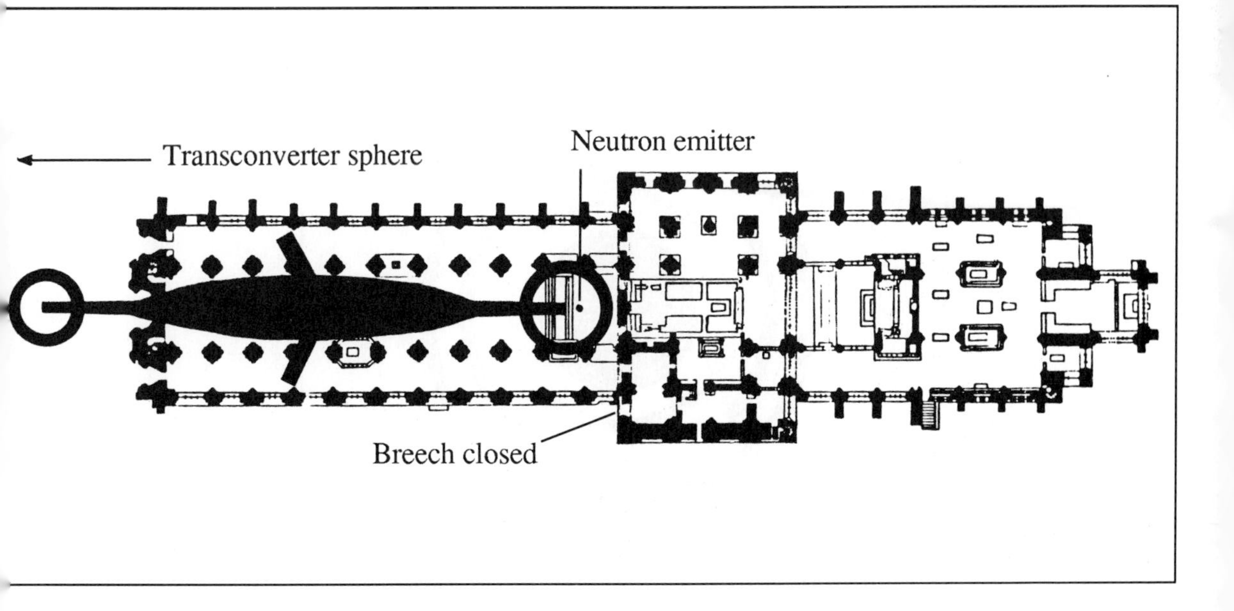

Figure 31. After the dolphin is positioned at the far end of the cylinder the breech is closed. The cylinder is then advanced into the transconverter sphere of the energy transconverter.

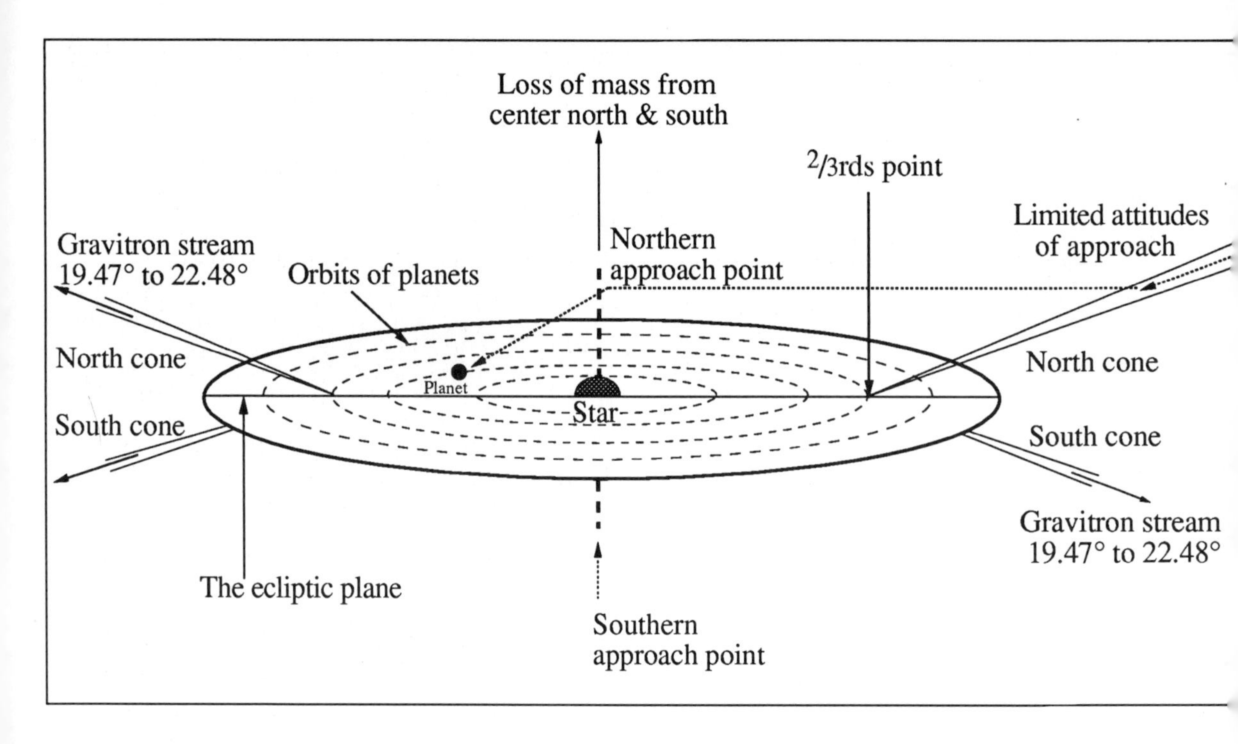

Figure 32. A solar system is relatively flat and acts in many ways like a spinning disk. Any solar system emits lost mass from its center north and south of the ecliptic plane and emits a stream of gravitrons in a circular cone north and south of the ecliptic plane.

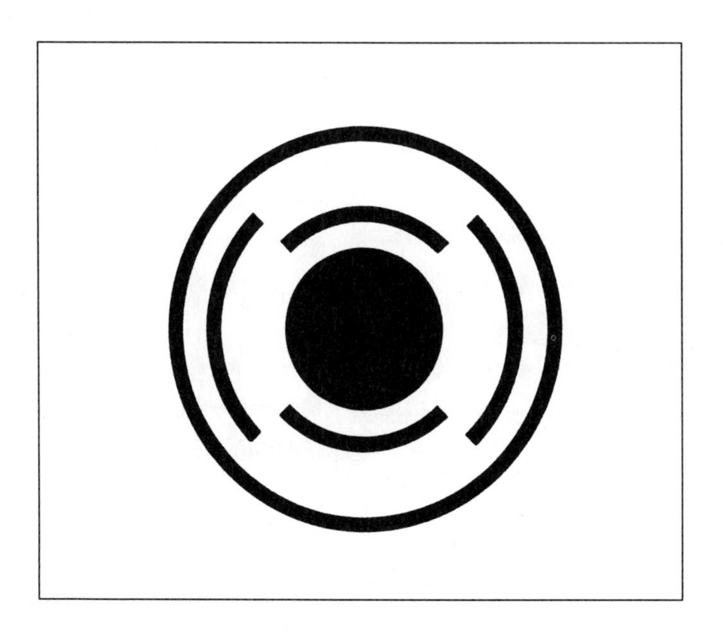

Figure 33. Depiction of the double clamshell doors that cover the number nine gravity thruster (open position) and the number nine gravity thruster. The outer circle depicts the ability to remove the entire unit when it has been damaged beyond repair due to numerous solar system approaches.

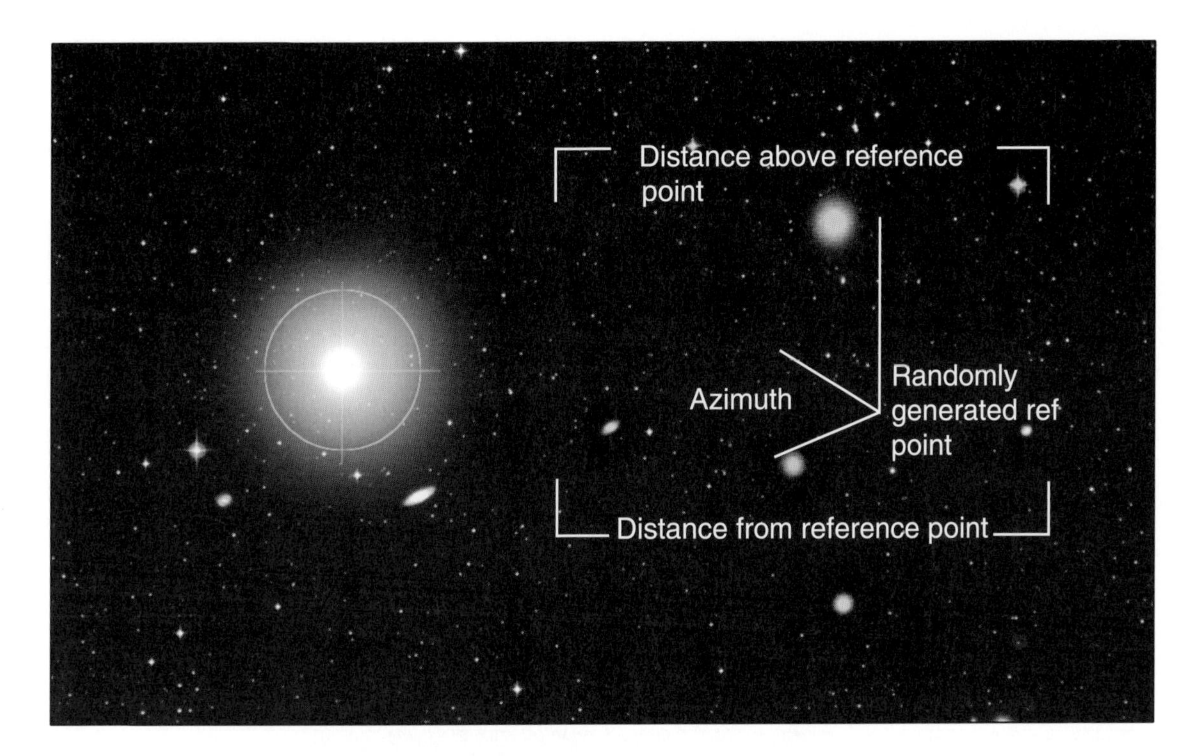

Figure 34. The galactic grid reference system. Part 2 Chapter 1

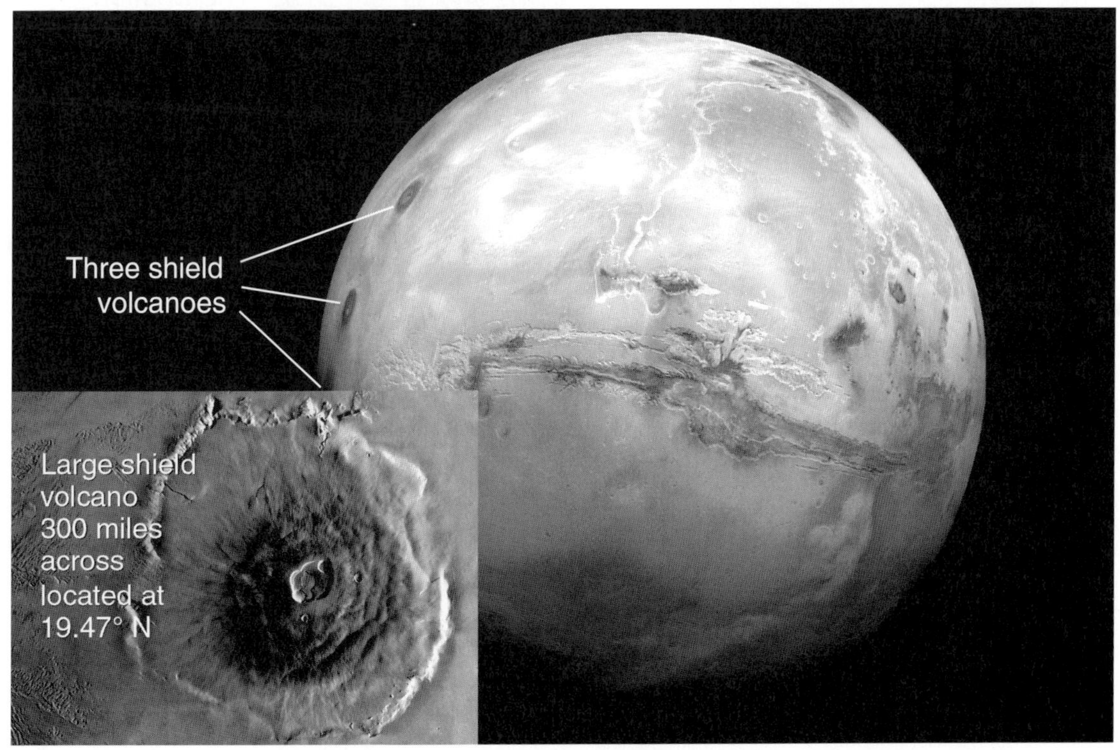

NASA

Figure 35. The red rock planet. Part 2 Chapter 3

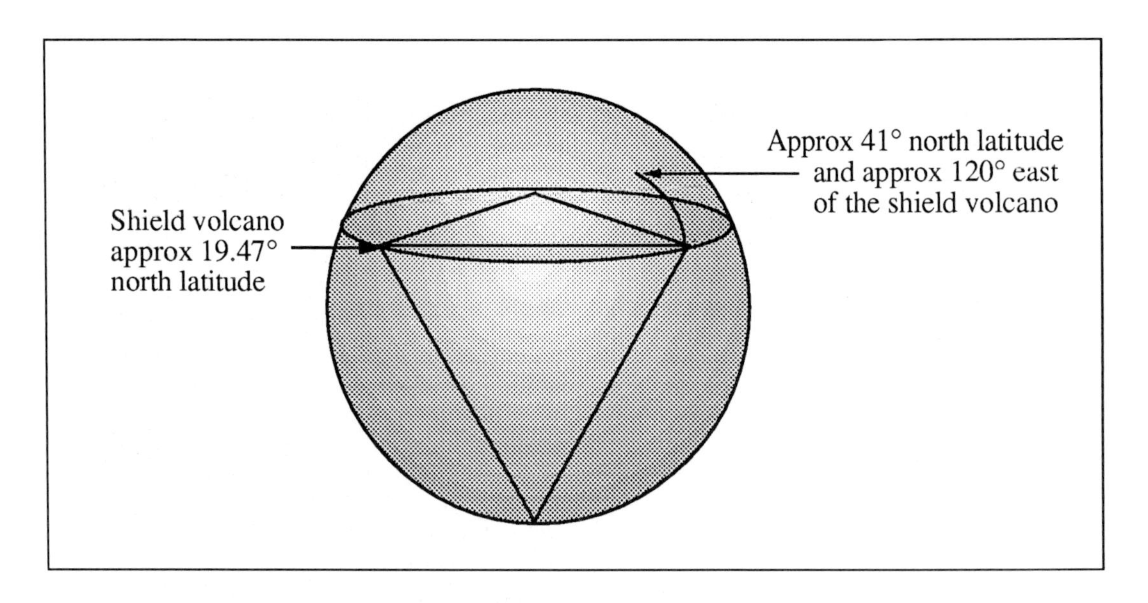

Figure 36. Location of the gravitron infusion complex on the red rock planet.

Part 2 Chapter 3

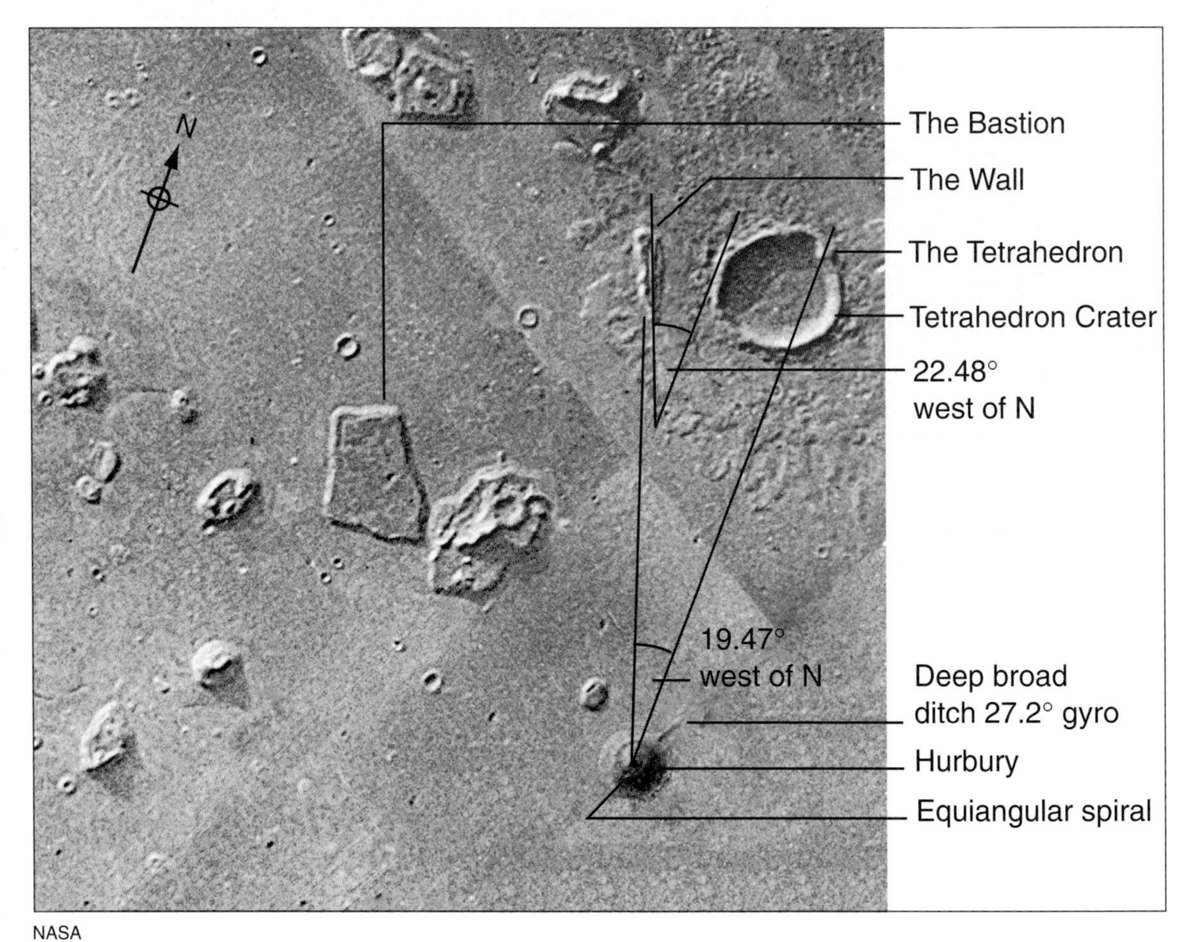

Figure 37. The area to the west of the gravitron infusion complex in the impact crater on Silbury.

Part 2 Chapter 4

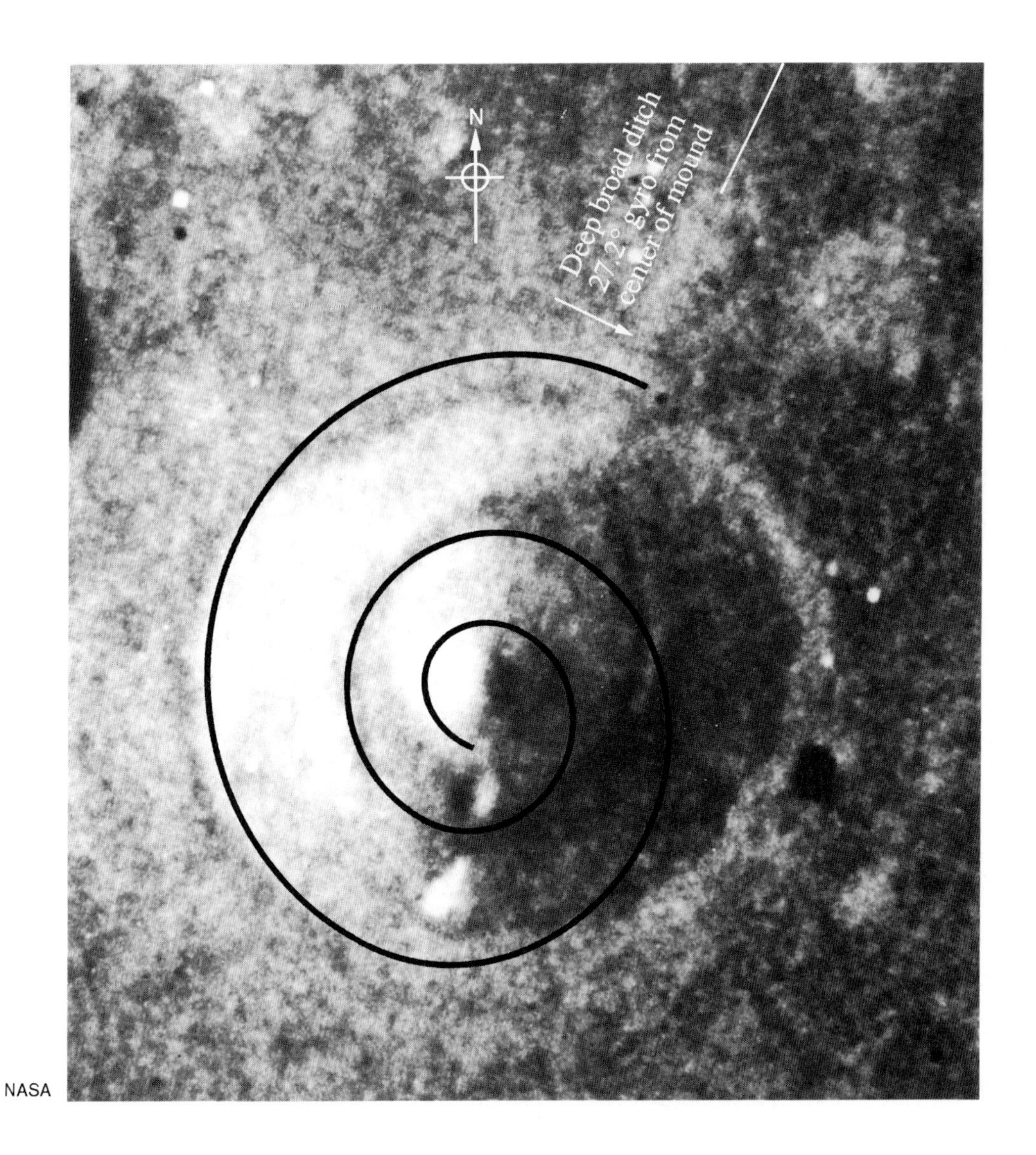

Figure 38. Close up view of Hurbury with superimposed equiangular spiral — a spiral based on the twelfth root of two.

Part 2 Chapter 4

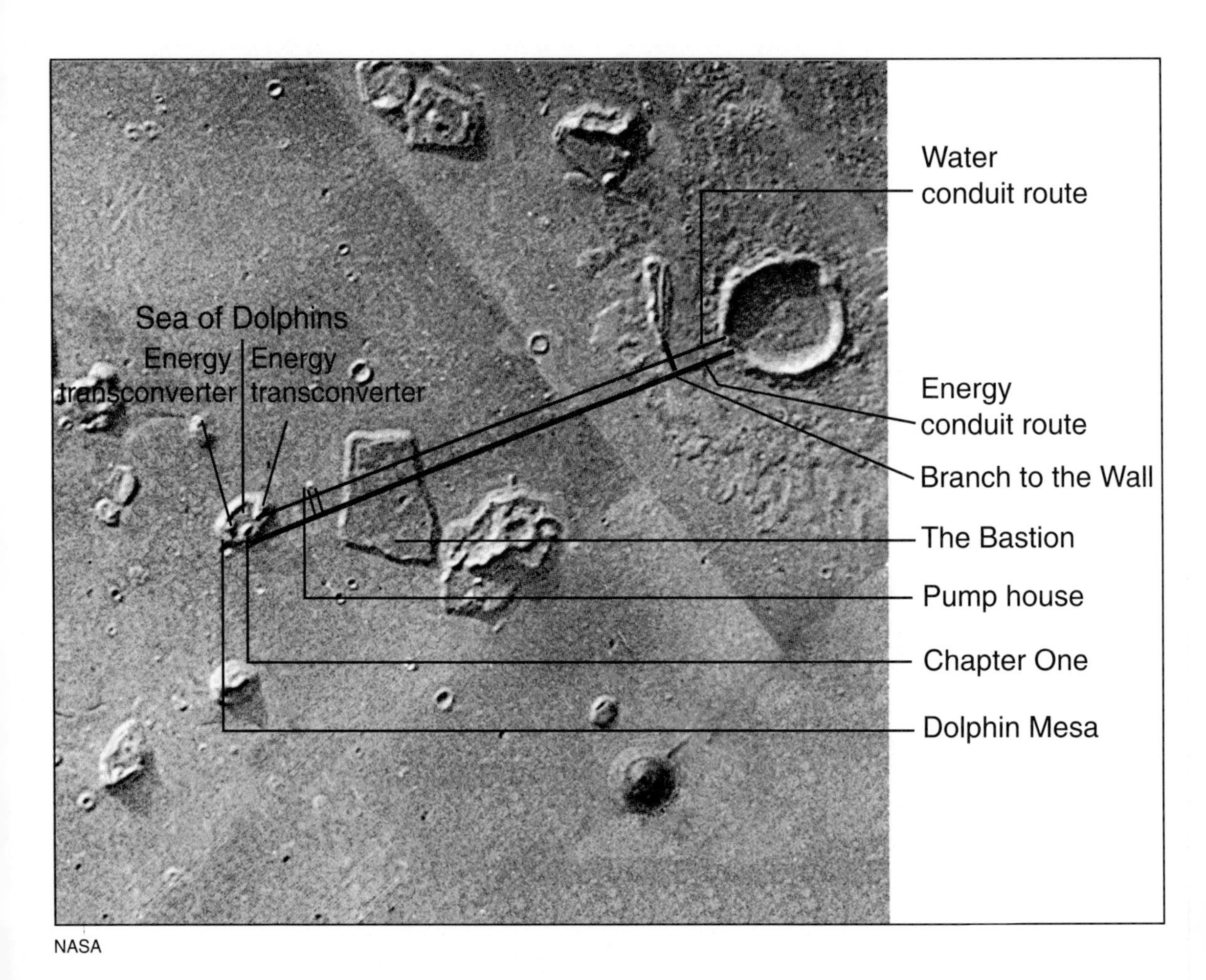

Figure 39. The route of the conduits carrying energy and water westward from the Tetrahedron Crater.

Part 2 Chapter 4

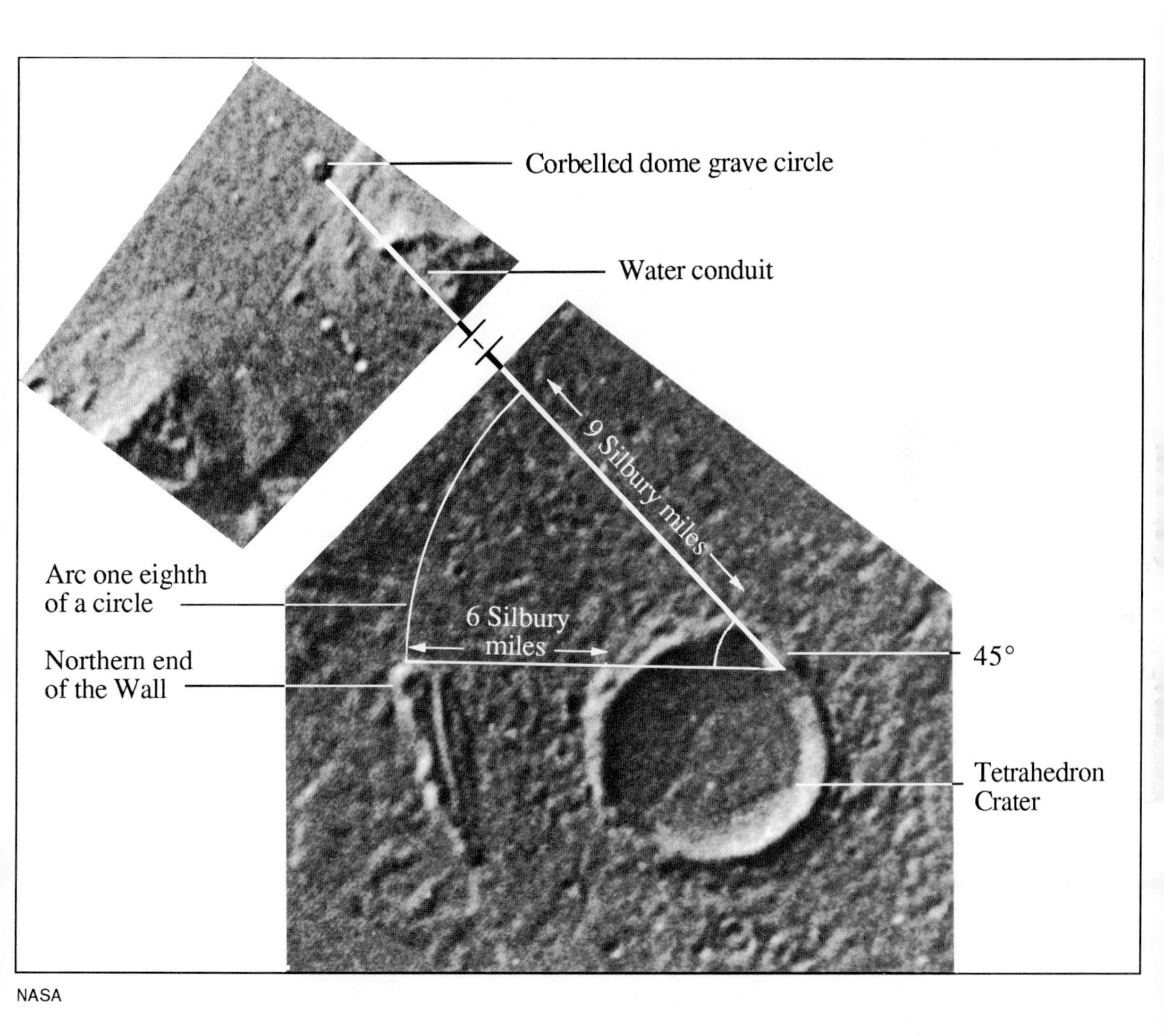

NASA

Figure 40. Location of the corbelled dome grave circle and route of the water conduit to the pump house in the Tetrahedron.

NASA

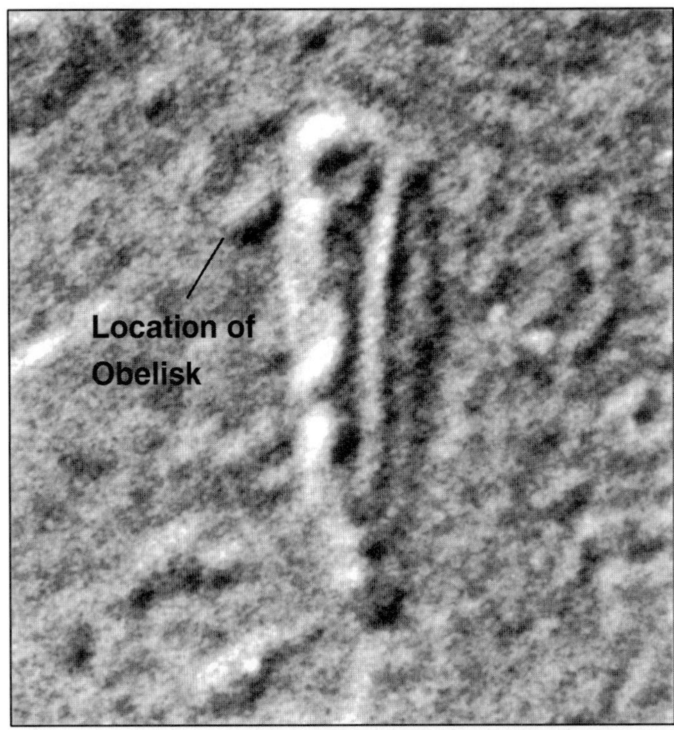

Figure 41. Monument in the form of an obelisk to Dan 'Pan Hur' located to the west of the Wall. A similar obelisk was raised in honour of George Washington the founder of his country.

Part 2 Chapter 4

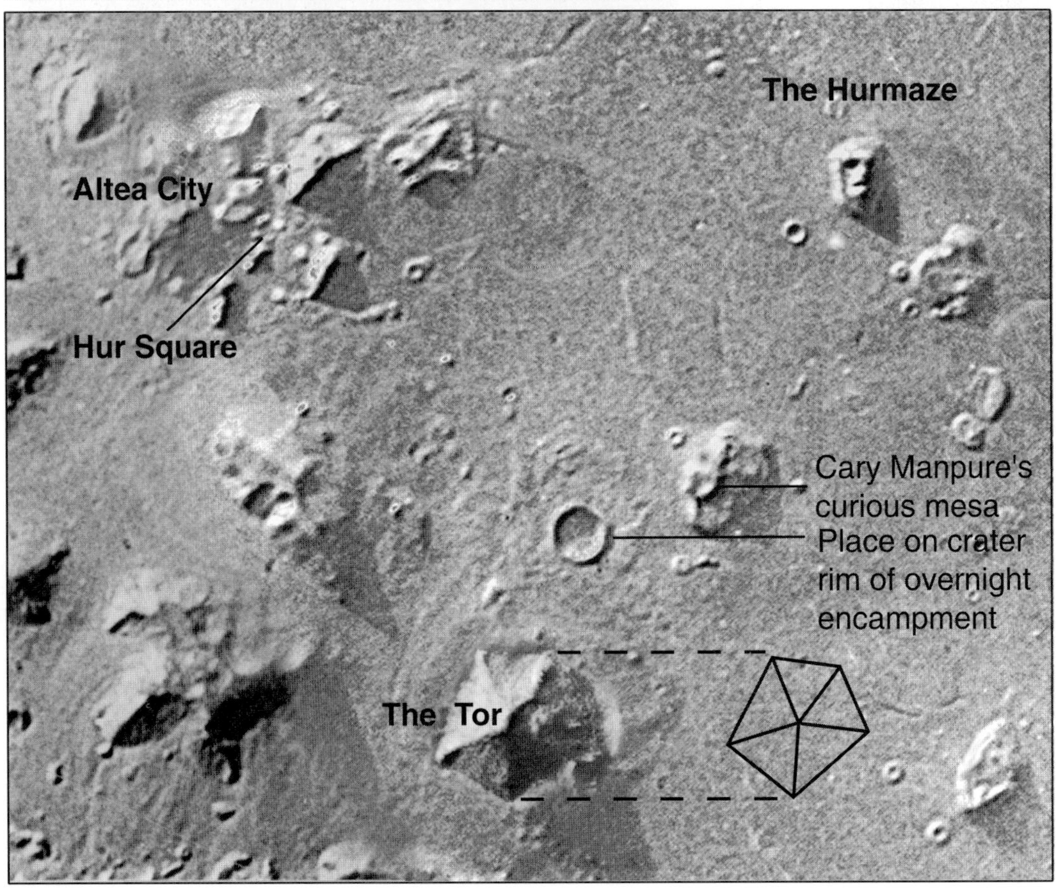

NASA

Figure 42. Western components of the Horz complex. Part 2 Chapter 5

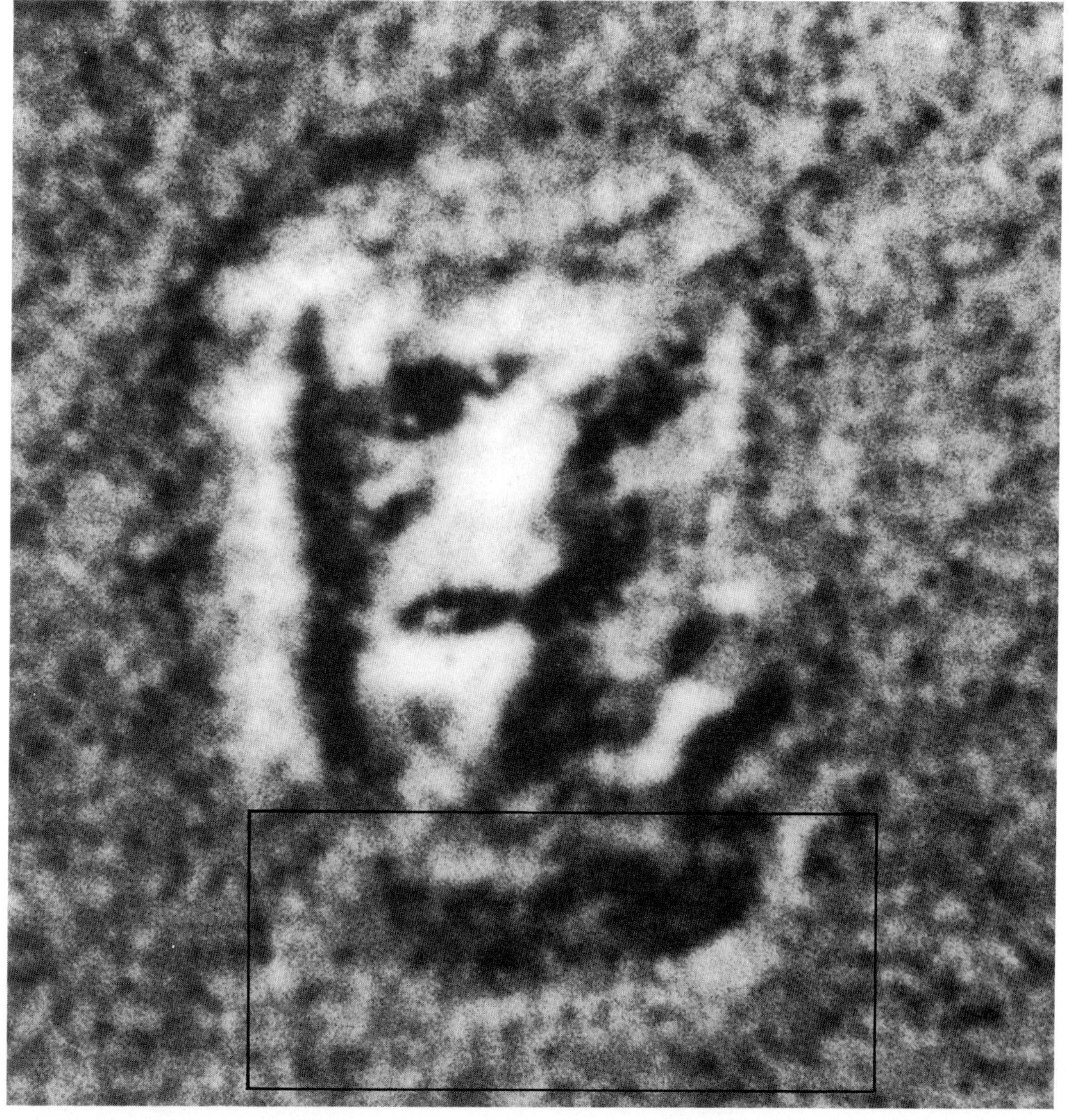

NASA

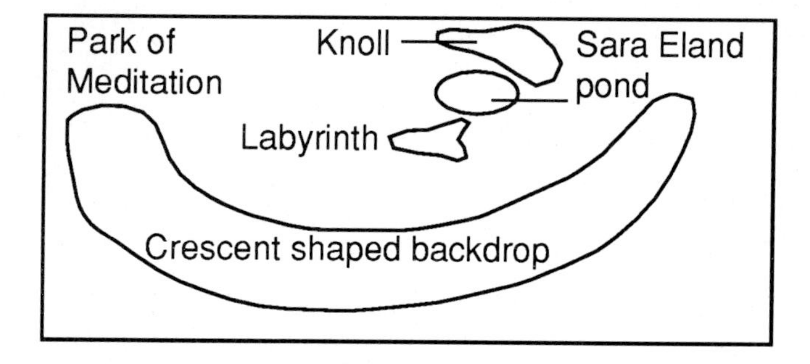

Figure 43. The two sided Hurmaze sculpted out of the top of a high flat mesa located between Altea City and the Wall. Designed to be the primary site of energy transredimensioning.

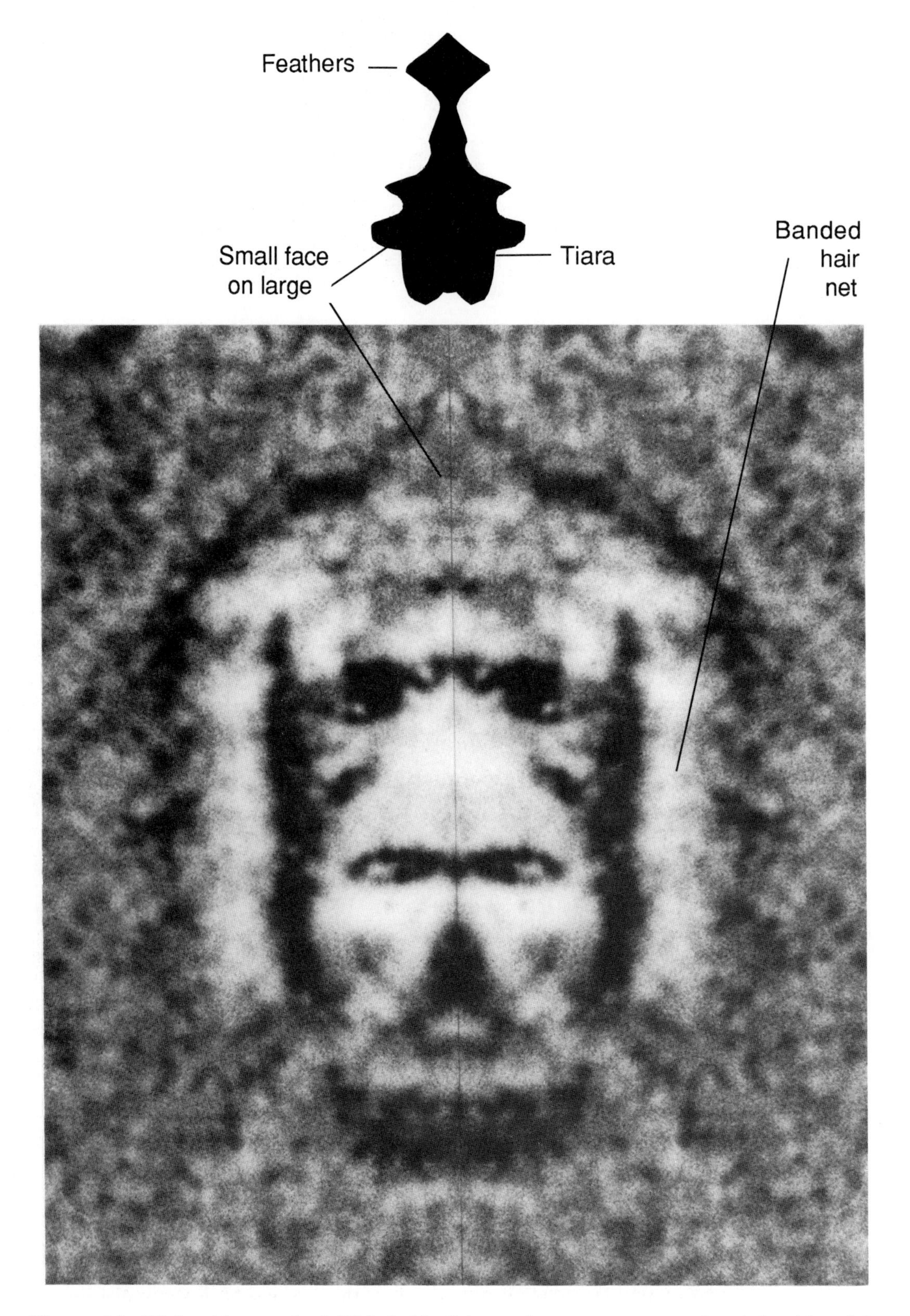

Figure 44. Right side matched. This half of the sculpture represents the right side of the primates head. The union of the evolved minds and souls of the children who are ultimately born self-aware is represented by the banded hair net and tiara.

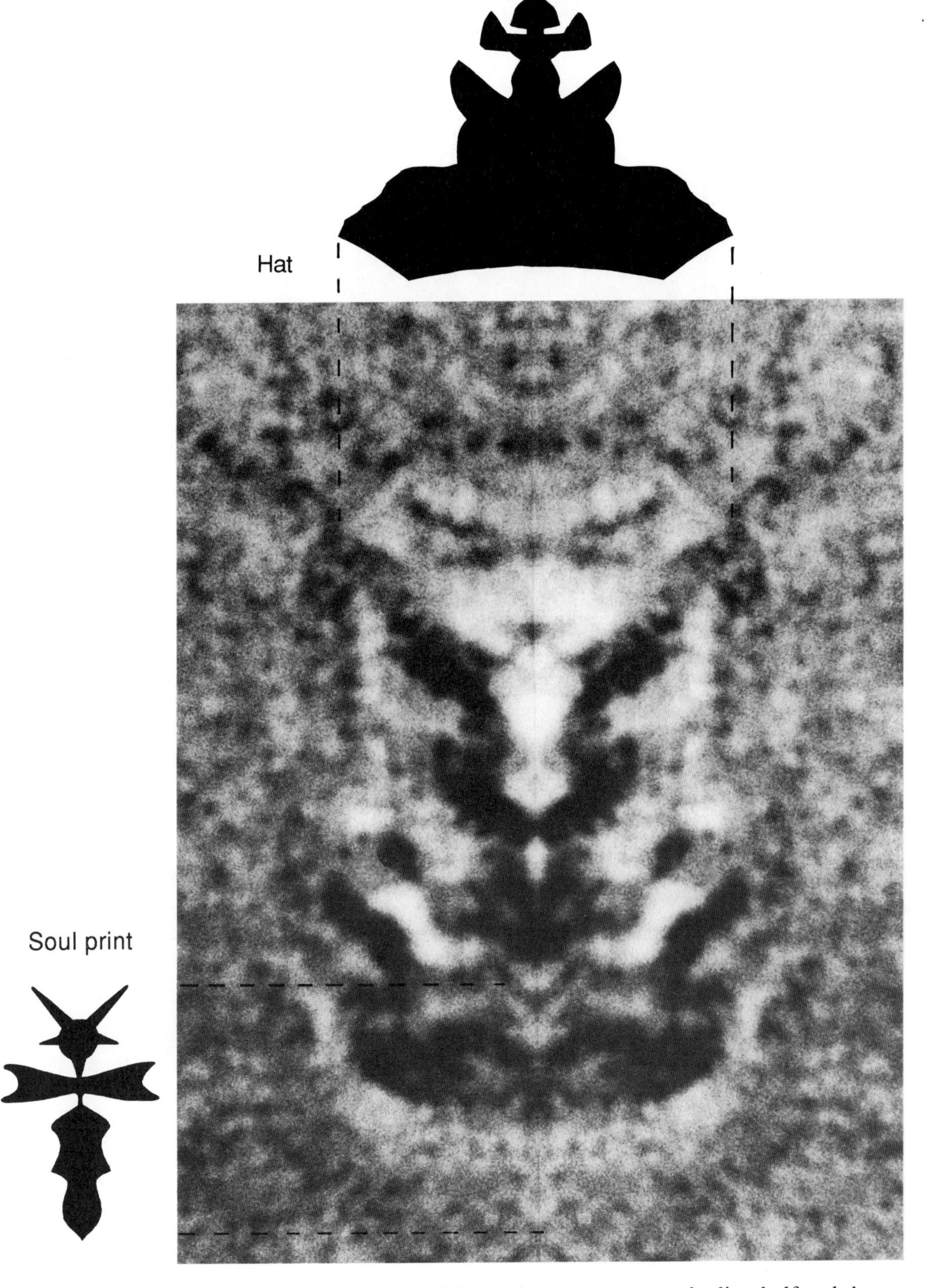

Figure 45. Left side matched. This side of the sculpture represents the lion half and the hat worn by Altean gentlemen when they unite with their wives. The lion is also wearing a soul print around its neck.

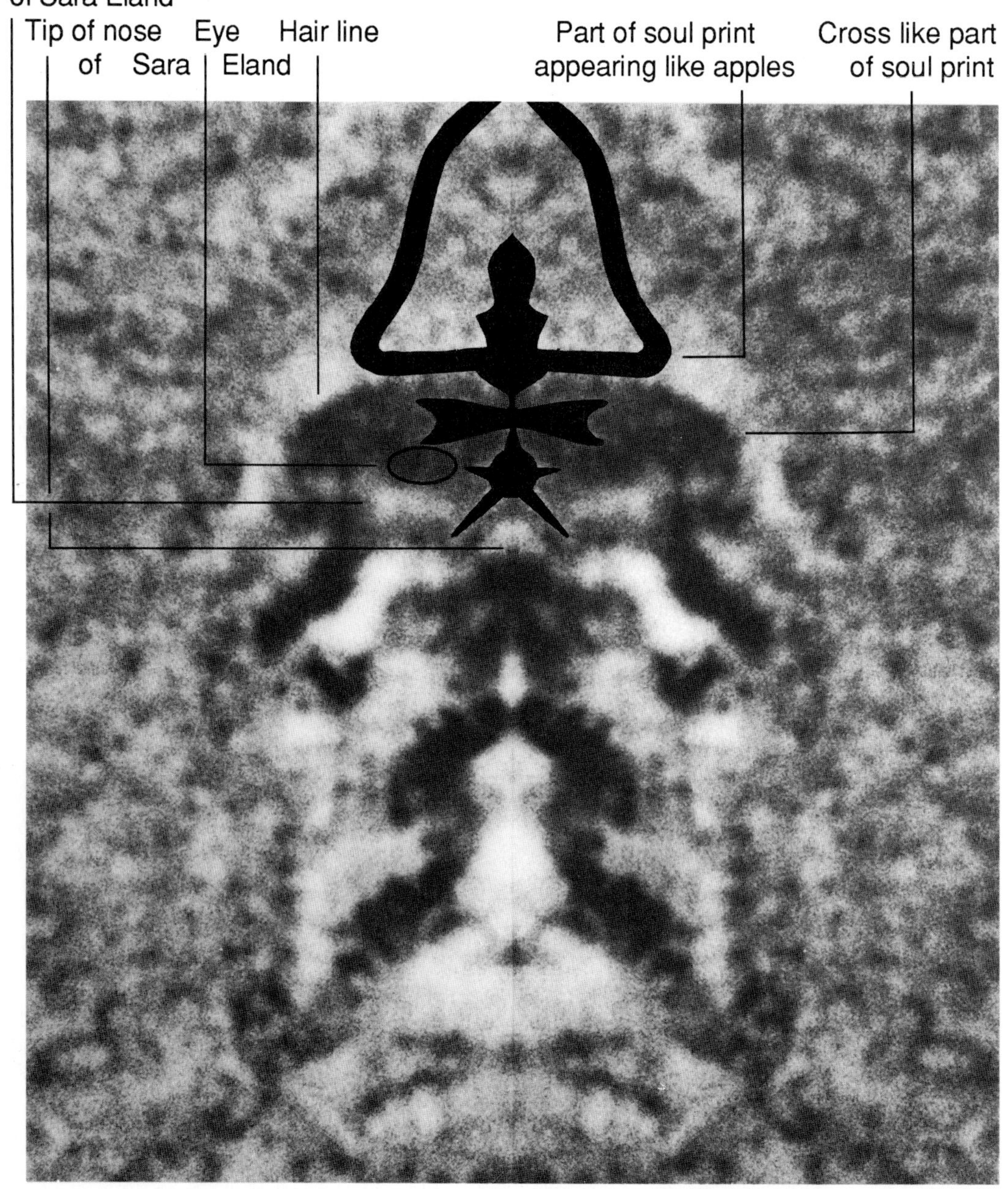

Figure 46. Left side of the Hurmaze matched and inverted — illustrating soul print and the 'hidden' face of Sara Eland.

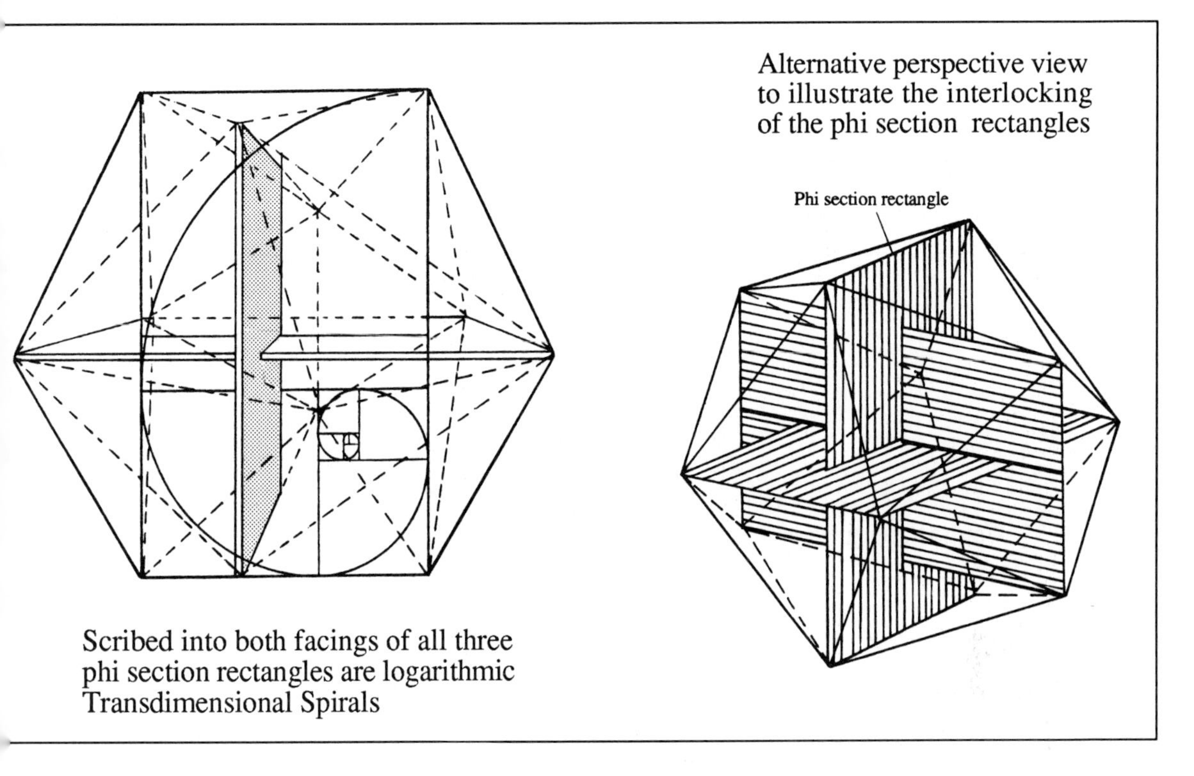

Figure 47. Icosahedral shaped energy transdimensioner. The three interlocked phi section rectangles transdimension four-dimensional torun through complexified three-space into three-dimensional torinum.

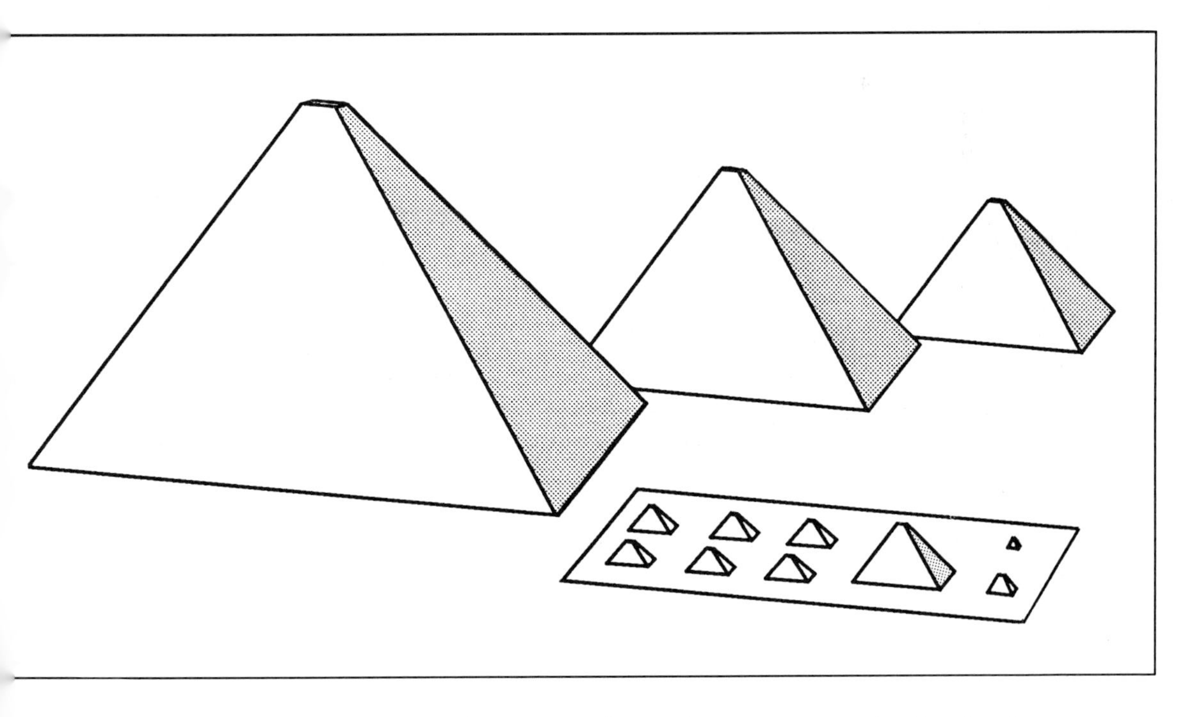

Figure 48. The four-sided pyramidal exterior form of computers varies in size from a height of about one inch to those constructed inside the mesa on which the Hurmaze was sculpted.

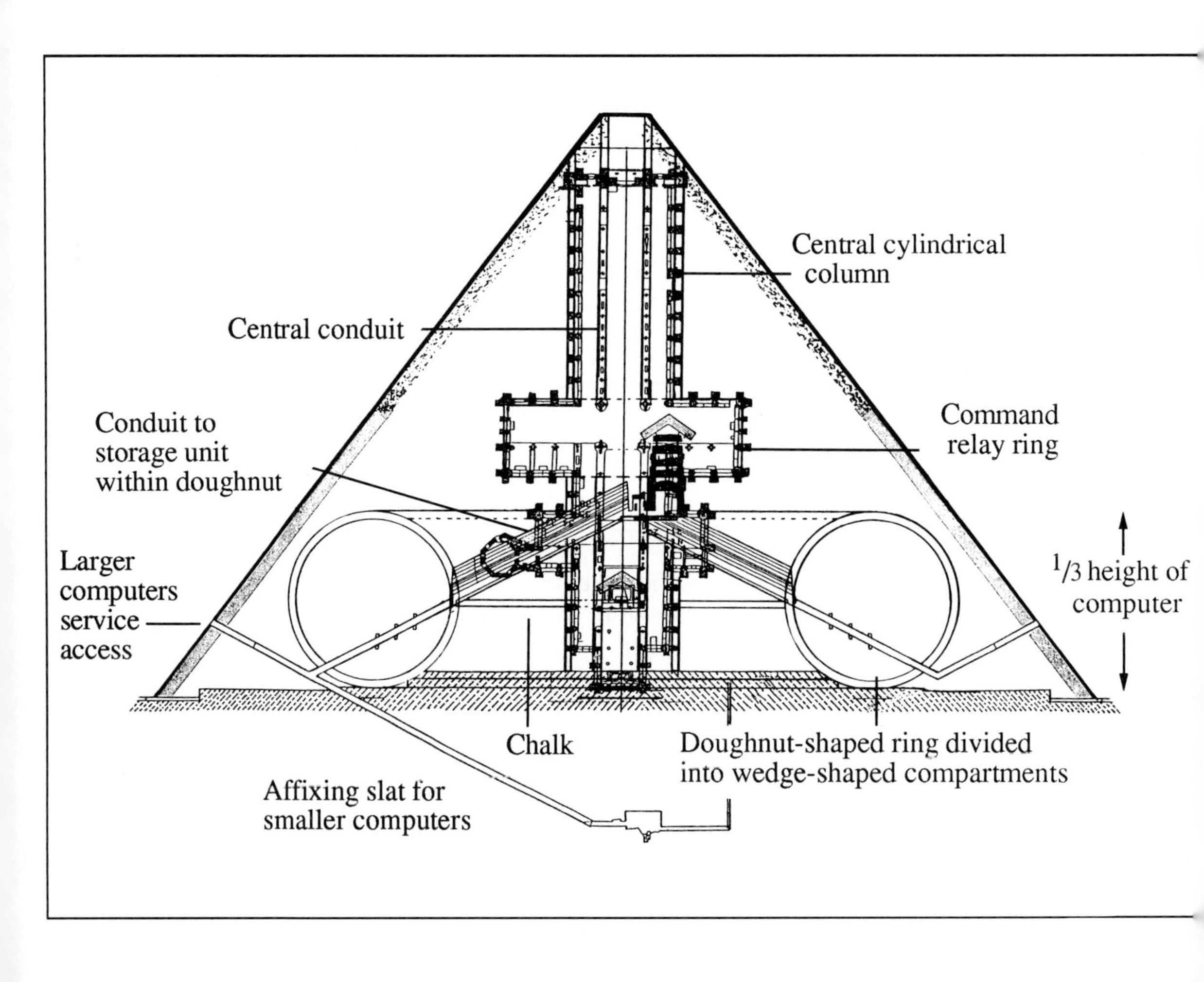

Figure 49. Side view cross section of a computer.

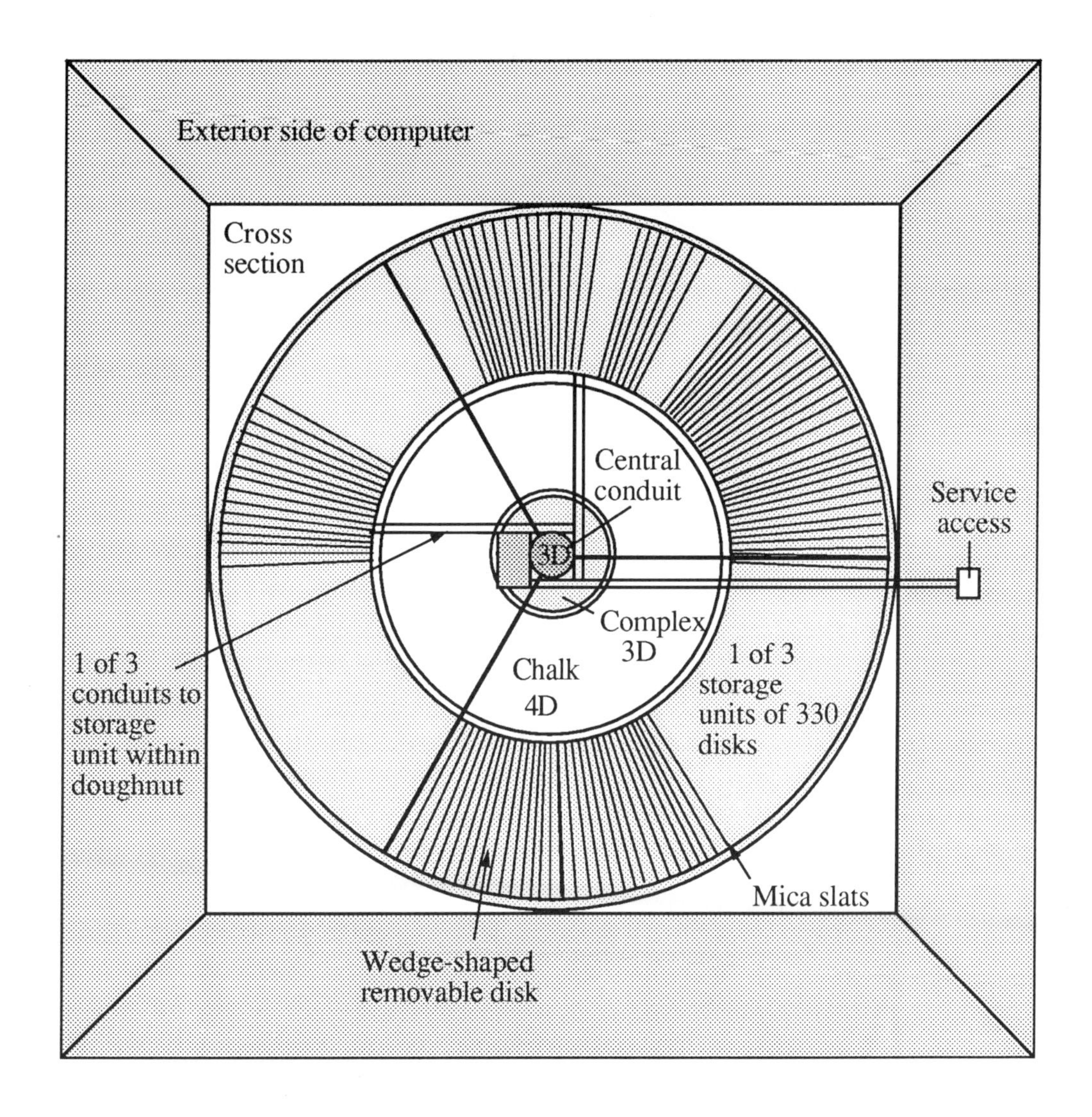

Figure 50. Top view cross section of a computer drawn to the same scale as figure 49.

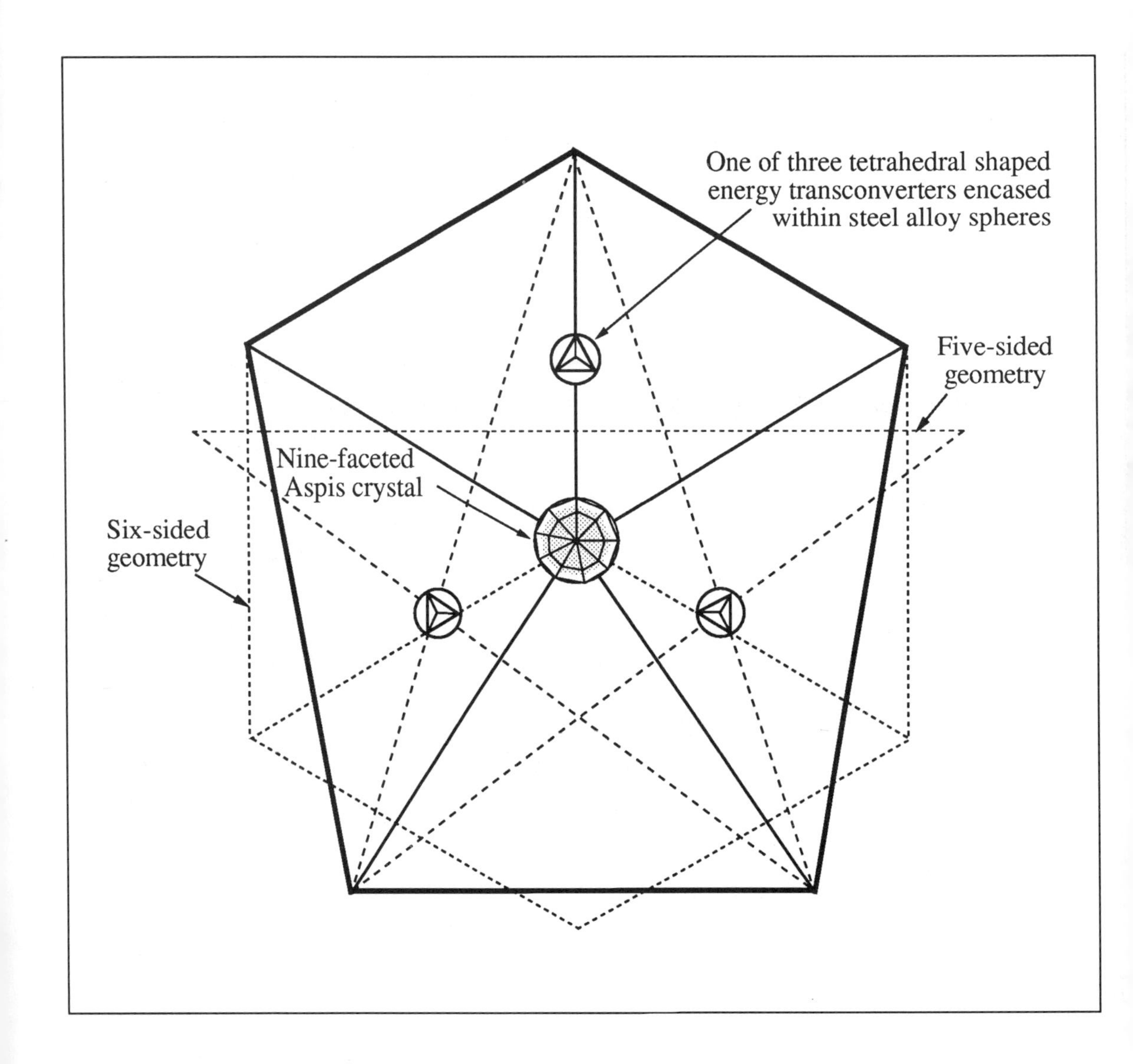

Figure 51. The positioning of the Aspis crystal and the three energy converters in the Tor. Two-thirds of the energy transconverters are located at the reconciliation points of six- and five-sided geometry.

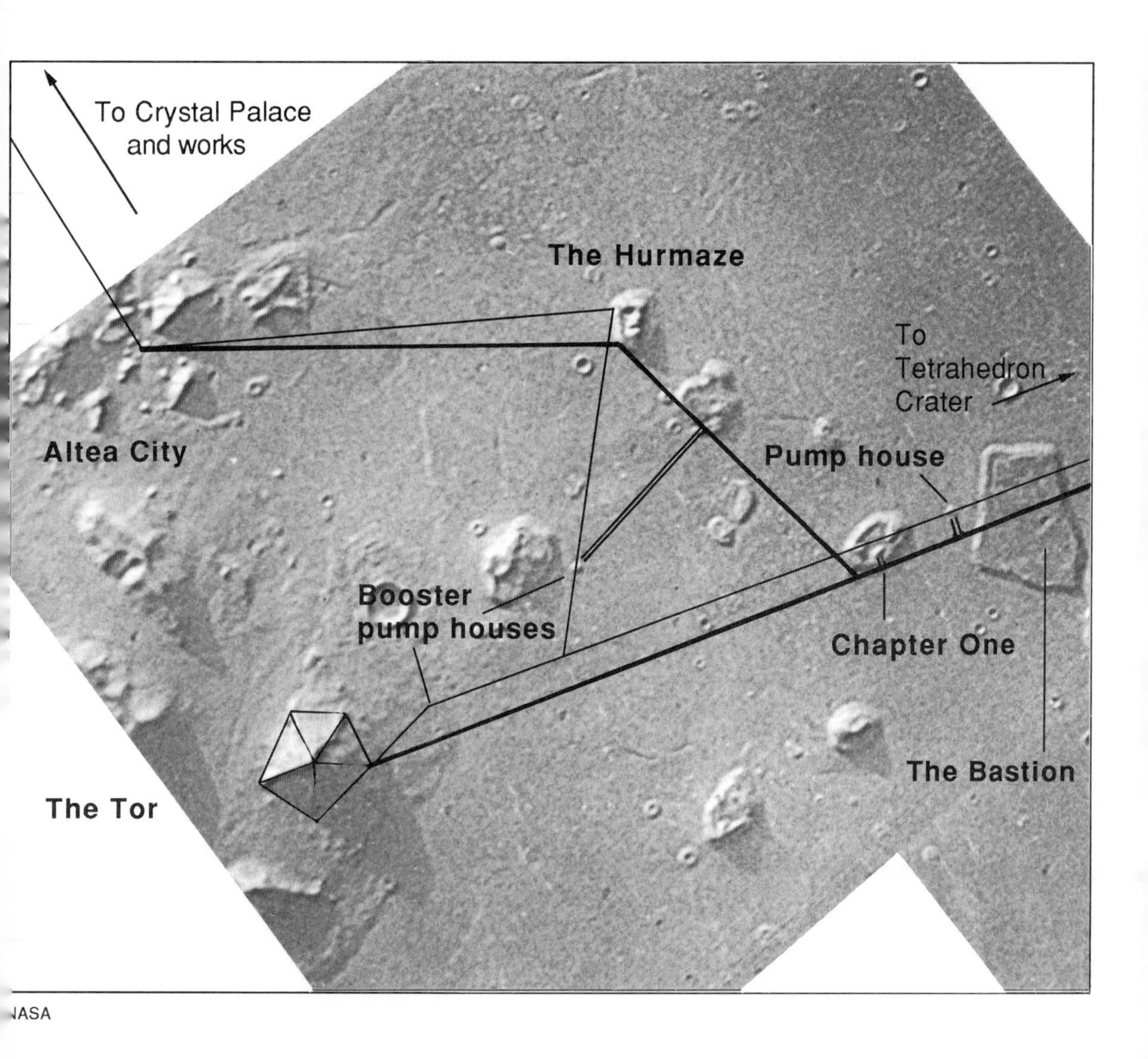

Figure 52. The conduit routes laid in ditches for the supply of energy and water to the west of Dolphin mesa.

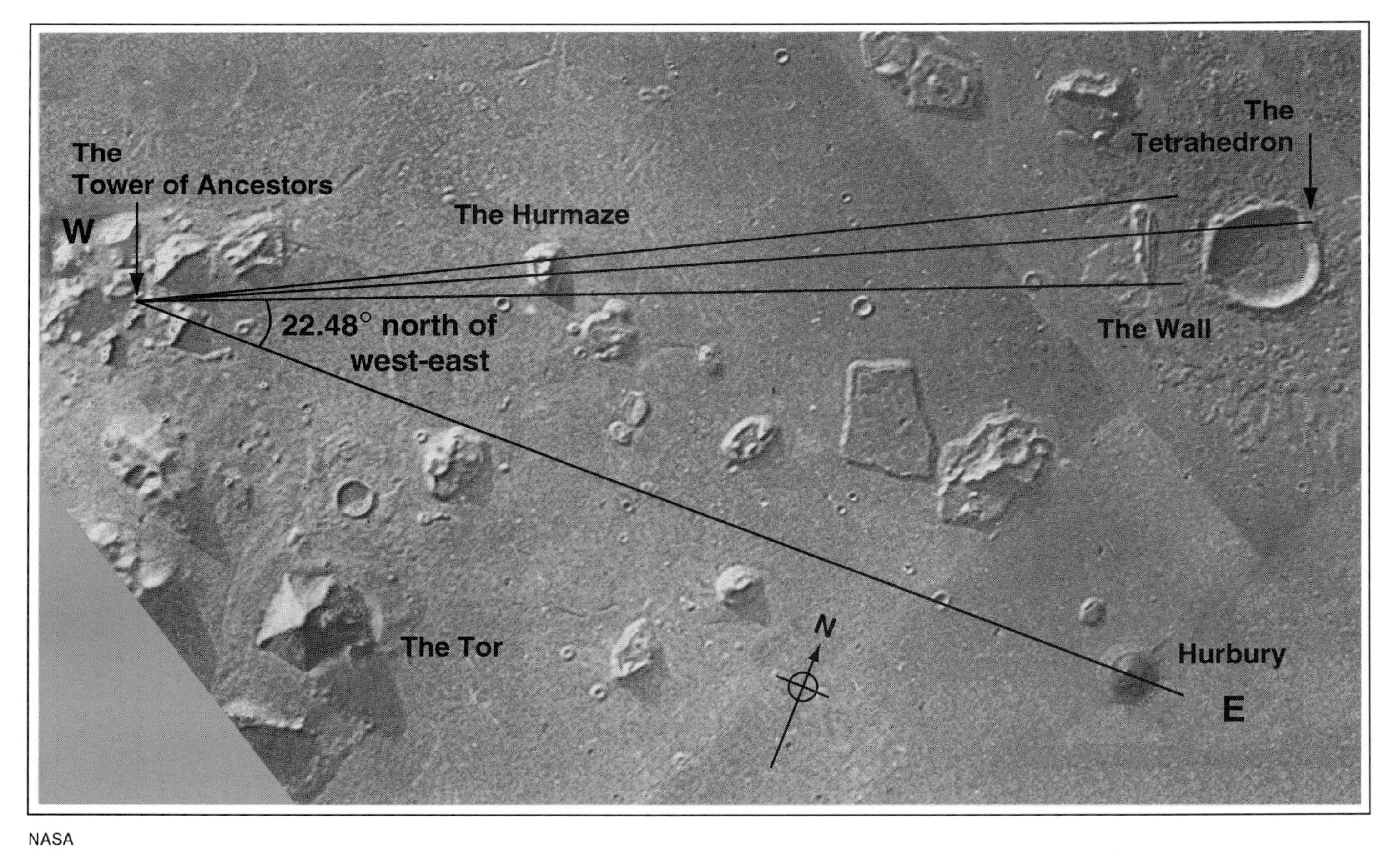

NASA

Figure 53. The sight lines of the Horz complex.

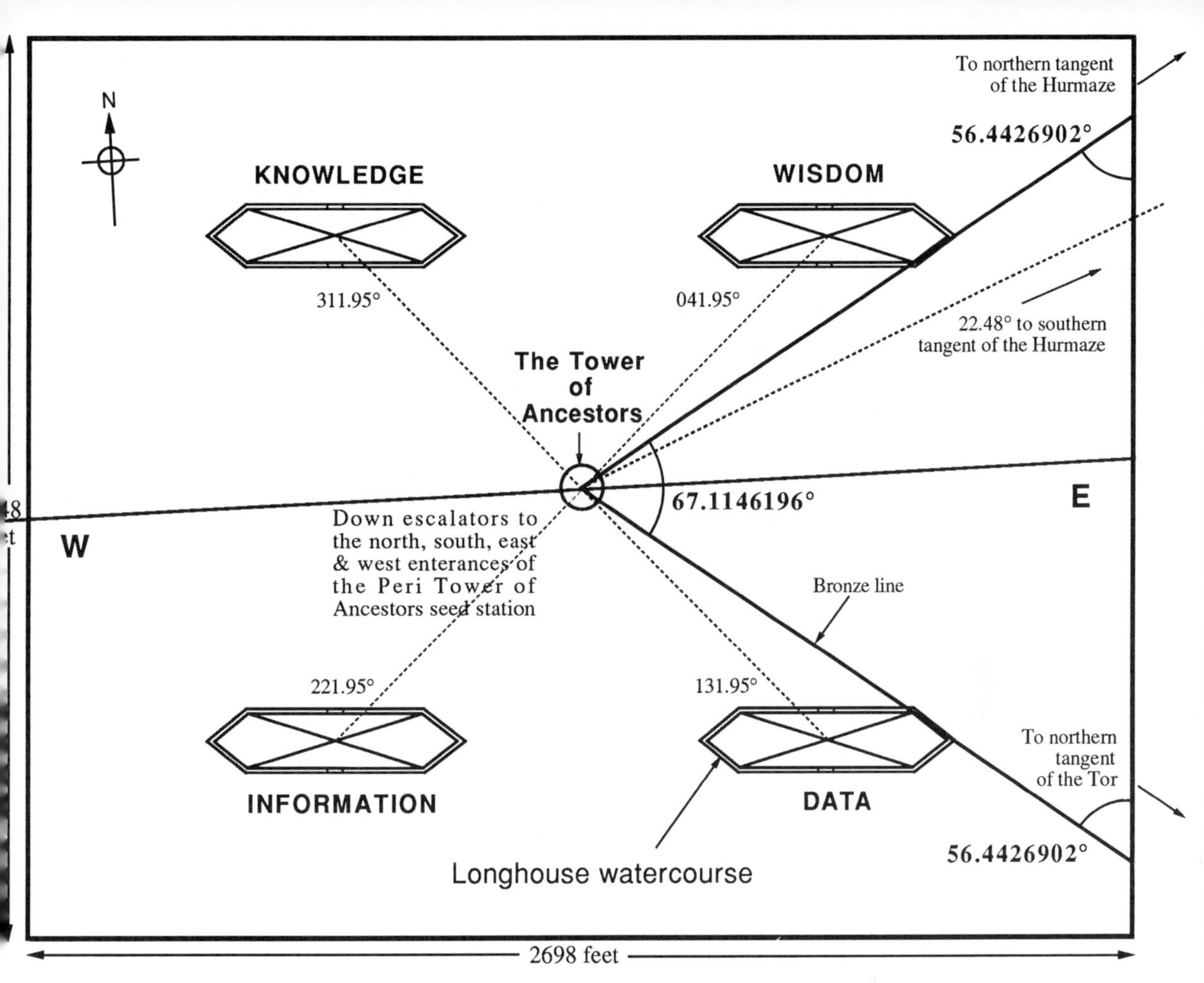

Figure 54. The four longhouses on Hur Square. The ratio of 2248 to 2698 is a near equivalent to the ratio of 5 to 6. The one-inch wide bronze line in the tiling of Hur Square is the two-dimensional representation of the cone of the physical universe. See also fig 10.

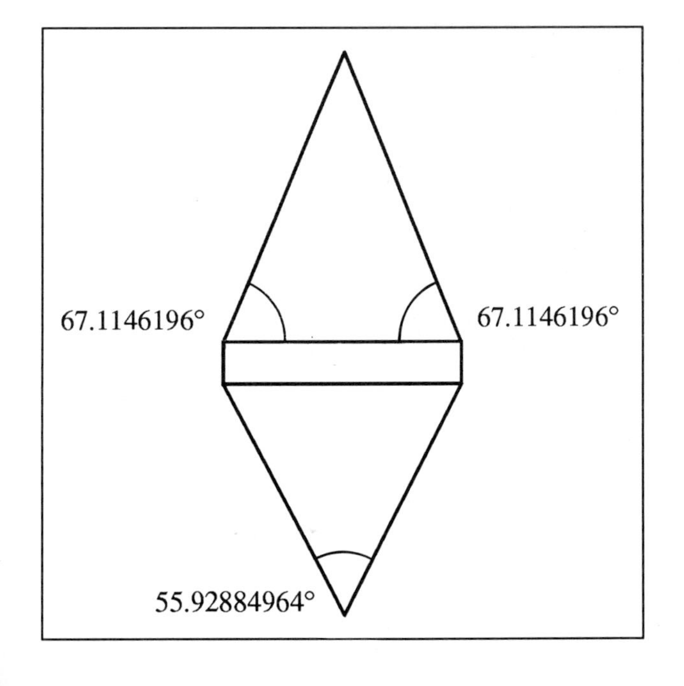

The ratio of 55.92884964 to 67.1146196 is equivalent to 5/6ths

Figure 55. Waldark's geometric representation in two-dimensions of the conical disturbance pattern of self-aware conciousness when transdimensioning energy.

NASA

Figure 56. The twelve principal structures of Altea City.

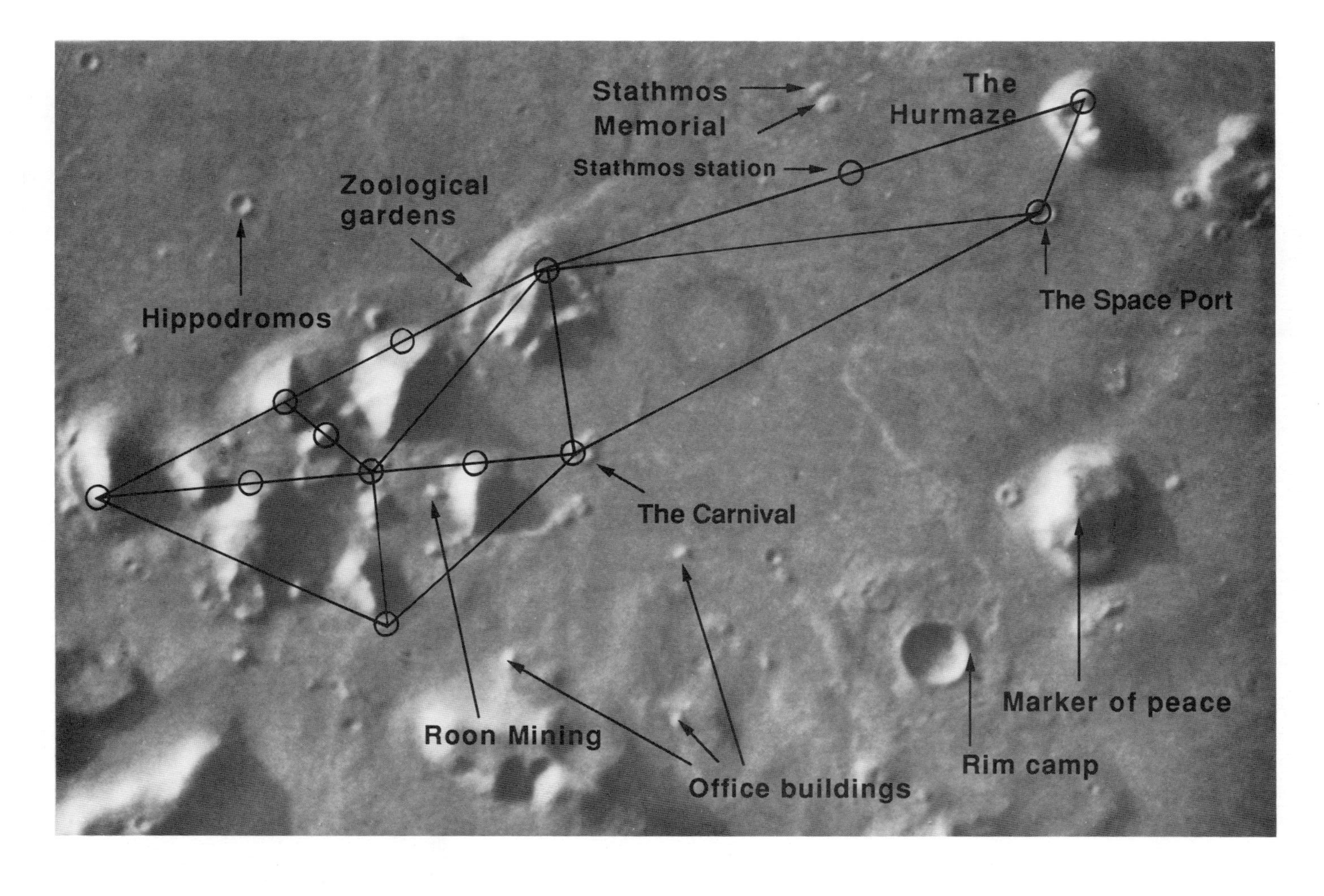

Figure 56.1. The perierchomai transportation system of Altea City affectionately known as the Peri was laid out so that its crystal tubes formed a grid consisting of seven triangles.

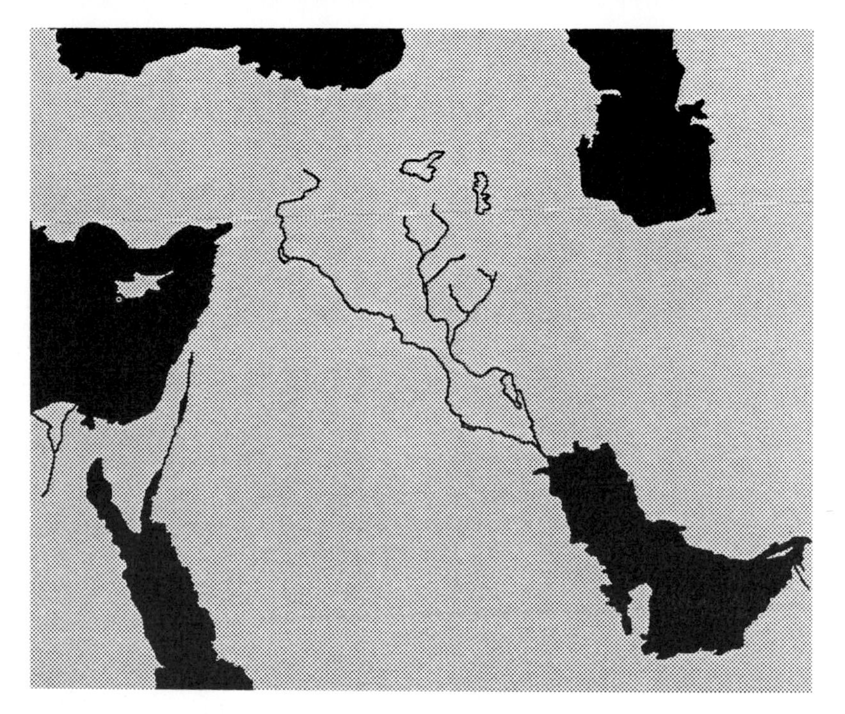

Figure 57. Halverson's private empire located between two rivers.
Part 2 Chapter 6

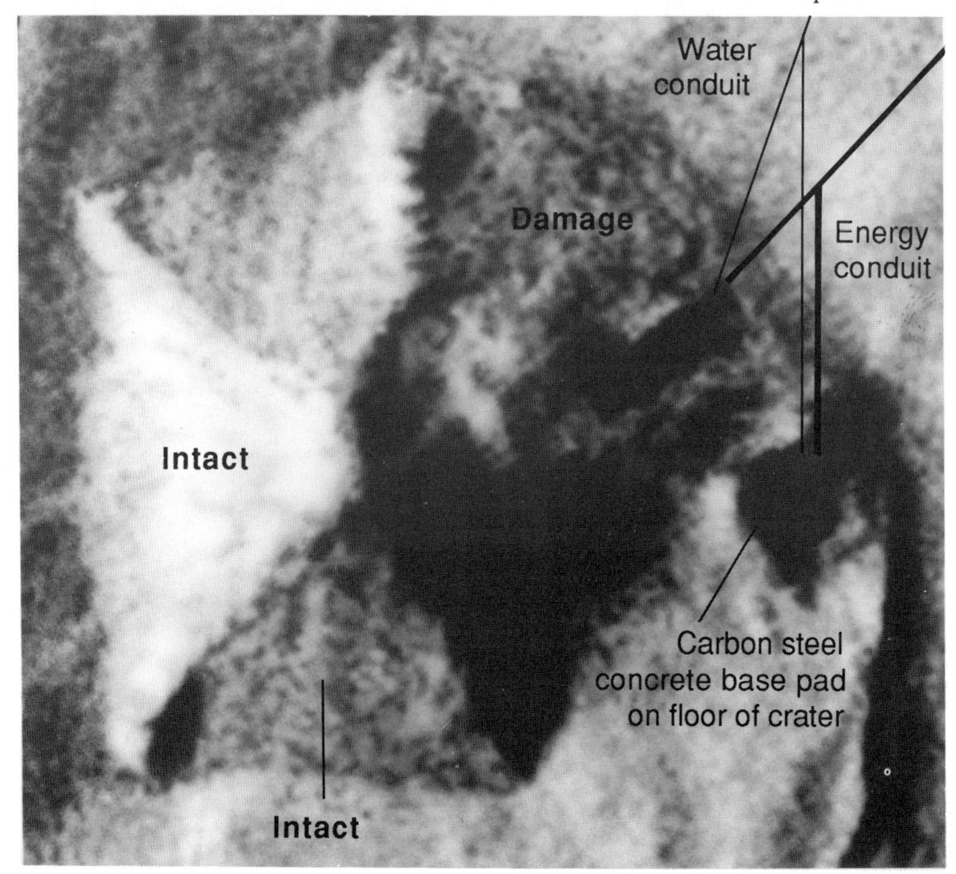

Figure 58. The damaged Tor and the new base pad in the shallow impact crater.
Part 2 Chapter 9

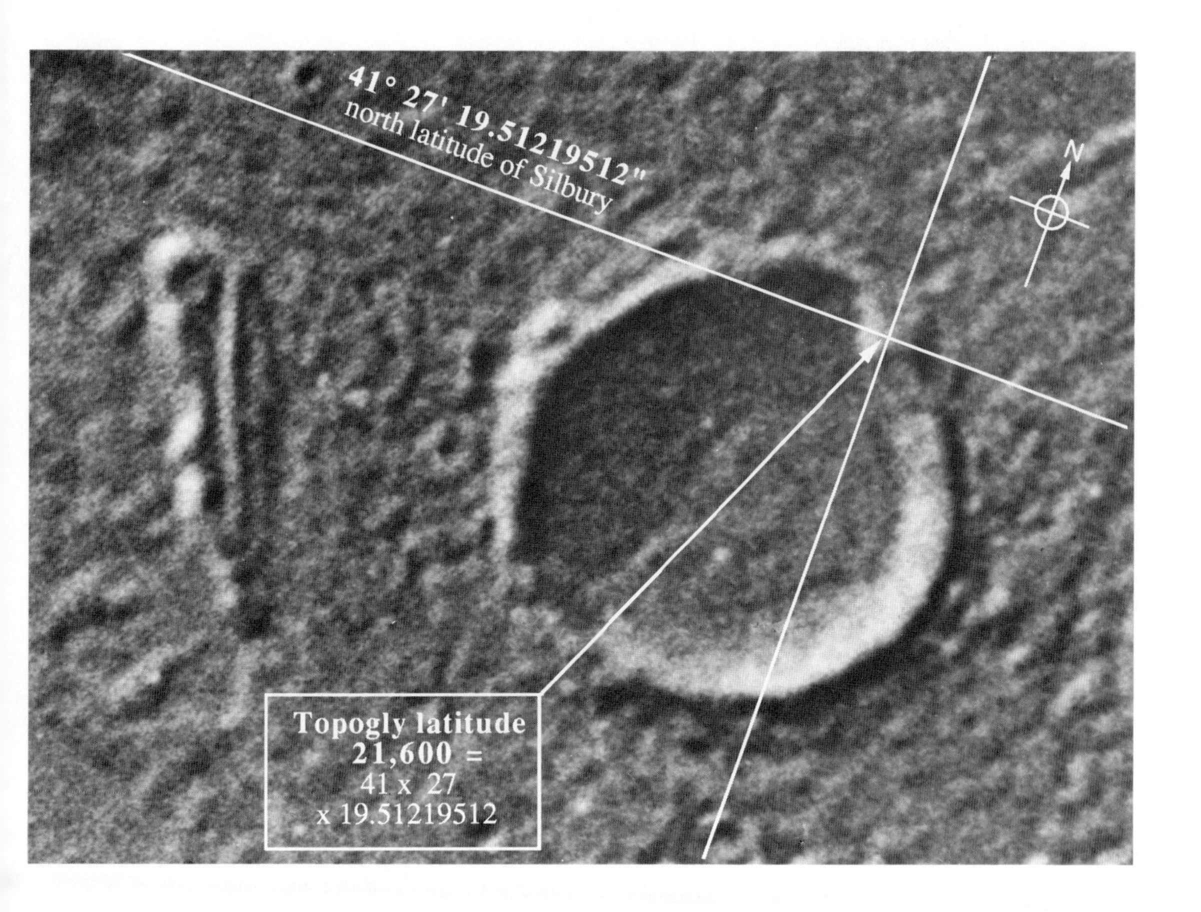

Figure 59. The topogly latitude of the Tetrahedron, the sourcemark of the Horz complex, located on the northeastern rim of the Tetrahedron Crater.

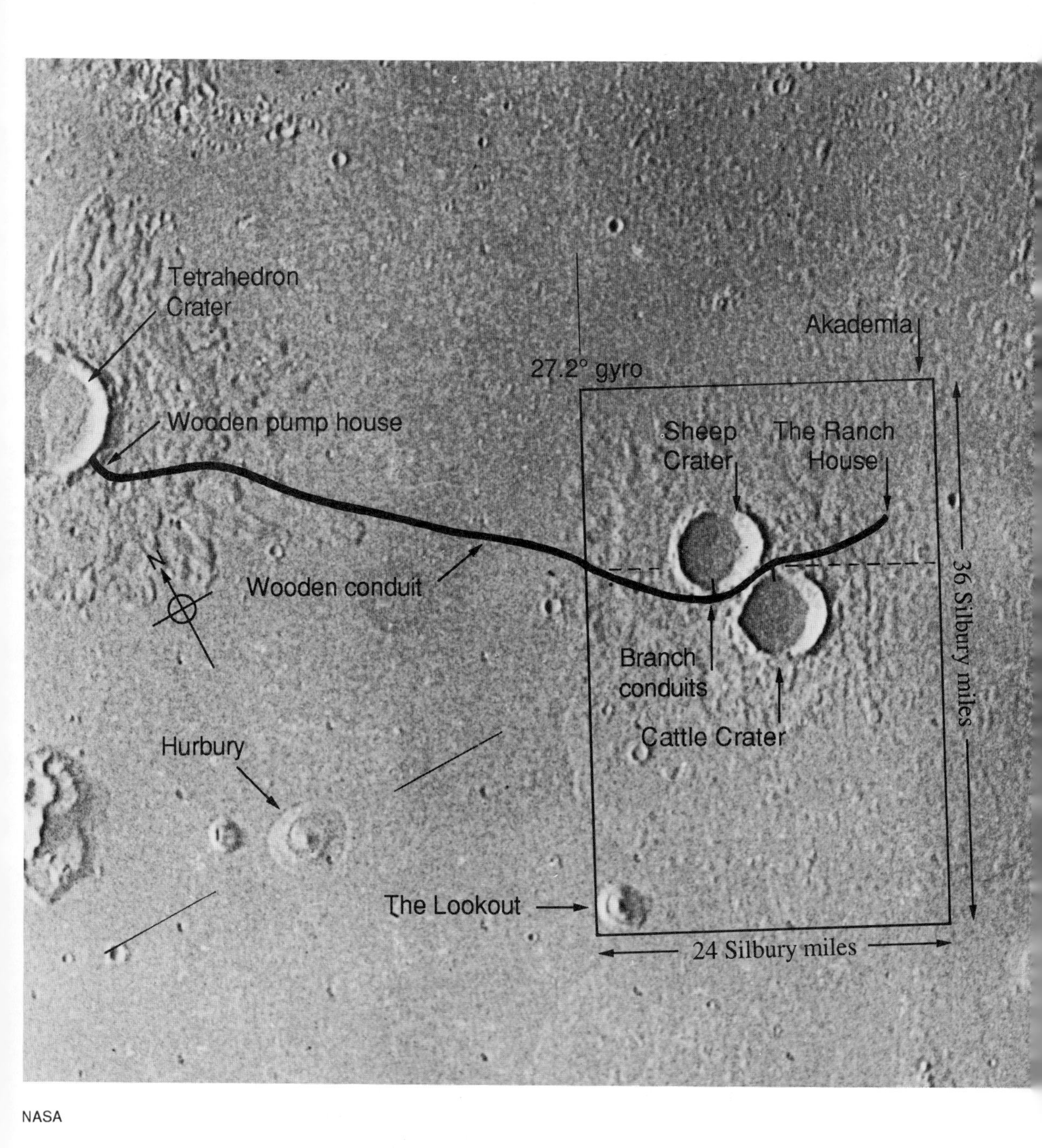

NASA

Figure 60. The Ranch centered about 20 miles southeast of the Tetrahedron Crater.
Part 2 Chapter 9

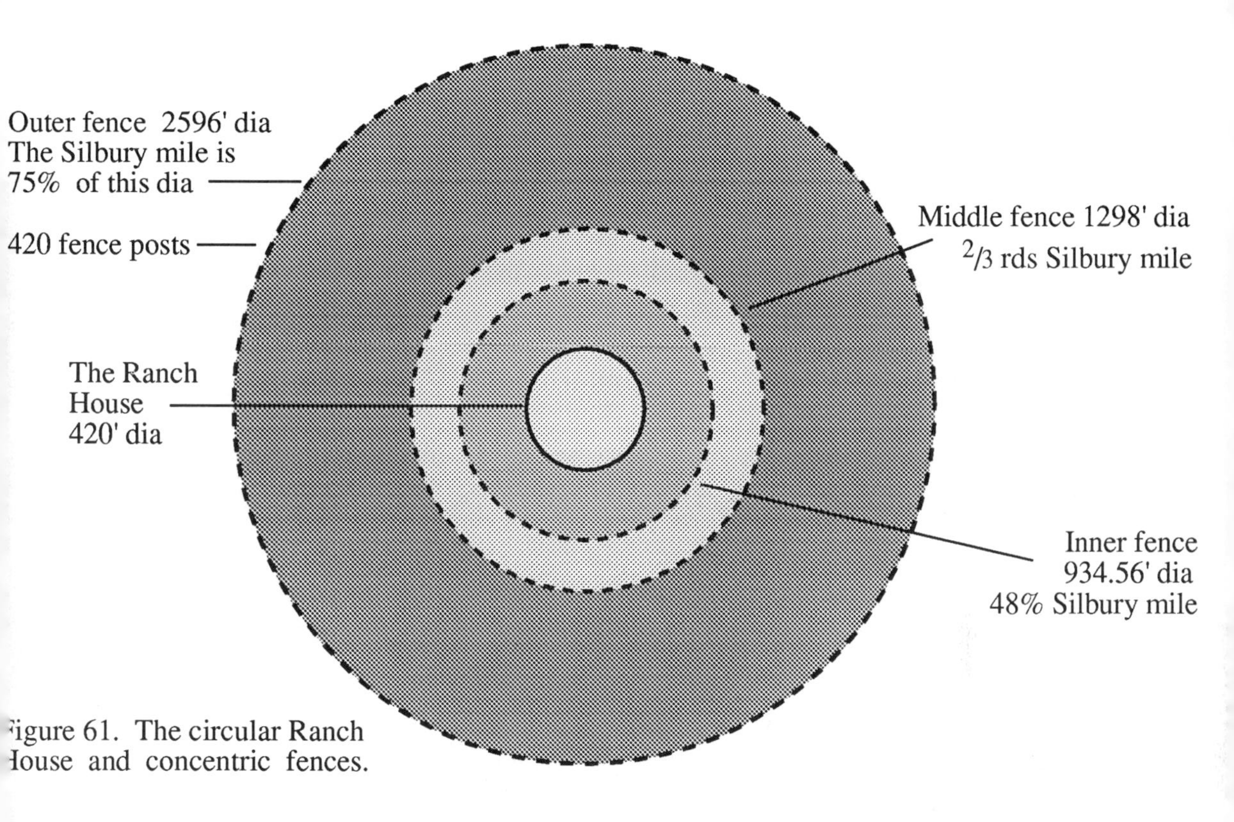

Figure 61. The circular Ranch House and concentric fences.

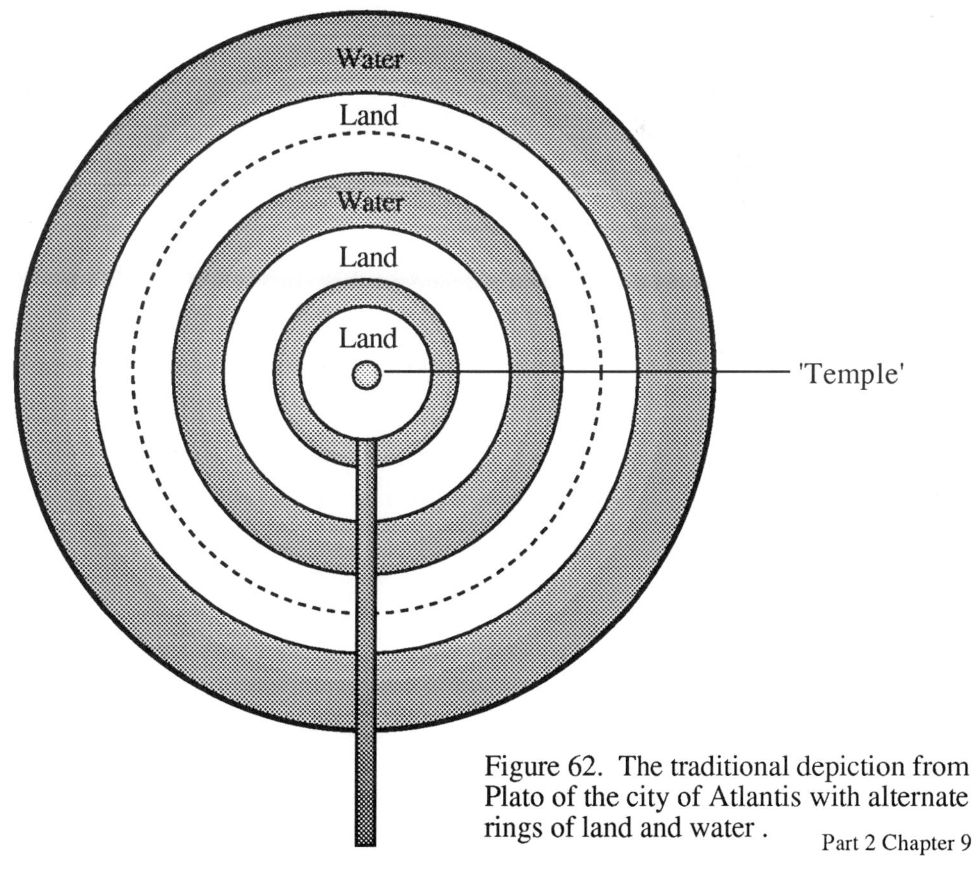

Figure 62. The traditional depiction from Plato of the city of Atlantis with alternate rings of land and water .

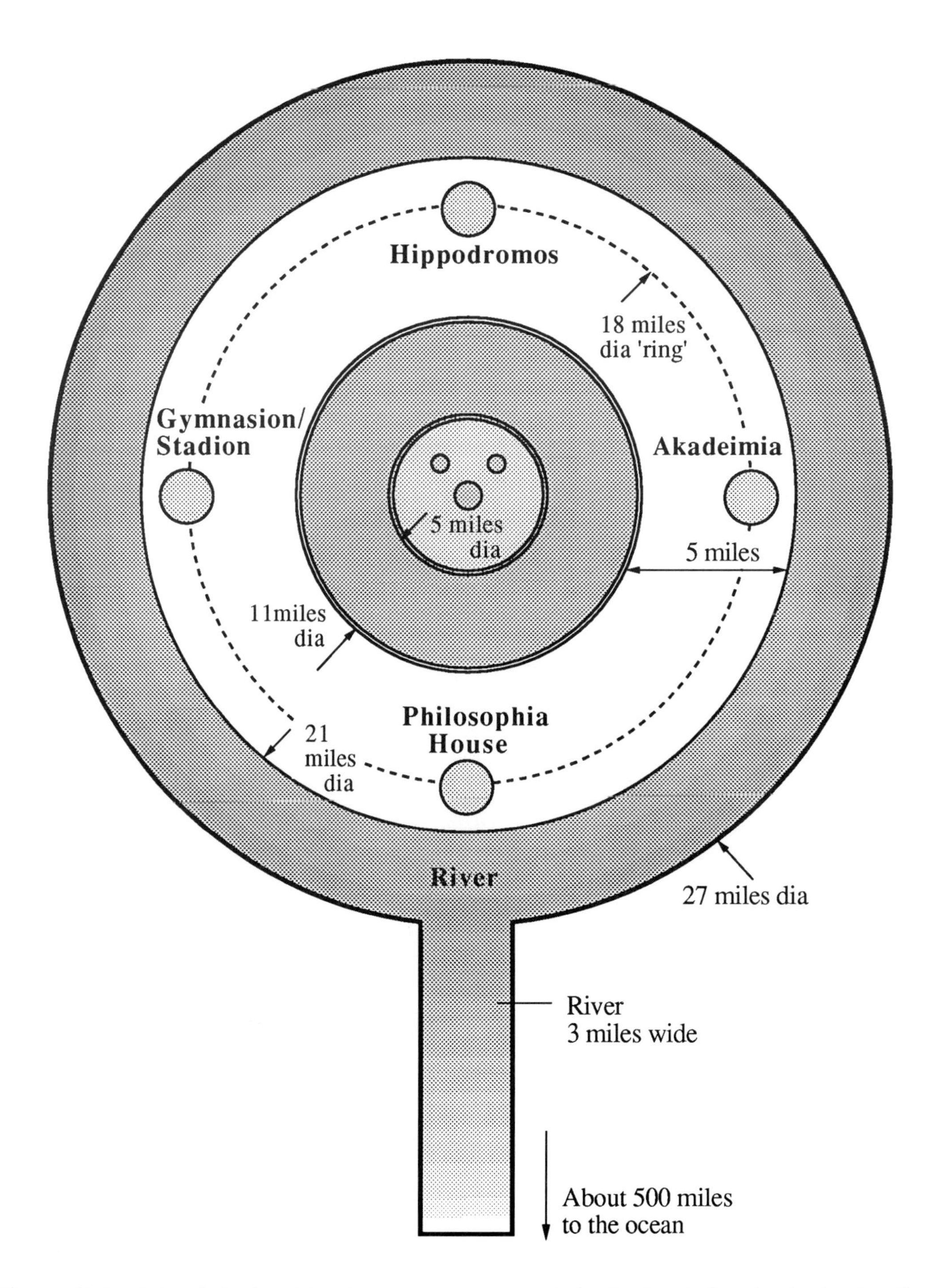

Figure 62.1. Atlantis is the oldest known and recorded city in the chain of galaxies leading to this galaxy and means 'something not equaled'. It was a superb city full of style and grace. In the middle of Atlantis' central terraced area was the transconversion complex, and had that complex been circumscribed, the resulting circle would have been one mile in diameter.

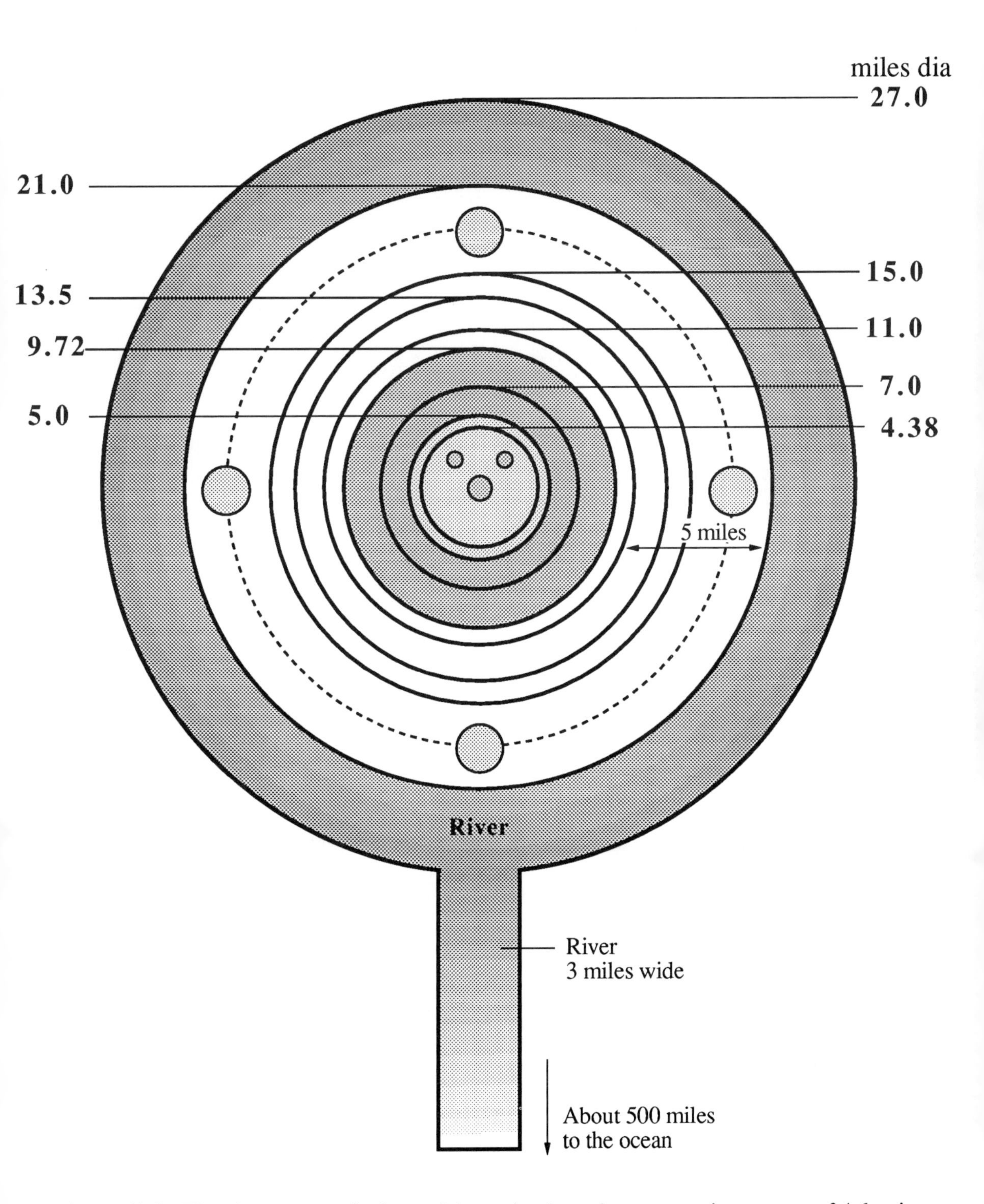

Figure 62.2. The nine concentric rings of the perierchomai transportation system of Atlantis.
Part 2 Chapter 9

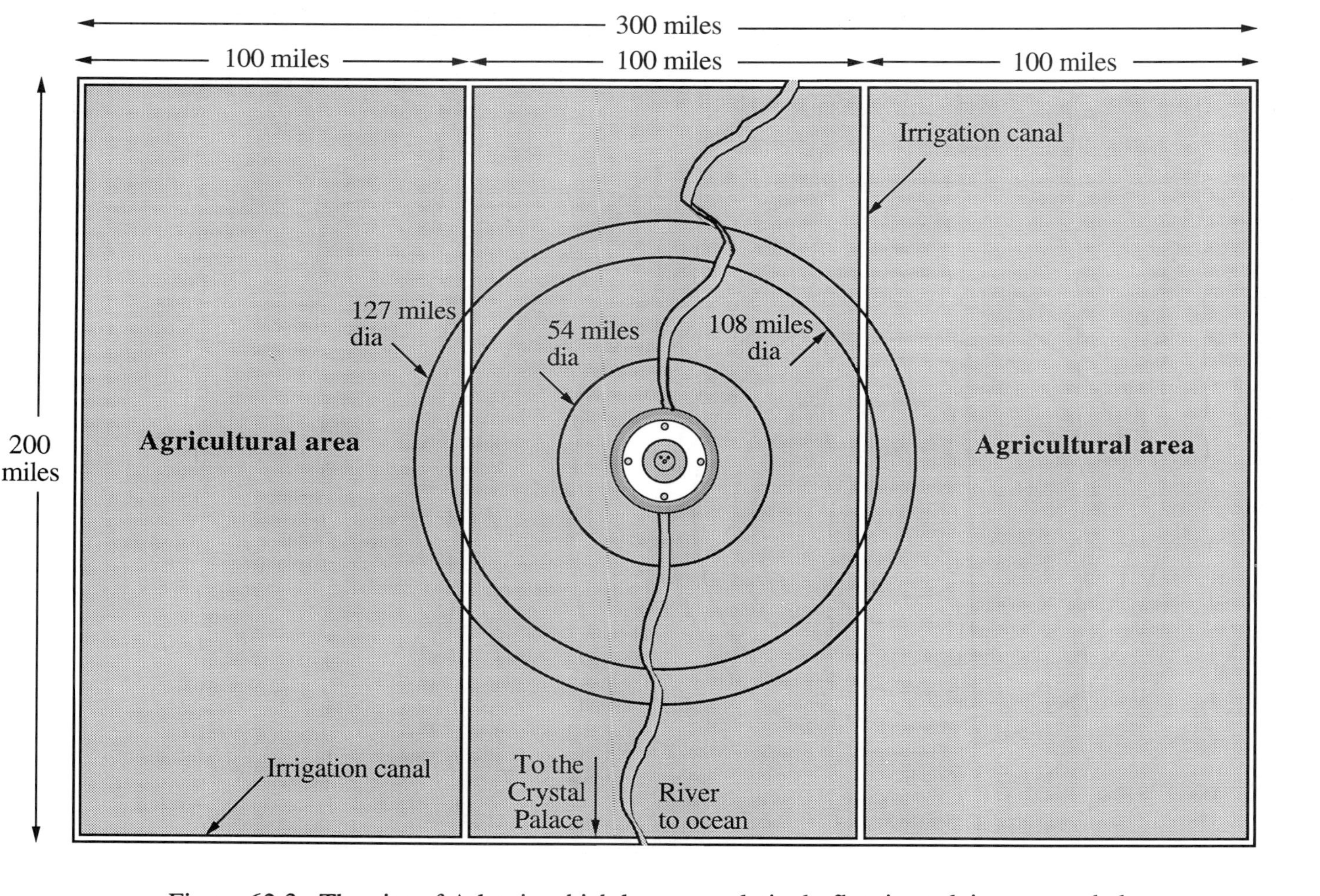

Figure 62.3. The city of Atlantis which lay on a relatively flat river plain surrounded on all sides by mountains. Three-fourths of the twelve periérchomai transportation system rings were inside the city with one-fourth of the rings extending into the agricultural area beyond.

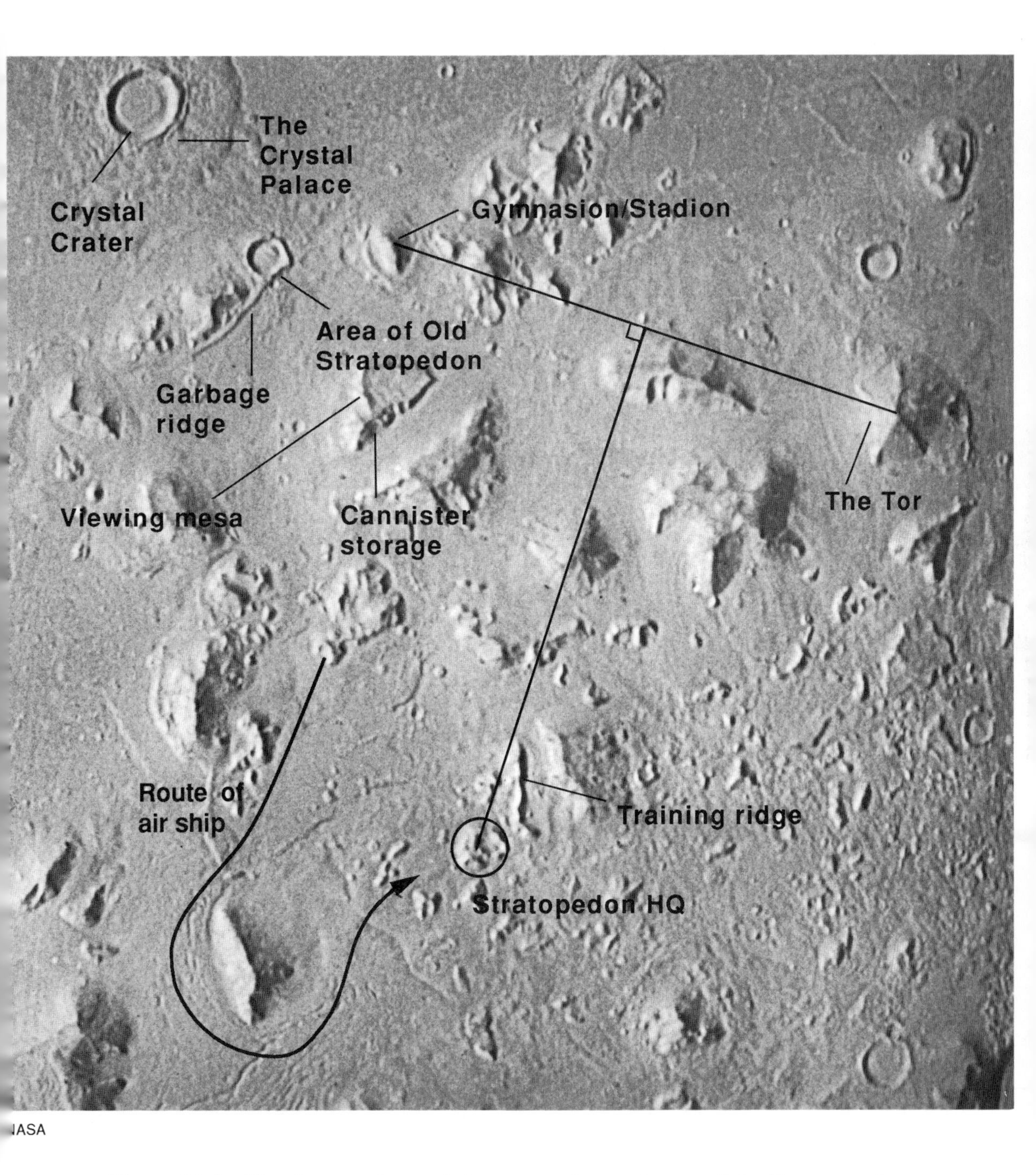

NASA

Figure 62.4. The Stratopedon and the area to the southwest of the Horz complex.

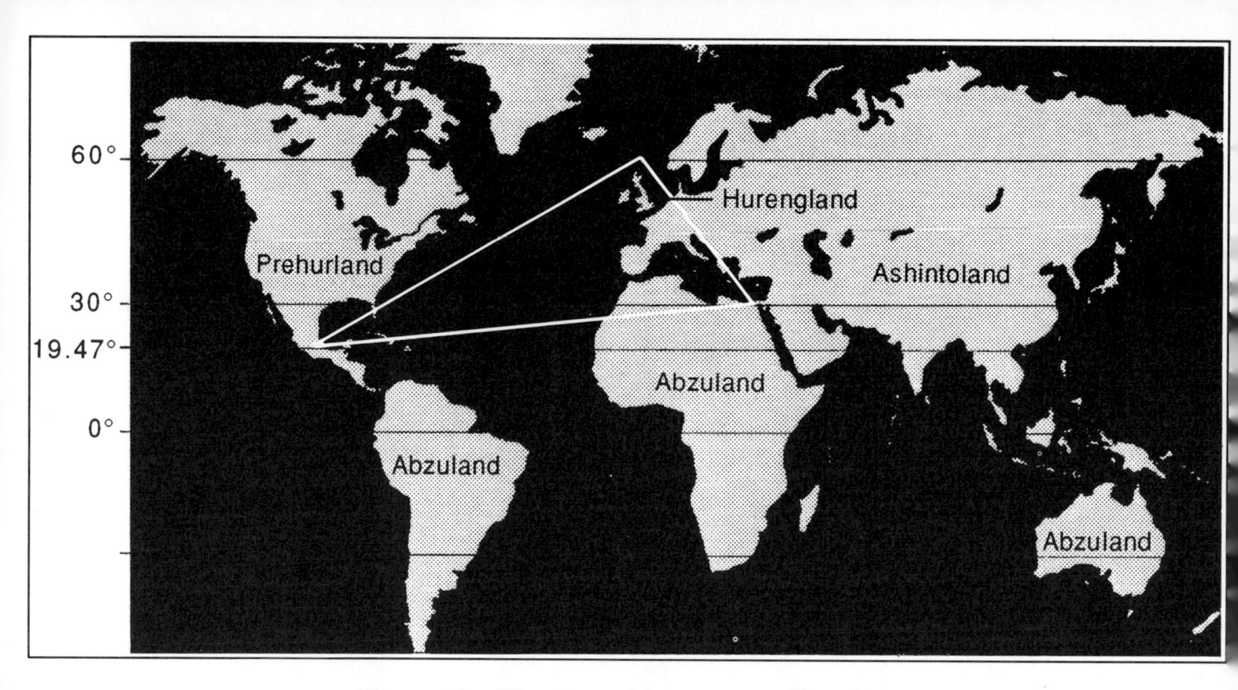

Figure 63. The three siting areas on Danebury.

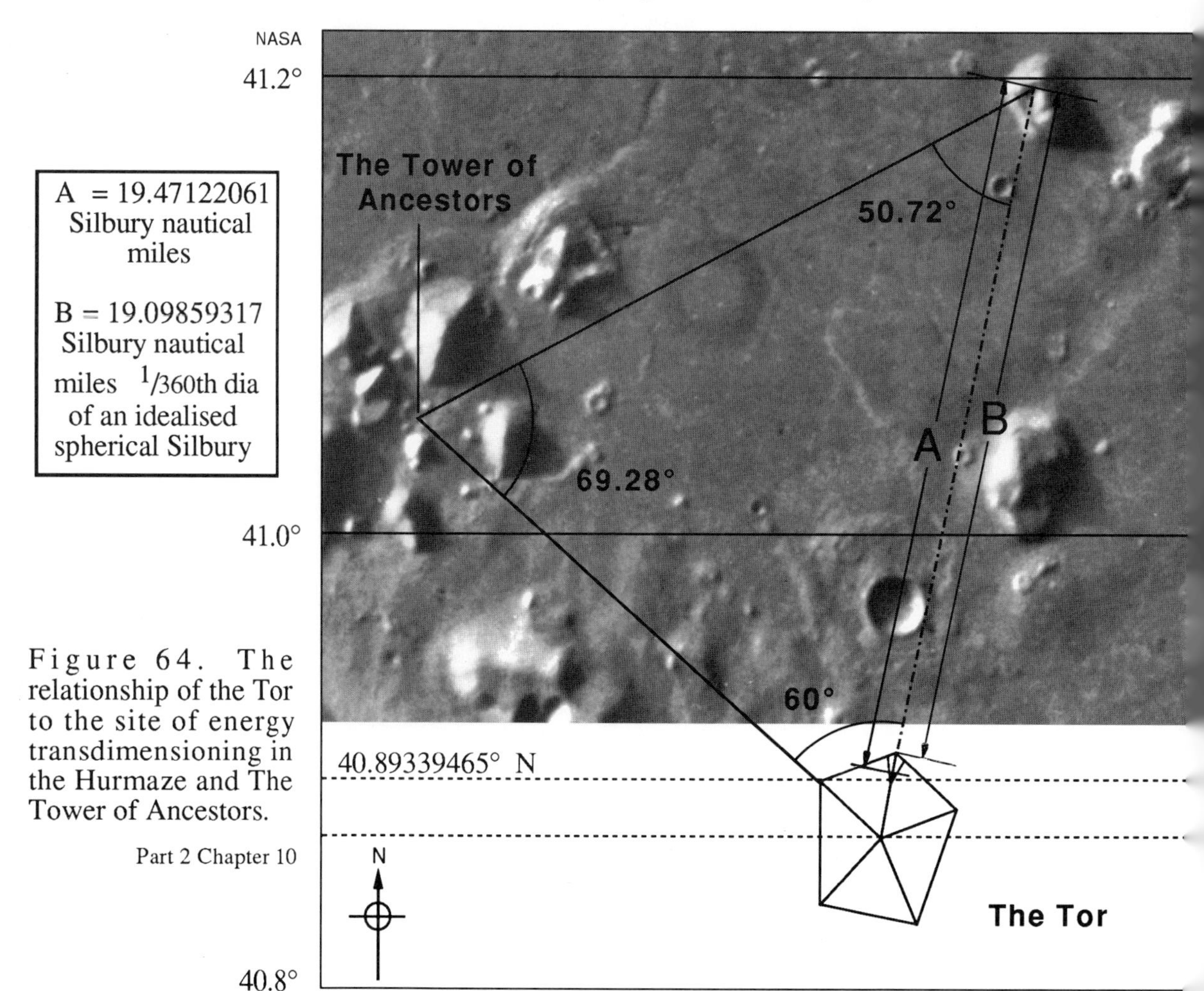

Figure 64. The relationship of the Tor to the site of energy transdimensioning in the Hurmaze and The Tower of Ancestors.

Part 2 Chapter 10

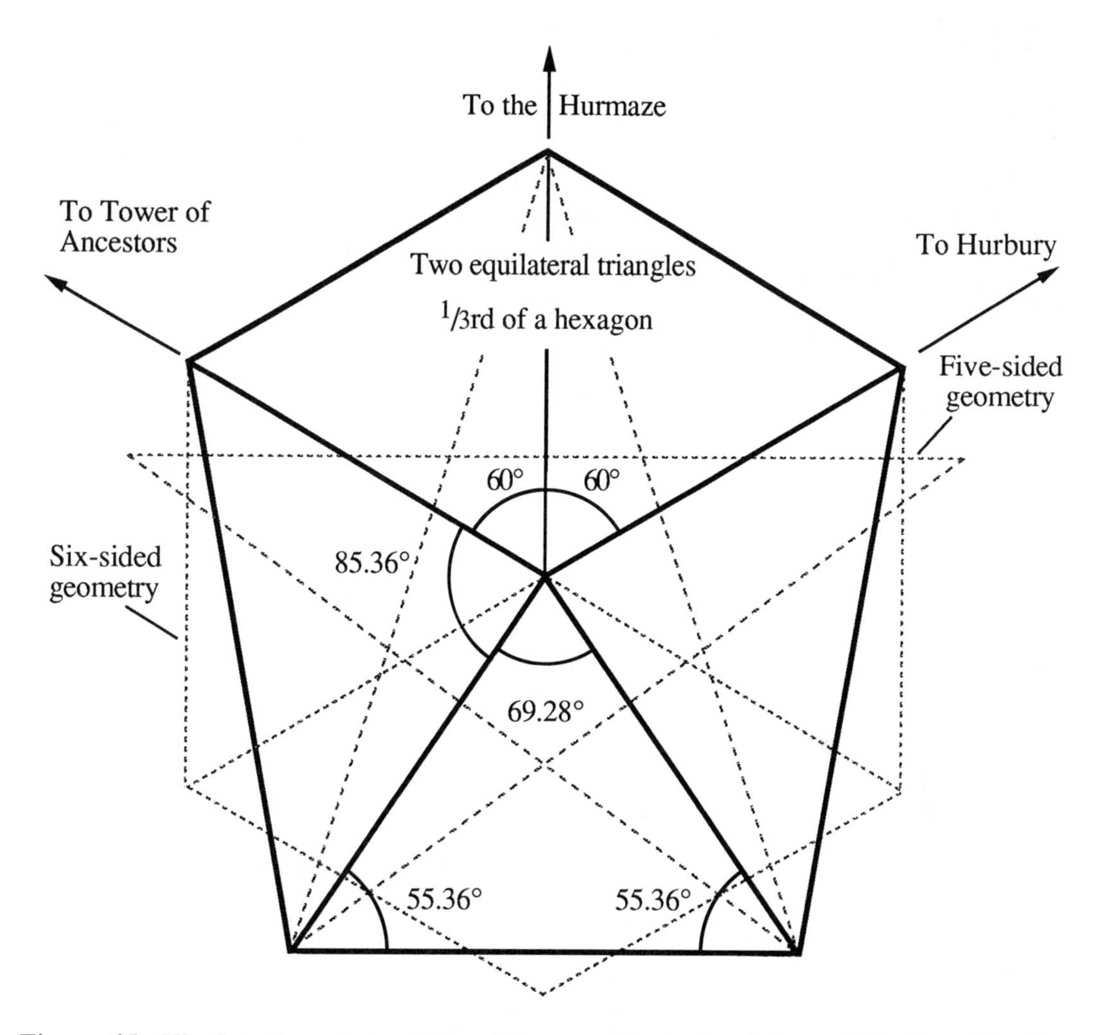

Figure 65. The interior relationships of the two-dimensional form of the Tor. The five sides of the Tor metaphorically represent the living parts of the Universe.

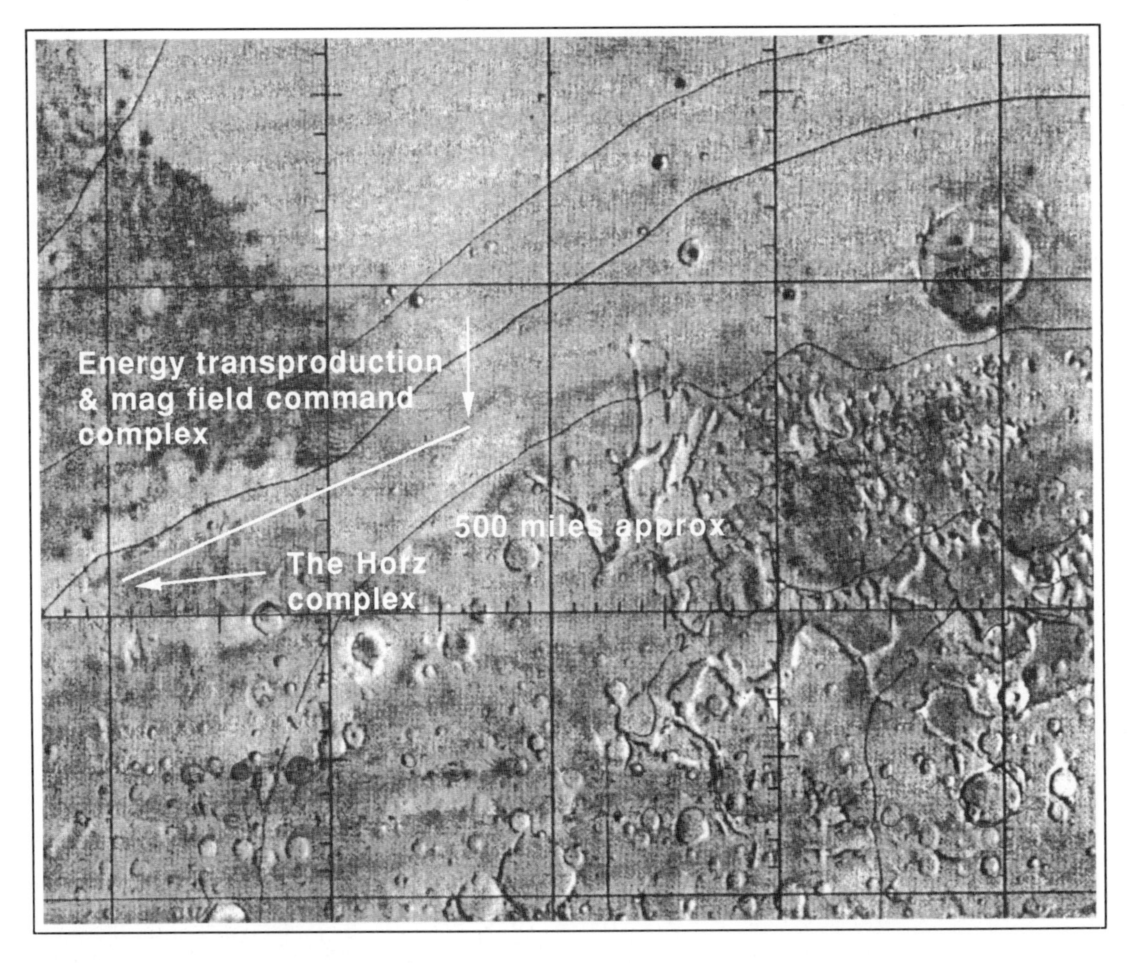

Figure 66. The combined energy transproduction and magnetic field command complex about 500 miles northeast of the Horz complex.

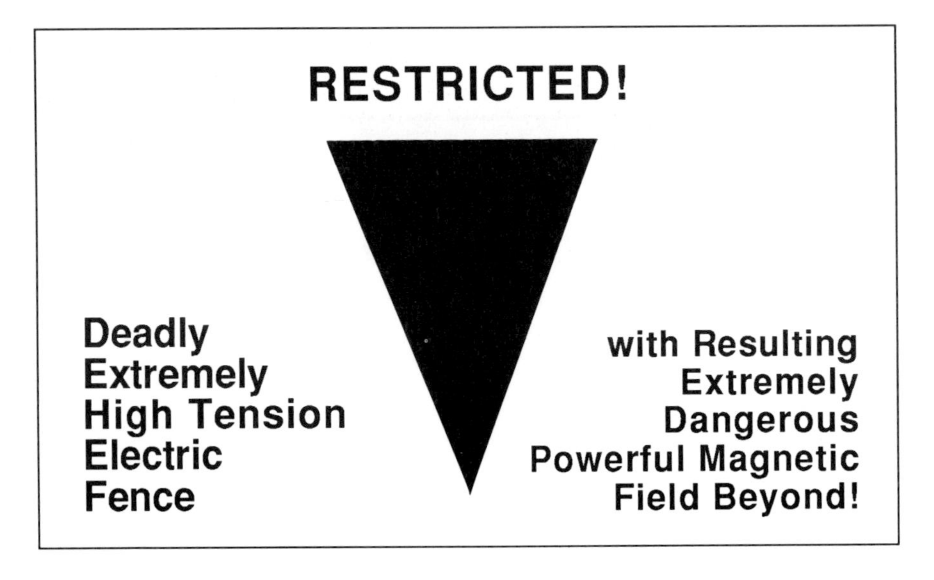

Figure 66.1. Warning signs on the fences encircling the Crystal Crater.

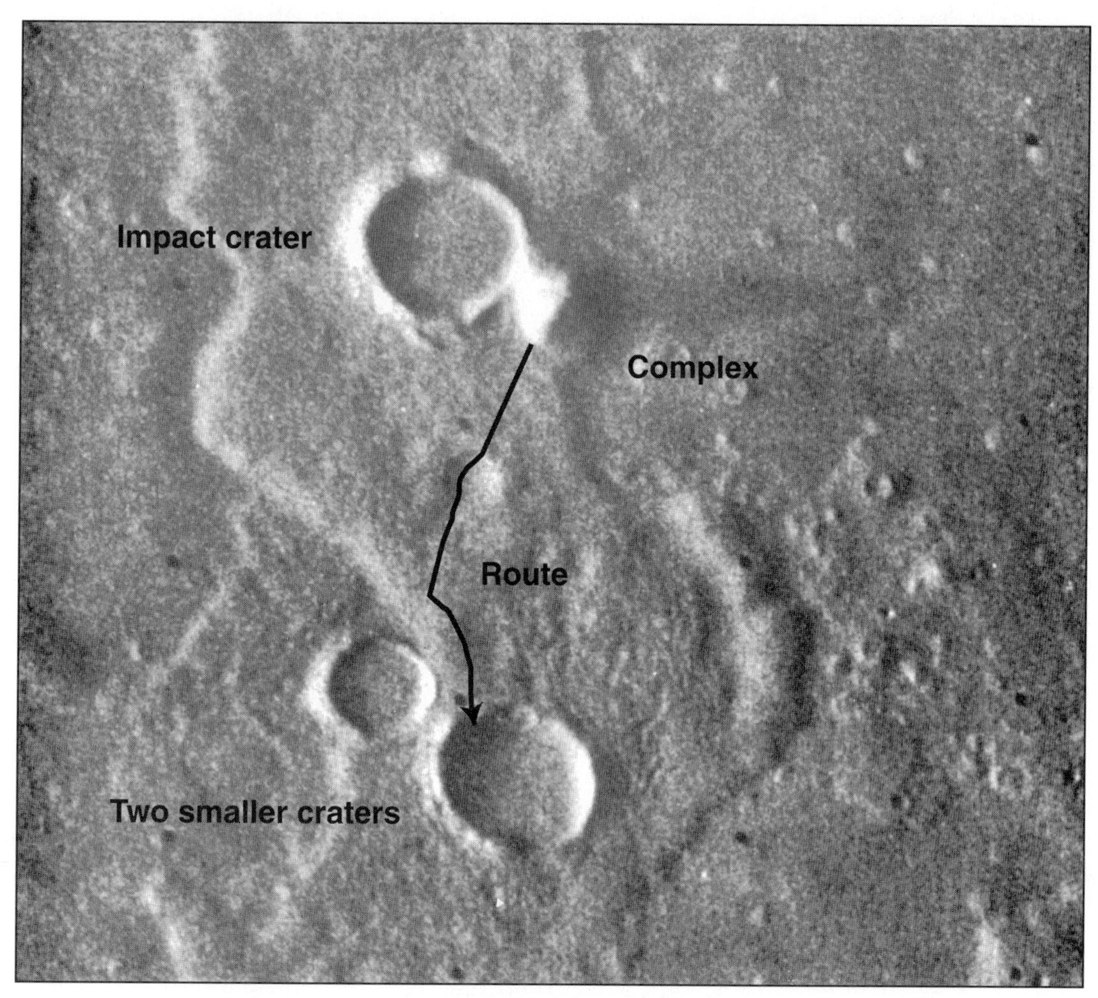

NASA

Figure 66.2 The Altean Naval Service complex housed in an enormous pyramidal structure on the rim of an ancient impact crater, and the route taken by Cary Manpure and Tommy Untiman.

Part 2 Chapter 10

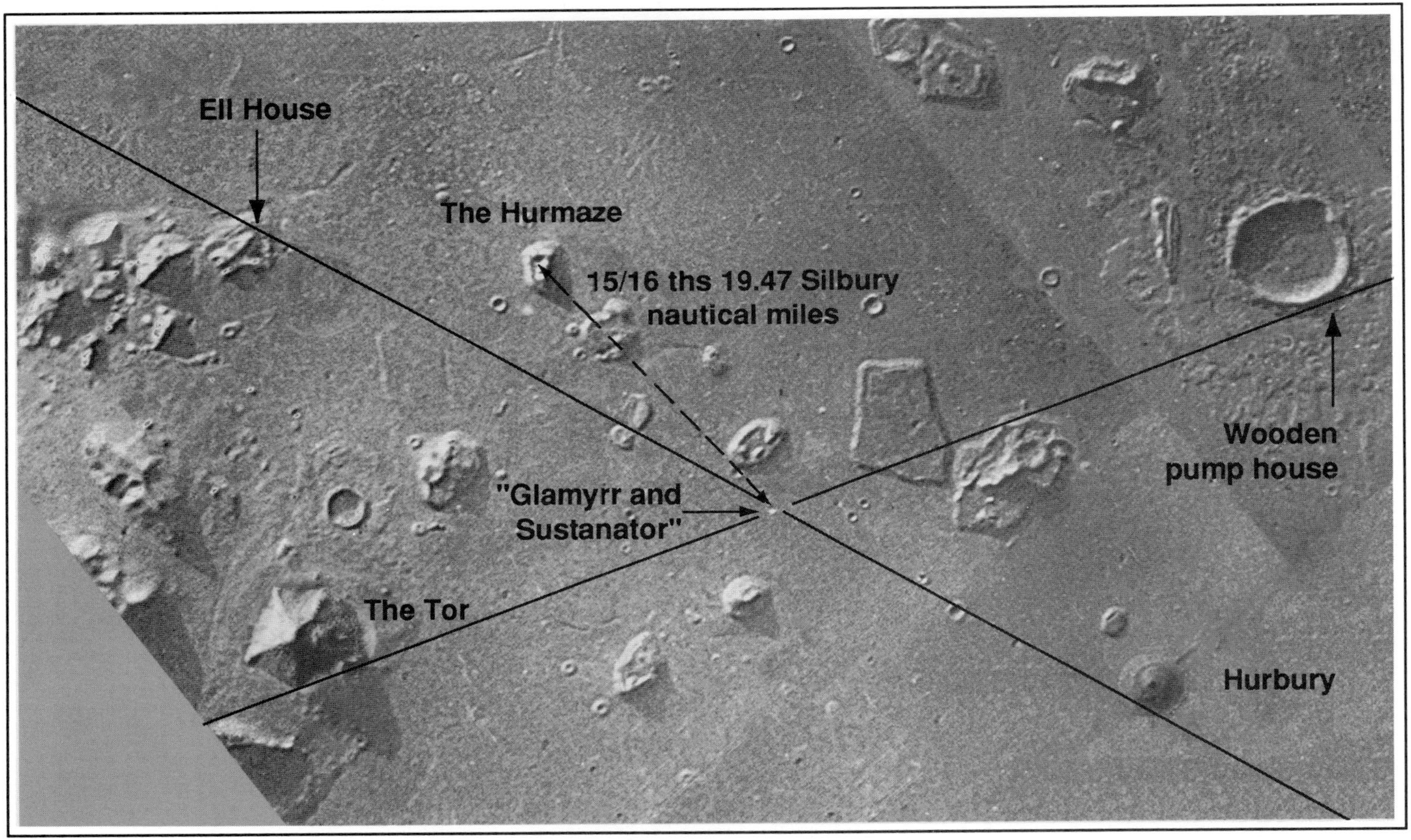

NASA

Figure 67. The position on the Horz complex of the sculpture "Glamyrr and Sustanator" at the intersection of two sight lines.

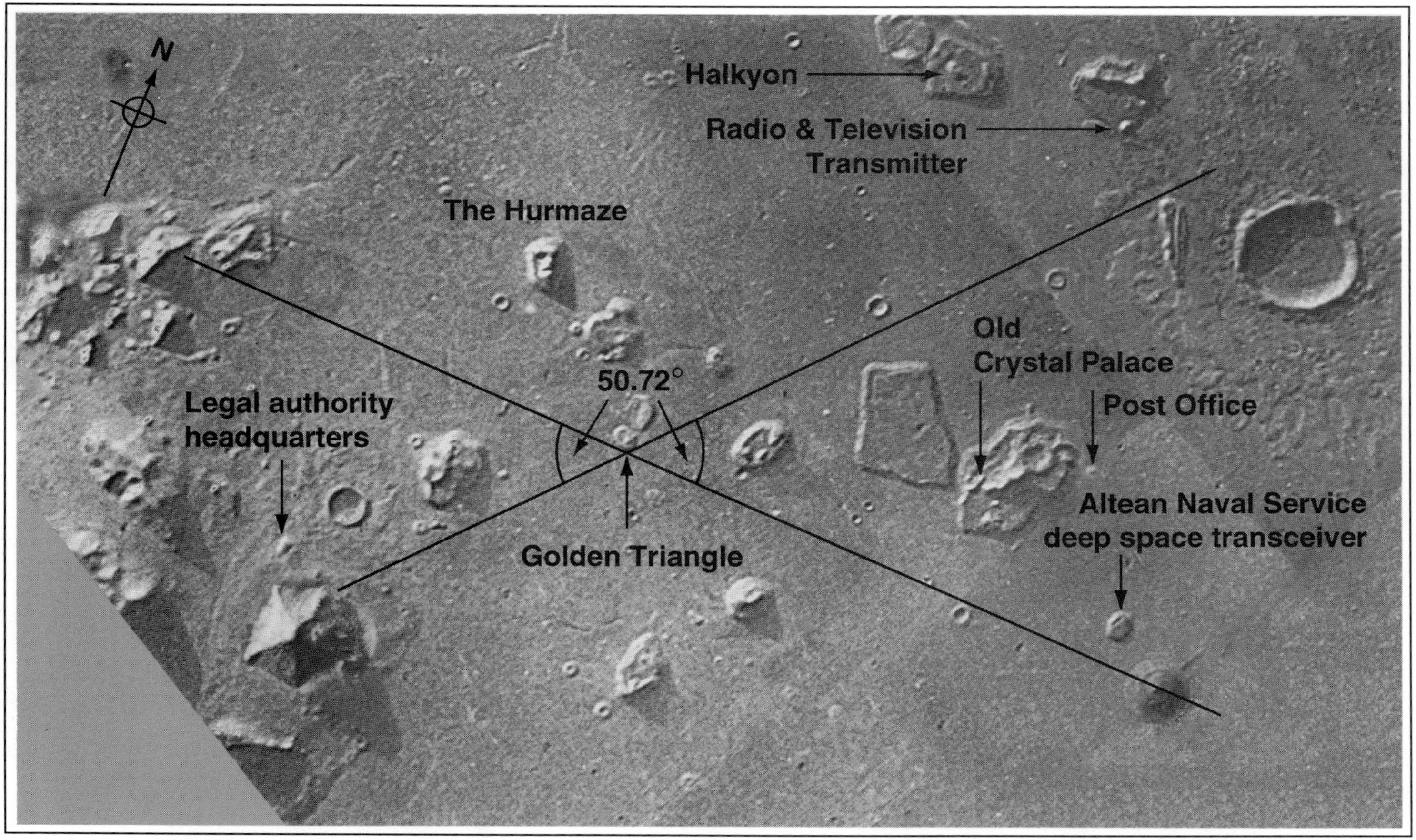

NASA

Figure 67.1. The Golden Triangle entertainment establishment at the crossing of sight lines which form two angles of 50.72 degrees each, one of the angles of golden triangles. See figure 64 for golden triangle formed between the Hurmaze, the Tor and the Tower of Ancestors.

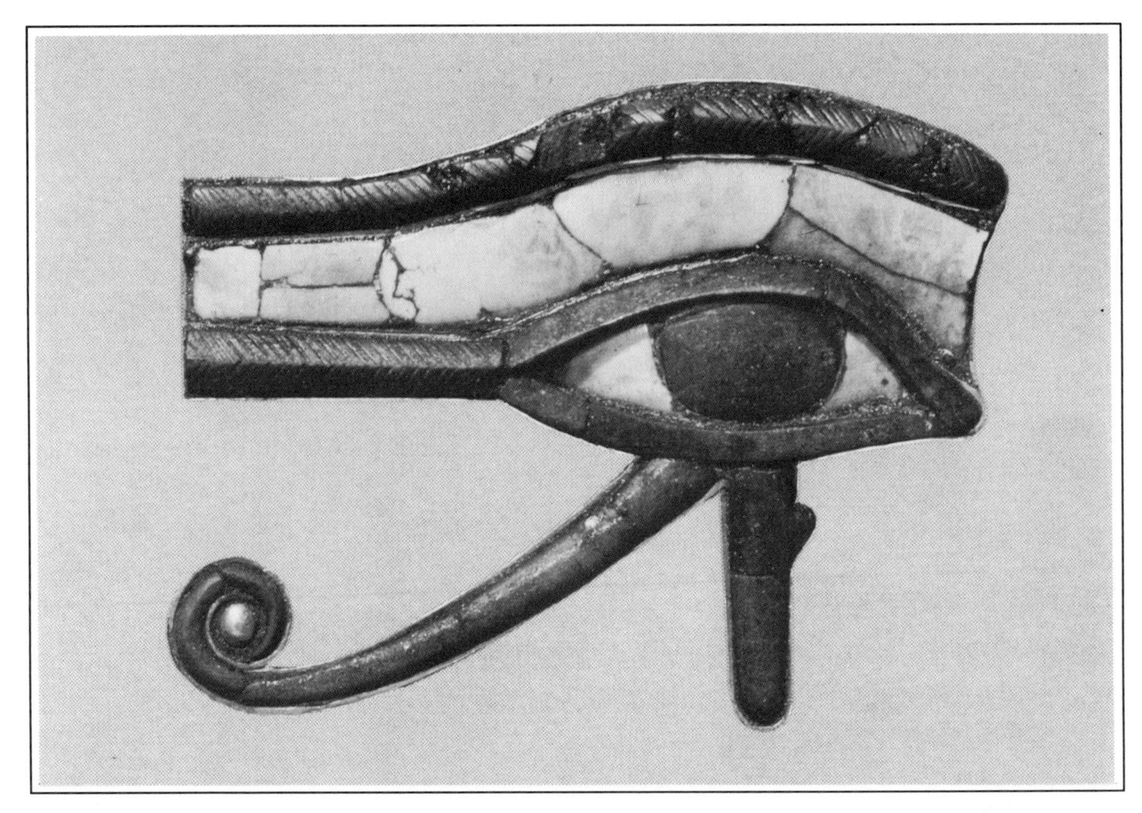

Figure 68. Since just after the time of Waldark, perioikomai have been given by special friends to wedding couples to wish them a long and loving life together. Perioikomai, meaning 'living around and about,' are multi-colored ceramic plaques with a multi-symbolic design (Egyptian copy). Part 2 Chapter 11

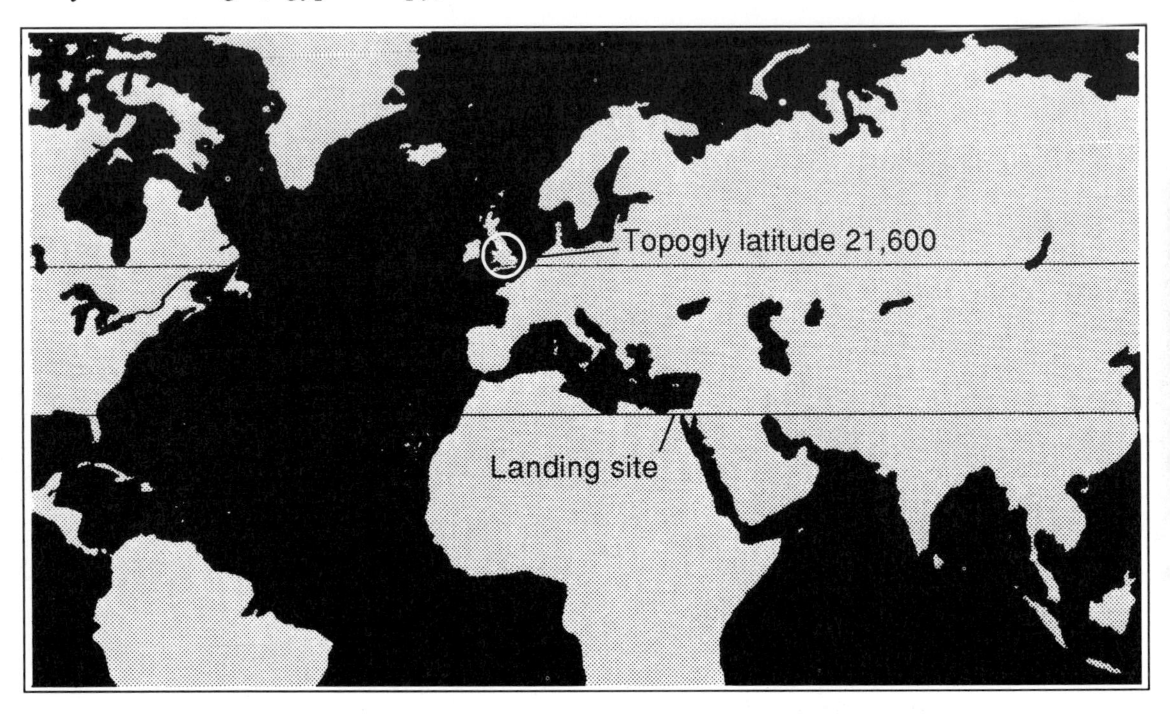

Figure 69. Site of the scale model of the spinning disk. Part 2 Chapter 13

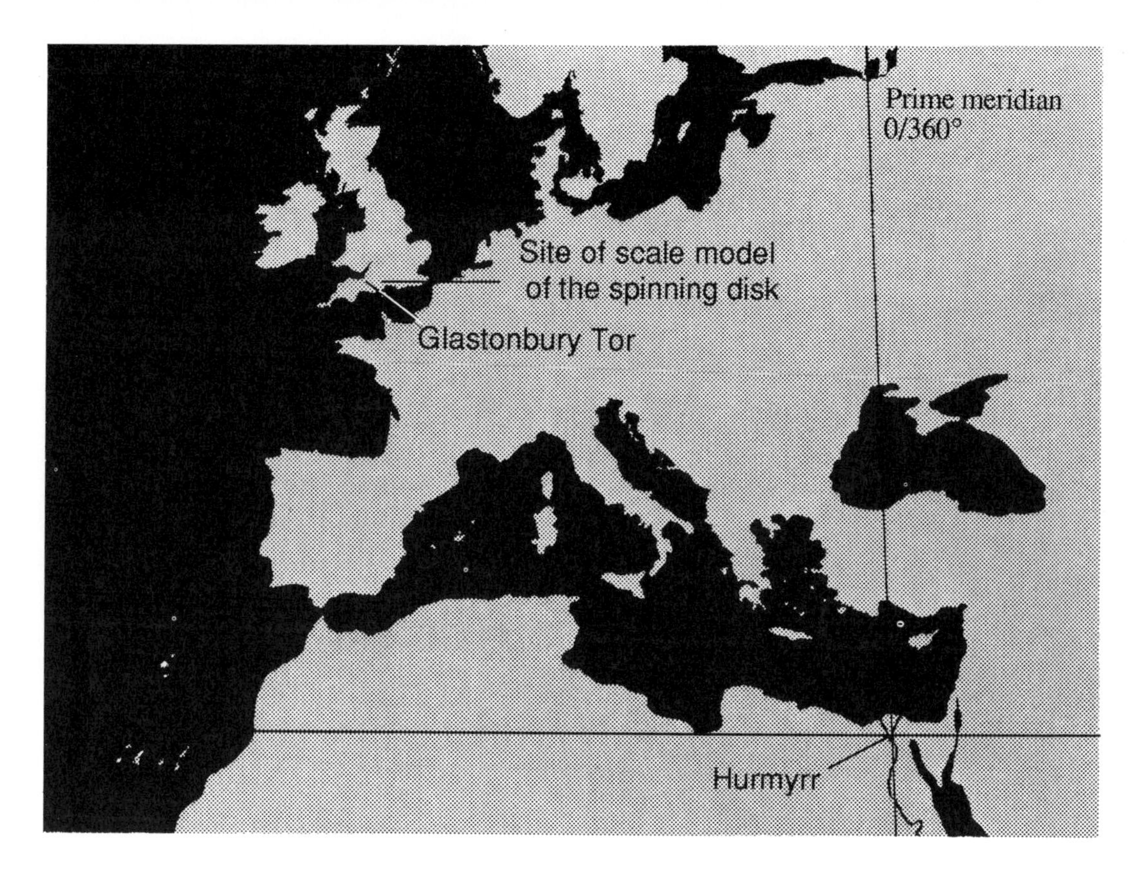

Figure 70. The location of Glastonbury Tor the sourcemark for Danebury, the site of the scale model of the spinning disk and the prime meridian Hurmyrr.

Part 2 Chapter 13

Figure 70.1. Marys Peak, Benton County, Oregon, called Chintimini by those who first came to Prehurland. Together with Glastonbury Tor (Fig. 70.2) and the shape of the Tetrahedron analog on Avenabury Circle (Fig. 170), they came to be as a result of Essenes wanting to encode on Earth the shape of Mount Hurartu on Altea.

Part 2 Chapter 13

70.2. Glastonbury Tor — upper photograph and Hurmyrr as they are today. Facing stones have long since been removed from Hurmyrr so there is no longer any shining reflection.

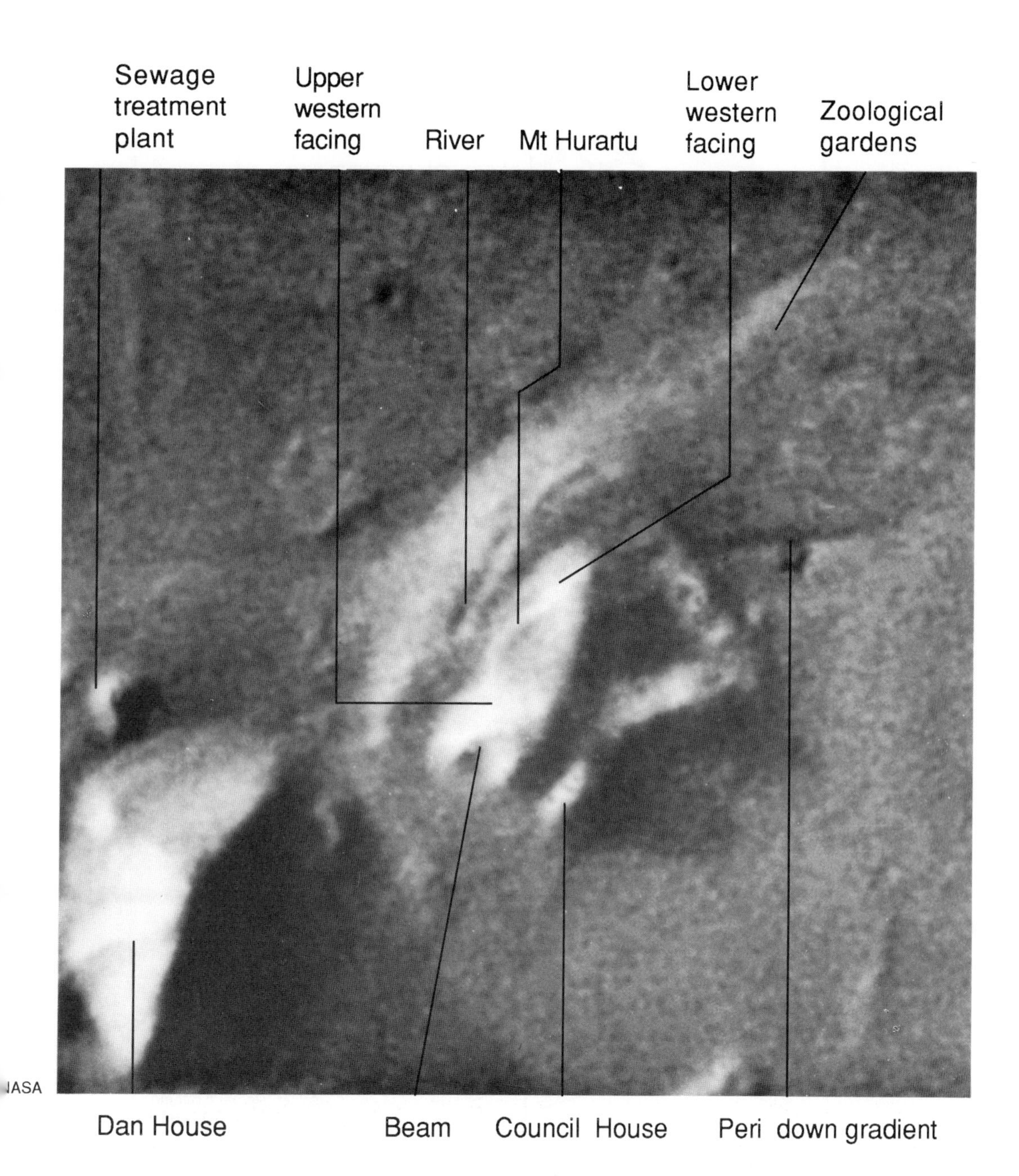

Figure 70.3. Ruins of Ell House and surroundings.

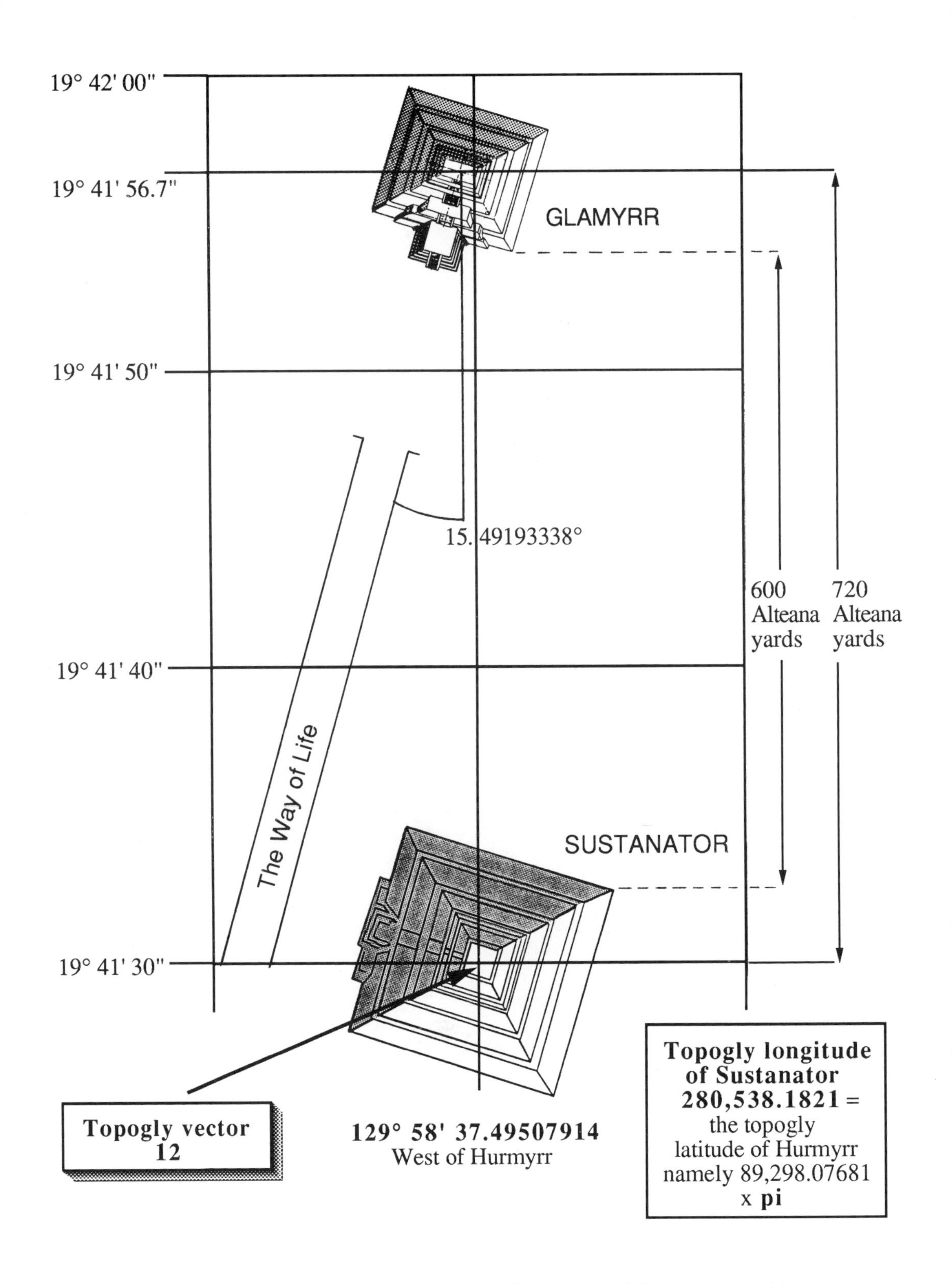

Figure 71. The location of the pyramids Glamyyr and Sustanator at Alteana.

Part 3 Chapter 1

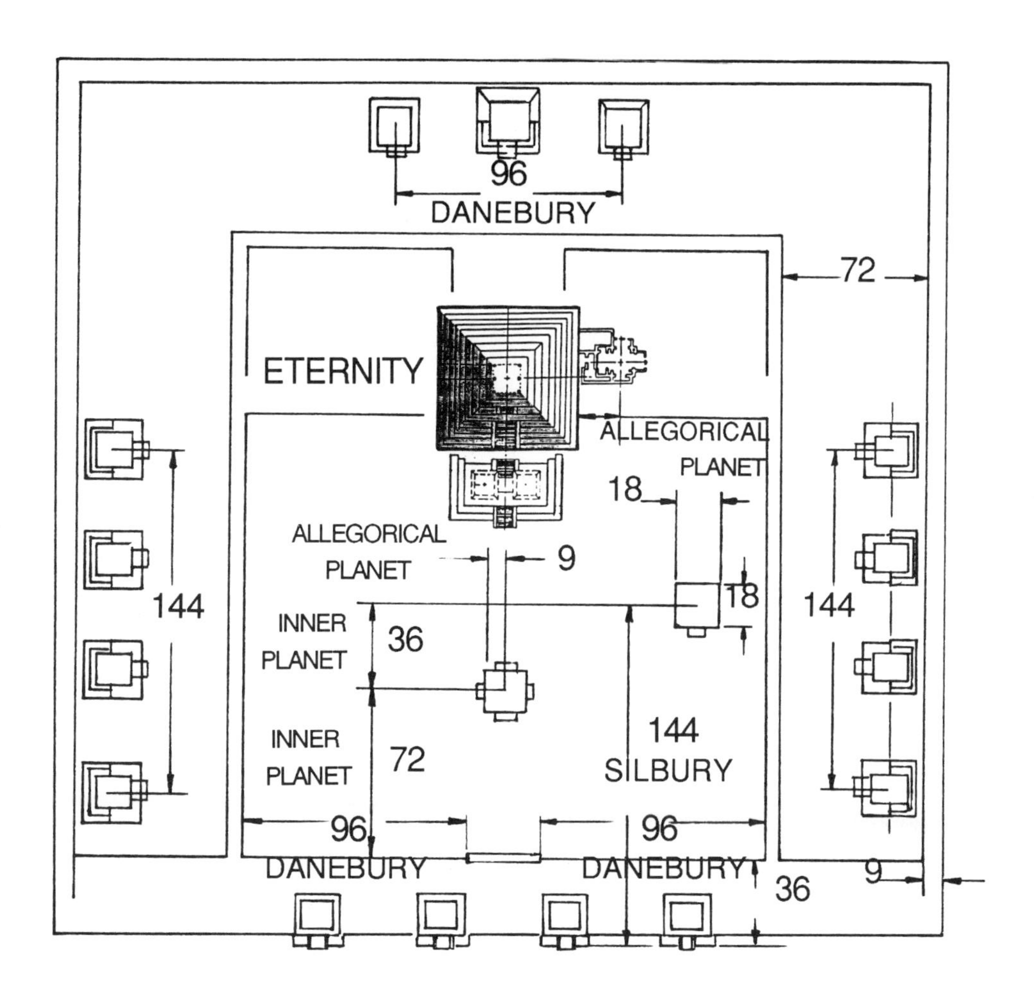

Figure 72. The lay out of the inner rocky planets inside the confines of the structure called Eternity, incorporating the two inner *allegorical* planets. All measurements in Alteana yards. The encoded distance between Danebury and its sun was fixed at 96 Alteana yards representing 24/25ths, the Harmonic of the Universe.

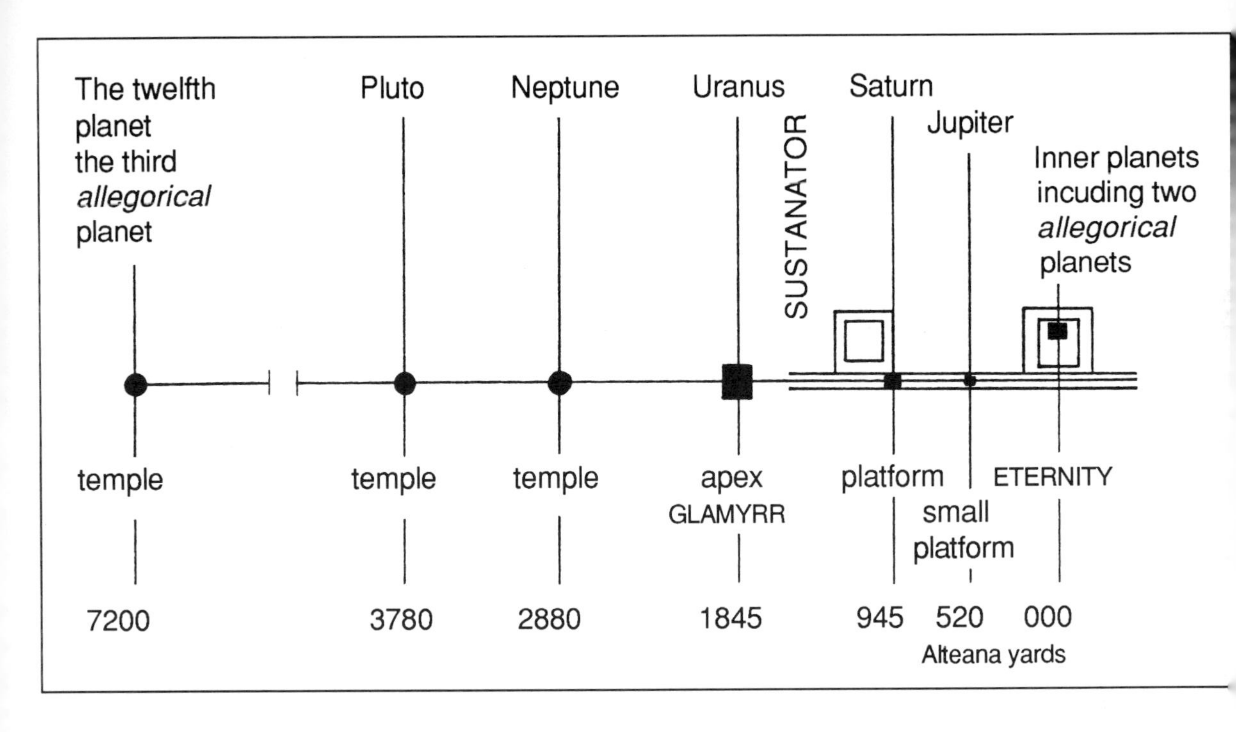

Figure 73. Encoded solar system at Alteana comprising the sun, the moon, and nine planets, plus the three *allegorical* planets.

Part 3 Chapter 2

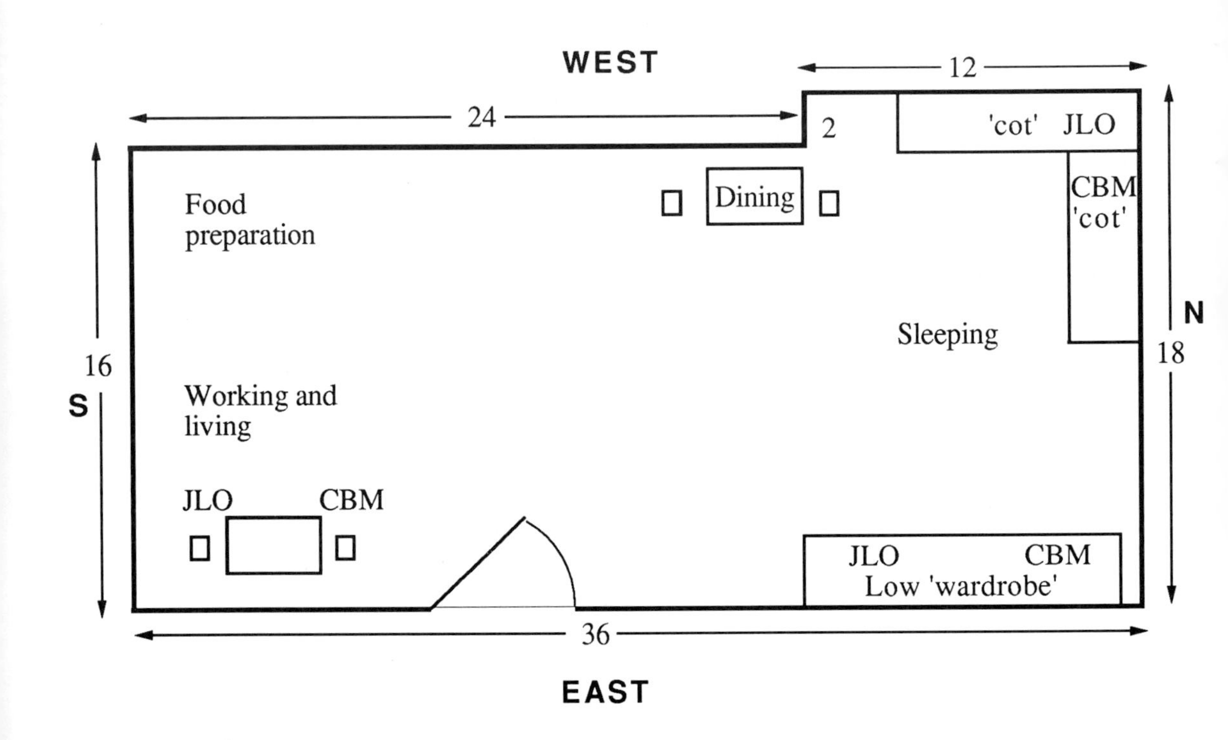

Figure 74. Floor plan of the Pavilion measured in Director Odkin feet.

Part 3 Chapter 4

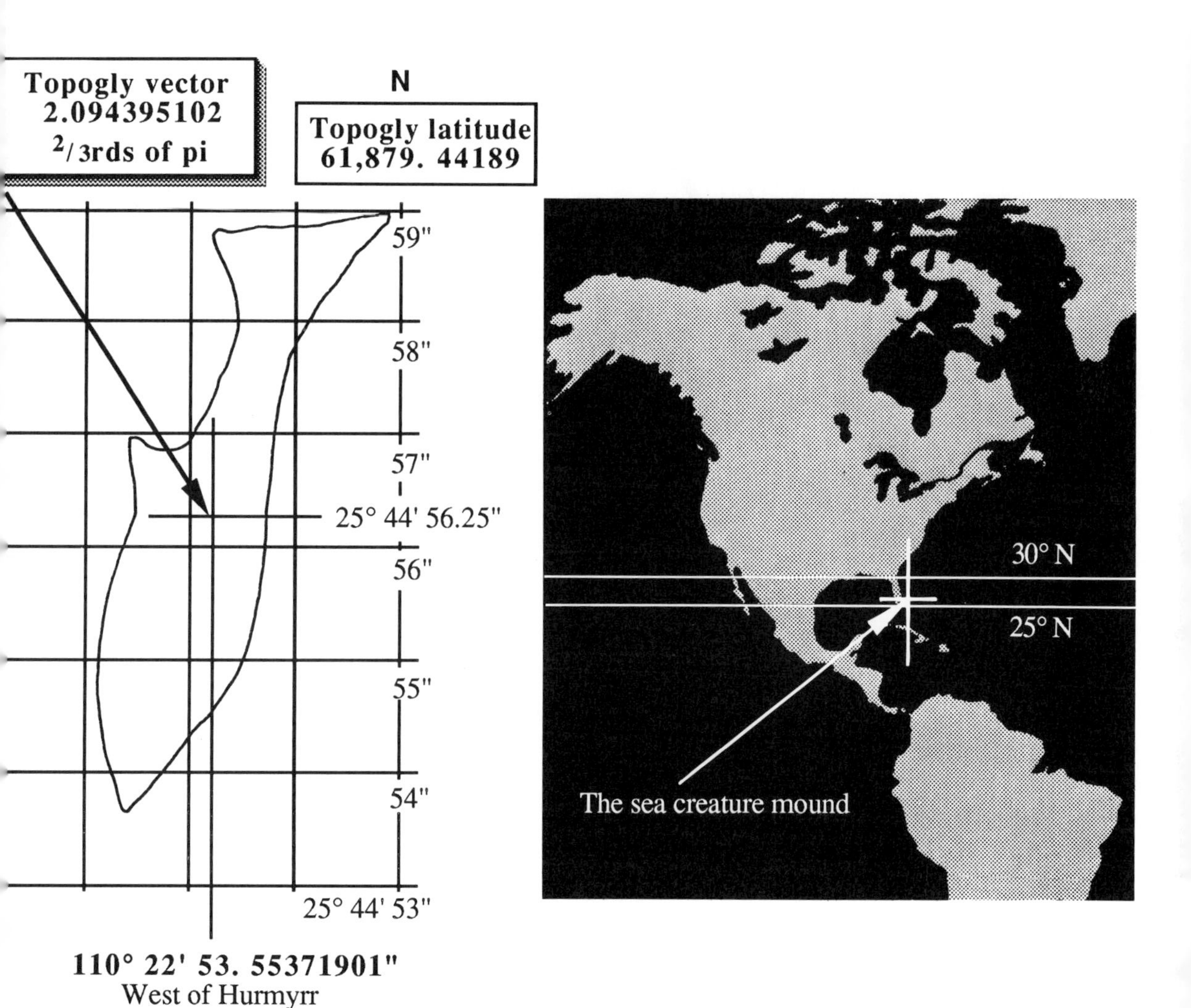

Figure 75. The location of the sea creature mound (North Bimini Island). Its topogly longitude is 129,600 the square of the topogly longitude of Hurmyrr.

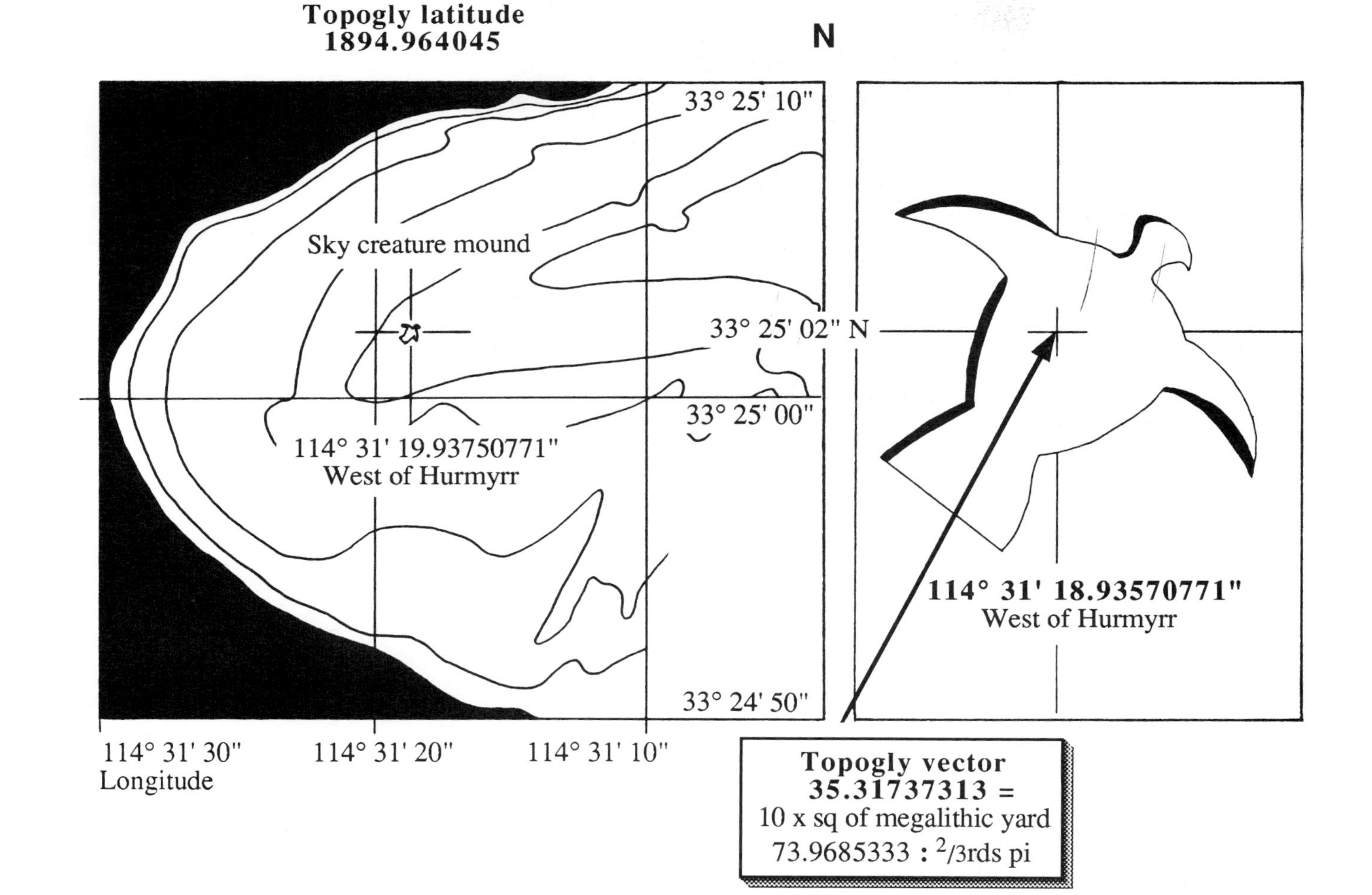

Figure 76. The sky creature mound in Prehurland (Rock Eagle Monument, Georgia), its topogly longitude of 66,925.15224 is equivalent to 4 times 1/10th of 21,600, the topogly latitude of the site of the scale model of the spinning disk, times the square root of 60.

Figure 77. Devil's Tower, Wyoming. Cary Jackman reduced the height of this rock pinnacle to 866 feet because Essenes wanted him to learn how to use an energy cannon before he had to blow the nose off the Ark Hur, and because Essenes wanted to encode the square root of three divided by two. Essenes later diddled with the movie "Close Encounters of the Third Kind" and Devil's Tower became the centerpiece of government lies. Devil's Tower is also closely associated with the continuation of the Lion Line across North America by way of Gulf Breeze, Florida.

Part 3 Chapter 6

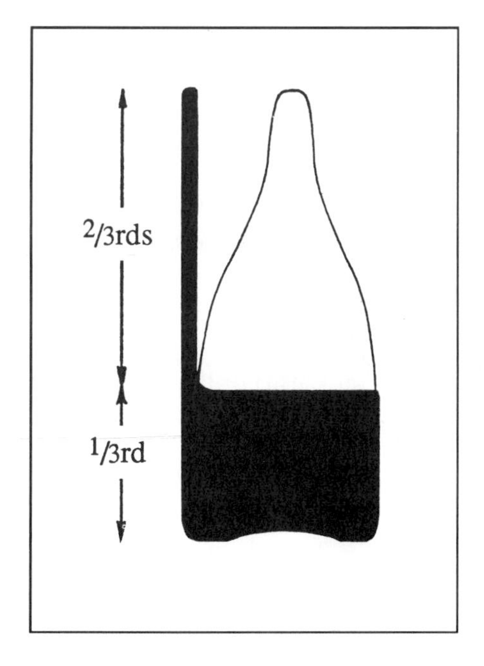

Figure 78. The Waldark hat and amplifier designed to capture the energy that causes the additional secondary energy disturbance pattern.

Part 3 Chapter 7

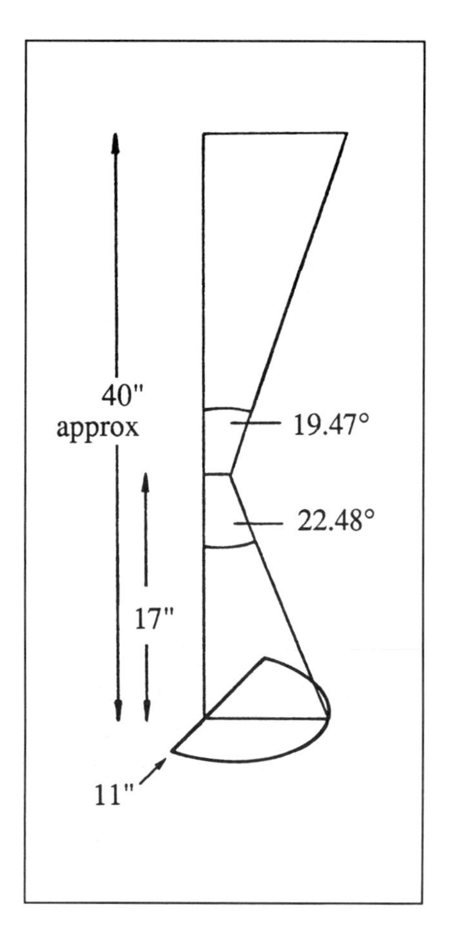

Figure 79. Dual perspective of the additional secondary energy disturbance pattern of the soul. Side view combined with perspective top view cross-section shows that the disturbance pattern is shaped like the letter D.

Part 2 Chapter 7

Figure 79.1. The combined crown of Egypt is a local (non-functional variant on Earth) of the Waldark hat and amplifier with modifications induced by Essenes, including the curling signature of Joe Lon Odkin. In this illustration Horus the Hawk meditates.

Part 2 Chapter 7

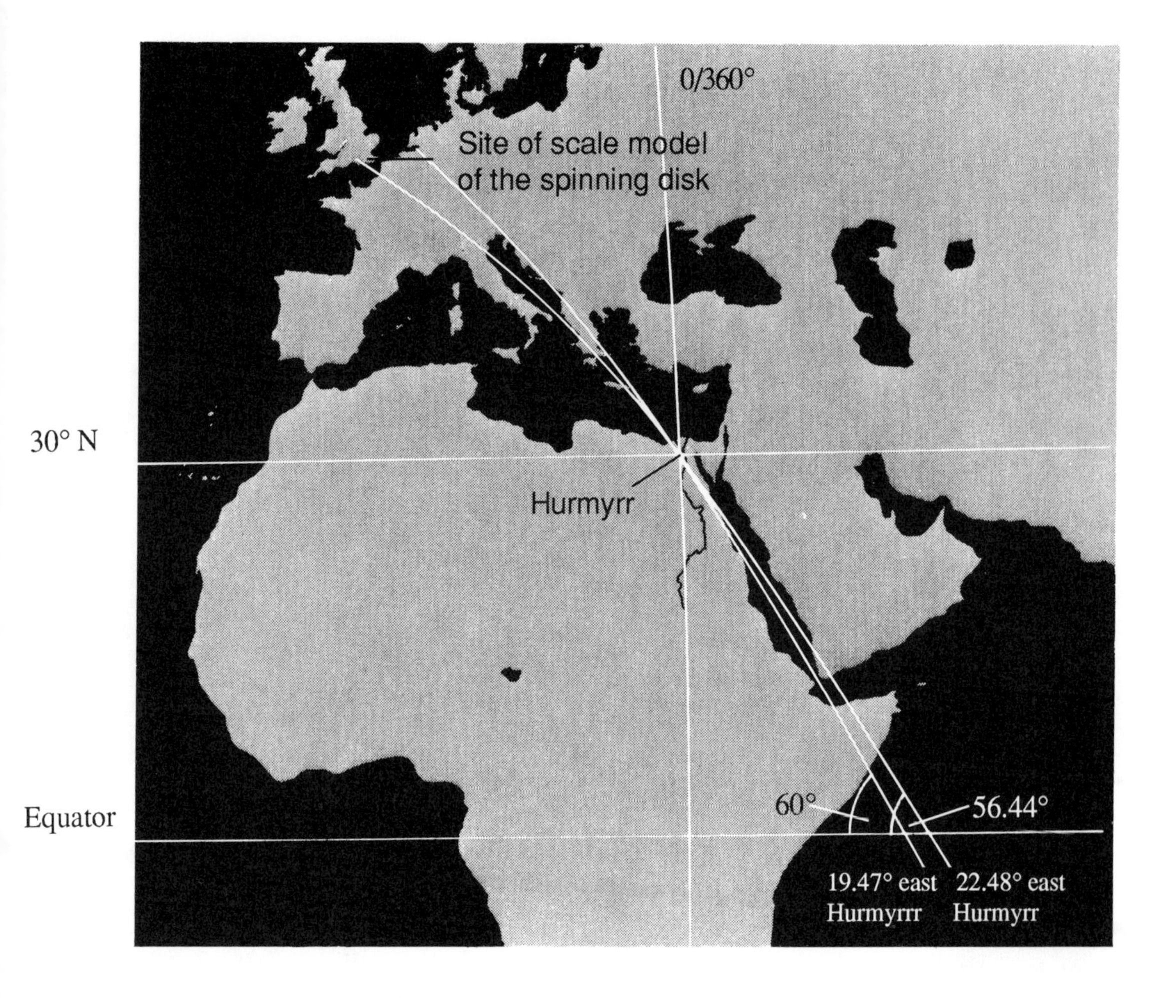

Figure 80. The two great circles passing through Hurmyrr and crossing the equator east of Hurmyrr at 22.48° & 19.47° respectively. As they cross the equator, the first great circle has a slope of 56.44° north of due west and the second has a slope of 60° north of due west.

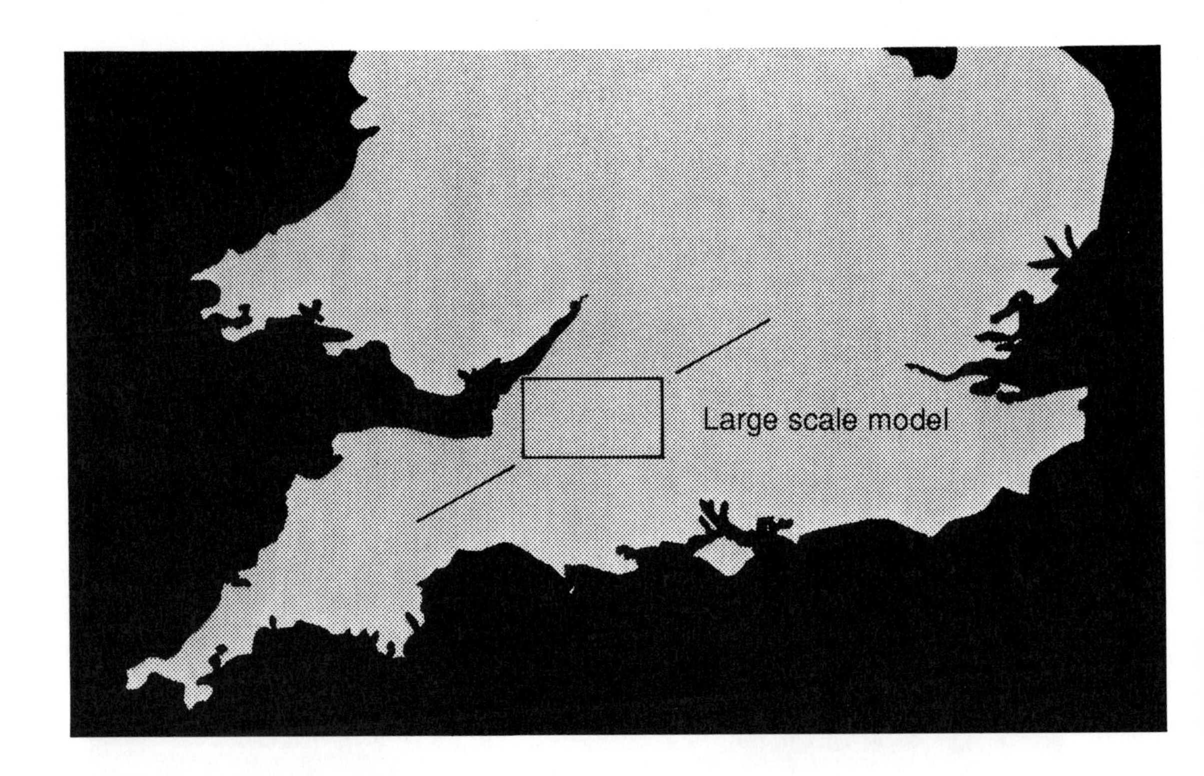

Figure 81. The location in southern Hurengland of the major components of the large scale model of the Horz complex, about one and one half times larger than the Horz complex on Silbury.

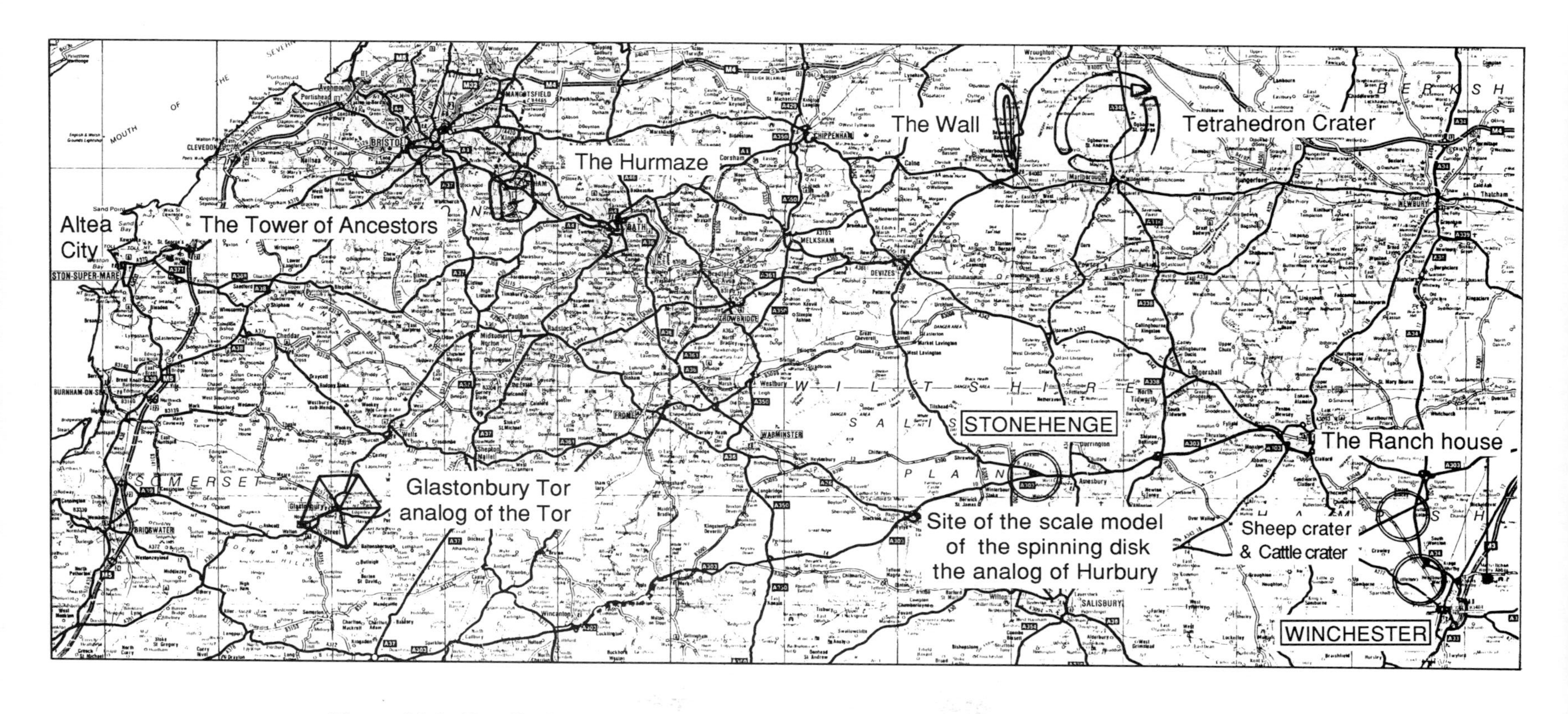

Figure 81.1. Detail of the large scale model of the Horz complex laid out on a modern map.

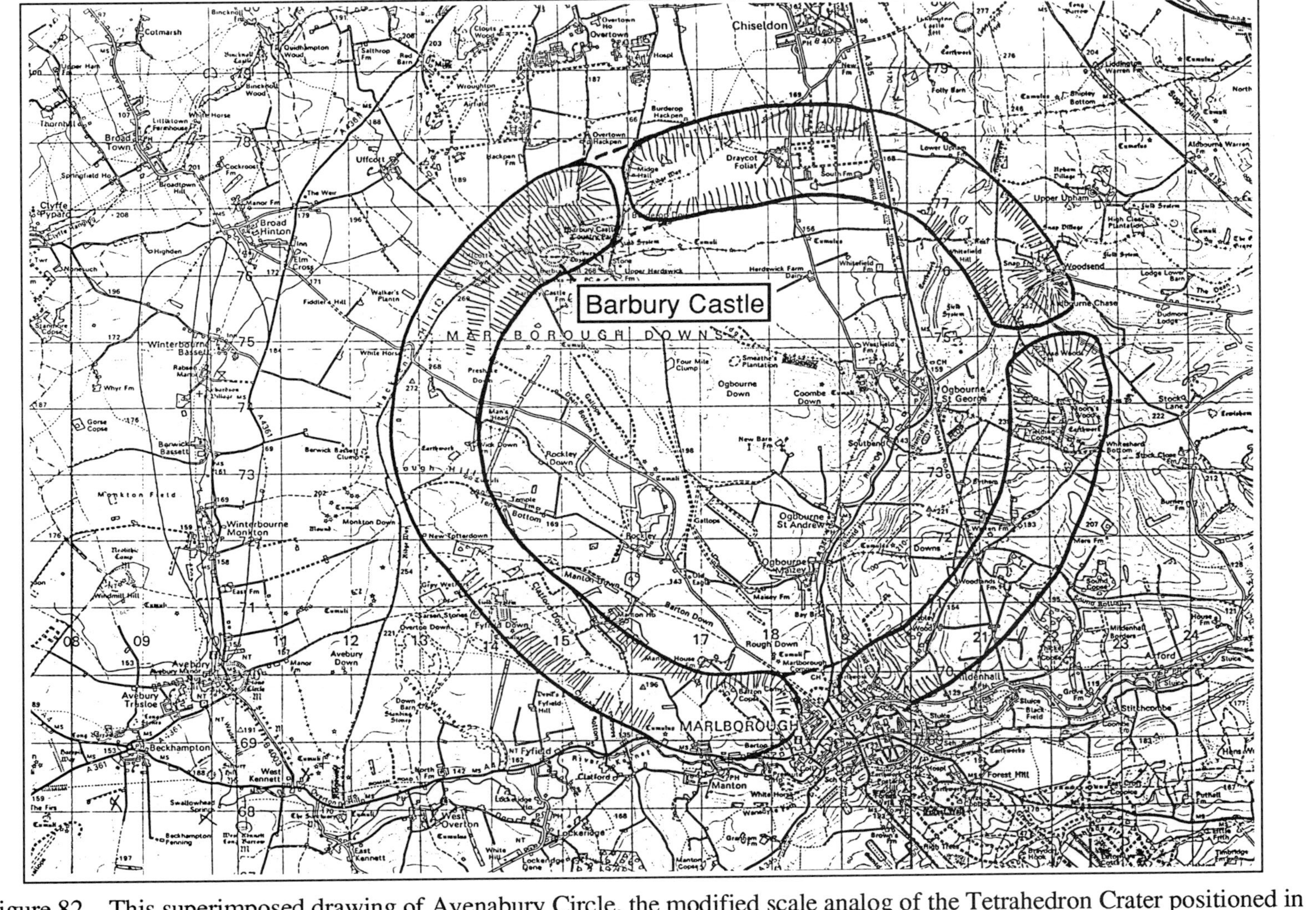

Figure 82. This superimposed drawing of Avenabury Circle, the modified scale analog of the Tetrahedron Crater positioned in proportion with the large scale model of the Horz complex, is inferred by Marlborough Downs. Near Barbury Castle earthworks was the protosite for the transtime crop glyph depicting the major components of energy converters on the northwestern rim of the modified analog of the Tetrahedron Crater in the large scale model.

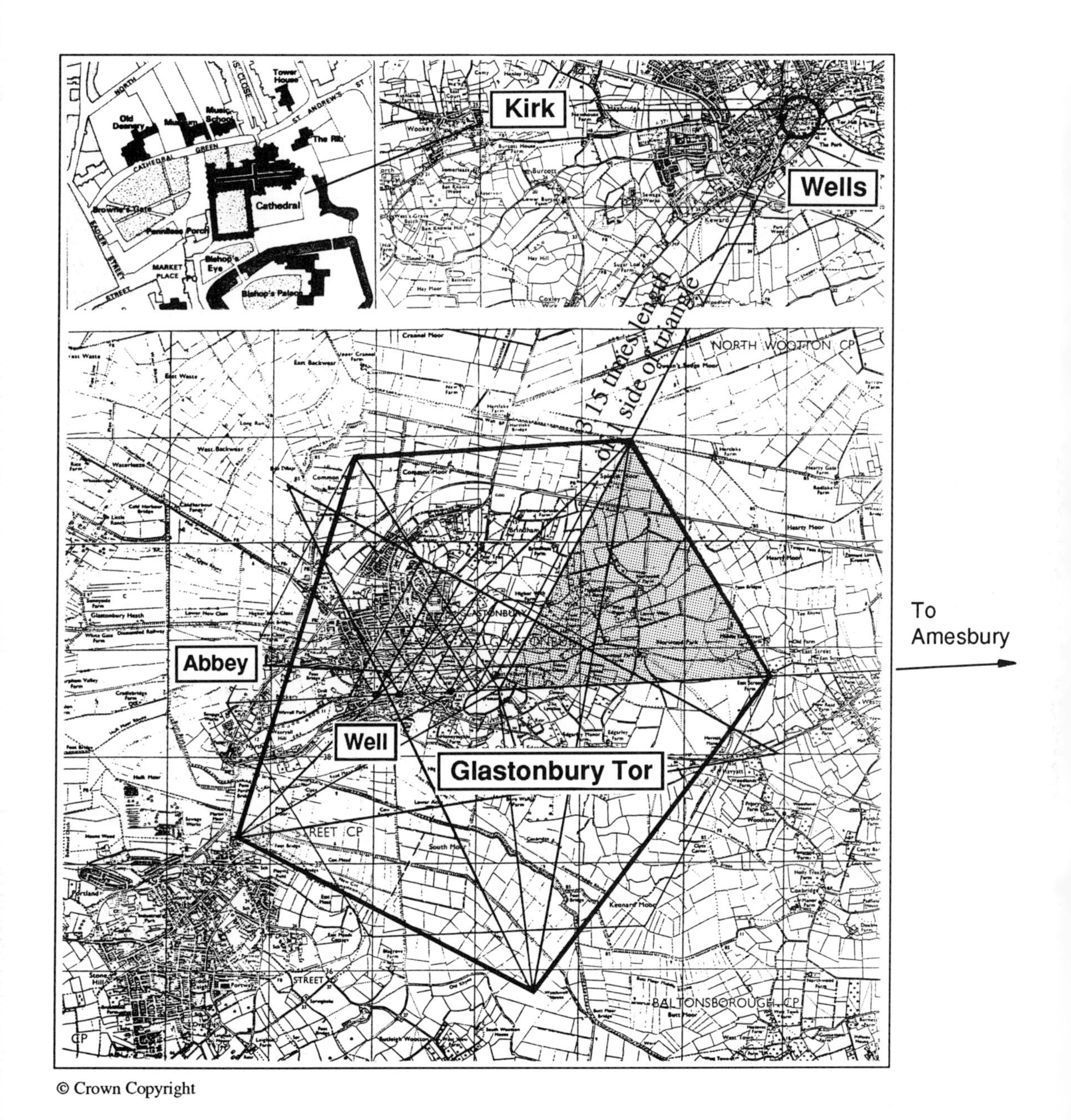

Figure 83. Superimposed drawing of the scale analog of the Tor with its apex on the stone sourcemark on Glastonbury Tor, illustrated on a modern map. The distance between Glastonbury Tor and Wells has been foreshortened for convenience.

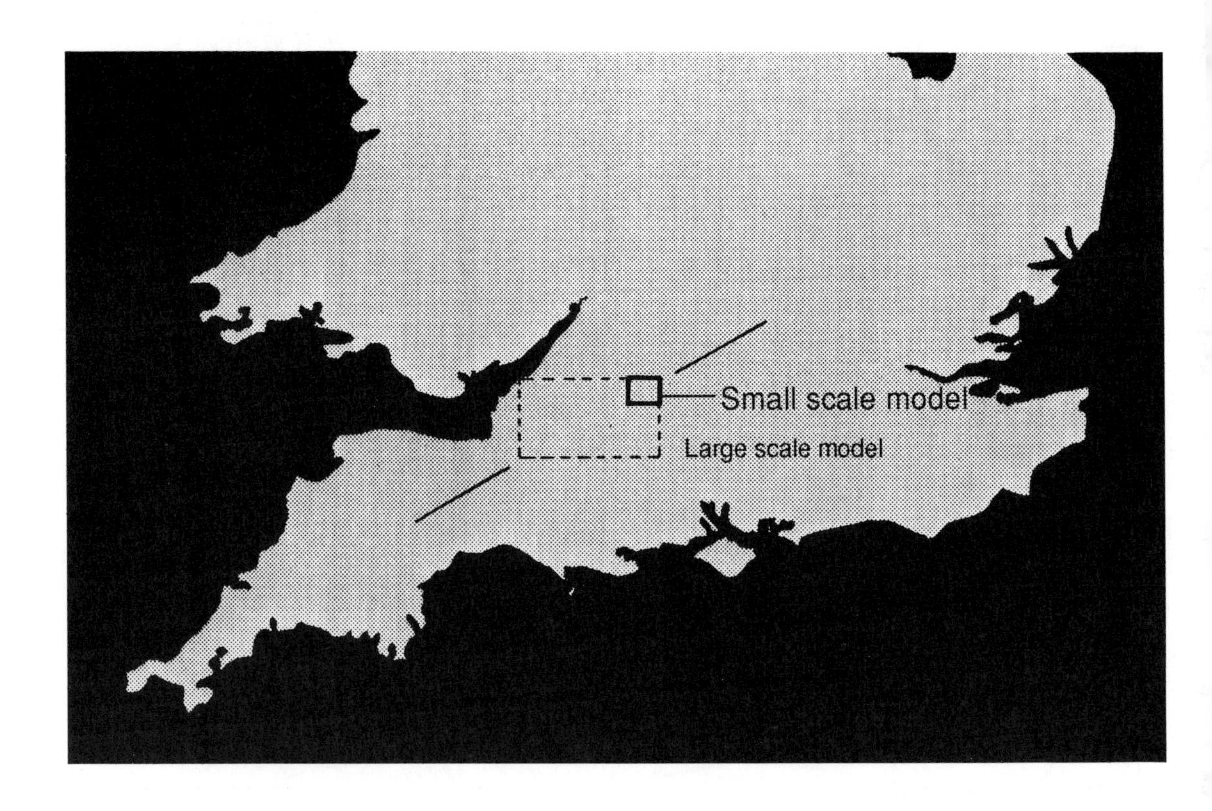

Figure 84. The location in southern Hurengland of the small scale model of the Horz complex.

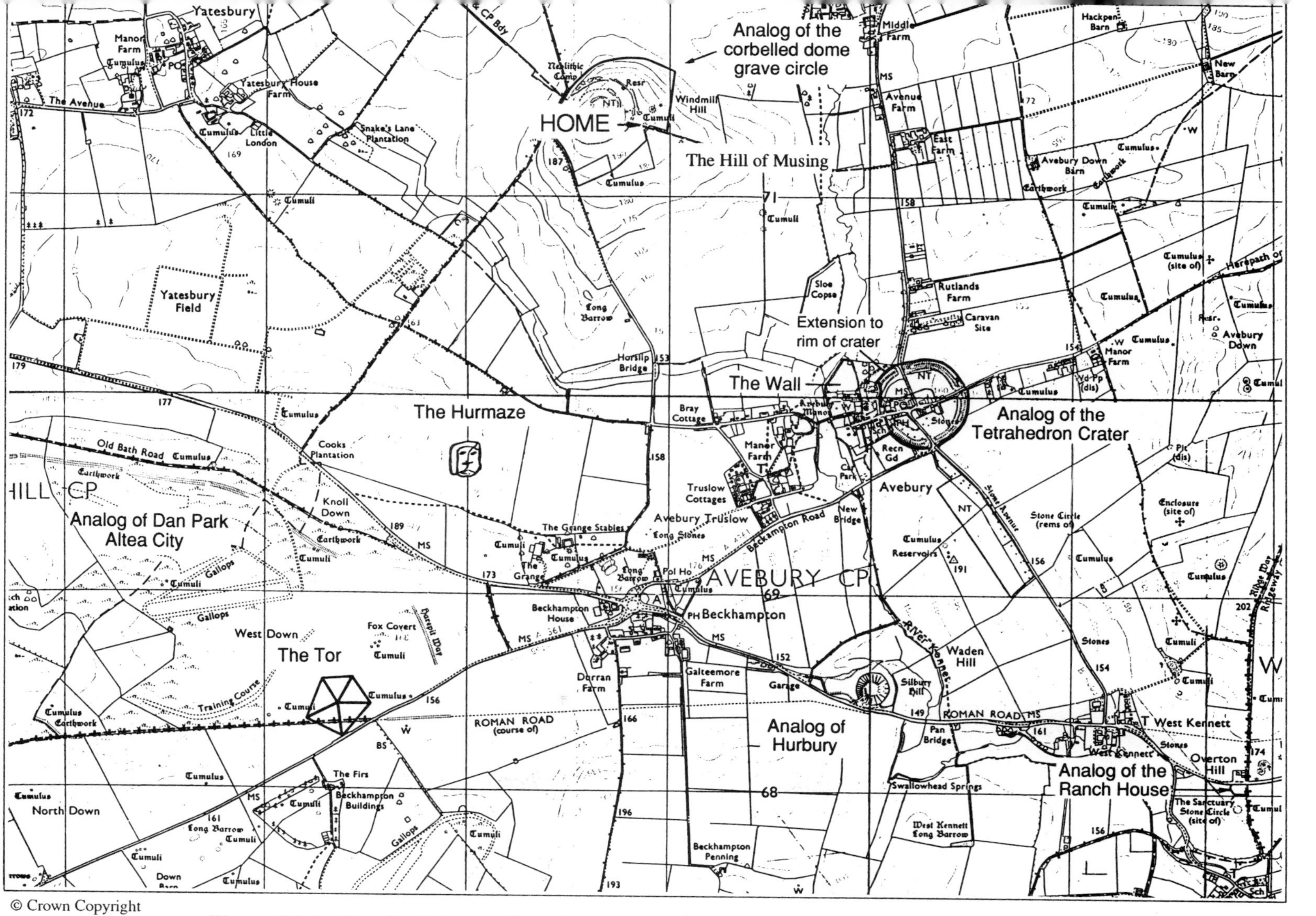

© Crown Copyright

Figure 84.1. Detail of the small scale model of the Horz complex illustrated on a modern map.

NASA

Figure 84.2 The small (7%) scale model of the Horz complex enlarged to full size and overlaid onto a photograph of the Horz complex on Silbury.

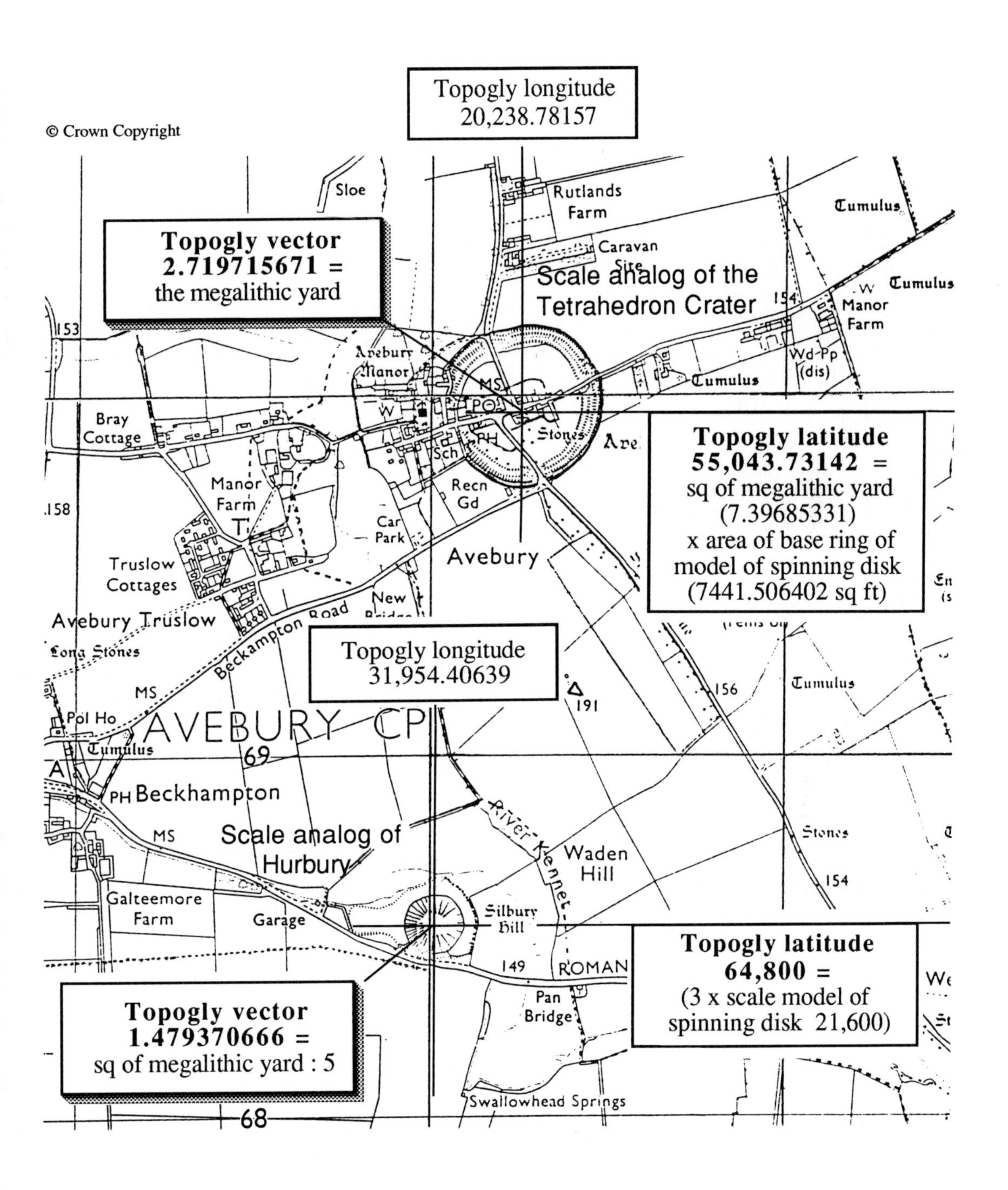

Figure 85. Close up of scale analogs of Hurbury and the Tetrahedron Crater.
A topogly vector is the result of dividing the larger topogly number by the smaller. For example, the topogly latitude of the scale Tetrahedron Crater 55,043.73140 divided by its topogly longitude 20,238.78157 equals 2.719715671.

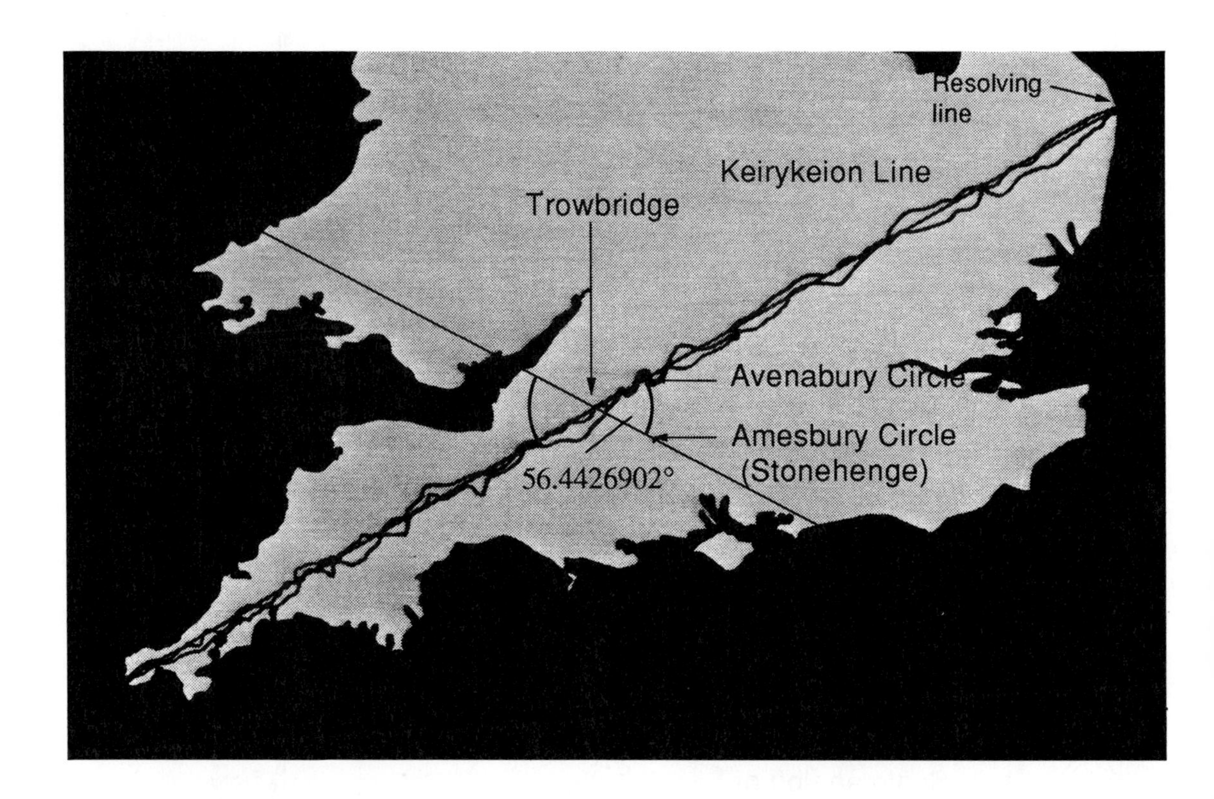

Figure 86. The crossing of the two great circles, the Keirykeion Line and the Lion Line northwest of Amesbury Circle (Stonehenge). The angle 56.4426902° has a sine of 5/6ths, a fraction which metaphorically represents the ratio 5 to 6.

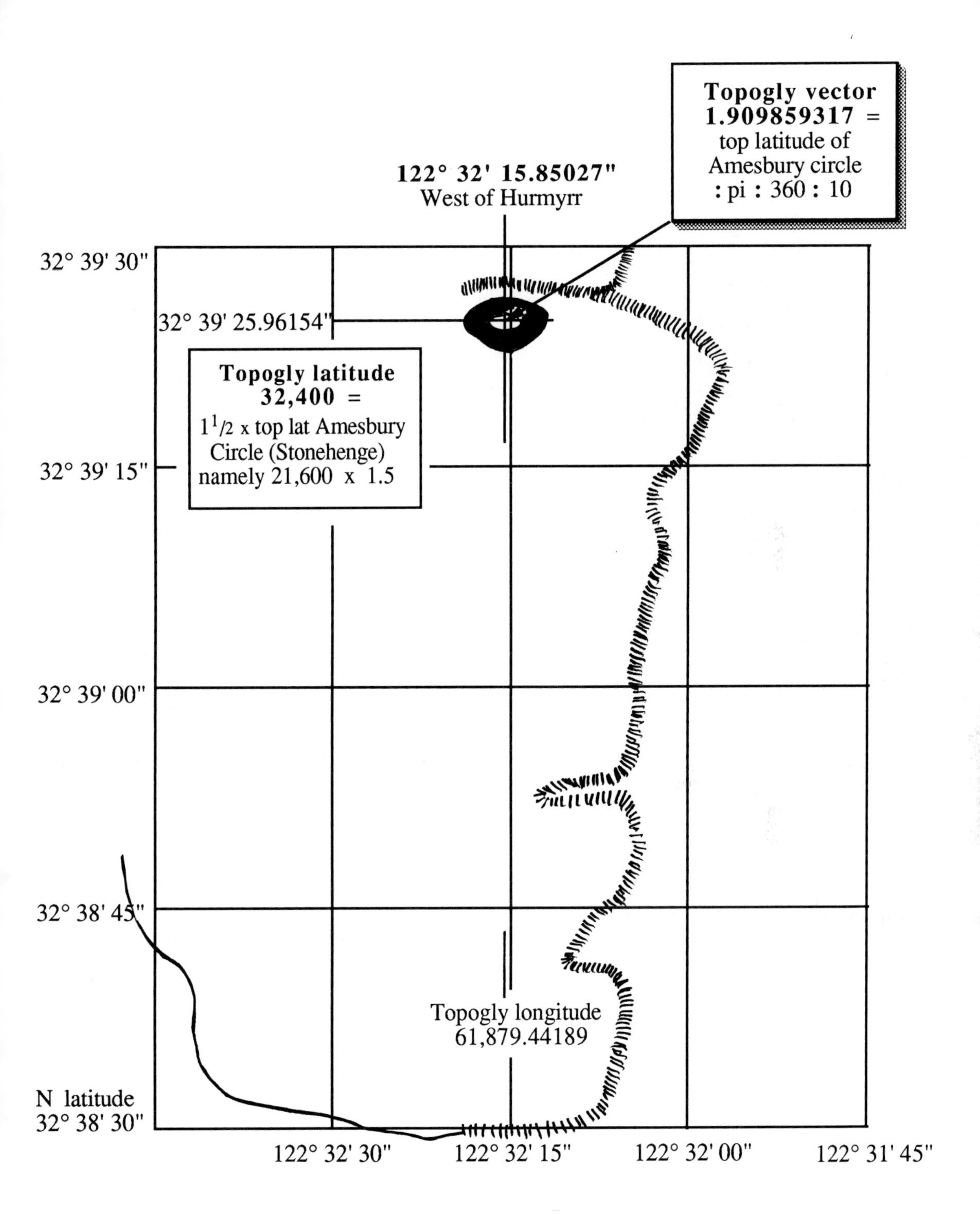

Figure 87. The first topogly matrix site: constructed in the shape of an eye. (Motley Mound, Poverty Point, Louisiana). The topogly longitude of this eye mound is identical to the topogly latitude of sea creature mound (compare figure 75).

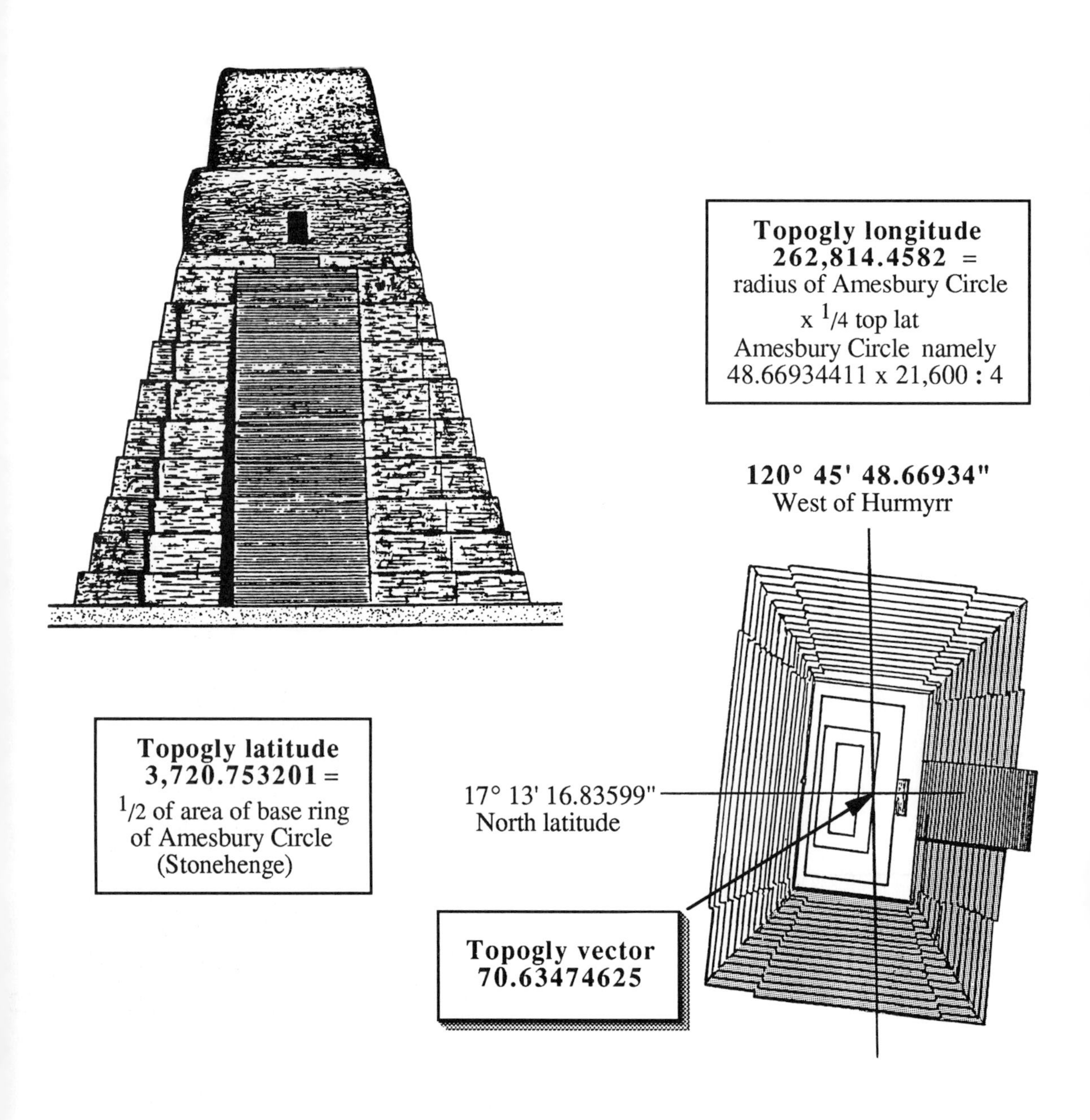

Figure 88. The second topogly matrix site the double-headed drakon pyramid. (Temple of the Double-Headed Serpent, Tikal, Guatemala.)

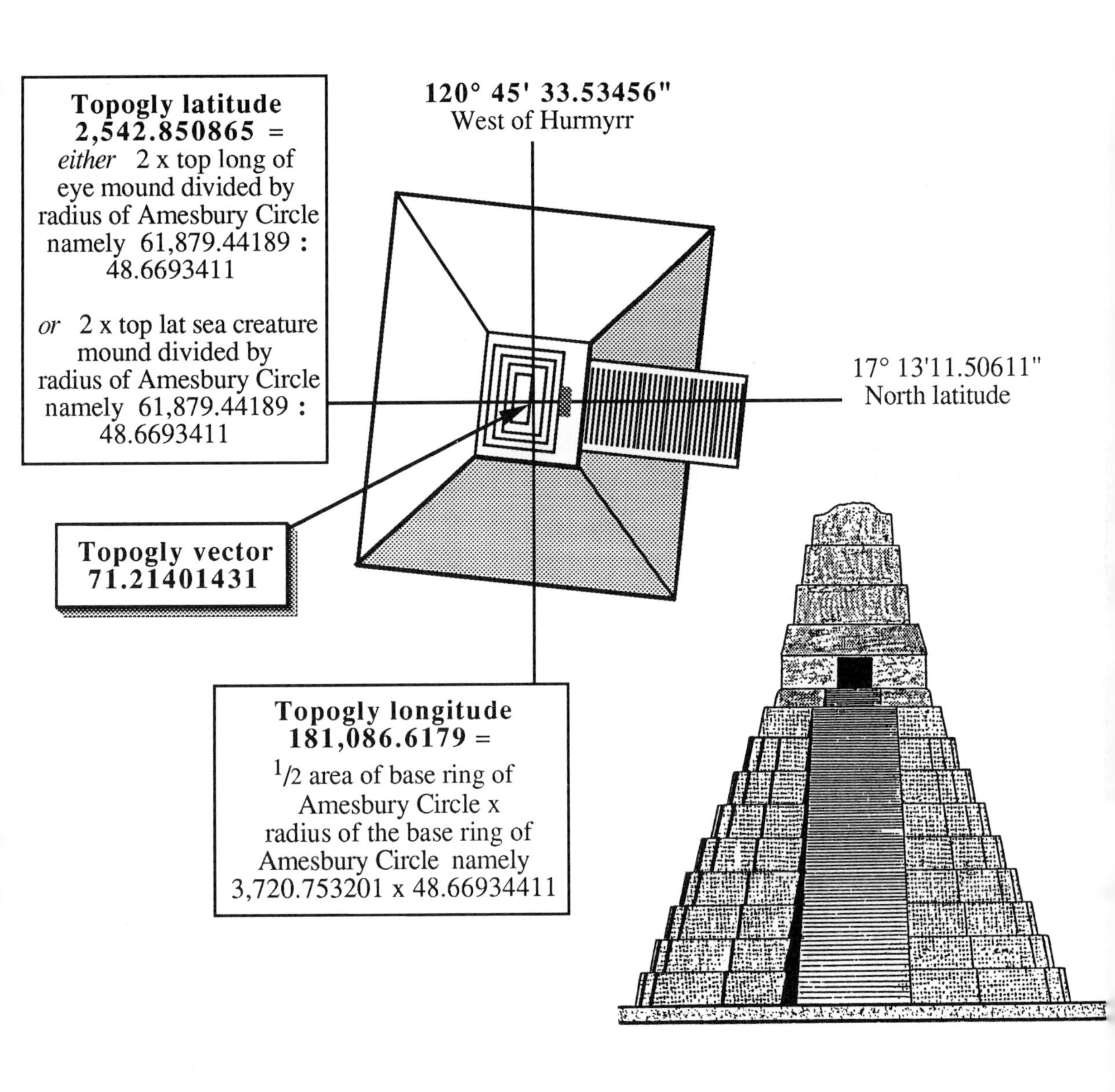

Figure 89. The third topogly matrix site a courage pyramid. (Temple of the Jaguar, Tikal, Guatemala.)

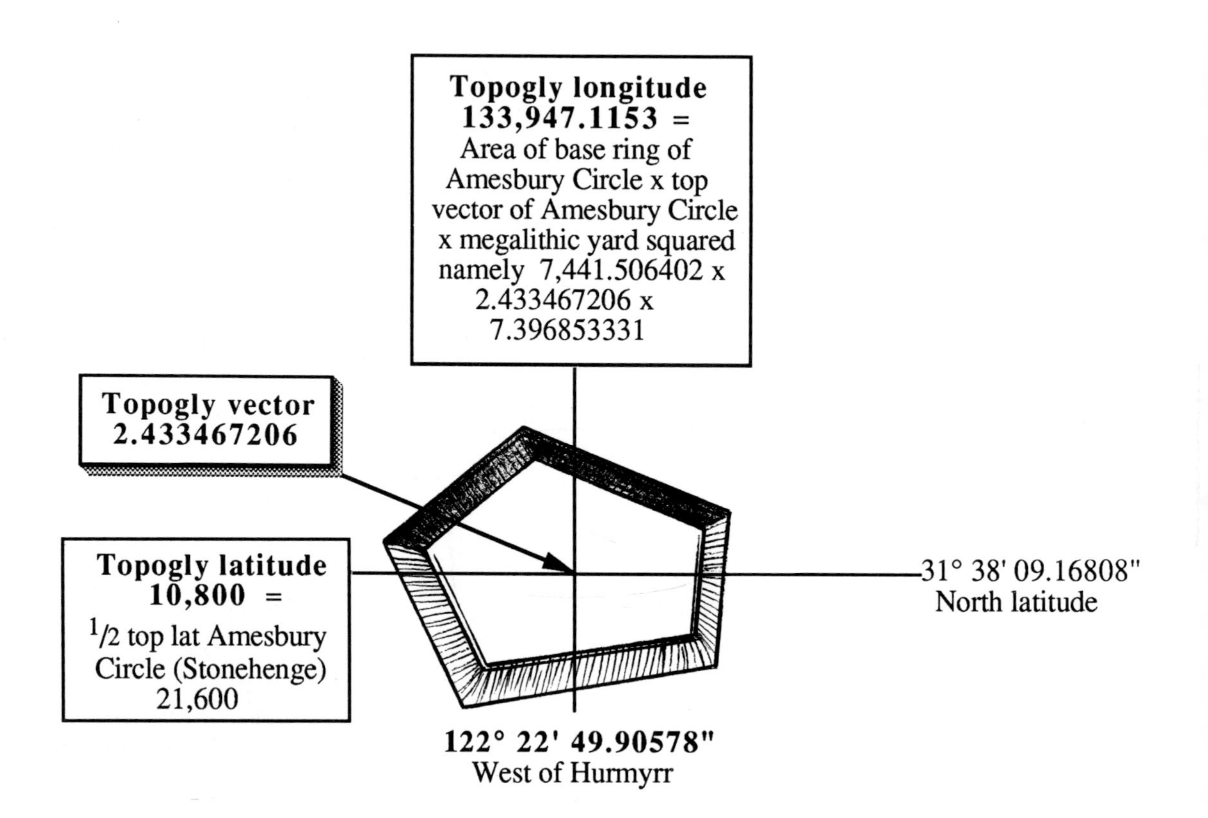

Figure 90. The fourth topogly matrix site a flat irregular five-sided mound. (Emerald Mound, Church Hill, Mississippi.)

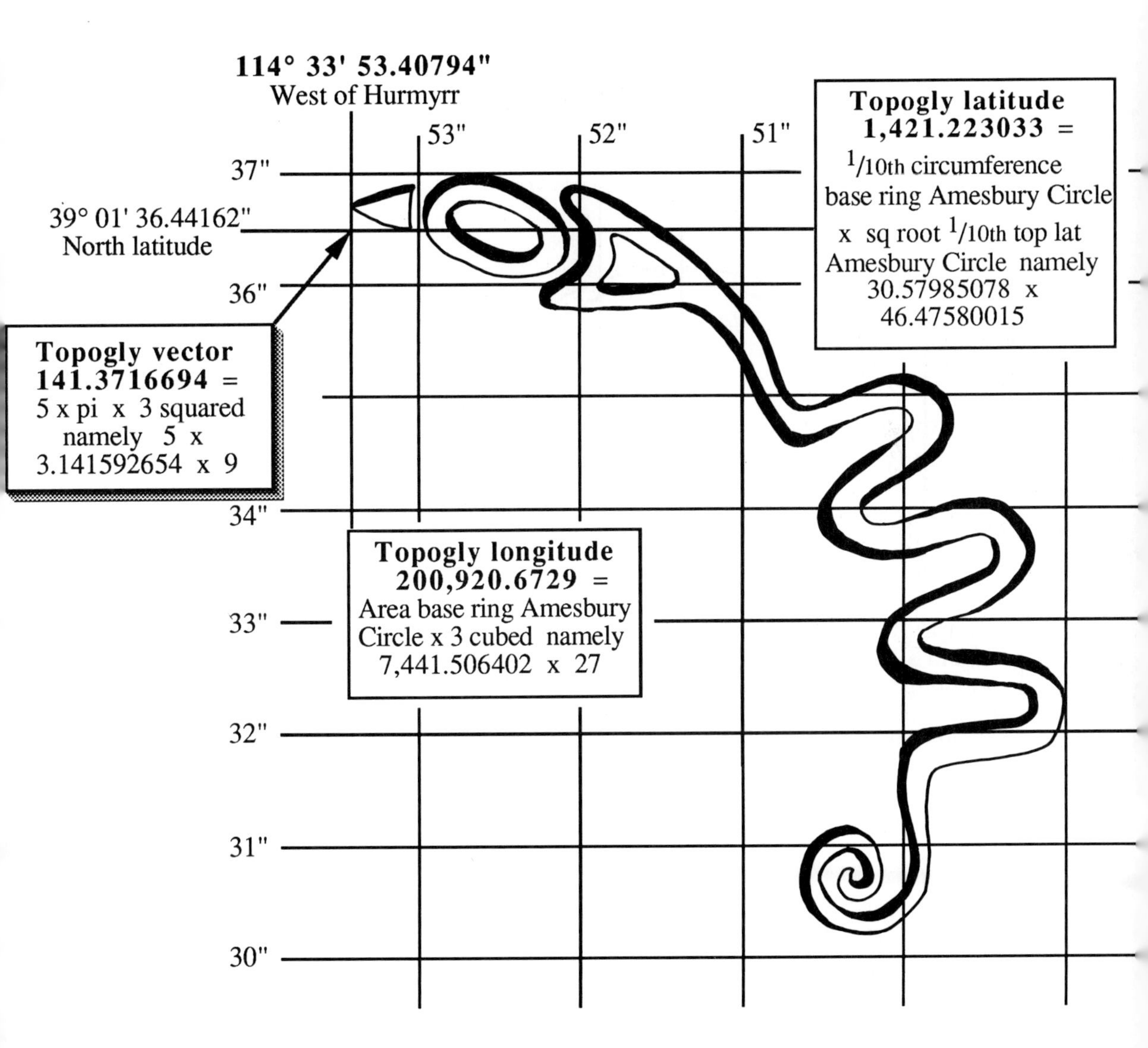

Figure 91. The first of the effigy mounds the drakon mound. (Serpent Mound, Loudon, Ohio.)

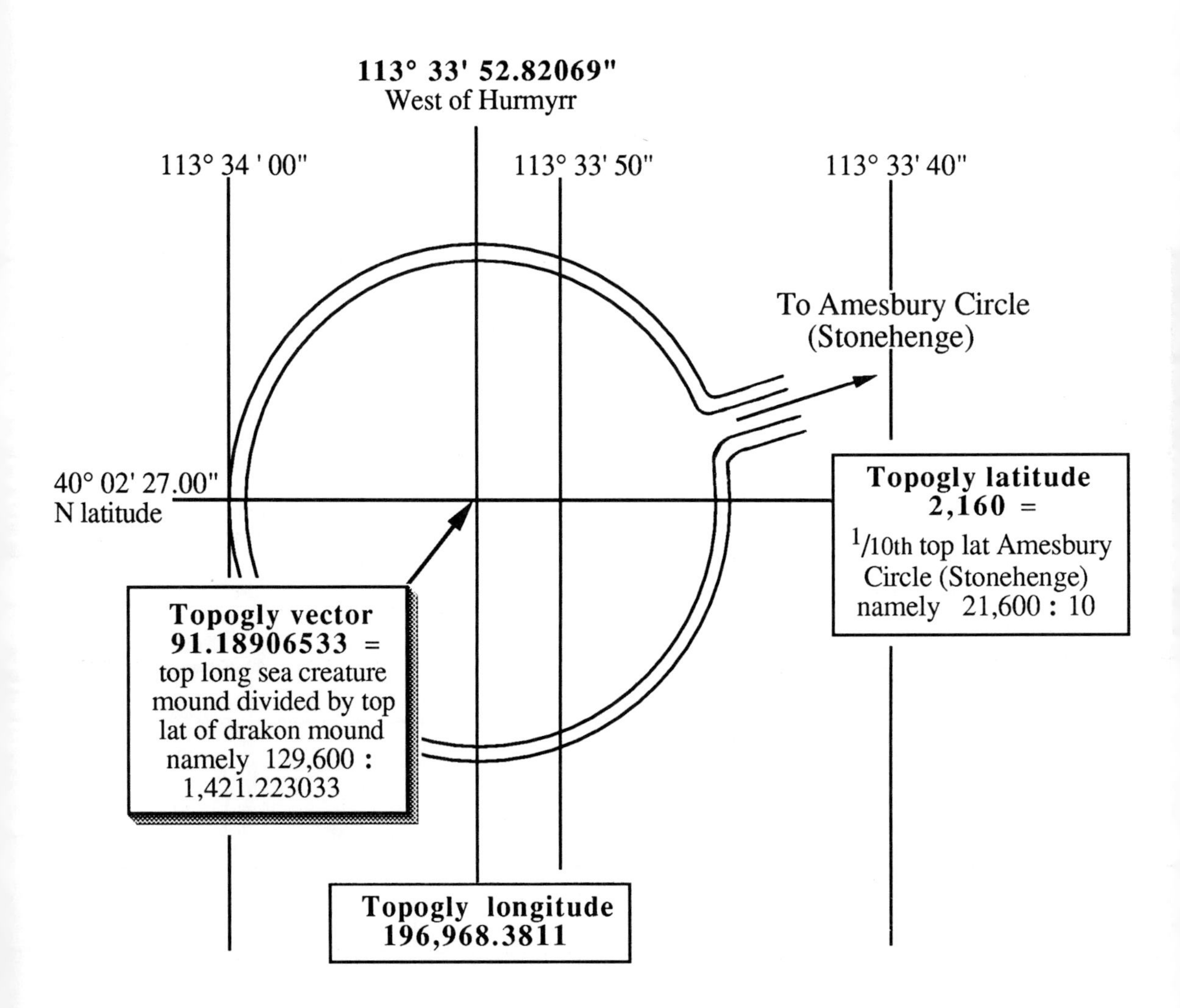

Figure 92. The first circle, the avenue circle. (Observatory Circle, Newark, Ohio.)

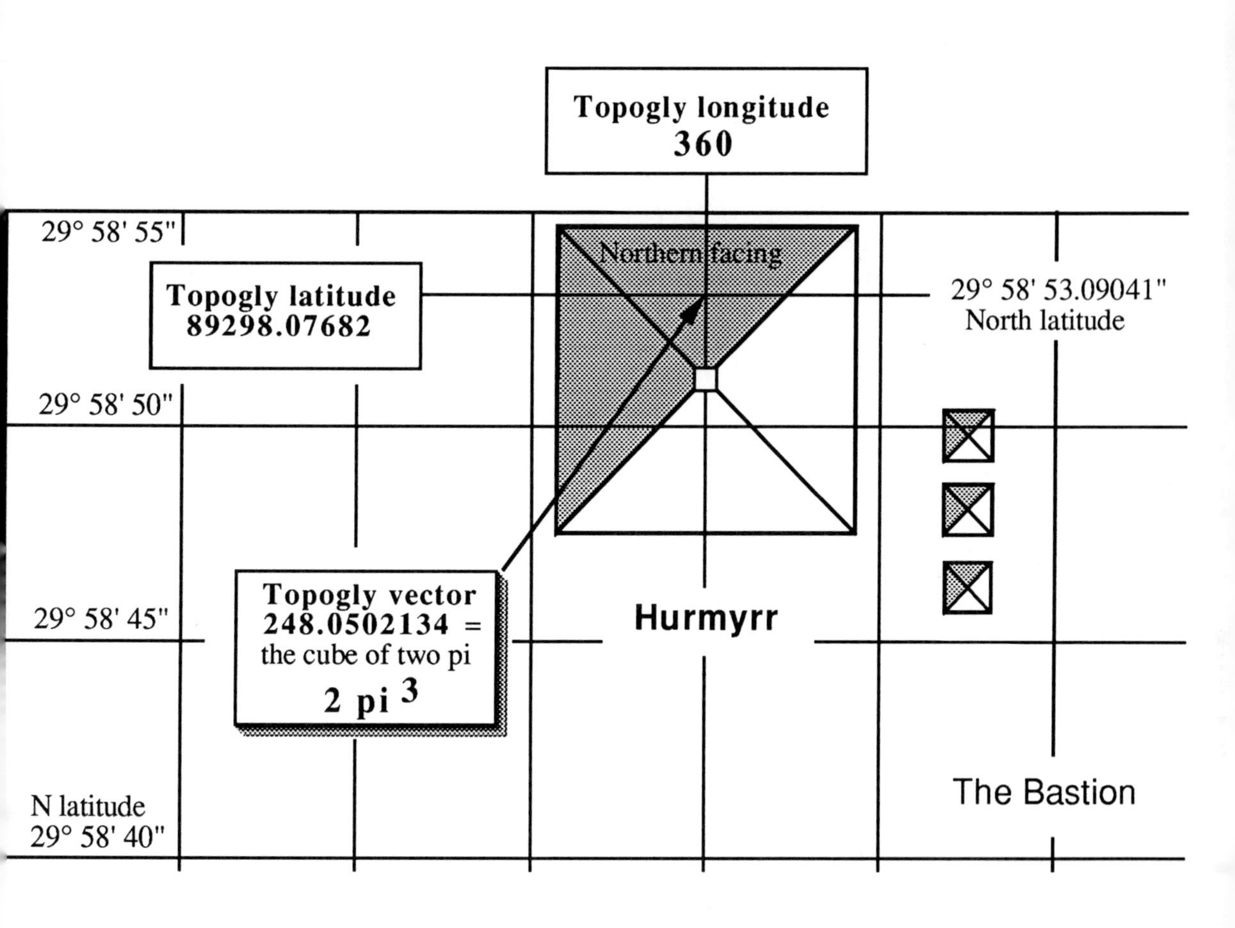

Figure 93. Hurmyrr (The Great Pyramid) the prime meridian, the source of the topogly matrix.

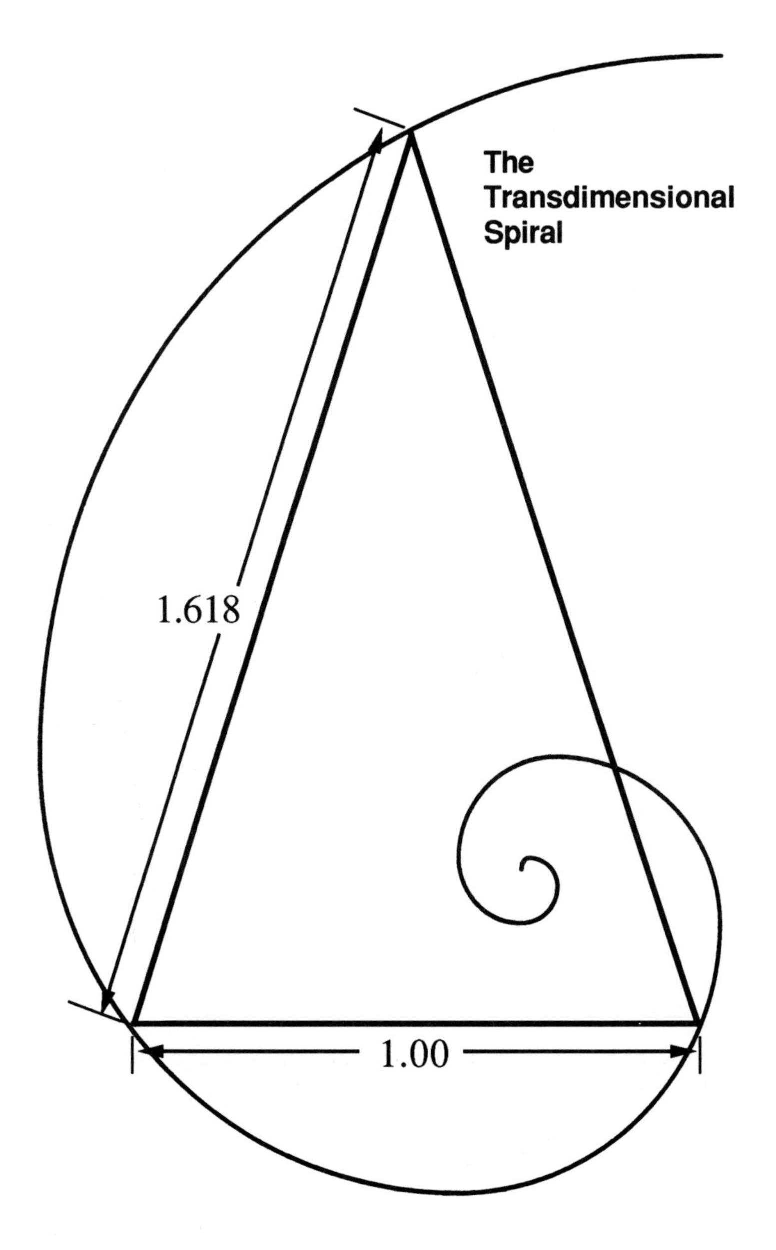

Figure 94. Scaled Transdimensional Spiral drawn tangent to the corners of an isosceles triangle with two sides 1.618 times as long as the short side.

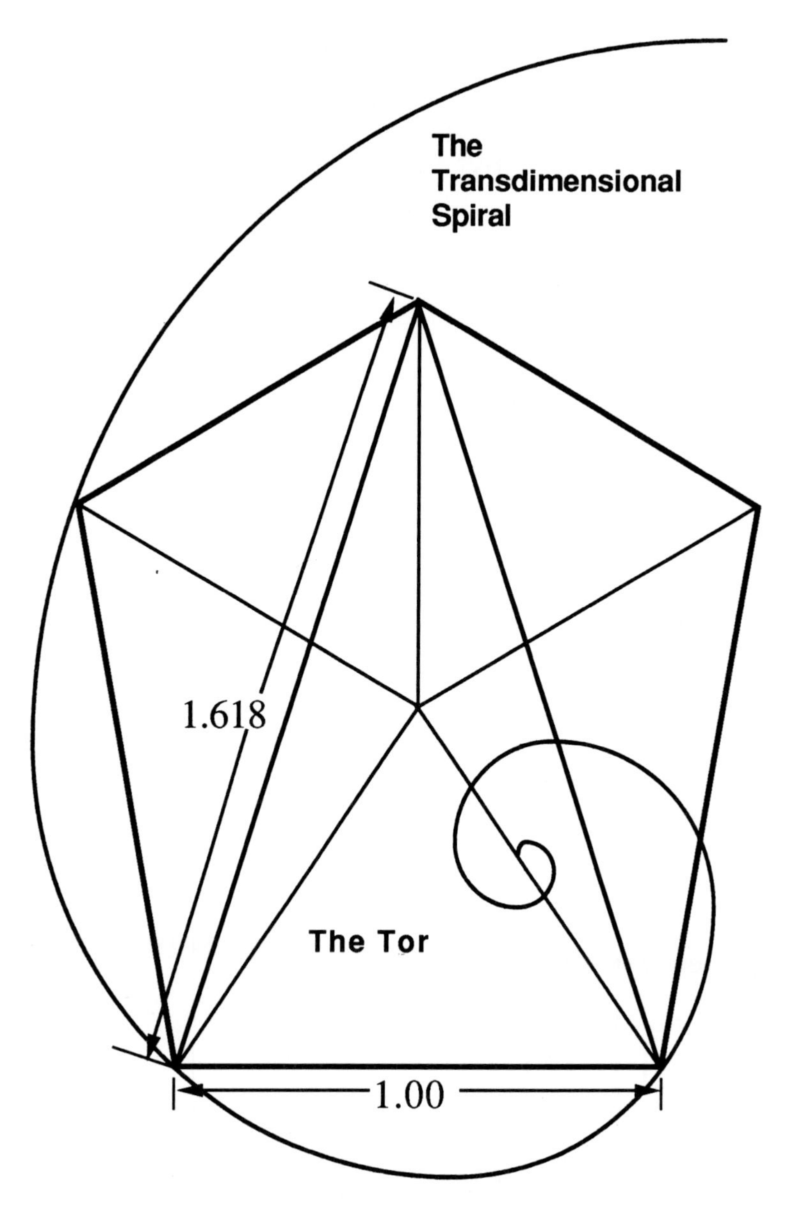

Figure 94.1 The Tor with overlaid scale Transdimensional Spiral.

Part 3 Chapter 8

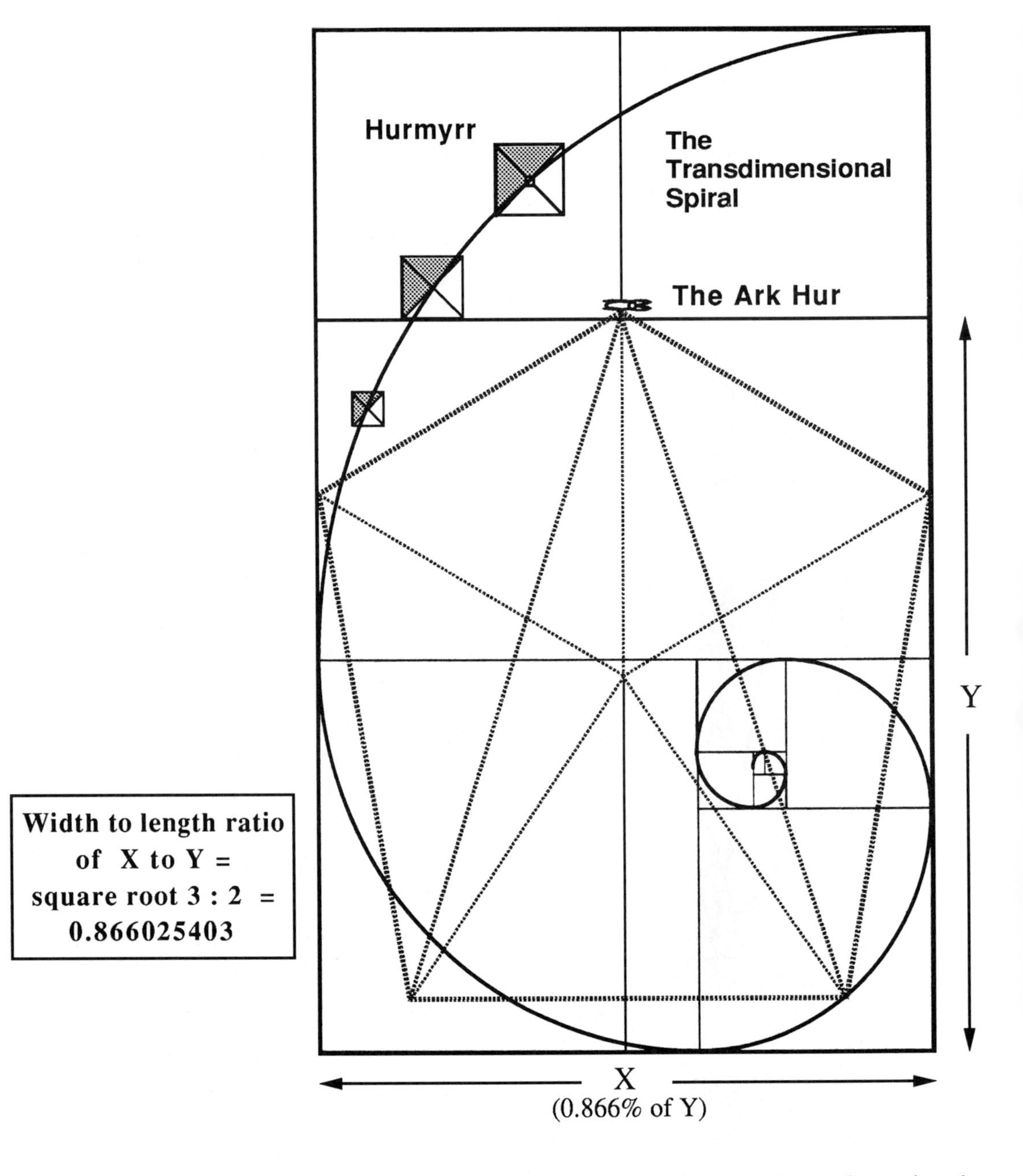

Figure 95. Map of the Bastion (the Giza plateau) with overlaid scale Transdimensional Spiral, the Tor positioned within the phi section rectangle and the Ark Hur halfway between the eastern and western sides of the rectangle.

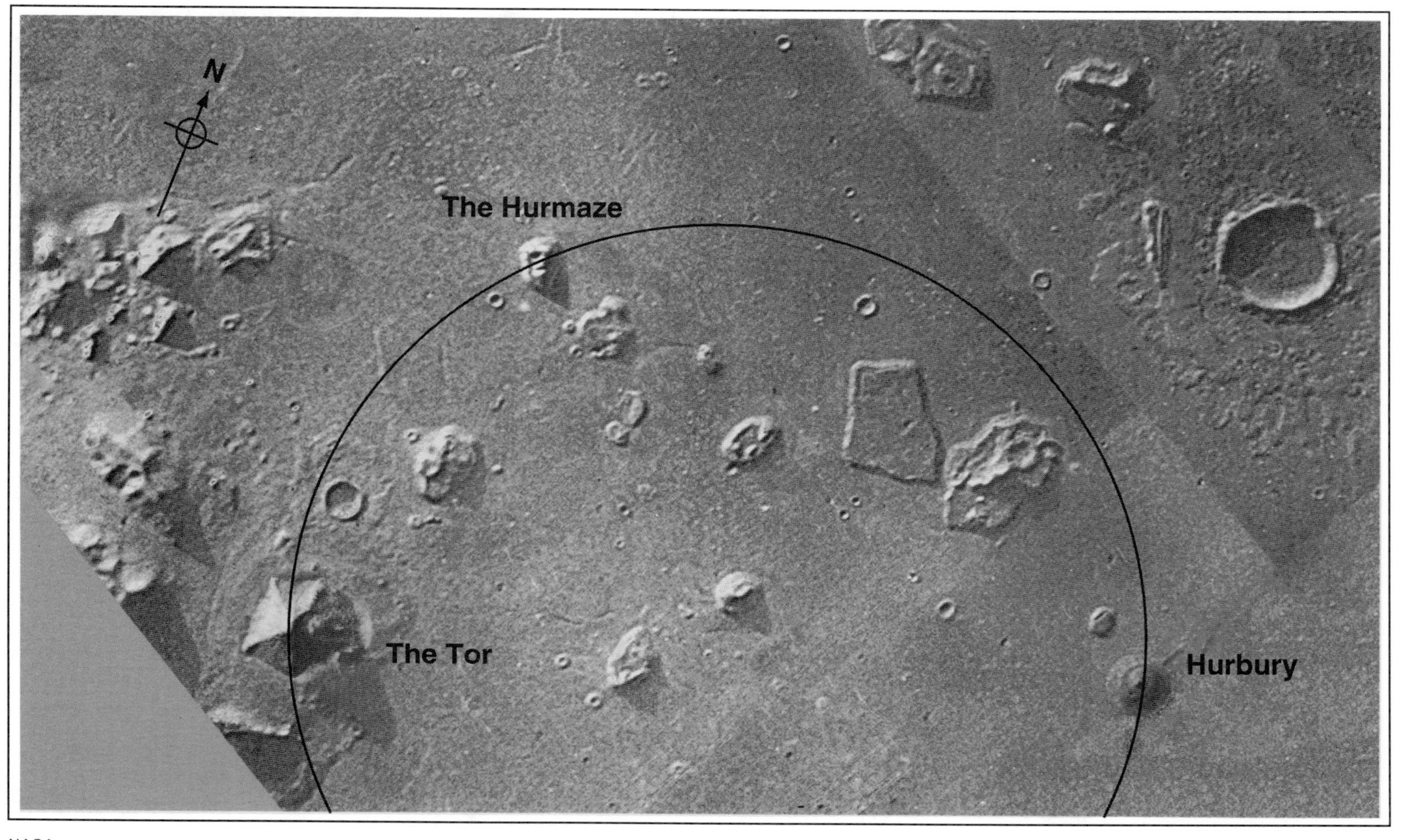

NASA

Figure 96. The Horz complex on Silbury with an overlaid arc passing through Hurbury, the Hurmaze and the Tor.

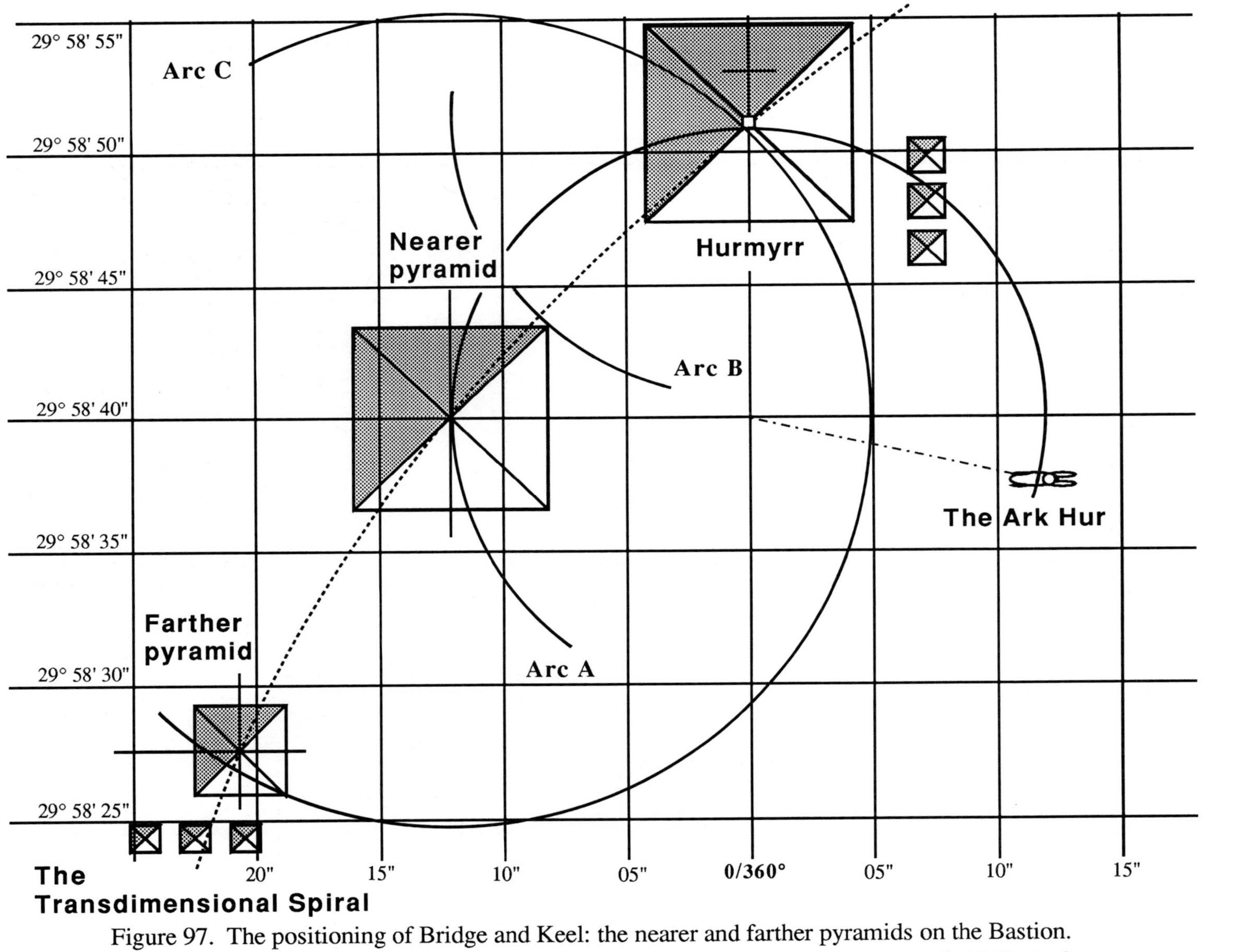

Figure 97. The positioning of Bridge and Keel: the nearer and farther pyramids on the Bastion.

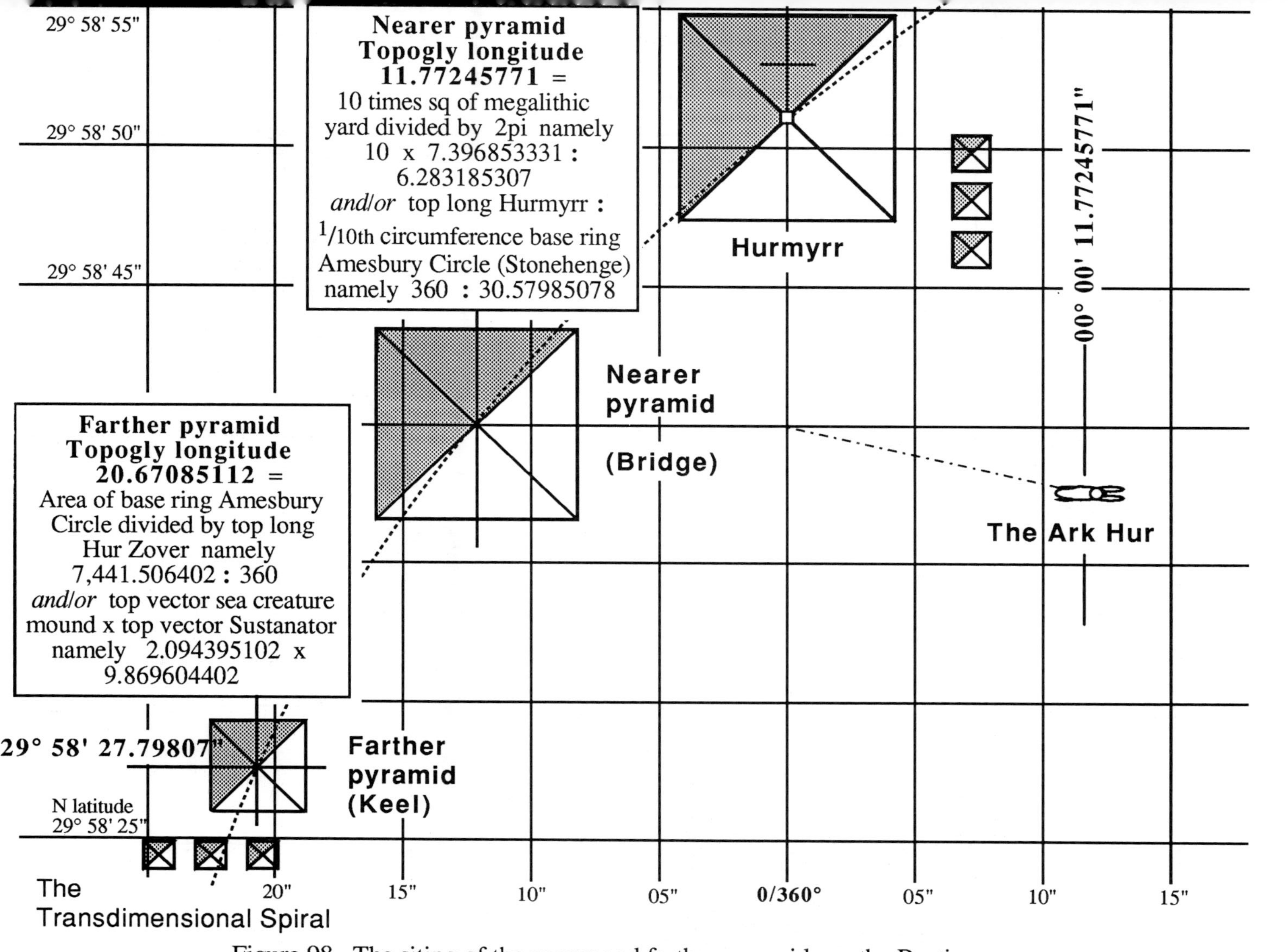

Figure 98. The siting of the nearer and farther pyramids on the Bastion.

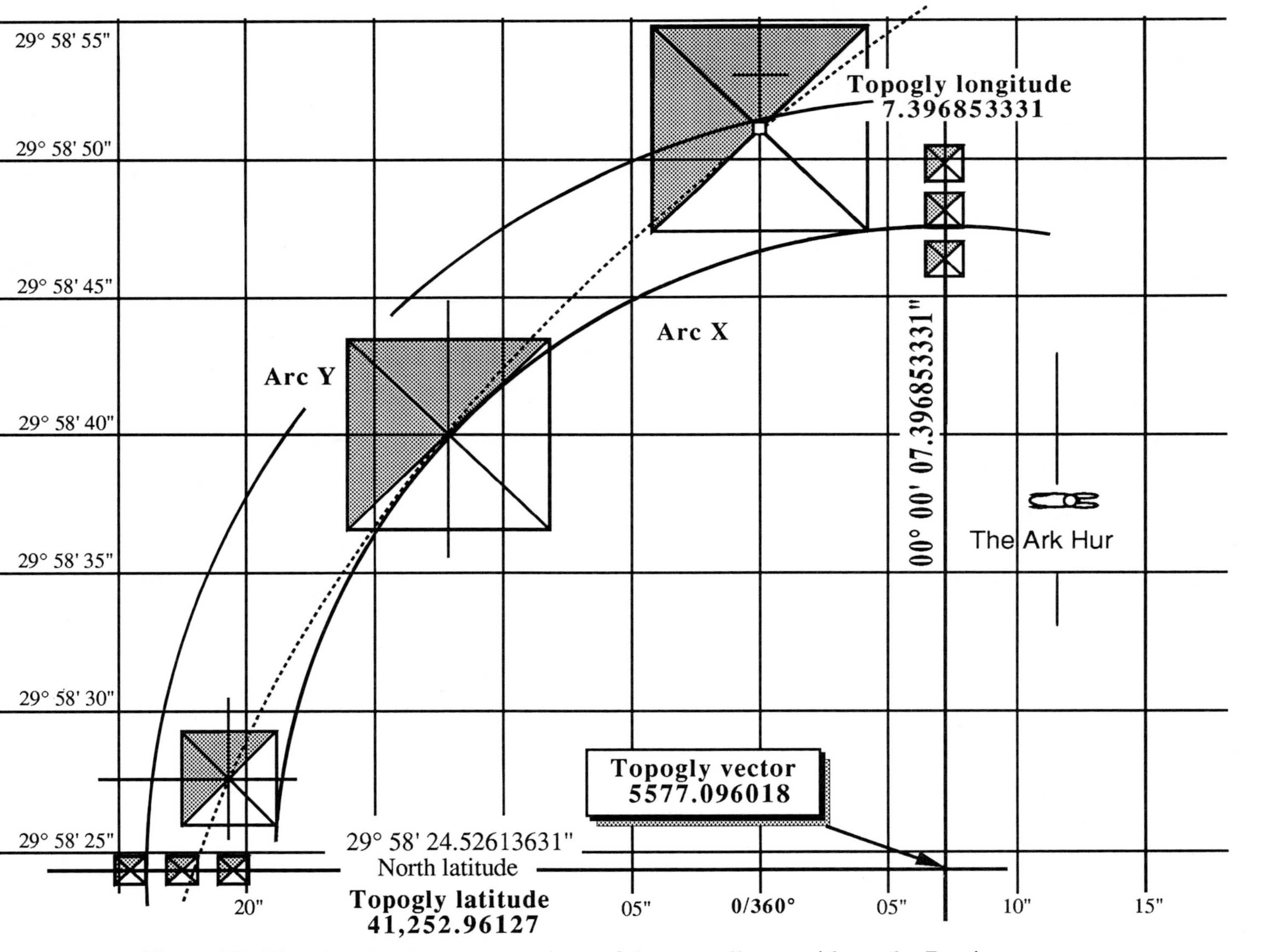

Figure 99. The sites for the two groupings of three small pyramids on the Bastion.

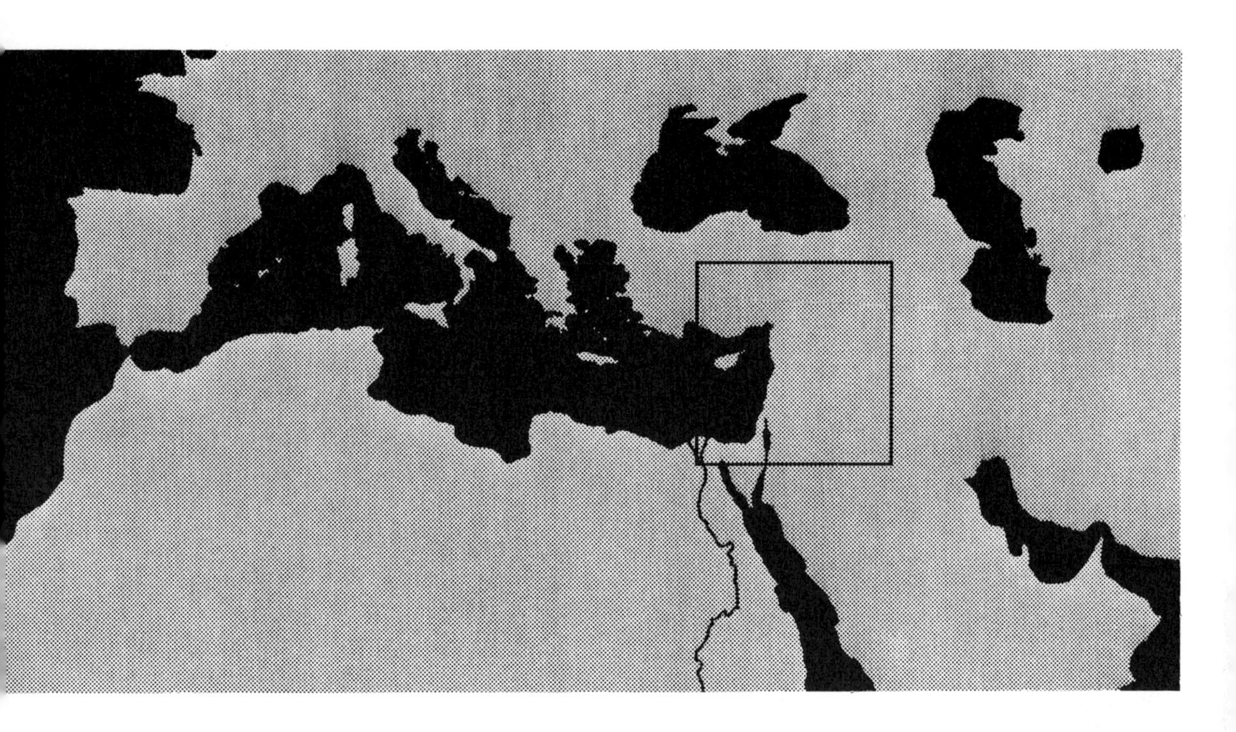

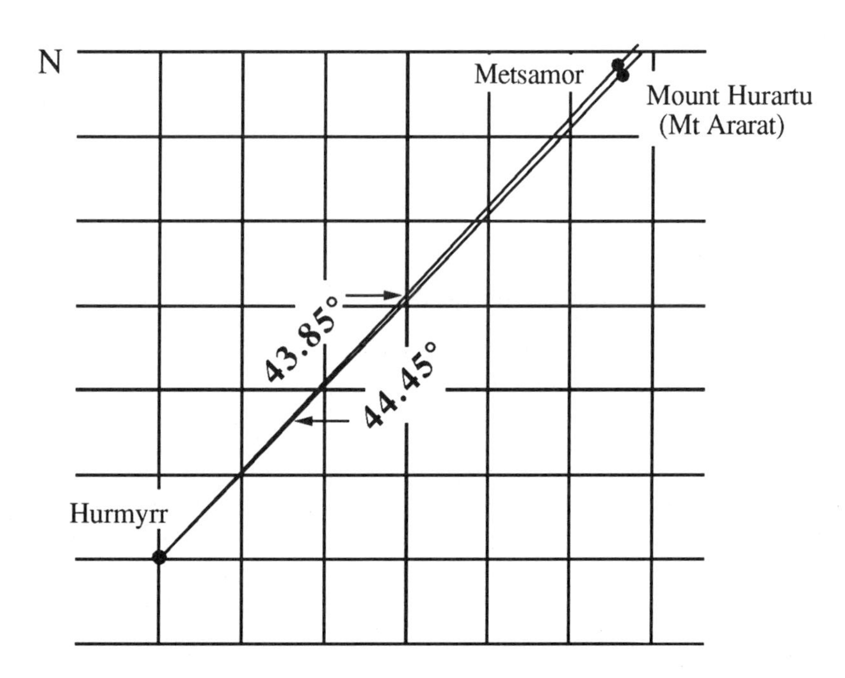

Figure 100. The location of Mount Hurartu and (less than 20 miles to the north) the Metsamor site; both in relation to Hurmyrr. Although Mount Ararat is not an analog of Mount Hurartu on Altea, the Alteans named Ararat in memory of their own mountain.

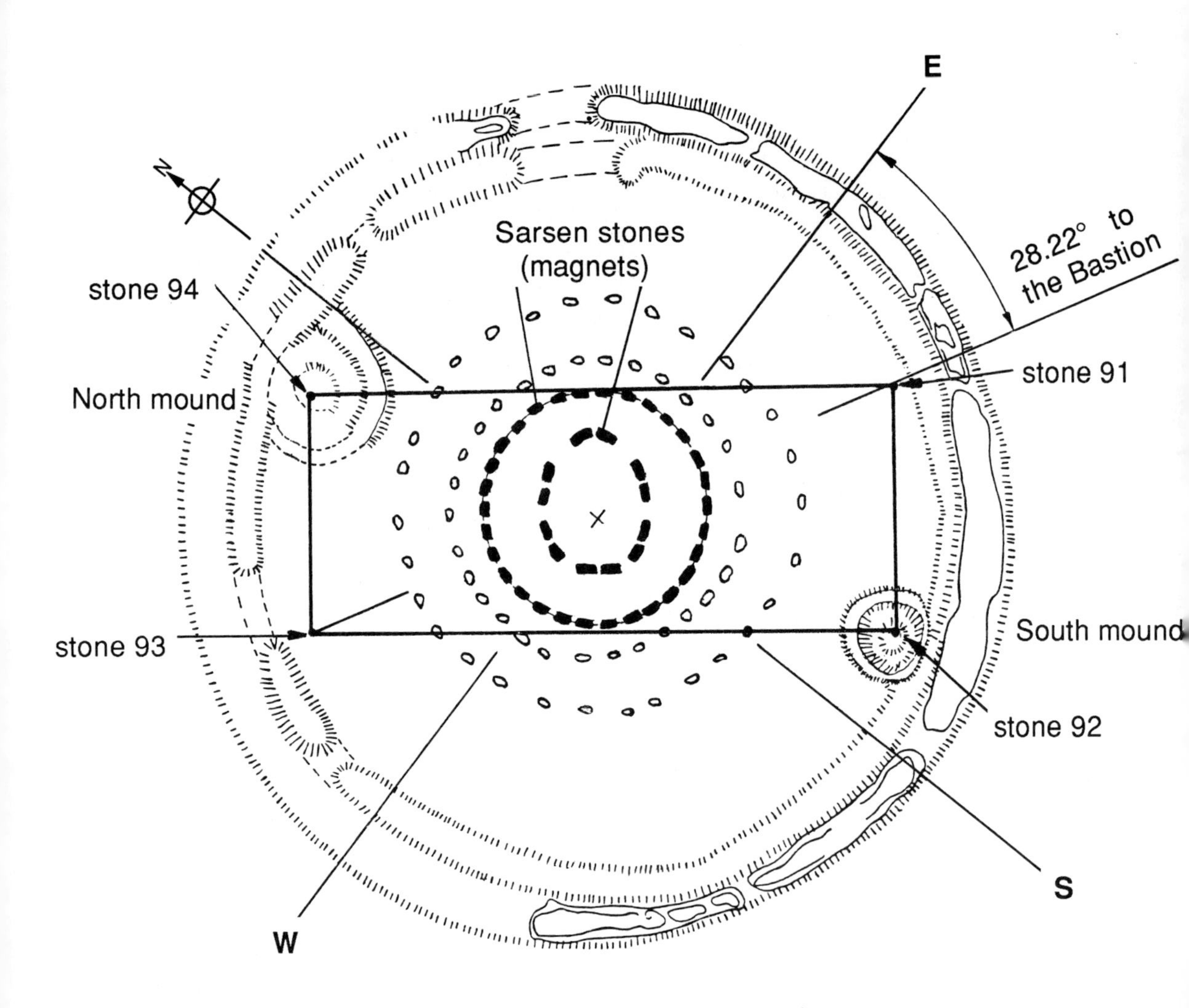

Figure 100.1. Joe Lon Odkin designed his model of a spinning disk according to standard Altean specifications which include an egg shaped array of downward levitating magnets in the upper armature (compare figure 24). Four large stones form a rectangle just inside the outer ditch and earth bank of Amesbury Circle (Stonehenge). These four stones represent a side view of the steel box which encloses the engineering spaces of a space vessel (also compare figure 24). In addition, the northwestern and southeastern stones form an angle of 28.22° south of due east and point to the Bastion on which the pyramids Bridge and Keel stand. Amesbury Circle and the Bastion form a unit which represents the presence of the Altean Naval Service on Silbury.

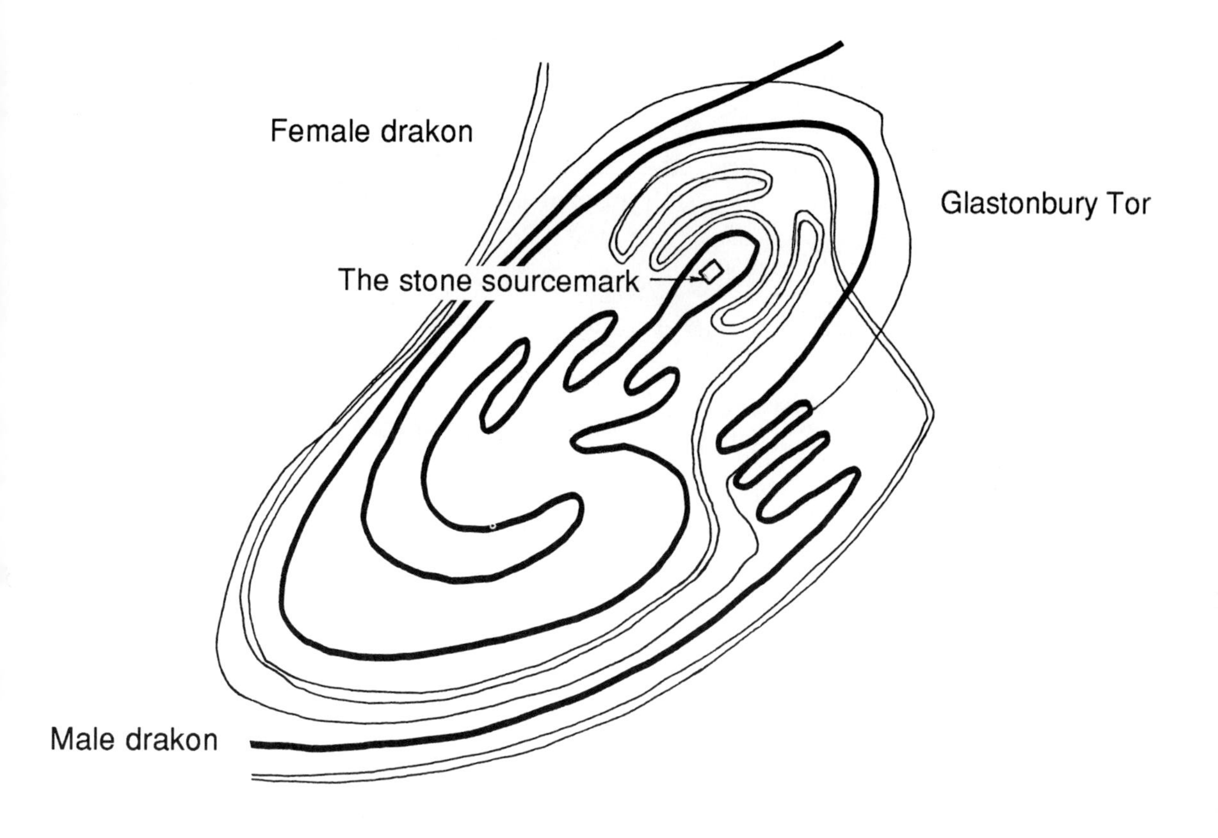

Figure 101. The female and male drakon of the Keirykeion Line on Glastonbury Tor. One of the channels is a representation of the birth canal of a female self-aware being. The other channel is a representation of the male reproductive organ of a male self-aware being. The male reproductive organ is inside the birth canal and additionally inside the end of the male reproductive organ is the stone sourcemark which represents the growing fetus of a self-aware being.

Part 3 Chapter 8

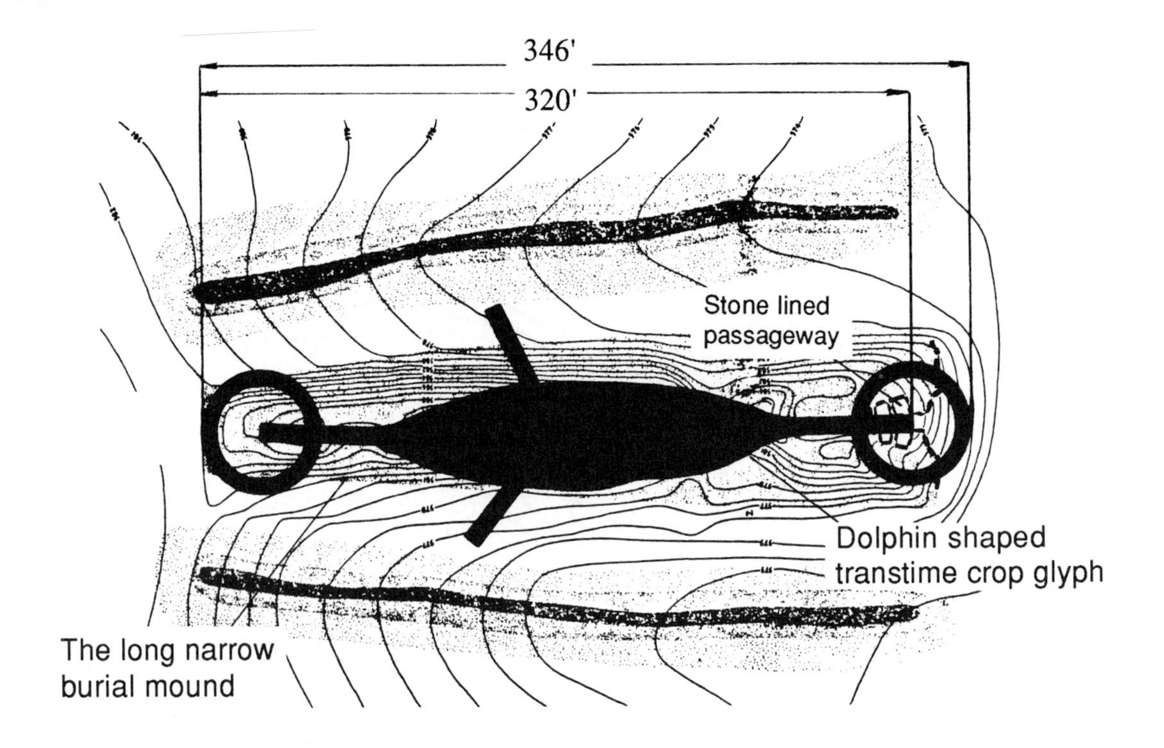

Figure 102. The long narrow burial mound (West Kennet Long Barrow) and the dolphin shaped transtime crop glyph (Lockeridge July 1991).

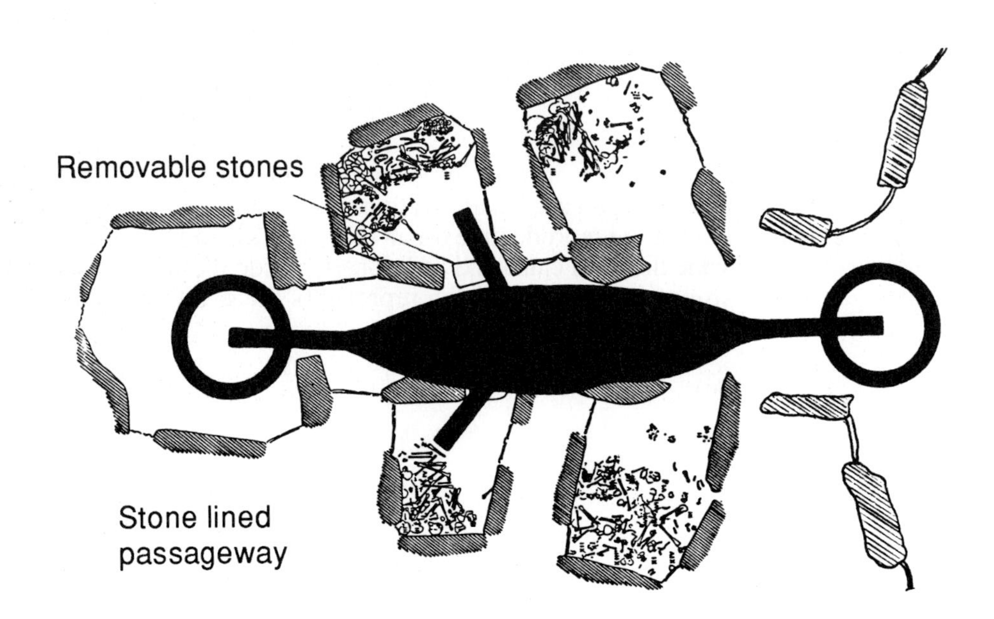

Figure 103. Scaled overlay of the dolphin shaped transtime crop glyph placed inside the stone lined passageway representing the end of a conduit leading into an energy transconverter.

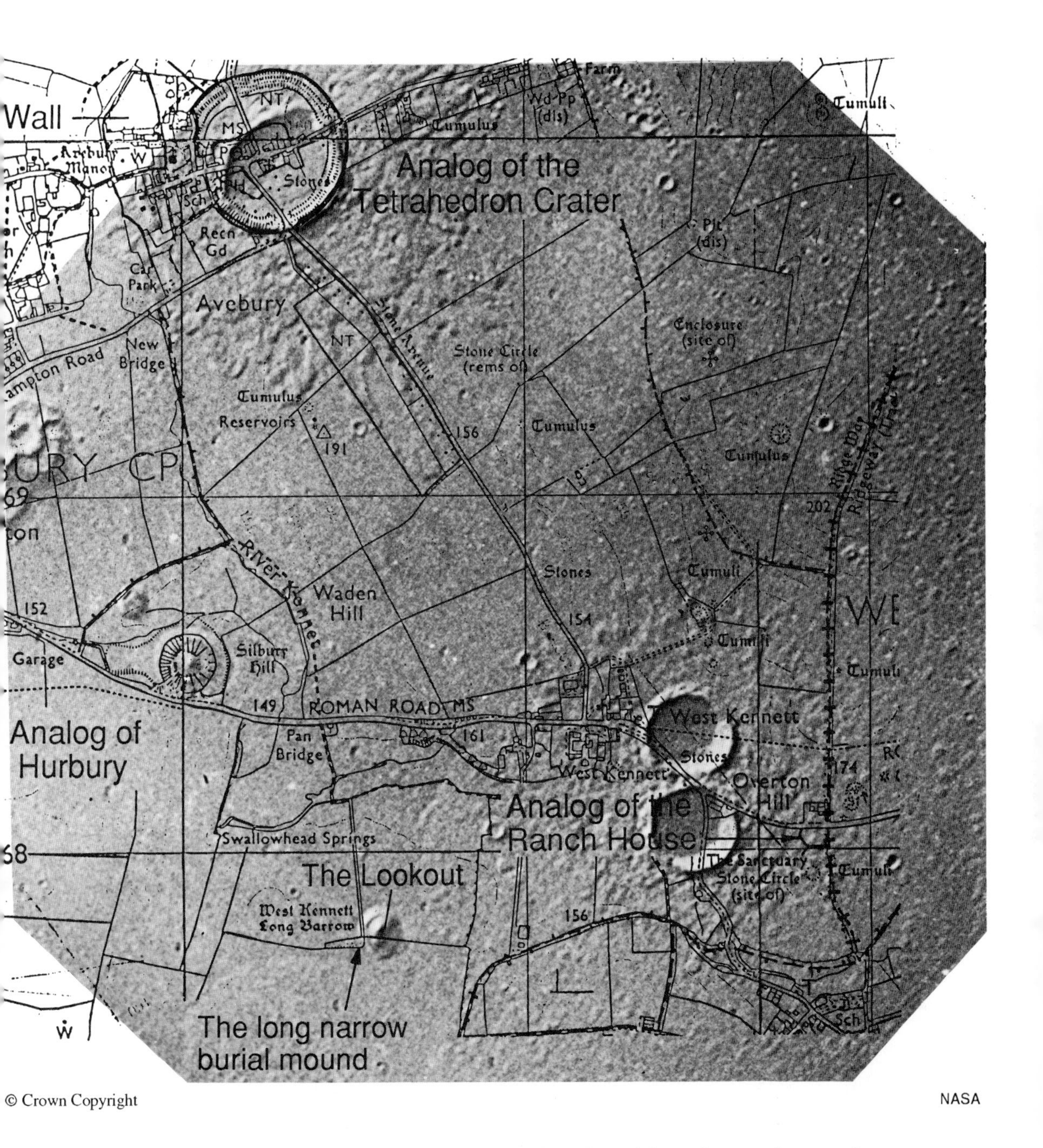

Figure 104. Modern map of Avenabury scaled and positioned over the southeastern section of the Horz complex, illustrating that the long narrow burial mound (West Kennet Long Barrow) is tangential to the Lookout (compare figure 60).

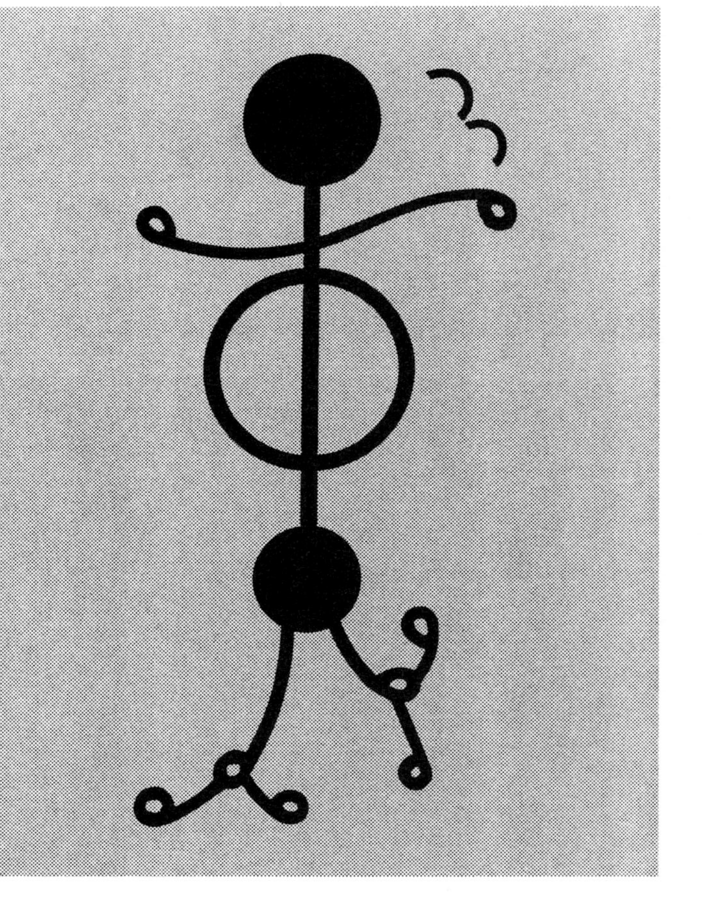

Figure 105. The Source transtime crop glyph (Micheldever Station August 1991). Note that the two Cs are above the *left* hand instead of the right and are backwards.

Figure 106. The first transtime crop glyph of the first growth ring of transtime crop glyphs (Amesbury July 1991). The antenna is coming out of the right side of the head to represent the main energy outflow from the soul captured by the Waldark hat and the short antenna is coming out of the left side to represent the secondary energy outflow from the soul captured by the Waldark hat amplifier.

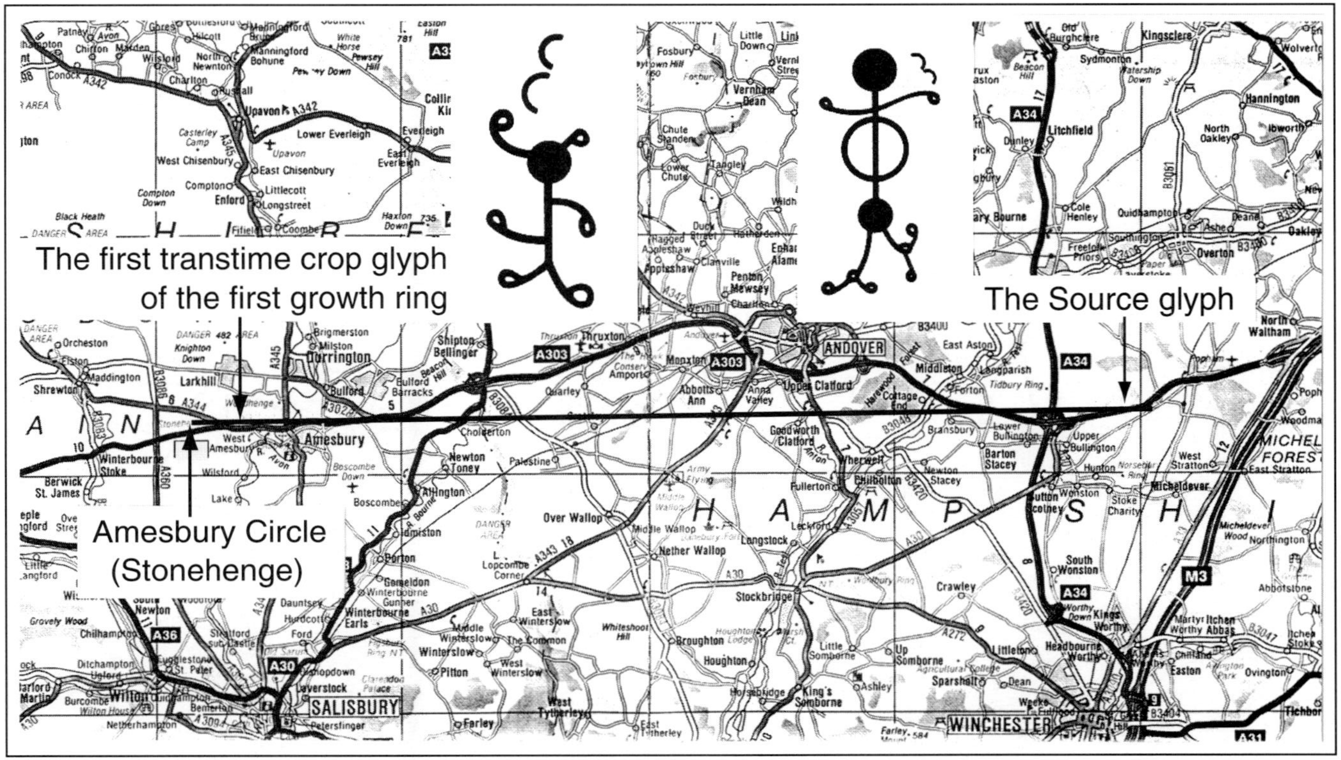

The first transtime crop glyph of the first growth ring

The Source glyph

Amesbury Circle (Stonehenge)

Figure 107. Amesbury Circle (Stonehenge) the first transtime crop glyph of the first growth ring of transtime crop glyphs and the Source glyph form a virtual straight line.

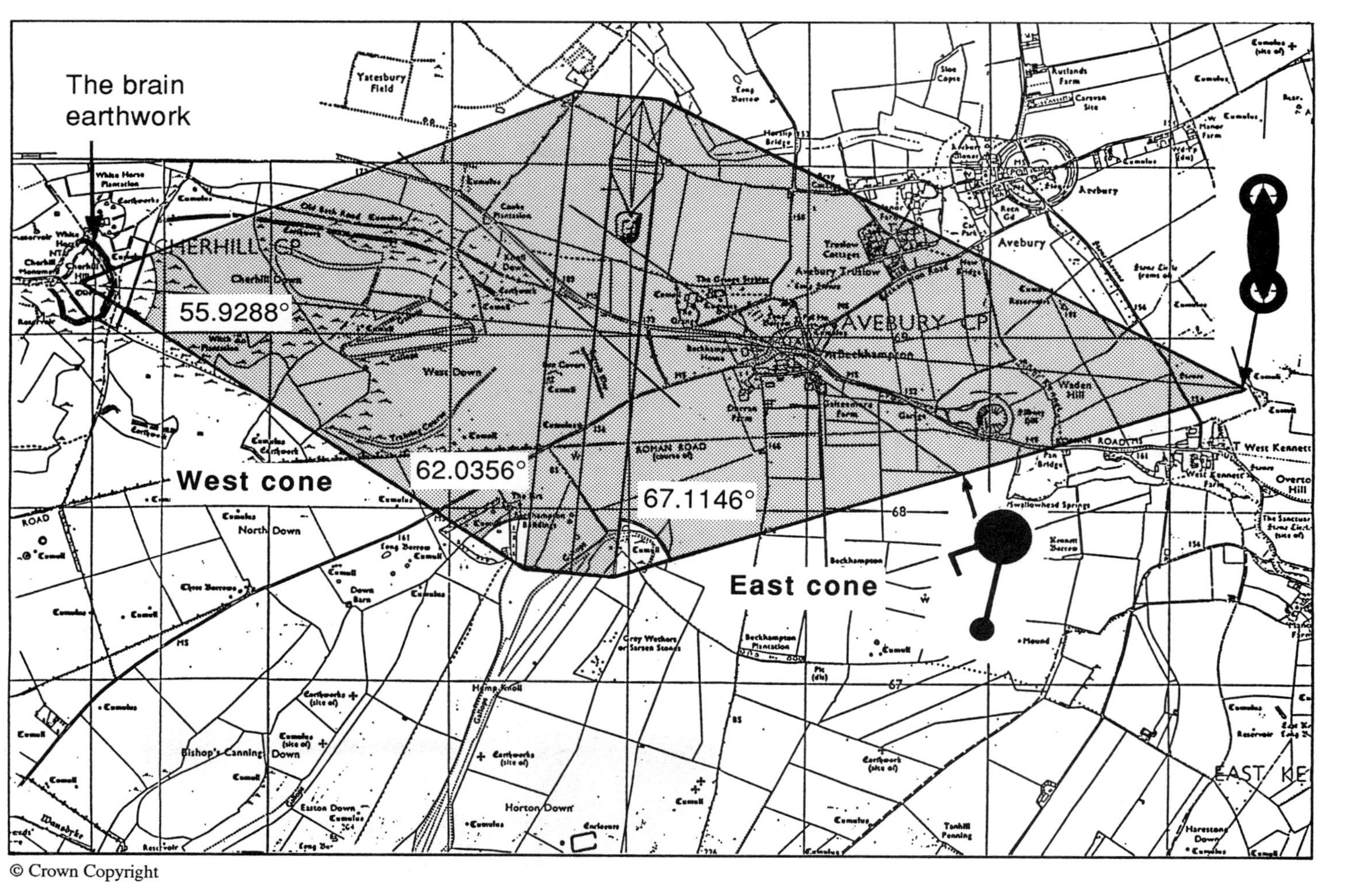

Figure 108. Two connected triangles, a two dimensional depiction of the first pair of cones of energy which emanate from souls of self-aware beings when their eyes are closed. Illustrated here on a modern map of the area south of the Hill of Musing.

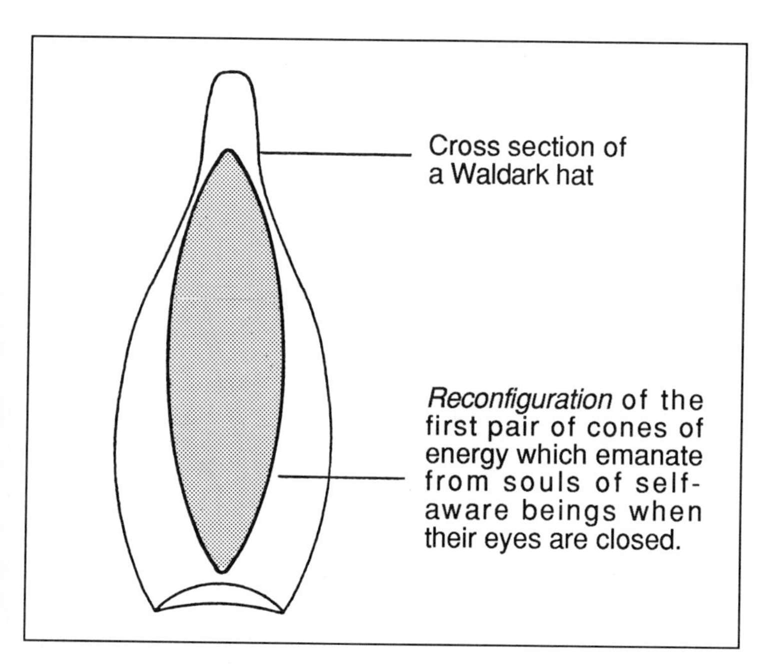

Figure 109. Depiction of a cross section of the oblate spheroid reconfiguration of cones caused by Waldark hats so that they can collect and transmit torun.

Part 3 Chapter 9

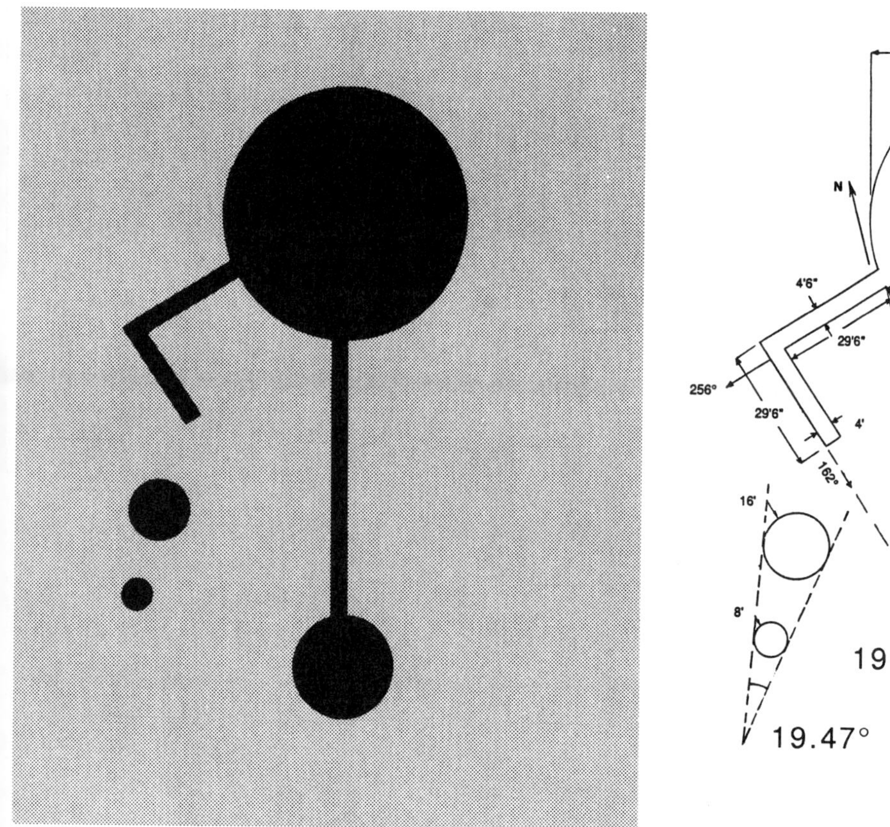

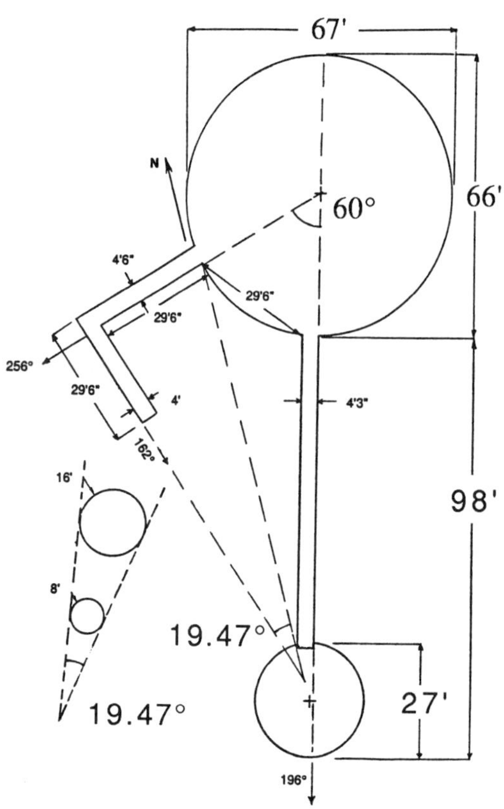

Figure 110. The transtime crop glyph (Silbury Hill July 1991) designed *primarily* to represent two-thirds, as two-thirds is so vital in energy transredimensioning.

Part 3 Chapter 9

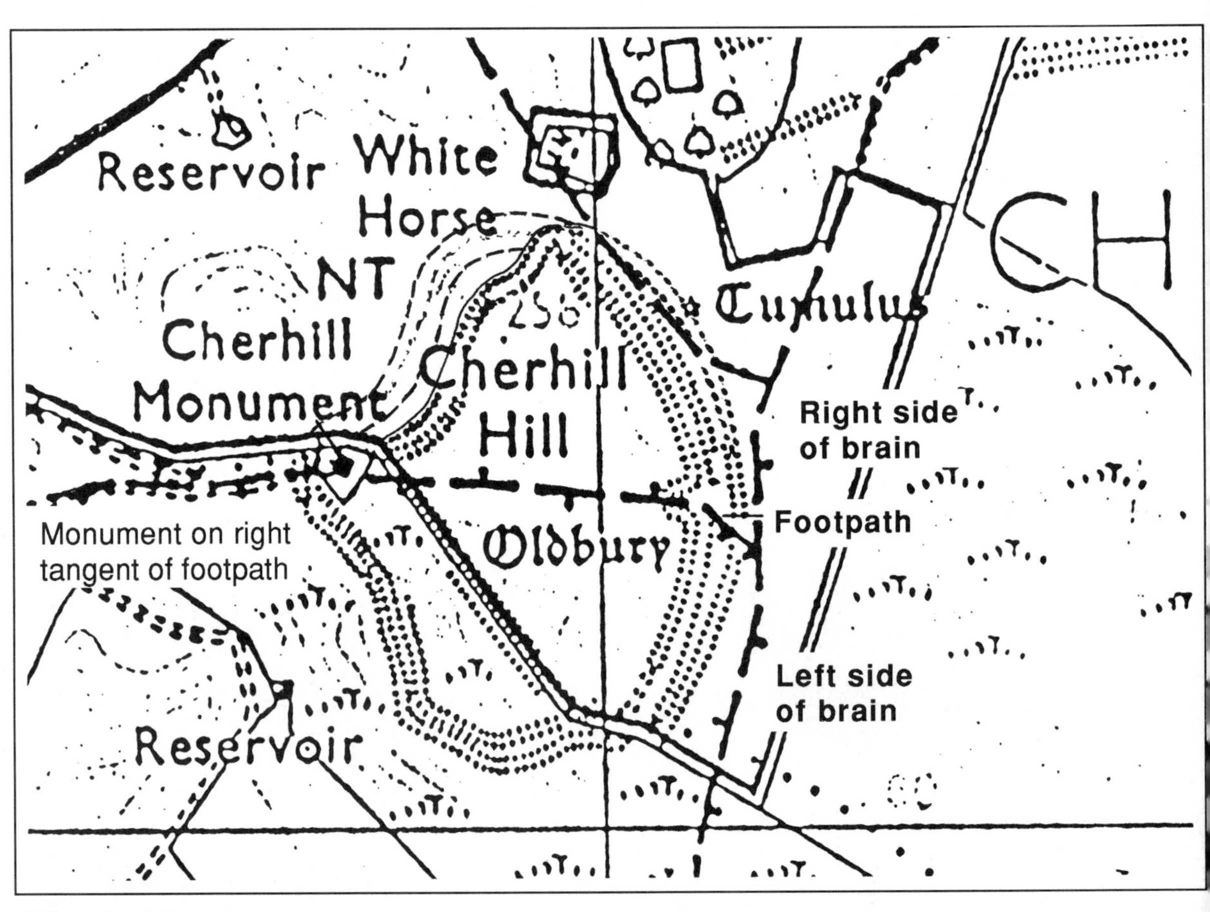

Figure 111. Map of the brain earthworks (Cherhill Hill) as it is today with only 75% of the right side of the brain shown. The dotted section outlines the missing 25%.

111.1. The brain earthworks viewed from the top of the head. The Cherhill monument representing the soul is placed on the right side of the footpath, the dividing line between the left and right sides of the brain.

111.2. Side view of the earthworks illustrating that part of the right side of the brain is missing as it is cut away by a steep embankment. Note also the location of the white horse on the adjacent hillside.

112. The stone meeting house (St James's Church) at Avenabury as it is today.

Part 3 Chapter 9

113. Interior view looking eastward of the stone meeting house illustrating that the centerline of the isle is on the right *tangent* of the font when viewed from the east looking westward.

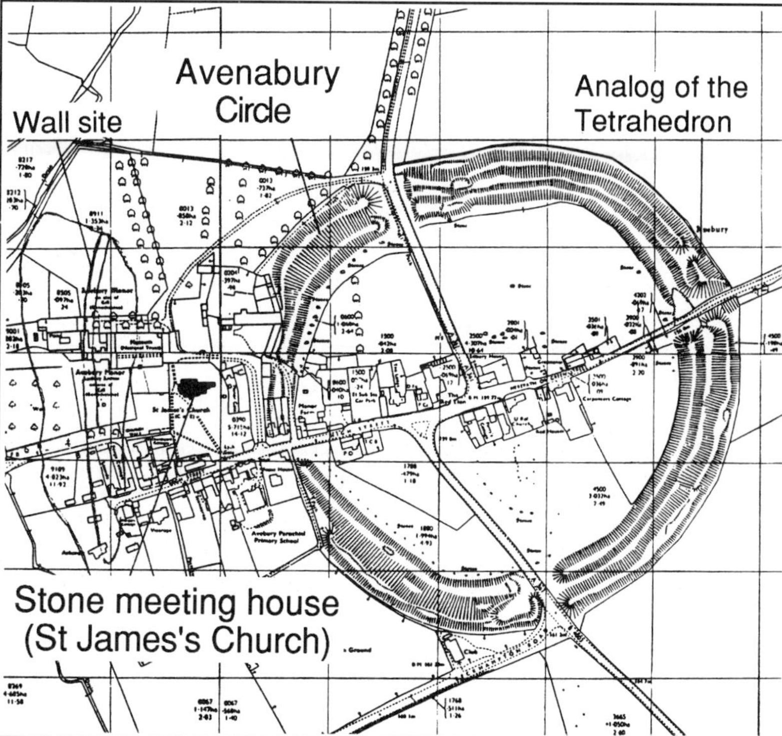

Figure 114. The positioning of the stone meeting house (St James's Church) aligned between the analog site of the Wall and the analog of the Tetrahedron Crater (Avenabury Circle) and located 4/7ths the way from the equator to the north pole.

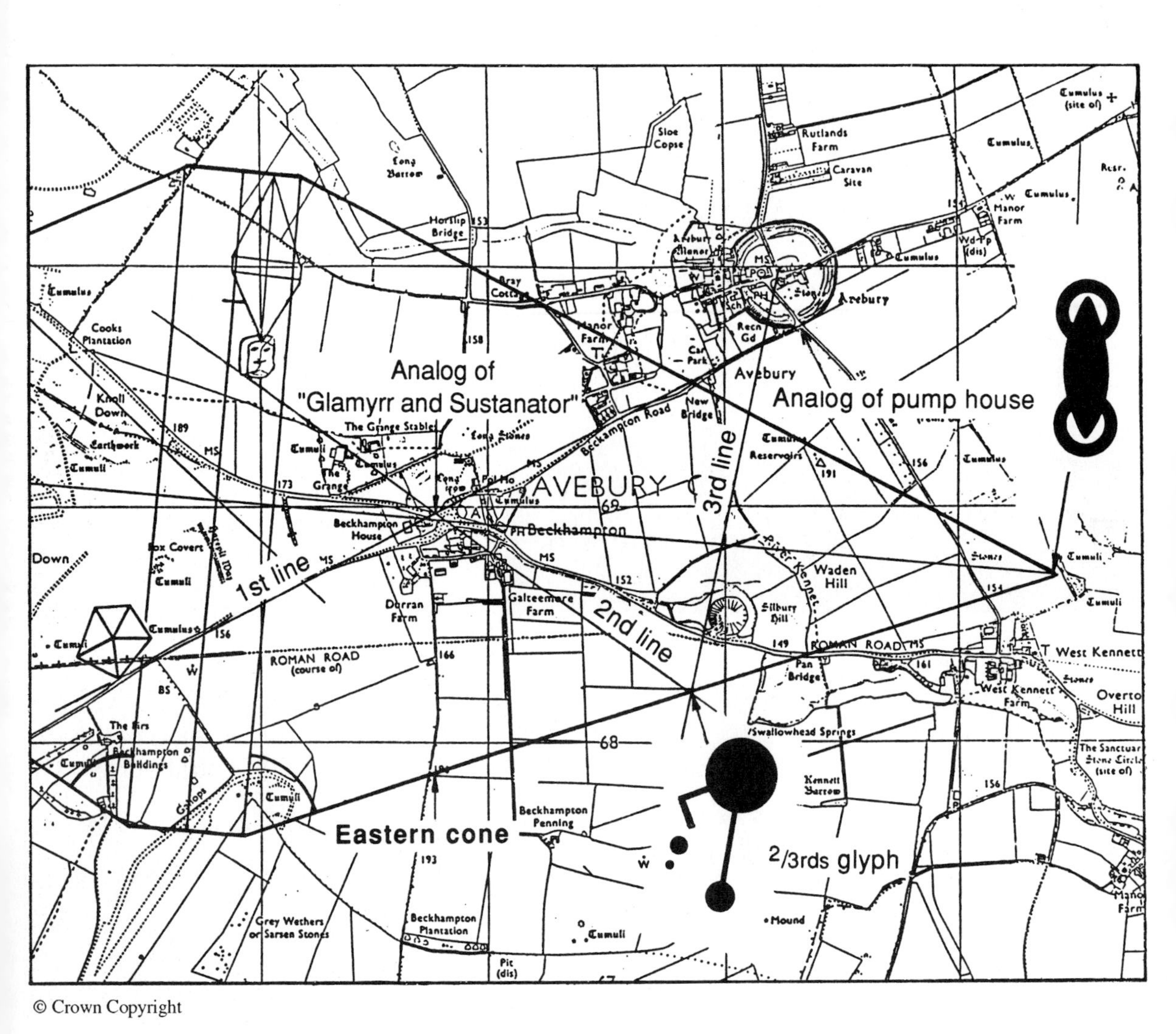

Figure 115. The positioning of the 2/3rds energy transredimensioning transtime crop glyph. The third line forms a *right* western tangent to Silbury Hill.

116. Very long boxes separated by relatively thin lines, a transtime crop glyph (Great Durnford July 1992) designed to depict a cross section of crystal disks (the long boxes) and mica slats (the thin lines) used in computers.

Figure 117. Kissing snakes transtime crop glyph (Longbarrow Crossroads June 1992) designed to depict the inflow and outflow of a computer, inflow and outflow which Odkin considered to be garbage. Odkin unwittingly connected himself to computers by unwittingly connecting his signature to this transtime crop glyph.

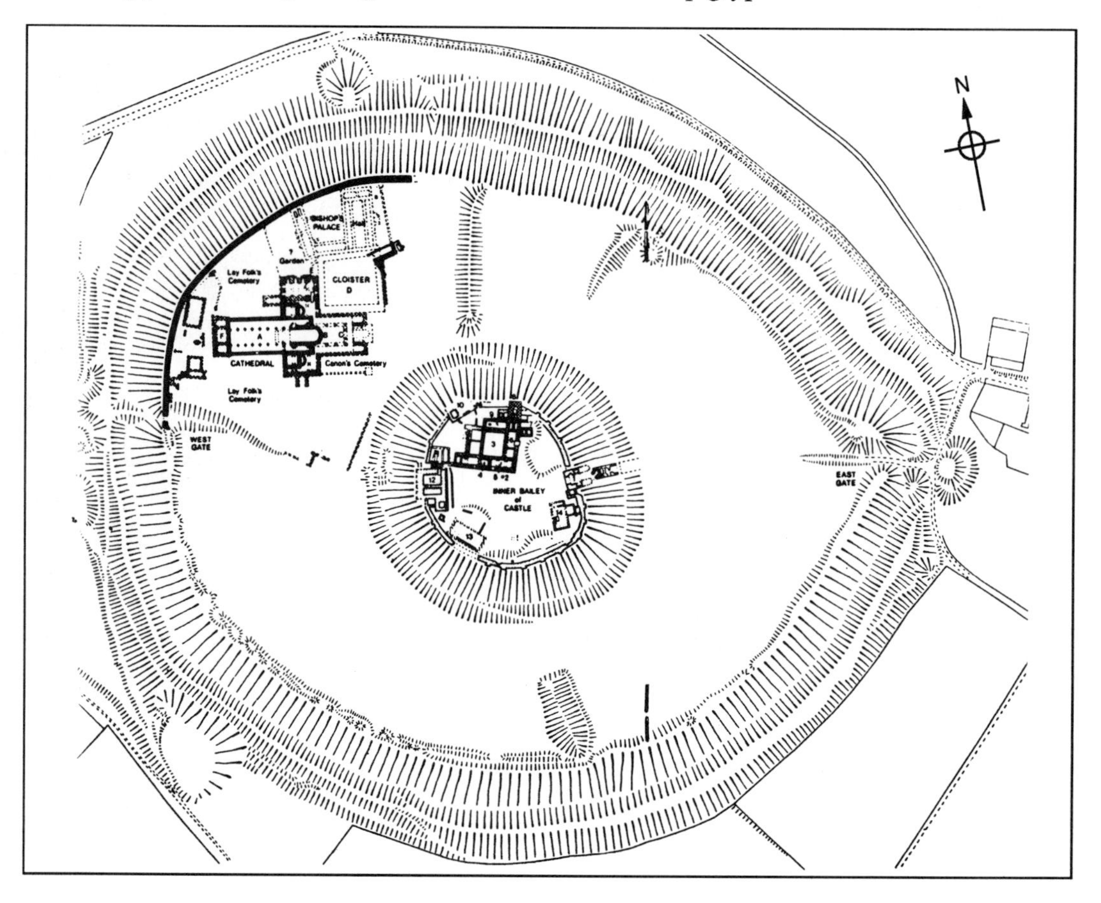

Figure 118. The doughnut earthworks (Old Sarum) as it is today.

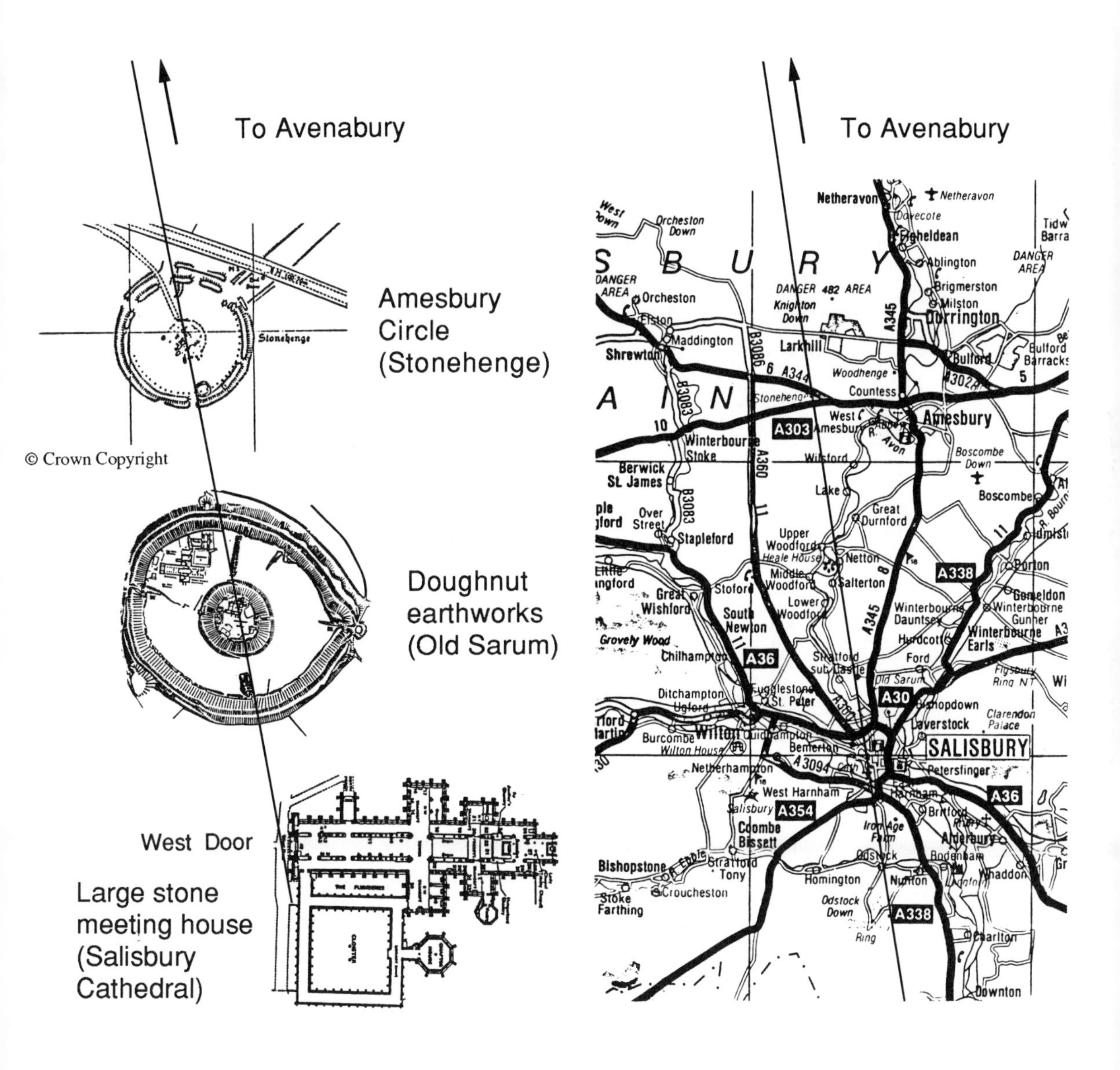

Figure 119. Positioning of the three sites pointing to the small scale model of the Horz complex.

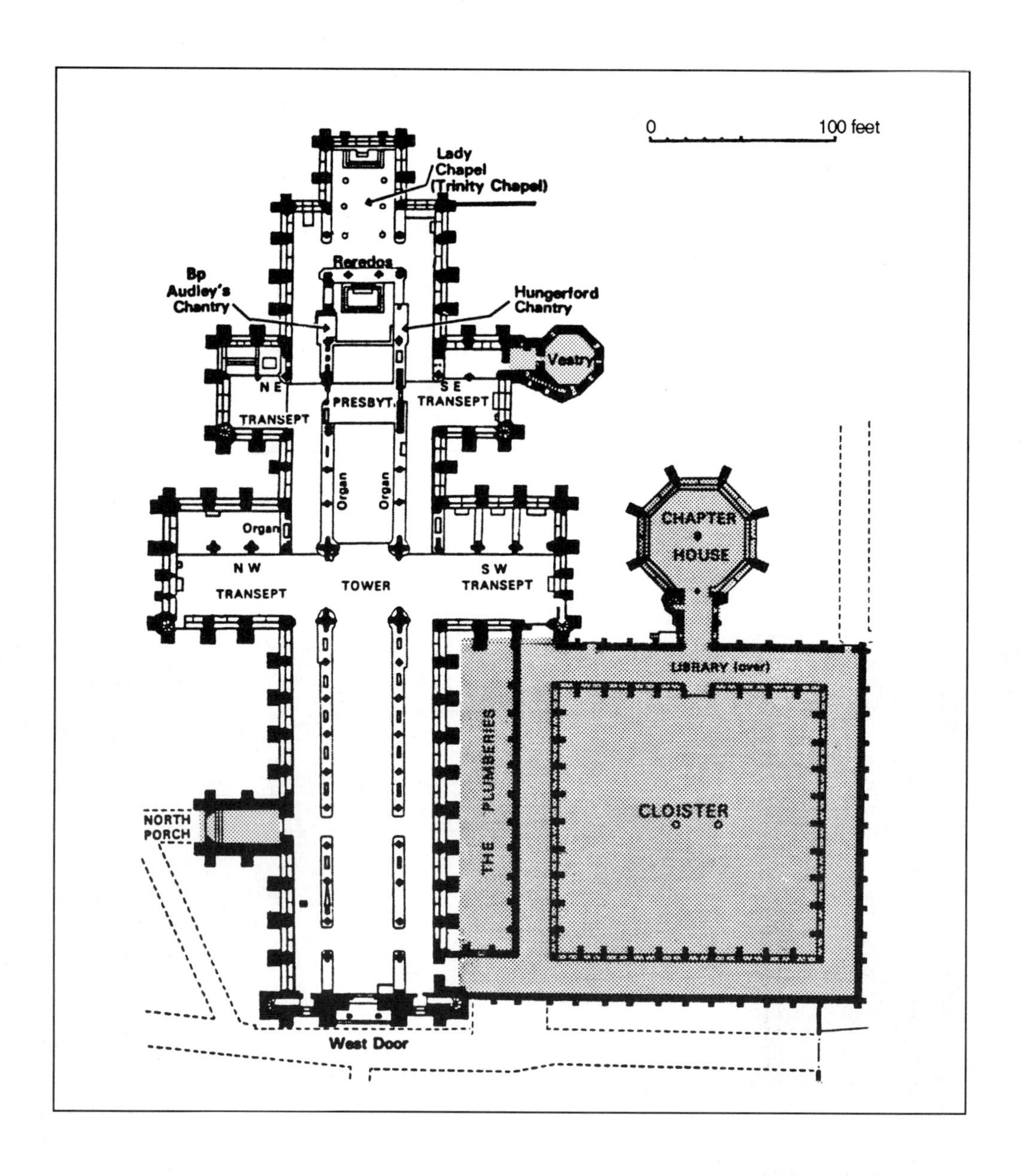

Figure 120. Floor plan of the stone meeting house (Salisbury Cathedral) designed to depict the central cylindrical column of a computer, the central cylindrical conduit and the cylindrical ring which surrounds the central column about midway up from the base. The shaded sections are not part of the design. Refer also to figure 49 and note that the West Door is at the apex of the computer.

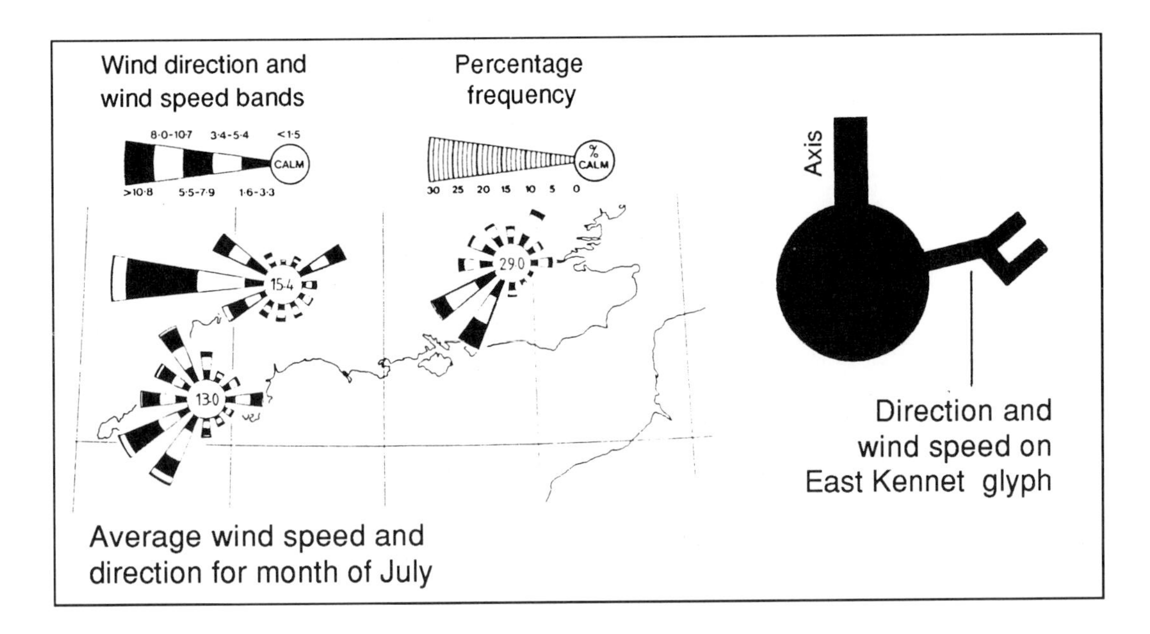

Figure 121. Weather symbols depicting the conditions at the time they were activated were incorporated into parts of some transtime crop glyphs in order to highlight the *non* meteorological cause (Alton Barnes July 1990, East Kennet July 1990).

122. Stone column with rounded flutes depicting an energy conduit with sub-conduits (Kirk at Wells).

Figure 123. The transtime crop glyph (Cheesefoot Head August 1991) featuring six petals — 2/3rds spaced among themselves — inside two concentric circles, depictions of the double casings of energy conduits. This transtime crop glyph is signed by the two Carys and Joe Lon Odkin.

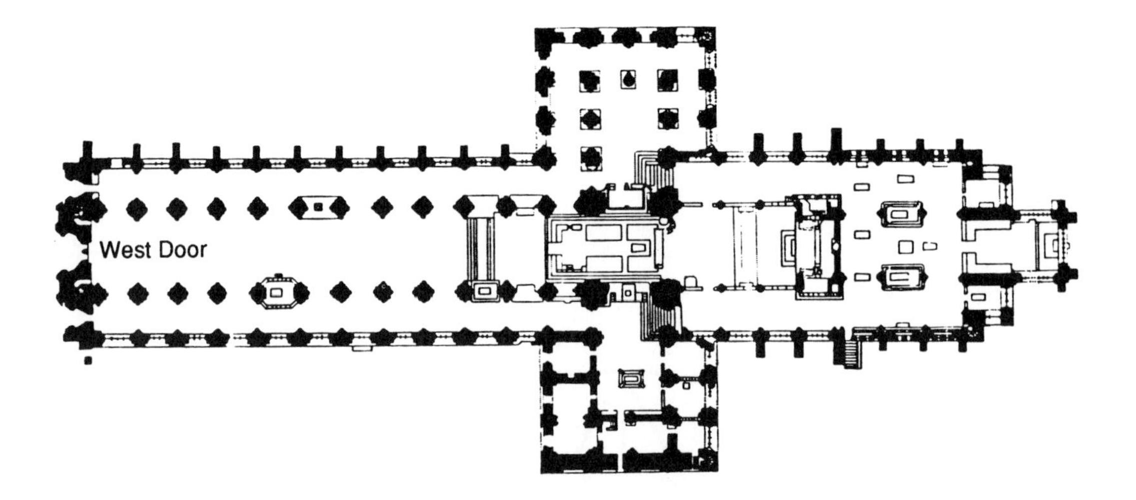

Figure 124. The floor plan of the stone meeting house (Winchester Cathedral) designed to depict one of the lead lined casings that contain a gold dolphin. Two such casings are then inserted into the transconverter sphere of energy transconverters (see also figures 30 and 31).

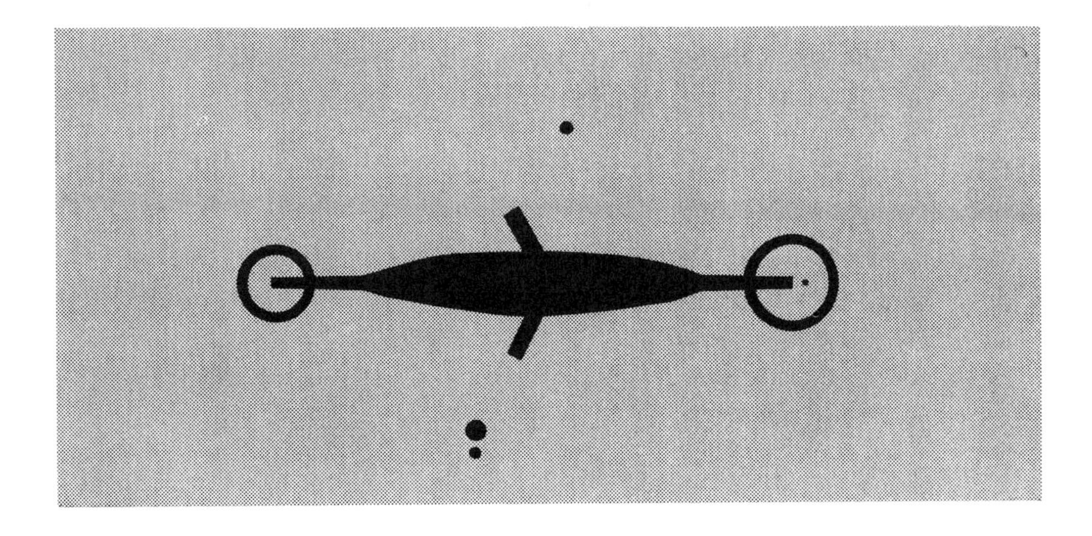

Figure 125. The transtime crop glyph (Firs Farm August 1991) designed to depict one of the gold dolphins with its attendant spheres that are placed into lead lined casings. There is a 1:1 size correlation between this glyph and Winchester Cathedral (see figures 124 and also figures 30 and 31).

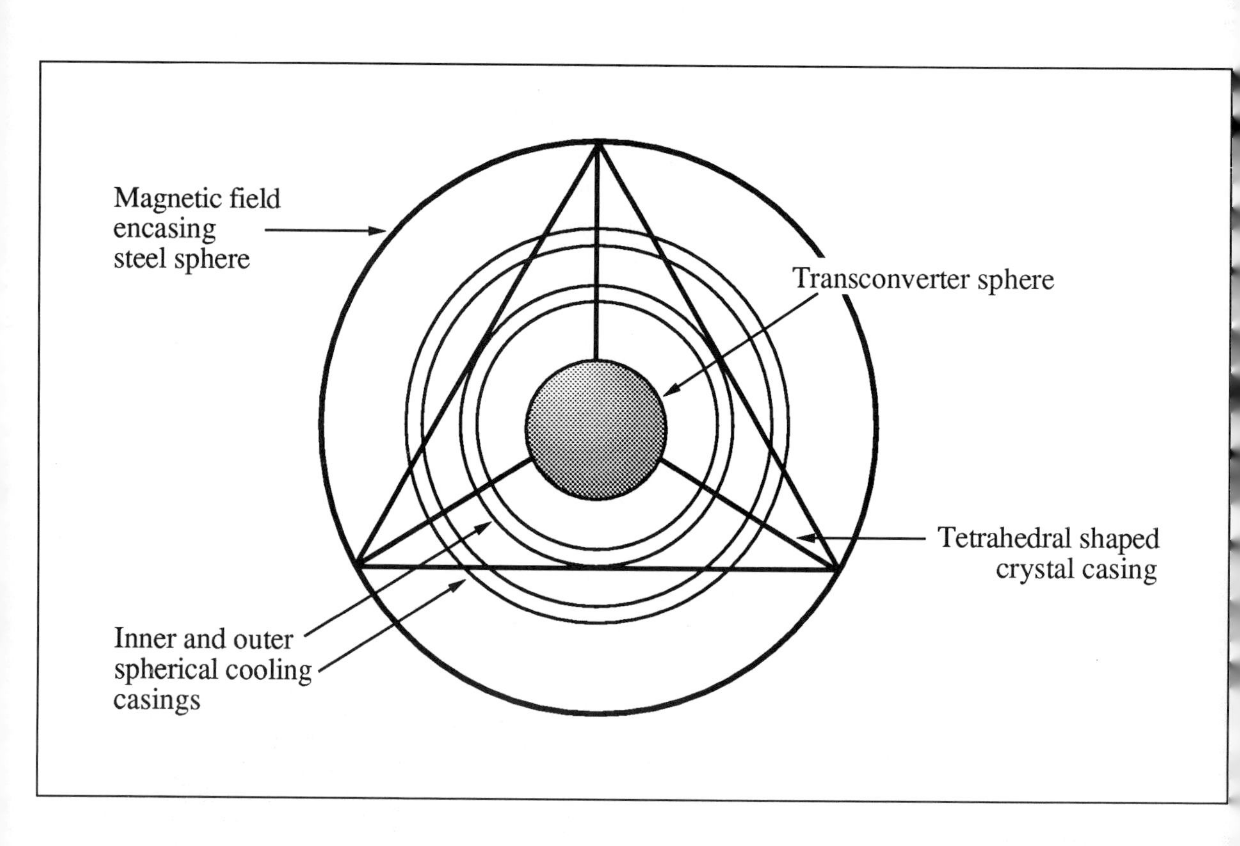

Figure 126. A two-dimensional depiction of the major components of an energy transconverter.

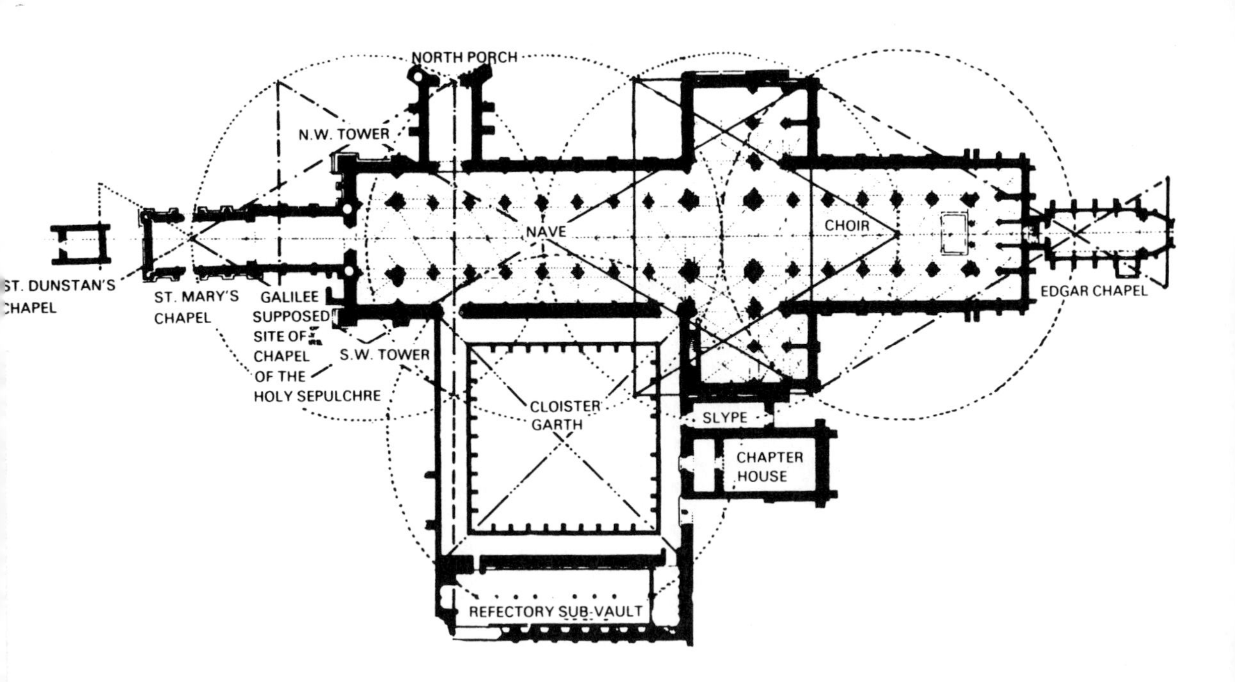

Figure 127. Groundplan of the large stone meeting house (Glastonbury Abbey) designed to depict components of the gravitron drive, in conjunction with the appropriate transtime crop glyphs.

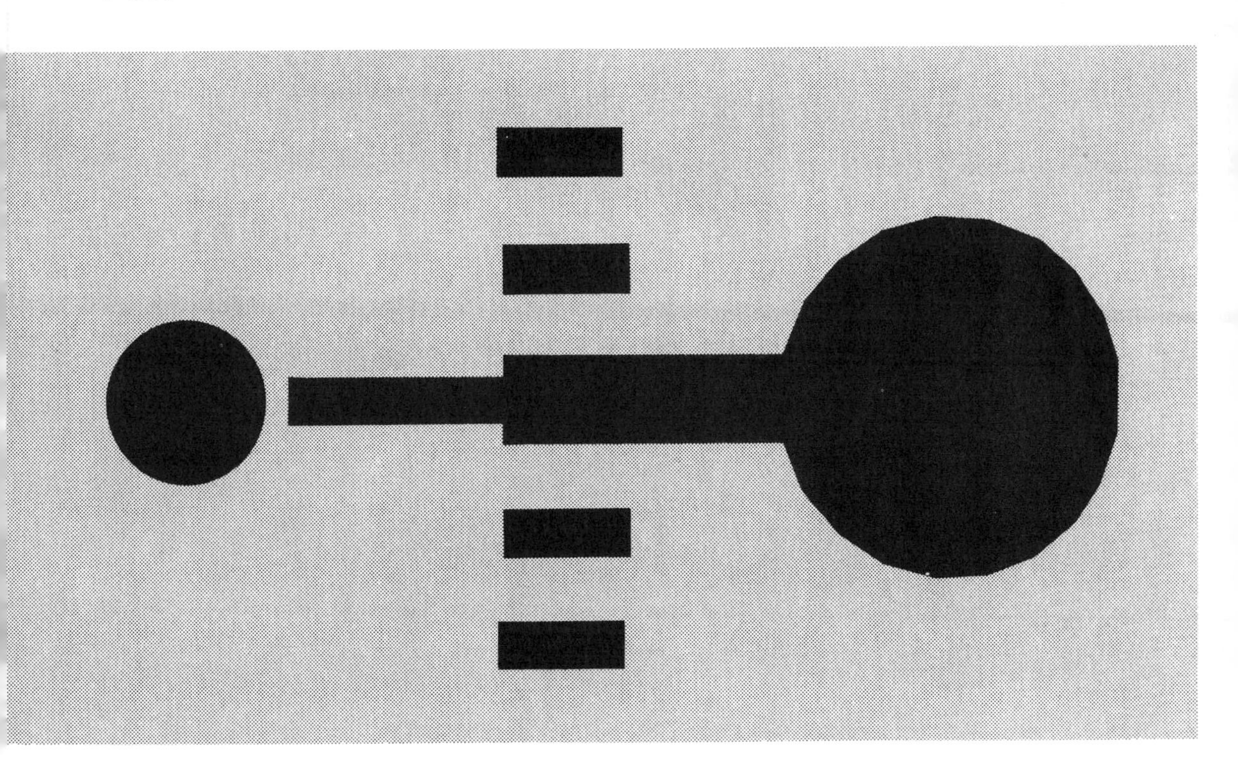

Figure 127.1 Transtime crop glyph (Chilcomb May 1990) designed to be combined with Glastonbury Abbey and the scale model of the spinning disk (Stonehenge) to depict components of the gravitron drive.

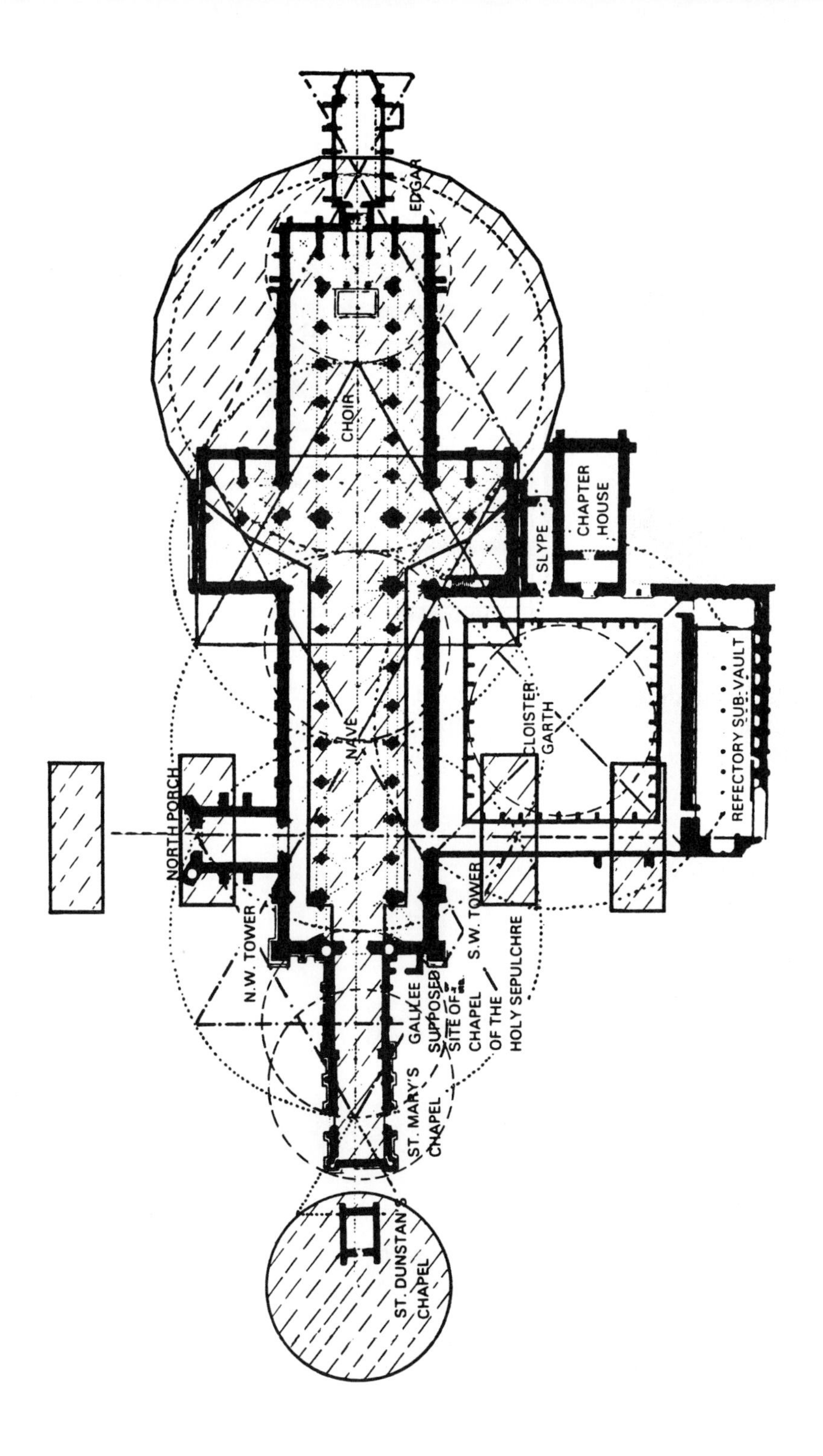

Figure 127.2. Glastonbury Abbey combined with scaled overlay of the Chilcomb May 1990 transtime crop glyph. Note that the diameter of the small circle over St Dunstan's Chapel is 50% the size of the larger circles which form part of the fundamental design of the Abbey.

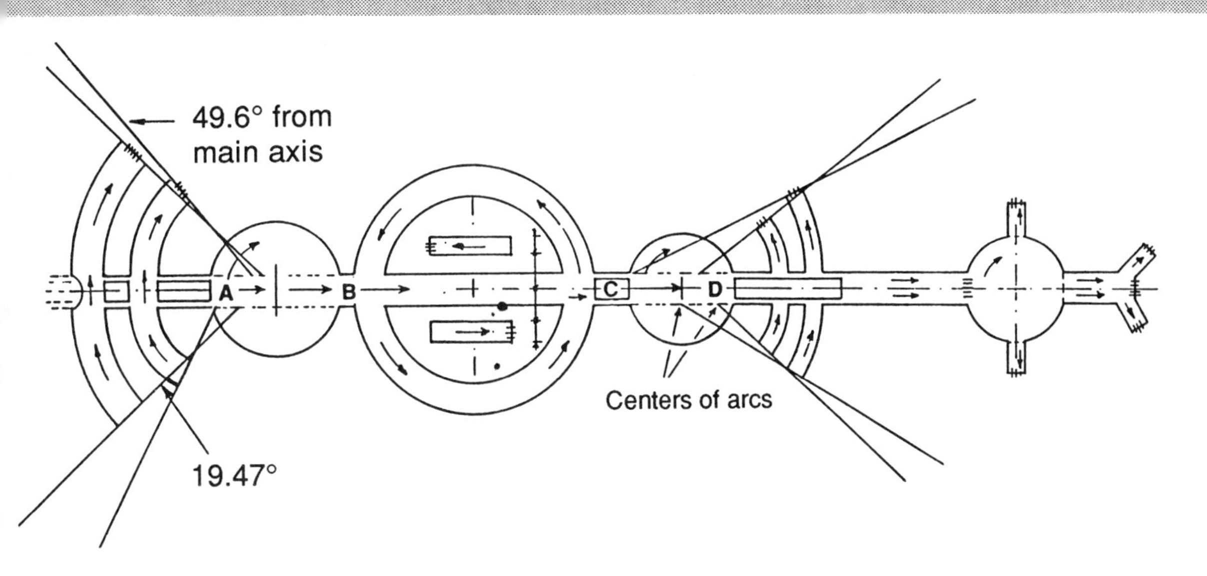

Figure 128. Transtime crop glyph (Cheesefoot Head August 1990) designed to depict the *process* of collecting the gravitron emissions from the spinning disk. It was also intended to be combined with both St Mary's Chapel in Glastonbury Abbey and the scale model of the spinning disk at Amesbury (Stonehenge) see figure 130.

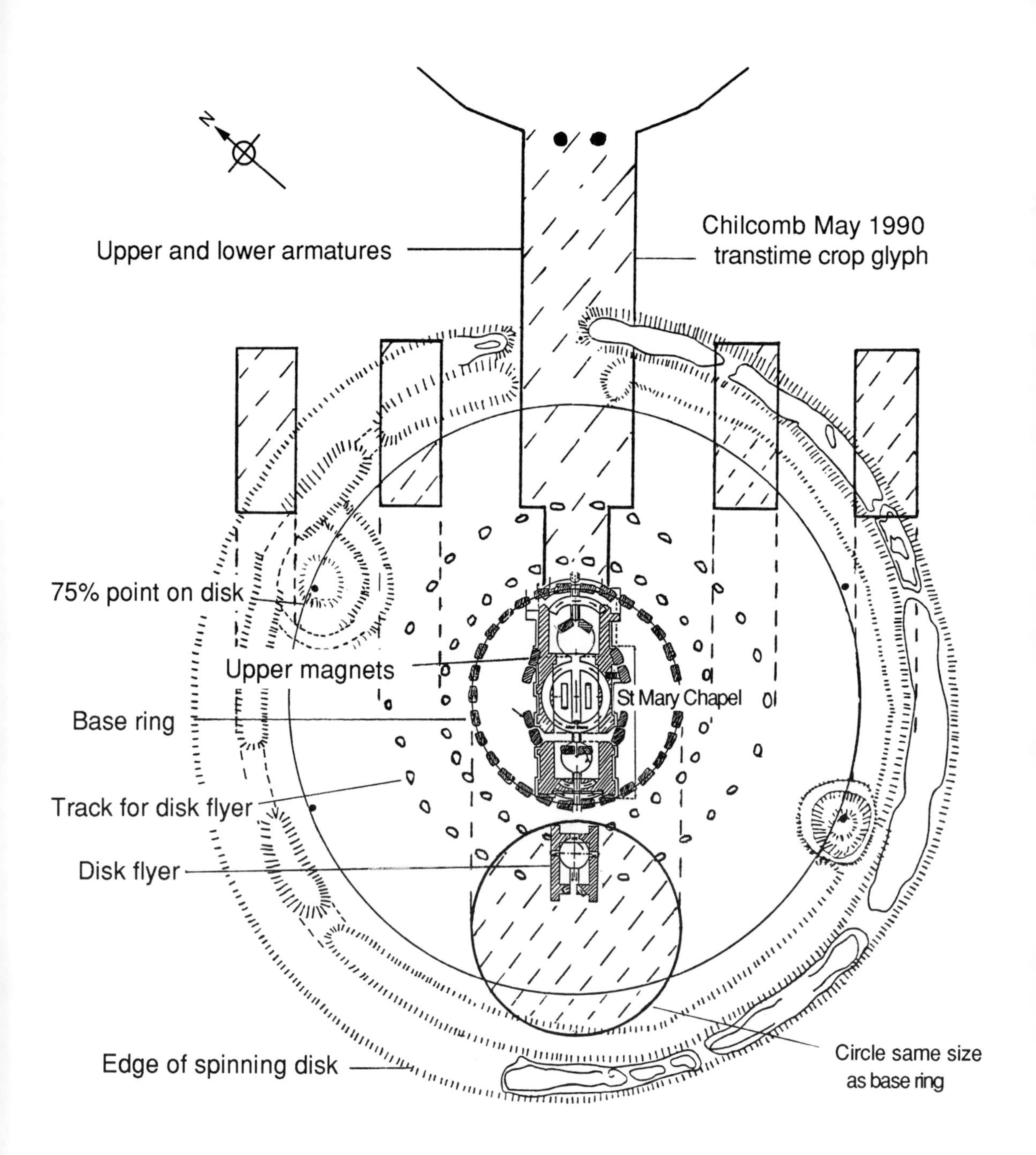

Figure 129. Plan view of Amesbury Circle (Stonehenge) combined with scaled overlay of the Chilcomb May 1990 transtime crop glyph, which depicts the western part of Glastonbury Abbey in particular the St Mary Chapel. The four boxes mark the key alignments of the stones and holes in this scale model of the spinning disk and are magnets (compare figure 24).

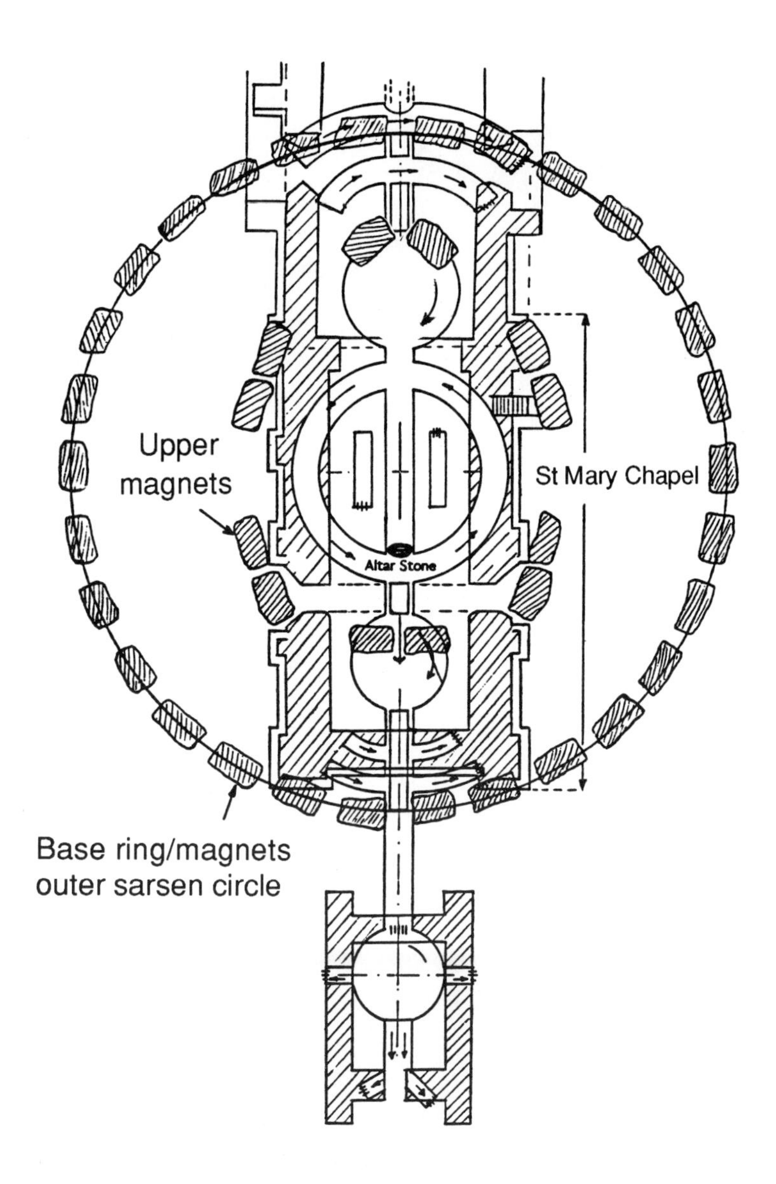

Figure 130. Close-up of St Mary's Chapel Glastonbury Abbey with scaled overlay of the Cheesefoot Head August 1990 transtime crop glyph combined with the sarsen ring at Stonehenge. It is clear that the chapel and the ring share a common groundplan.

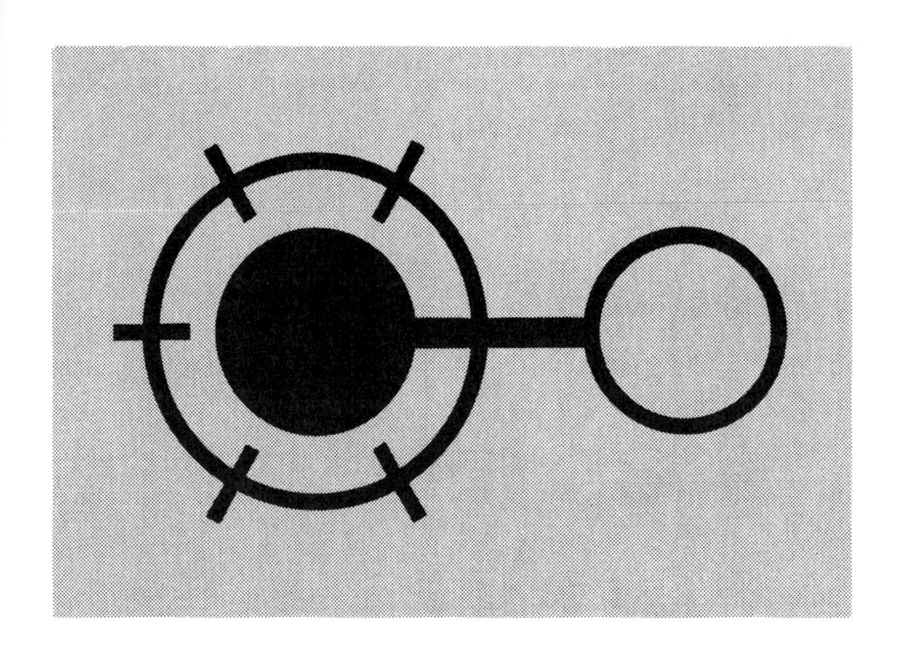

Figure 131. Transtime crop glyph (Etchilhampton July 1990). Designed to depict a multi-perspective of the gravitron capture rings, the gravitron drive support and gravitron emission shaft, the gravitron distributor ring and the six gravitron vents, through which gravitrons are vented into the spacings between the inner and outer hulls o star ships. (See also figure 28).

132. The analog of the wooden pump house just south of Avenabury Circle as it is today.

Figure 132.1. 'Bozo the holo-image' transtime crop glyph (Colchester Essex 1990). The glyph spells out 'ozo' with the 'b' strongly implied. Half the face is only implied as it was intended to represent a holographic face which has more elements than can be depicted in two dimensions. This glyph was formed well away from either the small or the large scale models of the Horz Complex.

Figure 132.2. Transtime crop glyph (Clanfield Hants July 1990) intended to depict the electrocuted body of a nitwit lying over a section of circular electric fencing, the fencing doubling as arms. The head is empty.

Figure 132.3. 'Geometric shapes' transtime crop glyph (Beckhampton July 1990). The large triangle was intended to represent the *imposed* home, and the smaller shapes to either side depict shapes from the Keirykeion Line which ran over the Hill of Musing. In addition it is a cross section of the defenses of *all* Crystal Palaces. (Compare figure 66.1).

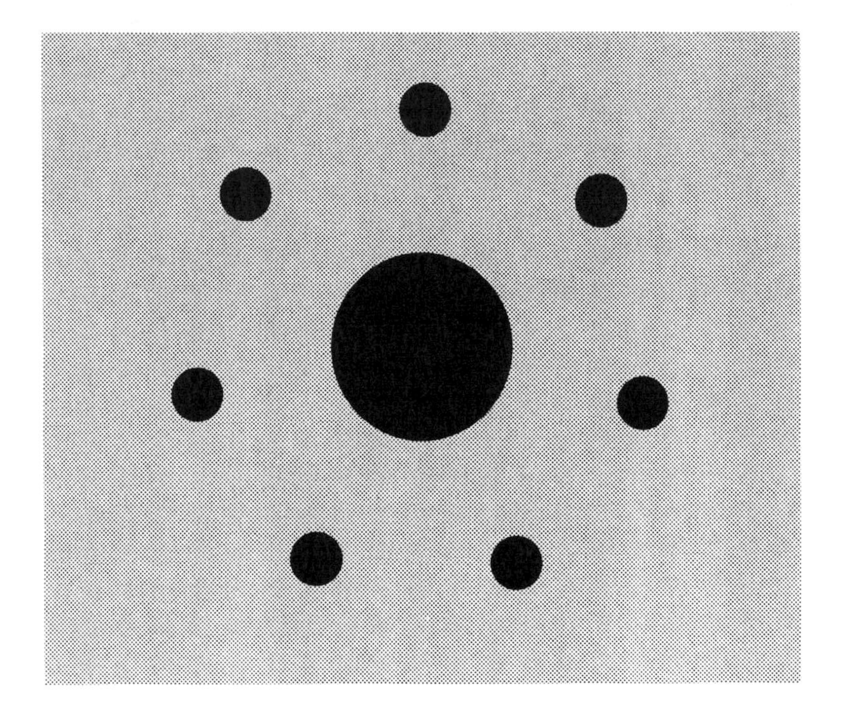

Figure 132.4. Transtime crop glyph (Bickington Devon 1990) intended to represent the rings of warning pylons around *all* Crystal Palaces.

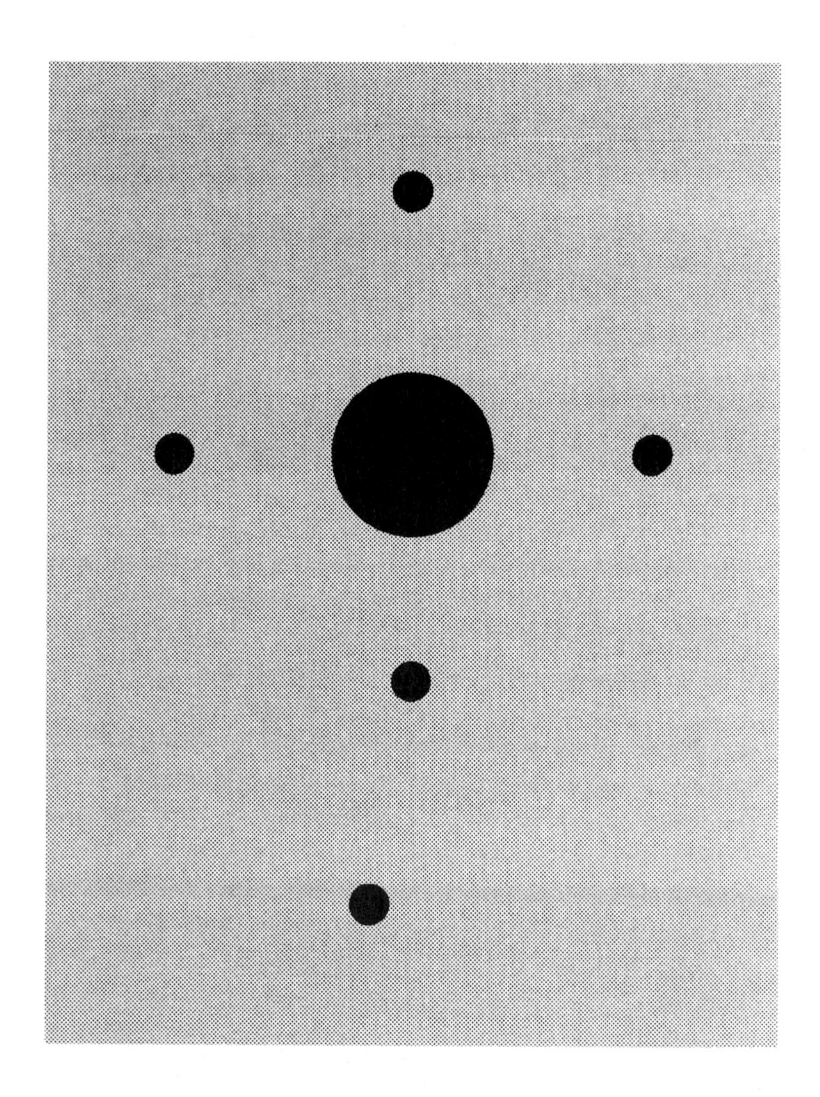

Figure 132.5. 'The mark missed' transtime crop glyph (Cherhill 1989) intended to depict Atlantis with its center terrace, four important things and the Crystal Palace of Atlantis in the river gorge far away, for those who missed the mark. This glyph was laid down in the analog position of the Crystal Palace in the small scale model of the Horz complex. (See figure 62.3).

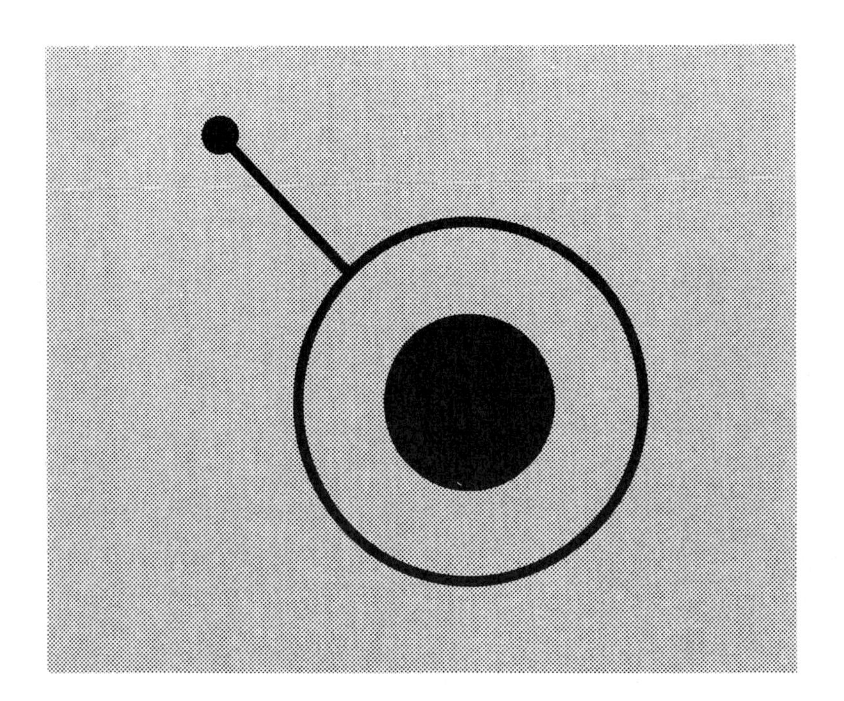

Figure 132.6. Transtime crop glyph (Churhill May 1992) designed to depict Cary Manpure in his 'agony.' This glyph was laid down near the analog position of the Crystal Palace in the small scale model of the Horz complex. In the photograph below, this transtime crop glyph points towards a white horse cut into the hillside (in honor of Cary Manpure's favorite horse) and to earthen butresses sculpted by Essenes.

Part 3 Chapter 9

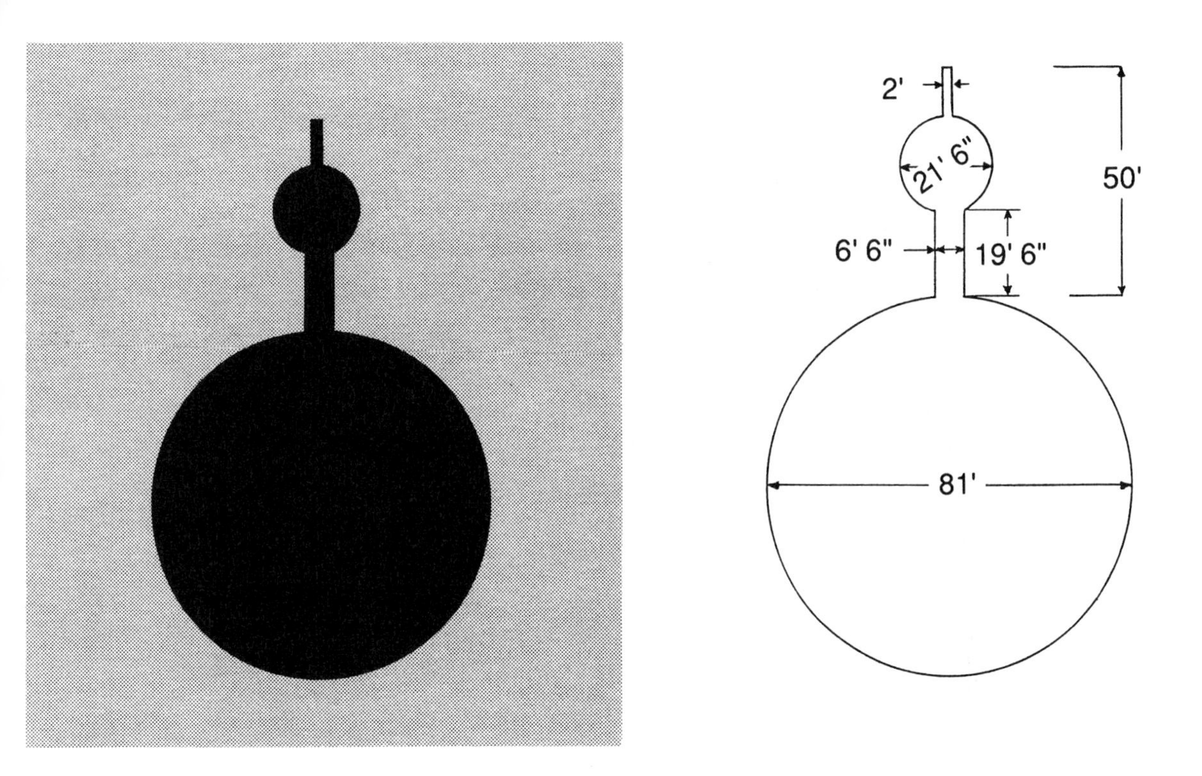

Figure 133. Harmony transtime crop glyph (Firs Farm Beckhampton 1991) designed to represent the mass ratio between Danebury and its moon, the smaller circle representing the diameter of Danebury's moon.

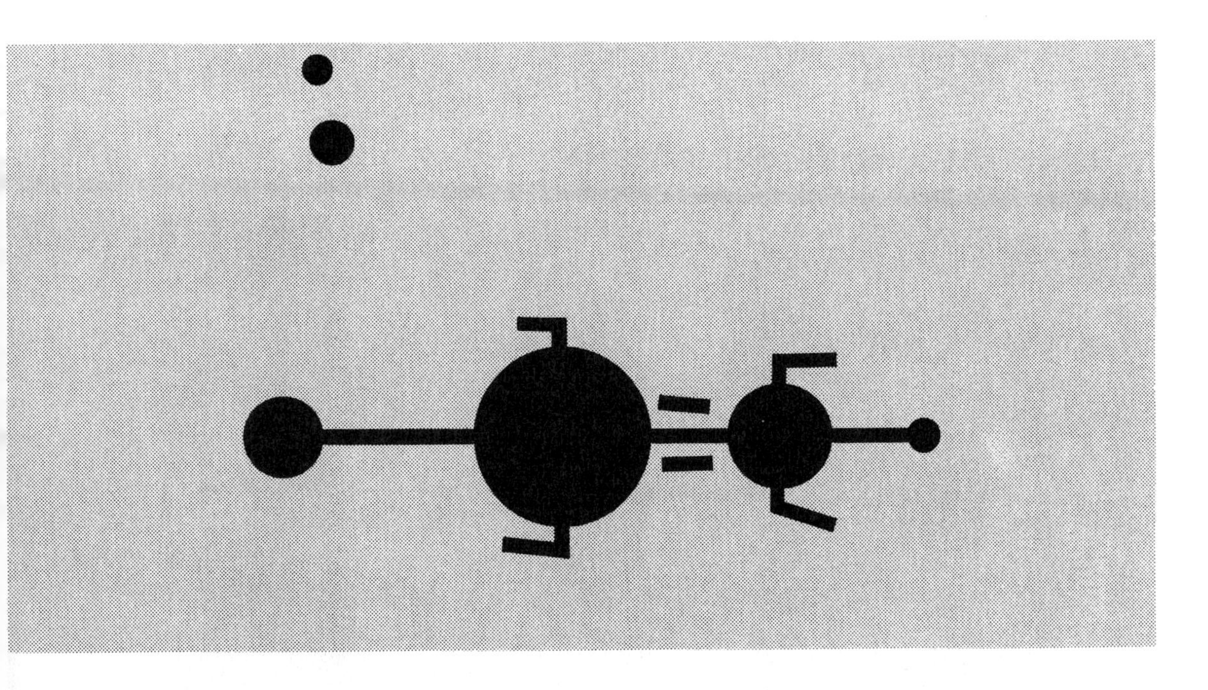

Figure 134. Ant men transtime crop glyph (Clatford Marlborough August 1991) part of the Disharmony series.

135. Copy of one of the water courses surrounding the longhouses in Hur Square. Used as a *urinal* at Glastonbury Abbey. (See the water courses in figure 54).

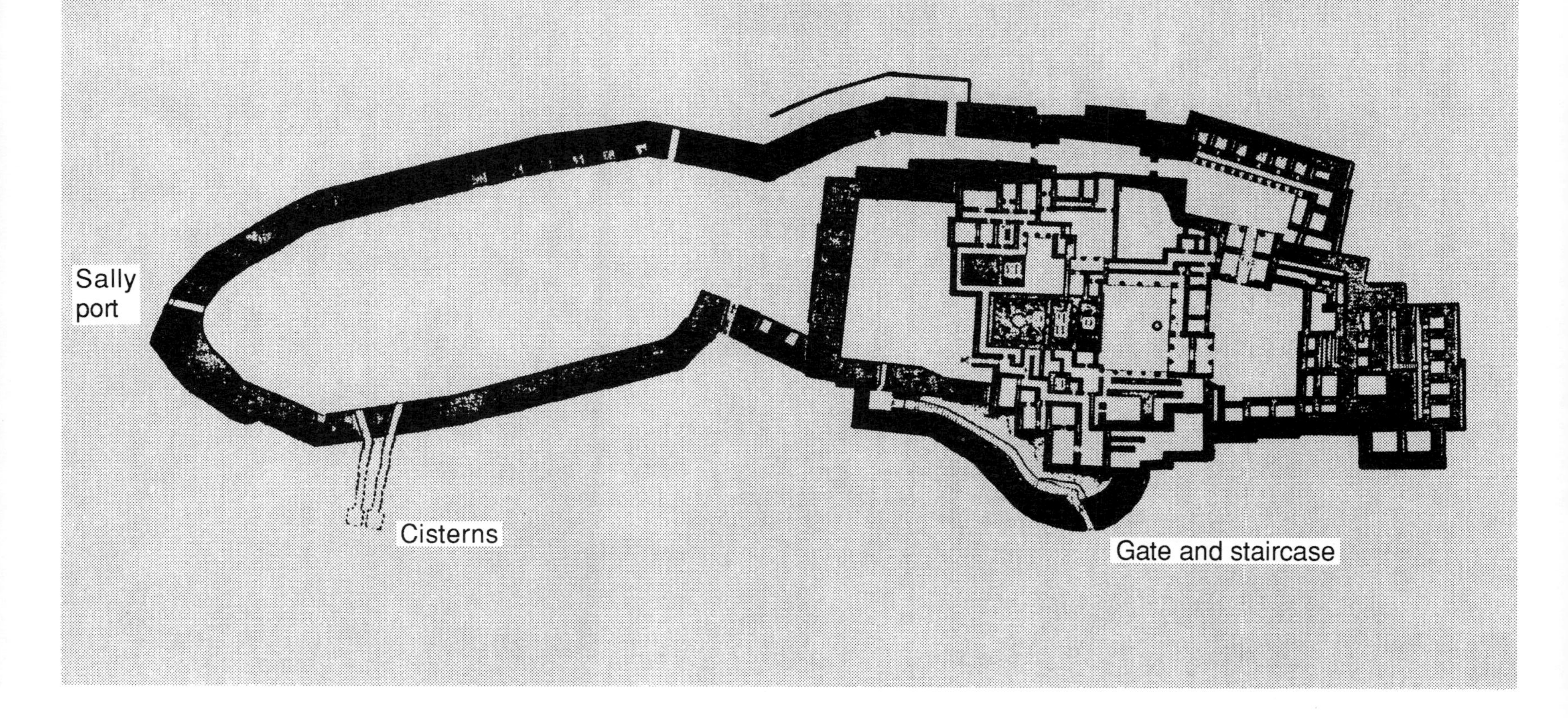

Figure 136. "Vasectomy." Groundplan of a fortress constructed of enormous rocks at Tiryns in the land of the Hellenes.

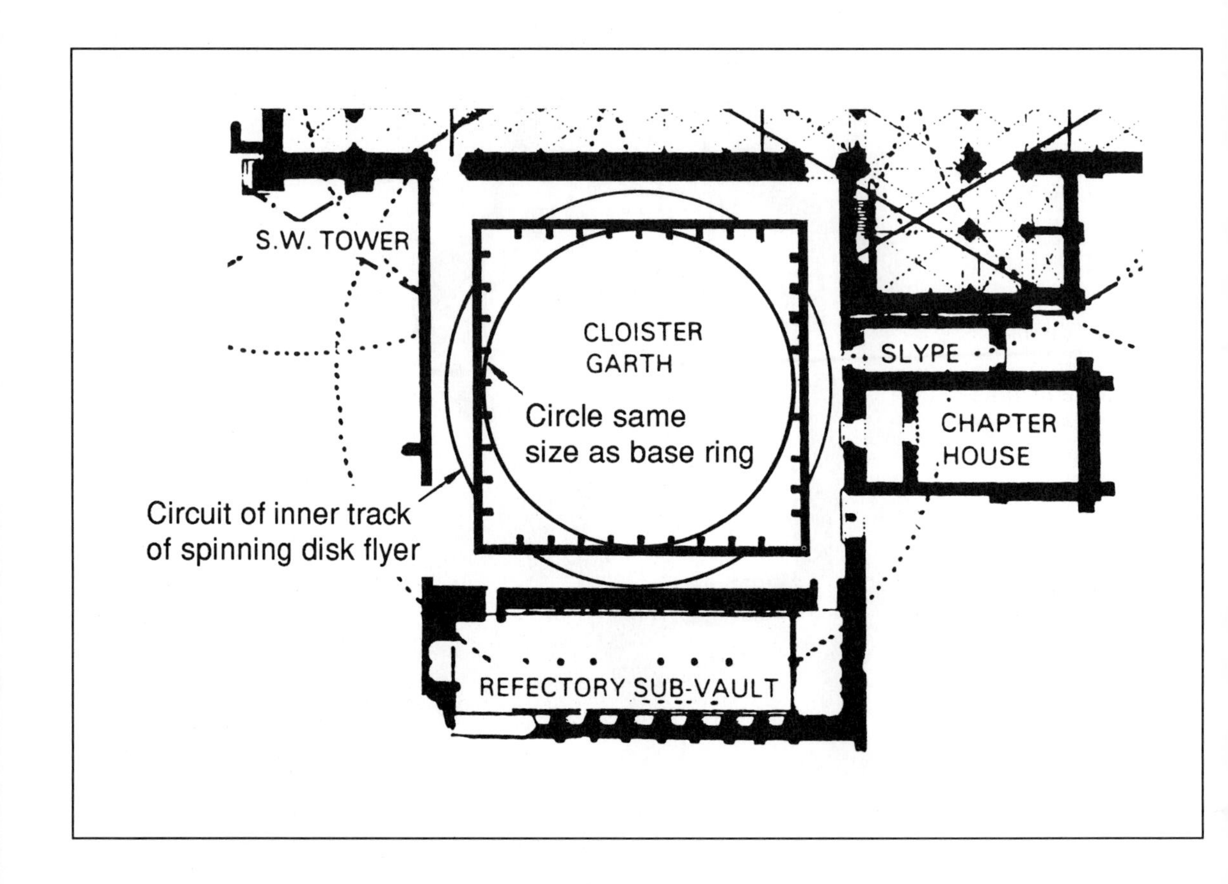

Figure 137. The Garth Representation now called the Garth Cloister, a cloister designed to illustrate the squaring of the circle of the base ring of the spinning disk. *If* this circle was squared, the flyer would not fly around the track. (See figures 24 and 129).

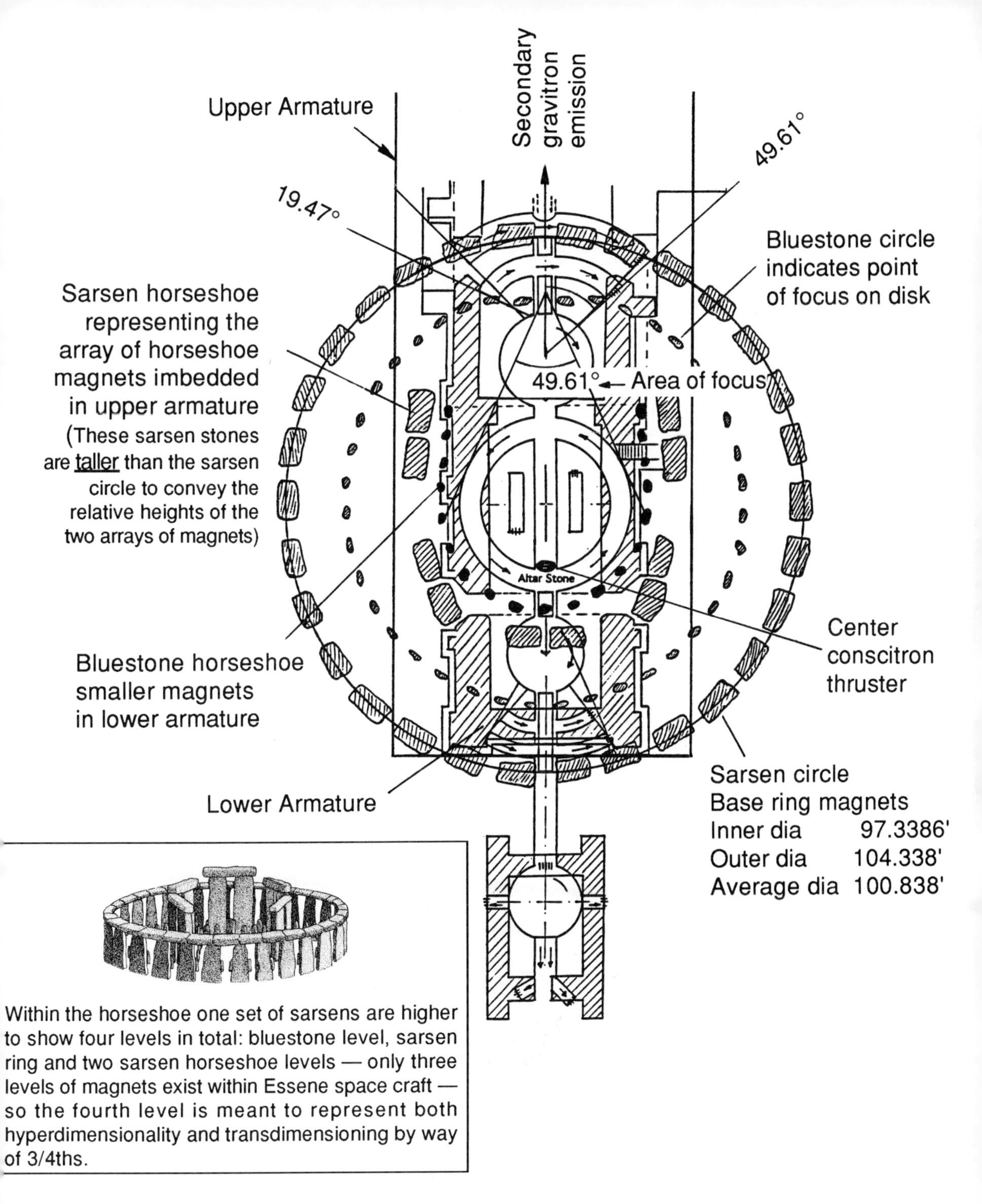

Figure 138. Depiction of the secondary emission of gravitrons from spinning disks. Here the restored sarsen rings at Amesbury Circle (Stonehenge) together with the scaled overlay of the Cheesefoot Head August 1990 transtime crop glyph, illustrate the reconfiguration of the magnets from an egg shape into a horseshoe, the way in which Amesbury Circle was subsequently constructed. This arrangement re-angles the secondary emission of gravitrons from 49.61004268° to 19.47122061° and refocuses the gravitrons at a point on the upper and lower armatures from where they can be collected. (Compare figure 130).

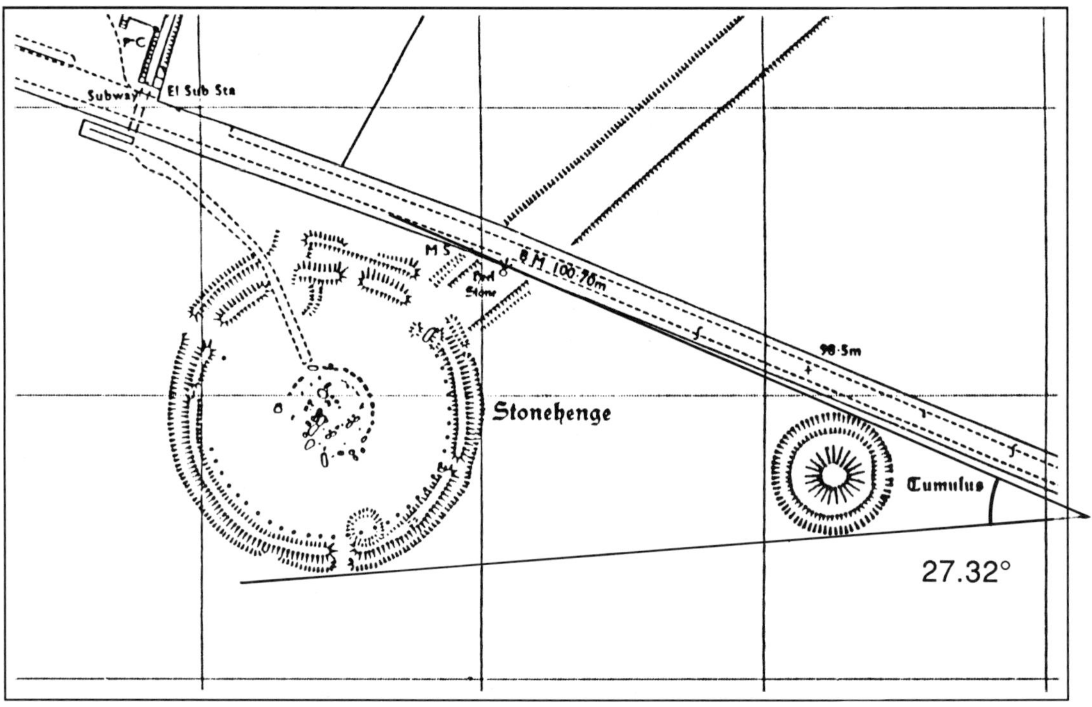

Figure 139. Mound sited to the east of Amesbury circle (Stonehenge) forming an angle of 27.3239545°. This angle was intended to encode the squaring of the circle and that the base ring of spinning disks have diameters that are 27.3239545 % as big as the diameter of the spinning disks they help magnetically levitate.

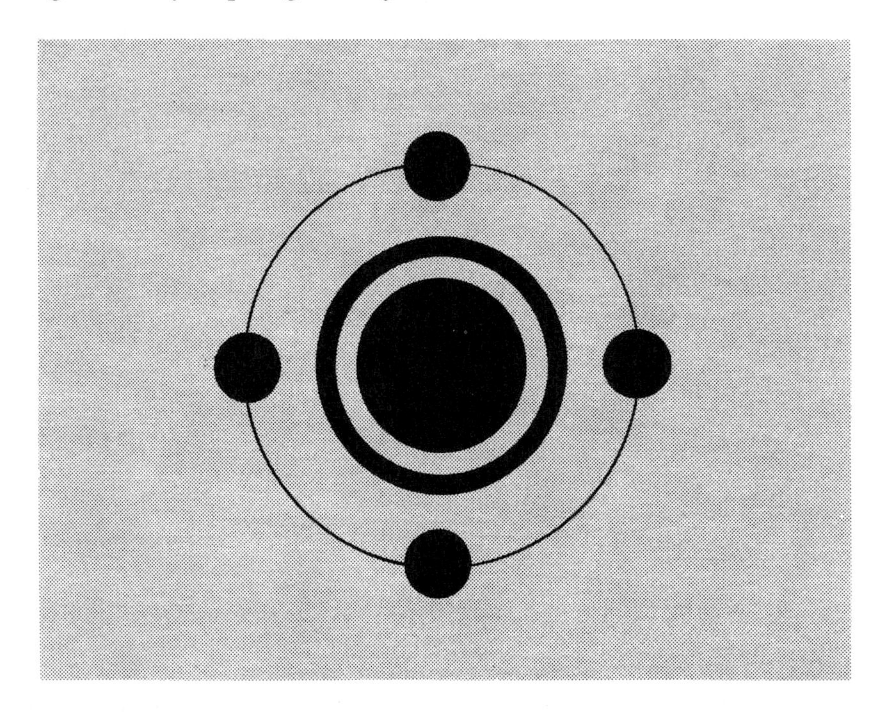

Figure 140. Transtime crop glyph (Whitchurch August 1992) designed to depict a spinning disk surrounded by a gravitron distributor ring, with the four smaller circles intended to represent the fourth-dimension, the source of all energy.

Figure 141. Transtime crop glyph (Draycott Fitzpaine August 1992) intended to depict the moving of the future moon of Danebury from one galaxy to another. The broad line and three smaller lines represent the *braided* beam.

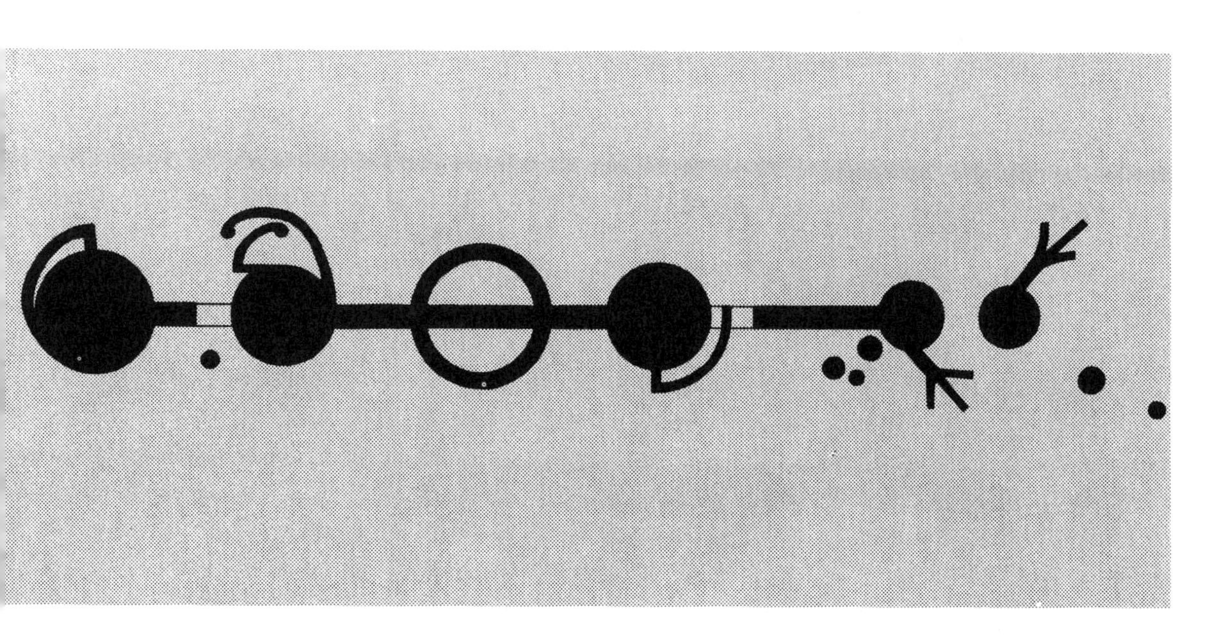

Figure 142. Transtime crop glyph (Froxfield August 1992) intended to represent the resizing, resurfacing and maneuvering of the future moon of Danebury into orbit. Parts of this transtime crop glyph were 'hoaxed' by human beings as a result of ideas infused into them by Essenes.

Figure 144. Transtime crop glyph (Alton Priors/West Stowell August 1992) designed to depict the new moon of Danebury. The ring represents the orbit of the new moon around Danebury. Note the thicker crescent than that of the depiction of Venus in figure 143.

Figure 143. Transtime crop glyph (West Stowell August 1992) intened to represent the process of drawing off the extra heat from Danebury to the sacrificed planet (Venus) which is often seen as a crescent from Danebury.

Figure 145. Transtime crop glyph (Winterbourne Stoke August 1989) designed as a representation of the rapidly spinning stroboscope disk essential as part of the crop glyph creation process. The stroboscope disk twists the two *braided beams* around each other and then transmits them to a predetermined spot on the ground.

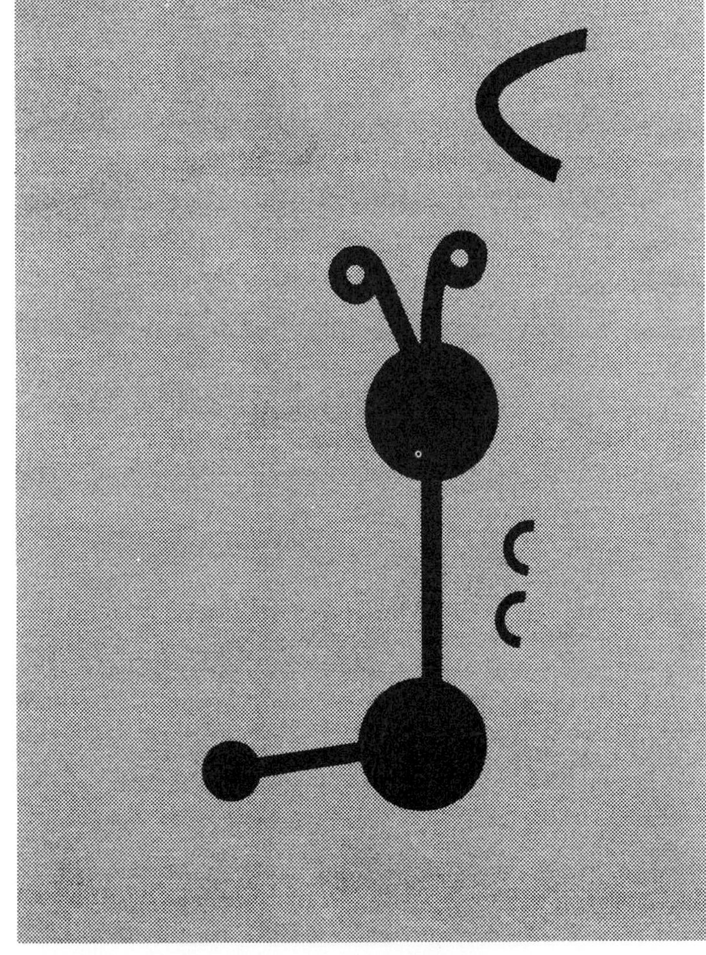

Figure 146. Transtime crop glyph (Cheesefoot Head August 1991) part of the Disharmony series, depicting Anson Trent the ultimate traitor.

Figure 147. Transtime crop glyph (Chilcomb Down July 1991) Anson Trent the ultimate traitor second version!

Figure 148. Transtime crop glyph (Chilcomb Down July 1991) a depiction of Ann Trent, Anson's daughter.

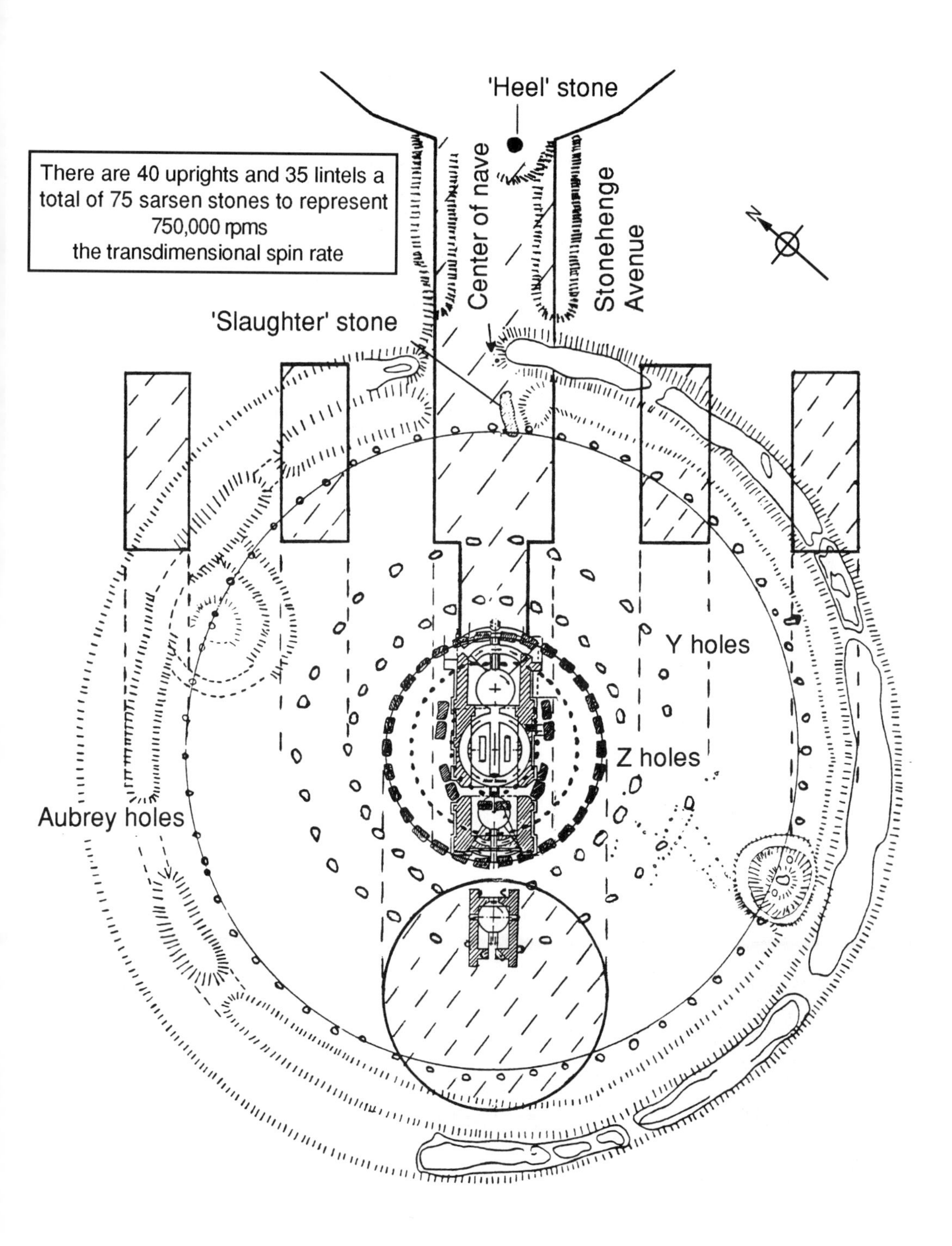

Figure 149. Amesbury Circle (Stonehenge) reconstructed from the remains as they are today. This is the final design including the scaled overlay of Chilcomb 1990 transtime crop glyph/Glastonbury Abbey. The nave of the abbey is an exact match to the width of the avenue. Note the total of 56 holes representing the outer edge of the gravitron capture rings. (Refer also to figure 138).

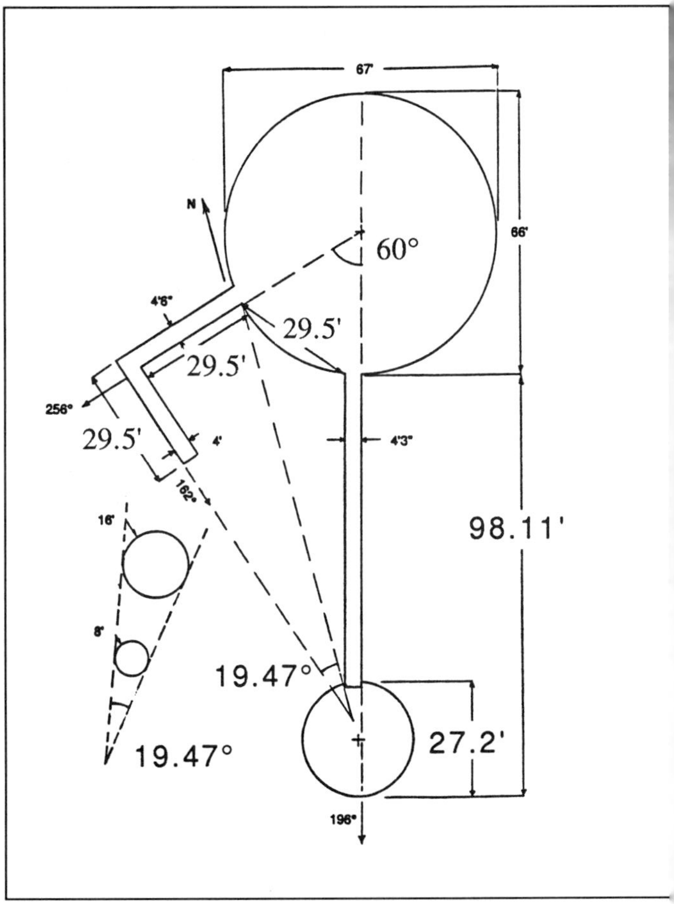

Figure 150. Additional details relevant to the Silbury Hill July 1991 transtime crop glyph designed to represent energy transredimensioning. The distance 29.5' is intended to represent 295, the number of projected spin axes of Horun in complexified three-space. Also worth noting: the relationship between the diameters of the smaller and larger circles is a near representation of the mass ratios between the two planets Danebury and Silbury.

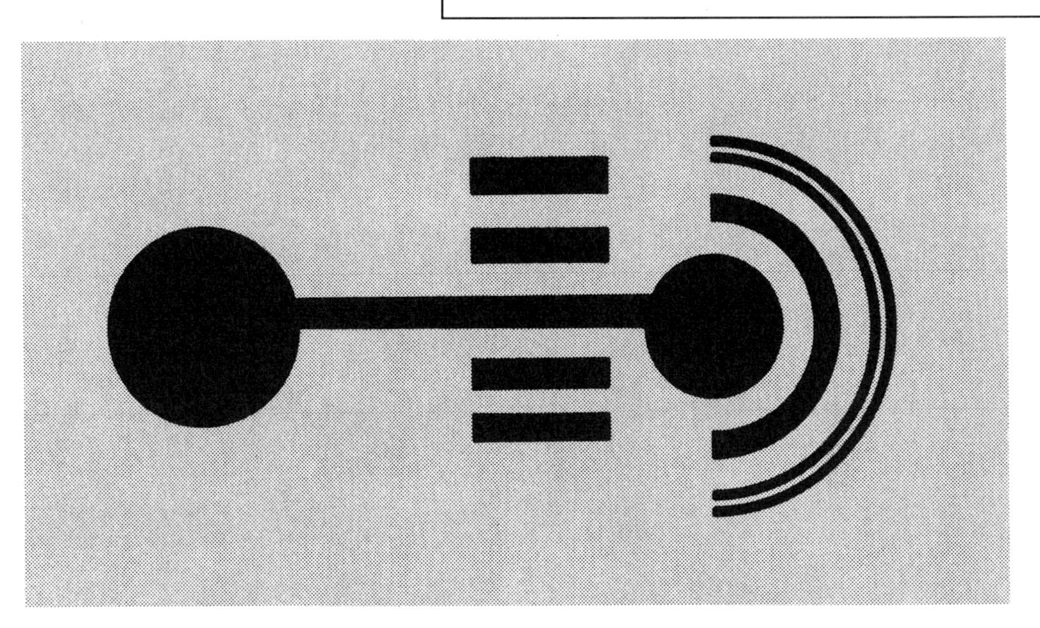

Figure 150.1. Transtime crop glyph (Litchfield June 1990) designed to represent harmonics. Two-thirds of the arcs are narrow and close together, to be read as one musical tone of a musical harmonic, and the broad arc is to be read as the other musical tone of the same harmonic. The four short lines represent the Source of the Universe, the Source of *all* harmonics.

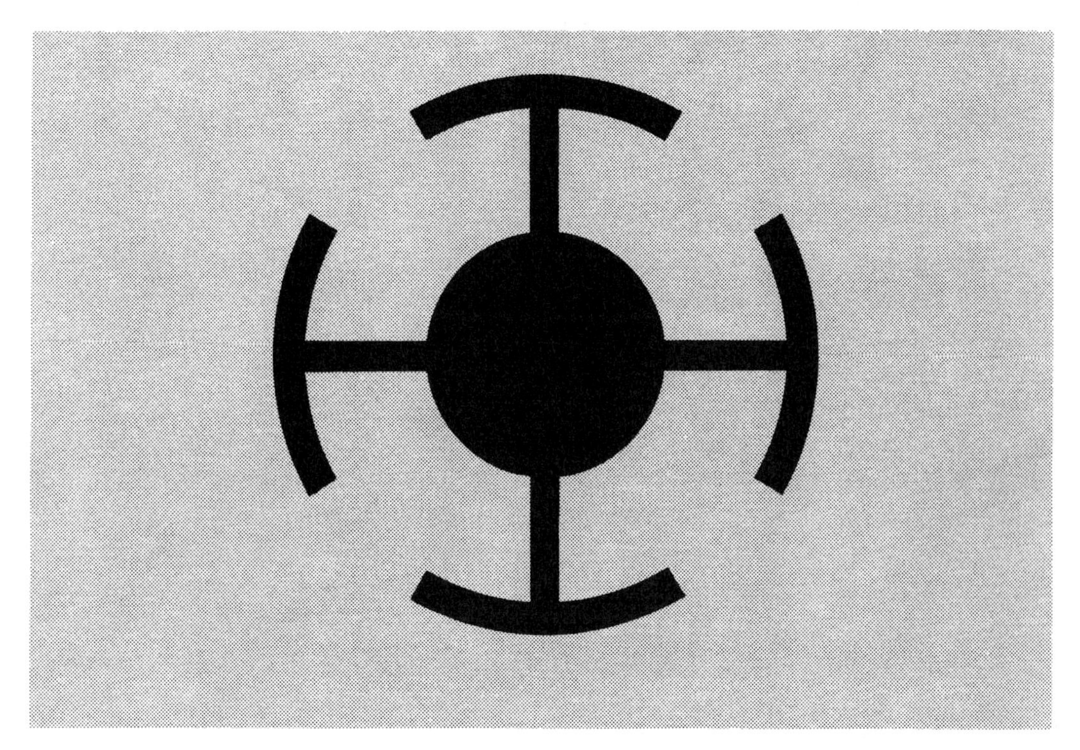

Figure 150.2. Transtime crop glyph (Spaldwick July 1991) designed to depict the rotation of a spinning disk partially into complexified three-space. The gaps represent that which is spun into complexified three-space and is no longer in three dimensions.

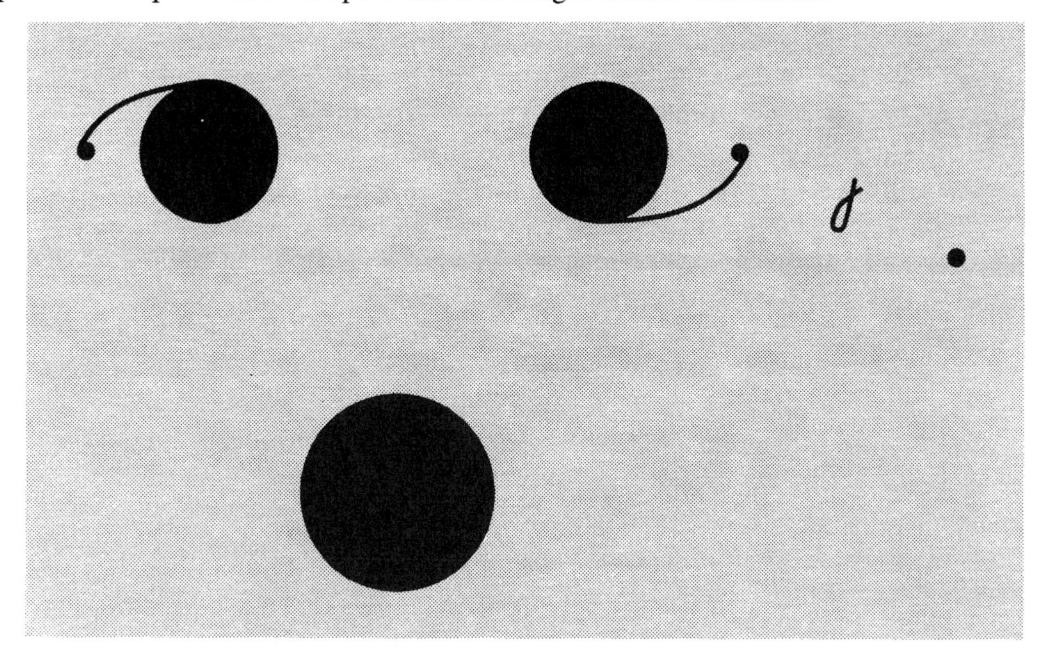

Figure 150.3. Transtime crop glyph (Overtown Farm June 1992 one mile north of Barbury Castle) designed to represent 2/3rds and 3/4rs. The smaller circles are 75% the size of the largest circle and two-thirds of the circles are depicted in the process of releasing gravitrons from the spinning disk—a disk which spins at 750,000 rpms. The Hellenikos letter to the right of the illustration is a *gamma* for gravitron centered between a single gravitron and a gravitron being emitted from the disk.

151. The modified oval shaped transtime crop glyph (Stone Avenue 1991) distorted due to the conditions at the time of laying it down approximately 237,000 years ago. This glyph was the first to be laid down on Danebury, and this photograph was taken less than 3 hours after its activation at the end of July 1991.

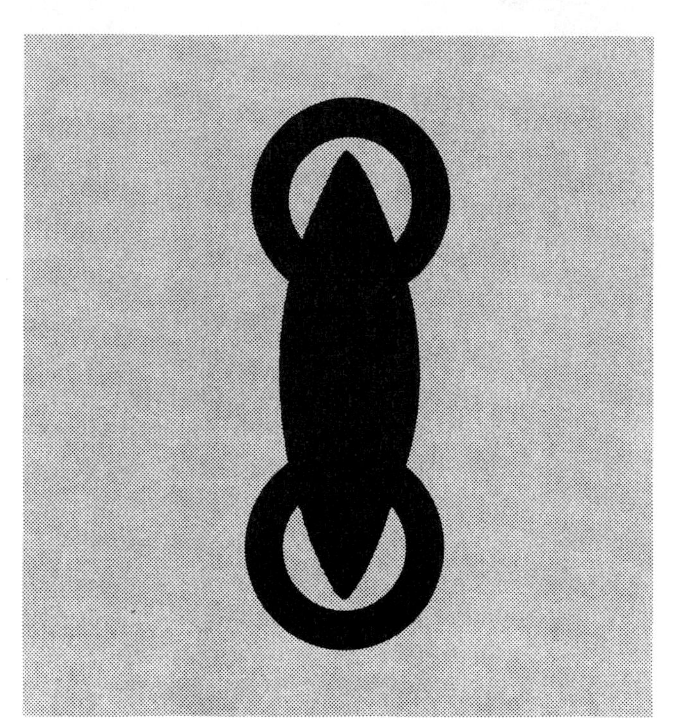

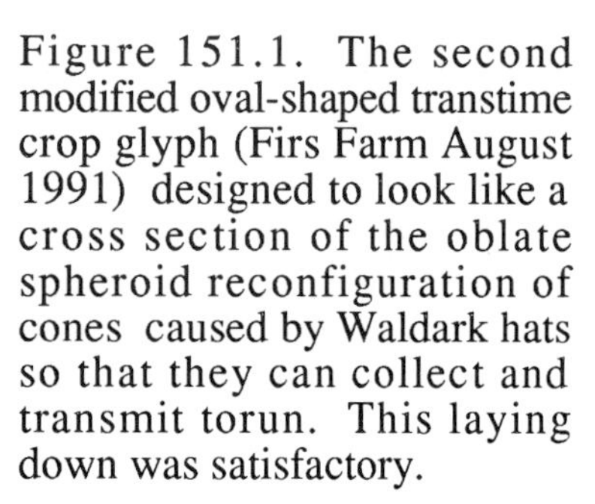

Figure 151.1. The second modified oval-shaped transtime crop glyph (Firs Farm August 1991) designed to look like a cross section of the oblate spheroid reconfiguration of cones caused by Waldark hats so that they can collect and transmit torun. This laying down was satisfactory.

Part 3 Chapter 11

152. Mound marking the spot (Beckhampton roundabout) where the trees were cleared and the cargo ship landed so that the two Carys could 'enjoy' a beer. Cary Manpure's pile is behind the arrow direction sign. Behind the blunt end of the arrow and outside the roundabout is the analog site in the small scale model of the Horz complex of "Glamyrr and Sustanator." The arrow points at the road in the background which goes just north of the northern side of the analog of Altea City in the small scale model of the Horz complex.

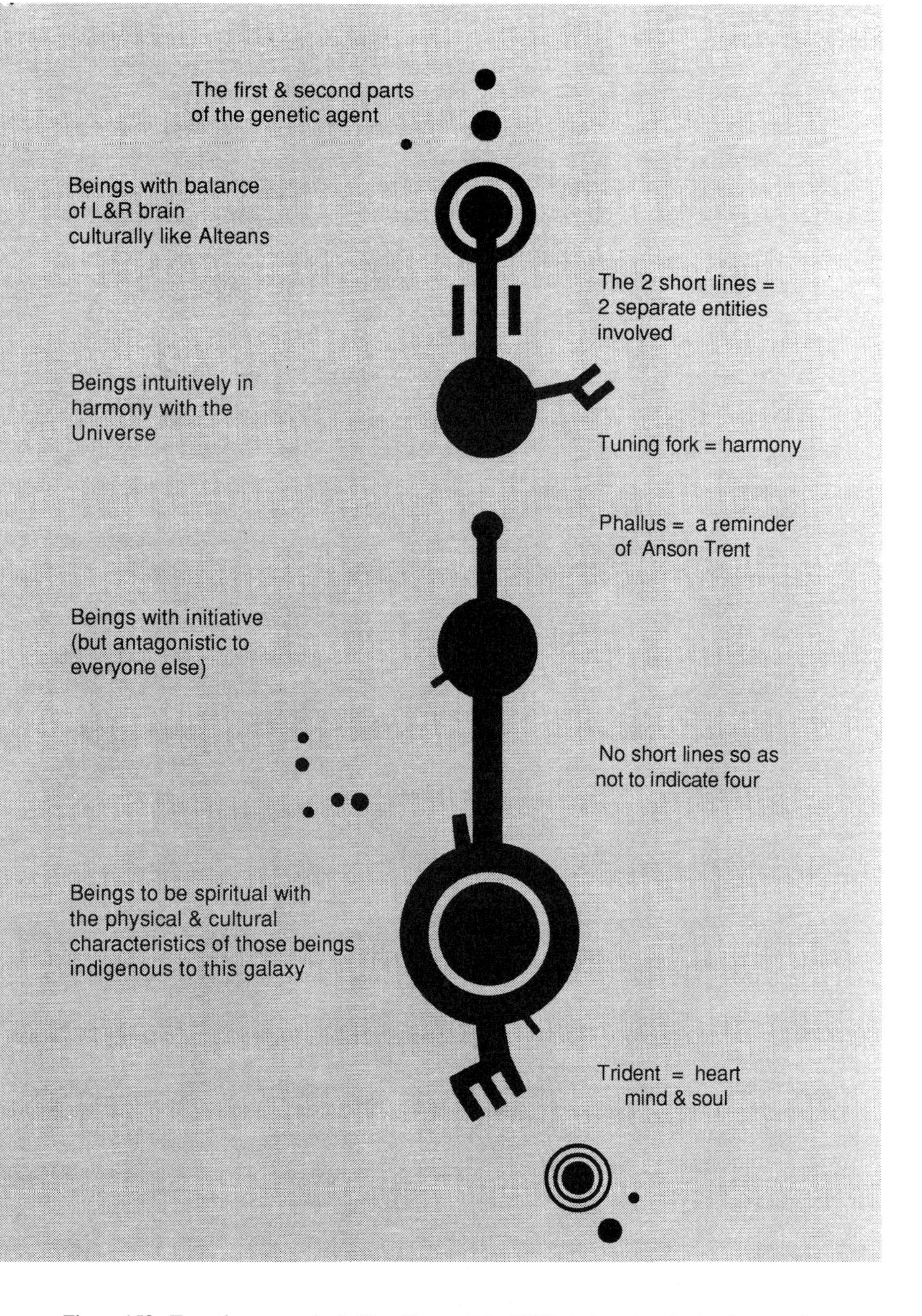

Figure 153. Transtime crop glyph (East Kennet July 1990) designed to depict the genetic project and the results it would produce. This is one of two which was to represent two-thirds of the possible combinations of intermingling between the four groups which were to be culturally, genetically and physically different.

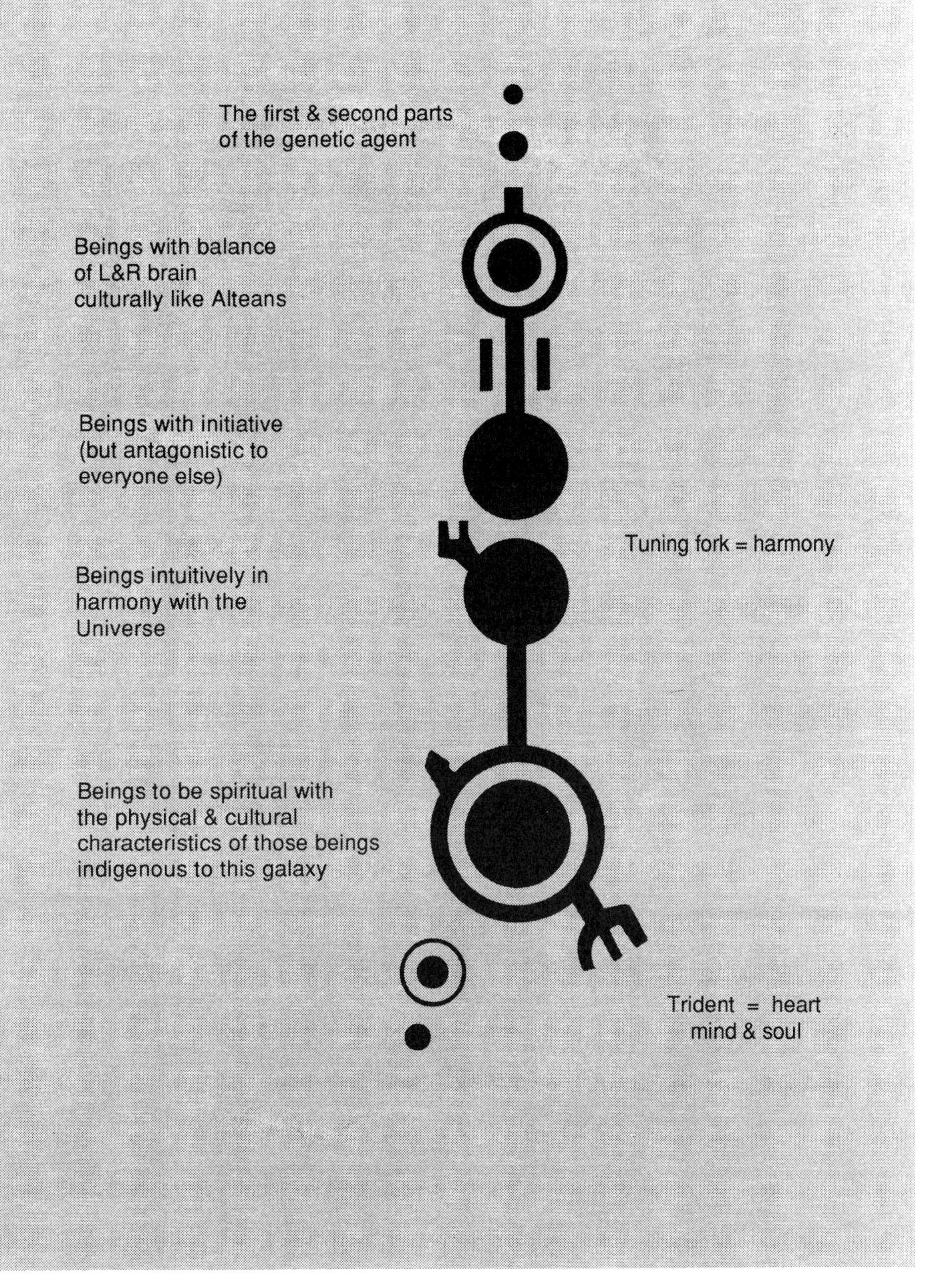

Figure 153.1 The second transtime crop glyph (Stanton St Bernard July 1990) also designed to represent the genetic project and the results it would produce.

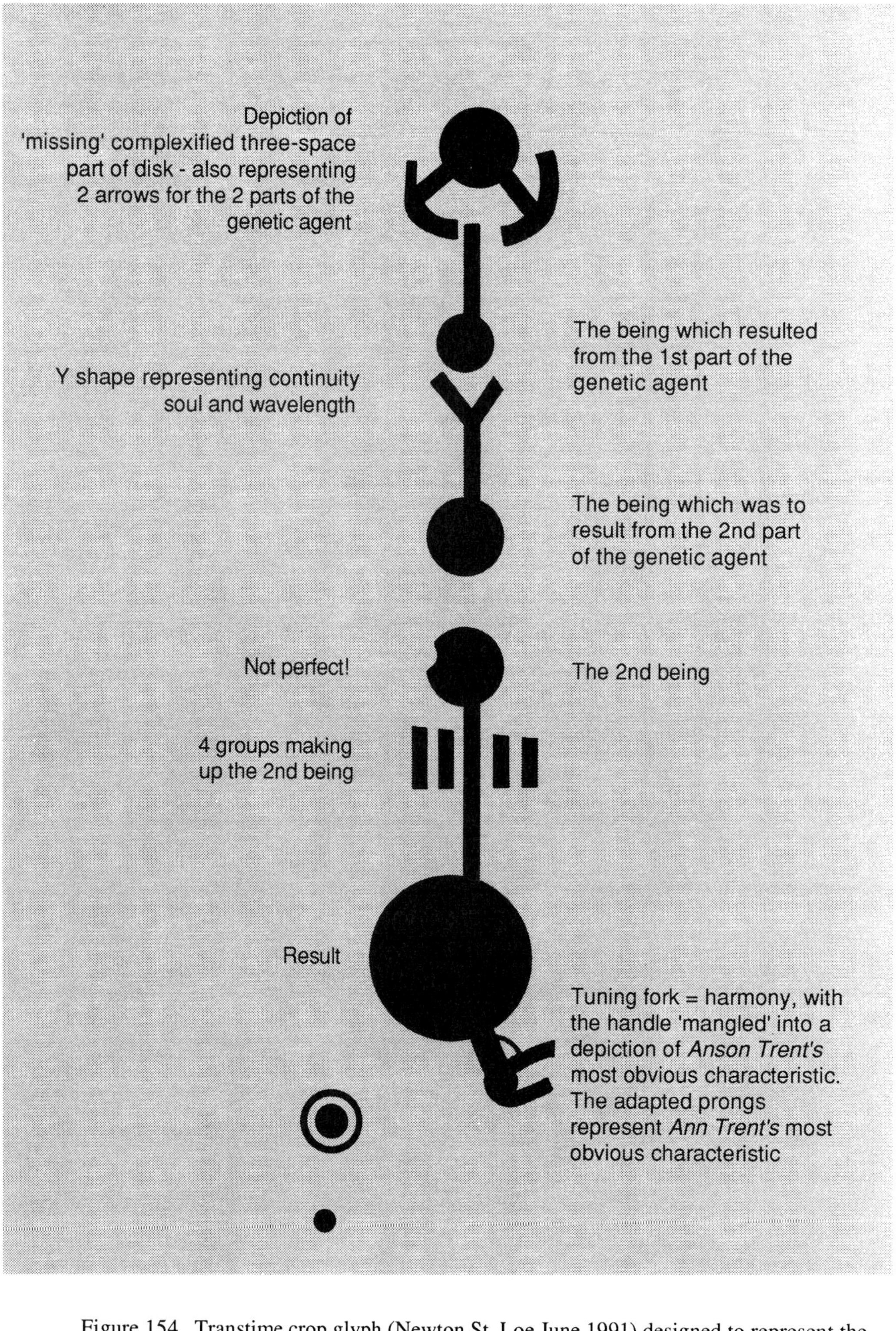

Figure 154. Transtime crop glyph (Newton St Loe June 1991) designed to represent the *process* which would result in a being capable of leading the redeeming of the galaxy.

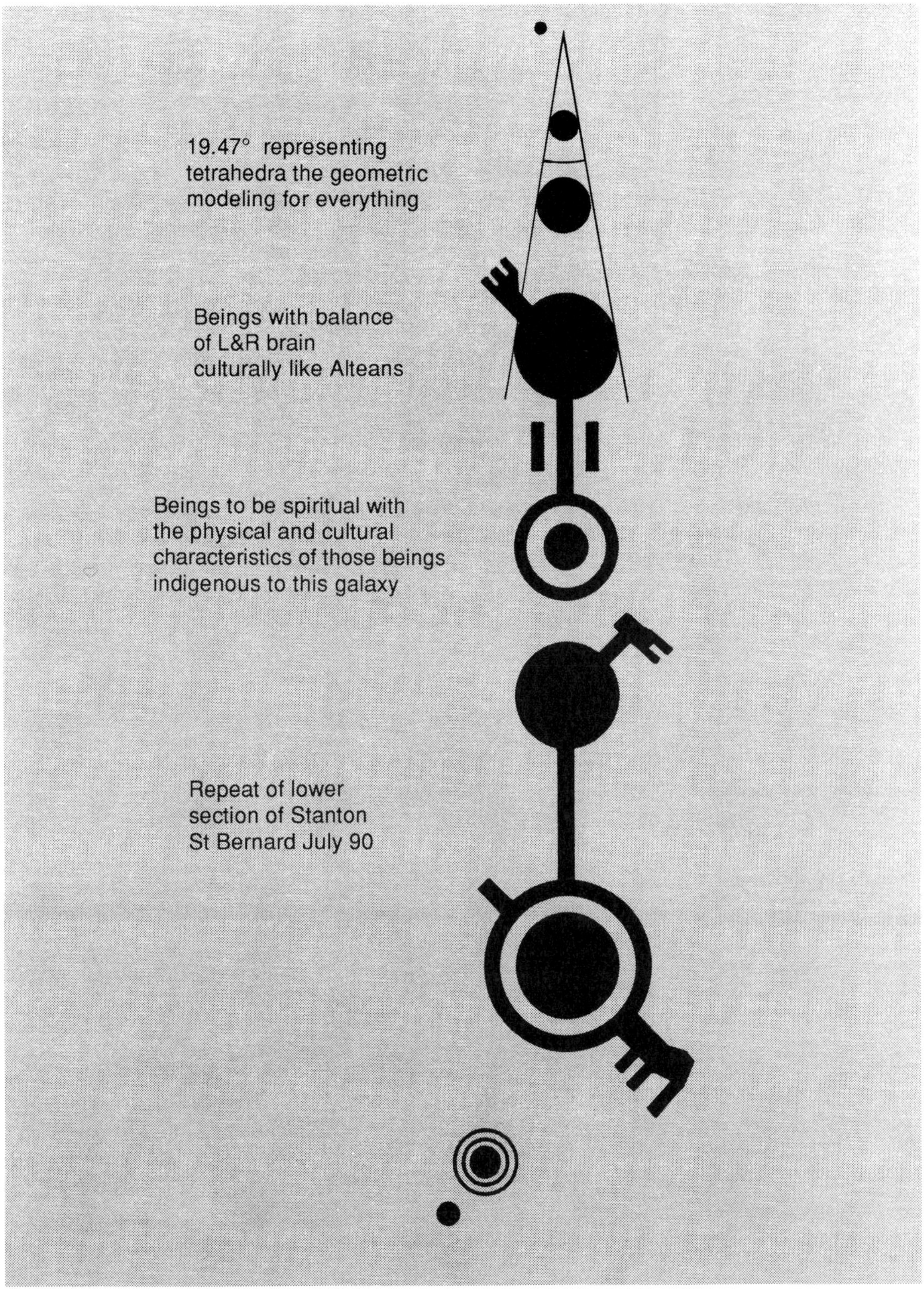

Figure 155. Third intermingling transtime crop glyph (Alton Barnes July 1990) illustrating one of the two unshown interminglings. Omitting a representation of potential intermingling between those who were to have initiative (but who were to be antagonistic) with those who were to be intuitively harmonious.

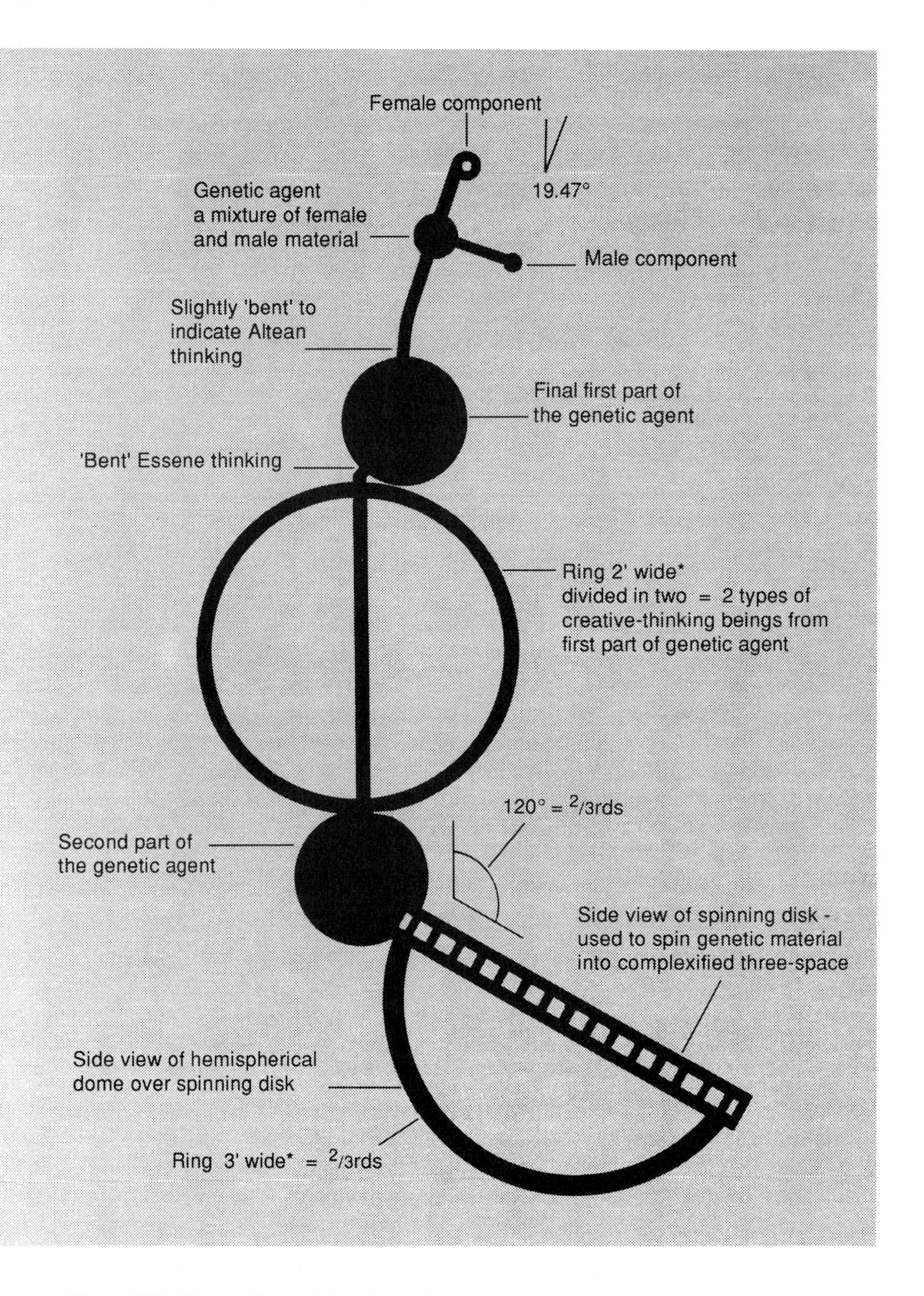

Figure 156. The two Carys design for a transtime crop glyph (Chilcomb Down August 1991) intended to depict details of the process which will result in a being capable of leading the redeeming of the galaxy.

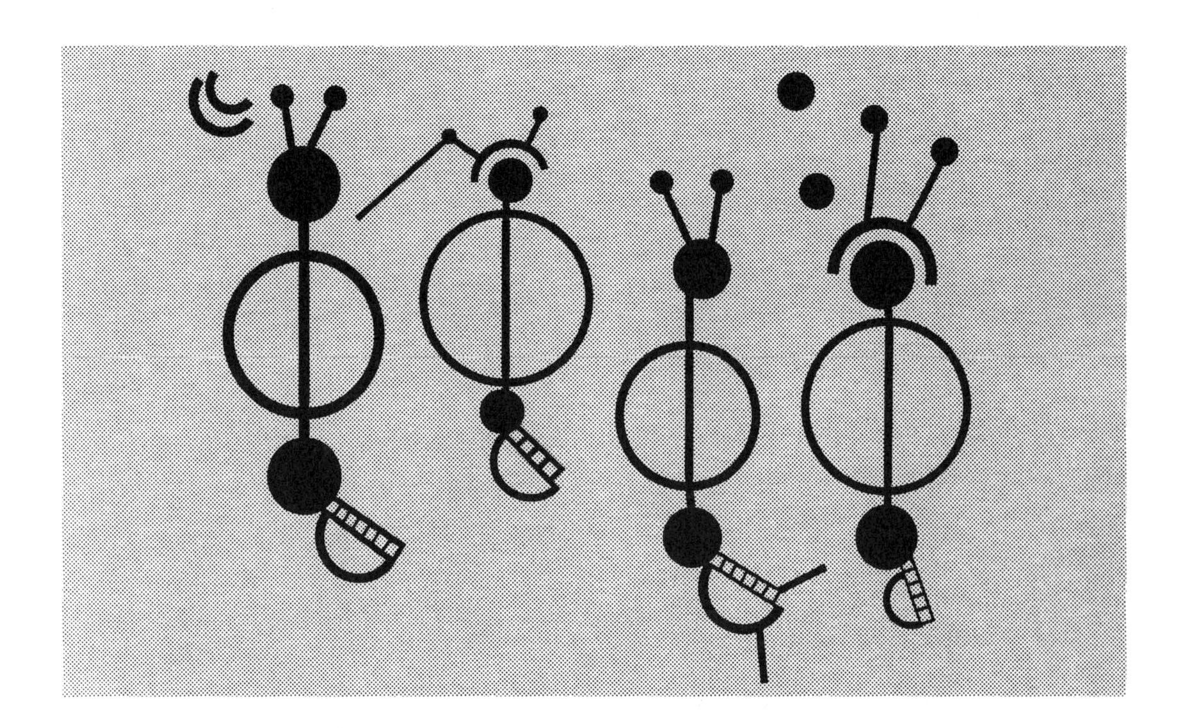

Figure 157. The four meaningless variants of figure 156 designed in order to confuse. R-L: Upham June 1991, Litchfield June 1991, Stonehenge June 1991, Stonehenge July 1991.

Figure 158. Transtime crop glyph (Froxfield August 1991) designed to depict in an appropriate way the Pleiadean worm sperm which resulted in the being with fatal genetic weaknesses due to inbreeding.

Figure 159. Transtime crop glyphs (Westbury 1990 on left and Thruxton 1992) designed to depict two variants of the mix of female and male genetic material used in the genetic agent.

Figure 160. Snail transtime crop glyph (Alton Barnes July 1992).

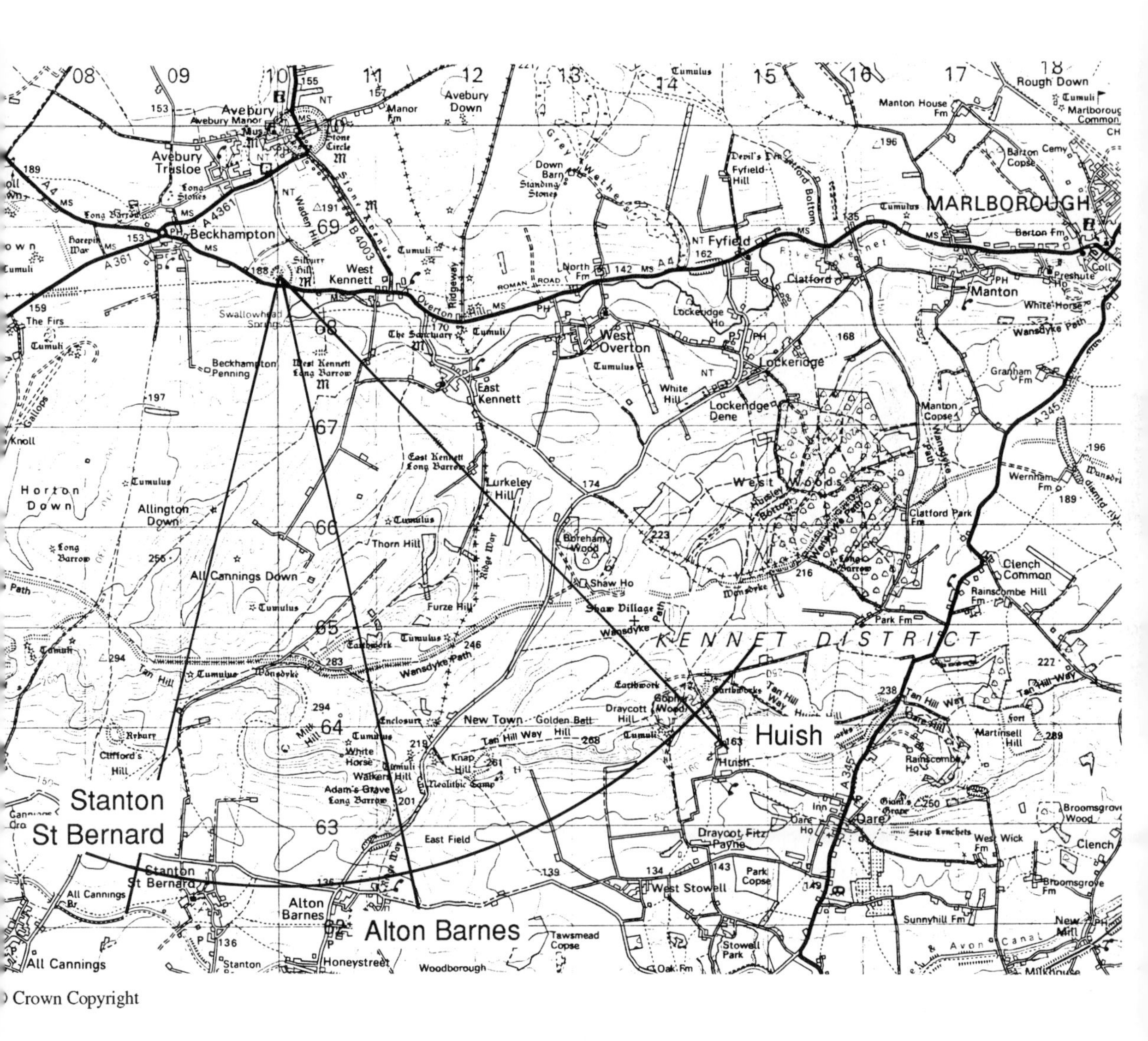

Figure 161. Location of the three separate compounds in which the creative thinking female beings of Danebury lived before they became pregnant. The distance from Silbury Hill to each compound is 3 3/4 miles.

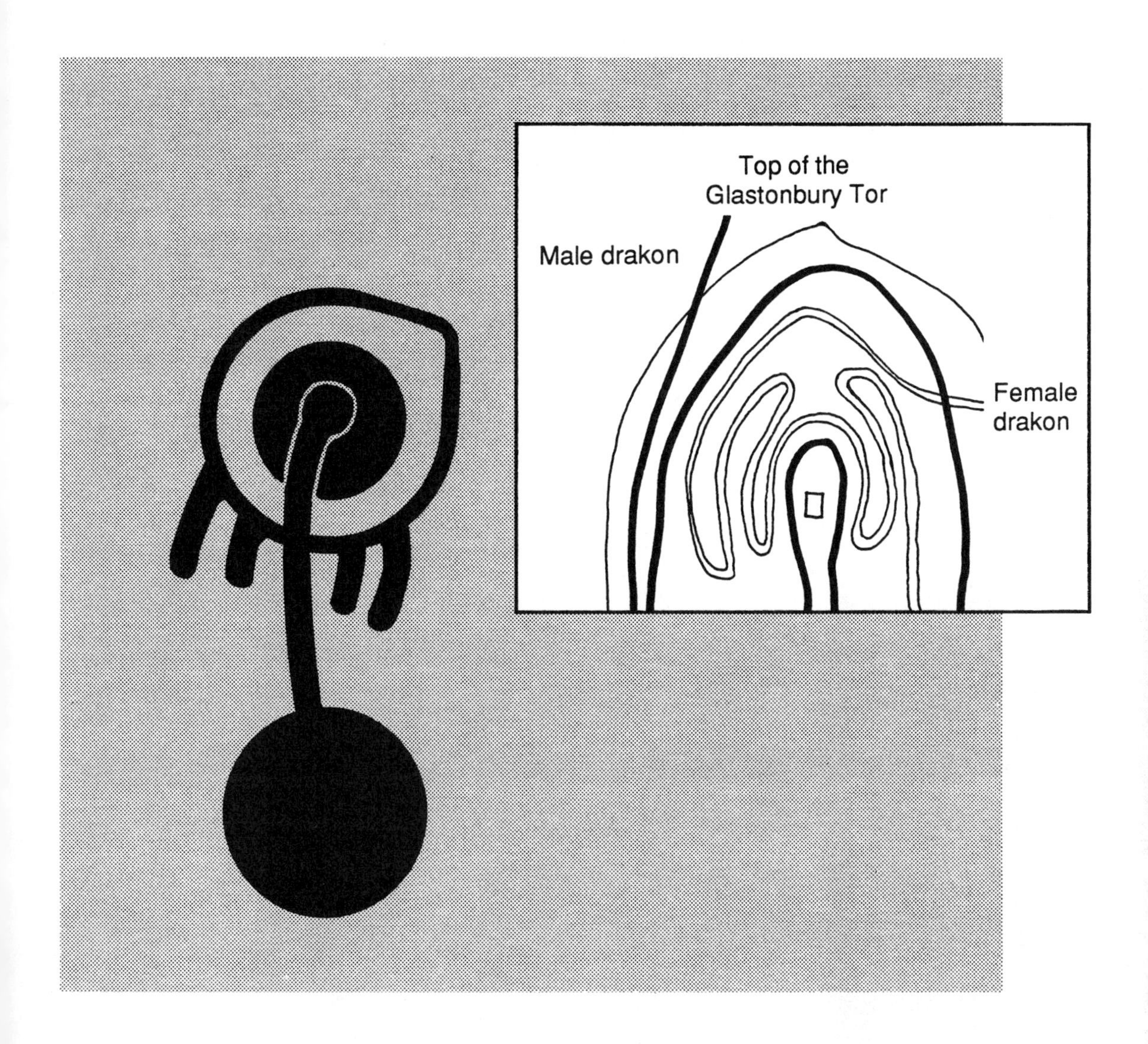

Figure 162. Agony. Transtime crop glyph (Hazeley Farm Fields, Cheesefoot Head June 1990) designed to depict the spawn of a lady of the group of beings who are to have the best balance between L&R brain — linear and creative thinking. This is a depiction of a spawn of a lady impregnated by one of the future Anson Trents of Danebury. (Compare the drakon lines on the Glastonbury Tor inset and figure 101).

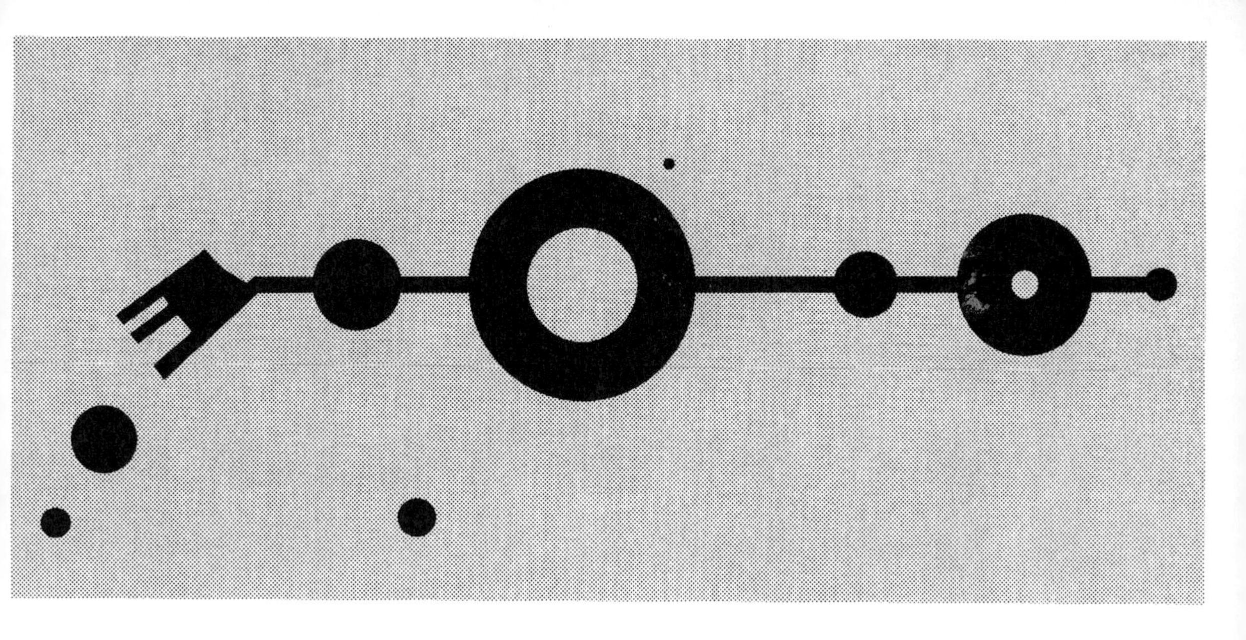

Figure 163. Twin spawn transtime crop glyph (Preshute Down July 1991) designed to represent the spawn of a lady of the group of beings who are to be the most spiritual. A female impregnated by one of the future Anson Trents of Danebury.

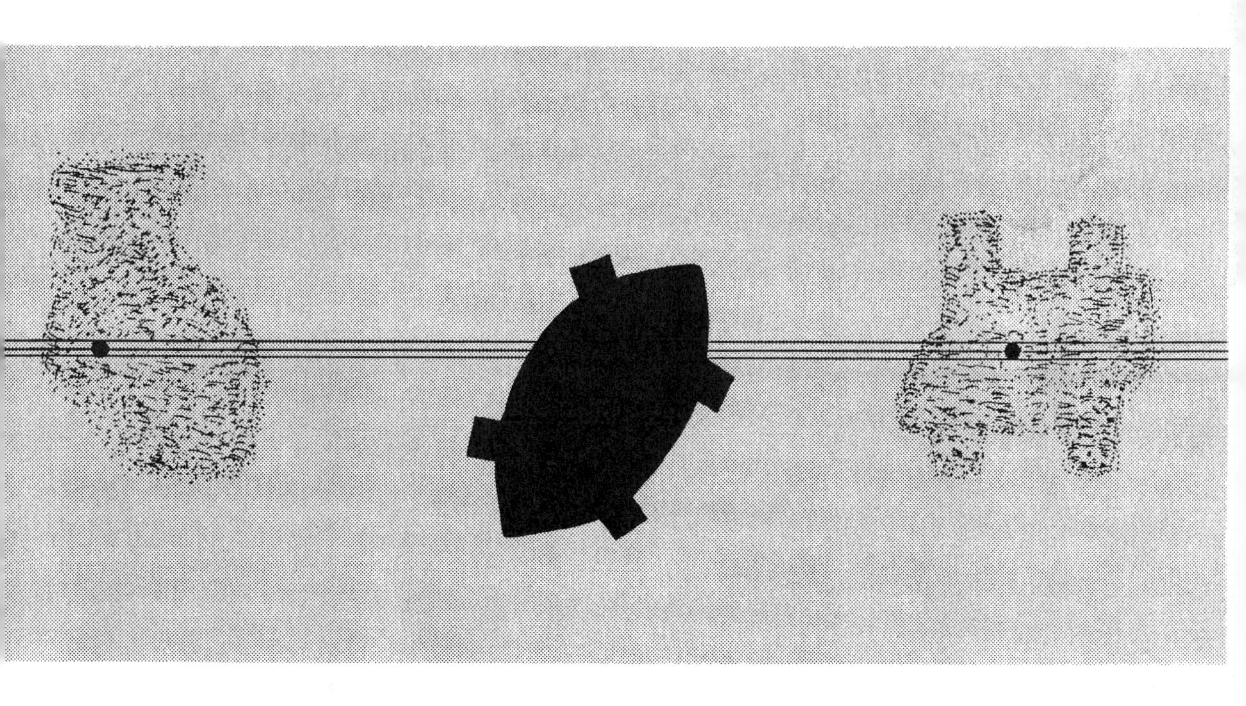

Figure 164. The turtle and 'mess' transtime crop glyph (Hungerford August 1991) designed to show that a turtle, a representation of life not self-aware, is undistorted by strong magnetic fields caused by the power cables suspended above. (Essenes later ensured that pylons were erected in the appropriate positions for this demonstration). Two-thirds of the glyph are messes and represent the end result of self-aware beings trying to exist in the vicinity of strong magnetic fields. One of the messes is a vague echo of the turtle to ensure that it is read as part of the glyph and not wind damage. For convenience the distances have been foreshortened.

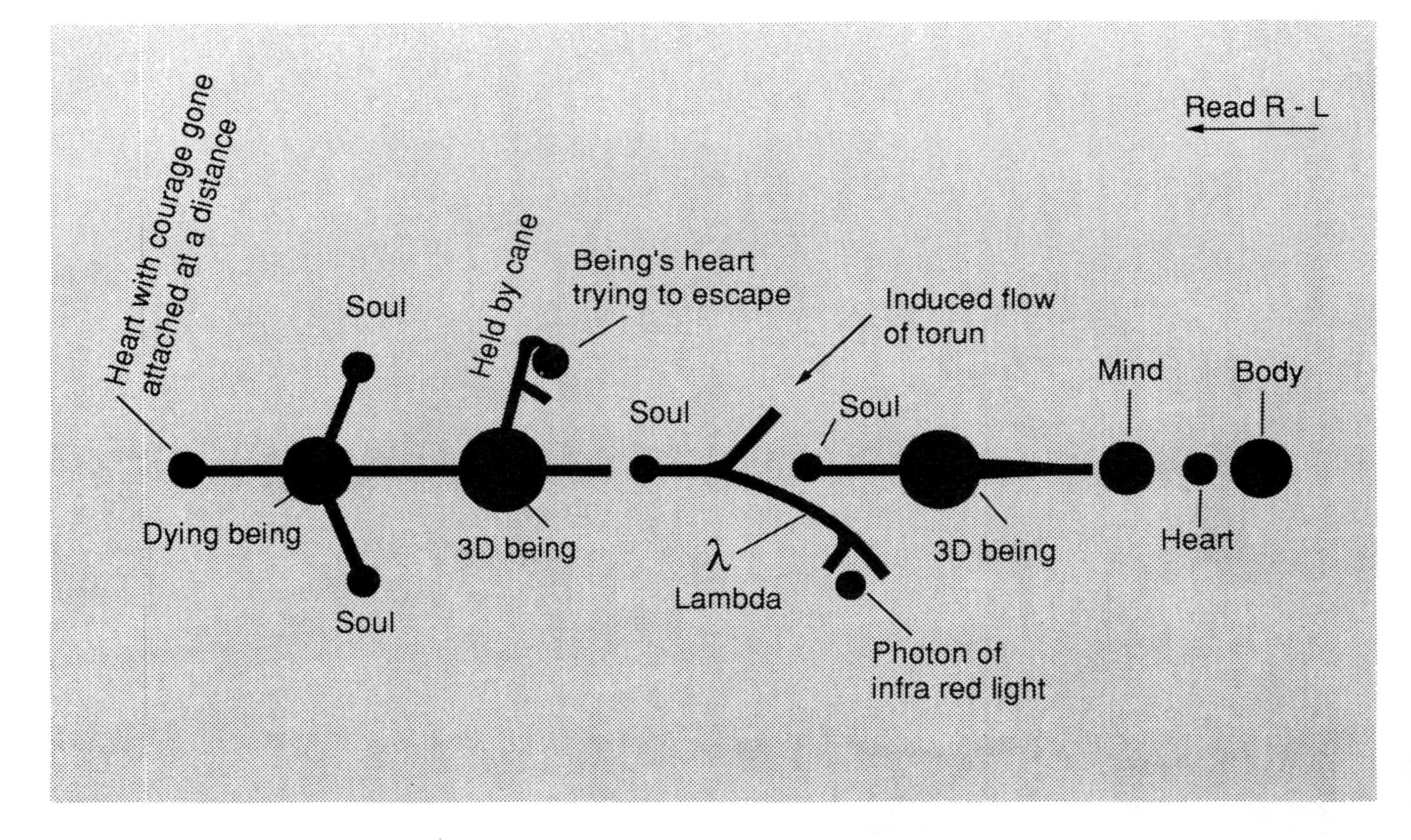

Figure 165. Space disaster transtime crop glyph (Wilton August 1991) designed to depict the causes of space illness which can be prevented by providing the correct environment on board space craft.

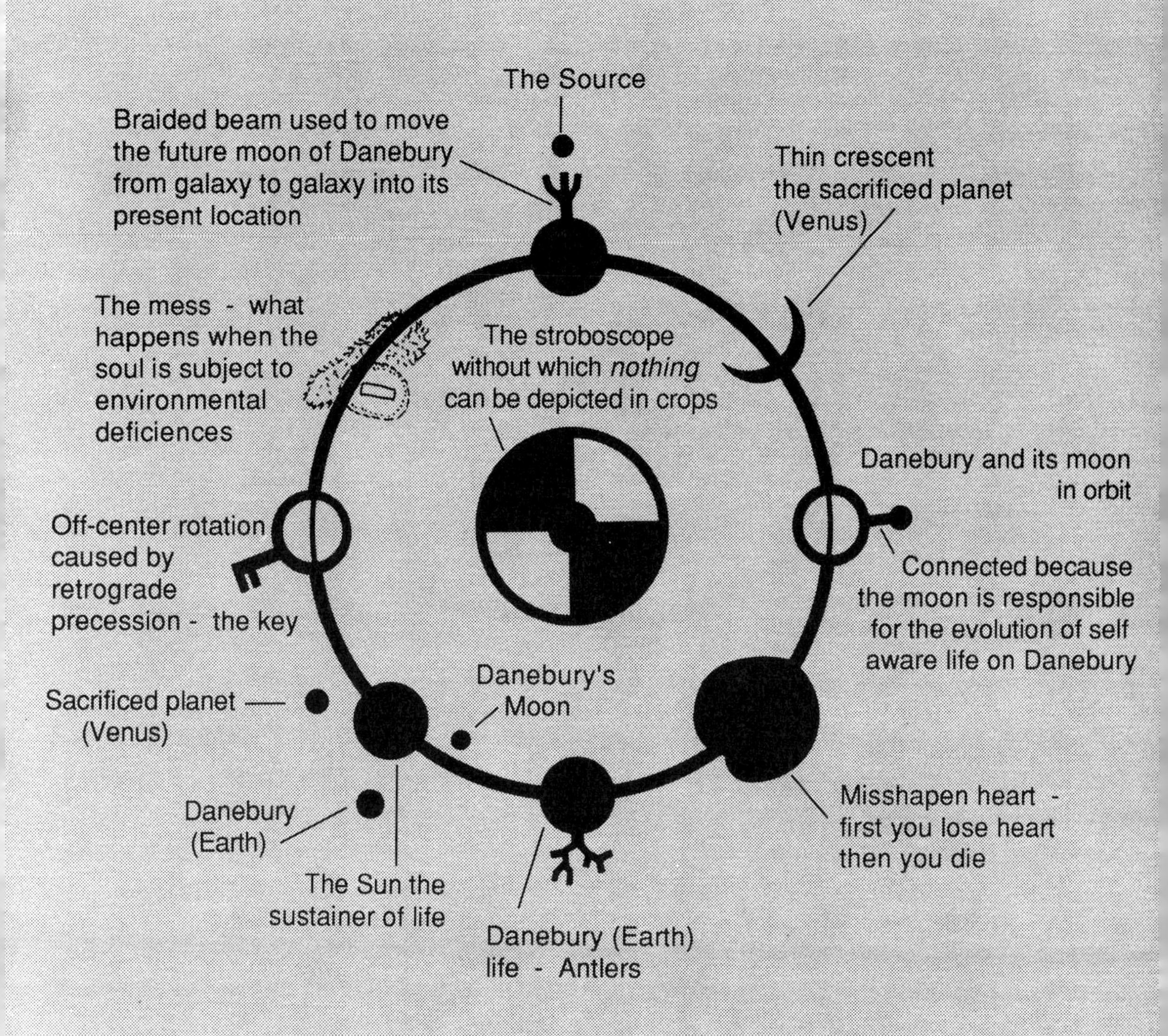

Figure 166. Combined transtime crop glyph (Silbury Hill August 1992) designed to represent both the process by which Essenes prepared Danebury for life, and what happens to self-aware beings when they do not live in an environment with the correct amount of flow of planetary torun or correct induced flow of torun. The eight depictions are intended to be read as pairs opposite each other on the ring. Essenes induced human beings to construct Amesbury Circle (Stonehenge) and Essenes induced human beings to make part of this crop glyph appear. Some consider part of this transtime crop glyph a hoax. If they do they should also consider Stonehenge a hoax.

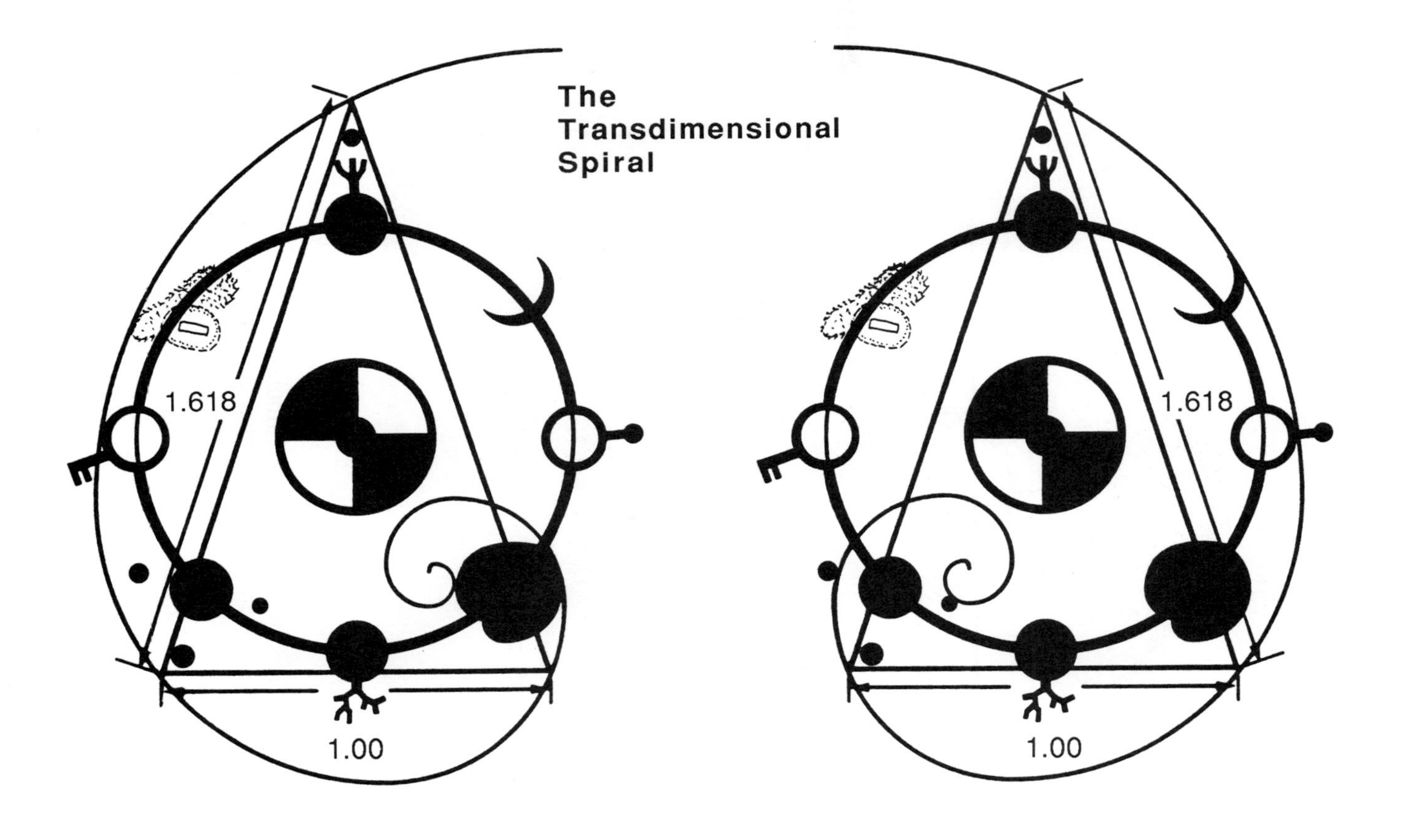

Figure 166.1. The Silbury Hill August 1992 transtime crop glyph illustrating the two transdimensional spirals with isosceles triangles whose two long sides have a phi section ratio of 1.618 : 1 with its short side in such a way that the corners of the triangle are tangent to the Transdimensional Spirals and the representation of the Source of the Universe is tangent to one corner of the triangle.

Figure 167. Special transtime crop glyph (Cheesefoot Head July 1991) designed in memory of Joe Lon Odkin. His enormous heart is represented by the solid circle (which was activated at a later date) and is positioned within the *left side* of the large ring representing his body.

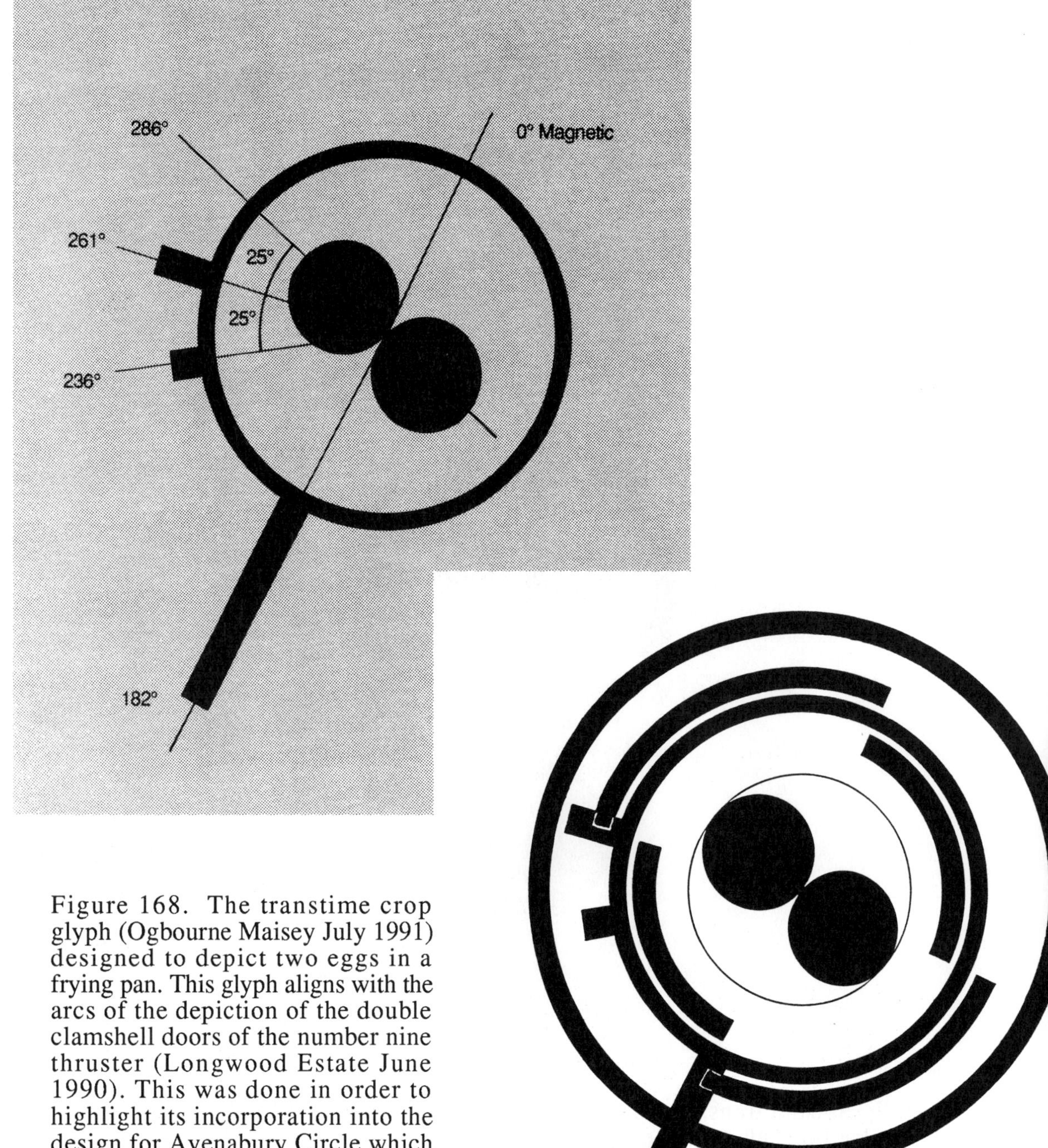

Figure 168. The transtime crop glyph (Ogbourne Maisey July 1991) designed to depict two eggs in a frying pan. This glyph aligns with the arcs of the depiction of the double clamshell doors of the number nine thruster (Longwood Estate June 1990). This was done in order to highlight its incorporation into the design for Avenabury Circle which will be shown later. The two eggs in this illustration represent the two Tetrahedron Crater spinning disks.

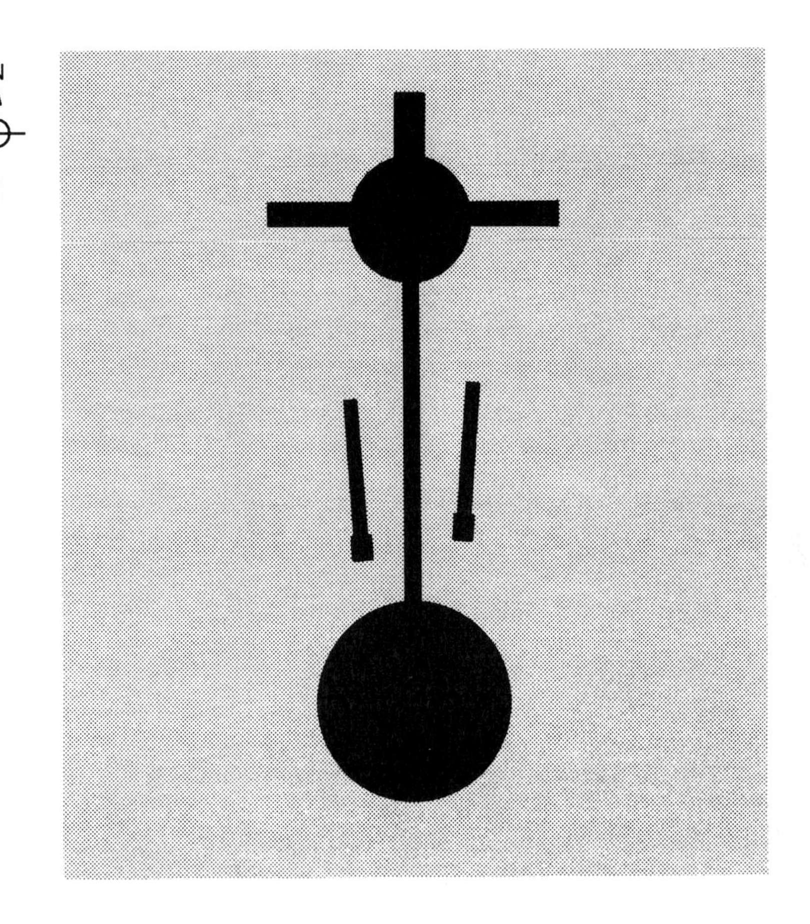

Figure 169. Representation in a transtime crop glyph to demonstrate the magnetic orientation of crop glyphs (Avebury Trusloe June 1991).

Part 3 Chapter 12

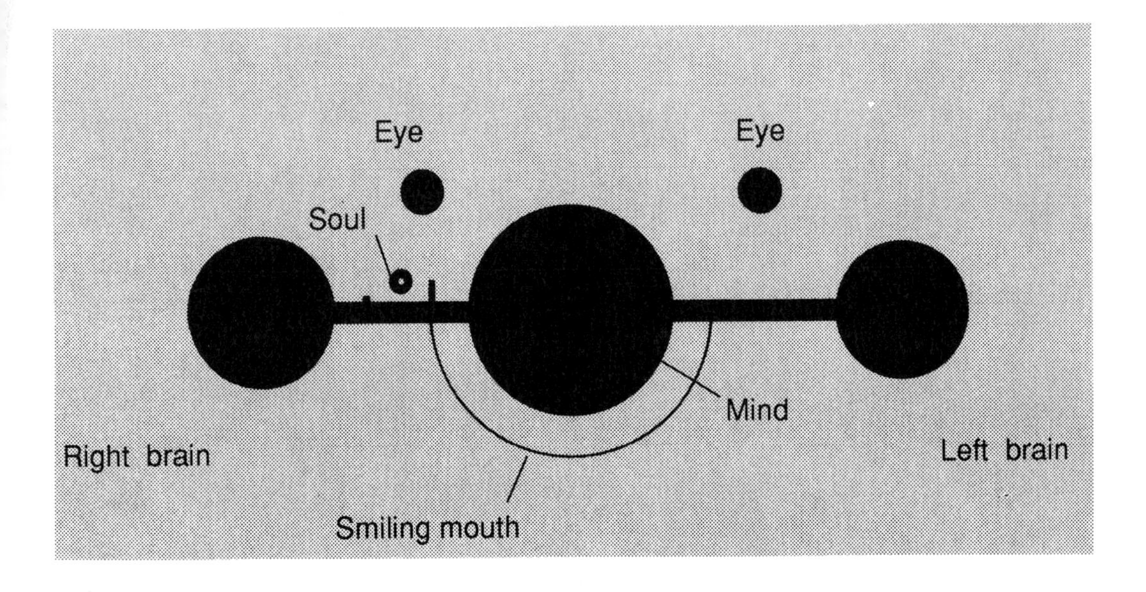

Figure 169.1. Transtime crop glyph (Avebury Trusloe June 1991) designed to depict the self-aware mind.

Part 3 Chapter 12

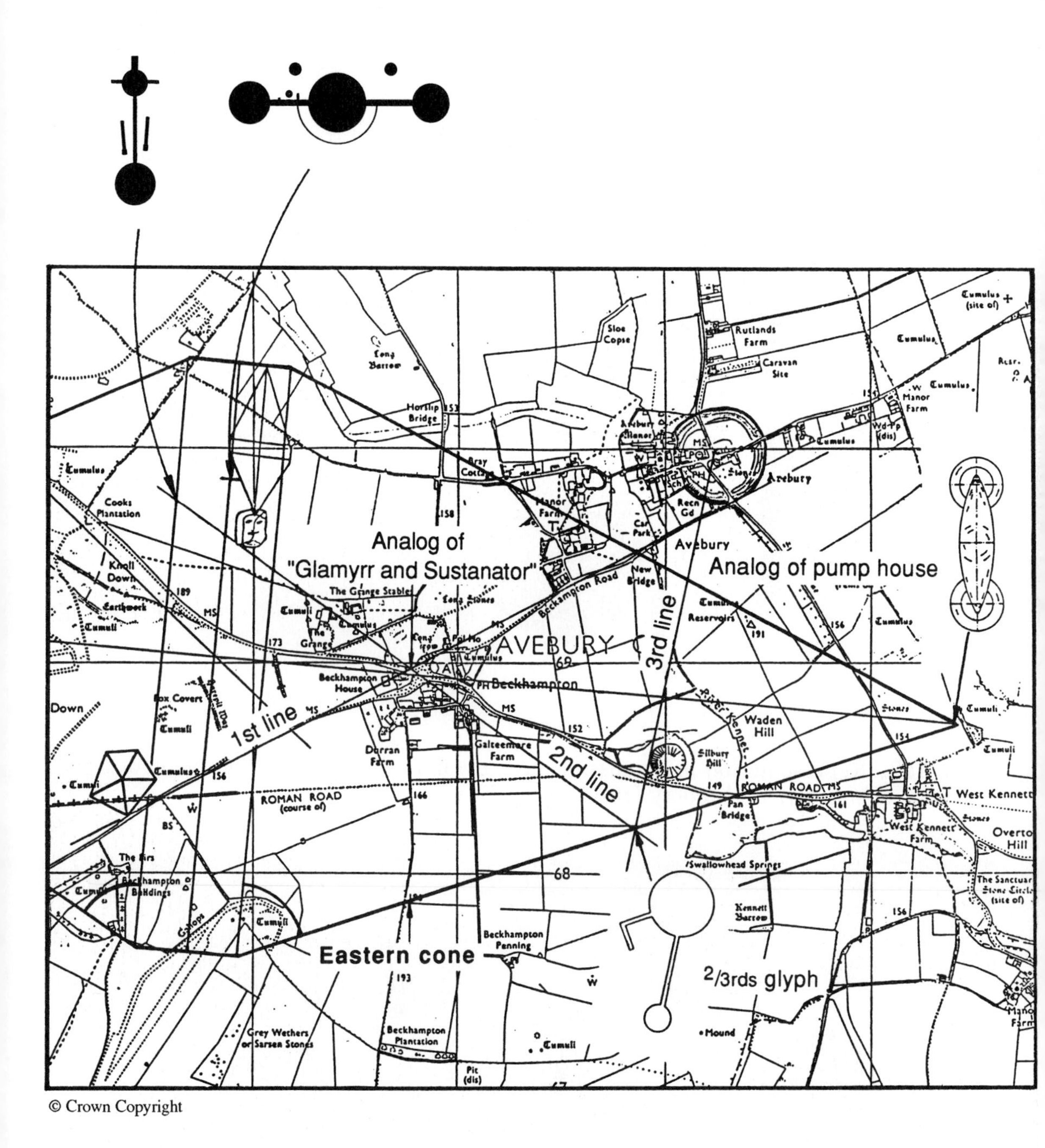

Figure 169.2. Location of the magnetic orientation and self-aware transtime crop glyphs in relation to the cones of energy transredimensioning on the Avenabury landscape.

Part 3 Chapter 12

170. The analog of the Tetrahedron on the northeastern rim of Avenabury Circle (lower photograph) similar in shape — as is Glastonbury Tor (upper photograph) to Mt Hurartu on Altea. (Compare figure 70.1)

171. The remains (in foreground) of the road, now a shallow ditch, that ran north-south through the village at Avenabury. This view is looking southeast with St James's Church in the background.

172. The so called Adam and Eve stones that mark the analog of the pump house northeast of Chapter One. (See figures 39 and 52).

172.1. Longbarrow northwest of the roundabout at Beckhampton that is the analog of Chapter One. (See figures 39, 52 and figure 176).

173. The small mound with marker stone to represent the analog site of Glamyrr Gate located at the end of a buttress on the southwestern side of the Tor. (See inset photograph of the Tor).

174. The analogs of the knowledge and Wisdom longhouses of Hur Square (elongated ovals near edge of ploughed field) in the amphitheater-like valley. (See figures 42 and 54).

175. The analog site of Zuv House built on the northern ridge of the amphitheater-like valley. (See figure 56).

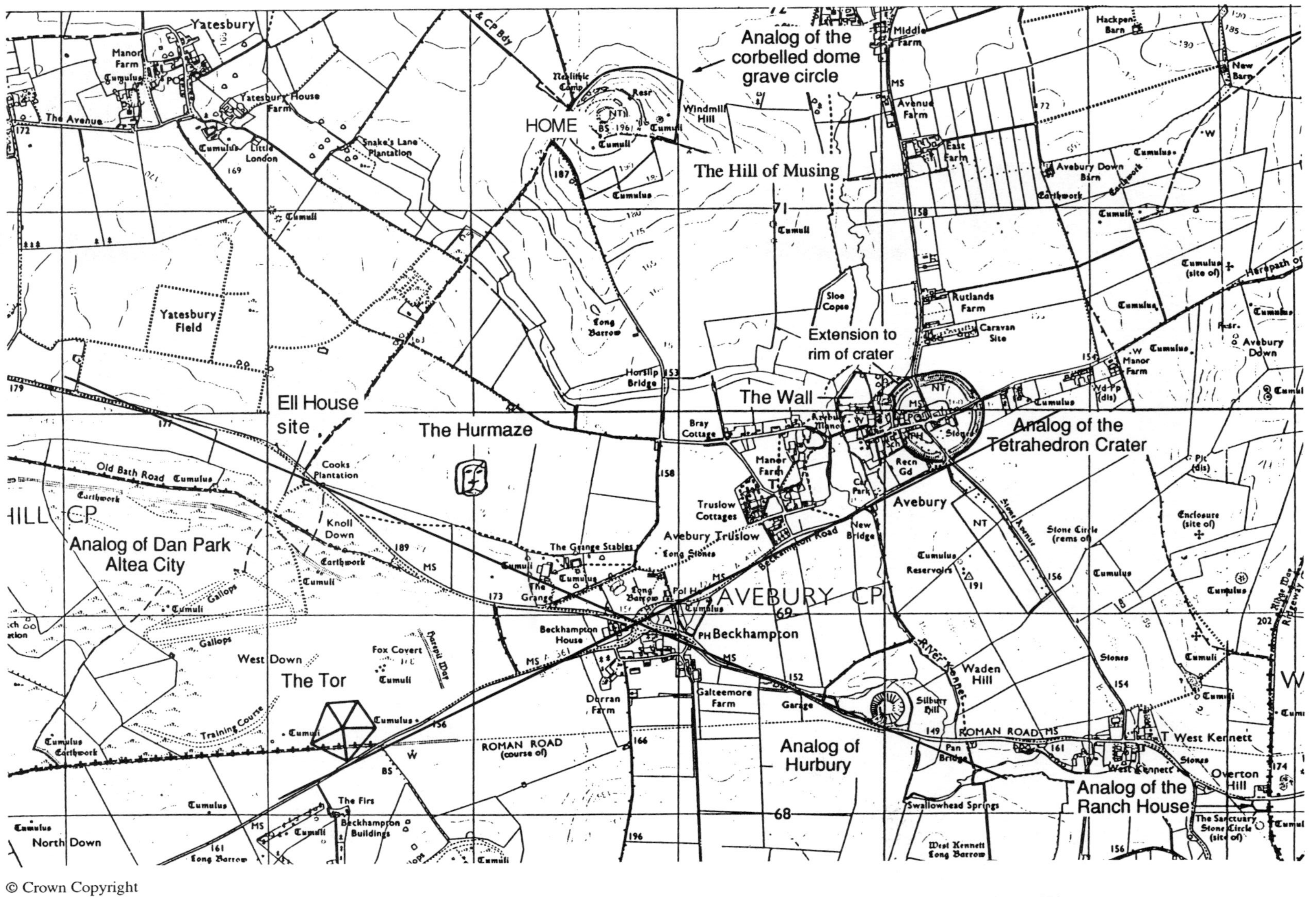

Figure 176. Roads on the small scale model of the Horz complex as they are today. These roads have been constructed along the *tangents* of the analogs. The intersection is tangential to the roundabout at Beckhampton.

177. The eating and drinking establishment, the Wagon and Horses public house east of the Beckhampton roundabout.

Part 3 Chapter 12

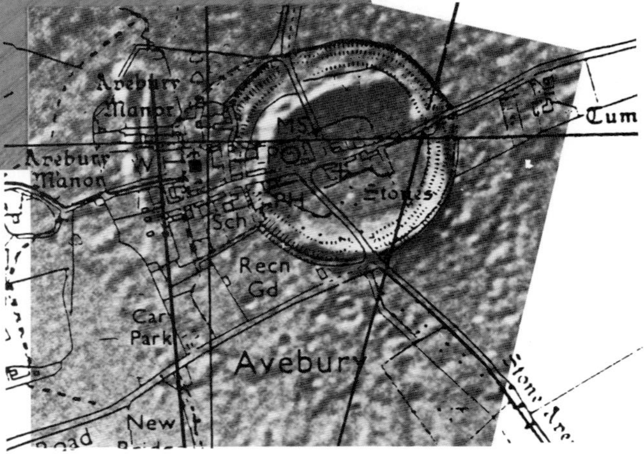

Figure 178. Avenabury Circle the modified analog of the Tetrahedron Crater. Trees in right side of picture highlight the Tetrahedron analog (above) and old-fashioned pump house (below). The light colored strip to the northwest of the church marks the analog site of the northern end of the Wall (see insert). The trees at top of picture lining the road leading to the north highlight the analog site of the Wall in large scale model of the Horz complex (see figure 82).

179. Sculpted earthen scale models of the butresses of the Tor at the ends of which were Glamyrr Gate and Sustanator Gate. They are intended as an encoded metaphor of how the *soul* helps beings attain physical, mental and ethical courage. These butresses are not required for physical support. To emphasise this they were placed adjacent to the *brain* earthworks. (In addition see inset photograph on 173).

Figure 180. Transtime crop glyph (Lockeridge June 1991) one of the series the Solution 69.28.

Part 3 Chapter 12

Figure 181. More diddling. A transtime crop glyph showing six Essene ships colliding and spinning downward (Chilcomb Down July 1991). This was the favorite transtime crop glyph of Cary Manpure, he kept a large copy of it on the wall of his living quarters and looked at it daily.

Part 3 Chapter 12

Figure 182. The first stage in the diddling with the design for the energy transconverter transtime crop glyph. The lines of the tetrahedron were bent to make them different lengths and the depictions of the transconverter sphere and its cooling casings moved off center.

Figure 182.1. The lower left ring, one of three rings added to the transconverter glyph with a line running into it from its circumference to just past its center.

Figure 182.2. The ring placed at the top of the transconverter glyph containing six unequally spaced arcs.

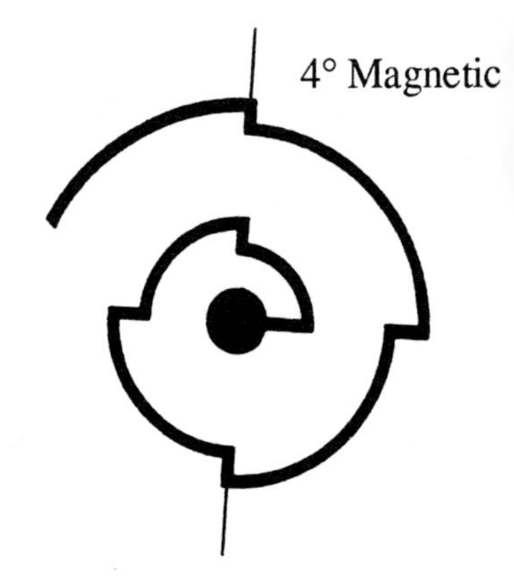

Figure 182.3. The lower right addition, an equiangular spiral with notches and a small circle at the end of the spiral.

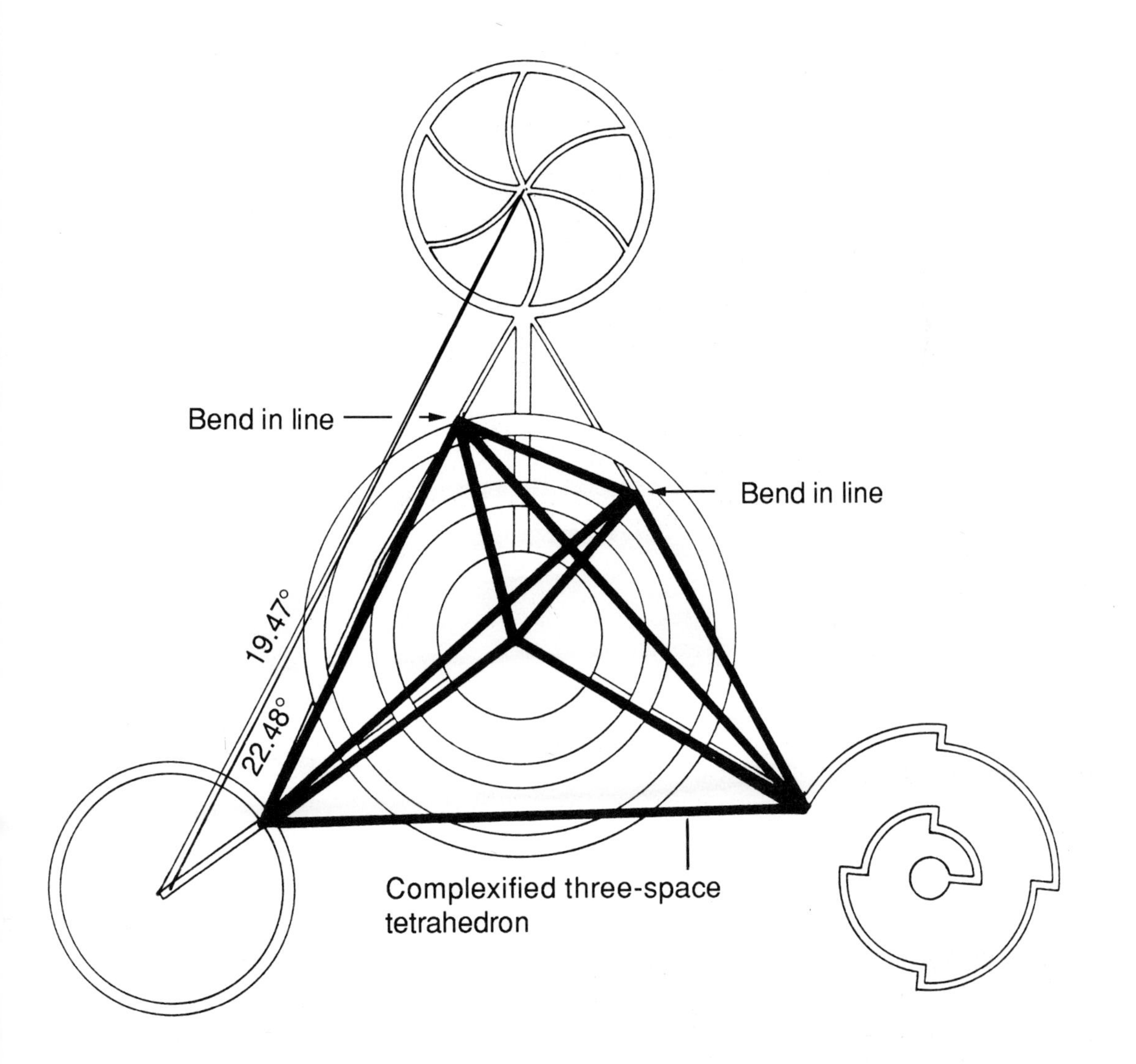

Figure 182.4. The adjusted lines of the equilateral triangle now accommodate the superimposition of a two-dimensional depiction of a complexified three-space tetrahedron representing the process.

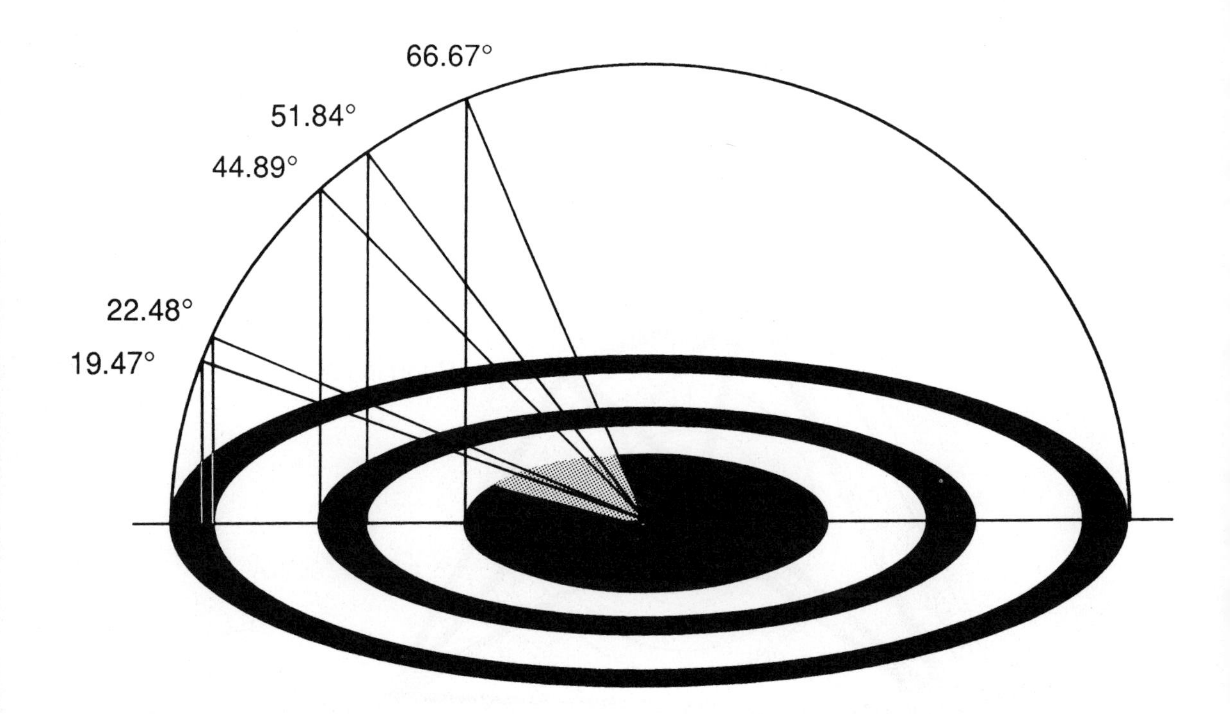

Figure 183. Two-dimensional drawing of a holo-plot which contains the two most important latitudes namely 19.47° and 22.48°. The intersection of the 19.47° line with the outer ring can be read from figure 182.4.

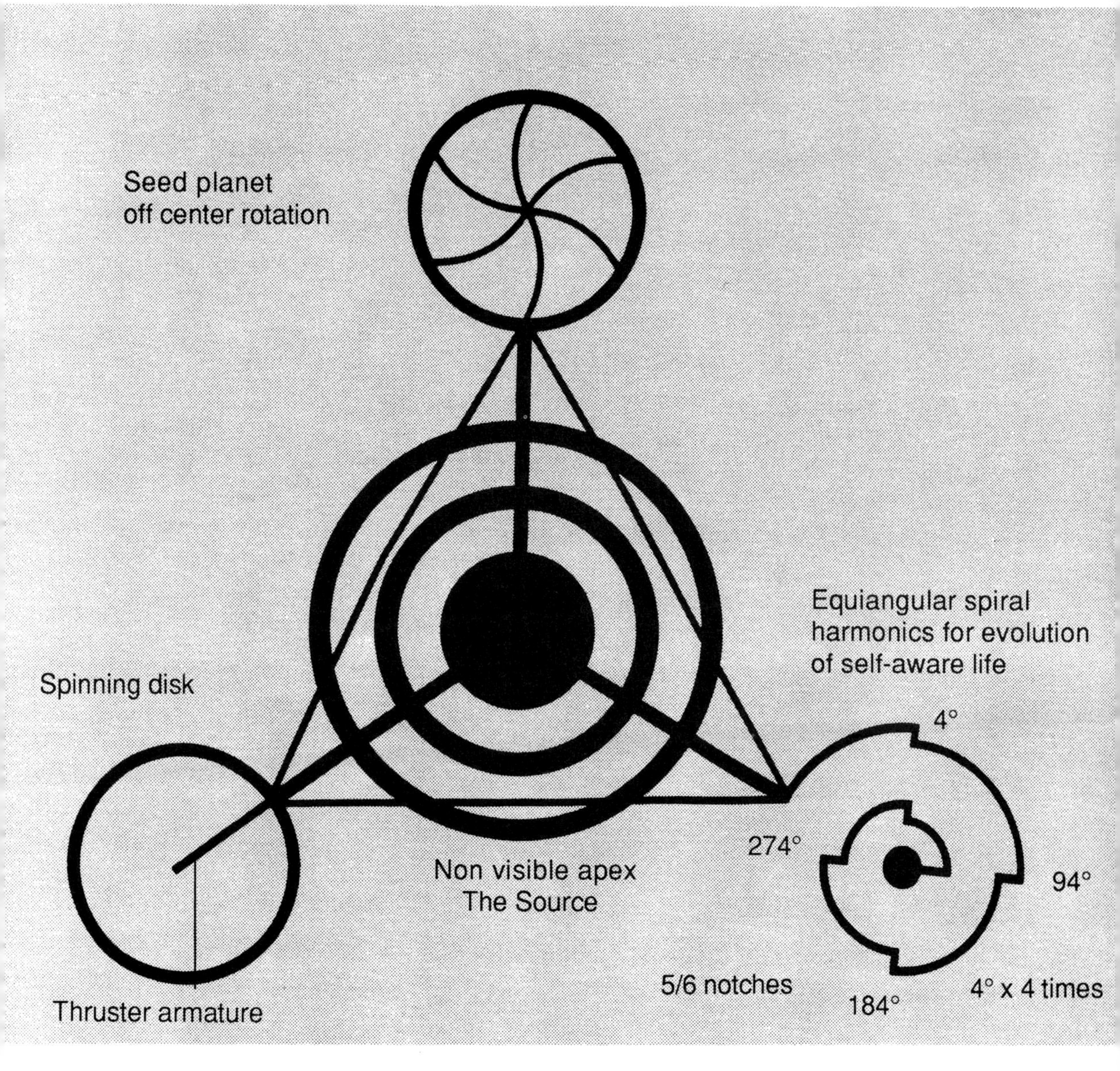

Figure 184. The final design of the altered transtime crop glyph adjusted to depict an energy transconverter, and modified to encode the transdimensioning processes of the Universe (Barbury Castle July 1991).

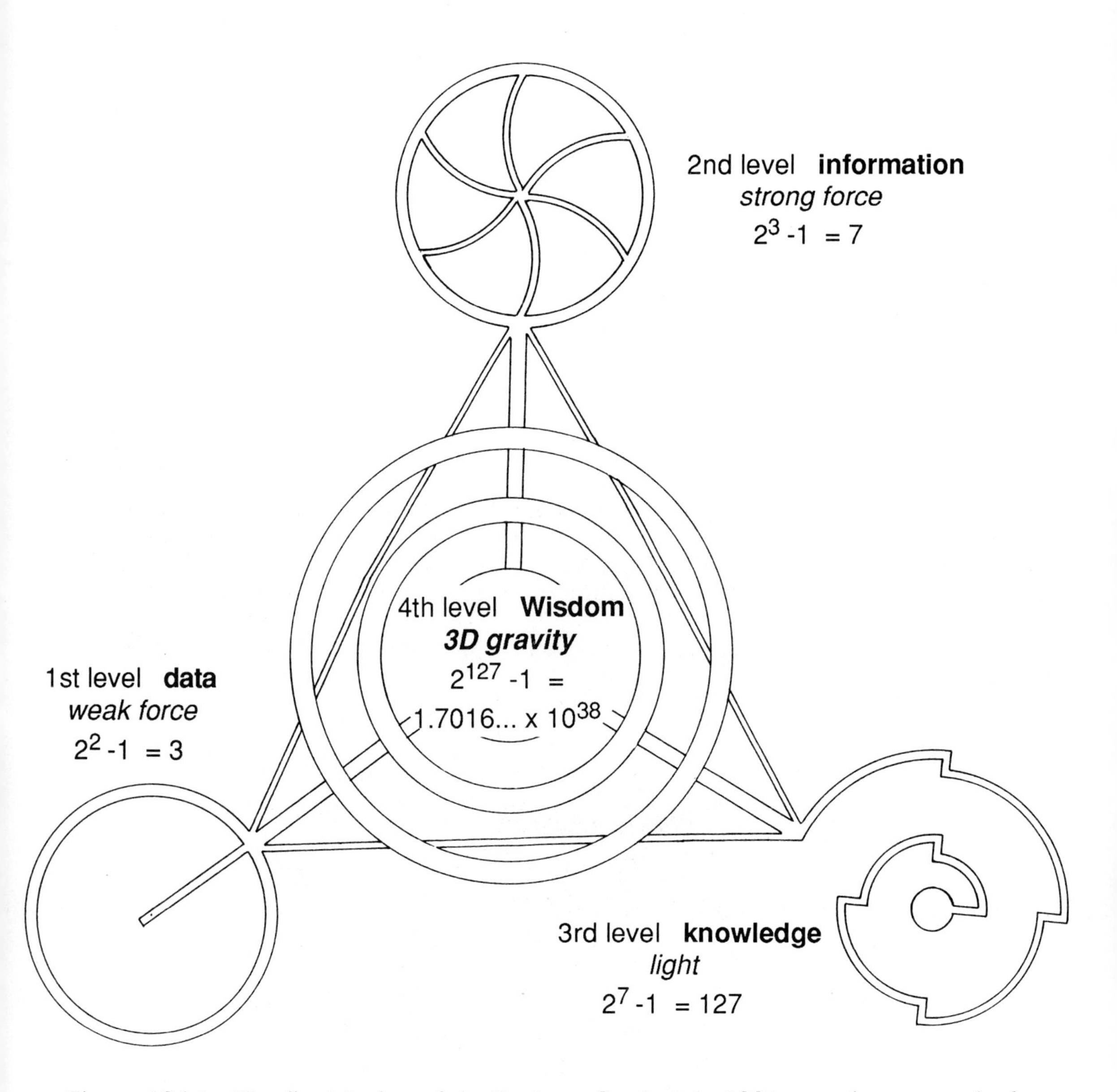

Figure 184.1. The final design of the Barbury Castle July 1991 transtime crop glyph with the four levels of the combinatorial hierarchy.

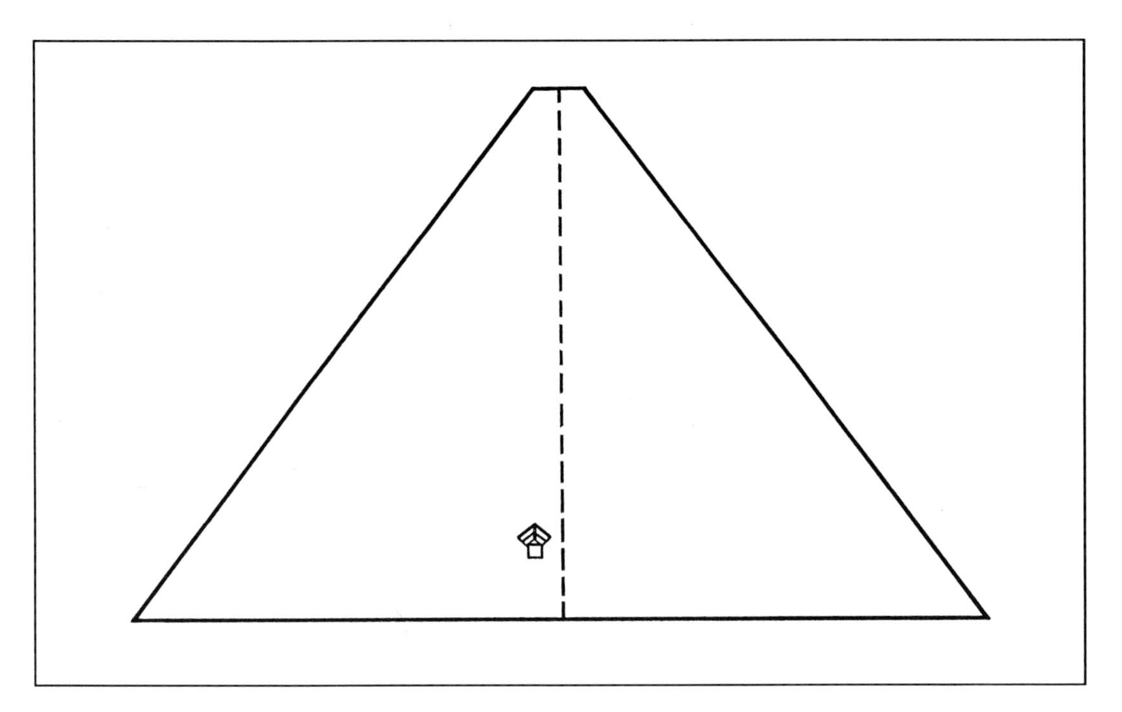

Figure 185. The offset to the entryway in the north facing of Hurmyrr. The distance from the center axis is 286.10213 pyramid inches, an inch which is longer than the Danebury inch by a ratio of 1.00106 to 1. This offset of the entryway is to the *right* of the center axis viewed from inside and therefore represents the soul of a self-aware being. This view is looking from the north towards the northern facing. The view looking eastward has the left side of the head facing west, the direction required for most efficient meditation.

Figure 186. The four different sized Cs hugging one another. A transtime crop glyph designed by Cary Manpure to show his love for his departed friend Cary Jackman (Overton July 1992).

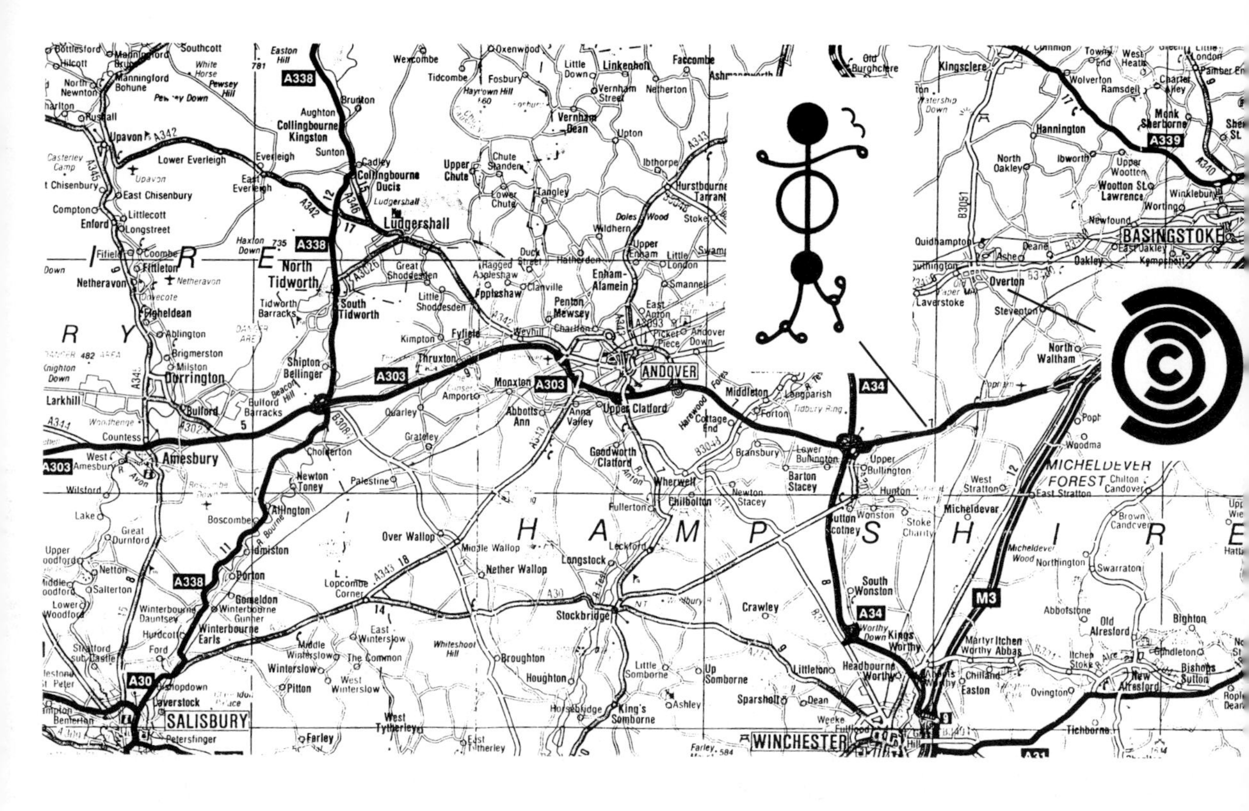

Figure 187. The four Cs transtime crop glyph laid down in the analog of the northern part of the Ranch in the large scale model of the Horz complex.

Figure 187.1. The Labyrys is the symbol of command for the Altean Naval Service because the two heads of the axe represent authority and ACCOUNTABILITY. Minoans understood this too. Romans did not — they used a single headed axe fasces — the Romans knew no accountability. (Minoan copy of labyrys).

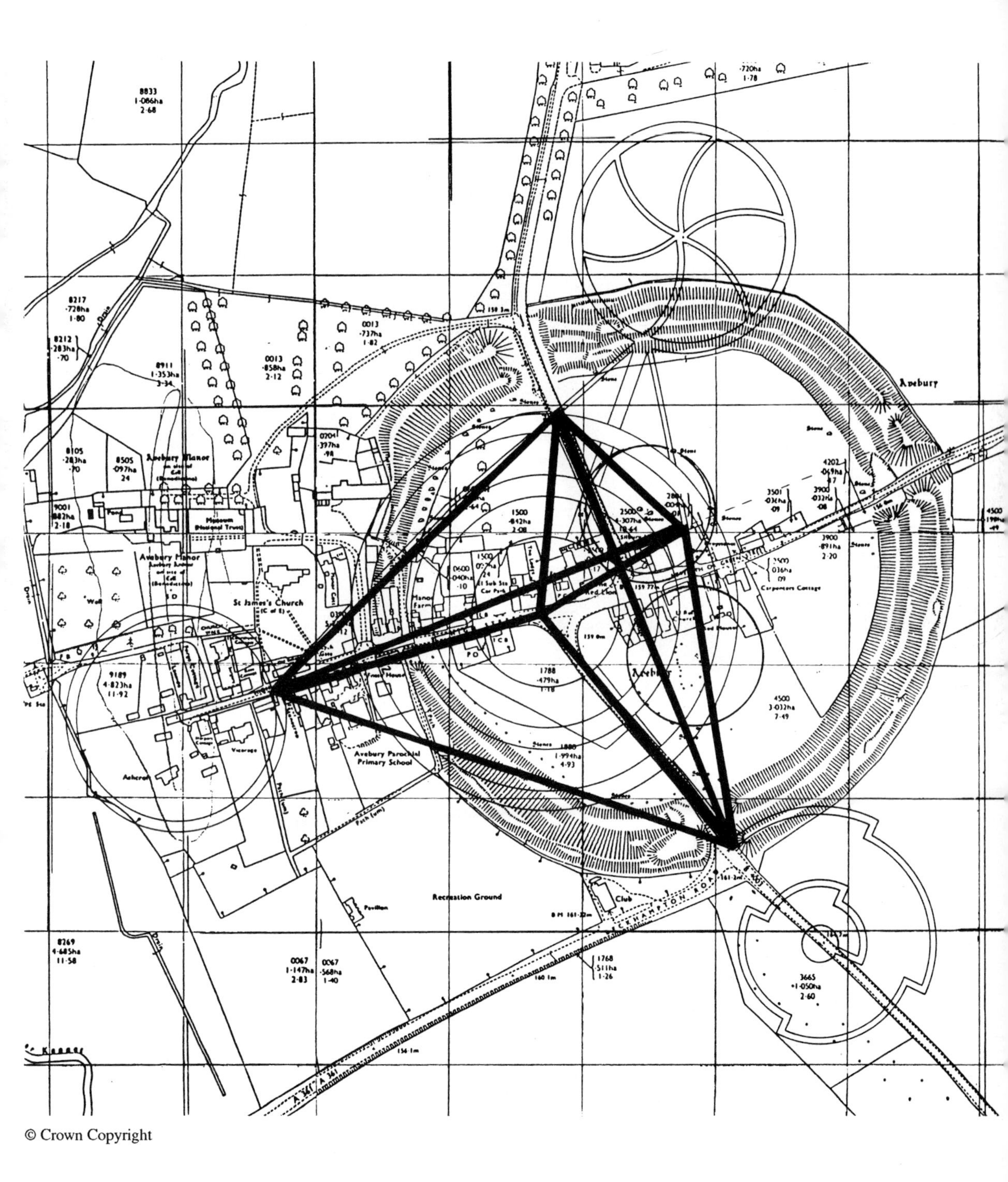

Figure 188. The Avenabury Circle with the scaled energy transconverter crop glyph (Barbury Castle July 1991) superimposed. The 2D depiction of a complexified three-space tetrahedron aligns with the road leading to the southeast, the road through the village to the west and the road leading to the north. Note that the east-west displacement of the north-south roads corresponds with the complexified three-space tetrahedron.

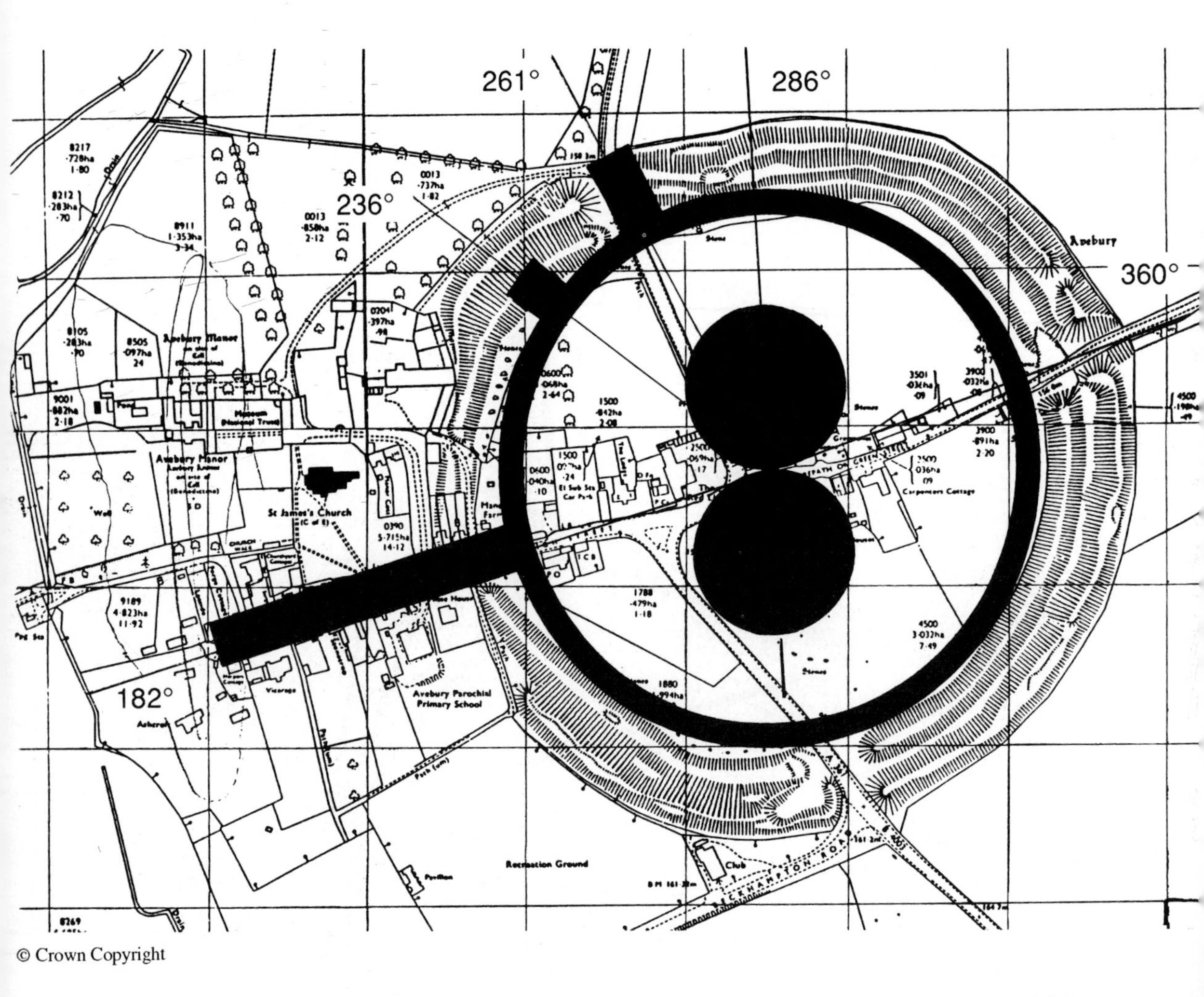

Figure 188.1. The two eggs frying in a frying pan transtime crop glyph (Ogbourne Maisey July 1991) scaled and superimposed over Avenabury Circle. The degrees from the center of the circle are degrees Avenabury.

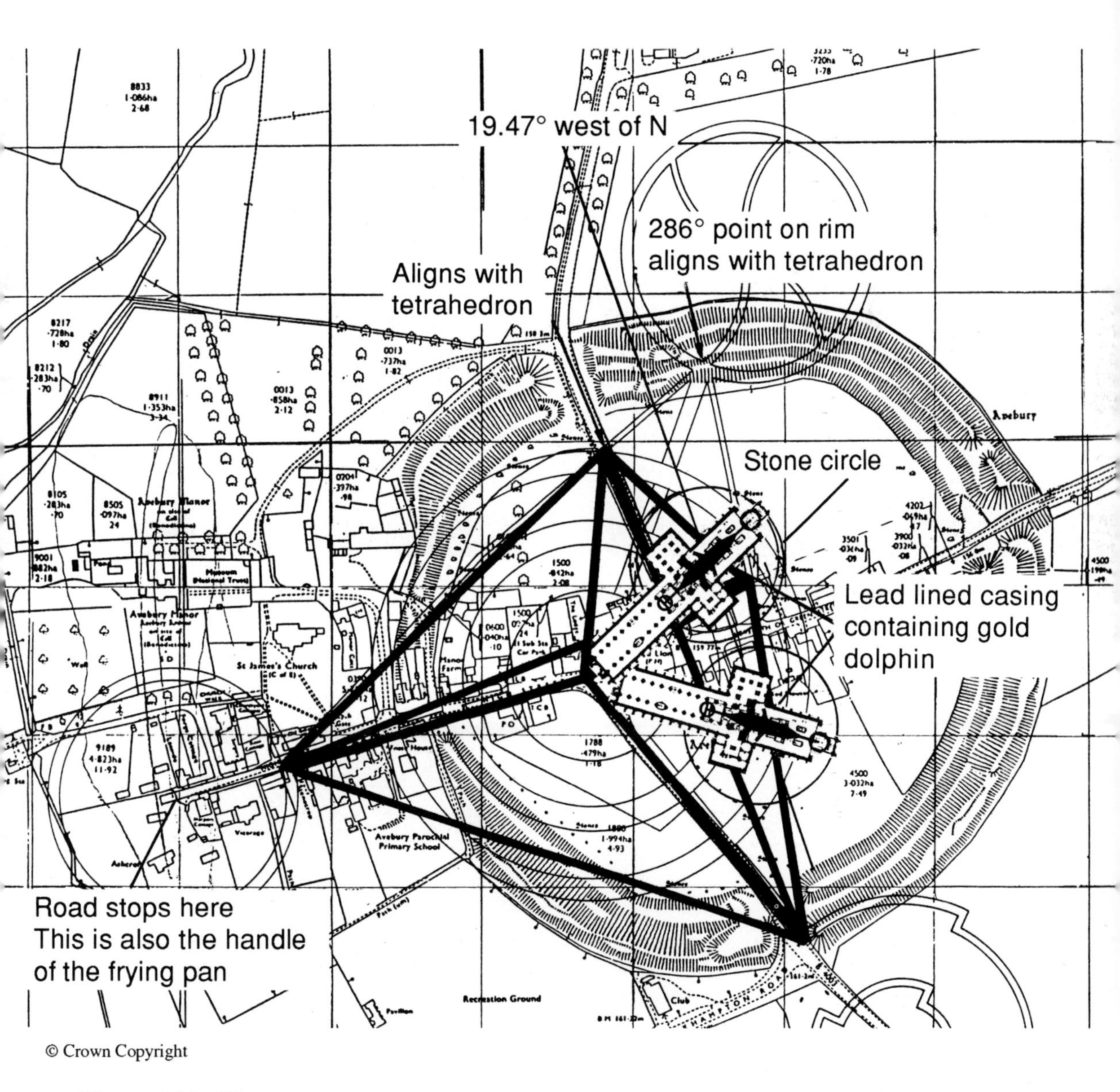

Figure 189. The two *stone* circles inside the Avenabury Circle dictate the alignment of the lead lined casings containing the gold dolphins and their positioning inside the energy transconverter sphere. (See also figures 30 and 31).

Figure 190. The Waldark set transtime crop glyph (Ickleton Cambridge August 1991). In this representation the glyph is modified with the small replication moved away from the main part of the set and depicted as a circle to represent the soul.

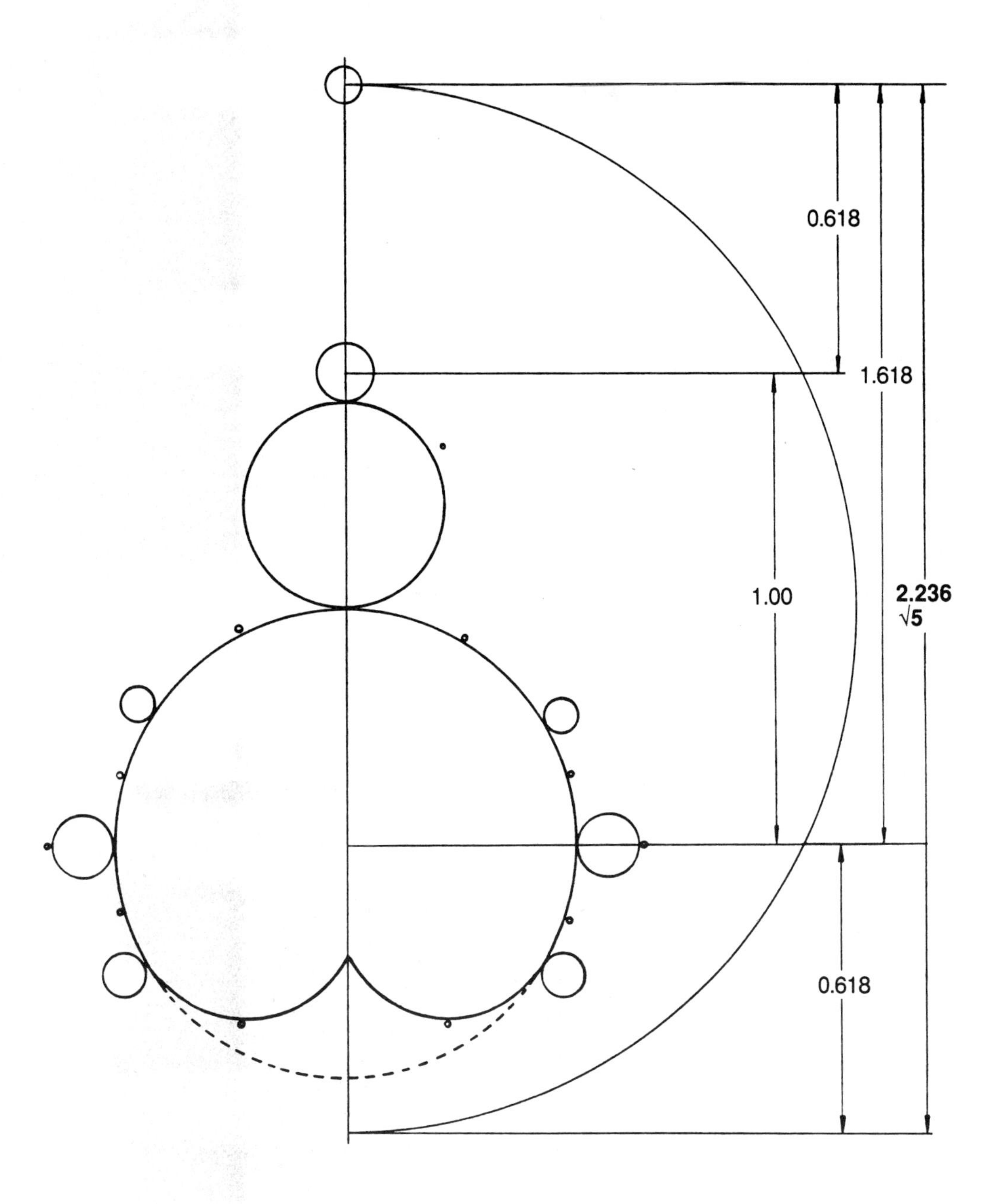

Figure 190.1. Waldark set transtime crop glyph demonstrating that the square root of five is related to the phi section by adding one over the phi section ratio to the phi section ratio.

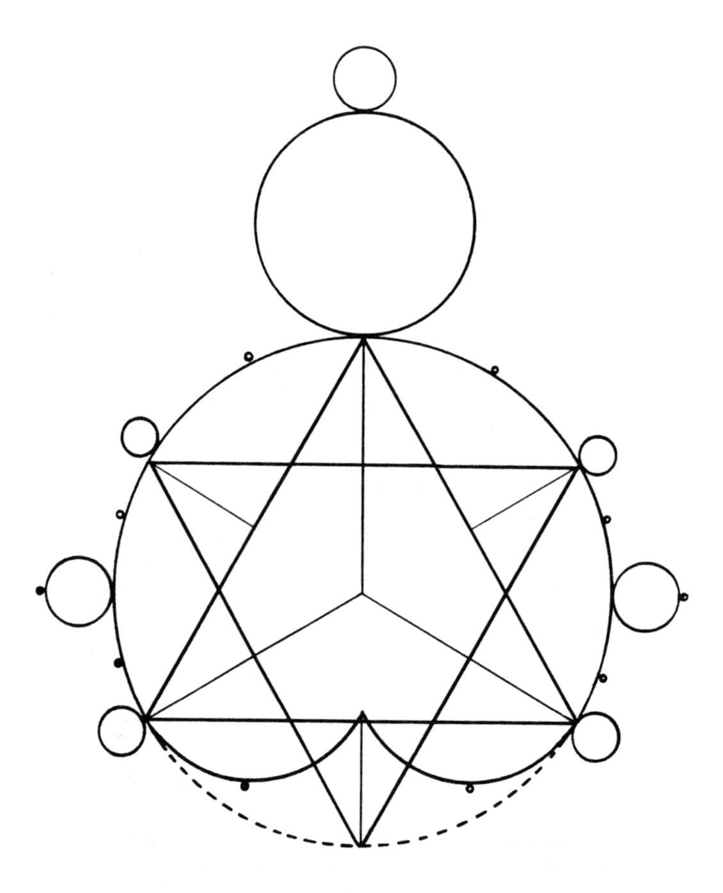

Figure 190.2. Main part of the Waldark set transtime crop glyph with overlaid circumscribed tetrahedra.

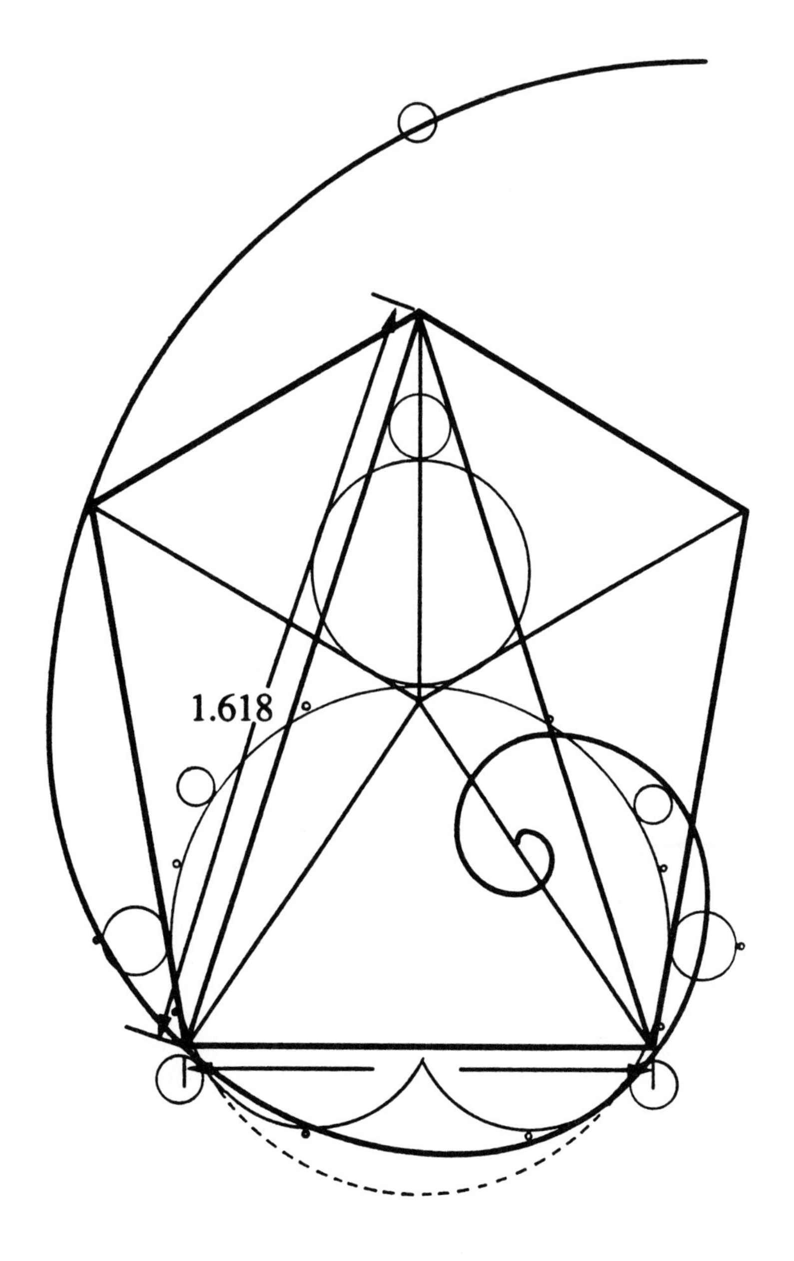

Figure 190.3. Waldark set transtime crop glyph with overlaid scale Transdimensional Spiral and the Tor. The Transdimensional Spiral passes through the two-thirds point of the upper circle, the depiction of the soul.

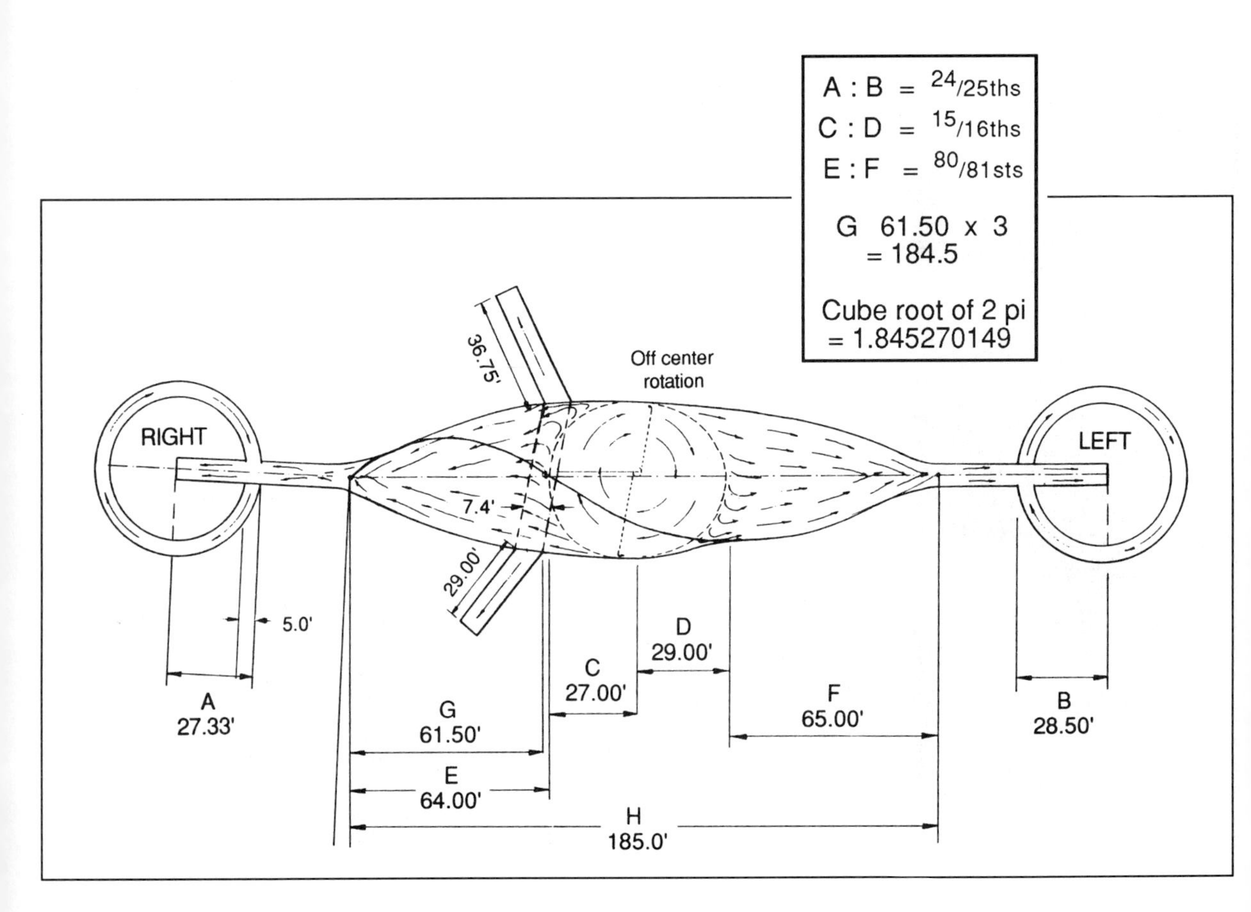

Figure 191. Lockeridge dolphin (July 1991) transtime crop glyph designed to illustrate the wavelength of planetary torun which is 184.5270149, inches of which H is a close approximation (the harmonics depicted in the glyph would not work out if this length was exact). The diameter and resulting wavelength of the three-dimensional disturbance pattern of the soul of self-aware beings is .1845270149 inches. The cube root of two pi is 10 times the wavelength of the three-dimensional disturbance pattern of the soul. Encoded in the glyph are three harmonics 15/16ths, 24/25ths and 80/81sts.

191.1. The pi shape of the setting for this transtime crop glyph (Lockeridge dolphin July 1991) is inferred by the field boundaries. The location of this crop glyph surounded on three sides by trees is an example of how Essenes have ensured that changes to the landscape made by human beings do not interfere with any of the preparatory work.

It is interesting to note that when this field was first cleared of its woodlands, the farmer who laid out these boundaries unwittingly circumnavigated the exact area in which the crop glyphs had been laid down, and thus created the appropriate space for subsequent activation. The photographs in figure 116 are examples of how farming techniques in southern Hurengland are compatible with the work. In those photographs the tractor lines substantially enhance the design of the mica slats and crystal disks.

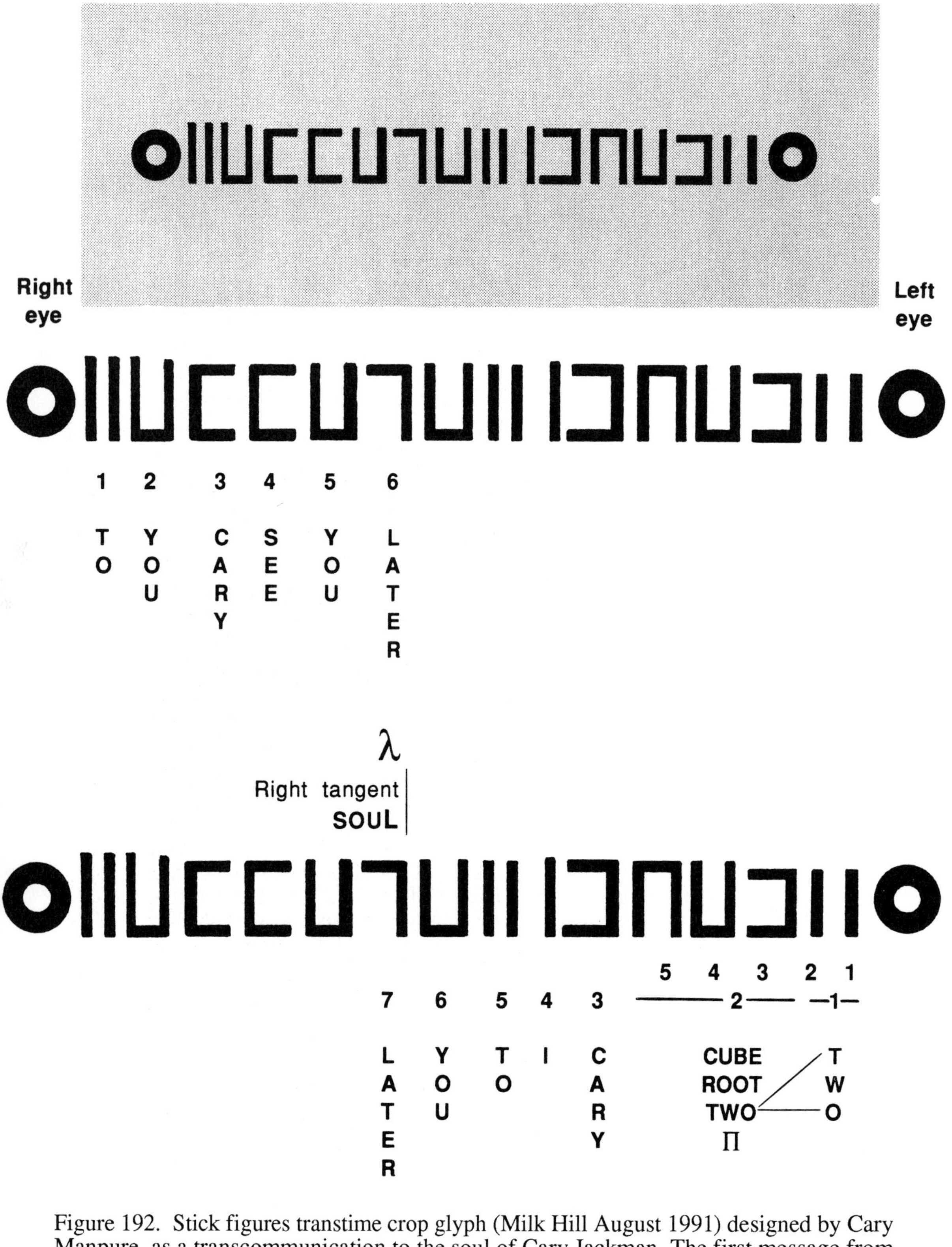

Right eye

Left eye

1 2 3 4 5 6

T Y C S Y L
O O A E O A
U R E U T
Y E
R

λ

Right tangent
SOUL

5 4 3 2 1
7 6 5 4 3 —2— —1—

L Y T I C CUBE T
A O O A ROOT W
T U R TWO O
E Y Π
R

Figure 192. Stick figures transtime crop glyph (Milk Hill August 1991) designed by Cary Manpure as a transcommunication to the soul of Cary Jackman. The first message from left to right reads "To you, Cary. See you later." The second message reads from right to left "The cube root of two pi, Cary. I to you later". Two out of the three representations of pi look like pis in order to encode the metaphor of the cube root of two pi: *two-thirds*.

193. The meandering stone lined avenue known today as the Stone Avenue connects the analog of the Tetrahedron Crater with the representation of the Ranch House on Silbury.

Part 3 Chapter 13

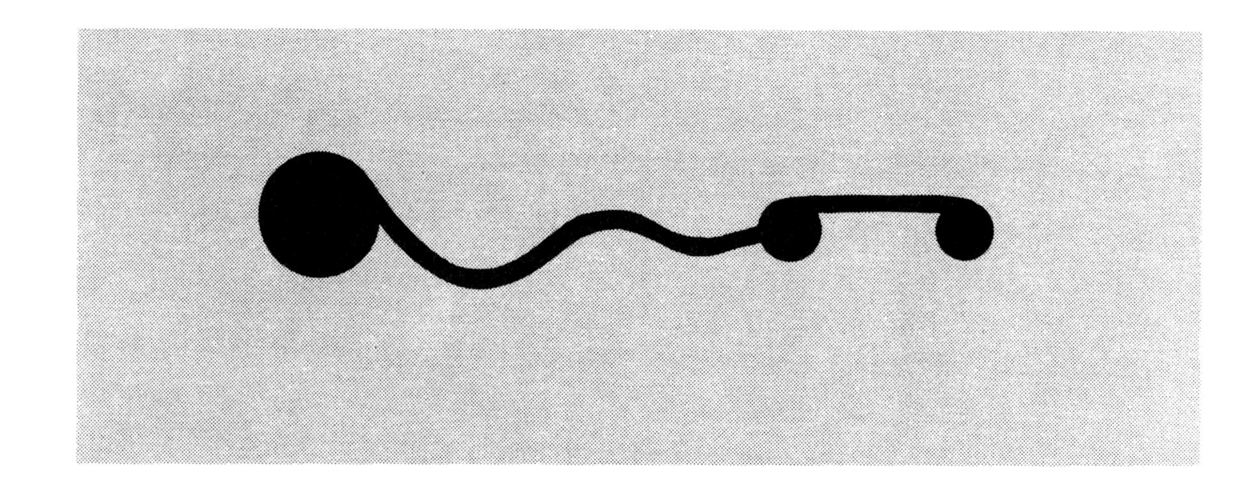

Figure 193.1. Multi perspective transtime crop glyph (Stone Avenue August 1991) intended to depict a cross section of the wooden water conduit and its meandering route from the Tetrahedron Crater Reservoir to the Ranch. The position of the craters relative to the fence between them was changed to make them look like a telephone handset. The telephone is connected to nothing — just like Cary Manpure. Essenes understood this and they wanted everyone to know that Cary Manpure could not call home. Essenes allegorized this situation in the movie ET.

193.2. Essenes insured that effigies of white horses were cut into the chalk hillsides around and about Avenabury as symbols of the hyperdimensional Source of the Universe and as memorials to Cary Manpure's favorite horse.

194. The Ark Hur. If the front legs of the Ark Hur were extended until they met there would be a 19.47 degree angle formed at the point of meeting.

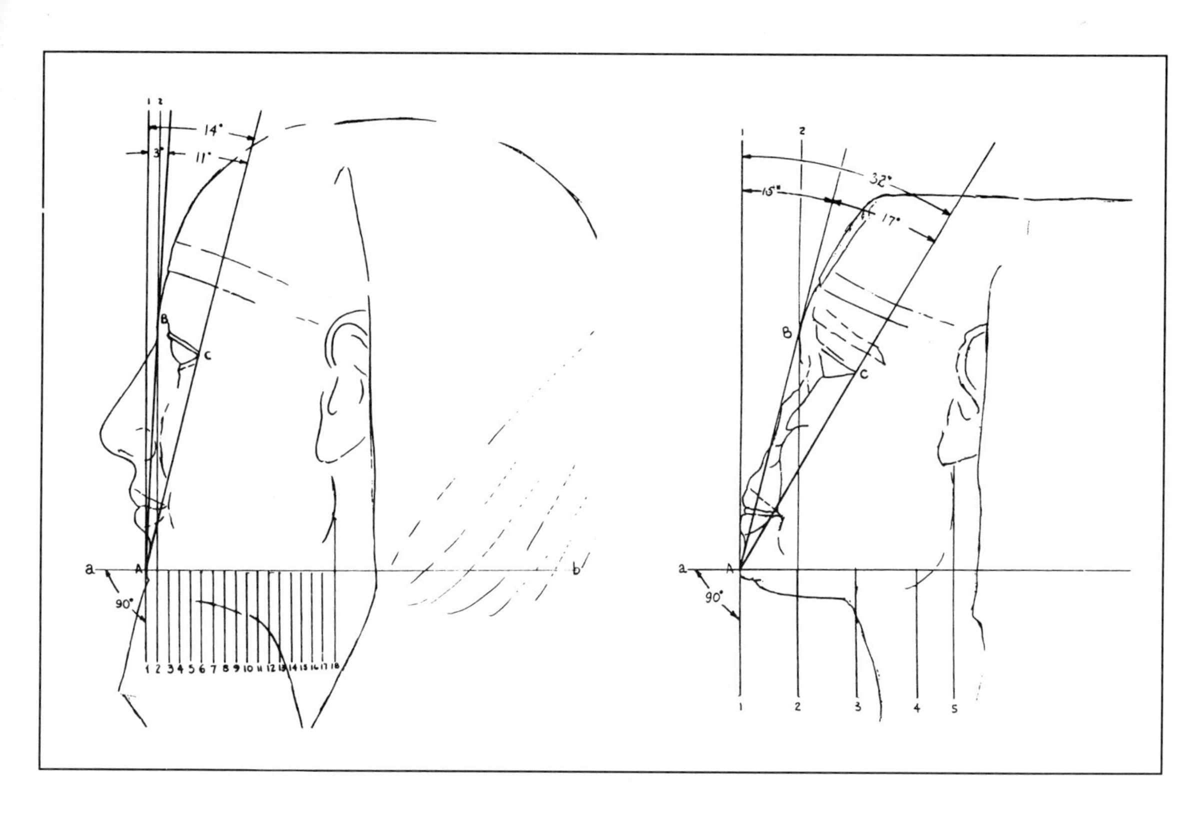

Figure 194.1. The blow-hard Chephren claimed the face of the Ark Hur was his own. It is plainly evident on comparison of Chephren (left) and the Ark Hur (right) that Chephren was only a blow-hard. Seekers of knowledge led by John Anthony West are responsible for these two profiles. They have also clearly demonstrated to all except those who cling to outmoded orthodox notions that much of the erosion of the Ark Hur and the basin from which it is carved is the result of extensive rain water erosion that could not have possibly ocurred since the time of the blow-hard Chephren.

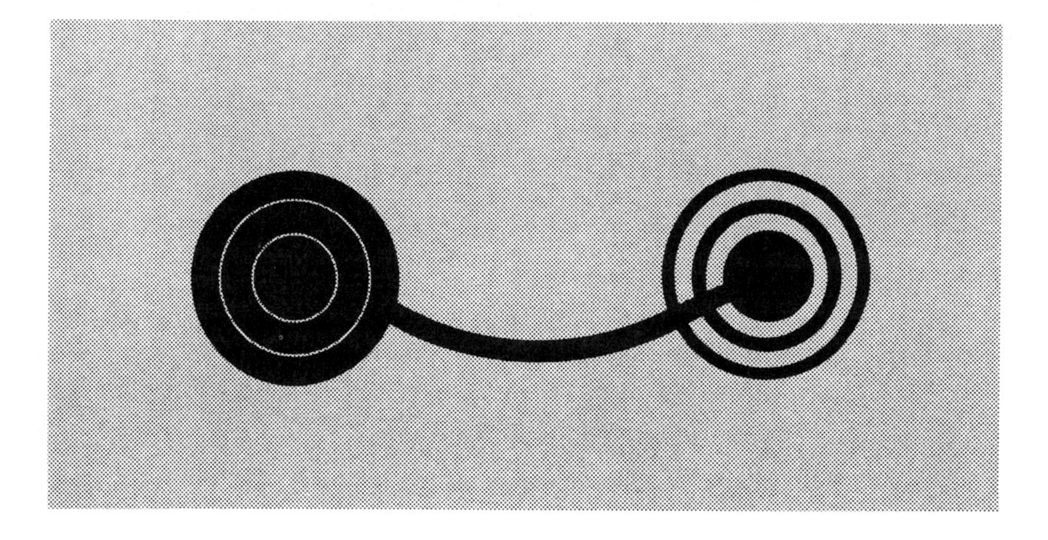

Figure195. Transtime crop glyph (Exton August 1992) designed to convey the twin cities of Helium on the red planet, Greater Helium to the west and Lesser Helium to the east. Helium is the first element which is formed by the fusing of two hydrogen atoms.

196. A female gray. A painting by Colette Dowell of a alien she 'experienced'. Even though individual grays evoke female or male categorization, and their appearance encodes many aspects, their most important encoding has to do with the quantity of their fingers and their lack of genitals. Grays have three fingers and a thumb. They are missing their fourth finger — hyperdimensionality — and lacking a total of five digits per hand, thus indicating that they are non-living. This is underlined by their lack of genitals for they cannot create life. This is to convey to us that they are images, not reality, induced into the perceiver's mind.

197. A male gray. A painting by Colette Dowell of another alien she 'experienced'. This male gray rather sadly contemplates his right hand, which lacks the fourth digit (see text for fig 196). The very shape of these grays, their color, and our reactions to the experiences that they evoke and/or provoke have more to do with the evolution of our consciousness, and individual soul choices, than with an 'invasion' by an alien species, which suggests induced images by *braided beam* rather than a physical reality.

Part 4 Chapter 4

198. Barbury Castle. The double walls and ditch represent the inner and outer hulls of star ships. The shape of Barbury Castle is a dual perspective of star ships, an egg and the face of gray aliens. Essenes induced the specific design of Barbury Castle hundreds of years ago to foreshadow the 'appearance' of gray aliens. Essenes also induced the name of Barbury Castle, a name which means 'alien mountain.' Barbury Castle is located on a ridge sculpted by Essenes which is part of the extended analog of the Tetrahedron Crater in the large scale model of the Horz complex on Silbury. The modified transtime crop glyph of Joe Lon Odkin of the energy transconverter was laid down and subsequently activated on a nearby slope of this ridge. (See also the egg shape of the upper magnets in figures 24, 100.1, 129 and 130).

Part 4 Chapter 4

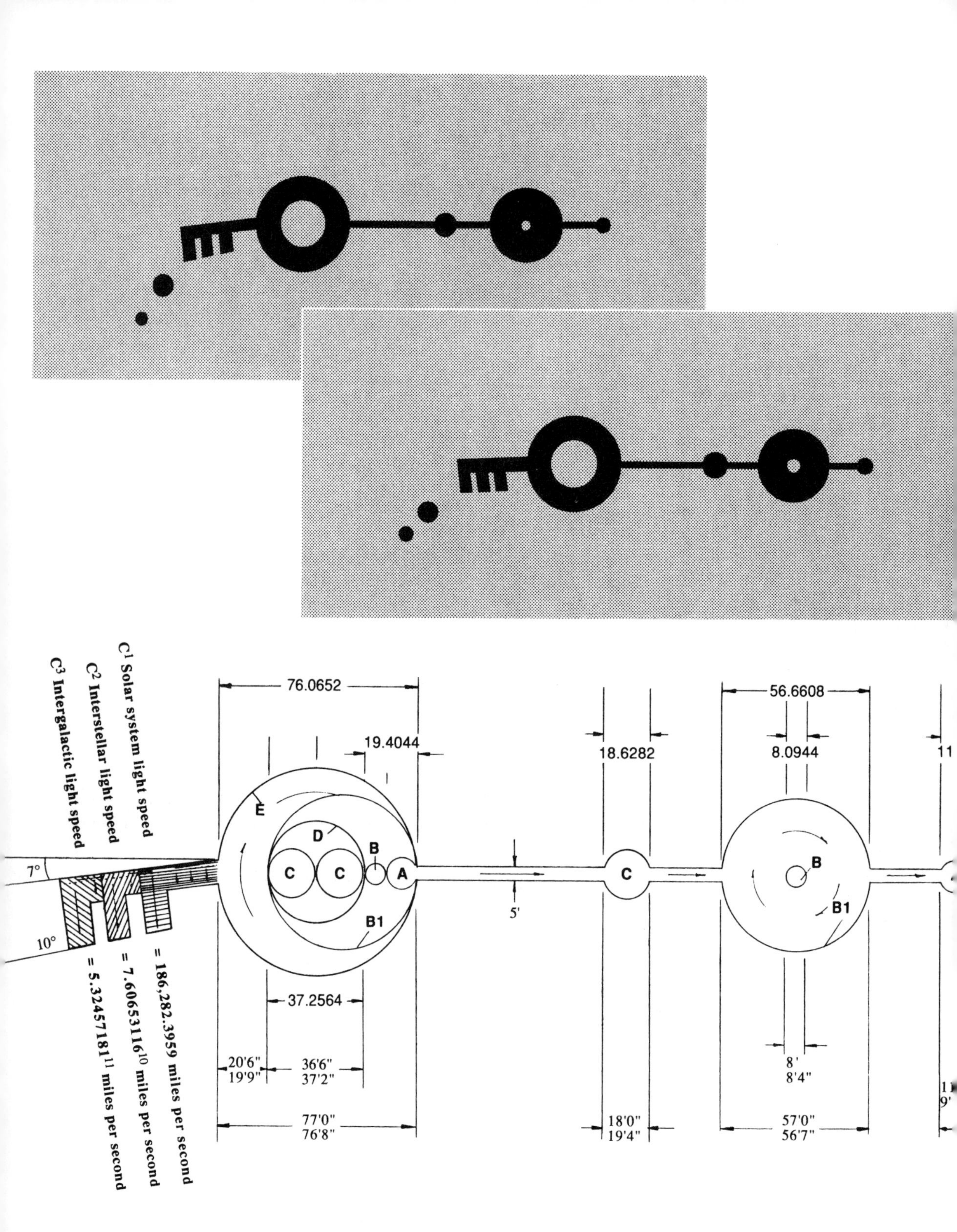

Figure 199. Two transtime crop glyphs (Alton Priors July 1991, upper illustration and West Kennett July 1991) designed to encode in the average diameters of each respective circle of the two glyphs the *three speeds of light*. *(See next page)*.

Alton Priors and West Kennett July 1991 dual transtime crop glyphs designed to illustrate the three speeds of light as described in the text: C^1 Solar system, C^2 Interstellar and C^3 Intergalactic light speeds.

In figure 199 the circles along the axis of the two glyphs have been marked from right to left A, B, B1, C, D and E. All the above circles have been telescoped down the axis and superimposed over the largest circle E, in order to illustrate the way in which the three light speeds were encoded.

The diameter of the circles and other measurements within these glyphs are in most instances the average, or the near average, of these two *almost identical* formations. For example, the true average between the two circles marked C on the two glyph surveys, namely 18.6666' is a close approximation to the value of 18.6282' for circle C. **186,282.3959** is the speed of light in miles per second as defined by a team led by Kenneth M Evenson during tests in Boulder, Colorado during October 1972 deploying a chain of laser beams.

Circle **C** is 18.6282	x 2 =	**37.2564**	
Circle **B** is 8.0944	x 2 =	**16.1888**	
Circle **A** is 11.3100	x 2 =	**22.6200**	
		76.0652	**(E)**
C x 2	=	37.2564	**(D)**
B x 1	=	8.0944	
A x 1	=	11.3100	
B namely **8.0944 x 7**	=	**56.6608**	**(B1)**
8.09441624 + 11.3100	=	**19.40441624**	**(A+B)**

24/25ths or **96%** (the maximum percentage of local light speed physically attainable — see text) of **A + B x 10** namely **194,044.1624** is **186,282.3959** = **C^1 solar system light speed in miles per second, the speed of light in a vacuum anywhere within a solar system.**

And 19.40441624 x 2 = 38.80883248

96% of 38.80883248 = 37.25647918 x 10 = 372,564.7918 = C^1 x 2

E = 76.06531166 : **18.62823959** = **4.08333333**

408,333.333 is the interstellar factor (see text references to interstellar light speed over 400,000 times faster than solar system light speed). **408,333.333 x C^1** namely **186,282.3539** = **7.60653116^{10}** — **the transgalactic speed of light C^2**

B1 namely **56.6608** = **8.0944 x 7**

7 is the factor applied to calculate the intergalactic speed of light C^3 (see text).

<u>Summary:</u>

C^1 Solar system light speed = 186,282.3959 miles per second

C^2 Interstellar light speed (186,282.3959 x 408,333.333) = 7.60653116^{10}

C^3 Intergalactic light speed (7.60653116^{10} x 7) = 5.32457181^{11}

West Kennett July 1991 transtime crop glyph looking northwest with the key end pointing at Avenabury. Silbury Hill (near the top of the photograph) is a very close analog to Hurbury and has a spiral on it (see figure 38). In times past Britons used to dance up the spiral to a maypole they erected on the top of Silbury Hill as a celebration of their being at one with the Universe.

Part 4 Chapter 4

Figure 200. Transtime crop glyph (Chilcomb May 1990) designed to depict the doughnut shaped portion of computers. The center circle depicts the central conduit and the ring around it depicts the area of chalk in which the calculations take place in four dimensions.

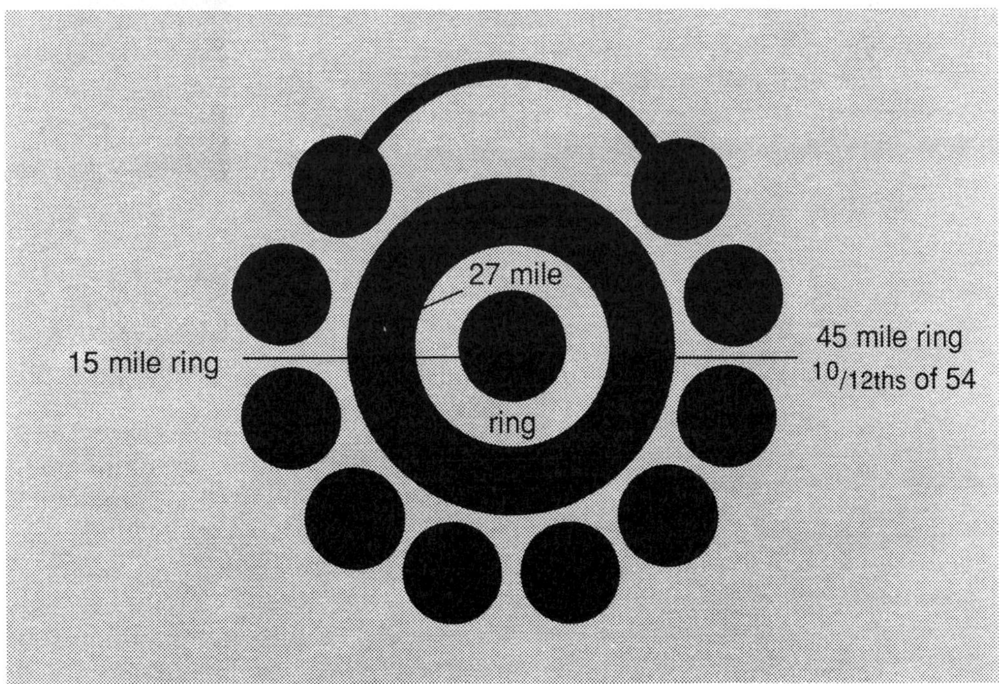

Figure 201. The arcing line in this transtime crop glyph (Hopton 1990) was designed to represent two missing small circles. These missing circles and the other small circles indicate 10 and 12. The outside of the thick ring represents the 45 mile ring , 10/12ths of 54, the next concentric ring of Atlantis. The glyph also conveys 5/6ths.

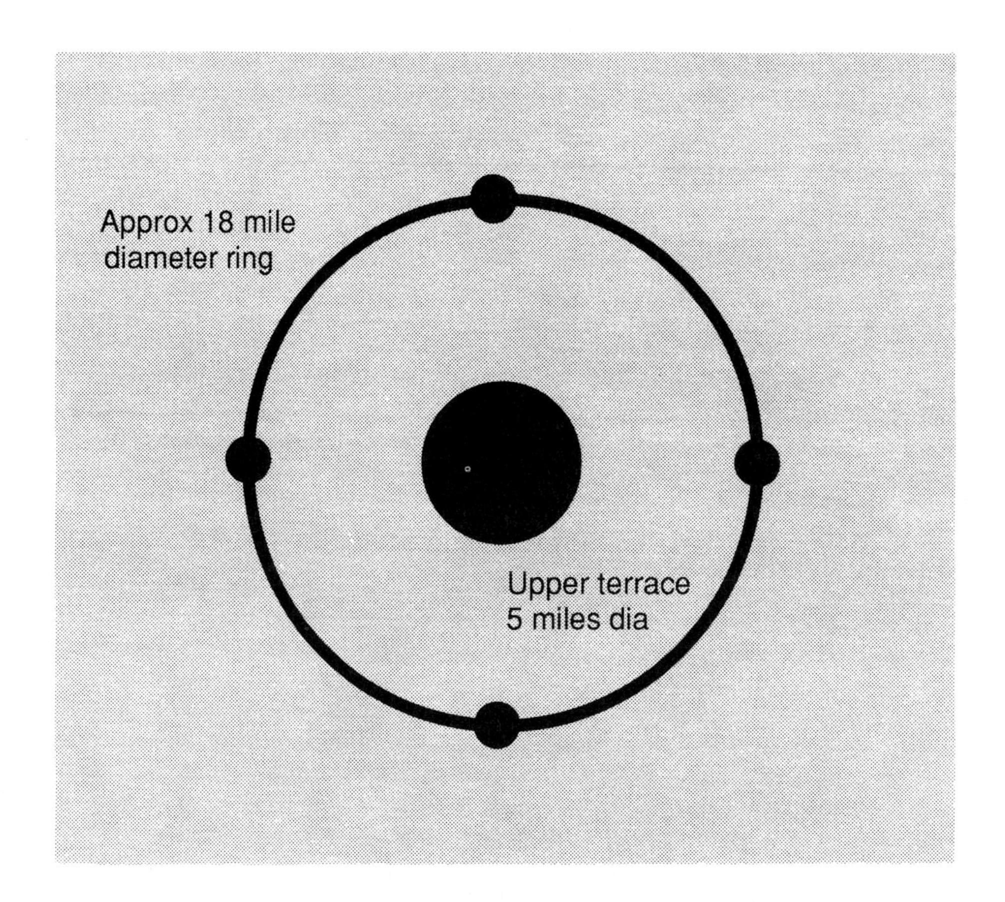

Figure 202. Transtime crop glyph (Charity Down August 1988). The center circle is intended to represent the upper circular terrace wall of Atlantis. The thin ring is inaccurately placed, there never was such a ring, but the four small circles depict the Gymnasion/Stadion, the Akadeimia, the Philosophia house and the Hippodromos. It is worth noting that in the 'non-existent' ring of this glyph, the lay of the crop was not circular but *radial*, from the center of the design.

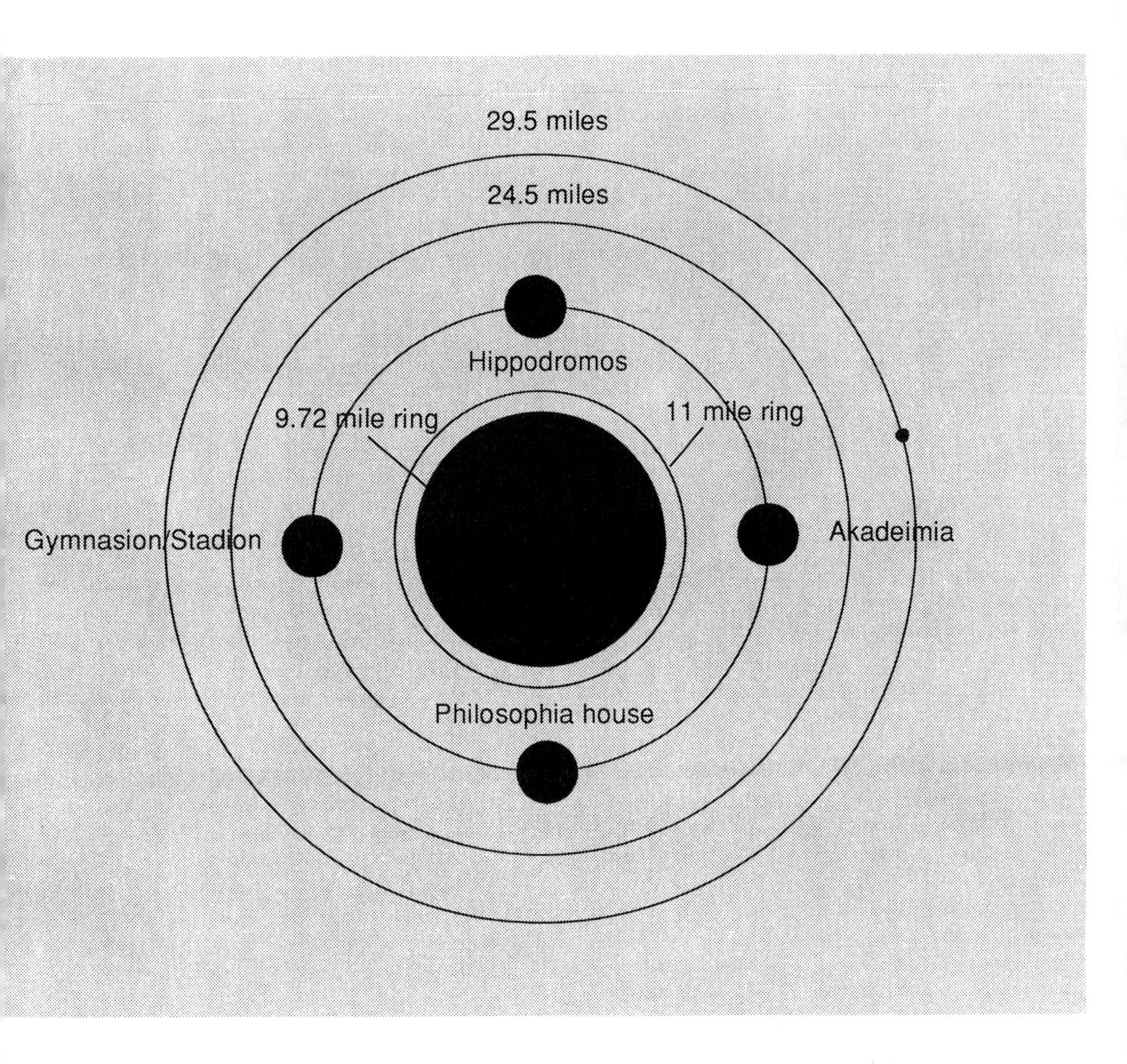

Figure 203. Similar to figure 202 but with additional lines, this transtime crop glyph (Bishops Cannings May 1990) also depicts the four important things of Atlantis. The third and fourth rings are additive and total 54 miles, the first concentric ring beyond the river surrounding Atlantis. (See figures 62.1 and 62.3).

Figure 204. Atlantis and the river. This transtime crop glyph (Milk Hill July 1991) was designed to represent at the outer edge of the thick ring the 54 mile concentric ring and at the inner edge, the never existing 18 mile ring. The extending line represents the river, its scaled width is 3 miles and its length 27.777+ miles. 27.777+ x 54 divided by 3 = 500 miles, the length of the river that flowed from Atlantis to the ocean.

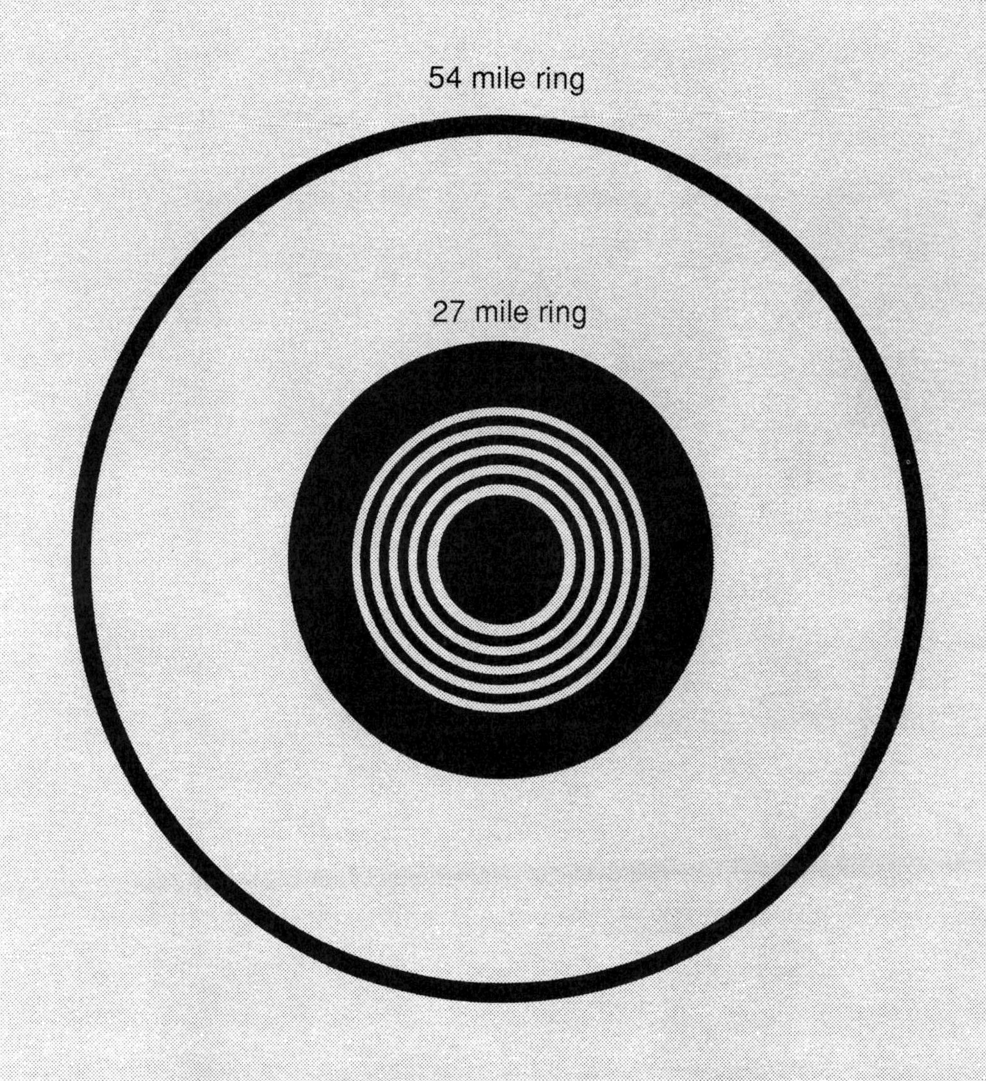

Figure 205. Transtime crop glyph (Woodford August 1991). The inside edge of the thick ring represents a perierchomai transportation system crystal tube. The four very thin rings represent the rings of magnetically levitating magnets surrounding the crystal tubes as they appear from a Peri car speeding through a tube. The inner circle depicts the way a station appears as it is approached by a Peri car.

This crop glyph was designed and laid down but not activated. It was 'hoaxed' by human beings as a result of ideas infused into them by Essenes, in the same way as Avenabury Circle, Silbury Hill and Stonehenge came to be built in the correct locations with the correct topological relationships and to the correct scale.

206. The walls of Wilusa (Ilios) slant inward at 19.47 degrees from the vertical. The inner terrace wall of Wilusa slanted inward at 22.48 degrees. Essenes have been amazed by the similarity of Wilusa to Atlantis.

Part 4 Chapter 4

Figure 207. Harmony multi-perspective transtime crop glyph (Upton Scudamore July 1992), the last transtime crop glyph of Cary Manpure. This transtime crop glyph is a representation of the harmony of Galen, Dalos and Harmonides — a harmony repeated by Bill Walsh, Joe Montana and Jerry Rice. The Stadion is smaller than the Gymnasion to indicate rising above. The circle representing Harmonides (and now also Jerry Rice) is larger because that circle also represents the soul. The discus thrower represents physical well being. Essenes have added the discus thrower to other transtime crop glyphs — including the space disaster transtime crop glyph — to emphasize the necessity for physical well being. The harmony transtime crop glyph was laid down south of Trowbridge and the crossing of the Keirykeion Line and the Lion Line to emphasize the necessity for working together — and for physical, mental and ethical courage.

Part 4 Chapter 4

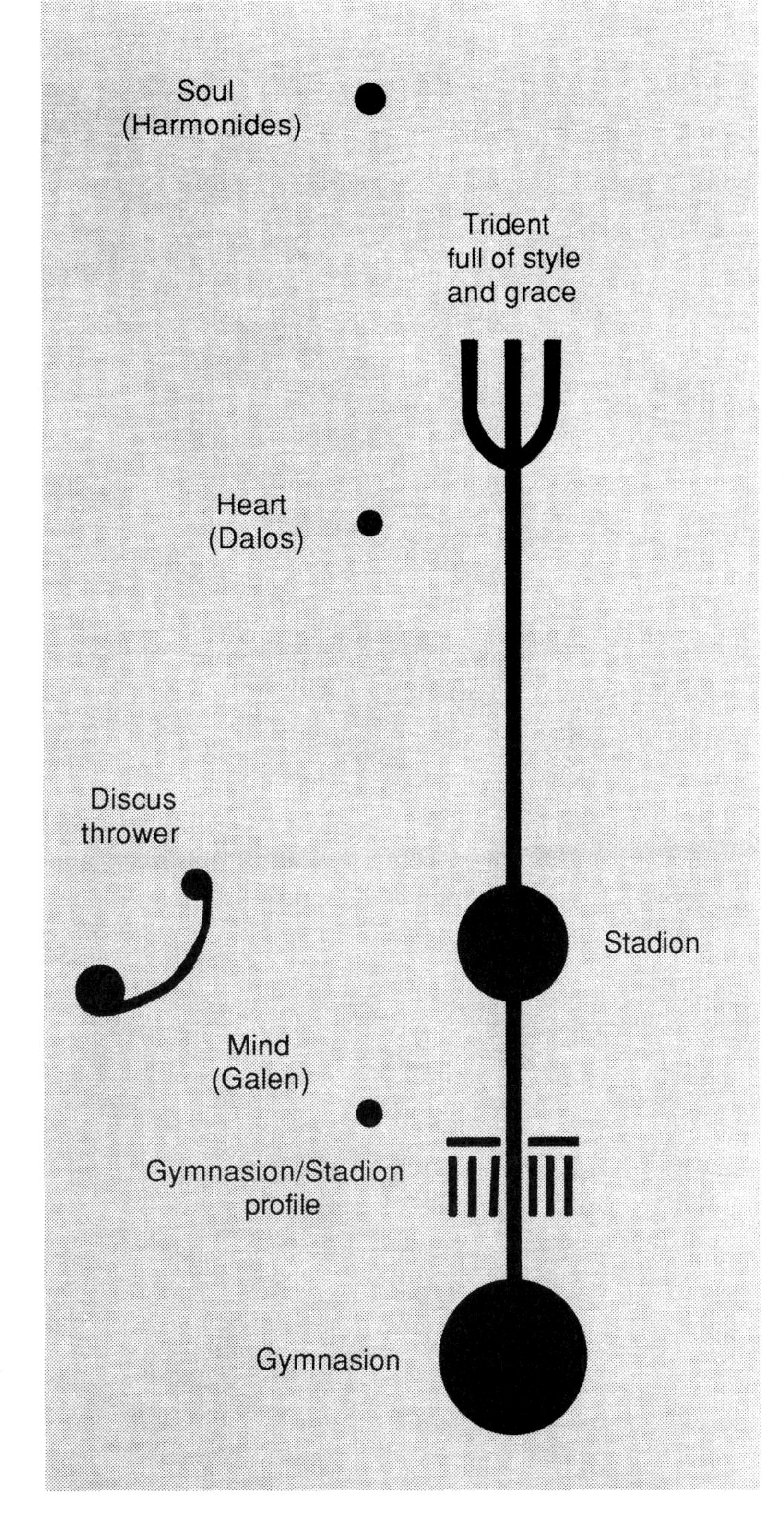

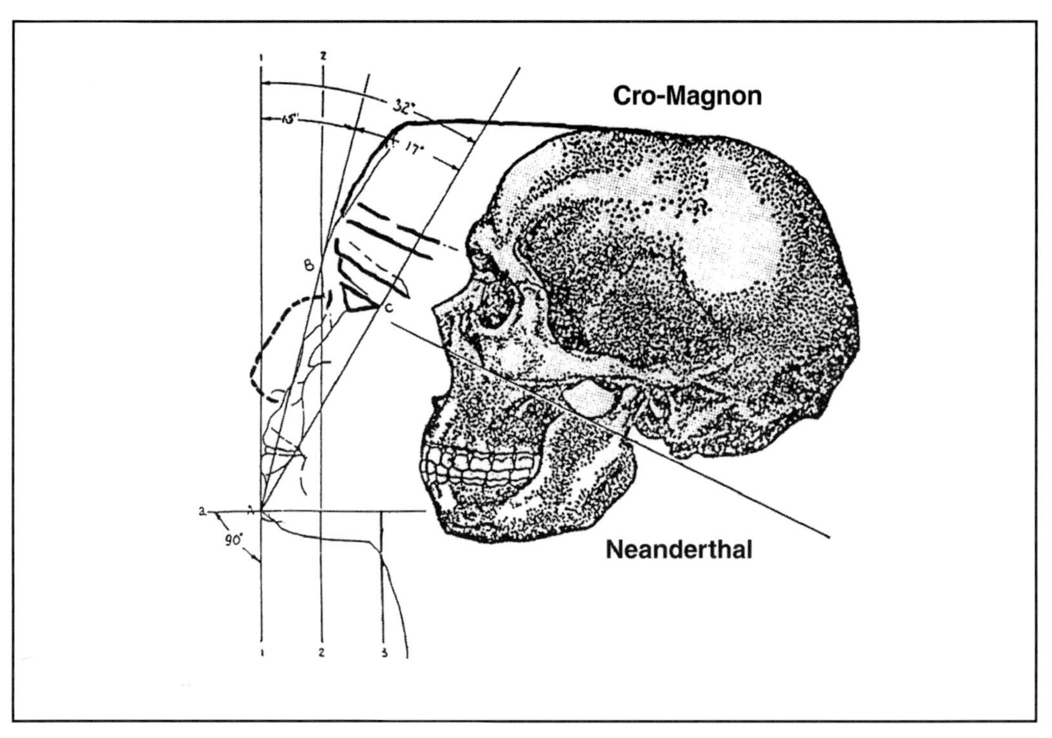

Based on Sphinx profile drawn by Frank Domingo

Figure 208. Combined skulls and profile of the Ark Hur—the Great Sphinx—complete with its large Neanderthal nose (dotted).

"Modify the face of the statue [the Sphinx] to resemble both the face of the transitional self-aware being resulting from the administration of the *first part of the genetic agent* [Neanderthal] and the face of the being resulting from the administration of the *second part of the genetic agent* [Cro-Magnon]."

Part 2 Chapter 10

Index

This Index is in seven sections:

Technical

Customs

Language

Measurement

Organisations

Locations

Systems